MW00565030

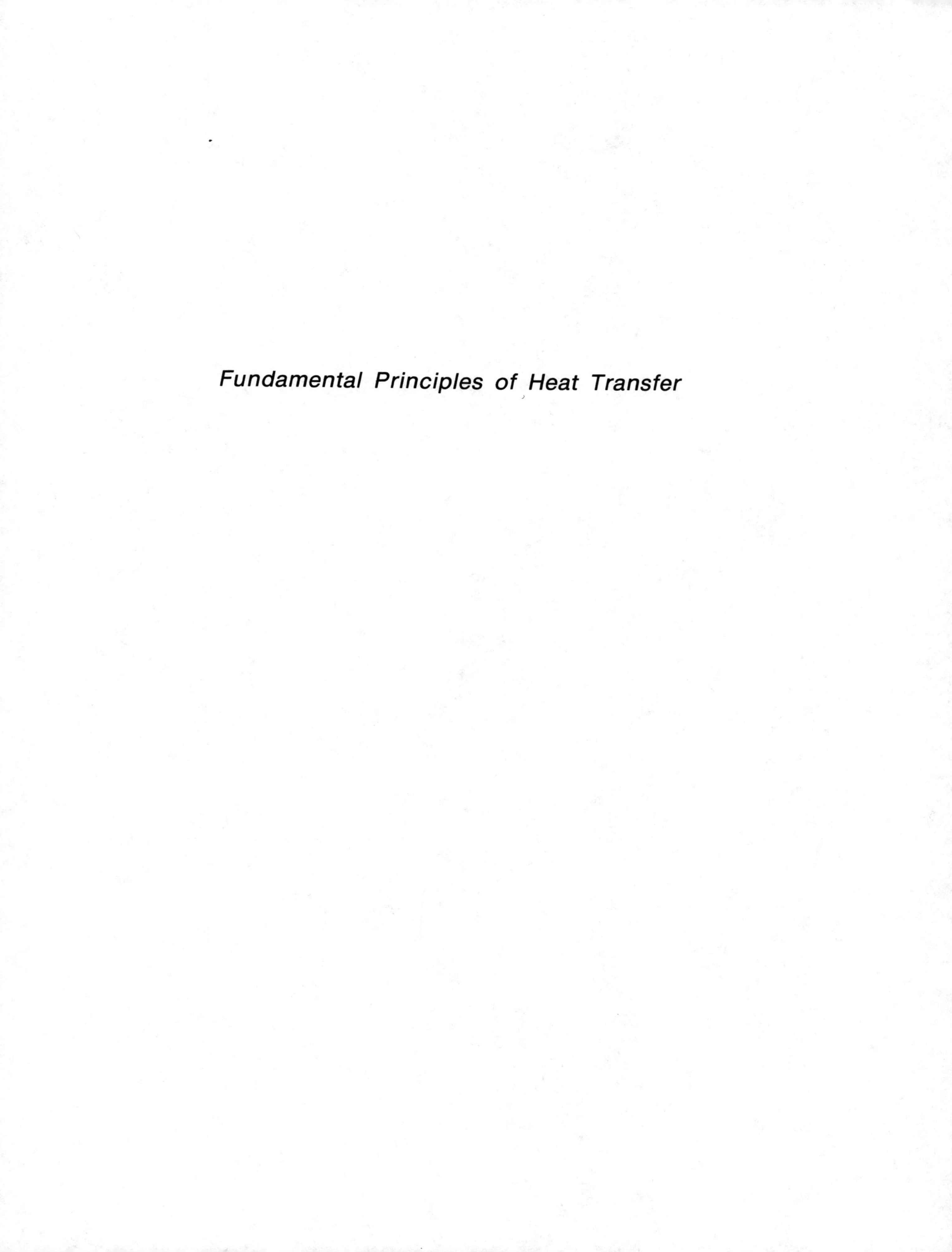

Fundamental Principles of Heat Transfer

Fundamental Principles of Heat Transfer

Stephen Whitaker
Professor of Chemical Engineering
University of California at Davis

Krieger Publishing Company
Malabar, Florida

Original Edition 1977
Reprint Edition 1983 w/corrections

Printed and Published by
ROBERT E. KRIEGER PUBLISHING COMPANY, INC.
KRIEGER DRIVE
MALABAR, FLORIDA 32950

Printed in the United States of America

Library of Congress Cataloging in Publication Data

Whitaker, Stephen.
Fundamental principles of heat transfer.

Reprint. Originally published: New York : Pergamon Press, c1977.
Bibliography: p.
Includes index.
1. Heat—Transmission. I. Title.
QC320.W46 1983 536'.2 82-13031
ISBN 0-89874-543-8
10 9 8 7

Contents

*It is recommended that sections marked with an asterisk be covered in an introductory course.

Preface

This book is intended to provide a comprehensive treatment of the fundamental aspects of conduction, convection, and radiation at an introductory level. While emphasis has been placed on careful and complete theoretical developments, numerous solved example problems and design problems have been included in order to illustrate the practical applications of fundamental principles. It has been assumed that students using this book will be familiar with thermodynamics and fluid mechanics. Familiarity with ordinary differential equations and vector analysis is also expected, as calculus is used predominantly in the presentation of theoretical results. When solutions to partial differential equations are required, the mathematical methods are presented in detail. Thus students who have not had a course in partial differential equations can attack the chapters on two-dimensional and transient heat conduction with confidence.

One can use this book for an introductory course in heat transfer for either Junior or Senior engineering students, although the material covering two-dimensional heat conduction, transient heat conduction, and non-black body radiation is more suitable for graduate study or a second undergraduate course. If used for a first course in heat transfer, one must choose the material judiciously in order to provide a balanced treatment of conduction, convection, and radiation. In the following paragraphs an outline for an introductory course consisting of 40 classroom hours is presented and is summarized in Table I. Alternate course outlines providing more flexible coverage of the material are also discussed and summarized in Tables II and III.

Suggested course outline

Chapter 1, *Introduction* (2 lectures). All the material in this chapter should be covered with one entire lecture devoted to the subject of radiation. Careful attention should be given to Design Problem I which begins the chapter, and the use of film heat transfer coefficients in formulating the flux condition at phase interfaces.

Chapter 2, *Steady, One-Dimensional Heat Conduction* (9 lectures). Every section in this chapter should be covered with the exception of Sec. 2.7 which introduces Bessel functions in the analysis of the annular fin. This chapter is perhaps the most important one in the book, and one must not give in to the urge to move on to the more challenging material in subsequent chapters for there is much to be learned from the study of one-dimensional heat conduction. Of particular importance is the specification and application of flux boundary conditions, the nature of approximate analysis as outlined in Sec. 2.6 which treats the rectangular fin, and the order-of-magnitude analysis which is covered in Sec. 2.9. The material covered in Sec. 2.10 represents an application of order-of-magnitude analysis, and can be assigned as reading material for the student in connection with the problems associated with Secs. 2.9 and 2.10.

Chapter 4, *Transient Heat Conduction* (3 lectures). The first three sections should be covered in this chapter. Section 4.1 provides a derivation of the transient heat conduction equation, and Sec. 4.2 treats the problem of negligible internal resistance. With careful planning both of these sections can be covered in one lecture. Section 4.3 covers transient heat conduction in a semi-infinite slab, both from the point of view of an exact solution and an approximate solution. The latter development builds upon the analysis presented in Sec. 2.6, and provides a lead in to the integral analysis of boundary layer flows presented in Chapter 5.

Chapter 5, *The Basic Equations of Momentum and Energy Transport* (7 lectures). It is recommended that every section, except Secs. 5.8, 5.10, and 5.11, be covered in this chapter. Section 5.8 provides the exact solution of forced convection for a flat plate, and it is felt that this material is unsuitable for an introductory course. Sections 5.10 and 5.11 deal with dimensional analysis and the exact solution for laminar free convection for a vertical, flat plate. While the importance of free convection cannot be denied, time requires that the discussion of this material be limited to the summaries of these two sections for an introductory course. It should be noted that Sec. 7.9, which presents the correlations for free convection, is part of the recommended introductory treatment.

The analysis of convective energy transport is based on the understanding and application of the thermal energy equation, and it is at this point that we come to one of the "crux moves" of the text. To rigorously derive the thermal energy equation one must understand kinematics, the laws of mechanics, and the first law of thermodynamics; however, these ideas can be grasped in no small amount of time. Those students who have had a careful treatment of these subjects in previous courses can move quickly through the first three sections of this chapter, and it is with this group in mind that brief summaries of these sections have been provided. For those students who are unfamiliar with the material in Secs. 5.1, 5.2, and 5.3 there are two alternatives: (1) Move directly to Sec. 5.4 and accept the presentation of the thermal energy equation without proof, or (2) devote approximately eight classroom hours to these three sections. If the former course of action is taken a qualitative lecture concerning the total energy equation, the mechanical energy equation and the thermal energy equation is certainly in order. If the latter course of action is elected one must be committed to eliminating either Chapters 6 and 7 or Chapters 8 and 9 from the introductory course. This choice may well be dictated by the content of other courses in the program. In summary, the suggested attack on Chapter 5 is to cover Secs. 5.1, 5.2, and 5.3 in one lecture so that six classroom hours can be devoted to Secs. 5.4, 5.5, 5.6, 5.7, and 5.9 along with brief discussions of the summaries of Secs. 5.8, 5.10, and 5.11.

Chapter 6, *Turbulent Flow* (2 lectures). The objective of this chapter is to derive the time-averaged transport equations and present a qualitative description of turbulent transport processes. Time averages are defined in Sec. 6.1, and the time-averaged transport equations are derived in Sec. 6.2. Both these sections can be covered in a single lecture. Section 6.3 presents a qualitative description of turbulent transport processes and can be covered in one lecture. The remaining two sections continue with a qualitative discussion of turbulence, and they are best left as additional reading for the interested student.

Chapter 7, *Macroscopic Balances* (6 lectures). Every section in this chapter should be covered; however, since dimensional analysis for forced convection was previously treated in Sec. 5.6 it may be sufficient to present an abbreviated version of Sec. 7.5. A summary of that section has been provided to aid in such a presentation. Since the material in Secs. 7.1 and 7.2 has probably been covered in a fluid mechanics course, one can normally cover the first three sections of this chapter in one lecture. Section 7.4 requires considerable discussion and two lectures should be allowed for this material. The remaining sections can be covered by means of problems assigned to the students; however, the subject of heat transfer in packed beds and tube bundles (Sec. 7.8) may be worthy of a lecture. Of particular importance is Design Problem VII, for if Chapter 11, *Design of Heat Exchangers*, is not covered, a careful discussion of the double-pipe heat exchanger is in order.

Chapter 8, *Thermal Radiation* (5 lectures). The treatment of radiation presented in this text is based on the photon transport equation, thus the derivation presented in Sec. 8.2 must be covered carefully. The photon transport equation illustrates the similarity between radiant energy transport and other transport processes; provides a sound basis for the analysis of absorption and emission phenomena; and gives rise to a logical basis for the specialized methods needed for the solution of radiant energy exchange problems. The material presented in Sec. 8.3 deals with the geometry of radiation at surfaces and must be discussed thoroughly for this section is referred to often in subsequent developments. Cavity or black body radiation is discussed in Sec. 8.4, and the thought experiments used in that development are extended in Sec. 8.5 in order to prove Kirchhoff's law. It is possible to state Kirchhoff's law as an accepted fact, and explain some of the consequences regarding α and ϵ without getting involved in the details of Sec. 8.5. As an aid to that kind of a treatment a brief summary of Sec. 8.5 has been prepared.

Chapter 9, *Radiant Energy Exchange* (4 lectures). For a first course in heat transfer, Secs. 9.1, 9.2, and 9.3 are recommended as being a satisfactory introduction to black body radiant energy exchange. The subject of radiant energy exchange between a gray body that cannot see itself and a black enclosure has been treated in Chapter 1 and the method of successive reflections (given in Sec. 9.7) can be used to analyze the infinite parallel plate problem. A comprehensive treatment of gray body radiation is generally beyond the scope of an introductory course, for the appropriate route to an understanding of that subject lies in the analysis of reradiating surfaces (Sec. 9.4), experimental measurements of emissivities (Sec. 9.5), properties of real surfaces (Sec. 9.6), and finally the matrix methods required to analyze the general gray body problem (Sec. 9.7).

Alternatives

The suggested course outline presented in the preceding paragraphs involves 38 lectures, presumably two class periods would be taken up with examinations thus bringing the total to 40 class periods. This course outline is listed in Table I for easy reference. It is entirely possible that the material in Sec. 6.3 is covered in a course on fluid mechanics, thus that section can be eliminated and one lecture saved.

The schedule indicated in Table I is indeed an extremely rigid one; however, there are alternatives

Table I Suggested Course Outline (38 lectures)

Chapter 1:	Secs. 1.1, 1.2, 1.3, 1.4, 1.5	Chapter 6:	Secs. 6.1, 6.2, 6.3
Chapter 2:	Secs. 2.1, 2.2, 2.3, 2.4, 2.5, 2.6, 2.9, 2.10	Chapter 7:	Secs. 7.1, 7.2, 7.3, 7.4, 7.5, 7.6, 7.7, 7.8, 7.9
Chapter 4:	Secs. 4.1, 4.2, 4.3	Chapter 8:	Secs. 8.1, 8.2, 8.3, 8.4, 8.5
Chapter 5:	Secs. 5.1, 5.2, 5.3, 5.4, 5.5, 5.6, 5.7, 5.9, 5.10	Chapter 9:	Secs. 9.1, 9.2, 9.3

which can provide some flexibility in the choice of material while still devoting a satisfactory amount of time to the fundamental concepts of conduction, convection, and radiation. The course outline is based on a commitment to the analysis of boundary layer phenomena; however, that subject can be eliminated by deleting Secs. 4.3, 5.7, and 5.9 with a savings of five lectures. In addition, if one deletes boundary layer phenomena the need for a study of order-of-magnitude analyses is considerably diminished and one could omit Secs. 2.9 and 2.10. This saves one more lecture and leads to the course outline given in Table II. The

Table II Suggested Course Outline Deleting Boundary Layer Phenomena and Order-of-Magnitude Analysis (32 lectures)

Chapter 1:	Secs. 1.1, 1.2, 1.3, 1.4, 1.5	Chapter 6:	Secs. 6.1, 6.2, 6.3
Chapter 2:	Secs. 2.1, 2.2, 2.3, 2.4, 2.5, 2.6	Chapter 7:	Secs. 7.1, 7.2, 7.3, 7.4, 7.5, 7.6, 7.7, 7.8, 7.9
Chapter 4:	Secs. 4.1, 4.2	Chapter 8:	Secs. 8.1, 8.2, 8.3, 8.4
Chapter 5:	Secs. 5.1, 5.2, 5.3, 5.4, 5.5, 5.6	Chapter 9:	Secs. 9.1, 9.2, 9.3

final time-saver would be the replacement of Secs. 5.1 through 5.5 with a single qualitative lecture outlining the derivation and simplification of the thermal energy equation as it is listed in the summary of Sec. 5.5. This would require that the treatment in Sec. 7.3 be restricted to fixed control volumes and Secs. 7.1 and 7.2 be deleted since the general transport theorem would not be available. The course outline for this approach is listed in Table III. Such a course would allow students to solve problems in conduction, convection, and radiation; however, a gap would be left in their understanding of the fundamental concepts. On the other hand, the time saved would allow individual instructors to pursue a variety of subjects such as two-dimensional heat conduction, numerical methods, non-black body radiation, boiling and condensation, and heat exchanger design.

Table III Suggested Course Outline Deleting Boundary Layer Phenomena, Order-of-Magnitude Analysis, and a Rigorous Treatment of the Thermal Energy Equation (28 lectures)

Chapter 1:	Secs. 1.1, 1.2, 1.3, 1.4, 1.5	Chapter 6:	Secs. 6.1, 6.2, 6.3
Chapter 2:	Secs. 2.1, 2.2, 2.3, 2.4, 2.5, 2.6	Chapter 7:	Secs. 7.3, 7.4, 7.5, 7.6, 7.7, 7.8, 7.9
Chapter 4:	Secs. 4.1, 4.2	Chapter 8:	Secs. 8.1, 8.2, 8.3, 8.4
Chapter 5:	Secs: 5.1–5.5 (qualitative), Sec. 5.6	Chapter 9:	Secs. 9.1, 9.2, 9.3

Problems

At the beginning of the first nine chapters there is a design problem which is used to illustrate the type of problems that one can solve after having mastered the material in each particular chapter. The main purpose of these problems is to serve as a motivating force; however, detailed solutions are given at the end of each chapter so these problems also serve as solved examples. In addition, there are problems at the end of each chapter dealing explicitly with the design problem, thus the design problems can be used as vehicles for studying special aspects of each chapter. For example, the first ten problems in Chapter 7 are concerned with Design Problem VII, and they are listed as Probs. VII-1, VII-2, through VII-10 to indicate that they deal directly with that specific design problem.

In addition to the solutions to the design problems, there are numerous solved example problems throughout the text. In order to provide motivation for studying these examples, there are problems at the end of each chapter which deal directly with the solved example problems. These problems are marked with an asterisk, and are generally somewhat simpler than the other problems.

In order to help in the assignment of problems there is a number in parentheses underneath each problem number indicating the section to which that problem pertains.

Acknowledgments

A number of able hands, including Barbara, Donna, Judy, and Connie, perservered for more years than they wish to remember in the preparation of this text. Their efforts are greatly appreciated. The treatment of radiation given in Chapters 8 and 9 is a departure from the traditional approach. It represents the results of many discussions with Dr. Alberto Cassano of the Universidad Nacional del Litoral in Argentina and Professor James Hurley of the Physics Department at Davis.

STEPHEN WHITAKER

Nomenclature†

Roman Letters

a_v	surface area per unit volume (345)
$a_{\lambda\omega}$	rate of absorption of $\lambda\omega$-photons (381)
A	area (3)
$\mathscr{A}$	area of a closed surface fixed in space (30)
$\mathscr{A}_a(t)$	area of an arbitrary closed surface moving in space (197, 306)
$\mathscr{A}_m(t)$	area of a closed material surface (26)
$A_e(t)$	area of entrances and exits (307)
$A_s(t)$	area of impenetrable moving surfaces (307)
A_s	area of impenetrable fixed surfaces (307)
$\mathscr{A}_{\lambda\omega}$	rate of absorption of radiant energy from $\lambda\omega$-photons (381)
b	length (48)
C	constant (51)
c	speed of light in free space (376)
c_v	constant volume heat capacity per unit mass (144)
c_p	constant pressure heat capacity per unit mass (7, 145, 213, 214)
d	distance (65)
D	diameter (43)
$\mathbf{d}$	rate of strain tensor in Gibbs notation (291)
D_p	particle diameter (347)
D_h	hydraulic diameter (296, 331)
e	internal energy (26)
E	electric field (29)
$e_{\lambda\omega}$	rate of emission of $\lambda\omega$-photons (381)
$\mathscr{E}_{\lambda\omega}$	rate of emission of radiant energy from $\lambda\omega$-photons (381)
$\mathbf{F}$	force vector (27)
F_{ij}	view factor (11, 408)
$\mathbf{g}$	gravity vector (29, 200)
g	magnitude of the gravity vector (254)
G	mass velocity (348, 490)
h	film heat transfer coefficient (13, 16, 193, 222), enthalpy (214), Planck's constant (381, 395)
h_{loc}	local film heat transfer coefficient (244, 311)
h_{avg}	average film heat transfer coefficient (244)
$h_{\ln}$	log-mean film heat transfer coefficient (316)
$\mathbf{i}, \mathbf{j}, \mathbf{k}$	unit base vectors for rectangular coordinates (4)
$I_0(x)$	modified Bessel function of the first kind of order zero (58, 60)
$I_1(x)$	modified Bessel function of the first kind of order one (61)
$I_{\lambda\omega}$	specific intensity (382)
$I_{b,\lambda\omega}$	black body specific intensity (395)
$\mathbf{j}$	electrical current density vector (29)
$J_0(x)$	Bessel function of the first kind of order zero (100)
J	radiosity (448)
k	thermal conductivity (4), Boltzmann's constant (395, 397)
$k^{(t)}$	turbulent thermal conductivity (287)
$K_0(x)$	modified Bessel function of the second kind of order zero (58, 62)
$K_1(x)$	modified Bessel function of the second kind of order one (61)
L	length (3)
ℓ	length (66)
ℓ_T	thermal mixing length (290)
ℓ_H	hydrodynamic mixing length (288)
$\dot{m}$	mass flow rate (7, 508)

†Symbols used consistently throughout the text are listed in this table. Page numbers in parentheses indicate where the symbol is defined. Several page numbers are given when appropriate.

$\mathbf{n}$ outwardly directed unit normal (27)
$n_{\lambda\omega}$ $\lambda\omega$-photon density (380)
NTU number of transfer units (526)
p absolute pressure (201)
$\mathcal{P}$ dimensionless pressure (222)
p_∞ absolute pressure far removed from an immersed body (228)
$\tilde{p}$ free convection pressure field (252)
p_{vap} vapor pressure (473)
$\mathbf{q}$ heat flux vector (4, 27)
$\mathbf{q}^R$ radiant heat flux vector (383)
$\bar{\mathbf{q}}^{(t)}$ turbulent heat flux vector (280)
$\bar{\mathbf{q}}^{(T)}$ total turbulent heat flux vector (280)
q_x, q_y, q_z scalar components of the heat flux vector in rectangular coordinates (4, 32)
q_r, q_θ, q_z scalar components of the heat flux vector in cylindrical coordinates (32)
$q^{(i)}_{\lambda\omega}$ specific incident flux (388)
$q_\lambda^{(i)}$ hemispherical incident flux (388)
$q^{(i)}$ total hemispherical incident flux (389)
$q_\omega^{(i)}$ total incident flux (390)
$q^{(a)}_{\lambda\omega}$ specific absorbed flux (390)
$q^{(r)}_{\lambda\omega}$ specific reflected flux (390)
$q^{(e)}_{\lambda\omega}$ specific emitted flux (390)
$q^{(e)}_{b,\lambda}$ black body hemispherical emitted flux (394, 396)
$q_b^{(e)}$ black body total hemispherical emitted flux (396)
$\dot{Q}$ total rate of heat transfer (3)
Q total heat transferred (30), volumetric flow rate (347, 361)
r, θ, z cylindrical coordinates (30)
r, θ, ϕ spherical coordinates (30)
r_c critical radius (45)
R, Θ, Z dimensionless cylindrical coordinates (320)
$\mathbf{r}$ position vector (200)
S an arbitrary scalar (195)
s_t transverse pitch (351)
s_ℓ longitudinal pitch (351)
S_t dimensionless transverse pitch (352)
S_ℓ dimensionless longitudinal pitch (352)
t time (27)
t^* dimensionless time (162, 221)
$\mathbf{t}_{(\mathbf{n})}$ stress vector (27, 200)
T temperature (3)
$\langle T \rangle$ average temperature (49, 287)
T_b bulk temperature (287, 312)
T_f film temperature (358)
T_{sat} saturation temperature (473)
T_∞ temperature far removed from an immersed body (228)
$\mathbf{T}$ stress tensor (200)
T_{ij} scalar components of the stress tensor (200)
$\mathbf{T}^T$ conjugate stress tensor (201)
u_0 characteristic velocity (220)
u_∞ velocity far removed from an immersed body (228)
$u_{\lambda\omega}$ $\lambda\omega$-photon energy density (381)
u^R radiant energy density (383)
$\mathbf{U}$ dimensionless velocity (221)
U overall heat transfer coefficient (14, 39, 43, 363, 512)
$\mathbf{U}$ unit tensor (201)
$\mathbf{v}$ fluid velocity vector (8, 26, 195)
$\tilde{\mathbf{v}}$ free convection velocity vector (252)
v magnitude of the velocity vector (26)
$\mathcal{V}$ volume fixed in space (30)
$\mathcal{V}_a(t)$ arbitrary volume moving in space (195, 306)
$\mathcal{V}_m(t)$ material volume (26)
$\mathbf{w}$ arbitrary velocity vector (194, 306)
x, y, z rectangular coordinates (30)
X, Y, Z dimensionless rectangular coordinates (222)
$Y_0(x)$ Bessel function of the second kind of order zero (100)

Dimensionless Groups

N_{Bi} Biot number (52)
N_{Re} Reynolds number (221)
N_{Pr} Prandtl number (221)
N_{BC} dimensionless number appearing in a boundary condition (222)
N_{Nu} Nusselt number (222, 311)
$N_{\text{Re},L}$ length Reynolds number (228)
N_{Gr} Grashof number (254)
N_{Ec} Eckert number (322)
N_k ratio of thermal conductivities (490)
N_α ratio of thermal diffusivities (490)
N_ρ ratio of densities (490)
N_{We} boiling Weber number (490)
N_ν ratio of kinematic viscosities (490)
N_{Bo} boiling number (490)
N_{Ve} velocity number (490)

Greek Letters

α thermal diffusivity (145), total absorptivity (402)
$\alpha^{(t)}$ turbulent thermal diffusivity (291)
$\alpha_{\lambda\omega}$ specific absorptivity (386, 401)
α_λ hemispherical absorptivity (401)
β coefficient of thermal expansion (145, 213, 253), ratio of lengths (85), contact angle (482)
$\beta(\lambda)$ extinction coefficient for light having a wavelength λ (382)
δ distance (35)
δ_T thermal boundary layer thickness (150, 227, 248, 251)
δ_H hydrodynamic boundary layer thickness (227, 248, 251)
δ_{ij} Kronecker delta, the scalar components of the unit tensor $\mathbf{U}$ (201)
ΔT temperature difference (3)
ΔT_{ln} log-mean temperature difference (316, 365, 513)
Δ_T dimensionless thermal boundary layer thickness (228)

Δ_H dimensionless hydrodynamic boundary layer thickness (228)
ΔH_{vap} heat of vaporization (475)
ϵ total emissivity (8, 402), void fraction (346), minimum effectiveness (526)
ϵ/D wall roughness ratio (320)
$\epsilon_{\lambda\omega}$ specific emissivity (399)
ϵ_λ hemispherical emissivity (401)
η similarity variable (151, 232, 234, 258)
Θ dimensionless temperature (50)
κ compressibility (145, 231), bulk coefficient of viscosity (201)
$\boldsymbol{\lambda}$ unit vector (28, 121, 254)
λ eigen value (85), wave length of light (376)
λ_c critical wave length (495)
Λ viscosity ratio (320, 326)
μ shear coefficient of viscosity (201)
μ_0 viscosity evaluated at the mean wall temperature (324)
μ_b viscosity evaluated at the mean bulk temperature (324)
$\mu^{(t)}$ turbulent viscosity (287)
ν kinematic viscosity (217, 221), frequency of light (376)
$\nu^{(t)}$ turbulent kinematic viscosity (291)
π 3.14159. . . . .
ρ density (26, 197)
$\tilde{\rho}$ free convection density difference (251)
$\rho_{\lambda\omega}$ specific reflectivity (390)
σ Stefan–Boltzmann constant (8, 397), specific electrical resistance (29), surface tension (476)
τ time constant (148)
$\boldsymbol{\tau}$ viscous stress tensor (201)
$\bar{\boldsymbol{\tau}}^{(t)}$ turbulent stress tensor
$\bar{\boldsymbol{\tau}}^{(T)}$ turbulent stress tensor plus the time arranged viscous stress tensor (281)
ϕ gravitational potential energy function (29)
Φ rate of heat generation (29)
Φ^* dimensionless rate of heat generation (168, 221, 254)
ψ stream function (121, 258)
Ψ dimensionless stream function (232)
ω frequency (158), solid angle (380)
$\boldsymbol{\Omega}$ unit vector indicating the direction of a photon flight path (380)

Mathematical Symbols

∇ vector operator, "grad" or "del" (6)
∇^2 scalar operator, "Laplacian" (33)
D/Dt material derivative (27, 195)
d/dt total derivative (194)
$\partial/\partial t$ partial derivative (143, 195)
$\langle\ \rangle$ area or volume average (49)
$\bar{}$ time average (273)
$\tilde{}$ free convection field (252)
$\mathbf{0}$ order-of-magnitude estimate (66)
$'$ turbulent fluctuation (274)

The Author

Stephen Whitaker (PhD, University of Delaware) is Professor of Chemical Engineering at the University of California, Davis. He spent several years as a research engineer with E. I. Du Pont de Nemours & Co., and taught at Northwestern University from 1961 to 1964. His research interests are transport processes in multi-phase systems, interfacial phenomena, and fluid mechanics. He is the author of *Introduction to Fluid Mechanics* published by Robert E. Krieger Publishing Company, Inc.

Design Problem I

The use of natural gas or fuel oil to heat homes and office buildings in the winter, and the use of electric power to operate air conditioners in the summer represent a significant consumption of natural resources. By natural resources we mean the obvious natural gas, fuel oil, and coal; in addition to the less obvious scenic coastline and the freely running river which may be destroyed by a power plant, the marine life which may be altered by thermal pollution, and the atmosphere which may be polluted by the effluents from combustion processes.

Insulated walls, as illustrated in Fig. I.1, help to conserve our natural resources while unfortunately increasing the capital outlay for home and office building construction. For the conditions indicated in Fig. I.1, calculate the new insulation thickness required to reduce the heat loss by 50 per cent and determine what fraction of the temperature drop occurs across the insulation.

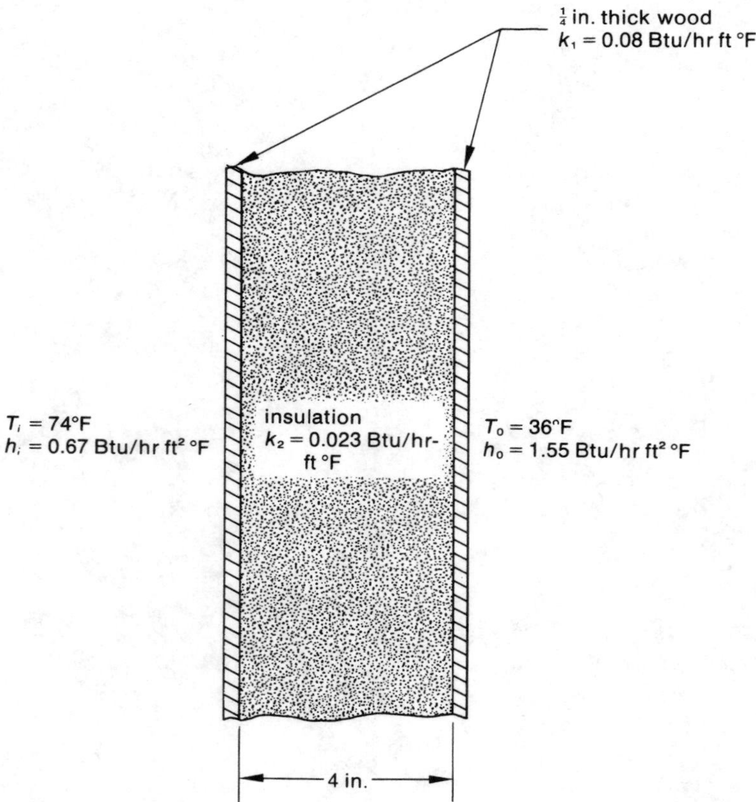

Fig. I.1 Heat transfer across a composite wall.

1

Introduction

The subject of heat transfer, or more generally the *transport of energy*, is of importance to all engineers and scientists, for it is energy, initially derived from the sun, on which the world runs. If we were to cut off the radiation from the sun we would soon find the world to be an uninhabitable, bleak sphere, and if we misuse the energy that is currently available to us a similar result may occur for other reasons.

At one time or another every engineer is likely to be confronted with a heat transfer problem. In the design of computer circuits electrical engineers may be concerned with temperature variations owing to electrical heating; civil and mechanical engineers may need to assess the importance of thermal stresses and strains in the structural design of high-speed aircraft and nuclear reactors; and chemical engineers are often required to design chemical reactors that operate at temperatures high enough so that the reaction rate is reasonably fast, but low enough so that product degradation or reactor burnout is not a problem. Agricultural engineers are interested in the radiative heat transfer that often leads to frost formation when the ambient air temperature is above the freezing point, and the energy transport processes associated with micro-meterology. The ecologist is concerned with a variety of heat transfer processes such as the "greenhouse" effect caused by the increasing carbon dioxide concentration in our atmosphere, and the effect of algae on the absorption of radiant energy in Lake Tahoe.

In an introductory text it is not possible to treat in depth any of the important special problems confronting engineers today, and we must be content with laying a solid foundation from which the student can proceed to the study of a variety of practical problems. In this chapter we will state the *fundamental postulates* governing the transport of energy, and describe briefly the *mechanisms* of energy transport.

*1.1 The Continuum Postulate

Throughout this text we will be examining processes that are satisfactorily described by the *continuum* or *field* equations. Thus, in the solids, liquids, and gases under consideration we will assume that the density, temperature, velocity, etc. are all smooth, continuous point functions. The continuum postulate is usually valid when the mean free path† is small compared to the characteristic dimension of the system under consideration. In high altitude flight the mean free path may become comparable to the characteristic dimension of the aircraft, and "slip flow" will occur. Under these conditions the velocity at

†The mean free path is the average distance travelled by molecules between collisions.

the fluid–solid interface undergoes a jump discontinuity and the fluid is thought of as "slipping" past the solid surface.

In the study of heat transfer the continuum postulate leads us to the assumption that the heat flux vector† $\mathbf{q}$ and the temperature T are continuous functions; however, there are many physical phenomena which are more easily described in terms of *discontinuous* functions. For example, the density at an air–water interface is treated as a discontinuous function. In actual fact the density is continuous, but undergoes an extremely rapid change as one passes from the gas phase into the liquid phase. Rather than become involved in the complexities of the large density gradients that occur at phase interfaces we allow for discontinuities in the density at phase interfaces. In Chapter 10 we will find that condensation and boiling are most easily treated by allowing for a discontinuity in $\mathbf{q}$ at the vapor–liquid interface; however, we will construct this discontinuity in a way which is consistent with the fundamental laws of physics.

*1.2 The Laws of Continuum Physics

The student should be familiar with all the fundamental postulates to be used in this text from previous courses in fluid mechanics and thermodynamics; however, it will be helpful to briefly review them here.

Conservation of mass

We state the principle of conservation of mass in the *rate* form as

$$\left\{\begin{matrix}\text{the time rate of}\\ \text{change of mass}\\ \text{of a body}\end{matrix}\right\} = 0 \tag{1.2-1}$$

Note that a body always contains the same *mass points* or the same *material,* thus the region in space occupied by a body will be referred to as a *material volume* and denoted by $\mathscr{V}_m(t)$. Often, in thermodynamics and fluid mechanics courses, a body is referred to as a *system* and its volume is denoted by V_{sys}. Since the word *system* has a variety of meanings we will use *material volume* to designate the space occupied by a body.

The laws of mechanics

The two fundamental laws of mechanics may be stated as:
(a) The balance of linear momentum

$$\left\{\begin{matrix}\text{the time rate of change}\\ \text{of the linear}\\ \text{momentum of a body}\end{matrix}\right\} = \left\{\begin{matrix}\text{the force}\\ \text{acting on}\\ \text{the body}\end{matrix}\right\} \tag{1.2-2}$$

(b) The balance of angular momentum

$$\left\{\begin{matrix}\text{the time rate of change}\\ \text{of the angular}\\ \text{momentum of a body}\end{matrix}\right\} = \left\{\begin{matrix}\text{the torque}\\ \text{acting on}\\ \text{the body}\end{matrix}\right\} \tag{1.2-3}$$

The linear momentum principle, Eq. 1.2-2, actually contains all three of Newton's laws of motion as they are traditionally presented in physics texts [1]. Clarification of the linear momentum principle is due largely to Euler, and following Truesdell [2] we refer to the balance of linear momentum as *Euler's first law of mechanics.* The angular momentum principle, or *Euler's second law of mechanics,* is not often awarded the prominence of Newton's laws or the linear momentum principle, yet it should stand equally with the first law as a separate fundamental postulate. This matter has been clarified by Truesdell [3] in an essay entitled "*Whence the Law of Moment of Momentum.*"

†The units of $\mathbf{q}$ are cal/sec cm^2 or something comparable.

The balance of energy

The general energy principle, often referred to as the first law of thermodynamics, can be expressed as

$$\left\{\begin{array}{l}\text{the time rate of change}\\ \text{of internal and kinetic}\\ \text{energy of a body}\end{array}\right\} = \left\{\begin{array}{l}\text{the rate at which energy}\\ \text{is supplied to the body}\\ \text{by "heat" and "work"}\end{array}\right\} + \left\{\begin{array}{l}\text{the rate at which electromagnetic}\\ \text{energy is accumulated or lost}\\ \text{from within the body}\end{array}\right\} \quad (1.2\text{-}4)$$

In Chapter 2 we will state more explicitly what is meant by heat and work, and in Chapter 5 we will show that the *total* energy equation (Eq. 1.2-4) contains both the *mechanical* energy equation, which is so useful in the analysis of incompressible flow processes, and the *thermal* energy equation. It is this latter energy equation which will prove to be the most suitable tool for the analysis of heat transfer processes. Note that the fundamental mass postulate is stated as a *conservation* principle, whereas the postulates concerning momentum, and energy were stated as *balance* principles. The reason for this is that only the mass of a body is conserved, while the linear momentum, angular momentum, and total energy of a body may increase or decrease depending on the action of the surroundings on the body.

*1.3 Mechanisms of Energy Transport

There are a variety of ways in which energy can be transported from one region to another, but from the continuum point of view all mechanisms can be satisfactorily categorized in terms of *conduction, convection,* and *radiation.* The mechanisms are listed in order of increasing complexity and we will study them in that order.

Conduction

The mechanism of conduction is perhaps best discussed in terms of an experiment that is often used to measure the *thermal conductivity* of gases and liquids. A schematic drawing of the apparatus is shown in Fig. 1.3.1. It consists of two parallel plates separated by a distance L. The lower plate is maintained at some temperature T_0 by a cool stream of fluid, while the upper plate is maintained at a higher temperature T_1 by an electrical heater. The heater output is measured in order to determine the energy per unit time† $\dot{Q}$ which flows from the top plate, through the test material, to the cold bottom plate.

If we vary the heater output, $\dot{Q}$, and the cell spacing, L, while measuring the temperature difference, $\Delta T = T_1 - T_0$, we obtain a series of values of the heat flux,‡ $\dot{Q}/A$, as a function of L and ΔT. Here A is the

†The dot over Q is used as a reminder that this term has the units of energy *per unit* time.

‡Note that the word *flux* has the meaning "..... per unit time per unit area" and that *heat* refers to *energy transported.*

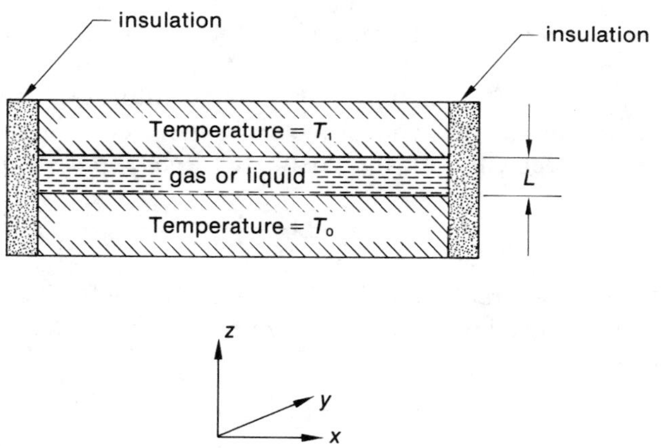

Fig. 1.3.1 Experimental determination of the thermal conductivity.

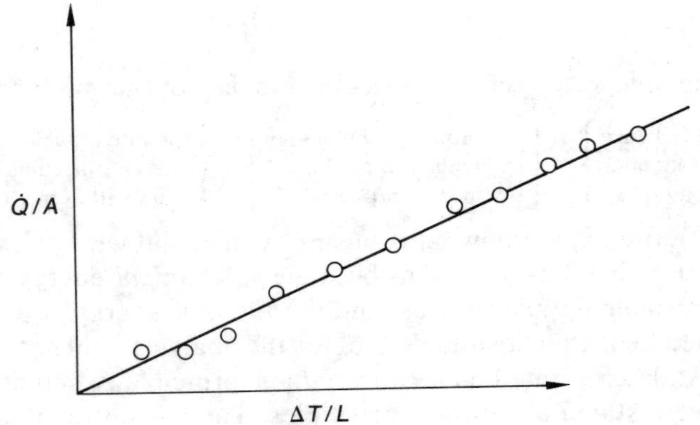

Fig. 1.3.2 Illustrative heat flux data versus $\Delta T/L$.

area over which the heat flow takes place, thus $\dot{Q}/A$ has the units of Btu/hr ft^2 in the British system, cal/sec cm^2 in the metric system, and joule/sec m^2 in the SI system. By experiment it has been found that $\dot{Q}/A$ is a *linear* function of $\Delta T/L$ as indicated in Fig. 1.3.2. The data can be represented by the following equation

$$\dot{Q}/A = k(T_1 - T_0)/L \tag{1.3-1}$$

where the coefficient k is the *thermal conductivity.* It exhibits a weak dependence on temperature and only a very slight dependence on pressure for both liquids and gases; however, it may depend strongly on the composition and structure for heterogeneous substances such as the common insulating materials used in building construction.

In dilute gases the energy is transported across the cell primarily by the motion of the molecules, while in liquids the transport takes place both by the migration of the molecules and by the interaction between neighboring molecules. In solids the mechanism is that of phonon transport [4]; however, we need not be overly concerned with any of these special mechanisms. We need only center our attention on the experimental observation that the rate of energy transport in the absence of macroscopic motion and radiation is a linear function of the temperature difference divided by the distance over which this difference is measured.†

We can *define* the mode of energy transport called *heat conduction* as follows:

> Heat conduction is the energy transported *over* and *above* that transported by macroscopic motion and radiation

In the apparatus shown in Fig. 1.3.1 there is certainly molecular motion taking place in the gas or liquid; however, the *mass average velocity* should be zero since the fluid is heated at the top and cooled at the bottom. At room temperatures radiant energy transport between the two plates is negligible and we can properly refer to $\dot{Q}$ as the rate of heat conduction. At high temperatures radiation cannot be neglected and the experimental determination of thermal conductivities is more complicated.

Eq. 1.3-1 is in complete agreement with the postulated *differential* or *point* relation

$$q_z = -k\left(\frac{\partial T}{\partial z}\right) \tag{1.3-2}$$

where q_z is the heat flux in the z-direction and has units of Btu/hr ft^2. The negative sign results from requiring that k be positive, thus heat flows in the negative z-direction (i.e., $q_z < 0$) when $\partial T/\partial z$ is positive. The heat flux vector is defined as

$$\mathbf{q} = \mathbf{i}q_x + \mathbf{j}q_y + \mathbf{k}q_z \tag{1.3-3}$$

†Departures from this linear relation do exist for rarefied gases and have been treated by Cha and McCoy [5].

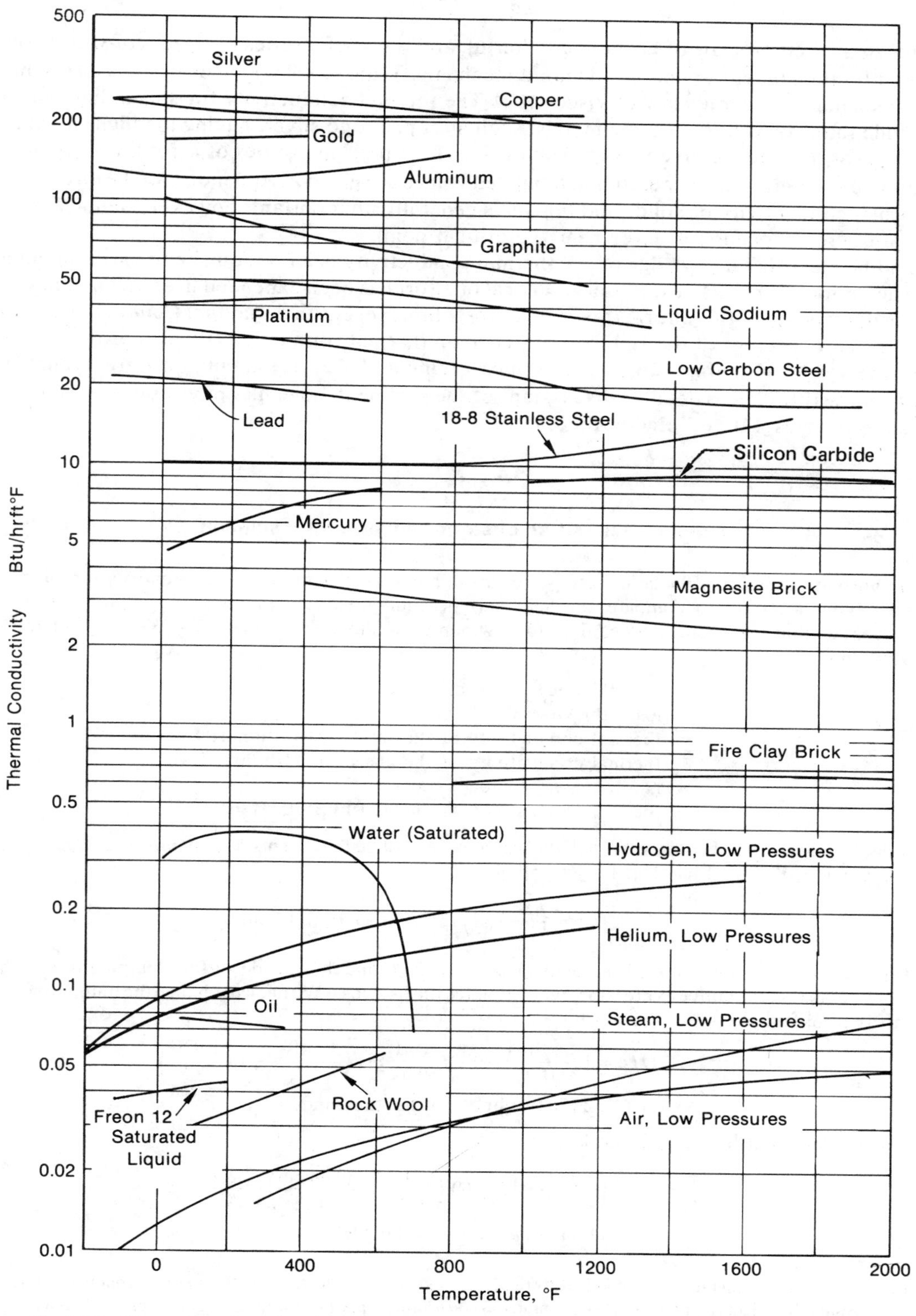

Fig. 1.3.3 Thermal conductivity of some solids, liquids, and gases. (From W. M. Rohsenow and H. Y. Choi, *Heat, Mass and Momentum Transfer*, Prentice-Hall, Inc., Englewood Cliffs, N.J. © 1961. By permission of the publisher.)

and the general form of Eq. 1.3-2 for an isotropic material† is

$$\mathbf{q} = -k\nabla T \tag{1.3-4}$$

This is known as Fourier's law of heat conduction [6], and is one of a series of *linear constitutive equations* encountered by the student in courses on solid mechanics (Hooke's law), electrical circuits (Ohm's law), and fluid mechanics (Newton's law of viscosity).‡ The thermal conductivity for solids, liquids, and gases covers a wide range of values with the metals, such as copper and silver, having the highest values, while liquids and gases have successively lower values. Fig. 1.3.3 presents values of k for a variety of materials as a function of temperature and additional tabulated values are given in Appendix A. The effect of pressure on the thermal conductivity of solids and liquids is generally unimportant; however, significant variations owing to pressure do occur for gases near the critical point.

It should be clear that knowledge of the thermal conductivity is a prerequisite to carrying out any heat transfer calculation, and because of this a great deal of effort has been expended in experimental studies. An outstanding description of this effort is given in a two-volume set entitled *Thermal Conductivity* edited by R. P. Tye [7]. The proceedings of the eighth conference on thermal conductivity [8] also provide an excellent entry into the world of thermal conductivity measurement. Extensive tabulations are available from a number of sources [9–12] and detailed discussions of the pertinent molecular physics can be found in books on solid state physics [13] and kinetic theory [14].

Example 1.3-1 Use of storm windows for insulation

In northern Minnesota the cold arctic winds make home heating in the winter months a serious problem. In this example we wish to compare the heat loss per unit area for windows and walls, and consider the improvement that can be made by adding storm windows as illustrated in Fig. 1.3.4. We are given the following information:

wall thickness: 10 cm
glass thickness: 0.5 cm
thermal conductivity of the wall: 0.05 Btu/hr ft °F
thermal conductivity of the glass: 0.4 Btu/hr ft °F
gap between windows: 3 cm
thermal conductivity of air: 0.013 Btu/hr ft °F

In order to calculate the heat flux through the window we assume that the inside and outside surface temperatures are 23°C and −17°C and use Eq. 1.3-1 to obtain

$$\dot{Q}/A = \left(\frac{0.4\ \text{Btu}}{\text{hr ft °F}}\right)[23°\text{C} - (-17°\text{C})]/0.5\ \text{cm}$$

The inside surface temperature will actually be less than 23°C and the outside surface temperature will be greater than −17°C so that the above expression overestimates the heat loss. We need to change the units from °C to °F and cm to ft to obtain

$$\dot{Q}/A = \left(\frac{0.4\ \text{Btu}}{\text{hr ft °F}}\right)(40°\text{C})\left(\frac{1}{0.5\ \text{cm}}\right)\left(\frac{30.48\ \text{cm}}{\text{ft}}\right)\left(\frac{1.8°\text{F}}{°\text{C}}\right)$$
$$= 1756\ \text{Btu/hr ft}^2, \quad \text{for the window}$$

A similar calculation for the wall leads to

$$\dot{Q}/A = \left(\frac{0.05\ \text{Btu}}{\text{hr ft °F}}\right)(40°\text{C})\left(\frac{1}{10\ \text{cm}}\right)\left(\frac{30.48\ \text{cm}}{\text{ft}}\right)\left(\frac{1.8°\text{F}}{°\text{C}}\right)$$
$$= 11.0\ \text{Btu/hr ft}^2, \quad \text{for the wall}$$

†For anisotropic materials this must be modified to read $q_i = -k_{ij}(\partial T/\partial x_j)$ where k_{ij} is the thermal conductivity tensor.

‡To be more explicit we might refer to Eq. 1.3-4 as a *material constitutive equation*, for the thermal conductivity is a property of the *material*.

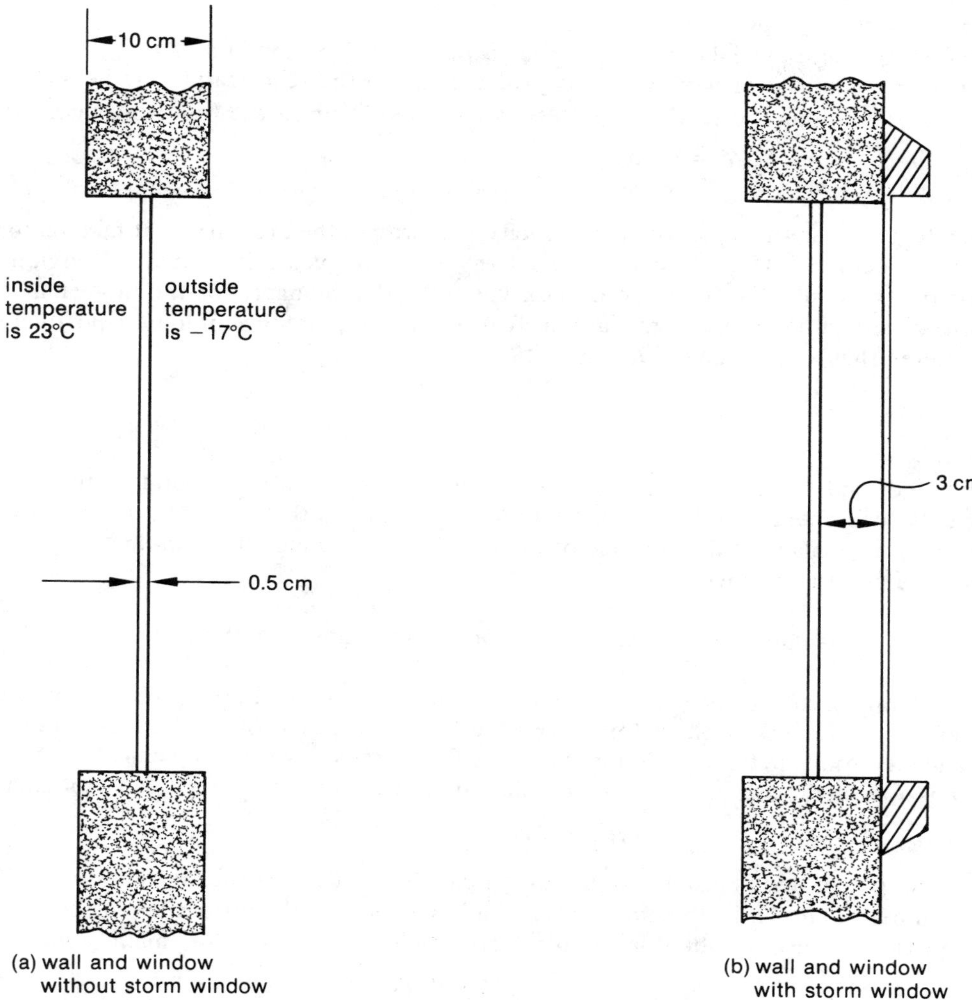

Fig. 1.3.4 Use of storm windows for insulation.

Here we see that the heat flux through the window is calculated to be 160 times larger than the heat flux through the walls. If only a small fraction of the wall space is taken up by windows, the loss of energy by conduction through the glass is still very significant and the use of storm windows to reduce this loss would appear to be worthwhile. It will be left as an exercise for the student to determine the heat flux when storm windows are used.

Convection

Convection refers to the energy transported as a result of *macroscopic* motion. This type of energy transport has been previously encountered by the student in a thermodynamics course. There, the macroscopic energy balances included terms of the type $\dot{m}c_p(T - T_0)$ where $\dot{m}$ is the mass flow rate, c_p the constant pressure heat capacity, and T_0 some reference temperature. These terms represented the *convection* of energy into and out of various control volumes.

If we return to our discussion of heat conduction for a dilute gas in our thermal conductivity cell, we note that essentially all the energy is transported by convection on the *microscopic* scale, i.e., by the motion of the gas molecules from one region into another, but on the *macroscopic* scale the energy transport is considered to be conduction. The point to be made here is that for obvious convenience we split the total nonradiative energy transport across a plane into two parts:

(a) that energy transport which is proportional to the mass flux, $\rho\mathbf{v}$, and

(b) the remaining energy transport which is proportional to the temperature gradient, ∇T.

In terms of these definitions the total energy flux vector is split up in the following manner:

$$\mathscr{E} = \underset{\text{convection}}{\rho \mathbf{v} e} + \underset{\text{conduction}}{\mathbf{q}} + \underset{\text{radiation}}{\mathbf{q}^R} \tag{1.3-5}$$

where ρ is the density, $\mathbf{v}$ is the mass average velocity vector, $\mathbf{q}$ is the ordinary heat flux vector, $\mathbf{q}^R$ is the radiant heat flux vector, and e is the internal energy per unit mass. It should be obvious that it is advantageous for us to split the total energy flux vector in this manner, for the molecular and atomic phenomena associated with the three terms are fairly distinct. Note that the continuum postulate discussed in Sec. 1.1 requires that $\mathscr{E}$ be a continuous function.

Radiation

If we place a hot body in an *evacuated* cavity having walls at a lower temperature than the body, the body will steadily lose energy until its temperature is the same as that of the surrounding cavity. This transfer of energy takes place in the absence of matter, thus, following our definition of heat conduction we may define radiation as follows:

Radiation is the energy transported in the absence of matter

Radiant energy is transported at the speed of light by means of photons. In the problems of interest to us, significant energy transfer takes place for wave lengths in the range of 10^{-2} cm (infrared) to 10^{-5} cm (ultraviolet), and electromagnetic radiation in this wave length region is naturally called *thermal radiation.* The rate of emission of radiant energy from a solid surface is given by the Stefan–Boltzmann law

$$\mathbf{q}^R \cdot \mathbf{n} = q^R = \epsilon\sigma T^4 \tag{1.3-6}$$

Here q^R is the energy emitted per unit time per unit area (Btu/hr ft^2), T is the absolute temperature of the body, ϵ is a parameter, known as the emissivity, which depends on the properties of the surface, and σ is a universal physical constant which is often referred to as the Stefan–Boltzmann constant.

$$\sigma = 1.71 \times 10^{-9} \text{ Btu/hr ft}^2\text{-}^\circ\text{R}^4$$

One of the most important characteristics of thermal radiation is that the rate of emission depends on the fourth power of the temperature, thus the rate increases rapidly with increasing temperature. Radiant energy transfer usually becomes significant for temperatures of the order of 200°F and may dominate the energy transfer process for temperatures of 1000°F and higher. In Chapters 8 and 9 we will develop methods for accurately calculating radiant energy transport rates; however, at this point we can analyze the radiant energy exchange that takes place between a body and a *black surface* which entirely surrounds the body. This situation is illustrated in Fig. 1.3.5, where we have indicated that the surrounding surface is at a uniform temperature, T_2. In order to focus our attention on the radiant energy transport we imagine that the enclosure is evacuated and that we have a means of controlling the temperature of the body.

We should note that the body we have shown in the enclosure "cannot see itself," i.e., all the radiation emitted from the body is incident upon the walls of the enclosure. The radiation which is emitted by the walls is more complex in that it can strike either the walls of the enclosure or the body. One might guess that keeping track of the radiation transport between the walls and the body could be very complex; however, this is not the case if we consider the surface of the enclosure to be a *black surface,* and the body in the enclosure to be a *black body.* A black surface or body is defined in the following way:

A black body or black surface absorbs all incident radiation

In addition, a black surface emits radiation according to

$$q^R = \sigma T^4, \quad \text{for a black surface} \tag{1.3-7}$$

thus the emissivity, ϵ, is 1.0 for a black surface.

In analyzing the radiant energy exchange process illustrated in Fig. 1.3.5, we first consider the case where the system is at equilibrium, i.e., the temperature of the body is T_2. For this case we can write

$$\begin{Bmatrix} \text{rate at which} \\ \text{radiant energy} \\ \text{is emitted from} \\ \text{the body} \end{Bmatrix} = \begin{Bmatrix} \text{rate at which} \\ \text{radiant energy} \\ \text{is absorbed by} \\ \text{the body} \end{Bmatrix} \tag{1.3-8}$$

If we designate the surface area of the body as A_1 we can use Eq. 1.3-7 to write

$$\begin{Bmatrix} \text{rate at which} \\ \text{radiant energy} \\ \text{is emitted from} \\ \text{the body} \end{Bmatrix} = A_1 \sigma T_2^4 \tag{1.3-9}$$

and it follows from Eq. 1.3-8 that

$$\begin{Bmatrix} \text{rate at which} \\ \text{radiant energy} \\ \text{is absorbed by} \\ \text{the body} \end{Bmatrix} = A_1 \sigma T_2^4 \tag{1.3-10}$$

We should note that $A_1 \sigma T_2^4$ represents the rate at which radiation is *incident* upon the body, and since we are considering a black body the *incident* radiation is equal to the *absorbed* radiation.

We now consider the case where the temperature of the body is increased to $T_1 > T_2$ by means of an

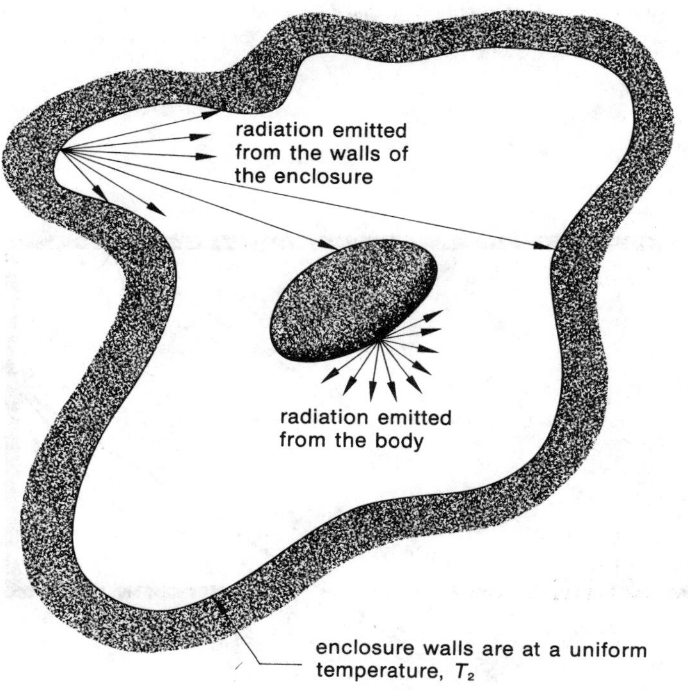

Fig. 1.3.5 Radiant energy exchange in an enclosure.

electric heater. An energy balance would require that

$$\left\{\begin{array}{l}\text{rate at which}\\ \text{energy is}\\ \text{transferred from}\\ \text{the body to}\\ \text{the walls}\end{array}\right\} = \left\{\begin{array}{l}\text{rate at which}\\ \text{radiant energy}\\ \text{is emitted}\\ \text{from the body}\end{array}\right\} - \left\{\begin{array}{l}\text{rate at which}\\ \text{radiant energy is}\\ \text{absorbed by the}\\ \text{body}\end{array}\right\} \tag{1.3-11}$$

We know from Eq. 1.3-7 that the rate at which energy is *emitted* from the body is $A_1\sigma T_1^4$, but what about the rate at which energy is absorbed by the body? This energy comes from the walls of the enclosure, and the radiation from the walls of the enclosure is not changed by changing the temperature of the body,† thus we can use Eq. 1.3-10 to find that the rate at which energy is *absorbed* by the body is $A_1\sigma T_2^4$. Expressing the rate at which energy is transferred from the body to the walls of the enclosure as $\dot{Q}_{12}$ we can now write Eq. 1.3-11 as

$$\dot{Q}_{12} = A_1\sigma T_1^4 - A_1\sigma T_2^4$$

or

$$\dot{Q}_{12} = A_1\sigma(T_1^4 - T_2^4), \quad \text{for a black body in a black enclosure} \tag{1.3-12}$$

It is most important to remember that Eq. 1.3-12 is valid only for a black body, which cannot see itself, in a black enclosure. From a practical point of view, if the enclosure is large compared to the body, it will act as a black enclosure even though some radiation is reflected from the walls. This phenomenon is easily observed by looking at a window of a house in which all the lights are turned off. If the window is small compared to the size of the room, it will appear to be black simply because all the visible radiation which enters the window from the outside is absorbed in the room. This situation is illustrated in Fig. 1.3.6.

We can extend our analysis of radiant energy exchange in an enclosure to a more realistic system, provided we retain the restriction that the walls of the enclosure are black. Since this means that the walls of the enclosure absorb all incident radiation we only require that the enclosure be very large compared to

†This would not be true if the walls could reflect radiation. In that case some of the radiation emitted by the body would be reflected back to the body, thus the *incident* radiation would be influenced by the temperature of the body.

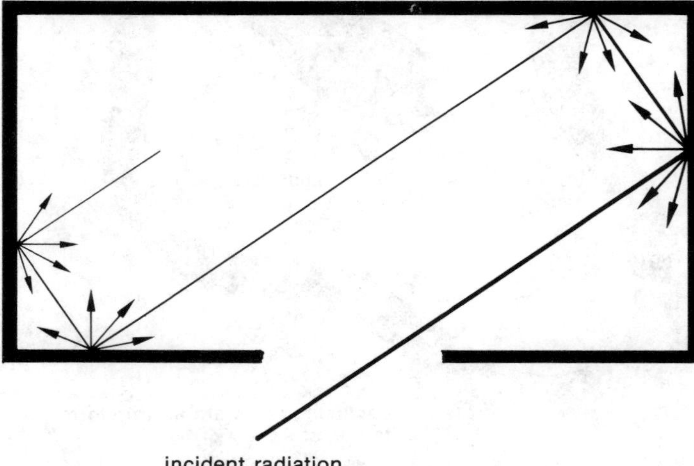

Fig. 1.3.6 Absorption of radiation in an enclosure which reflects some of the incident radiation.

the body. Consider now that the body emits radiation according to the Stefan–Boltzmann law given by Eq. 13.3-6

$$\left\{\begin{array}{l}\text{rate at which}\\ \text{radiant energy}\\ \text{is emitted from}\\ \text{the body}\end{array}\right\} = \epsilon A_1 \sigma T_1^4 \tag{1.3-13}$$

Real surfaces always absorb some fraction of the incident radiation, and we designate this fraction as α, the absorptivity, so that the rate at which radiant energy is absorbed by the body is given by

$$\left\{\begin{array}{l}\text{rate at which}\\ \text{radiant energy}\\ \text{is absorbed}\\ \text{by the body}\end{array}\right\} = \underset{\substack{\uparrow \\ \text{fraction} \\ \text{absorbed}}}{\alpha} \qquad \underset{\substack{\uparrow \\ \text{incident} \\ \text{radiation}}}{A_1 \sigma T_2^4} \tag{1.3-14}$$

Eq. 1.3-14 naturally reduces to Eq. 1.3-10 for a black body, i.e., $\alpha = 1.0$. Substitution of Eqs. 1.3-13 and 1.3-14 into 1.3-11 leads to

$$\dot{Q}_{12} = A_1 \sigma(\epsilon T_1^4 - \alpha T_2^4) \tag{1.3-15}$$

For a black body, $\epsilon = \alpha = 1.0$, and Eq. 1.3-15 reduces to Eq. 1.3-12.

The black body or black surface represents the simplest and crudest possible model of real surfaces. An improvement is the *gray body* model which is defined as

A gray body is a body for which $\alpha = \epsilon$

Our expression for the radiant energy exchange between a gray body and a black enclosure, or a very large enclosure is

$$\dot{Q}_{12} = \epsilon A_1 \sigma(T_1^4 - T_2^4), \quad \text{gray body in a black enclosure} \tag{1.3-16}$$

It is important to note that Eq. 1.3-16 is quite a reasonable approximation for the radiant energy exchange between any real body and a large enclosure, provided T_1 and T_2 do not differ by more than 200°F. The reason for this is that one can prove for *any* body that $\alpha \rightarrow \epsilon$ as $T_2 \rightarrow T_1$ (see Prob. 8-14, and the experimental data discussed in Sec. 9.6), thus Eq. 1.3-16 is exact for an arbitrary body in a large enclosure as T_1 approaches T_2.

When a black body can see itself, the rate at which it emits radiation is less than $A_1 \sigma T_1^4$ because some of the emitted radiation is incident upon the body itself. This situation is taken care of by the introduction of a geometrical factor, called a view factor, which is defined as

$$F_{12} = \left\{\begin{array}{l}\text{fraction of radiant energy}\\ \text{leaving surface 1 which}\\ \text{is incident upon surface 2}\end{array}\right\} \tag{1.3-17}$$

For a black body in a black enclosure Eq. 1.3-9 is modified to,

$$\left\{\begin{array}{l}\text{rate at which radiant}\\ \text{energy is emitted}\\ \text{from the body}\end{array}\right\} = A_1 F_{12} \sigma T_2^4 \tag{1.3-18}$$

and it follows that Eq. 1.3-10 takes the form

$$\left\{\begin{array}{l}\text{rate at which radiant}\\ \text{energy is absorbed}\\ \text{by the body}\end{array}\right\} = A_1 F_{12} \sigma T_2^4 \tag{1.3-19}$$

For the non-equilibrium case Eq. 1.3-12 quite naturally takes the form

$$\dot{Q}_{12} = A_1 F_{12} \sigma(T_1^4 - T_2^4), \quad \text{for a black body in a black enclosure} \tag{1.3-20}$$

It is not so obvious, but one can prove (see Ex. 9.7-1) that when a gray body can see itself, i.e., $F_{12} < 1$, we must write Eq. 1.3-16 as

$$\dot{Q}_{12} = \frac{\epsilon A_1 F_{12}\sigma}{[\epsilon + F_{12}(1-\epsilon)]}(T_1^4 - T_2^4), \quad \text{gray body in a black enclosure} \tag{1.3-21}$$

One must always be careful to remember the restrictions that apply to Eq. 1.3-21; they will be discussed again in greater detail in Chapters 8 and 9.

Example 1.3-2 Radiation losses from an uninsulated steam pipe

An uninsulated steel pipe carrying saturated steam at 99 psig (330°F) has an outside diameter of 1.24 in. and is 100 ft long. We wish to calculate the heat loss owing to radiation in a large room at 70°F and estimate the cost per year in energy losses.

Because the dimensions of the room will be large compared to the pipe diameter we can approximate the process as a gray body in a black enclosure. Since the surface of a straight pipe cannot see itself, Eq. 1.3-21 reduces to Eq. 1.3-16 and the radiation loss can be expressed as

$$\dot{Q} = \pi D L \epsilon \sigma (T_1^4 - T_2^4)$$

Remember that T_1 and T_2 represent absolute temperatures so that

$$T_1 = (330 + 459.67)°\text{R}$$

$$T_2 = (70 + 459.67)°\text{R}$$

From Table 9.6-2 we estimate the emissivity as $\epsilon = 0.7$ and the rate of energy loss owing to radiation is given by

$$\dot{Q} = (3.14)(1.24\ \text{in.})(100\ \text{ft})(0.7)\left(\frac{1.71\times 10^{-9}\ \text{Btu}}{\text{hr}\,\text{ft}^2\,°\text{R}^4}\right)[(790°\text{R})^4 - (530°\text{R})^4]\left(\frac{1\ \text{ft}}{12\ \text{in.}}\right)$$

$$= 1.21\times 10^4\ \text{Btu/hr}$$

In a year's time the radiant energy loss will be

$$\begin{Bmatrix}\text{radiant}\\ \text{energy loss}\\ \text{per year}\end{Bmatrix} = 1.06\times 10^8\ \text{Btu}$$

and converting this to kilowatt hours gives

$$\begin{Bmatrix}\text{radiant}\\ \text{energy loss}\\ \text{per year}\end{Bmatrix} = 3.11\times 10^4\ \text{kWh}$$

A representative cost of energy at an industrial site could be taken to be $1\frac{1}{2}$ cents per kilowatt hour, thus the cost owing to radiant energy losses is

$$\begin{Bmatrix}\text{cost of radiant}\\ \text{energy loss}\\ \text{per year}\end{Bmatrix} = \$466$$

We should remember that energy losses also occur owing to convection and conduction. In any event, it is obvious that the cost is significant and insulation is in order.

When T_1 and T_2 differ by less than 200°F, we can put Eq. 1.3-20 into a more convenient form. This is done by expressing T_1 and T_2 in terms of the average temperature and the temperature difference,

$$T_1 = T_{av} + (T_1 - T_2)/2$$

$$T_2 = T_{av} - (T_1 - T_2)/2$$

where the average temperature is given by

$$T_{av} = (T_1 + T_2)/2$$

One can easily show that the temperature difference in Eq. 1.3-20 can be expressed as

$$T_1^4 - T_2^4 = 4T_{av}^3(T_1 - T_2) + T_{av}(T_1 - T_2)^3 \tag{1.3-22}$$

Since $T_{av} \sim 500°R$ we can see that

$$4T_{av}^3(T_1 - T_2) \gg T_{av}(T_1 - T_2)^3$$

provided $(T_1 - T_2)$ is less than 200°F. Under these circumstances Eq. 1.3-20 takes the form

$$\dot{Q}_{12} = A_1F_{12}4\sigma T_{av}^3(T_1 - T_2), \quad \text{black body in a black enclosure for } |T_1 - T_2| \leq 200°\text{F} \tag{1.3-23}$$

The average net radiant energy heat flux, $\dot{Q}_{12}/A_1 = \langle q^R \rangle_{net}$ can be expressed as

$$\langle q^R \rangle_{net} = \left(F_{12}4\sigma T_{av}^3\right)(T_1 - T_2) \tag{1.3-24}$$

or in terms of a radiation film heat transfer coefficient

$$\langle q^R \rangle_{net} = h_r(T_1 - T_2) \tag{1.3-25}$$

where h_r is given by

$$h_r = 4F_{12}\sigma T_{av}^3 \tag{1.3-26}$$

Several values of h_r are listed in Table 1.3-1 for the case where $F_{12} = 1.0$. There we can see that radiant energy transfer becomes important relative to free convection for temperatures on the order of 100°F and can dominate the heat transfer process for quiescent air at room temperatures.

Combined mechanisms

In many, if not most, real processes one must deal with all three mechanisms of energy transport. To illustrate, let us consider the steady heat transfer taking place between a hot liquid in a metal tank and the surrounding air. This process is illustrated in Fig. 1.3.7. Part (a) shows the velocity profile that is established as the less dense air near the hot surface rises owing to buoyancy forces. Energy transported as a result of this type of fluid motion is referred to as *free convection.* Part (b) shows two temperature profiles, one being the profile for free convection, and the other being the profile that would occur if air were blown past the tank (*forced convection*). The effect of radiation on the temperature profile is left as an exercise for the student. The heat flux in the walls of the tank is related to the temperature gradient by

$$q_x = -k\left(\frac{dT}{dx}\right), \quad \text{in the walls of the tank} \tag{1.3-27}$$

The heat flux in the air is not easily determined as the fluid motion makes the process much more complex. However, at the surface of the tank the fluid velocity is zero and we can write

$$q_x|_{air} = -k_{air}\left(\frac{dT_{air}}{dx}\right), \quad \text{at the surface of the tank} \tag{1.3-28}$$

Very often we find it convenient to correlate experimentally determined values of the heat flux $q_x|_{air}$ in terms of a *film heat transfer coefficient, h.* This is defined by the equation†

$$q_x|_{air} \equiv h_{air}(T_0 - T_a), \quad \text{at the surface of the tank} \tag{1.3-29}$$

†Eq. 1.3-29 is often referred to as "Newton's Law of Cooling." This is somewhat of a misnomer since it applies equally well to heating or cooling situations, and in actual fact Eq. 1.3-29 should be referred to as a *process constitutive equation* since h_{air} is a *process* variable.

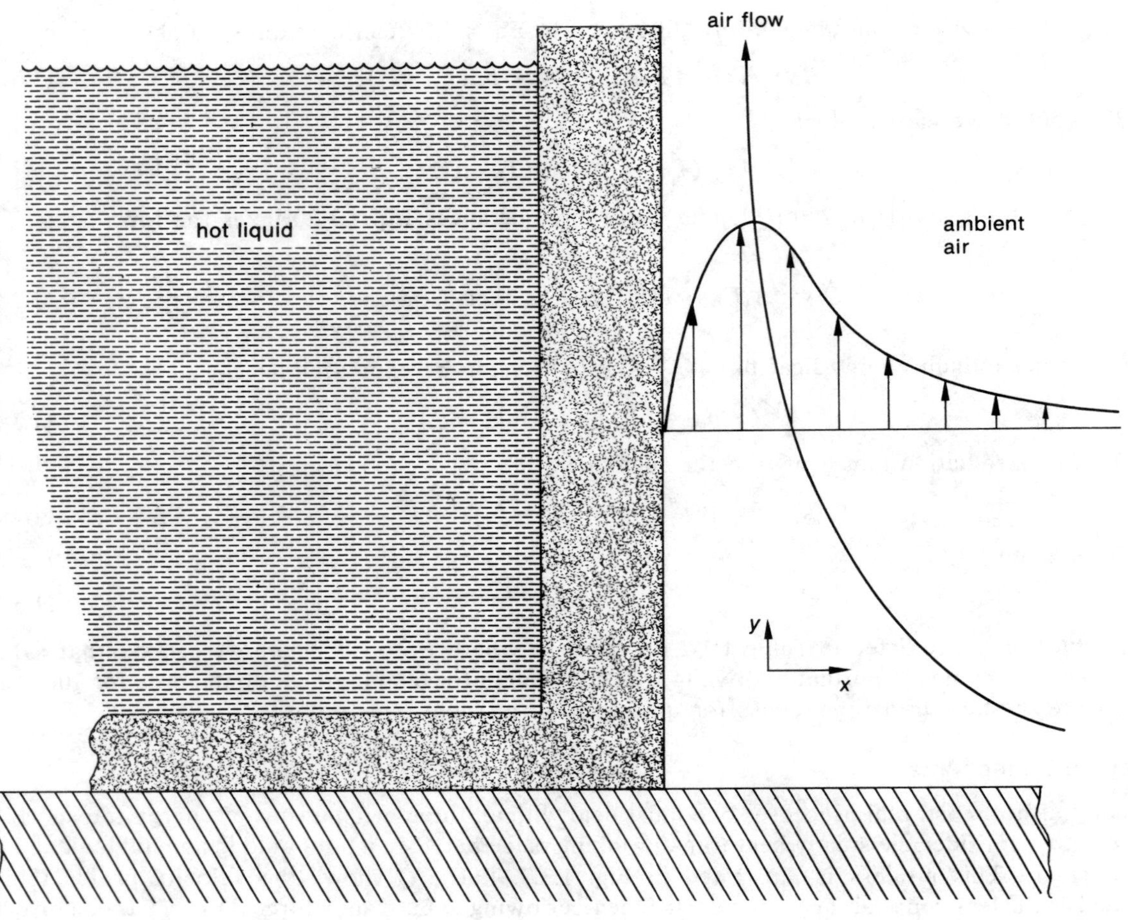

Fig. 1.3.7a Velocity and temperature profiles for a hot liquid in a tank.

Here T_0 is the temperature of the outer surface of the tank and T_a is the ambient temperature of the air far removed from the tank. The film heat transfer coefficient h depends on the velocity field and physical properties of the air in a complex manner. If air is blown past the surface at a high velocity, large values of h_{air} are observed and h_{air} is independent of $(T_0 - T_a)$. If air is not blown past the surface but rises slowly owing to buoyancy effects, small values of h_{air} are observed and they are proportional to $(T_0 - T_a)^{1/4}$. In Chapters 5, 6, and 7 we will investigate the problem of calculating, measuring, and correlating heat transfer coefficients, but for the present we will proceed on the assumption that expressions such as that given by Eq. 1.3-29 adequately represent the heat flux at *phase interfaces.*

The importance of film heat transfer coefficients stems from the fact that they can be used to determine an *overall* heat transfer coefficient U *defined* by the equation

$$\dot{Q} \equiv UA(T_\ell - T_a) \tag{1.3-30}$$

where U is given by†

$$\frac{1}{U} = \left[\frac{1}{h_{\text{liq}}} + \frac{1}{k/L} + \frac{1}{h_{\text{air}}}\right] \tag{1.3-31}$$

†Derivation of Eq. 1.3-31 is illustrated in the solution of Design Problem I.

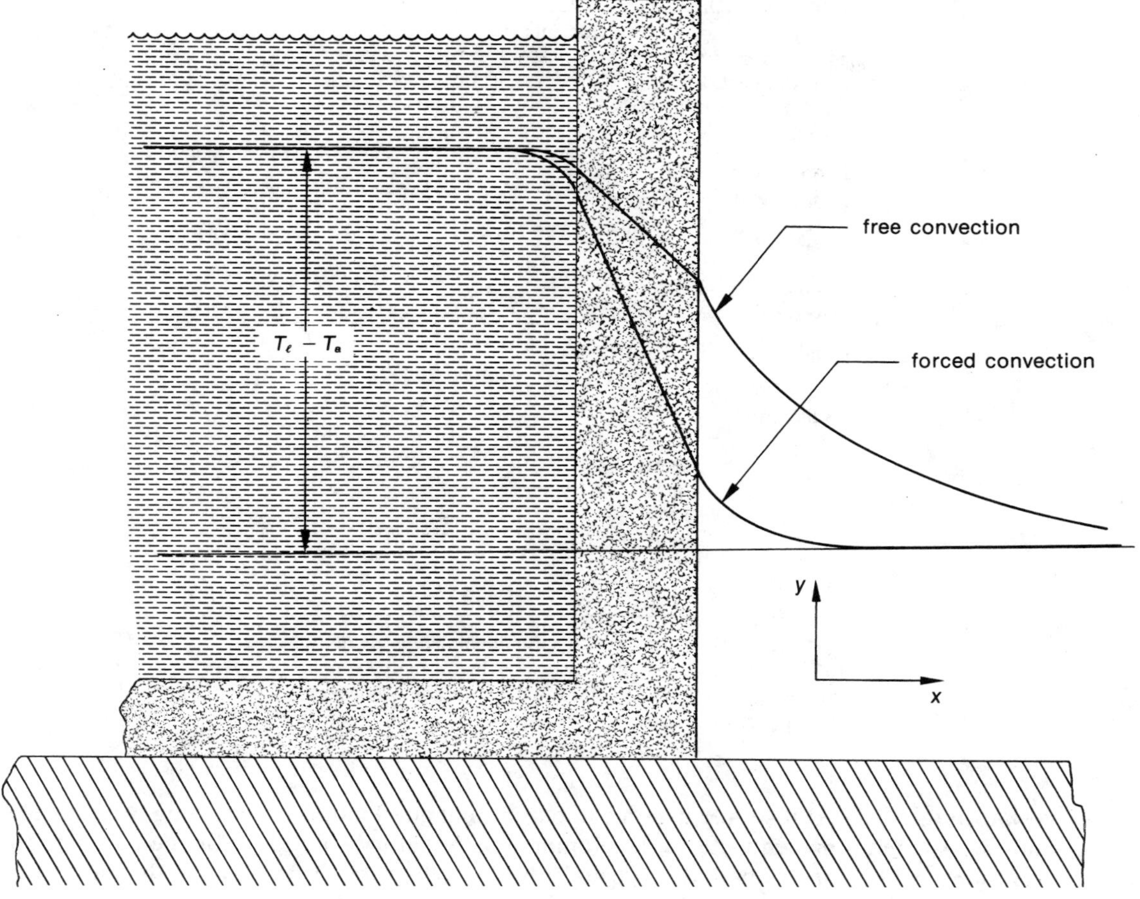

Fig. 1.3.7b Temperature profiles.

Here h_{liq} is the *liquid-side* film heat transfer coefficient, k is the thermal conductivity of the wall material, L is the thickness of the wall, and h_{air} is the *air-side* film heat transfer coefficient. The value of knowing the overall coefficient U should be obvious, for if it is known that we can calculate the rate at which energy is transferred from the hot liquid to the surrounding air knowing only the temperature of the hot liquid T_ℓ and the temperature of the ambient air, T_a. Some representative values for film heat transfer coefficients are given in Table 1.3-1.

It should be noted at this point how very important it is to be able to sketch temperature profiles such as those shown in Fig. 1.3.7, and to have some idea how these profiles will change as the air flow rate is changed, or the thermal conductivity of the wall is changed, etc. The necessity for having a good "feel" for the temperature field would perhaps appear more reasonable if we stopped to think about some of the problems that have been successfully solved in earlier courses. You should remember from a course in solid mechanics or "strength of materials" that the key step in developing the design equations for beams (the Euler–Bernoulli beam theory) was the shrewd guess as to the nature of the stress and strain fields; i.e., deducing which components of the stress and strain tensors were zero or negligible. In the analysis of flow problems, you should have been introduced to the idea that some knowledge of the velocity field was required in order to develop a satisfactory solution. For example, in the analysis of laminar flow in a tube, the velocity profile is assumed to be independent of the axial position; the analysis of boundary layer flows rests upon the knowledge that viscous forces are important only in a very thin region near the solid surface; and the analysis of a variety of turbulent flow phenomena in closed conduits is based on the knowledge that the velocity profiles are nearly flat.

Table 1.3-1 Order-of-Magnitude of Film Heat Transfer Coefficients

	h, Btu/hrft²°F
Free Convection	
air	0.1–1
water	1–10
Forced Convection	
air, superheated steam	5–50
water	50–2000
oil	10–300
Boiling	
water	500–10000
Condensation	
steam	1000–20000
Radiation†	
T_{av} = 100°F	1.20
200°F	1.96
300°F	3.00
400°F	4.35
800°F	13.7
1200°F	31.3
1600°F	59.8

†The radiation film heat transfer coefficient is given by $4\sigma T_{av}^3$ and represents the case of a black body, which cannot see itself, in a black enclosure for values of $|T_1 - T_2|$ less than 200°F.

As you work through this text it should become apparent that good intuition regarding the nature of the temperature profile is often a prerequisite to developing a satisfactory solution. For the easier problems where exact solutions can be constructed, this type of intuition is less important, but for the more complex problems where our best hope is to obtain an approximate solution, it is often necessary that one be able to make a reasonable guess regarding the temperature field.

Example 1.3-3 Effect of film heat transfer coefficients on the storm window decision

In light of the previous discussion on combined mechanisms of heat transfer we would now like to repeat the calculation given in Ex. 1.3-1. On the inside of the window the fluid motion is most likely caused by buoyancy forces as the cold air flows downward by the window and the wall. On the outside, forced convection is more probable since we are primarily concerned with the effect of the cold arctic winds.

In Chapters 5, 6, and 7 we will develop techniques for predicting appropriate values for the film heat transfer coefficients, but at this point we will simply take some representative values for free and forced convection from Table 1.3-1. We are therefore given the following information:

wall thickness: 10 cm
glass thickness: 0.5 cm
thermal conductivity of the wall: 0.05 Btu/hrft°F
thermal conductivity of the glass: 0.4 Btu/hrft°F
inside film heat transfer coefficient: $h_i = 0.55$ Btu/hrft²°F
outside film heat transfer coefficient: $h_o = 12$ Btu/hrft²°F

We can now use Eqs. 1.3-10 and 1.3-11 to express the heat flux as

$$\dot{Q}/A = \frac{T_i - T_o}{\dfrac{1}{h_i} + \dfrac{1}{k/L} + \dfrac{1}{h_o}}$$

where $T_i = 23°C$ and $T_o = -17°C$. Substitution of the appropriate values leads to the following expression for the heat flux in the wall.

$$\dot{Q}/A = \frac{(40)(1.8)\ \text{Btu/hr ft}^2}{\left(\underset{\substack{\uparrow\\ \text{inside air}\\ \text{resistance}}}{1.82} + \underset{\substack{\uparrow\\ \text{wall}\\ \text{resistance}}}{6.56} + \underset{\substack{\uparrow\\ \text{outside air}\\ \text{resistance}}}{0.083}\right)}$$

Here we note that h_i^{-1}, L/k, and h_o^{-1} can be thought of as resistances to the transfer of heat, and for the case under consideration the resistances of the inside air film and the wall are the most significant. Carrying out the numerical calculations leads to

$$\dot{Q}/A = 8.51\ \text{Btu/hr ft}^2, \qquad \text{for the wall}$$

A similar calculation for the window leads to

$$\dot{Q}/A = \frac{(40)(1.8)\ \text{Btu/hr ft}^2}{\left(\underset{\substack{\uparrow\\ \text{inside air}\\ \text{resistance}}}{1.82} + \underset{\substack{\uparrow\\ \text{window}\\ \text{resistance}}}{0.041} + \underset{\substack{\uparrow\\ \text{outside air}\\ \text{resistance}}}{0.083}\right)}$$

Here we see that the resistance of the glass is quite small and the resistance of the inside air film dominates the process. Carrying out the numerical calculations leads to

$$\dot{Q}/A = 37.0\ \text{Btu/hr ft}^2, \qquad \text{for the window}$$

Comparing this result with that given in Ex. 1.3-1 indicates that taking the resistance of the inside air film into account leads to a greatly reduced heat flux through the window. Still, the loss through the window is large and storm windows may be appropriate.

*1.4 Units

In previous courses in chemistry, physics, and engineering the student has undoubtedly come in contact with the British system of units (lb_m, ft, sec), the metric system (g, cm, sec), and the SI system (kg, m, sec). Until recently the British system predominated in engineering applications while the metric system was generally preferred by chemists and physicists. For the engineer, converting from one set of units to another is a fact of life, and no serious difficulties are encountered when centimeters must be changed to feet, or grams to pounds mass. However, things are not so simple when one tries to thread a $\frac{3}{8}$-in. nut on a 10-mm bolt, and a universal system of units has considerable appeal.

At the 11th Conférence Générale des Poids et Mesures[15] in 1960 a system of units based on the kilogram, meter, second, and ampere was formally recommended for international use and given the full title "Système International d'Unités" which is abbreviated as SI. The system is constructed from six basic units and two supplementary units which are listed in Table 1.4-1. The unit of force is taken to be a

Table 1.4-1 Basic SI Units

Physical Quantity	Name of Unit	Symbol†
length	meter	m
mass	kilogram	kg
time	second	s
electric current	ampere	A
temperature	degree Kelvin	°K
luminous intensity	candela	cd
plane angle	radian	rad
solid angle	steradian	sr

†These symbols will be used consistently with the exception that the second will be denoted by sec.

Table 1.4-2 Derived SI Units

Physical Quantity	Name of Unit	Definition	Symbol†
force	newton	$kg\,m/s^2$	N
energy	joule	$kg\,m^2/s^2$	J
power	watt	J/s	W
electric charge	coulomb	A s	C
electric potential difference	volt	J/A s	V
electric resistance	ohm	V/A	Ω
electric capacitance	farad	A s/V	F
magnetic flux	weber	V s	Wb
inductance	henry	V s/A	H
luminous flux	lumen	cd sr	lm
frequency	hertz	cycle/second	Hz
area	square meter	m^2	
volume	cubic meter	m^3	
density	kilogram/cubic meter	kg/m^3	
pressure	newton/square meter	N/m^3	
thermal diffusivity	square meter/second	m^2/s	
coefficient of viscosity	newton second/square meter	$N\,s/m^2$	

†These symbols will be used consistently with the exception that the second will be denoted by sec.

newton and is given by Newton's second law as

$$1 \text{ newton} = 1 \text{ kilogram} \times 1 \text{ meter/sec}^2 \tag{1.4-1}$$

Energy and work are, of course, equivalent and the unit of energy is chosen to be a joule.

$$1 \text{ joule} = 1 \text{ newton} \times 1 \text{ meter} \tag{1.4-2}$$

Other derived SI units are listed in Table 1.4-2. Such a system has the advantage that no numerical factors (such as $g_c = 32.17\ \text{lb}_m\,\text{ft/lb}_f\,\text{sec}^2$ or $J = 778\ \text{ft}\,\text{lb}_f/\text{Btu}$) are required for the conversion of units.

Although the use of a universally consistent set of units is an appealing idea, it is unlikely that engineers will enjoy this luxury in the near future. To a large extent the engineer functions in a zone between the scientist and the consumer, and he must be adept at converting from one set of units to another. To help in the conversion of units a number of conversion factors are given in Table 1.4-3.

*1.5 Design Objectives

Our design objectives in this text are directed toward the determination of (1) the temperature field, and (2) the heat flux at phase interfaces. The former is required if there are limitations on the maximum and minimum temperature in the system or if a temperature dependent process is occurring in the system, and the latter is required if we are to determine the amount of energy transferred from one phase to another. Thinking back to previous courses, the student should remember encountering similar pairs of design objectives. In a course on solid mechanics one wished to determine (1) the displacement vector field, and (2) the stress field. The former being required to satisfy geometric limitations on the deformation of the solid, while the latter is required to insure that the yield stress is not exceeded, thus causing the structure to fail. In a previous course on fluid mechanics the design objectives† were to determine (1) the velocity field, and (2) the stress field. The former is required in the calculation of flow rates, while the latter is necessary in order to determine pressure drops and drag forces.

Throughout this text we hope to point out, wherever applicable, the similarities between solid

†Note that throughout this discussion we are neglecting the ultimate design objective which is to "do the best job for the least cost."

Table 1.4-3 Units and Conversion Factors

Mass	Length	Time
1 lb$_m$ = 453.6 g	1 in. = 2.54 cm	1 minute = 60 sec
1 ton (short) = 2000 lb$_m$	1 angstrom = 10^{-8} cm	1 hour = 60 min
1 ton (long) = 2240 lb$_m$	1 micron = 10^{-4} cm	1 day = 24 hr
1 kg = 1000 g	1 ft = 0.3048 m	
1 slug = 32.17 lb$_m$	1 mile = 1.609 km	
	1 meter = 10^2 cm	
	1 yard = 0.9144 m	
Force	Area	Volume
1 newton = 10^5 dyne	1 in^2 = 6.452 cm^2	1 in^3 = 16.39 cm^3
1 dyne = 2.248×10^{-6} lb$_f$	1 ft^2 = 9.29×10^{-2} m^2	1 ft^3 = 2.83×10^{-2} m^3
1 poundal = 3.108×10^{-2} lb$_f$	1 acre = 4.35×10^4 ft^2	1 gal (US) = 231 in^3
1 lb$_f$ = 4.448 newton	1 square mile = 2.59 km^2	1 quart (liq) = 0.25 gal (US)
		1 barrel = 31.5 gal (US)
		1 gal (Imperial) = 1 gal (US)
Pressure	Energy	Power
1 atm = 14.7 lb$_f$/in^2	1 cal = 4.187 joule	1 horsepower = 745.7 watt
1 lb$_f$/in^2 = 6.89×10^3 N/m^2	1 Btu = 252 cal	1 horsepower = 42.6 Btu/min
1 torr = 133.3 N/m^2	1 erg = 10^{-7} joule	1 watt = 9.51×10^{-4} Btu/sec
1 atm = 1.013×10^6 dyne/cm^2	1 Btu = 1055 watt sec	1 ft lb$_f$/sec = 1.356 watt
	1 ft lb$_f$ = 1.356 joule	
Temperature	Viscosity	Thermal Conductivity
1°C = 1.8°F	1 poise = 1 g/cm sec	1 Btu/hr ft °F = 1.731 watt/meter °C
°K = °C + 273.16	1 centipoise = 10^{-3} kg/m sec	1 cal/cm sec °C = 242 Btu/hr ft °F
°R = °F + 459.69	1 poise = 6.72×10^{-2} lb$_m$/ft sec	
°F = (1.8)°C + 32	1 centipoise = 2.09×10^{-5} lb$_f$ sec/ft^2	
	1 poise = 0.1 newton sec/m^2	
Thermal Diffusivity and Kinematic Viscosity	Heat Capacity	Heat Transfer Coefficient
1 m^2/sec = 3.875×10^4 ft^2/hr	1 J/kg°C = 2.39×10^{-4} Btu/lb$_m$ °F	1 watt/m^2°C = 0.1761 Btu/hr ft^2°F
1 cm^2/sec = 10^{-4} m^2/sec	1 Btu/lb$_m$°F = 1 cal/g°C	1 cal/cm^2 sec °C = 7373 Btu/hr ft^2°F
1 stokes = 1 cm^2/sec	1 Chu/lb$_m$°C = 1 Btu/lb$_m$ °F	1 joule/sec cm^2°C = 1761 Btu/hr ft^2°F

mechanics, fluid mechanics, and heat transfer, both in terms of the theoretical developments, the design objectives, and problem-solving techniques.

Solution to design problem I

We begin with the result given by Eq. 1.3-1 indicating that the heat flux owing to conduction can be expressed as

$$\dot{Q}/A = k\Delta T/L \tag{I-1}$$

and the result given by Eq. 1.3-29 indicating that the heat flux at a phase interface can be expressed as

$$\dot{Q}/A = h\Delta T \tag{I-2}$$

Referring to the interface temperatures indicated in Fig. I.2 we can write

$$\{\text{heat flux from the inner air to surface 1}\} = \dot{Q}/A = h_i(T_i - T_1) \tag{I-3a}$$

$$\{\text{heat flux from surface 1 to surface 2}\} = \dot{Q}/A = k_1(T_1 - T_2)/L_1 \tag{I-3b}$$

$$\{\text{heat flux from surface 2 to surface 3}\} = \dot{Q}/A = k_2(T_2 - T_3)/L_2 \tag{I-3c}$$

$$\{\text{heat flux from surface 3 to surface 4}\} = \dot{Q}/A = k_1(T_3 - T_4)/L_1 \tag{I-3d}$$

$$\{\text{heat flux from surface 4 to the outside air}\} = \dot{Q}/A = h_o(T_4 - T_o) \tag{I-3e}$$

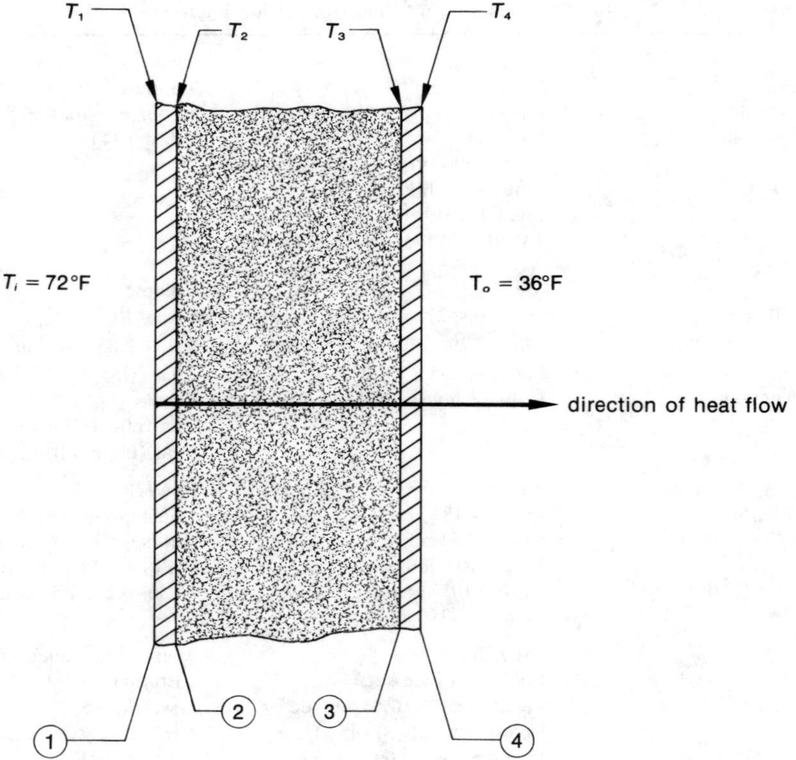

Fig. 1.2 Interface temperatures in a composite wall.

Here we have represented the thickness of the wood by L_1 and the thickness of the insulation by L_2. In addition we have assumed that the heat flux is constant throughout the wall. This requires that the process be steady and that heat flows in only one direction as indicated in Fig. I.2. We can rearrange Eqs. I-3 to obtain

$$T_i - T_1 = \frac{\dot{Q}/A}{h_i} \tag{I-4a}$$

$$T_1 - T_2 = \frac{\dot{Q}/A}{\left(\frac{k_1}{L_1}\right)} \tag{I-4b}$$

$$T_2 - T_3 = \frac{\dot{Q}/A}{\left(\frac{k_2}{L_2}\right)} \tag{I-4c}$$

$$T_3 - T_4 = \frac{\dot{Q}/A}{\left(\frac{k_1}{L_1}\right)} \tag{I-4d}$$

$$T_4 - T_o = \frac{\dot{Q}/A}{h_o} \tag{I-4e}$$

Summing Eqs. I-4 will eliminate the interface temperatures and provide an expression for $\dot{Q}/A$ in terms of only the inside and outside temperatures.

$$\dot{Q}/A = \frac{T_i - T_o}{\left[\frac{1}{h_i} + \frac{L_1}{k_1} + \frac{L_2}{k_2} + \frac{L_1}{k_1} + \frac{1}{h_o}\right]} \tag{I-5}$$

If we now substitute the following values:

$$T_i = 72°\text{F} \qquad k_1 = 0.08\ \text{Btu/hr ft °F}$$
$$T_o = 36°\text{F} \qquad k_2 = 0.023\ \text{Btu/hr ft °F}$$
$$L_1 = \tfrac{1}{4}\ \text{in.} \qquad h_i = 0.67\ \text{Btu/hr ft}^2\ \text{°F}$$
$$L_2 = 4\ \text{in.} \qquad h_o = 1.55\ \text{Btu/hr ft}^2\ \text{°F}$$

we find

$$(\dot{Q}/A) = \frac{(36)\ \text{Btu/hr ft}^2}{\underset{\substack{\uparrow\\ \text{inside}\\ \text{resistance}}}{1.49} + \underset{\substack{\uparrow\\ \text{resistance}\\ \text{of wood}}}{2(0.26)} + \underset{\substack{\uparrow\\ \text{resistance}\\ \text{of insulation}}}{14.5} + \underset{\substack{\uparrow\\ \text{outside}\\ \text{resistance}}}{0.64}} = 2.1\ \text{Btu/hr ft}^2$$

If we designate the insulation thickness required to reduce the heat loss by 50 per cent by L_2' we can write

$$(\dot{Q}/A)' = \tfrac{1}{2}(\dot{Q}/A), \qquad \text{for } L_2 = L_2'$$

Eq. I-5 can now be used to obtain an expression for L_2'

$$L_2' = k_2\left\{2\left[\frac{1}{h_i} + \frac{2L_1}{k_1} + \frac{L_2}{k_2} + \frac{1}{h_o}\right] - \left[\frac{1}{h_i} + \frac{2L_1}{k_1} + \frac{1}{h_o}\right]\right\} \tag{I-6}$$

Substituting the appropriate numerical values yields

$$L_2' = 8\tfrac{3}{4}\ \text{in.}$$

In order to determine the fraction of the temperature drop that occurs across the insulation, we can substitute Eq. I-5 into Eq. I-4c and rearrange to obtain

$$\left\{\begin{array}{l}\text{fraction of temperature}\\ \text{drop occurring across}\\ \text{the insulation}\end{array}\right\} = \frac{T_2 - T_3}{T_i - T_o} = \frac{(L_2/k_2)}{\left[\frac{1}{h_i} + \frac{2L_1}{k_1} + \frac{L_2}{k_2} + \frac{1}{h_o}\right]}. \tag{I-7}$$

For the 4 in. thick insulation this fraction is 0.84 and for the $8\tfrac{3}{4}$-in. thickness the fraction is 0.92. This clearly indicates that the major resistance to heat transfer is the insulation.

PROBLEMS†

I-1. Derive Eq. I-6.

I-2. Compute the heat flux through a $\tfrac{1}{4}$ in. thick glass plate which is subjected to the same temperature conditions as the composite wall described in Design Problem I. If 30 per cent of the wall space in a house is composed of $\tfrac{1}{4}$ in. thick glass plate and the remainder is composed of the type of wall described in Design Problem I, what fraction of the total heat loss is lost through the glass plate? Take the insulation thickness to be 4 in. and the thermal conductivity of the glass to be 0.36 Btu/hr ft °F.

***I-3.** In Chapter 5 it will be shown that the air between the window and the storm window illustrated in Fig. 1.3.4 can be considered stagnant for the purpose of calculating the heat flux through the window–storm window configuration. Take the thermal conductivity of air to be 0.013 Btu/hr ft °F, and use the information given in Examples 1.3-1 and 1.3-3 to determine the effect of the storm window on the heat flux through the window. Assume that the thickness of the glass in the storm window is also 0.5 cm.

1-1. At the interface between two static fluids the pressures in the two phases are related by
(1.1)

$$p_{\text{I}} = p_{\text{II}} + \sigma\left(\frac{1}{R_1} + \frac{1}{R_2}\right)$$

†Problems numbered I-1, I-2, etc. deal directly with Design Problem I, and problems marked with an asterisk (*) are concerned with the solved example problems.

where σ is the interfacial tension and R_1 and R_2 are the two radii of curvature. Does this expression violate the continuum postulate? Is it consistent with the laws of mechanics?

1-2. (1.2) The statement of the first law of thermodynamics given by Eq. 1.2-4 contains no explicit reference to *potential energy*; however, changes in potential energy are indeed included. Can you indicate where the potential energy will arise in a more thorough explanation of the terms in Eq. 1.2-4?

***1-3.** (1.3) Repeat the calculation given in Ex. 1.3-1 when the thickness of the wall is 5 in. and the thickness of the glass is $\frac{1}{4}$ in.

***1-4.** (1.3) If the pressure in the steam line described in Ex. 1.3-2 is raised to 200 psig (388°F), what is the cost of radiant energy loss per year?

***1-5.** (1.3) On those days when there is no wind the situation described in Ex. 1.3-3 is considerably changed, and the outside film heat transfer coefficient is reduced to a value representative of a *free-convection* situation. Repeat the calculation given in Ex. 1.3-3 for $h_o = 0.62$ Btu/hr ft²°F in order to assess the effect of the windows on calm days.

1-6. (1.3) For the process illustrated in Fig. 1.3.7a sketch temperature profiles for the following idealized cases:
(a) The thermal conductivity of the wall material tends to infinity.
(b) The thermal conductivity of the wall material tends to zero.
(c) The thermal conductivity of the liquid in the tank tends to infinity.

1-7. (1.3) Sketch the velocity profile in the tank in Fig. 1.3.7a that would result from free convection.

1-8. (1.3) Sketch the time-dependent temperature profile for the system shown in Fig. 1.3.7a if the hot liquid is suddenly replaced by a cold liquid.

1-9. (1.3) *Black body* surfaces are idealized surfaces which absorb *all* incident radiation and emit radiation according to the law

$$q^R = \sigma T^4$$

If two infinite parallel plates at temperatures T_1 and T_2 behave as black bodies, show that the net radiant energy flux between them is given by

$$q^R_{\text{net}} = 4\sigma T^3_{\text{av}}(T_1 - T_2)$$

provided $(T_1 - T_2) \ll T_{\text{av}}$ where $T_{\text{av}} = (T_1 + T_2)/2$.

1-10. (1.3) A radiator in a home heating system operates at a surface temperature of 53°C. Determine the rate at which it *emits* radiant energy per unit area in both the British and SI system of units if it behaves as a black body.

1-11. (1.3) Air at 68°F blows over a hot metal surface maintained at 320°F. If the heat transfer coefficient is 4.6 Btu/hr ft²°F and the surface area is 2.5 ft², how much energy is lost in a ten-minute period owing to convection? Owing to black body radiation in 68°F surroundings?

1-12. (1.3) A hemispherical tent perched on the top of a high peak on a clear night can be considered as radiating into a 0°K "sink," in addition to exchanging radiation with the surroundings. If the tent fabric provides a negligible resistance to heat transfer and the inside and outside heat transfer coefficients are $h_i = 0.4$ Btu/hr ft²°F and $h_o = 2.0$ Btu/hr ft²°F, what is the rate of energy loss from the tent for an outside temperature 15°F and an inside temperature of 58°F? Take the tent diameter to be 6 ft and the emissivity of the tent fabric to be 0.7.

1-13. (1.3) The temperature at the outer surface of a bare steam pipe is measured as 228°F when the ambient temperature is 64°F. If the heat transfer coefficient owing to convection to the surrounding air is 3.1 Btu/hr ft²°F and the emissivity is 0.8, determine the fraction of the total heat loss due to radiation. Compute the cost (in dollars per year) of the energy loss for a 1.24-in. outer diameter pipe which is 100 ft long. Take the cost of energy to be 0.015 dollars per kilowatt hour.

1-14. (1.3) Show how Eq. 1.3-1 can be derived from Eq. 1.3-2. List your assumptions carefully.

1-15. (1.3) Professor J. P. Holman has observed that in an air-conditioned (72°F) classroom in Texas the students attend summer classes in shorts, sandals, and skimpy shirts and are quite comfortable. In the winter the same students wear wool slacks, long-sleeve shirts, and sweaters and are equally comfortable with the room temperature maintained at 75°F. Explain this anomaly, paying careful attention to radiant energy transport.†

†This problem will be considered more rigorously in Ex. 8.4-1 and Ex. 9.1-1.

1-16. Using the conversion factors given in Table 1.4-3 convert
(1.4) (a) joules to Btu
(b) horsepower to cal/sec
(c) lb_f/in^2 to dyne/cm^2
(d) newton to lb_f

1-17. Reconstruct Table 1.3-1 using SI units of J/sec m^2 °K.
(1.4)

REFERENCES

1. Sears, F. W., *Principles of Physics I: Mechanics, Heat, and Sound,* Addison-Wesley Press, Inc., 1945.
2. Truesdell, C., "A Program Toward Rediscovering the Rational Mechanics of the Age of Reason," *Archives for the History of Exact Sciences* **1**, 31 (1961).
3. Truesdell, C., *Essays in the History of Mechanics*, Springer-Verlag New York Inc., 1968.
4. Ziman, J., "The Thermal Properties)of Materials," *Scientific American* **217**, 181 (1967).
5. Cha, C. Y., and McCoy, B. J., "Third-Order Constitutive Equations and Transport in Rarefied Gases," *J. Chem. Phy.* **56**, 3265 (1972).
6. Fourier, J. B. J., *Theorie Analytique de la chaleur,* Gauthier-Villars, 1822, English translation by Alexander Freeman, Dover Publications, Inc., New York, 1955.
7. *Thermal Conductivity,* edited by R. P. Tye, Academic Press, New York, 1969.
8. *Proceedings of the Eighth Conference on Thermal Conductivity,* edited by C. Y. Ho and R. E. Taylor, Plenum Press, New York, 1969.
9. *Chemical Engineers Handbook,* Third Edition, edited by J. H. Perry, McGraw-Hill Book Co., Inc., New York, 1950.
10. Tsederberg, N. V., *Thermal Conductivity of Gases and Liquids,* The M.I.T. Press, Cambridge, Mass., 1965.
11. *Thermophysical Properties Research Center Data Book,* Thermophysical Properties Research Center, Purdue University, Lafayette, Indiana.
12. *Handbook of Chemistry and Physics,* edited by R. C. Weast, The Chemical Rubber Co., Cleveland, Ohio.
13. Weiss, R. J., *Solid State Physics for Metallurgists,* Chap. IX, Addison-Wesley Pub. Co., Inc., Reading, Mass., 1963.
14. Hirschfelder, J. O., Curtiss, C. F., and Bird, R. B., *Molecular Theory of Gases and Liquids,* John Wiley & Sons, Inc., New York, 1954.
15. *Comptes Rendus des Séances de la Onzième Conférence Générale des Poids et Mesures,* Gauthier-Villars, Paris, 1960.

Design Problem II

A chemical reactor, which can contain fluids as hot as 800°F, is situated in an open area where both plant personnel and visitors can come in contact with it. The walls of the reactor vessel are 1 in. thick steel ($k_1 = 20$ Btu/hr ft °F), and the inside film heat transfer coefficient is relatively high ($h_1 = 12$ Btu/hr ft^2°F) owing to the motion of the reacting fluids.

Under the present circumstances the steel surface of the reactor can be quite hot and visitors have burned their hands when they inadvertently touched the reactor walls. Insulation is available which has a thermal conductivity of 0.12 Btu/hr ft °F. Would you please consider the possibility of insulating this reactor and recommend a course of action that will prevent further injuries to visitors or plant personnel. The outer film heat transfer coefficient will depend on the temperature difference between the surface and the ambient air; however, for the purposes of this problem you may take this coefficient, h_2, to be 1.5 Btu/hr ft^2°F.

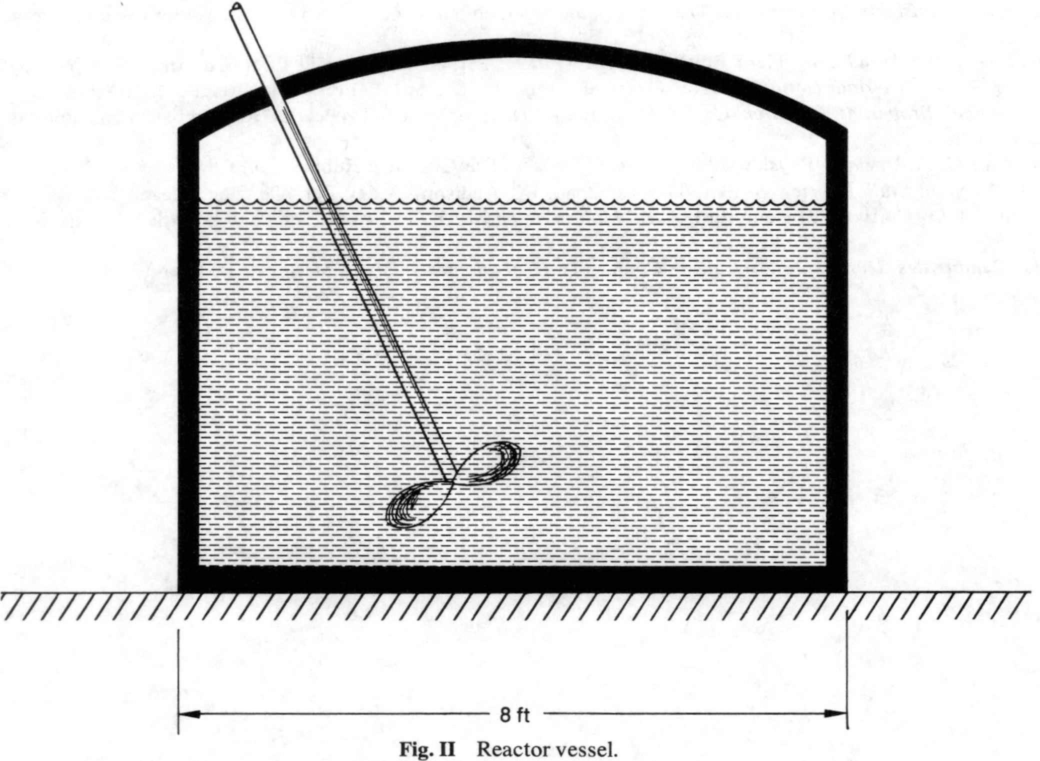

Fig. II Reactor vessel.

2

Steady, One-Dimensional Heat Conduction

In this chapter we will treat the simplest possible type of heat transfer process, i.e., energy transport in the absence of convection and radiation (heat conduction), independent of time (steady), and only one component of the heat flux vector being nonzero (one-dimensional). The student should not be encouraged by the simplicity of this material to treat it lightly, because the practical applications are significant, and certain fundamental ideas will be established in this chapter which are continually used throughout the text.

We have already encountered some steady, one-dimensional, conduction problems in Chapter 1, and in this chapter we will give a more precise derivation of the governing differential equations along with a more thorough discussion of the boundary conditions that must be imposed at phase interfaces. Problems in cylindrical and spherical coordinates will be analyzed, and we will discuss the use of extended surfaces (fins) to enhance overall heat transfer rates.

Summary of Section 2.1

In this section we discuss in some detail the fundamental energy postulate, or the first law of thermodynamics. In its rate form, this postulate is stated as:

> The time rate of change of the internal and kinetic energy of a body is equal to the rate at which heat is transmitted to the body plus the rate at which work is done on the body plus the rate at which electromagnetic energy is liberated within the body

This statement is made more explicit by using the language of calculus, thus leading us to

$$\frac{D}{Dt}\int_{\mathscr{V}_m(t)}\left(\rho e+\frac{1}{2}\rho v^2\right)dV=-\int_{\mathscr{A}_m(t)}\mathbf{q}\cdot\mathbf{n}\,dA+\int_{\mathscr{A}_m(t)}\mathbf{t}_{(\mathbf{n})}\cdot\mathbf{v}\,dA+\int_{\mathscr{V}_m(t)}\rho\mathbf{g}\cdot\mathbf{v}\,dV+\int_{\mathscr{V}_m(t)}\Phi\,dV \tag{2.1-13}$$

The left-hand-side of Eq. 2.1-13 represents the time rate of change of the internal and kinetic energy of the body. Here e is the internal energy per unit mass and is assumed to be a function of the local state of the system even though the system is not at equilibrium. This assumption is often referred to as the *principle of local equilibrium.*

The first term on the right-hand-side of Eq. 2.1-13 represents the rate at which heat is transmitted to the body at the surface of the body, $\mathscr{A}_m(t)$. The second term represents the rate at which surface work is done on the body, while the third term represents the rate at which body forces (gravitational, electrostatic, and electromagnetic) do work on the body. The last term on the right-hand-side of Eq. 2.1-13 represents the rate of heat generation owing to electromagnetic effects.

The complete form of the fundamental energy postulate is not required for our study of steady, one-dimensional heat conduction. Under steady conditions with $\mathbf{v} = 0$, Eq. 2.1-13 reduces to

$$0 = -\int_{\mathscr{A}} \mathbf{q} \cdot \mathbf{n} \, dA + \int_{\mathscr{V}} \Phi \, dV \tag{2.2-1}$$

which is the first equation of Sec. 2.2. In words, Eq. 2.2-1 simply states that

$$\left\{\begin{array}{l}\text{the rate at which}\\ \text{energy enters}\\ \text{the body by conduction}\end{array}\right\} + \left\{\begin{array}{l}\text{the rate at which energy is}\\ \text{generated within the body}\\ \text{by electromagnetic heating}\end{array}\right\} = \left\{\begin{array}{l}\text{the rate at which}\\ \text{energy leaves}\\ \text{the body by conduction}\end{array}\right\} \tag{2.2-4}$$

This statement has considerable intuitive appeal and is sufficient for solving all of the problems in Chapter 2. For this reason some students may wish to skip Sec. 2.1; however, the complete statement of the fundamental energy postulate must be understood in order to analyze the convective heat transfer processes presented in Chapters 5, 6, 7, 10, and 11.

*2.1 The Fundamental Energy Postulate

The fundamental energy postulate may be stated in words as

$$\left\{\begin{array}{l}\text{the time rate of change}\\ \text{of internal and kinetic}\\ \text{energy of a body}\end{array}\right\} = \left\{\begin{array}{l}\text{the rate at which non-mechanical}\\ \text{energy is transferred to the body,}\\ \text{i.e., the rate at which ``heat'' is}\\ \text{transferred to the body}\end{array}\right\}$$
$$+ \left\{\begin{array}{l}\text{the rate at which mechanical energy}\\ \text{is transferred to the body by means}\\ \text{of surface forces, i.e., the rate at}\\ \text{which surface ``work'' is done on the}\\ \text{body}\end{array}\right\}$$
$$+ \left\{\begin{array}{l}\text{the rate at which mechanical energy}\\ \text{is transferred to the body by means}\\ \text{of body forces, i.e., the rate at}\\ \text{which body force ``work'' is done on}\\ \text{the body}\end{array}\right\}$$
$$+ \left\{\begin{array}{l}\text{the rate at which electromagnetic}\\ \text{energy is liberated within the body}\end{array}\right\} \tag{2.1-1}$$

It should be noted at this point that *heat* and *work* are simply two different mechanisms by which energy can be transferred to a body. We wish to apply Eq. 2.1-1 to the body illustrated in Fig. 2.1.1. The region occupied by a body is referred to as a *material volume* and is denoted by $\mathscr{V}_m(t)$, and the surface bounding the body is a *material surface* and is designated by $\mathscr{A}_m(t)$. If we use e to represent the internal energy per unit mass and note that $\frac{1}{2}\rho v^2$ is the *kinetic energy per unit volume*,† Then the internal and kinetic energy of a body is

$$\left\{\begin{array}{l}\text{internal and}\\ \text{kinetic energy}\\ \text{of a body}\end{array}\right\} = \int_{\mathscr{V}_m(t)} \left(\rho e + \frac{1}{2}\rho v^2\right) dV \tag{2.1-2}$$

†The magnitude v of the velocity vector $\mathbf{v}$ is given by $v = \sqrt{\mathbf{v} \cdot \mathbf{v}}$.

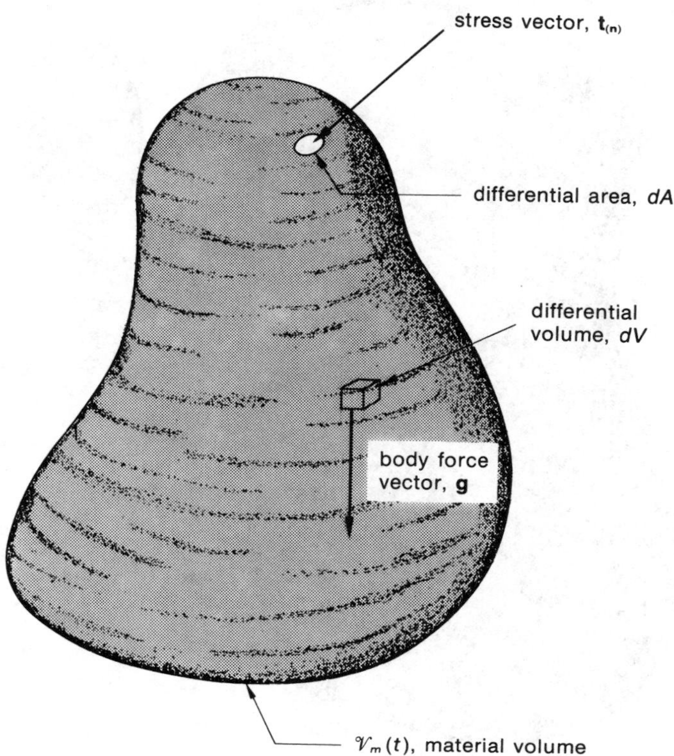

Fig. 2.1.1 A material volume.

The first term on the left-hand-side of Eq. 2.1-1 may now be written as

$$\begin{Bmatrix} \text{time rate of change of} \\ \text{internal and kinetic} \\ \text{energy of a body} \end{Bmatrix} = \frac{D}{Dt} \int_{\mathscr{V}_m(t)} \left(\rho e + \frac{1}{2} \rho v^2 \right) dV \tag{2.1-3}$$

Here the derivative D/Dt is referred to as the *material derivative*, for it represents the time rate of change that would be measured by an observer moving with the *material*.† The second term in Eq. 2.1-1 can be expressed as

$$\begin{Bmatrix} \text{the rate at which} \\ \text{heat is transferred} \\ \text{to the body} \end{Bmatrix} = - \int_{\mathscr{A}_m(t)} \mathbf{q} \cdot \mathbf{n} \, dA \tag{2.1-4}$$

In effect, Eq. 2.1-4 is a *definition* of the heat flux vector, i.e., $\mathbf{q}$ is a vector such that when it is dotted with the outwardly directed unit normal, multiplied by -1, and integrated over the entire surface yields the rate at which non-mechanical energy (*heat*) is transferred to the body at its boundaries.

If we focus our attention on an element of surface dA, we can express the force $d\mathbf{F}$ acting on the element in terms of the stress vector $\mathbf{t}_{(\mathbf{n})}$ by the equation

$$d\mathbf{F} = \mathbf{t}_{(\mathbf{n})} \, dA \tag{2.1-5}$$

The stress vector, generally defined in courses on solid and fluid mechanics [1, 2, 3], is the *vector force per unit area* acting on a surface having an outwardly directed unit normal, $\mathbf{n}$. Let us now consider the work done on a moving surface area element during the time Δt. This process is illustrated in Fig. 2.1.2 where the element dA is shown moving through a distance ΔL in the direction denoted by the unit vector $\boldsymbol{\lambda}$. The

†Time derivatives are discussed in more detail in Chapter 5; however, the present qualitative description of the material derivative is entirely satisfactory for our work in this chapter.

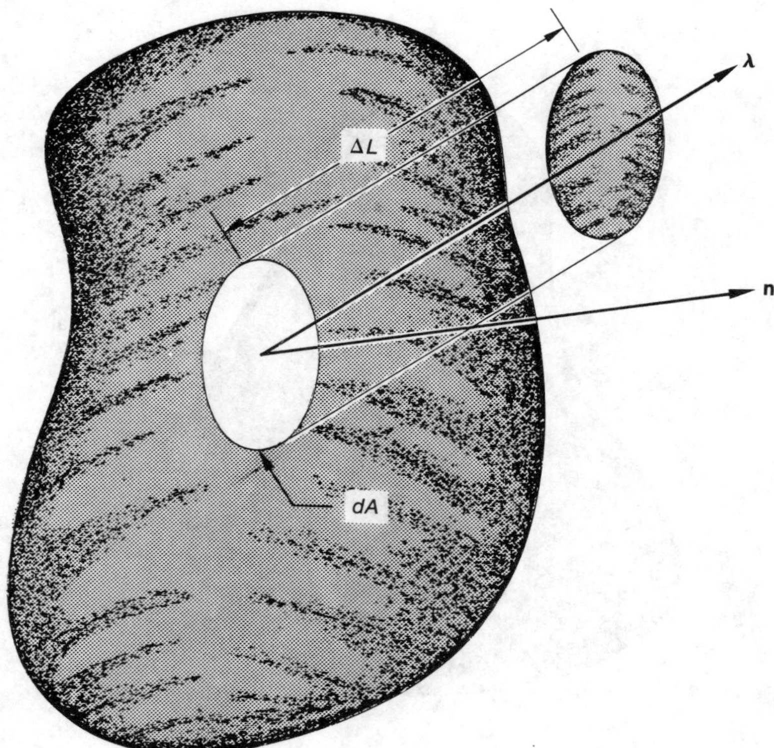

Fig. 2.1.2 Work done on an element of surface area.

velocity vector $\mathbf{v}$ can be represented in terms of the magnitude v and $\boldsymbol{\lambda}$ as

$$\mathbf{v} = \boldsymbol{\lambda} v \tag{2.1-6}$$

Now, we know that the work done on dA is the force acting in the $\boldsymbol{\lambda}$-direction times the distance ΔL,

$$\left\{\begin{matrix}\text{work done on the}\\ \text{surface element}\\ dA\end{matrix}\right\} = \mathbf{t}_{(\mathbf{n})} \cdot \boldsymbol{\lambda}\, \Delta L\, dA \tag{2.1-7}$$

and the *rate* of work is given by

$$\left\{\begin{matrix}\text{rate of work done}\\ \text{on the surface}\\ \text{element } dA\end{matrix}\right\} = \lim_{\Delta t \to 0} \left[\mathbf{t}_{(\mathbf{n})} \cdot \boldsymbol{\lambda} \frac{\Delta L}{\Delta t}\right] dA \tag{2.1-8}$$

However, the limit of $(\Delta L/\Delta t)$ as $\Delta t \to 0$ is just the magnitude of the velocity v, and we can use Eq. 2.1-6 to write

$$\left\{\begin{matrix}\text{rate of work done}\\ \text{on the surface}\\ \text{element } dA\end{matrix}\right\} = \mathbf{t}_{(\mathbf{n})} \cdot \mathbf{v}\, dA \tag{2.1-9}$$

Integrating over the surface area $\mathscr{A}_m(t)$ gives the third term in Eq. 2.1-1.

$$\left\{\begin{matrix}\text{the rate at which}\\ \text{surface work is done}\\ \text{on the body}\end{matrix}\right\} = \int_{\mathscr{A}_m(t)} \mathbf{t}_{(\mathbf{n})} \cdot \mathbf{v}\, dA \tag{2.1-10}$$

The extension of these ideas to calculating the rate at which work is done on the body by body forces such as gravity is straightforward, and we write the fourth term in Eq. 2.1-1 as

$$\left\{\begin{array}{l}\text{the rate at which}\\ \text{body force work is}\\ \text{done on the body}\end{array}\right\} = \int_{\mathcal{V}_m(t)} \rho \mathbf{g} \cdot \mathbf{v} \, dV \tag{2.1-11}$$

If we designate the energy source–sink per unit volume per unit time as Φ, the last term in Eq. 2.1-1 becomes

$$\left\{\begin{array}{l}\text{the rate at which electromagnetic}\\ \text{energy is liberated within the}\\ \text{body}\end{array}\right\} = \int_{\mathcal{V}_m(t)} \Phi \, dV \tag{2.1-12}$$

Here Φ is positive for an energy source and negative for a sink. If E is the electric field (volts) and $\mathbf{j}$ is the current density vector (amperes per square centimeter) Φ is given by

$$\Phi = -\nabla E \cdot \mathbf{j}$$

If the material obeys Ohm's law

$$\nabla E = -\sigma \mathbf{j}$$

where σ is the specific resistances (ohm-cm), we can express the rate of energy generation per unit volume as

$$\Phi = \sigma j^2, \quad \text{source due to electrical heating}$$

Substituting Eqs. 2.1-3, 2.1-4, 2.1-10, 2.1-11, and 2.1-12 into Eq. 2.1-1 gives us a symbolic representation of the fundamental energy postulate:

$$\frac{D}{Dt}\int_{\mathcal{V}_m(t)} \left(\rho e + \frac{1}{2}\rho v^2\right) dV = -\int_{\mathcal{A}_m(t)} \mathbf{q} \cdot \mathbf{n} \, dA + \int_{\mathcal{A}_m(t)} \mathbf{t}_{(\mathbf{n})} \cdot \mathbf{v} \, dA + \int_{\mathcal{V}_m(t)} \rho \mathbf{g} \cdot \mathbf{v} \, dV + \int_{\mathcal{V}_m(t)} \Phi \, dV \tag{2.1-13}$$

In order to connect Eq. 2.1-13 a little more closely to the form usually encountered in a thermodynamics text, we need to show that the second-last term in Eq. 2.1-13 is indeed the *time rate of change of potential energy* of the body when $\mathbf{g}$ represents a time-independent conservative force field. Representing the body force vector in terms of the negative gradient of a scalar† gives

$$\mathbf{g} = -\nabla \phi \tag{2.1-14}$$

and we may use the special form of the Reynolds transport theorem‡ to write

$$\int_{\mathcal{V}_m(t)} \rho \mathbf{g} \cdot \mathbf{v} \, dV = -\int_{\mathcal{V}_m(t)} (\rho \nabla \phi) \cdot \mathbf{v} \, dV = \frac{D}{Dt}\int_{\mathcal{V}_m(t)} \rho \phi \, dV \tag{2.1-15}$$

provided ϕ is independent of time. This last step is based on material presented in detail in Chapter 5. It will be passed over lightly here for two reasons: (1) The student may have already encountered this development in a course in fluid mechanics, and (2) the final result is intuitively quite appealing. Substitution of Eq. 2.1-15 into Eq. 2.1-13 gives

$$\frac{D}{Dt}\int_{\mathcal{V}_m(t)} \left(\rho e + \frac{1}{2}\rho v^2 + \rho\phi\right) dV = -\int_{\mathcal{A}_m(t)} \mathbf{q} \cdot \mathbf{n} \, dA + \int_{\mathcal{A}_m(t)} \mathbf{t}_{(\mathbf{n})} \cdot \mathbf{v} \, dA + \int_{\mathcal{V}_m(t)} \Phi \, dV \tag{2.1-16}$$

In terms of the nomenclature used in thermodynamics texts we would write

$$\dot{U} + \dot{KE} + \dot{PE} = \dot{Q} + \dot{W} \tag{2.1-17}$$

where the electromagnetic source term has been neglected for the moment. Here $\dot{U}$ represents the *time rate of change* of the *total* internal energy of the body, or the *system* in the nomenclature of thermodynamics. If we integrate Eq. 2.1-17 with respect to time we obtain a form of the fundamental

†Any conservative force can be represented as the gradient of a scalar.
‡See Reference 3, Chapter 4 and note that $D\phi/Dt = \mathbf{v} \cdot \nabla\phi$ when ϕ is independent of time.

energy postulate generally encountered in thermodynamics texts

$$\Delta U + \Delta KE + \Delta PE = Q + W \tag{2.1-18}$$

Here

$$\Delta U = U(t_2) - U(t_1)$$

$$Q = \int_{t_1}^{t_2} \dot{Q}\, dt \qquad \text{and} \qquad W = \int_{t_1}^{t_2} \dot{W}\, dt$$

Although Eq. 2.1-18 is undoubtedly a familiar expression, we will make use of the more informative expresson of the fundamental energy postulate given by Eq. 2.1-16.

In our statement of the fundamental energy postulate we assume that e is a continuous function of the spatial coordinates and time, and in addition that e is a function of the *local state* of the system even though the system is not at equilibrium. From the thermodynamic point of view, Eq. 2.1-18 would be the correct statement of the fundamental energy postulate with the restriction that the system was in equilibrium at the times t_1 and t_2. There is, of course, ample evidence that the more general statement given by Eq. 2.1-16 is valid for a wide range of circumstances with the possible exception of those cases where extremely high gradients exist.

*2.2 Steady Heat Conduction

If we consider that class of problems for which $\mathbf{v} = 0$ and all functions are independent of time, Eq. 2.1-16 reduces to an especially simple form

$$0 = -\int_{\mathscr{A}} \mathbf{q} \cdot \mathbf{n}\, dA + \int_{\mathscr{V}} \Phi\, dV \tag{2.2-1}$$

Here the material surface area $\mathscr{A}_m(t)$ has been replaced by $\mathscr{A}$, indicating that the surface is fixed in space. Application of the divergence theorem and putting both terms under the same integral sign gives

$$0 = \int_{\mathscr{V}} [-\nabla \cdot \mathbf{q} + \Phi]\, dV \tag{2.2-2}$$

If we assume that $\mathbf{q}$ a.ıd its derivatives are continuous, and note that the limits of integration are arbitrary, we conclude that the integrand must be *identically* equal to zero.

$$0 = -\nabla \cdot \mathbf{q} + \Phi \tag{2.2-3}$$

Expressions for Eq. 2.2-3 in rectangular, cylindrical, and spherical coordinates are listed in Table 2.2-1. The scalar components of $\mathbf{q}$ in cylindrical and spherical coordinates are to be interpreted as the projections of $\mathbf{q}$ onto tangents to the coordinate curves. The discussion of vector equations in curvilinear coordinates is straightforward, but tedious, and will not be discussed in this text since the subject is adequately treated elsewhere [4, 5, 6].

Table 2.2-1 Steady Heat Conduction Equation in Terms of the Components of the Heat Flux Vector

rectangular (x, y, z)

$$0 = -\left(\frac{\partial q_x}{\partial x} + \frac{\partial q_y}{\partial y} + \frac{\partial q_z}{\partial z}\right) + \Phi \tag{a}$$

cylindrical (r, θ, z)

$$0 = -\left[\frac{1}{r}\frac{\partial}{\partial r}(r q_r) + \frac{1}{r}\left(\frac{\partial q_\theta}{\partial \theta}\right) + \frac{\partial q_z}{\partial z}\right] + \Phi \tag{b}$$

spherical (r, θ, ϕ)

$$0 = -\left[\frac{1}{r^2}\frac{\partial}{\partial r}(r^2 q_r) + \frac{1}{r \sin\theta}\frac{\partial}{\partial \theta}(q_\theta \sin\theta) + \frac{1}{r\sin\theta}\left(\frac{\partial q_\phi}{\partial \phi}\right)\right] + \Phi \tag{c}$$

Alternate method

Before continuing our analysis of steady heat conduction, it may be helpful to rederive Eq. 2.2-3 from a different point of view. Returning to Eq. 2.2-1 we note that heat is transferred *to* the body over portions of the surface area for which $\mathbf{q}\cdot\mathbf{n}$ is *negative*, i.e., $\mathbf{q}$ is pointing inwardly toward the body. It follows that

$$\int_{A_1} \mathbf{q}\cdot\mathbf{n}\,dA < 0, \quad \text{for heat transferred } \textit{to} \text{ the body}$$

$$\int_{A_2} \mathbf{q}\cdot\mathbf{n}\,dA > 0, \quad \text{for heat transferred } \textit{from} \text{ the body}$$

where $A_1 + A_2 = \mathscr{A}$. We can now express Eq. 2.2-1 in words as

$$\left\{\begin{matrix}\text{the rate at which}\\ \text{energy enters the}\\ \text{body by conduction}\end{matrix}\right\} + \left\{\begin{matrix}\text{the rate at which energy is}\\ \text{generated within the body}\\ \text{by electromagnetic heating}\end{matrix}\right\} = \left\{\begin{matrix}\text{the rate at which}\\ \text{energy leaves the}\\ \text{body by conduction}\end{matrix}\right\} \tag{2.2-4}$$

$$-\int_{A_1} \mathbf{q}\cdot\mathbf{n}\,dA \quad + \quad \int_{\mathscr{V}} \Phi\,dV \quad = \quad \int_{A_2} \mathbf{q}\cdot\mathbf{n}\,dA \quad .$$

We would like now to apply this word equation to the cube shown in Fig. 2.2.1 to obtain

$$\overbrace{\langle q_x\rangle|_x\,\Delta y\,\Delta z + \langle q_y\rangle|_y\,\Delta x\,\Delta z + \langle q_z\rangle|_z\,\Delta x\,\Delta y}^{\text{rate at which energy enters the cube}} + \overbrace{\langle\Phi\rangle\Delta x\,\Delta y\,\Delta z}^{\text{rate at which energy is generated in the cube}}$$
$$= \underbrace{\langle q_x\rangle|_{x+\Delta x}\,\Delta y\,\Delta z + \langle q_y\rangle|_{y+\Delta y}\,\Delta x\,\Delta z + \langle q_z\rangle|_{z+\Delta z}\,\Delta x\,\Delta y}_{\text{rate at which energy leaves the cube}} \tag{2.2-5}$$

Here the term $\langle q_x\rangle$ refers to the average value of q_x over the surface area $\Delta y\,\Delta z$, and $\langle\Phi\rangle$ is the average rate of heat generation in the volume $\Delta x\,\Delta y\,\Delta z$. The direction of the various heat fluxes is indicated by the arrows in Fig. 2.2.1. We can divide Eq. 2.2-5 by the volume $\Delta x\,\Delta y\,\Delta z$ and put all the terms on the right-hand-side to obtain

$$0 = -\left\{\left(\frac{\langle q_x\rangle|_{x+\Delta x} - \langle q_x\rangle|_x}{\Delta x}\right) + \left(\frac{\langle q_y\rangle|_{y+\Delta y} - \langle q_y\rangle|_y}{\Delta y}\right) + \left(\frac{\langle q_z\rangle|_{z+\Delta z} - \langle q_z\rangle|_z}{\Delta z}\right)\right\} + \langle\Phi\rangle \tag{2.2-6}$$

If we take the limit as Δx, Δy, and Δz simultaneously tend to zero Eq. 2.2-6 is expressed as

$$0 = -\left\{\lim_{\Delta x\to 0}\left(\frac{\langle q_x\rangle|_{x+\Delta x} - \langle q_x\rangle|_x}{\Delta x}\right) + \lim_{\Delta y\to 0}\left(\frac{\langle q_y\rangle|_{y+\Delta y} - \langle q_y\rangle|_y}{\Delta y}\right) + \lim_{\Delta z\to 0}\left(\frac{\langle q_z\rangle|_{z+\Delta z} - \langle q_z\rangle|_z}{\Delta z}\right)\right\} + \Phi \tag{2.2-7}$$

Each term in this equation represents a partial derivative and the result of the limiting process is

$$0 = -\left(\frac{\partial q_x}{\partial x} + \frac{\partial q_y}{\partial y} + \frac{\partial q_z}{\partial z}\right) + \Phi \tag{2.2-8}$$

which is simply Eq. 2.2-3 for rectangular Cartesian coordinates.

In general, Eq. 2.2-8 or the general form given by Eq. 2.2-3 is not solvable for there are three unknowns (the scalar components of $\mathbf{q}$) and only one equation. A constitutive equation is in order here, and if we use Fourier's law of heat conduction for isotropic materials†

$$\mathbf{q} = -k\nabla T \tag{2.2-9}$$

our steady heat conduction equation reduces to

$$0 = \nabla\cdot(k\nabla T) + \Phi \tag{2.2-10}$$

†The scalar components of Eq. 2.2-9 are given in Table 2.2-2 for rectangular, cylindrical, and spherical coordinates. Remember that for anisotropic material Fourier's law must be modified to read $q_i = -k_{ij}(\partial T/\partial x_j)$ where k_{ij} is the thermal conductivity tensor.

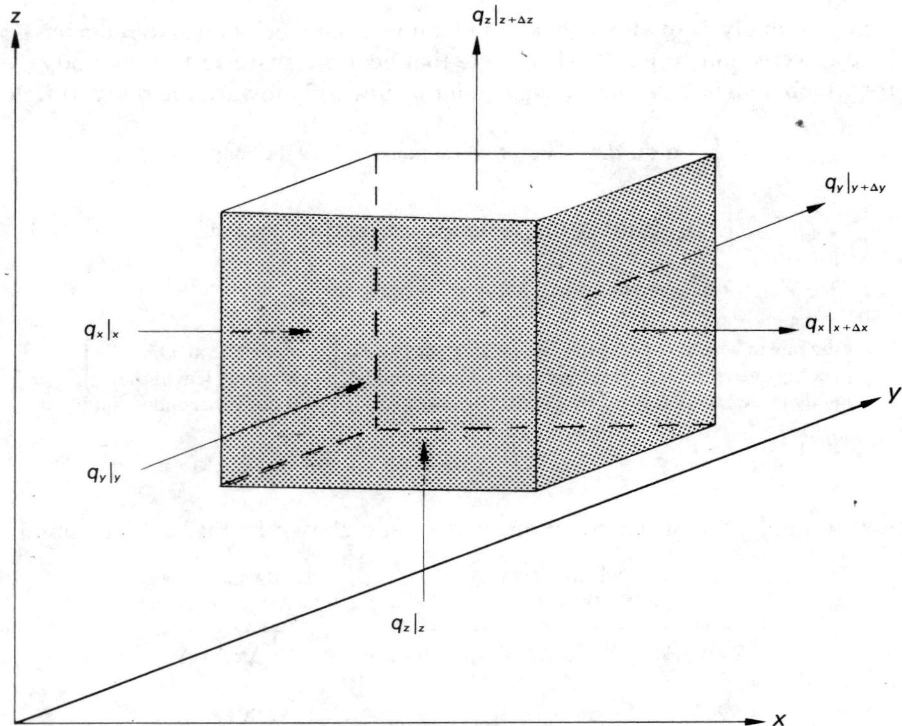

Fig. 2.2.1 Steady heat conduction in a cube.

Table 2.2-2 Scalar Components of the Heat Flux Vector **q**

rectangular (x, y, z)

$$q_x = -k\left(\frac{\partial T}{\partial x}\right) \qquad q_y = -k\left(\frac{\partial T}{\partial y}\right) \qquad q_z = -k\left(\frac{\partial T}{\partial z}\right) \tag{a}$$

cylindrical (r, θ, z)

$$q_r = -k\left(\frac{\partial T}{\partial r}\right) \qquad q_\theta = -k\left(\frac{1}{r}\frac{\partial T}{\partial \theta}\right) \qquad q_z = -k\left(\frac{\partial T}{\partial z}\right) \tag{b}$$

spherical (r, θ, ϕ)

$$q_r = -k\left(\frac{\partial T}{\partial r}\right) \qquad q_\theta = -k\left(\frac{1}{r}\frac{\partial T}{\partial \theta}\right) \qquad q_\phi = -k\left(\frac{1}{r \sin\theta}\frac{\partial T}{\partial \phi}\right) \tag{c}$$

Table 2.2-3 Steady Heat Conduction Equation in Terms of the Temperature for a Constant Thermal Conductivity

rectangular (x, y, z)

$$0 = \left(\frac{\partial^2 T}{\partial x^2} + \frac{\partial^2 T}{\partial y^2} + \frac{\partial^2 T}{\partial z^2}\right) + \Phi/k \tag{a}$$

cylindrical (r, θ, z)

$$0 = \left[\frac{1}{r}\frac{\partial}{\partial r}\left(r\frac{\partial T}{\partial r}\right) + \frac{1}{r^2}\left(\frac{\partial^2 T}{\partial \theta^2}\right) + \frac{\partial^2 T}{\partial z^2}\right] + \Phi/k \tag{b}$$

spherical (r, θ, ϕ)

$$0 = \left[\frac{1}{r^2}\frac{\partial}{\partial r}\left(r^2\frac{\partial T}{\partial r}\right) + \frac{1}{r^2 \sin\theta}\frac{\partial}{\partial \theta}\left(\sin\theta\frac{\partial T}{\partial \theta}\right) + \frac{1}{r^2 \sin^2\theta}\left(\frac{\partial^2 T}{\partial \phi^2}\right)\right] + \Phi/k \tag{c}$$

Although the thermal conductivity k will always vary with the temperature and therefore be a function of the spatial coordinates, this variation can often be neglected and Eq. 2.2-10 reduces to

$$0 = \nabla^2 T + \Phi/k. \tag{2.2-11}$$

Here ∇^2 is used to represent the Laplacian where $\nabla^2 = \nabla \cdot \nabla$. Eq. 2.2-11 is given in rectangular, cylindrical, and spherical coordinates in Table 2.2-3. Solutions of Eq. 2.2-11 subject to appropriate boundary conditions, will provide us with both the temperature and heat flux vector field.

*2.3 Steady, One-Dimensional Heat Conduction in Rectangular Coordinates

The simplest steady, one-dimensional heat conduction problem is that of heat conduction across a plane wall of infinite extent in the y- and z-directions but finite in the x-direction. If the conditions at the surface of the wall are independent of y and z, the temperature T will only be a function of x, and q_x will be the only nonzero component of the heat flux vector. We first consider the case, illustrated in Fig. 2.3.1, where the surface temperatures are specified.

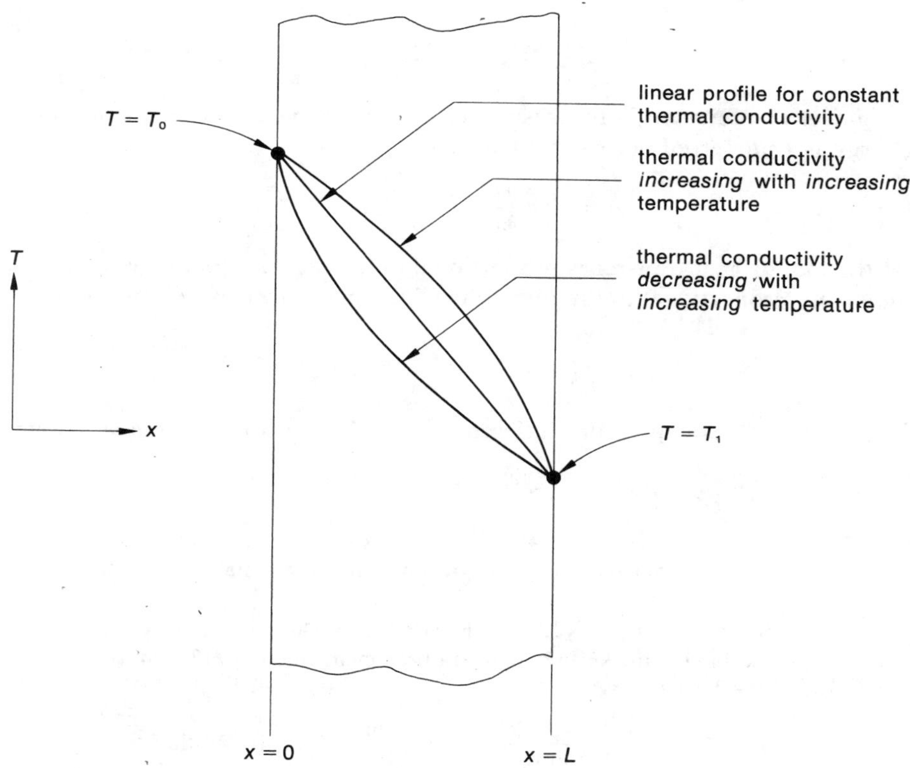

Fig. 2.3.1 Steady heat conduction in a flat plate.

Specified surface temperatures

If we restrict our analysis to the case of constant thermal conductivity, the appropriate form of the steady-state heat conduction equation is

$$0 = \left(\frac{\partial^2 T}{\partial x^2} + \frac{\partial^2 T}{\partial y^2} + \frac{\partial^2 T}{\partial z^2}\right) \tag{2.3-1}$$

We may further simplify the problem by assuming the plate to be infinite in the y- and z-directions. This requires that T be either independent of y and z or periodic in y and z. Since the temperatures at $x = 0$ and $x = L$ are not functions of y or z the periodic dependence of T can be dismissed and Eq. 2.3-1 reduces to

$$0 = \frac{\partial^2 T}{\partial x^2} = \frac{d^2 T}{dx^2} \tag{2.3-2}$$

It goes without saying that infinite flat plates do not exist in the real world, and when we analyze such a hypothetical configuration we are doing so with the hope of discovering the *dominant* features of the temperature field for a plate which is much larger in the y- and z-directions than it is in the x-direction.

The general solution of Eq. 2.3-2 is readily deduced as

$$T = A + Bx \tag{2.3-3}$$

which is subject to the boundary conditions

B.C.1 $$T = T_0, \qquad x = 0 \tag{2.3-4}$$

B.C.2 $$T = T_1, \qquad x = L \tag{2.3-5}$$

Eqs. 2.3-4 and 2.3-5 can be used to evaluate the constants of integration, A and B, and the temperature field is given by

$$T = T_0 - (T_0 - T_1)\left(\frac{x}{L}\right) \tag{2.3-6}$$

Most often the engineer is interested in this result because it can be used to compute the heat flux or the rate at which energy is transferred across the flat plate.

$$q_x = -k\frac{\partial T}{\partial x} = \left(\frac{k}{L}\right)(T_0 - T_1) \tag{2.3-7}$$

Here we see that the rate of heat transfer is proportional to the thermal conductivity and the temperature difference and inversely proportional to the thickness of the plate, L. It is helpful to think of Eq. 2.3-7 in the form

$$\text{heat flow} = \frac{\text{driving force}}{\text{resistance}} \tag{2.3-8}$$

where the driving force is the temperature difference, $T_0 - T_1$, and the resistance is given by

$$\text{resistance} = L/k \tag{2.3-9}$$

Example 2.3-1 Heat transfer through a slab

As an example of the use of Eq. 2.3-7, let us calculate the rate at which energy is transferred across a plate 4 ft by 6 ft and $\frac{1}{4}$ in. thick, having the surface temperatures maintained at 212°F and 70°F. If the plate is steel, $k = 25$ Btu/hr ft °F and the heat flux is

$$q_x|_{\text{steel}} = \underbrace{\left\{\frac{(25\ \text{Btu hr}^{-1}\text{ft}^{-1}\text{°F}^{-1})(142\text{°F})}{(0.25\ \text{in.})}\right\}}_{\text{original terms in Eq. 2.3-7}}\underbrace{\left\{\frac{12\ \text{in.}}{\text{ft}}\right\}}_{\text{conversion factor}} = 17 \times 10^4\ \text{Btu/hr ft}^2$$

and the total rate of energy transfer is

$$\dot{Q} = \left(\frac{17 \times 10^4\ \text{Btu}}{\text{hr ft}^2}\right)(24\ \text{ft}^2) = 4.09 \times 10^6\ \text{Btu/hr}$$

Specified heat flux

If the heat flux, i.e., q_x, is specified the problem is nearly trivial for q_x is generally what we wish to find. If, in addition, we want to know the temperature field we again start with Eq. 2.3-1 and are quickly led, by the same set of assumptions to

$$T = A + Bx \tag{2.3-10}$$

which is subject to the condition specifying the heat flux

B.C.1 $$q_x = q_0, \qquad 0 \leqslant x \leqslant L \tag{2.3-11}$$

Since there are two constants of integration in Eq. 2.3-10, we obviously need another boundary condition in order to specify the temperature field. Taking this to be

B.C.2 $$T = T_0, \qquad x = 0 \tag{2.3-12}$$

we may solve for B as follows:

B.C.1 $$q_x = q_0 = -k\frac{\partial T}{\partial x} = -kB \tag{2.3-13}$$

or

$$B = -q_0/k$$

Imposing the second boundary condition

B.C.2 $$T = T_0 = A \tag{2.3-14}$$

determines A and the temperature field is given by

$$T = T_0 - \left(\frac{q_0}{k}\right)x \tag{2.3-15}$$

Specified fluid temperatures and film heat transfer coefficients

Although we are a long way from having a thorough understanding of heat transfer at fluid–solid interfaces we may use the *definition* of a film heat transfer coefficient to analyze the steady heat conduction in a flat plate surrounded by two fluids. This situation is shown in Fig. 2.3.2. We can *define* a film heat transfer coefficient for the fluid–solid interface at $x = 0$ by the expression

$$q_x|_{x=0} = h_0(T_0 - T|_{x=0}) \tag{2.3-16}$$

Similarly the film heat transfer coefficient at $x = L$ is defined by

$$q_x|_{x=L} = h_1(T|_{x=L} - T_1) \tag{2.3-17}$$

In order to develop some physical intuition for the film heat transfer coefficient we might note, as we did in Eq. 1.3-28, that the heat flux at $x = L$ can also be expressed as

$$q_x|_{x=L} = -k_{\text{liq}}\left(\frac{\partial T_{\text{liq}}}{\partial x}\right)_{x=L} \tag{2.3-18}$$

since the fluid velocity is zero at the solid–liquid interface and conduction is the only mode of energy transport.† We cannot use this expression to calculate the heat flux unless we first determine the temperature field in the liquid; however, it can be used to give us a "picture" of the film heat transfer coefficient. Referring to the temperature profile in Fig. 2.3.2 we see that,

$$\left(\frac{\partial T_{\text{liq}}}{\partial x}\right)_{x=L} = \frac{T_1 - T|_{x=L}}{\delta} \tag{2.3-19}$$

and Eq. 2.3-18 can be expressed as

$$q_x|_{x=L} = \left(\frac{k_{\text{liq}}}{\delta}\right)(T|_{x=L} - T_1) \tag{2.3-20}$$

†Refer to Eq. 1.3-5 and neglect the radiant energy heat flux.

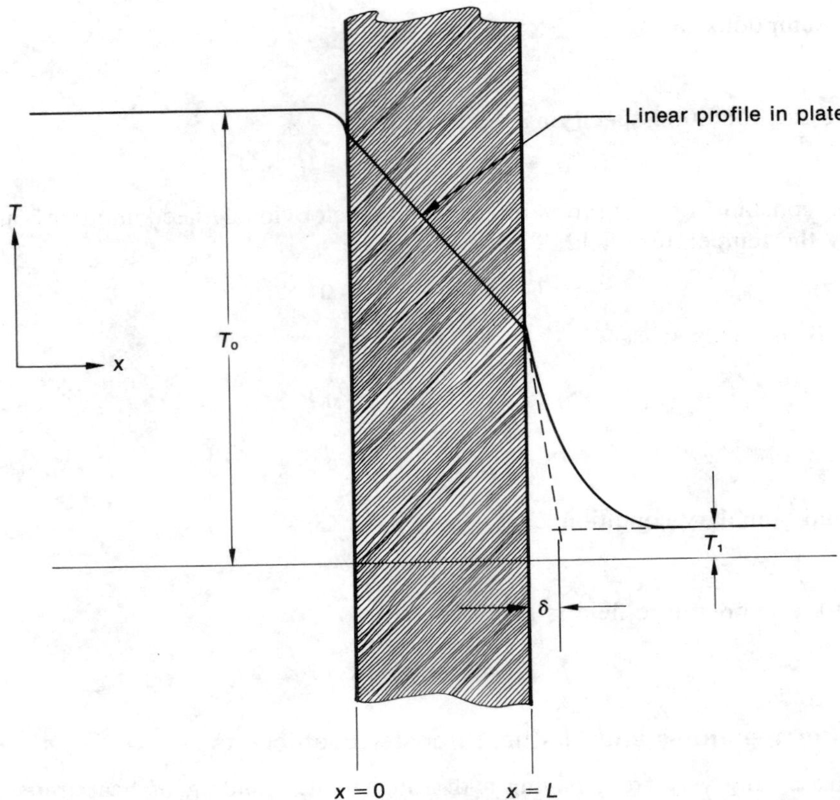

Fig. 2.3.2 Steady heat conduction in a flat plate bounded by two fluids.

Comparing this result with Eq. 2.3-17 indicates that h_1 is given by

$$h_1 = \left(\frac{k_{\text{liq}}}{\delta}\right) \tag{2.3-21}$$

where δ is thought of as a hypothetical film of liquid in which only conduction occurs.

If we now proceed to determine the temperature profile in the plate we quickly find that T is given by

$$T = A + Bx \tag{2.3-22}$$

where the constants of integration are to be determined by the conditions

B.C.1
$$q_x|_{x=0} = -k\left(\frac{\partial T}{\partial x}\right)_{x=0} \tag{2.3-23}$$

or

$$h_0(T_0 - T) = -k\left(\frac{\partial T}{\partial x}\right), \qquad x = 0$$

and

B.C.2
$$q_x|_{x=L} = -k\left(\frac{\partial T}{\partial x}\right)_{x=L} \tag{2.3-24}$$

or

$$h_1(T - T_1) = -k\left(\frac{\partial T}{\partial x}\right), \qquad x = L$$

Substitution of Eq. 2.3-22 into B.C.1 yields

B.C.1
$$h_0(T_0 - A) = -kB \tag{2.3-25}$$

while the second boundary condition provides the result

B.C.2
$$h_1(A + BL - T_1) = -kB \tag{2.3-26}$$

These two equations may be used to solve for A and B yielding

$$A = T_0 + \left(\frac{k}{h_0}\right) B$$

$$B = \frac{-h_1(T_0 - T_1)}{L\left[\left(\frac{k}{L}\right)\left(\frac{h_1}{h_0} + 1\right) + h_1\right]}$$

This result can be used to determine the temperature profile within the plate; however, the quantity of general interest is the heat flux q_x which is given by,

$$q_x = -k\left(\frac{\partial T}{\partial x}\right) = -kB \tag{2.3-27}$$

or

$$q_x = \frac{T_0 - T_1}{\frac{1}{h_0} + \frac{L}{k} + \frac{1}{h_1}} \tag{2.3-28}$$

If we define an *overall* heat transfer coefficient U by

$$\frac{1}{U} = \frac{1}{h_0} + \frac{L}{k} + \frac{1}{h_1} \tag{2.3-29}$$

we can express the heat flux in the especially simple form

$$q_x = U(T_0 - T_1) \tag{2.3-30}$$

Note that if we think of these heat transfer coefficients as the inverse of a *resistance* and write,

$$R = \frac{1}{U}$$

$$r_0 = \frac{1}{h_0}$$

$$r_{\text{plate}} = \frac{1}{k/L}$$

$$r_1 = \frac{1}{h_1}$$

then the *total resistance* R of the plate plus the two surrounding fluids could be expressed as the sum,

$$R = r_0 + r_{\text{plate}} + r_1$$

i.e., the thermal resistances act in *series* and may be summed to yield the total resistance. This analogy between thermal resistance and electrical resistance has been utilized to solve a number of complex heat transfer problems [7].

Composite plates

Another example of steady, one-dimensional heat conduction is that of heat transfer across a composite plate such as that shown in Fig. 2.3.3. This actually represents a simplified version of Design Problem I; however, it will be worthwhile to examine a problem of this type once again.

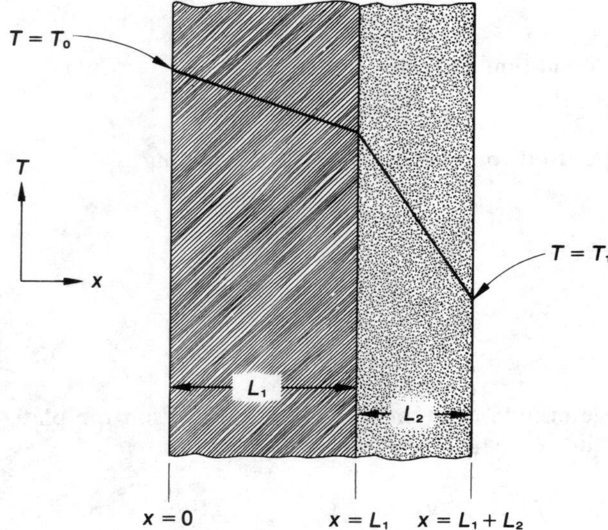

Fig. 2.3.3 Steady heat conduction in a composite flat plate.

The governing differential equation for the temperature is

$$\frac{d^2T}{dx^2} = 0 \tag{2.3-31}$$

and the solution is

$$T = A + Bx \tag{2.3-32}$$

provided the thermal conductivity is constant. In treating this problem we will be careful about defining the temperature in each of the two distinct regions and write

$$T = T_{(1)} = A_{(1)} + B_{(1)}x, \qquad 0 \leq x \leq L_1 \tag{2.3-33a}$$

$$T = T_{(2)} = A_{(2)} + B_{(2)}x, \qquad L_1 \leq x \leq L_1 + L_2 \tag{2.3-33b}$$

The device of labeling the temperature, i.e., $T_{(1)}$ and $T_{(2)}$, for each region will prove to be helpful when we impose the boundary conditions. Two obvious boundary conditions are derived from the fact that the temperature is specified at $x = 0$ and $x = L_1 + L_2$ and we write

B.C.1 $$T_{(1)} = T_0, \qquad x = 0 \tag{2.3-34}$$

B.C.2 $$T_{(2)} = T_1, \qquad x = L_1 + L_2 \tag{2.3-35}$$

We need two more boundary conditions in order to completely specify the temperature profile, and these are obtained by imposing the conditions of *continuity of temperature* and *continuity of the normal component of the heat flux vector.* This yields†

B.C.3 $$T_{(1)} = T_{(2)}, \qquad x = L_1, \quad \text{continuity of temperature} \tag{2.3-36}$$

B.C.4 $$-k_1\left(\frac{dT_{(1)}}{dx}\right) = -k_2\left(\frac{dT_{(2)}}{dx}\right), \qquad x = L_1, \quad \text{continuity of } \mathbf{q}\cdot\mathbf{n} \tag{2.3-37}$$

The boundary conditions can now be used to determine the constants of integration appearing in Eqs. 2.3-33.

†Here we are assuming that the different materials are continuous at the interface, i.e., there is no air gap, or cement, glue, etc. at the interface.

$$A_{(1)} = T_0$$

$$B_{(1)} = -\frac{(T_0 - T_1)}{k_1\left(\dfrac{L_1}{k_1} + \dfrac{L_2}{k_2}\right)}$$

$$A_{(2)} = T_0 - L_1\left(\frac{k_2}{k_1} - 1\right)\left[\frac{T_0 - T_1}{k_2\left(\dfrac{L_1}{k_1} + \dfrac{L_2}{k_2}\right)}\right]$$

$$B_{(2)} = -\frac{(T_0 - T_1)}{k_2\left(\dfrac{L_1}{k_1} + \dfrac{L_2}{k_2}\right)}$$

As in the previous example we are generally interested in the heat flux q_x rather than the temperature profile; the former is given by

$$q_x = -k_1\left(\frac{dT_{(1)}}{dx}\right) = U(T_0 - T_1) \tag{2.3-38}$$

where the overall heat transfer coefficient is given by

$$\frac{1}{U} = \frac{L_1}{k_1} + \frac{L_2}{k_2} \tag{2.3-39}$$

Our analysis of this problem was based on the governing differential equation, its solution, and the appropriate boundary conditions. This approach is more complex than the one given in the solution of Design Problem I; however, it illustrates very nicely how the boundary conditions are constructed at phase interfaces.

Uniform heat generation

When heat is generated uniformly throughout a flat plate, the one-dimensional heat conduction equation becomes

$$0 = \frac{d}{dx}\left(k\frac{dT}{dx}\right) + \Phi \tag{2.3-40}$$

For constant thermal conductivity this reduces to

$$0 = \frac{d^2T}{dx^2} + \Phi/k \tag{2.3-41}$$

which may be integrated to yield

$$T = A + Bx - \left(\frac{\Phi}{k}\right)\frac{x^2}{2} \tag{2.3-42}$$

Considering the simple case of specified surface temperatures, we write the boundary conditions as

B.C.1 $$T = T_0, \quad x = 0 \tag{2.3-43}$$

B.C.2 $$T = T_1, \quad x = L \tag{2.3-44}$$

Solving for the constants of A and B, we obtain

$$T = T_0 - (T_0 - T_1)\left(\frac{x}{L}\right) + \frac{\Phi}{2k}(L - x)x \tag{2.3-45}$$

This result is plotted in Fig. 2.3.4.

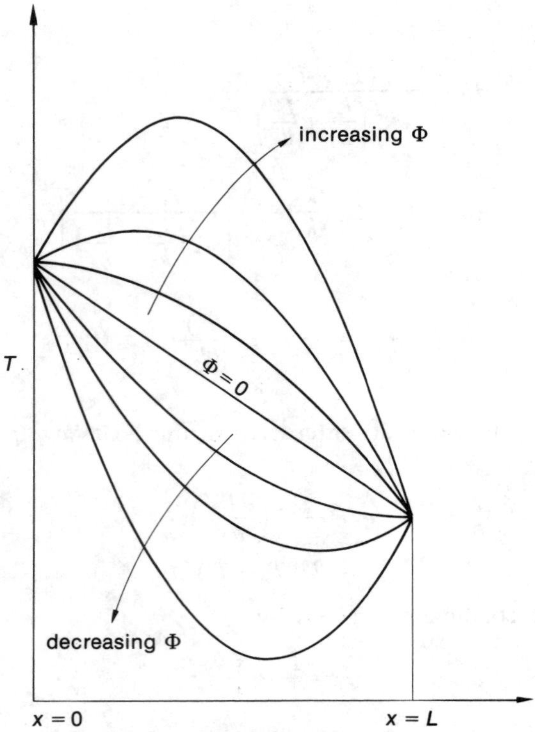

Fig. 2.3.4 Temperature distribution in a flat plate with a heat source or sink.

Example 2.3-2 Determination of the maximum temperature

If a copper plate of thickness 1 in. is subject to a uniform heat generation rate of 24×10^6 Btu/hr ft³, what is the maximum temperature in the plate if its surfaces are maintained at 212°F and 72°F?

From Eq. 2.3-45 we can locate the position of the maximum temperature by the expression

$$\frac{dT}{dx} = 0 = -\frac{(T_0 - T_1)}{L} + \frac{\Phi}{2k}(L - 2x)$$

Thus we find the value of x for which the temperature is a maximum is given by

$$x_{\max} = \frac{L}{2} - \frac{k(T_0 - T_1)}{\Phi L}$$

Note that we require $k(T_0 - T_1)/\Phi L \leq L/2$ in order that this expression for $x_{\max}$ be valid. For values of $k(T_0 - T_1)/\Phi L$ greater than $L/2$ there is no maximum temperature other than T_0 or T_1. Substituting the expression for $x_{\max}$ into Eq. 2.3-45 yields an expression for the maximum temperature

$$T_{\max} = T_0 + \frac{\Phi}{2k}\left[\frac{L}{2} - \frac{k(T_0 - T_1)}{\Phi L}\right]^2$$

From Fig. 1.3.3 we obtain the thermal conductivity, thus we have all the data we need.

$$\begin{aligned} k &= 220 \text{ Btu/hr ft °F} \\ \Phi &= 24 \times 10^6 \text{ Btu/hr ft}^3 \\ T_0 &= 212\text{°F} \\ T_1 &= 72\text{°F} \\ L &= (1/12) \text{ ft} \end{aligned}$$

The calculated maximum temperature is

$$T_{\max} = 212\text{°F} + \frac{(24 \times 10^6 \text{ Btu/hr ft}^3)}{(2)(220 \text{ Btu/hr ft °F})}\left[\frac{\text{ft}}{24} - \frac{(220 \text{ Btu/hr ft °F})(140\text{°F})}{(24 \times 10^6 \text{ Btu/hr ft}^3)(1/12 \text{ ft})}\right]^2 = 249.6\text{°F}$$

*2.4 Steady, One-Dimensional Heat Conduction in Cylindrical Coordinates

The study of heat transfer in the radial direction for cylindrical coordinates is of immense practical value since pipes are so commonly used to transport process streams. The water in automobile cooling systems is cooled in radiators consisting of a bundle of tubes; steam lines in industrial plants must be insulated against loss of heat owing to radial heat conduction; and a relatively efficient heat exchanger for cooling or heating process streams can be constructed from two concentric pipes. In such a heat exchanger one stream passes through the central pipe and the other flows through the annular region; the energy transfer taking place by heat conduction in the radial direction. In this section we consider just the single case of a composite pipe bounded by fluids on the inside and outside at temperatures T_0 and T_1 respectively. This configuration and a sketch of the temperature profile are shown in Fig. 2.4.1.† We begin our analysis with Eq. (*b*) in Table 2.2-3 and set $\Phi = 0$ to obtain

$$0 = \left[\frac{1}{r}\frac{\partial}{\partial r}\left(r\frac{\partial T}{\partial r}\right) + \frac{1}{r^2}\left(\frac{\partial^2 T}{\partial \theta^2}\right) + \frac{\partial^2 T}{\partial z^2}\right] \tag{2.4-1}$$

If we assume that the process under consideration is axially symmetric, the temperature is independent of θ

†Here we assume that the surrounding fluids are flowing at a sufficiently rapid rate so that the temperature is uniform in the fluid except in a thin region near the pipe.

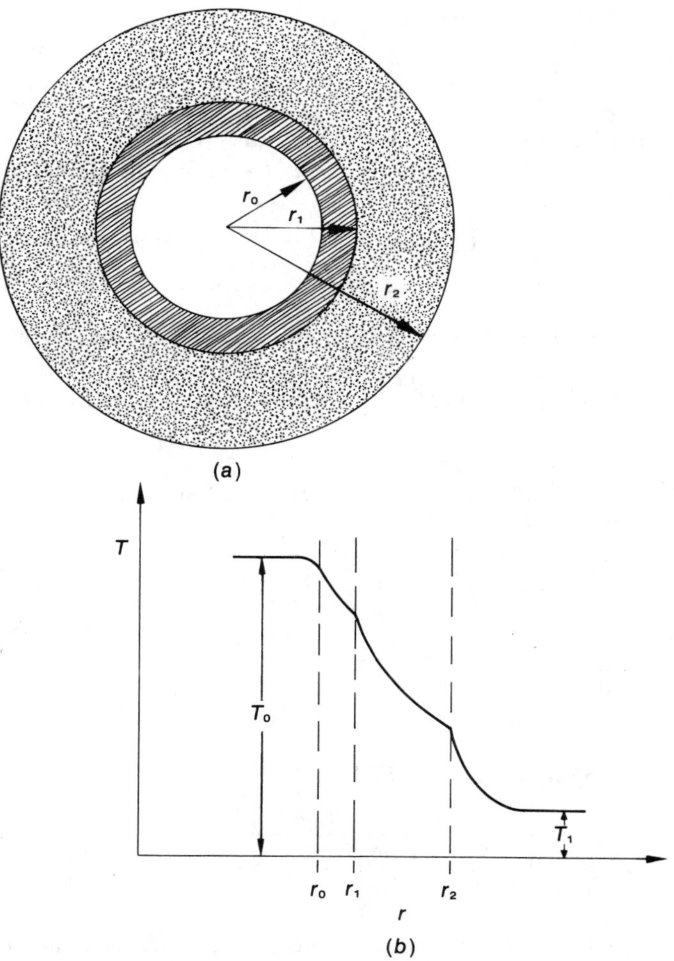

Fig. 2.4.1 Radial heat conduction in a composite pipe.

so that $\partial^2 T/\partial\theta^2 = 0$ and Eq. 2.4-1 reduces to

$$0 = \left[\frac{1}{r}\frac{\partial}{\partial r}\left(r\frac{\partial T}{\partial r}\right) + \frac{\partial^2 T}{\partial z^2}\right] \tag{2.4-2}$$

The assumption of symmetry is generally a reasonable one for many practical cases; however, it is rarely strictly satisfied. For example, in an automobile radiator the heat transfer coefficient is probably higher on the side of the radiator tube facing the oncoming air, thus a variation of h_{air} exists around the tube and the temperature in the tube will depend on θ. Nevertheless, the conduction in the θ-direction will still be small compared to the conduction in the r-direction. Under these conditions the assumption of symmetry will lead to a reasonable result provided an average film heat transfer coefficient is used. If we further assume that the variation of T in the z-direction is small, we obtain†

$$0 = \frac{1}{r}\left[\frac{d}{dr}\left(r\frac{dT}{dr}\right)\right] \tag{2.4-3}$$

Multiplying by r and integrating once gives

$$r\frac{dT}{dr} = A \tag{2.4-4}$$

Dividing by r and integrating again yields an expression for the temperature

$$T = A \ln r + B \tag{2.4-5}$$

Often one encounters Eq. 2.4-3 in the expanded form

$$0 = \left(\frac{d^2 T}{dr^2}\right) + \frac{1}{r}\left(\frac{dT}{dr}\right)$$

and other methods [8, 9] must be used to obtain the solution.

At this point we follow the procedure used in the case of a composite slab and express the temperature field in terms of $T_{(1)}$ and $T_{(2)}$ where

$$T_{(1)} = A_{(1)} \ln r + B_{(1)}, \qquad r_0 \leq r \leq r_1 \tag{2.4-6}$$

$$T_{(2)} = A_{(2)} \ln r + B_{(2)}, \qquad r_1 \leq r \leq r_2 \tag{2.4-7}$$

The constants of integration will be determined by application of the following boundary conditions:

B.C.1 $$h_0(T_0 - T_{(1)}) = -k_1\left(\frac{dT_{(1)}}{dr}\right), \qquad r = r_0, \quad \text{continuity of heat flux} \tag{2.4-8}$$

B.C.2 $$T_{(1)} = T_{(2)}, \qquad r = r_1, \quad \text{continuity of temperature} \tag{2.4-9}$$

B.C.3 $$-k_1\left(\frac{\partial T_{(1)}}{\partial r}\right) = -k_2\left(\frac{\partial T_{(2)}}{\partial r}\right), \qquad r = r_1, \quad \text{continuity of heat flux} \tag{2.4-10}$$

B.C.4 $$-k_2\left(\frac{\partial T_{(2)}}{\partial r}\right) = h_1(T_{(2)} - T_1), \qquad r = r_2, \quad \text{continuity of heat flux} \tag{2.4-11}$$

After some tedious algebraic manipulation we find

$$A_{(1)} = -\frac{(T_0 - T_1)}{\left[\left(\frac{k_1}{h_1 r_2}\right) + \left(\frac{k_1}{k_2}\right)\ln\left(\frac{r_2}{r_1}\right) + \ln\left(\frac{r_1}{r_0}\right) + \left(\frac{k_1}{h_0 r_0}\right)\right]}$$

†Here the partial derivatives have been replaced by total derivatives since T is assumed to depend only on r.

$$B_{(1)} = T_1 + A_{(1)}\left[\left(\frac{k_1}{k_2}\right)\ln\left(\frac{r_1}{r_2}\right) - \ln r_1 - \left(\frac{k_1}{h_1 r_2}\right)\right]$$

$$A_{(2)} = \left(\frac{k_1}{k_2}\right) A_{(1)}$$

$$B_{(2)} = T_1 - A_{(1)}\left[\left(\frac{k_1}{h_1 r_2}\right) + \left(\frac{k_1}{k_2}\right)\ln r_2\right]$$

With the constants of integration, Eqs. 2.4-6 and 2.4-7 completely determine the temperature profile. Of prime importance is the heat transfer rate for a pipe of length L. This is given by

$$\begin{aligned}\dot{Q} &= 2\pi r_2 L q_r|_{r=r_2} \\ &= -2\pi r_2 L k_2\left(\frac{\partial T_{(2)}}{\partial r}\right)_{r=r_2} \\ &= \frac{-2\pi r_2 L k_2 A_{(2)}}{r_2} \\ &= \frac{2\pi L k_2 (T_0 - T_1)(k_1/k_2)}{\left[\frac{k_1}{h_1 r_2} + \left(\frac{k_1}{k_2}\right)\ln\left(\frac{r_2}{r_1}\right) + \ln\left(\frac{r_1}{r_0}\right) + \frac{k_1}{h_0 r_0}\right]} \\ &= \frac{2\pi k_1 L (T_0 - T_1)}{\left[\left(\frac{k_1}{h_1 r_2}\right) + \left(\frac{k_1}{k_2}\right)\ln\left(\frac{r_2}{r_1}\right) + \ln\left(\frac{r_1}{r_0}\right) + \frac{k_1}{h_0 r_0}\right]}\end{aligned} \tag{2.4-12}$$

We can rearrange this expression for the total heat flux so that it takes a form similar to that for the composite flat plate

$$\dot{Q} = \frac{(2\pi r_2)L(T_0 - T_1)}{\left[\frac{1}{h_0}(r_2/r_0) + \left(\frac{r_1}{k_1}\right)(r_2/r_1)\ln(r_1/r_0) + \left(\frac{r_2}{k_2}\right)\ln(r_2/r_1) + \frac{1}{h_1}\right]}$$

or

$$\dot{Q} = U_o A_o (T_0 - T_1) \tag{2.4-13}$$

where U_0^{-1} is the sum of the resistances.

$$\frac{1}{U_o} = \frac{1}{h_0}(r_2/r_0) + \left(\frac{r_1}{k_1}\right)(r_2/r_1)\ln(r_1/r_0) + \left(\frac{r_2}{k_2}\right)\ln(r_2/r_1) + \frac{1}{h_1}$$

Here A_o represents the "outer" area and U_o represents the overall heat transfer coefficient *based on the outer area.* A similar expression for $\dot{Q}$ can be obtained in terms of A_i and U_i, the "inner" area and the overall heat transfer coefficient *based on the inner area.*

Example 2.4-1 Heat loss in an insulated pipe

As an example of the application of the expression for $\dot{Q}$ given by Eq. 2.4-13, we consider the rate of heat loss from an insulated steam pipe. We are given the following conditions:

length of pipe:	$L = 100$ ft
inner diameter of pipe:	$D_0 = 1.0$ in.
outer diameter of pipe:	$D_1 = 1.24$ in.
outer diameter of insulation:	$D_2 = 2$ in.

inside film heat transfer coefficient for condensing saturated steam:	$h_0 = 800$ Btu/hr ft^2°F
outside film heat transfer coefficient for air:	$h_1 = 2$ Btu/hr ft^2°F
thermal conductivity for the pipe:	$k_1 = 28$ Btu/hr ft °F
thermal conductivity of insulating material:	$k_2 = 0.035$ Btu/hr ft °F
temperature of condensing steam inside the pipe:	$T_0 = 235$°F
temperature of air outside the pipe:	$T_1 = 78$°F

If we neglect the energy loss due to radiation and if the assumption of symmetry that was made in the course of developing Eq. 2.4-13 is satisfactory, we calculate the rate of heat loss to be

$$\dot{Q} = \frac{2(3.14)(1.0\text{ in.})(100\text{ ft})(235°\text{F} - 78°\text{F})}{\left(\frac{\text{hr ft}^2\,°\text{F}}{800\text{ Btu}}\right)\left(\frac{2.0}{1.0}\right) + \frac{0.62\text{ in.}}{28\text{ Btu/hr ft °F}}\left(\frac{2.0}{1.24}\right)\ln\left(\frac{1.24}{1.0}\right) + \frac{1.0\text{ in.}}{0.035\text{ Btu/hr ft °F}}\ln\left(\frac{2.0}{1.24}\right) + \frac{\text{hr ft}^2\,°\text{F}}{2.0\text{ Btu}}}$$

Carrying out the calculations for the denominator allows us to put this expression in the form

$$\dot{Q} = \frac{2(3.14)(1.0\text{ in.})(100\text{ ft})(235°\text{F} - 78°\text{F})\text{ Btu/hr ft}^2\,°\text{F}}{\underset{\substack{\uparrow \\ \text{inside film} \\ \text{resistance}}}{0.025} + \underset{\substack{\uparrow \\ \text{pipe wall} \\ \text{resistance}}}{0.00064} + \underset{\substack{\uparrow \\ \text{insulation} \\ \text{resistance}}}{1.138} + \underset{\substack{\uparrow \\ \text{outside film} \\ \text{resistance}}}{0.500}}$$

Here we see that the insulation and the surrounding air are responsible for a major portion of the resistance to heat transfer, while the pipe wall gives rise to a negligible resistance and the resistance owing to the condensing steam film is small. Completing the calculation we find

$$\dot{Q} = 4941\text{ Btu/hr}$$

If the cost of energy is $1\frac{1}{2}$ cents per kilowatt hour† the energy loss in this example results in an energy cost given by

$$\{\text{energy cost}\} = \left(\frac{491\text{ Btu}}{\text{hr}}\right)\left(\frac{\$0.015}{\text{kWh}}\right)\left(\frac{252\text{ cal}}{\text{Btu}}\right)\left(\frac{1.62\times 10^{-6}\text{ kWh}}{\text{cal}}\right)$$
$$= \$0.0217/\text{hr}$$
$$= \$190/\text{yr}$$

Here we see that the energy loss for this 100-ft section of steam line costs on the order of \$190 per year as compared to \$601 per year if no insulation is used. This difference must be considered in light of the cost of insulating the line and maintaining the insulation. For example, increasing the thickness of the insulation would reduce the loss; however, this would require a larger capital outlay and perhaps increase the maintenance costs. Obviously there is an *economic* optimum for this process, and in searching for this optimum one should be aware of the existence of a *critical* insulation thickness which must be exceeded if the addition of more insulation is to give the desired effect. Thus we will show in the following paragraphs that under certain circumstances the energy loss *increases* with increasing insulation thickness. This phenomenon results from the fact that the heat flux $q_r|_{r=r_2}$ decreases with increasing r_2 more slowly than r_2 increases when $r_2 < r_c$, where r_c is the critical radius. This results in the product $2\pi r_2 q_r|_{r=r_2}$ increasing with increasing r_2.

Critical insulation thickness

In order to demonstrate the effect of insulation on the heat loss from a pipe, we need only make use of Eq. 2.4-13. However, in order to simplify the analysis, we will consider the idealized case

†This is approximately the cost of energy supplied by an industrial steam power plant to a large user. Home owners usually pay from 2 to 5 cents per kilowatt hour.

$$h_0 \to \infty, \qquad k_1 \to \infty$$

Thus we assume that the resistance to heat transfer is entirely in the insulation and in the air surrounding the pipe. From the previous example of the heat loss in an insulated pipe, we can see that this is a reasonable assumption for many practical cases. Making these assumptions, Eq. 2.4-13 reduces to

$$\dot{Q} = \frac{2\pi r_2 L (T_0 - T_1)}{\left(\frac{r_2}{k_2}\right) \ln (r_2/r_1) + \frac{1}{h_1}} \tag{2.4-14}$$

If we plot $\dot{Q}/2\pi L(T_0 - T_1)$ versus r_2 we obtain curves of the type shown in Fig. 2.4.2. The shape of the curve of course depends on the values of k_2 and h_1; however, all curves will have the important characteristic that $\dot{Q}$ will be a maximum for $r_2 = r_c$. This means that the addition of insulation to a pipe having a radius less than r_c will *increase* the heat loss unless sufficient insulation is added so that the radius of the pipe plus insulation is greater than r_c.

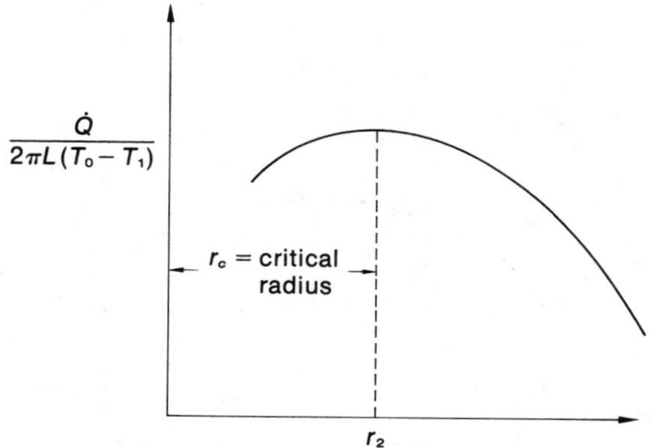

Fig. 2.4.2 Heat loss from an insulated pipe as a function of radius.

We can obtain a useful expression for r_c by locating the maximum in $\dot{Q}$ by means of Eq. 2.4-14. Differentiating $\dot{Q}$ with respect to r_2 and setting the result equal to zero,

$$\left(\frac{\partial \dot{Q}}{\partial r_2}\right) = 0 = \frac{\left[\left(\frac{r_2}{k_2}\right) \ln (r_2/r_1) + \frac{1}{h_1}\right] - r_2 \left[\left(\frac{1}{k_2}\right) \ln (r_2/r_1) + \frac{1}{k_2}\right]}{\left[\left(\frac{r_2}{k_2}\right) \ln (r_2/r_1) + \frac{1}{h_1}\right]^2} \tag{2.4-15}$$

Solving for $r_2 = r_c$ yields

$$r_c = k_2/h_1 \tag{2.4-16}$$

Choosing some representative values for k_2 (the thermal conductivity of the insulation) and h_1 (the air film heat transfer coefficient) yields

$$r_c = \frac{0.035 \text{ Btu/hr ft °F}}{2 \text{ Btu/hr ft}^2 \text{°F}} = 0.21 \text{ in.}$$

Here we see that the critical radius is relatively small, thus the phenomenon of a maximum heat loss is of importance only for small pipes or wires. For larger pipes the heat loss always decreases with increasing insulation thickness as indicated in Fig. 2.4.3.

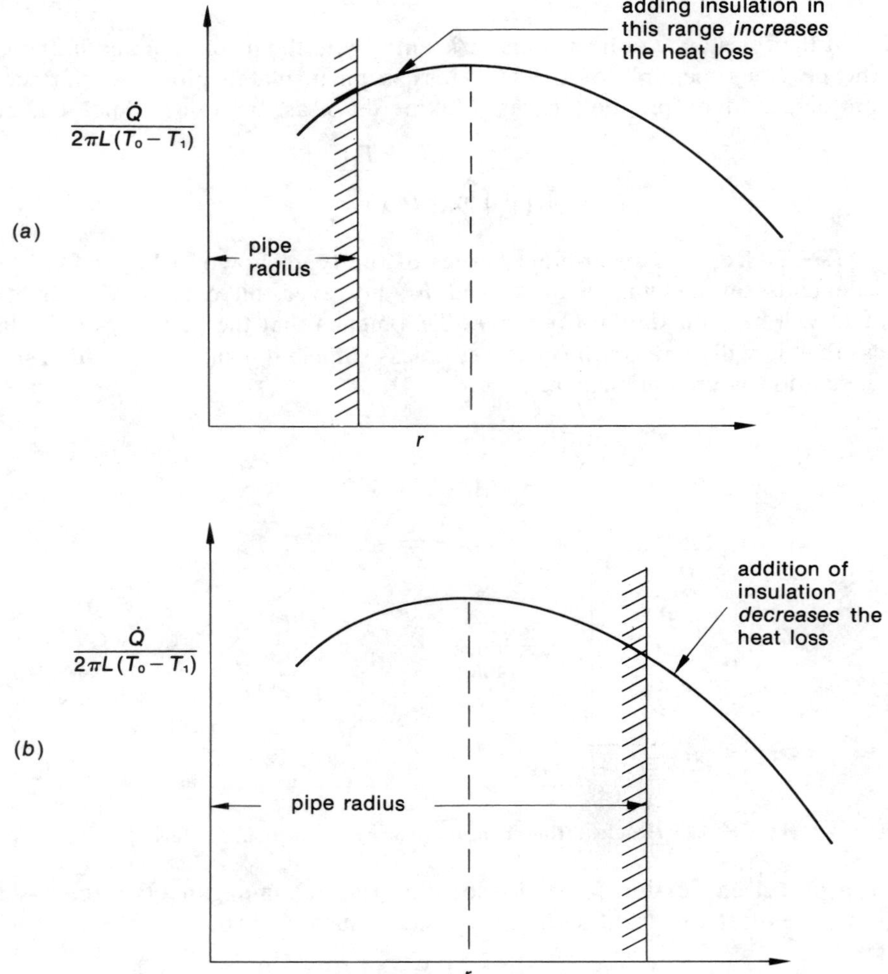

Fig. 2.4.3 Effect of insulation on the heat loss from small and large pipes.

*2.5 Steady, One-Dimensional Heat Conduction in Spherical Coordinates

Heat conduction in spherical coordinates is much less important than either rectangular or cylindrical coordinates since this type of geometry is encountered only occasionally in practical heat transfer problems. Nevertheless, it will be instructive to work through one example in spherical coordinates to complete our study of steady, one-dimensional heat transfer.

We will consider the simplest possible case; that of a spherical shell having its inner and outer surfaces maintained at the temperatures T_0 and T_1 respectively. This configuration is illustrated in Fig. 2.5.1. We begin the analysis with Eq. (c) in Table 2.2-3 assuming that $\Phi = 0$.

$$0 = \left[\frac{1}{r^2}\frac{\partial}{\partial r}\left(r^2\frac{\partial T}{\partial r}\right) + \frac{1}{r^2 \sin\theta}\frac{\partial}{\partial \theta}\left(\sin\theta\frac{\partial T}{\partial \theta}\right) + \frac{1}{r^2\sin^2\theta}\left(\frac{\partial^2 T}{\partial \phi^2}\right)\right] \tag{2.5-1}$$

The assumption that T is independent of θ and ϕ must be made if the process is to be one-dimensional (i.e., T is only a function of r), and Eq. 2.5-1 reduces to

$$0 = \frac{1}{r^2}\left[\frac{d}{dr}\left(r^2\frac{dT}{dr}\right)\right] \tag{2.5-2}$$

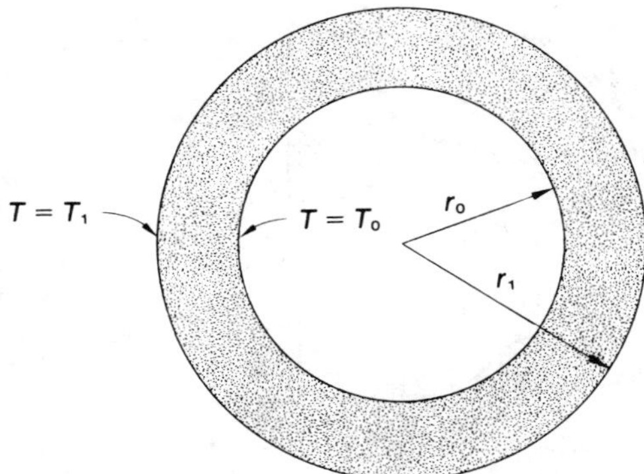

Fig. 2.5.1 Steady, one-dimensional heat conduction in a spherical shell.

Multiplying by $r^2\,dr$ and integrating yields

$$r^2\frac{dT}{dr} = C_1 \tag{2.5-3}$$

Dividing by r^2 and multiplying by dr allows us to separate the variables, and integration then yields

$$T = -\frac{C_1}{r} + C_2 \tag{2.5-4}$$

The boundary conditions may be expressed as

B.C.1 $$T = T_0, \qquad r = r_0 \tag{2.5-5}$$

B.C.2 $$T = T_1, \qquad r = r_1 \tag{2.5-6}$$

Use of these two conditions allows us to determine the two constants of integration and the temperature distribution is given by

$$T = T_0 - (T_0 - T_1)\left(\frac{r_0/r - 1}{r_0/r_1 - 1}\right) \tag{2.5-7}$$

The total rate of heat transfer from the sphere to the surroundings is given by

$$\dot{Q} = 4\pi r_1{}^2 q_r\big|_{r=r_1} \tag{2.5-8}$$

or

$$\dot{Q} = 4\pi k\frac{(T_0 - T_1)}{\left(\frac{1}{r_0} - \frac{1}{r_1}\right)} \tag{2.5-9}$$

A variety of other one-dimensional problems exist in spherical coordinates; however, they will be left as problems for the student.

*2.6 Extended Surfaces†—The Rectangular Fin

When the overall heat transfer rate is limited by a low rate of heat transfer between a solid surface and a surrounding fluid, extended surfaces, or fins, may often be used to improve the overall transfer rate. In essence the fins are used to increase the area; however the overall heat transfer rate is not a simple function of the area when fins are used, and we must analyze the problem in some detail if we are to develop satisfactory design equations for finned surfaces. Such surfaces have probably been observed by the student on air-cooled automobile engines, and on some steam heaters.

Some examples of finned surfaces are shown in Fig. 2.6.1. The configuration of the extended surface usually depends on the type of fluid motion occurring over the extended surface, and whenever possible

†This subject is treated in considerable detail in a recent book by D. Q. Kern and A. D. Kraus, *Extended Surface Heat Transfer*, McGraw-Hill Book Co., Inc., New York, 1972.

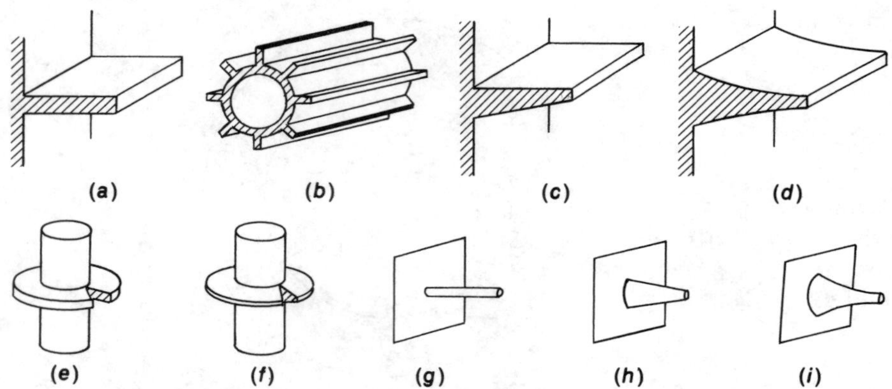

Fig. 2.6.1 Examples of finned surfaces: (*a*) Longitudinal fin of rectangular profile; (*b*) cylindrical tube equipped with fins of rectangular profile; (*c*) longitudinal fin of trapezoidal profile; (*d*) longitudinal fin of parabolic profile; (*e*) cylindrical tube equipped with radial fin of rectangular profile; (*f*) cylindrical tube equipped with radial fin of truncated conical profile; (*g*) cylindrical spine; (*h*) truncated conical spine; (*i*) parabolic spine. (Adapted from *Extended Surface Heat Transfer* by D. Q. Kern and A. D. Kraus, McGraw-Hill Book Co., Inc., New York, 1972.)

one will choose an arrangement of fins which will enhance the fluid motion and provide the highest possible film heat transfer coefficient.

In this section we will confine our attention to rectangular fins such as the one illustrated in Fig. 2.6.2. There we have shown a portion of a fin of thickness b and length L attached to a wall of unspecified thickness. Our objective here is to determine the heat flux over the surface area of the fin under steady conditions. Assuming constant thermal conductivity and no sources or sinks, our steady heat conduction equation, Eq. 2.2-10, takes the form

$$\frac{\partial^2 T}{\partial x^2} + \frac{\partial^2 T}{\partial y^2} + \frac{\partial^2 T}{\partial z^2} = 0 \tag{2.6-1}$$

If the length of the fin in the y-direction is much greater than L, we can assume† that the temperature

†See Secs. 2.9 and 2.10 for a detailed discussion of this point.

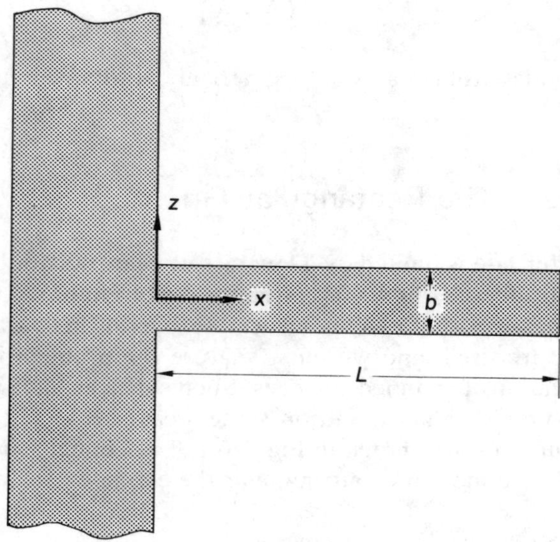

Fig. 2.6.2 Rectangular fin.

is independent of y and our governing differential equation reduces to

$$\frac{\partial^2 T}{\partial x^2} + \frac{\partial^2 T}{\partial z^2} = 0 \tag{2.6-2}$$

It must be remembered that we are not particularly interested in the temperature field, our objective being to determine the heat flux at the *phase interface*; however, the temperature field will lead us to this quantity. With an appropriate set of boundary conditions we can solve Eq. 2.6-2 to obtain the temperature field and hence the desired interphase heat flux.

If the flow past the fin is symmetrical, i.e., the flow field is the same above and below the fin, we could make the intuitive[10] assumption of symmetry and write

B.C.1
$$\frac{\partial T}{\partial z} = 0, \qquad z = 0 \tag{2.6-3}$$

It is quite likely that the film heat transfer coefficient varies over the length of the fin; however, as a simplifying approximation we will assume it is constant and write

B.C.2
$$-k\frac{\partial T}{\partial z} = h(T - T_a), \qquad z = b/2 \tag{2.6-4}$$

The effect of variations in h along the fin has been studied by Stachiewicz[11], and a correction factor given which brings the constant h analysis presented here into agreement with experimental data. In Eq. 2.6-4 the *ambient* temperature is designated by T_a, and we have discarded the condition at $z = -b/2$ since the temperature profile has been assumed to be symmetric. At the end of the fin a similar representation takes the form

B.C.3
$$-k\frac{\partial T}{\partial x} = h_{\text{end}}(T - T_a), \qquad x = L \tag{2.6-5}$$

Here we have written the film heat transfer coefficient as h_{end} since it is likely to be quite different from the heat transfer coefficient over the other surfaces of the fin. We still need to specify the temperature at $x = 0$, and without committing ourselves to the exact meaning of T_0 we write

B.C.4
$$T = T_0, \qquad x = 0 \tag{2.6-6}$$

Here we have assumed that the temperature at the base of the fin is constant and given by T_0. We are now confronted by a *differential equation*, Eq. 2.6-2 and *four boundary conditions*, Eqs. 2.6-3, 2.6-4, 2.6-5, and 2.6-6. Although we have not yet discussed the solution of *partial* differential equations, the student might guess that such solutions could become quite tedious and the effort is probably not justified for a problem which is already only an approximate description of the real process.

Very often an engineer is confronted with complex processes which do not justify the effort required to obtain an "exact" solution, and quite often his route to an approximate solution has some of the characteristics to be illustrated in this example. Rather than seek a complete solution giving point values of the temperature, $T(x, z)$, let us try instead to determine the variation of the *average* temperature.

Integrating Eq. 2.6-2 from $z = 0$ to $z = +b/2$ yields

$$\int_0^{b/2} \frac{\partial^2 T}{\partial x^2}\,dz + \int_0^{b/2} \frac{\partial^2 T}{\partial z^2}\,dz = 0$$

Interchanging differentiation and integration in the first integral and evaluating the second gives

$$\frac{\partial^2}{\partial x^2}\int_0^{b/2} T\,dz + \left.\frac{\partial T}{\partial z}\right|_{z=b/2} - \left.\frac{\partial T}{\partial z}\right|_{z=0} = 0 \tag{2.6-7}$$

Here we see that integration gives rise to boundary conditions 1 and 2 in our governing equation. Making use of Eqs. 2.6-3 and 2.6-4, and defining the average temperature $\langle T\rangle$ by

$$\langle T\rangle = \frac{2}{b}\int_0^{b/2} T\,dz \tag{2.6-8}$$

we may write Eq. 2.6-7 as†

$$\frac{d^2\langle T\rangle}{dx^2} - \frac{2h}{kb}\left(T|_{z=b/2} - T_a\right) = 0 \tag{2.6-9}$$

Here we encounter some difficulty, for our defining equation contains *two* unknowns,‡ $\langle T\rangle$ and $T|_{z=b/2}$, and is thus indeterminate.

In order to proceed we need to sketch some temperature profiles for a rectangular fin, and this has been done in Fig. 2.6.3. The three curves shown in Fig. 2.6.3 are simply intuitive versions of the temperature profile at some arbitrary point along the fin. Curve (a) represents the profile for a fin having a *low* thermal conductivity; curve (b) is for a *high* thermal conductivity; and curve (c) is for the limiting case of an *infinite* thermal conductivity.

From these curves we can feel confident that if the thermal conductivity is sufficiently§ high we can write

$$\langle T\rangle \sim T|_{z=b/2} \tag{2.6-10}$$

Defining the dimensionless temperature¶ as

$$\Theta = \frac{\langle T\rangle - T_a}{T_0 - T_a}$$

†The partial derivative is replaced by the ordinary derivative since $\langle T\rangle$ is a function only of x.
‡The ambient temperature is a *parameter* which must be specified.
§Later we will attempt to determine what is meant by "sufficiently" using an order-of-magnitude analysis of B.C.2.
¶Throughout the text dimensionless temperatures will be represented by Θ.

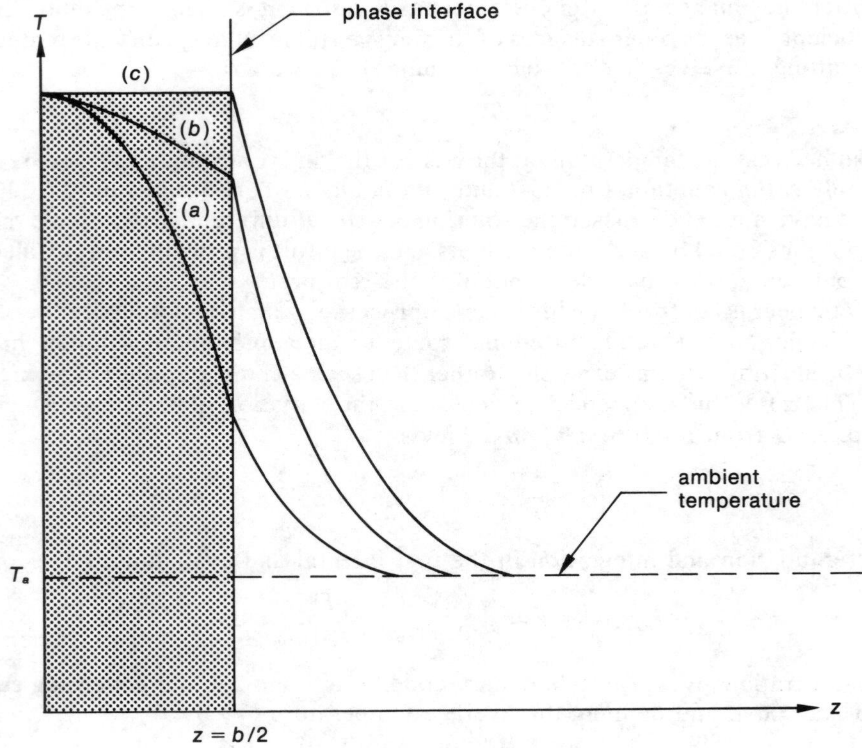

Fig. 2.6.3 Temperature profiles for a rectangular fin.

we can now express Eq. 2.6-9 as

$$\frac{d^2\Theta}{dx^2} - \left(\frac{2h}{kb}\right)\Theta = 0 \tag{2.6-11}$$

Boundary conditions 3 and 4 can be expressed as

B.C.3′ $$-k\frac{\partial\langle T\rangle}{\partial x} = h_{\text{end}}(\langle T\rangle - T_a), \qquad x = L \tag{2.6-12}$$

B.C.4′ $$\langle T\rangle = T_0, \qquad x = 0 \tag{2.6-13}$$

Here we have simply integrated Eqs. 2.6-5 and 2.6-6 from $z = 0$ to $z = b/2$ and imposed the definition of the average temperature given by Eq. 2.6-8. In terms of the dimensionless temperature these boundary conditions become

B.C.3″ $$-k\frac{d\Theta}{dx} = h_{\text{end}}\,\Theta, \qquad x = L \tag{2.6-14}$$

B.C.4″ $$\Theta = 1, \qquad x = 0 \tag{2.6-15}$$

The solution of Eq. 2.6-11 is obtained by assuming a solution of the form,

$$\Theta = Ce^{mx} \tag{2.6-16}$$

substituting into Eq. 2.6-11 to obtain the characteristic equation

$$m^2 - \frac{2h}{kb} = 0 \tag{2.6-17}$$

Thus Θ is given by

$$\Theta = C_1 \exp(x\sqrt{2h/kb}) + C_2 \exp(-x\sqrt{2h/kb}) \tag{2.6-18}$$

The constants of integration may be determined in terms of the boundary conditions given by Eqs. 2.6-14 and 2.6-15 and the final result is

$$\Theta = \frac{\cosh m(L-x) + \left(\frac{n}{m}\right)\sinh m(L-x)}{\cosh mL + \left(\frac{n}{m}\right)\sinh mL} \tag{2.6-19}$$

where

$$m = \sqrt{2h/kb}$$

$$n = h_{\text{end}}/k$$

Before going on to the determination of the increased heat transfer rate resulting from the fin, we must establish under what circumstances the approximation expressed by Eq. 2.6-10 is valid. To do this we turn our attention to B.C.2 and make the following order-of-magnitude estimate†

$$\frac{\partial T}{\partial Z} = \mathbf{0}\left(\frac{\Delta T}{b/2}\right) \tag{2.6-20}$$

Here ΔT represents the temperature difference between the centerline of the fin and the surface of the fin, thus

$$\Delta T = T|_{z=0} - T|_{z=b/2} \tag{2.6-21}$$

†The symbol **0** should be read as "order-of-magnitude of . . ." Order-of-magnitude analysis is discussed in Sec. 2.9.

We can now rearrange B.C.2 in the form

$$\frac{\Delta T}{T|_{z=b/2} - T_a} = \mathbf{0}\left(\frac{hb}{2k}\right) \tag{2.6-22}$$

From the temperature profiles shown in Fig. 2.6.3 it is clear that our analysis should be satisfactory when

$$\frac{\Delta T}{T|_{z=b/2} - T_a} \ll 1$$

or in terms of the governing parameters,

$$\frac{hb}{2k} \ll 1$$

The dimensionless group (hL/k), where L is some characteristic length, is encountered often in heat transfer problems and is known as the Biot number. For this particular case the characteristic length is $b/2$ and we write the Biot number as

$$N_{Bi} = hb/2k$$

and require that $N_{Bi} \ll 1$ in order that our analysis be valid. This requires that b be small, k be large, and h be small. But there would be no reason for constructing a fin under any circumstances but these;† thus, the practical considerations of the problem necessarily restrict the applications of the analysis to cases for which Eq. 2.6-10 is justified. A more thorough analysis [12] indicates that the solution given here is accurate to within 1 per cent provided $N_{Bi} \leq 0.1$.

The solution for the temperature distribution can be simplified somewhat if we assume that

$$h_{end} \sim h \tag{2.6-23}$$

Under these conditions the ratio n/m in Eq. 2.6-19 takes the form

$$\frac{n}{m} = \sqrt{\frac{hb}{2k}} = N_{Bi}^{1/2}, \quad \text{for } h_{end} = h \tag{2.6-24}$$

Thus if N_{Bi} is quite small, say on the order of 10^{-2}, it follows that $N_{Bi}^{1/2}$ is still small compared to unity and Eq. 2.6-19 may be simplified to

$$\Theta = \frac{\cosh [N_{Bi}^{1/2} 2(L-x)/b]}{\cosh [N_{Bi}^{1/2} 2L/b]}, \quad \text{for } h_{end} = h \text{ and } N_{Bi} \ll 1 \tag{2.6-25}$$

It will be helpful to have some idea of the circumstances for which Eq. 2.6-25 is valid. In computing an order-of-magnitude for $N_{Bi}^{1/2}$ we first examine Table 1.3-1 to conclude that

$$h = \mathbf{0}(10 \text{ Btu/hr ft}^2 {}^\circ\text{F})$$

This gives us an upper bound for natural convection, although it is perhaps a bit low for forced convection. For the fin thickness we estimate

$$b = \mathbf{0}(\tfrac{1}{8} \text{ in.})$$

and for the fin thermal conductivity we examine Fig. 1.3.3 to obtain

$$k = \mathbf{0}(10 \text{ Btu/hr ft} {}^\circ\text{F})$$

Thus we find that

$$N_{Bi}^{1/2} = \mathbf{0}(10^{-1})$$

†It should be obvious that there is little point in constructing a fin having a low thermal conductivity, nor would one use fins if h were large. Clearly, large values of b would defeat the purpose of the fin.

and Eq. 2.6-25 is a reasonably good approximation to the temperature distribution in a fin for most practical conditions. We can now use Eq. 2.6-25 to calculate the heat transfer rate for the fin. This is given by

$$\left\{\begin{matrix}\text{heat transfer rate for}\\ \text{the fin per unit length}\\ \text{in the } y\text{-direction}\end{matrix}\right\} = b\langle q_x\rangle|_{x=0}$$

$$= -bk\frac{d\langle T\rangle}{dx}\bigg|_{x=0} \tag{2.6-26}$$

$$= -bk(T_0 - T_a)\frac{d\Theta}{dx}\bigg|_{x=0}$$

Evaluating $d\Theta/dx$ at $x = 0$ gives

$$\left\{\begin{matrix}\text{heat transfer rate for}\\ \text{the fin per unit length}\\ \text{in the } y\text{-direction}\end{matrix}\right\} = 2N_{\text{Bi}}^{1/2}[\tanh(2N_{\text{Bi}}^{1/2}L/b)]k(T_0 - T_a) \tag{2.6-27}$$

Alternate derivation

There is an alternative approach to solving this problem which will be instructive for us to explore. Going back to Eqs. 2.6-2 through 2.6-6 we again consider the difficulty of obtaining an exact solution of the point equations. As a general rule when the point equations present great difficulties we should immediately consider the possibility of obtaining an approximate solution by means of the macroscopic balance equation. In the study of fluid flow this usually must be done when the flow is turbulent. For the case at hand, a macroscopic balance for the control volume shown in Fig. 2.6.4 would not be satisfactory at

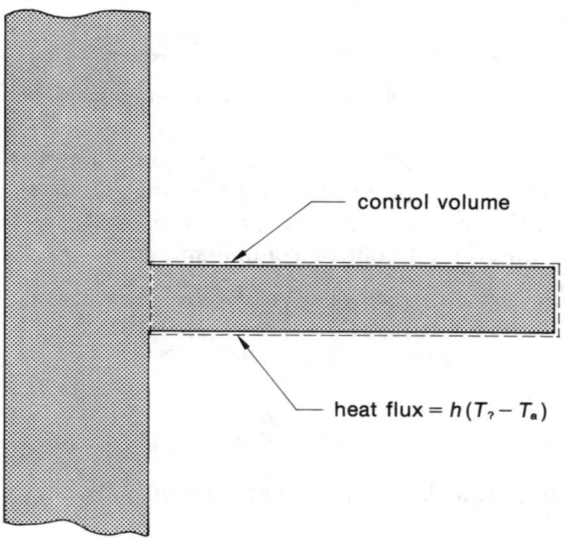

Fig. 2.6.4 Control volume for macroscopic balance analysis of rectangular fin.

all for we would have a very difficult time estimating the heat flux at the surface of the fin. At the base of the fin we know that the flux could be estimated as

$$q_z|_{z=b/2} \sim h(T_0 - T_a), \qquad x = 0$$

However, our *intuition* tells us that the *temperature of the fin varies in the x-direction* and we must have a good estimate of this variation if we are to satisfactorily compute the total heat flux from the fin. There is a rule† regarding macroscopic balances and their application to this type of problem which states:

> If some quantity such as the temperature varies continuously in the x-direction and we wish to *determine* this variation, the macroscopic balance must be made differential in the x-direction

It should be clear that we wish to develop a differential–macroscopic balance by using the control volume shown in Fig. 2.6.5. This type of analysis should be reminiscent of that encountered in the analysis of

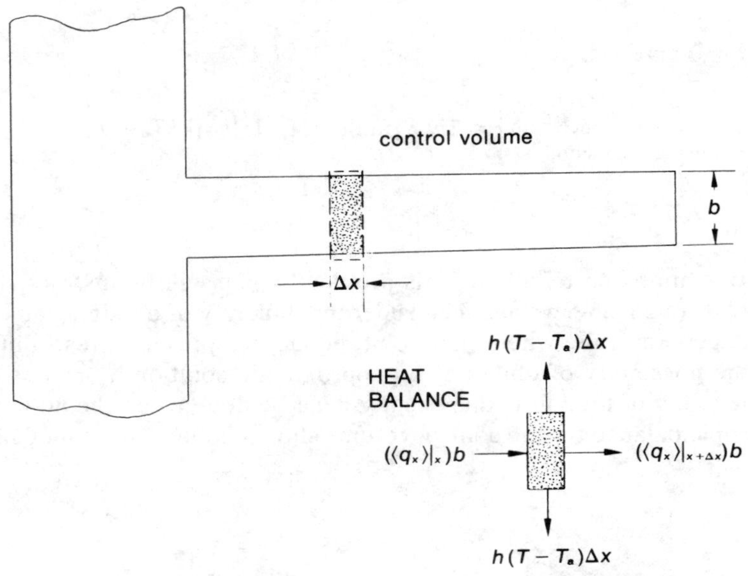

Fig. 2.6.5 Control volume for a differential–macroscopic balance.

beams in a strength of materials course. There, it may be remembered, it was necessary to know the shear force V, and bending moment M, as a function of x. The governing equations were derived by applying the laws of mechanics to a differential section of the beam such as that shown in Fig. 2.6.6.

The energy balance on the differential control volume shown in Fig. 2.6.5 could be stated as

$$\left\{\begin{array}{l}\text{heat flux into the control}\\ \text{volume per unit length}\\ \text{in the } y\text{-direction}\end{array}\right\} = \left\{\begin{array}{l}\text{heat flux out of the control}\\ \text{volume per unit length}\\ \text{in the } y\text{-direction}\end{array}\right\}$$

and written explicitly in the form

$$\langle q_x \rangle|_x b = 2h(T|_{z=b/2} - T_a)\Delta x + \langle q_x \rangle|_{x+\Delta x} b \tag{2.6-28}$$

Here $\langle q_x \rangle$ represents the *average* heat flux and is given explicitly by

$$\langle q_x \rangle = \frac{1}{b}\int_{z=-b/2}^{z=+b/2} q_x \, dz \tag{2.6-29}$$

Rearranging Eq. 2.6-28, dividing by Δx and taking the limit $\Delta x \to 0$ yields

$$-\frac{d\langle q_x \rangle}{dx} = \frac{2h}{b}(T|_{z=b/2} - T_a) \tag{2.6-30}$$

Making use of Fourier's law in the averaged form

†See Reference 3, page 273.

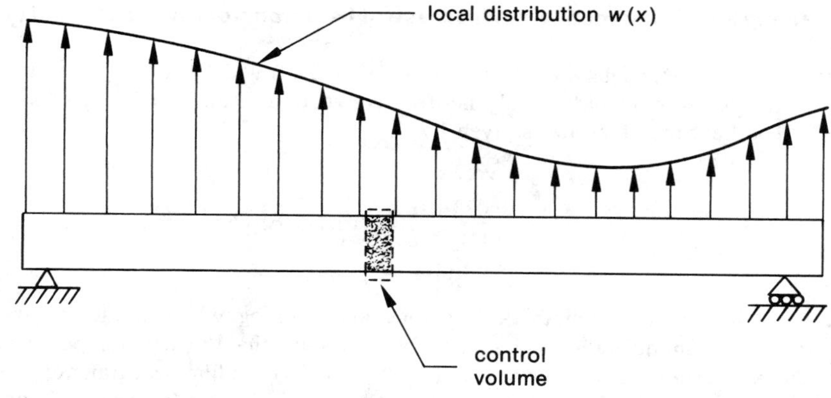

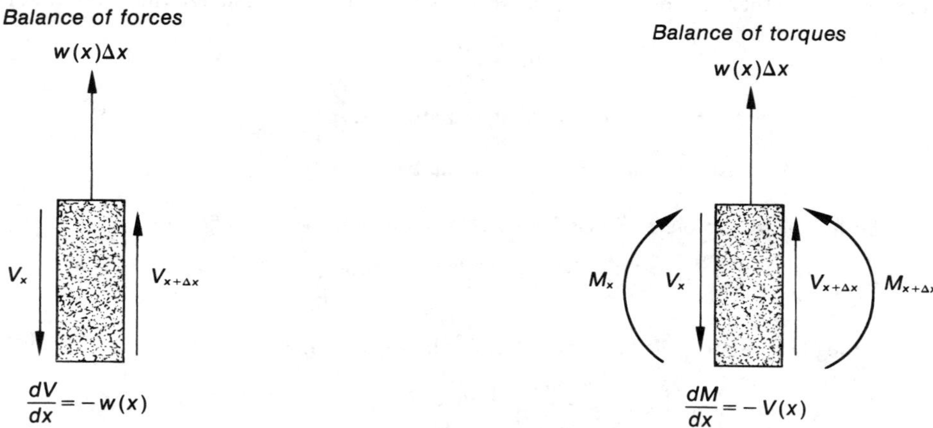

Fig. 2.6.6 Analysis of beams.

$$\langle q_x \rangle = -\left\langle k \frac{dT}{dx} \right\rangle$$

and assuming the thermal conductivity is constant to obtain†

$$\langle q_x \rangle = -k \frac{d\langle T \rangle}{dx}$$

allows us to write Eq. 2.6-30,

$$\frac{d^2\langle T \rangle}{dx^2} - \frac{2h}{kb}(T|_{z=b/2} - T_a) = 0 \tag{2.6-31}$$

This is the same expression previously obtained by direct integration of the partial differential equation, and from here on the analysis is the same. It is important to carefully consider both approaches to this problem. The first approach is more mathematical and forces us to be precise in defining averages and making approximations regarding the surface temperature and the average temperature. The second approach gives us a better "picture" of the process, and this is helpful for we must have this good picture of any process if we are going to make reasonable assumptions in route to an approximate solution.

†The average of the derivative is equal to the derivative of the average, since the limits of integration in the average are independent of x. This represents an application of the Leibnitz rule discussed in Chapter 4 following Eq. 4.3-27.

Example 2.6-1 Estimating the increase in heat transfer rate at a finned surface

We consider in this example a flat steel surface 6 ft high and 4 ft wide. The temperature of the plate is 180°F, the ambient air temperature is 68°F, and the free-convection heat transfer coefficient is taken to be 0.09 Btu/hr ft²°F. The heat transfer rate is given by

$$\dot{Q} = hA\,\Delta T$$
$$= \left(\frac{0.09\text{ Btu}}{\text{hr ft}^2\,°\text{F}}\right)(24\text{ ft}^2)(112°\text{F})$$
$$= 242\text{ Btu/hr}$$

If we add 25 vertical fins which are $\frac{1}{8}$ in. thick, 1 in. wide, and 6 ft long, what will the heat transfer rate be? This problem raises two important questions. Is it reasonable to assume that the plate temperature, and therefore the temperature at the base of the fin, will remain at 180°F? What will the film heat transfer coefficient for the fins be, and how will the presence of fins affect the film heat transfer coefficient for the area between the fins? These are important questions; however, at this stage in our studies we will avoid them and take the plate temperature to be 180°F and the film heat transfer coefficient to be 0.09 Btu/hr ft²°F.

We can estimate the thermal conductivity of steel to be 20 Btu/hr ft °F and determine the Biot number to be

$$N_{\text{Bi}} = \frac{hb}{2k} = 8.6 \times 10^{-6}$$

We can now use Eq. 2.6-27 to calculate the heat transfer rate per fin as

$$\{\text{heat transfer rate per fin}\} = 2HN_{\text{Bi}}^{1/2}[\tanh(2N_{\text{Bi}}^{1/2}L/b)]k(T_0 - T_a)$$

where H is the height of the plate. Since $2N_{\text{Bi}}^{1/2}L/b \ll 1$ this can be simplified to

$$\{\text{heat transfer rate per fin}\} = 4HN_{\text{Bi}}Lk(T_0 - T_a)/b$$
$$= 3.7\text{ Btu/hr}$$

The area of the plate not occupied by fins is 22.4 ft² and the total heat transfer rate for the finished surface is

$$\dot{Q}_{\text{finned surface}} = \left(\frac{0.09\text{ Btu}}{\text{hr ft}^2\,°\text{F}}\right)(22.4\text{ ft}^2)(112°\text{F}) + (25)(3.7\text{ Btu/hr})$$
$$= 318\text{ Btu/hr}$$

This amounts to an increase of about 30 per cent and it should be apparent that much longer fins are needed if the expense of adding fins is to be justified. If the width of the fins were increased from 1 to 3 in., we would obtain

$$\{\text{heat transfer rate per fin}\} = 11.1\text{ Btu/hr}$$

and the overall heat transfer rate for the finned surface would be

$$\dot{Q}_{\text{finned surface}} = 504\text{ Btu/hr}$$

This amounts to an increase of over 100 per cent. Note that when $2N_{\text{Bi}}^{1/2}L/b \ll 1$, the heat transfer rate from each fin is a linear function of L. This occurs because the temperature of the fin is essentially constant at a value of T_0. As the value of $2N_{\text{Bi}}^{1/2}L/b$ becomes larger, the average temperature of the fin must decrease and the fin becomes less efficient.

2.7 The Annular Fin

Because of the prevalent use of pipes for transporting process fluids, the annular fin illustrated in Fig. 2.7.1 is of considerable practical importance. The essential nature of the use of extended surfaces to increase heat transfer rates has been described in the previous section and will be amplified in Sec. 2.8. The material discussed in this section will not necessarily enhance our understanding of the phenomena, and the main purpose here is to introduce the student to the use of Bessel functions in the solution of heat

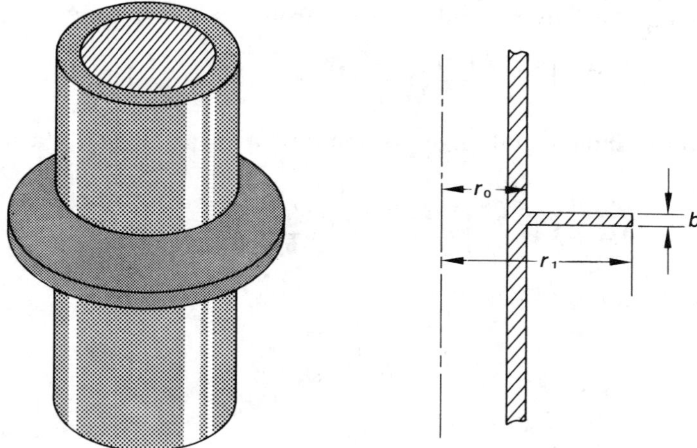

Fig. 2.7.1 The annular fin of uniform thickness.

transfer problems in cylindrical coordinates. Those students who have had a course in partial differential equations can skim through this material rapidly; those students who are more interested in phenomena and less interested in mathematics can skip the entire section with no ill effects; and those students who are interested in learning how to solve ordinary differential equations with nonconstant coefficients can proceed.

We begin the analysis with the steady-state heat conduction equation in cylindrical coordinates given in Table 2.2-3:

$$0 = \left[\frac{1}{r}\frac{\partial}{\partial r}\left(r\frac{\partial T}{\partial r}\right) + \frac{1}{r^2}\left(\frac{\partial^2 T}{\partial \theta^2}\right) + \left(\frac{\partial^2 T}{\partial z^2}\right)\right] \tag{2.7-1}$$

Here we have already made the assumption that the thermal conductivity k is constant. If we assume axial symmetry Eq. 2.7-1 simplifies to†

$$0 = \left[\frac{1}{r}\frac{\partial}{\partial r}\left(r\frac{\partial T}{\partial r}\right) + \left(\frac{\partial^2 T}{\partial z^2}\right)\right] \tag{2.7-2}$$

Our analysis will follow that given in Sec. 2.6 in that we will be content to settle for an approximate solution of Eq. 2.7-2 for the case where temperature variations within the fin are small. The boundary conditions are given as

B.C.1 $$T = T_0, \qquad r = r_0 \tag{2.7-3}$$

B.C.2 $$-k\left(\frac{\partial T}{\partial z}\right) = h(T - T_a), \qquad z = +b/2 \tag{2.7-4a}$$

B.C.3 $$-k\left(\frac{\partial T}{\partial z}\right) = h(T_a - T), \qquad z = -b/2 \tag{2.7-4b}$$

B.C.4 $$-k\left(\frac{\partial T}{\partial r}\right) = h_{\text{end}}(T - T_a), \qquad r = r_1 \tag{2.7-5}$$

Boundary condition 1 would be suitable for describing that case where the major resistance to heat transfer is in the fluid surrounding the pipe, and T_0 would represent the fluid temperature in the pipe. The second boundary condition implies that h is constant over the entire surface of the fin except for the end where the heat transfer coefficient is given by h_{end}.

†The effect of circumferential variation of the temperature resulting from variations in the film heat transfer coefficient has been investigated by K. N. Newhouse, "Temperature Distributions in Circular Fins of Rectangular Profile," *Trans. ASME, Journal of Heat Transfer* **86**, 563 (1964).

If we now multiply Eq. 2.7-2 by dz and integrate from $z = -b/2$ to $z = +b/2$ we obtain

$$0 = \int_{z=-b/2}^{z=+b/2} \frac{1}{r}\frac{\partial}{\partial r}\left(r\frac{\partial T}{\partial r}\right) dz + \int_{z=-b/2}^{z=+b/2} \left(\frac{\partial^2 T}{\partial Z^2}\right) dz \tag{2.7-6}$$

Interchanging differentiation and integration in the first term and carrying out the integration in the second term gives

$$0 = \frac{1}{r}\frac{\partial}{\partial r}\left(r\frac{\partial}{\partial r}\int_{z=-b/2}^{z=+b/2} T\,dz\right) + \frac{\partial T}{\partial z}\bigg|_{z=+b/2} - \frac{\partial T}{\partial z}\bigg|_{z=-b/2} \tag{2.7-7}$$

Defining the average temperature $\langle T\rangle$ as

$$\langle T\rangle = \frac{1}{b}\int_{z=-b/2}^{z=+b/2} T\,dz \tag{2.7-8}$$

and making use of B.C.2 and B.C.3 gives

$$0 = \frac{1}{r}\frac{\partial}{\partial r}\left[r\frac{\partial}{\partial r}(b\langle T\rangle)\right] - \frac{2h}{k}(T|_{z=\pm b/2} - T_a) \tag{2.7-9}$$

Following the discussion given in Sec. 2.6 we make the assumption

$$\langle T\rangle \sim T|_{z=\pm b/2}$$

define a dimensionless temperature Θ as

$$\Theta = \frac{\langle T\rangle - T_a}{T_0 - T_a} \tag{2.7-10}$$

and rearrange Eq. 2.7-10 to obtain

$$\left(\frac{d^2\Theta}{dr^2}\right) + \frac{1}{r}\left(\frac{d\Theta}{dr}\right) - \left(\frac{2h}{kb}\right)\Theta = 0 \tag{2.7-11}$$

Here we encounter an ordinary, second-order, nonconstant coefficient differential equation which cannot be solved by the methods discussed in Sec. 2.4. The solution is given by

$$\Theta = C_1 I_0(\lambda r) + C_2 K_0(\lambda r) \tag{2.7-12}$$

where I_0 = modified Bessel function of the first kind of order zero, K_0 = modified Bessel function of the second kind of order zero, $\lambda = \sqrt{2h/kb}$, and C_1, C_2 = constants of integration. Often Bessel functions have not been encountered by the student in previous engineering courses, and we need to show how these functions arise and what their special characteristics are. Before doing so it should be pointed out that Bessel functions are really not much different from the sine and cosine functions or the exponential function. They may seem a bit mysterious, but only because they appear less often in engineering analysis at the undergraduate level.

The route to a solution of Eq. 2.7-11 lies in the use of the Frobenius method [13] where one assumes† that the solution can be represented in terms of a power series in r. Thus we assume that Θ can be expressed as

$$\Theta = \sum_{n=0}^{\infty} A_n r^n \tag{2.7-13}$$

Substitution of this expression into Eq. 2.7-11 yields

$$\sum_{n=2}^{\infty} A_n n(n-1) r^{n-2} + \frac{1}{r}\sum_{n=1}^{\infty} A_n n r^{n-1} - \lambda^2 \sum_{n=0}^{\infty} A_n r^n = 0 \tag{2.7-14}$$

†Remember that previous solutions to more simple equations have been obtained by *assuming* solutions of the form, e^{mx}.

We can rearrange this expression to take the form

$$\sum_{n=2}^{\infty} (A_n n(n-1) + A_n n - \lambda^2 A_{n-2}) r^{n-2} + A_1 r^{-1} = 0 \tag{2.7-15}$$

Since this infinite series will be equal to zero if and only if the coefficient of every power of r is zero, we obtain

$$A_1 = 0 \tag{2.7-16}$$

$$A_n = \frac{\lambda^2}{n^2} A_{n-2} \tag{2.7-17}$$

Writing out the individual terms we find

$$A_0 = A_0$$

$$A_1 = 0$$

$$A_2 = \frac{\lambda^2}{2^2} A_0$$

$$A_3 = 0$$

$$A_4 = \frac{\lambda^2}{4^2} A_2 = \frac{\lambda^4}{4^2 2^2} A_0$$

$$A_5 = 0$$

$$A_6 = \frac{\lambda^2}{6^2} A_4 = \frac{\lambda^4}{6^2 4^2} A_2 = \frac{\lambda^6}{6^2 4^2 2^2} A_0$$

A general expression for this sequence is

$$A_1 = A_3 = A_5 = \cdots = 0$$

$$A_{2n} = \left[\frac{\lambda^{2n}}{(2n)^2(2n-2)^2(2n-4)^2 \cdots (2)^2}\right] A_0$$

Factoring out a 2 from each term in the denominator of the expression for A_{2n} yields

$$A_{2n} = \frac{\lambda^{2n}}{2^2(n)^2 2^2(n-1)^2 2^2(n-2)^2 \cdots 2^2(1)^2} A_0$$

Further rearrangement gives

$$A_{2n} = \frac{\lambda^{2n}}{2^{2n}[n(n-1)(n-2)\cdots(1)][n(n-1)(n-2)\cdots(1)]} A_0$$

Finally we obtain a compact form for A_{2n}

$$A_{2n} = \left[\frac{\lambda^{2n}}{2^{2n}(n!)^2}\right] A_0$$

Returning to Eq. 2.7-13 we obtain a solution for Θ

$$\Theta = C_1 \sum_{n=0}^{\infty} \frac{(\lambda r)^{2n}}{2^{2n}(n!)^2} \tag{2.7-18}$$

Here we have replaced the coefficient A_0, which factors out of every term in the series, with C_1 so as to use the traditional symbol for a constant of integration. Following established convention we represent the infinite series by $I_0(\lambda r)$ and write

$$I_0(\lambda r) = \sum_{n=0}^{\infty} \frac{(\lambda r)^{2n}}{2^{2n}(n!)^2}$$

A plot of $I_0(\lambda r)$ is shown in Fig. 2.7.2 indicating that $I_0(\lambda r)$ is a function reminiscent of the exponential function so often encountered in the solution of *constant coefficient* ordinary differential equations.

We now have *one* solution of Eq. 2.7-11, and in order to obtain a complete solution we need a second solution. Before attacking this problem let us simplify Eq. 2.7-11 somewhat by changing the independent variable so as to eliminate the parameter $\lambda = \sqrt{2h/kb}$. This can be accomplished by making the substitution

$$\xi = \lambda r = \sqrt{2h/kb}\, r$$

This transforms Eq. 2.7-11 to

$$\left(\frac{d^2\Theta}{d\xi^2}\right) + \frac{1}{\xi}\left(\frac{d\Theta}{d\xi}\right) - \Theta = 0 \tag{2.7-19}$$

We have already shown that one solution of this equation is

$$\Theta_1 = C_1 I_0(\xi) \tag{2.7-20}$$

and in order to find a second solution we seek a function $\Psi(\xi)$ having the property that $\Psi(\xi)I_0(\xi)$ is a

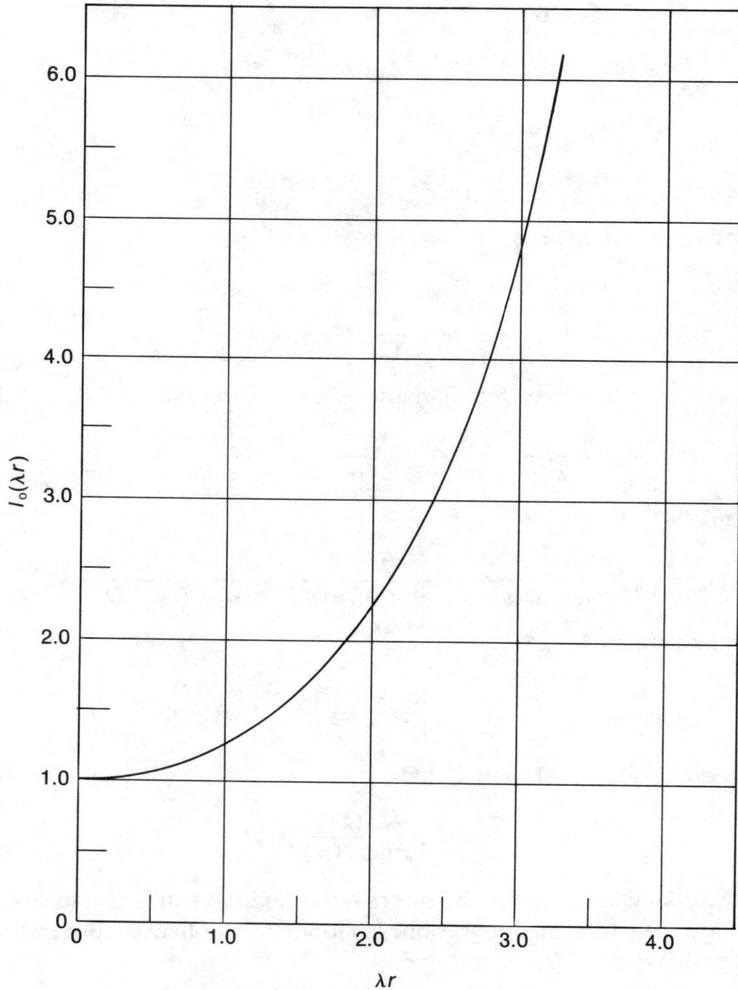

Fig. 2.7.2 Modified Bessel function of the first kind of order zero.

solution to the differential equation. Substituting

$$\Theta_2 = \Psi I_0 \tag{2.7-21}$$

into Eq. 2.7-19 gives

$$I_0\left(\frac{d^2\Psi}{d\xi^2}\right) + \Psi\left(\frac{d^2 I_0}{d\xi^2}\right) + 2\left(\frac{dI_0}{d\xi}\right)\left(\frac{d\Psi}{d\xi}\right) + \frac{1}{\xi}\left[I_0\left(\frac{d\Psi}{d\xi}\right) + \Psi\left(\frac{dI_0}{d\xi}\right)\right] - \Psi I_0 = 0$$

This may be arranged in the form

$$\Psi\left\{\left(\frac{d^2 I_0}{d\xi^2}\right) + \frac{1}{\xi}\left(\frac{dI_0}{d\xi}\right) - I_0\right\} + \left[2\left(\frac{dI_0}{d\xi}\right)\frac{d\Psi}{d\xi} + I_0\left(\frac{d^2\Psi}{d\xi^2}\right) + \frac{I_0}{\xi}\left(\frac{d\Psi}{d\xi}\right)\right] = 0 \tag{2.7-22}$$

The term in braces, { }, is zero since I_0 is a solution of the differential equation, and we are left with

$$\left(\frac{d^2\Psi}{d\xi^2}\right) + \left[\frac{1}{\xi} + \frac{2}{I_0}\left(\frac{dI_0}{d\xi}\right)\right]\left(\frac{d\Psi}{d\xi}\right) = 0 \tag{2.7-23}$$

This equation can be solved by reducing the order and separating variables. The solution is

$$\Psi = C_2 \int \frac{d\xi}{\xi I_0^2(\xi)} + C_3 \tag{2.7-24}$$

and substituting into Eq. 2.7-21 we find our second solution to be

$$\Theta_2(\xi) = C_2 I_0(\xi) \int \frac{d\xi}{\xi I_0^2(\xi)} + C_3 I_0(\xi) \tag{2.7-25}$$

In light of the first solution given by Eq. 2.7-20 there is no loss in generality by setting C_3 equal to zero, and we express the complete solution of Eq. 2.7-19 as

$$\Theta = C_1 I_0(\lambda r) + C_2 K_0(\lambda r) \tag{2.7-26}$$

where $K_0(\lambda r)$ is given by

$$K_0(\lambda r) = I_0(\lambda r) \int \frac{d(\lambda r)}{\lambda r I_0^2(\lambda r)} \tag{2.7-27}$$

and is plotted in Fig. 2.7.3.

The values of the Bessel functions encountered in this problem are available in tables just as values of the cosine, hyperbolic tangent, exponential function, etc. are tabulated in any table of integrals. A short list of values is given in Appendix B. The result given by Eq. 2.7-26 is generally a bit imposing simply because we are unaccustomed to working with Bessel functions. Any apprehension about these functions should be quickly dispelled, for they are nothing more than another member of a large class of transcendental functions, several of which (i.e., the trigonometric and exponential functions) the student is quite familiar with. Like the sine and cosine these functions have integrals and derivatives which are also tabulated. These are given by

$$\frac{d}{d\xi}(K_0(\xi)) = -K_1(\xi) \tag{2.7-28}$$

$$\frac{d}{d\xi}(I_0(\xi)) = I_1(\xi) \tag{2.7-29}$$

where $K_1(\xi)$ is a modified Bessel function of the second kind of order one, and $I_1(\xi)$ is a modified Bessel function of the first kind of order one. Values of these functions are also available in Appendix B.

Returning now to the physical problem under investigation, we rewrite the boundary conditions given by Eqs. 2.7-3 and 2.7-5 first in terms of $\langle T \rangle$ and then in terms of Θ:

B.C.1′
$$\langle T \rangle = T_0, \qquad r = r_0 \tag{2.7-30}$$

B.C.3′
$$-k\frac{\partial \langle T \rangle}{\partial r} = h_{\text{end}}(\langle T \rangle - T_a), \qquad r = r_1 \tag{2.7-31}$$

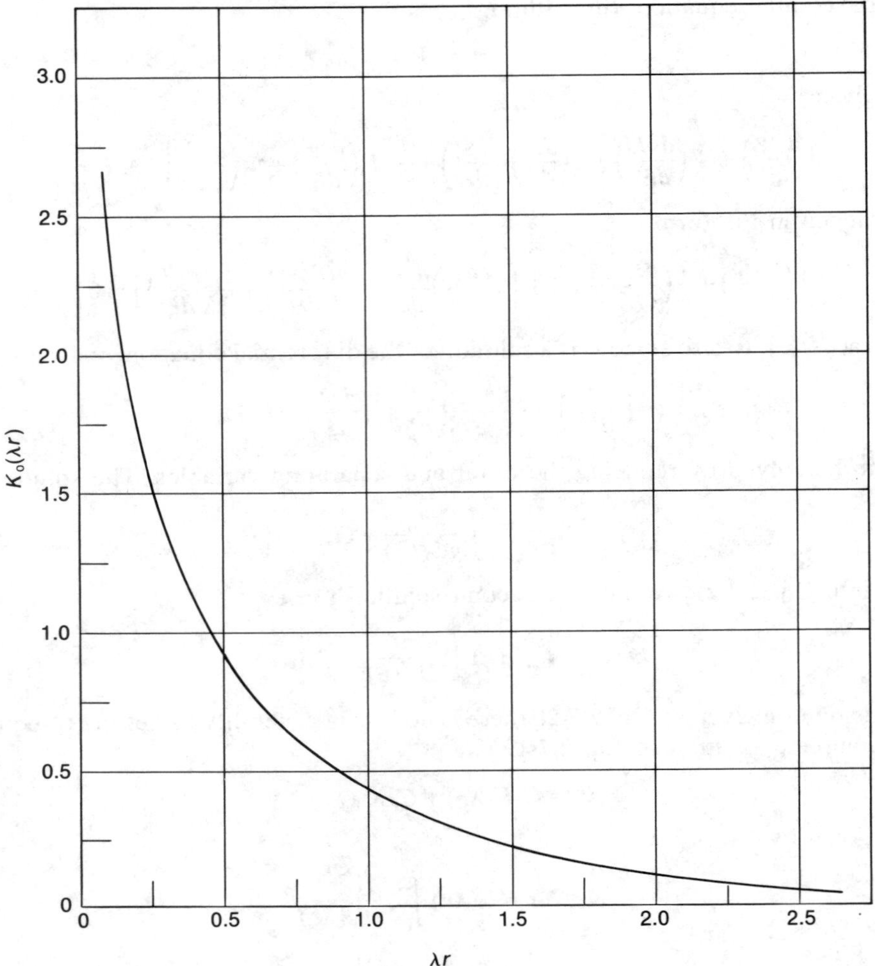

Fig. 2.7.3 Modified Bessel function of the second kind of order zero.

Note that B.C.2 and B.C.3 have already been incorporated into the derivation of Eq. 2.7-11 and do not play a part in the analysis for the average temperature. In terms of Θ the boundary conditions become

B.C.1″ $$\Theta = 1, \qquad r = r_0 \tag{2.7-32}$$

B.C.2″ $$-\frac{\partial \Theta}{\partial (\lambda r)} = \left(\frac{h_{end}}{k\lambda}\right)\Theta, \qquad r = r_1 \tag{2.7-33}$$

These two boundary conditions can be used to determine the constants of integration in Eq. 2.7-26 and the result is

$$C_1 = \frac{K_1(\lambda r_1) - (h_{end}/k\lambda)K_0(\lambda r_1)}{\{I_1(\lambda r_1)K_0(\lambda r_0) + I_0(\lambda r_0)K_1(\lambda r_1) + (h_{end}/k\lambda)[I_0(\lambda r_1)K_0(\lambda r_0) - I_0(\lambda r_0)K_0(\lambda r_1)]\}}$$

$$C_2 = \frac{1 - C_1 I_0(\lambda r_0)}{K_0(\lambda r_0)}$$

If we write $h_{end}/k\lambda$ as

$$\left(\frac{h_{end}}{k\lambda}\right) = \left(\frac{h_{end}}{h}\right)^{1/2} \sqrt{\frac{h_{end} b}{2k}}$$

assume that h_{end} is the same order-of-magnitude as h, and remember (see Sec. 2.6) that the analysis is only valid if

$$\sqrt{\frac{hb}{2k}} \ll 1$$

we conclude that

$$\frac{h_{\text{end}}}{k\lambda} \ll 1$$

is a necessary restriction in this analysis. Under these circumstances we can simplify the expressions for C_1 and C_2.

$$C_1 \sim \frac{K_1(\lambda r_1)}{I_1(\lambda r_1)K_0(\lambda r_0) + I_0(\lambda r_0)K_1(\lambda r_1)}$$

$$C_2 \sim \frac{I_1(\lambda r_1)}{I_1(\lambda r_1)K_0(\lambda r_0) + I_0(\lambda r_0)K_1(\lambda r_1)}$$

Our mathematical analysis is now complete, and we need only calculate the quantity of interest, i.e., the rate at which heat is transferred from the fin to the surroundings. This is given by

$$\begin{aligned}\dot{Q} &= \langle q_r \rangle|_{r=r_0} b(2\pi r_0) \\ &= -k \frac{\partial \langle T \rangle}{\partial r}\bigg|_{r=r_0} b(2\pi r_0) \\ &= -\lambda k (T_0 - T_a) \frac{\partial \Theta}{\partial (\lambda r)}\bigg|_{r=r_0} b(2\pi r_0)\end{aligned}$$

Substitution of Eq. 2.7-26 and making use of the expressions for C_1 and C_2 gives

$$\dot{Q} = 2\pi r_0 \lambda b k (T_0 - T_a) \left\{ \frac{K_1(\lambda r_0) I_1(\lambda r_1) - K_1(\lambda r_1) I_1(\lambda r_0)}{K_0(\lambda r_0) I_1(\lambda r_1) + K_1(\lambda r_1) I_0(\lambda r_0)} \right\} \tag{2.7-34}$$

In order to put this result in a more compact form we will define the following dimensionless variables:

$$\dot{\mathcal{Q}} = \dot{Q}/\dot{Q}_{\max}, \quad \text{dimensionless rate of heat transfer}$$

$$\Lambda = \lambda r_0 = \sqrt{\left(\frac{2hr_0}{k}\right)\left(\frac{r_0}{b}\right)}$$

$$\mathcal{R} = r_1/r_0$$

Here $\dot{Q}_{\max}$ is the maximum rate of heat transfer and is given by

$$\dot{Q}_{\max} = 2\pi h (r_1^2 - r_0^2)(T_0 - T_a)$$

The dimensionless rate of heat transfer $\dot{\mathcal{Q}}$ can now be written as

$$\dot{\mathcal{Q}} = \frac{2}{(\mathcal{R}^2 - 1)\Lambda} \left\{ \frac{K_1(\Lambda) I_1(\Lambda \mathcal{R}) - K_1(\Lambda \mathcal{R}) I_1(\Lambda)}{K_0(\Lambda) I_1(\Lambda \mathcal{R}) + K_1(\Lambda \mathcal{R}) I_0(\Lambda)} \right\} \tag{2.7-35}$$

This result, along with the tabulated values of the Bessel functions given in Appendix B, may be used to compute the heat transfer rate from an annular fin. The quantity $\dot{\mathcal{Q}} \times 100$ is often referred to as the *fin efficiency*. When the temperature of the fin is uniform and equal to the base temperature, T_0, the fin efficiency is 100 per cent.

Example 2.7-1 Heat transfer rate from an annular fin

If a steel fin of inner radius $\frac{1}{2}$ in., outer radius 2 in., and thickness $\frac{3}{32}$ in. is attached to a pipe having a surface temperature of 190°F, what is the heat transfer rate if the ambient air temperature is 70°F? We are given the data

$$h = 0.06\ \text{Btu/hr ft}^2\,°\text{F}$$
$$k = 20\ \text{Btu/hr ft}\,°\text{F}$$

From the data given we find that

$$\lambda = \sqrt{2h/kb} = 0.88\ \text{ft}^{-1}$$

Thus our system satisfies the condition

$$\frac{h_{\text{end}}}{k\lambda} \ll 1$$

The dimensionless quantities Λ and $\mathcal{R}$ take on the values

$$\Lambda = 0.037$$
$$\mathcal{R} = 4$$

and Eq. 2.7-35 yields

$$\dot{\mathcal{Q}} = 0.99$$

The heat transfer rate $\dot{Q}$ is now given by

$$\dot{Q} = 0.99[2\pi h(r_1^2 - r_0^2)(T_0 - T_a)]$$
$$= 1.17\ \text{Btu/hr}$$

*2.8 Fin Effectiveness

Fins are only used to enhance the rate of heat transfer when the interphase heat transfer rate is low enough so that the expense of adding fins is justified. This generally occurs when energy is being transferred to or from a gas and there are restrictions on the size of the heat transfer device. In the absence of this latter restriction one would simply increase the area for heat transfer by enlarging the unfinned surface whatever it may be. If one is cooling a process stream by means of ambient air, it is generally much less expensive to simply extend the length of the pipe rather than become involved in the costly process of adding fins to the pipe. Examples of the size restriction are found in air-cooled engines where the cylinder heads are often finned, cooling coils in refrigerators, and in some home heating units.

For most cases of importance, the temperature profile in a system that is in need of a finned surface is similar to that shown in Fig. 2.8.1. That temperature profile indicates a relatively small resistence to heat transfer in the process stream and across the metal wall, while the major portion of the resistence occurs in the gas film. In Fig. 2.8.1b we have shown a temperature profile representative of a finned surface which doubles the heat transfer rate. This means that the magnitude of the slope of the temperature profile in the wall also doubles and the temperature at the base of the fin is lowered from T_0 (without fins) to T_0^* (with fins). If the lowering of the surface temperature is negligible, i.e., $(T_0 - T_0^*)/(T_0 - T_a) \ll 1$, we can perform a relatively simple analysis to determine the effectiveness of a finned surface. Knowing this we would be in a position to decide whether the addition of fins would be economically sound. We will define the effectiveness η as

$$\eta = \{\text{fin effectiveness}\} = \frac{(\text{rate of heat transfer with fins})}{(\text{rate of heat transfer without fins})}$$

and restrict our discussion to the rectangular fin which was analyzed in Sec. 2.6. These fins are assumed to be spaced a distance d from one another as shown in Fig. 2.8.2. In addition to the assumptions made in Sec. 2.6 we will make the following two in this development:

A.1 The film heat transfer coefficients is constant over the fin, the wall and the end of the fin

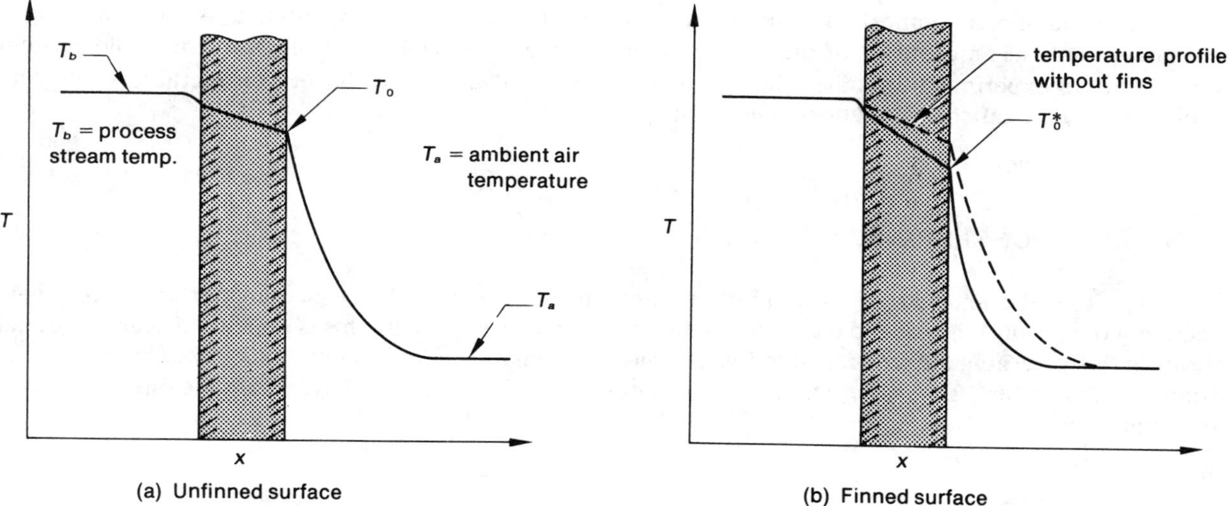

Fig. 2.8.1 Temperature profiles for a surface with and without fins.

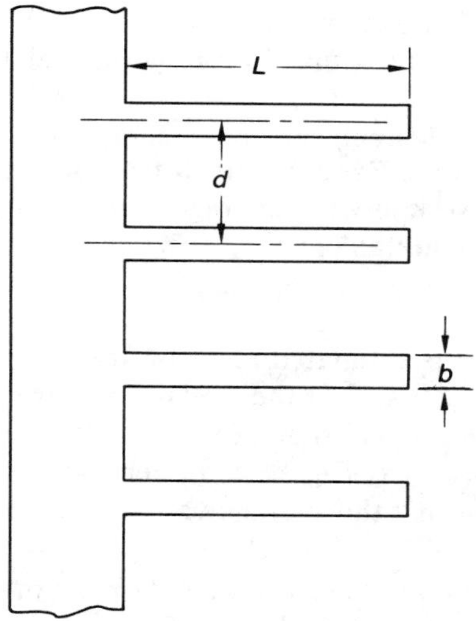

Fig. 2.8.2 Finned surface.

A.2
$$(T_0 - T_0^*)/(T_0 - T_a) \ll 1$$

On the basis of these assumptions we can write

$$\{\text{rate of heat transfer without fin per unit length}\} = ndh(T_0 - T_a)$$

$$\{\text{rate of heat transfer with fins per unit length}\} = n(d - b)h(T_0 - T_a) + nmbk(T_0 - T_a)[\tanh(mL)]$$

Here we are considering a surface with n fins. Our fin effectiveness can now be expressed as

$$\eta = \left(1 - \frac{b}{d}\right) + \left[\frac{\tanh(2N_{\text{Bi}}^{1/2}L/b)}{N_{\text{Bi}}^{1/2}(d/b)}\right] \tag{2.8-1}$$

Given the geometry of the finned surface, i.e., b, d, and L, the thermal conductivity of the fin, and the film heat transfer coefficient we can immediately *estimate* the improvement in the heat transfer rate. Note that there are a number of important assumptions that went into this development, thus Eq. 2.8-1 can be considered only as an *estimate* of the fin effectiveness. A precise analysis of the problem would certainly involve some experimental studies, but even there our analysis would be of considerable value for it probably gives a satisfactory upper bound on η.

*2.9 Order-of-Magnitude Analysis

Very often the analysis of a complex process can be simplified by neglecting certain effects while retaining (hopefully) the essential characteristics of the process. Usually this is done by discarding certain terms in the governing differential equations, or by approximating complex boundary conditions with some simpler form. In Sec. 2.6 we were able to turn a complex problem into a relatively simple one by means of the approximation

$$\langle T \rangle \sim T|_{z=b/2} \tag{2.9-1}$$

which we decided was quite satisfactory provided $(hb/2k) \ll 1$. In this case the range of validity of our solution was determined by an *order-of-magnitude analysis* and the tacit assumption that "small causes lead to small effects." Birkhoff [10] has commented on the fallibility of this assumption, and one must be constantly alerted to the possibility that the assumption, and thus the order-of-magnitude analysis, will fail. The student should already be aware of one such failure; namely the fact that a *small* wall roughness in a pipe leads not to a small change in the pressure drop-flow rate relation for turbulent flow, but to a *large* change.

In performing an order-of-magnitude analysis, one generally attempts to estimate the average value of some function over the region of interest. For example, if the volumetric flow rate in a pipe having a cross-sectional area of 1 ft^2 is 172 ft^3/sec, we know the average value of the velocity is 172 ft/sec and we would express our order-of-magnitude estimate as

$$v_z = \mathbf{0}(172 \text{ ft/sec}) \tag{2.9-2}$$

This is to be read as: The velocity v_z is estimated to be on the order of 172 ft/sec. Keep in mind that for laminar flow the velocity varies between zero at the wall to 344 ft/sec at the centerline, while for turbulent flow the velocity is very nearly equal to 172 ft/sec over most of the pipe. In both cases we express the estimate of the order-of-magnitude of v_z by Eq. 2.9-2. In general, if we say that the order-of-magnitude of some function is $\mathcal{M}$, we feel confident that the average value, or more correctly the average of the *absolute* value, lies between $0.1\mathcal{M}$ and $10\mathcal{M}$.

In order to put our discussion in concrete terms we *define* the order-of-magnitude of some function as the average of the absolute value of the function. For the function $f(x)$ in the region $0 \leq x \leq L$ we write,

$$\{\text{order-of-magnitude of } f(x)\} \equiv \frac{1}{L}\int_0^L |f|\, dx \tag{2.9-3}$$

and for the function $g(x, y)$ in the region $0 \leq x \leq L$ and $0 \leq y \leq \ell$ we write

$$\{\text{order-of-magnitude of } g(x, y)\} \equiv \frac{1}{\ell L}\int_0^\ell \int_0^L |g(x, y)|\, dx\, dy \tag{2.9-4}$$

Estimating the order-of-magnitude of some function is relatively easy; the *estimate* simply being our best guess of the average of the absolute value. Keep in mind that, in this discussion, there is a difference between the *order-of-magnitude* of a function which is a defined quantity and the *estimate of the order-of-magnitude*. For the example cited, the order-of-magnitude of v_z is 172 ft/sec, and our estimate is *perfect*, being also 172 ft/sec.

While estimating the order-of-magnitude of a function is straightforward, the estimate of the order-of-magnitude of the derivative is another matter, and we must develop some consistent method of making this estimate. Consider the derivative df/dx in the region $0 \leq x \leq L$. According to our definition

$$\left\{\text{order-of-magnitude of } \frac{df}{dx}\right\} = \frac{1}{L}\int_0^L \left|\frac{df}{dx}\right| dx \tag{2.9-5}$$

For the moment let us simplify our problem by assuming that f is a monotonic function of x so that

$$\frac{df}{dx} = \left|\frac{df}{dx}\right|$$

if f increases with x, and

$$\left(\frac{df}{dx}\right) = -\left|\frac{df}{dx}\right|$$

if f decreases with x. Since we are not concerned with the sign, but only the order-of-magnitude we can replace Eq. 2.9-5 with

$$\left\{\text{order-of-magnitude of } \frac{df}{dx}\right\} = \frac{1}{L}\int_0^L \left(\frac{df}{dx}\right) dx = \frac{1}{L}[f(L) - f(0)] \tag{2.9-6}$$

Returning now to the order-of-magnitude of $f(x)$ and retaining the restriction that the function be monotonic we write

$$\{\text{order-of-magnitude of } f(x)\} = \frac{1}{L}\int_0^L f(x)\, dx = f(\xi), \quad 0 \leq \xi \leq L \tag{2.9-7}$$

Here we have simply used the mean value theorem to express the integral in terms of the integrand evaluated at some point $x = \xi$.

Now, if $f(x)$ is a reasonably smooth function we might argue that both $f(L)$ and $f(0)$ are the same order-of-magnitude as $f(\xi)$ and estimate the order-of-magnitude as

$$f(L) = \mathbf{0}\{f(\xi)\} = \mathbf{0}(f) \tag{2.9-8}$$

$$f(0) = \mathbf{0}\{f(\xi)\} = \mathbf{0}(f) \tag{2.9-8b}$$

From this we conclude that

$$f(L) - f(0) = \mathbf{0}(f)$$

and we estimate the order-of-magnitude of the derivative to be

$$\left(\frac{df}{dx}\right) = \mathbf{0}(f)/L \tag{2.9-9}$$

In order that this estimate be of any value to us, it is imperative that we have some reasonable picture of the function $f(x)$. For example if we consider the problem of flow in a pipe we would estimate v_z as

$$v_z = \mathbf{0}(\langle v_z \rangle) \tag{2.9-10}$$

and the derivative becomes

$$\left(\frac{dv_z}{dr}\right) = \mathbf{0}(\langle v_z \rangle / r_0) \tag{2.9-11}$$

where $\langle v_z \rangle$ is the average value and r_0 is the radius of the pipe. If the flow is laminar the derivative varies from zero at the centerline to $4\langle v_z \rangle / r_0$ at the wall and Eq. 2.9-11 is not a bad estimate. If the flow is turbulent we find

$$\left(\frac{dv_z}{dr}\right) \ll \frac{\langle v_z \rangle}{r_0}, \quad \text{in the core region} \tag{2.9-12}$$

$$\left(\frac{dv_z}{dr}\right) \gg \frac{\langle v_z \rangle}{r_0}, \quad \text{in the viscous sublayer} \tag{2.9-13}$$

Under these circumstances, Eq. 2.9-11 is not at all a satisfactory estimate of the order-of-magnitude of dv_z/dr. It is apparent then that we must have some idea of how the function behaves before we can make a good estimate.

Extending the definitions given by Eqs. 2.9-3 and 2.9-5 we can define the order-of-magnitude of the second derivative as

$$\{\text{order-of-magnitude of } d^2f/dx^2\} \equiv \frac{1}{L}\int_0^L \left|\frac{d^2f}{dx^2}\right| dx \tag{2.9-14}$$

If we now restrict ourselves to functions having monotonic first derivatives we can discard the absolute value sign in Eq. 2.9-14 and write

$$\{\text{order-of-magnitude of } d^2f/dx^2\} = \frac{1}{L}\left[\left.\frac{df}{dx}\right|_{x=L} - \left.\frac{df}{dx}\right|_{x=0}\right] \tag{2.9-15}$$

Making use of Eq. 2.9-9 we write

$$\left.\frac{df}{dx}\right|_{x=L} = \mathbf{0}(f)/L$$

$$\left.\frac{df}{dx}\right|_{x=0} = \mathbf{0}(f)/L$$

and our estimate of the order-of-magnitude of the second derivative becomes

$$\left(\frac{d^2f}{dx^2}\right) = \mathbf{0}(f)/L^2 \tag{2.9-16}$$

This result could be generalized to

$$\left(\frac{d^nf}{dx^n}\right) = \mathbf{0}(f)/L^n \tag{2.9-17}$$

In order to test this method of estimating the order-of-magnitude, we will apply Eqs. 2.9-9 and 2.9-16 to the four functions shown in Fig. 2.9.1. In each case the average value of the function is A and the estimates of the order-of-magnitude of the first and second derivatives are

$$\left(\frac{df}{dx}\right) = \mathbf{0}(f)/L = A/L \tag{2.9-18}$$

$$\left(\frac{d^2f}{dx^2}\right) = \mathbf{0}(f)/L^2 = A/L^2 \tag{2.9-19}$$

The order-of-magnitude, defined by Eqs. 2.9-5 and 2.9-14, is readily calculated and is compared with the estimate in Table 2.9-1. Here we see that the estimates of the order-of-magnitude are not unreasonable, although they certainly could be improved if more information regarding the nature of the function were incorporated into the analysis. For example if we knew the *shape* but not the exact form of each curve, we would make the following order-of-magnitude estimates:

Curve 1

$$\left(\frac{df}{dx}\right) \ll \mathbf{0}(A/L), \qquad \left(\frac{d^2f}{dx^2}\right) \ll \mathbf{0}(A/L^2)$$

Curve 2

$$\left(\frac{df}{dx}\right) \sim A/L, \qquad \left(\frac{d^2f}{dx^2}\right) \ll \mathbf{0}(A/L^2)$$

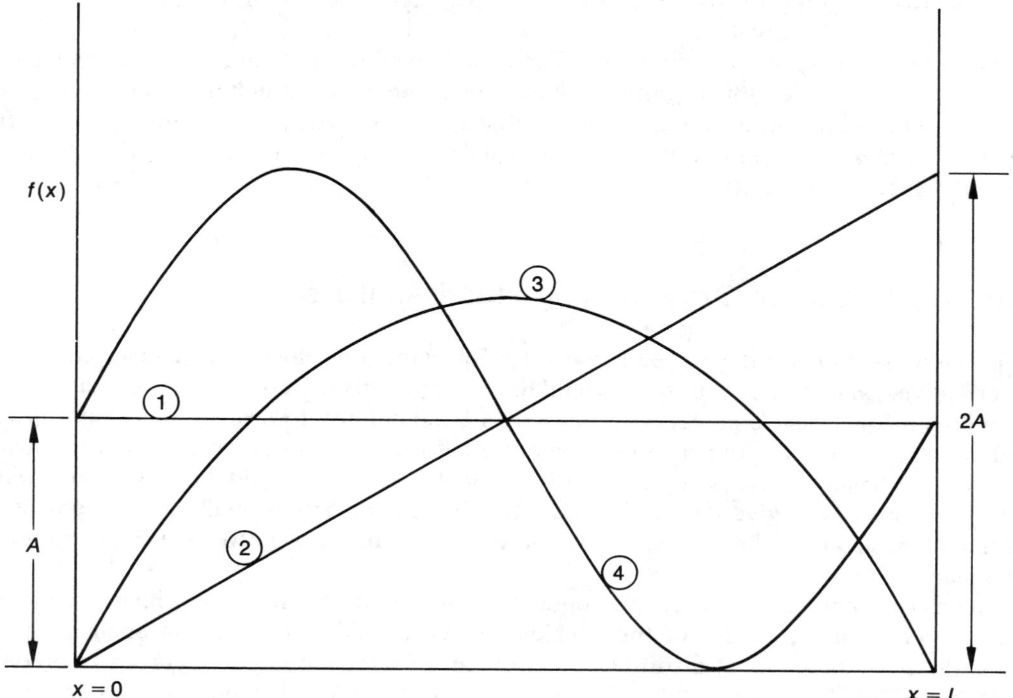

Fig. 2.9.1 Trial functions for order-of-magnitude estimate.
1. $f(x) = A$
2. $f(x) = 2A(x/L)$
3. $f(x) = 6A[(x/L) - (x/L)^2]$
4. $f(x) = A[1 + \sin 2\pi(x/L)]$

Table 2.9-1 Comparison of the Order-of-Magnitude with the Estimate of the Order-of-Magnitude

Curve	$\left(\frac{df}{dx}\right)$		$\left(\frac{d^2f}{dx^2}\right)$	
	Order-of-Magnitude	Estimate of the Order-of-Magnitude	Order-of-Magnitude	Estimate of the Order-of-Magnitude
1	0	(A/L)	0	(A/L^2)
2	$2(A/L)$	(A/L)	0	(A/L^2)
3	$3(A/L)$	(A/L)	$12(A/L^2)$	(A/L^2)
4	$4(A/L)$	(A/L)	$8\pi(A/L^2)$	(A/L^2)

These estimates (especially for the second derivatives) are in much closer agreement with the calculated order-of-magnitude. They follow intuitively from the statements: "The function is essentially constant" (curve 1), and "the function is essentially linear" (curve 2). The order-of-magnitude estimates for curve 4 could be improved if we knew that the first derivative changed sign at $x = L/4$, and the second derivative changed sign at $x = L/2$. Under these circumstances the order-of-magnitude estimates would take the form

Curve 4

$$\left(\frac{df}{dx}\right) = \frac{0(f)}{L/4} = 4A/L$$

Curve 4

$$\left(\frac{d^2f}{dx^2}\right) = \frac{0(f)}{(L/2)^2} = 4A/L^2$$

Here we see improved agreement with the listed order-of-magnitude of $4(A/L)$ for the first derivative and $8\pi(A/L^2)$ for the second derivative.

In using an order-of-magnitude estimate one can usually distinguish between two terms which differ by a factor of 100 (i.e., two orders-of-magnitude); however, if the estimate indicates that two terms differ in magnitude by only a factor of 10, it may turn out that they are actually equal in magnitude. In order to effectively use an order-of-magnitude estimate to simplify an analysis one must be daring, lucky, and quick to retreat in the face of adversity.

*2.10 An Application of Order-of-Magnitude Analysis

In the previous section we developed some rules for estimating the order-of-magnitude of functions and their derivatives, and in this section we would like to apply this material to the problem of determining when a two-dimensional heat conduction process can be simplified to a one-dimensional process.

Throughout this chapter a number of one-dimensional heat conduction processes were analyzed. For practical purposes these processes were one-dimensional because we *said* they were one-dimensional. Often some justification was given by saying that "the thickness is much smaller than the width," or "the plate is infinite in the y- and z-directions"; however, the fact remains: the processes were one-dimensional because we said so.

The problems encountered in this chapter could be solved with relative ease primarily because the title of the chapter indicated the nature of the problems to be considered. When an engineer encounters a problem outside of an educational institution, there is no *title* indicating the methods to be employed in order to develop a satisfactory solution. If an engineer is to work independently and develop new and better solutions to both new and old problems, he must be capable of discerning the *essential features* of the process under investigation. The search for these essential features usually requires considerable experience and judicious use of order-of-magnitude analysis.

As an example we will consider the heat transfer process illustrated in Fig. 2.10.1. Distasteful as it may be, we will assume that the slab of thickness b and width L is infinite in the z-direction so that the temperature is only a function of x and y. If L is much, much larger than b ($L \gg b$) our previous experience would suggest that the heat flux could be expressed as

$$q_y = k(T_0 - T_1)/b \tag{2.10-1}$$

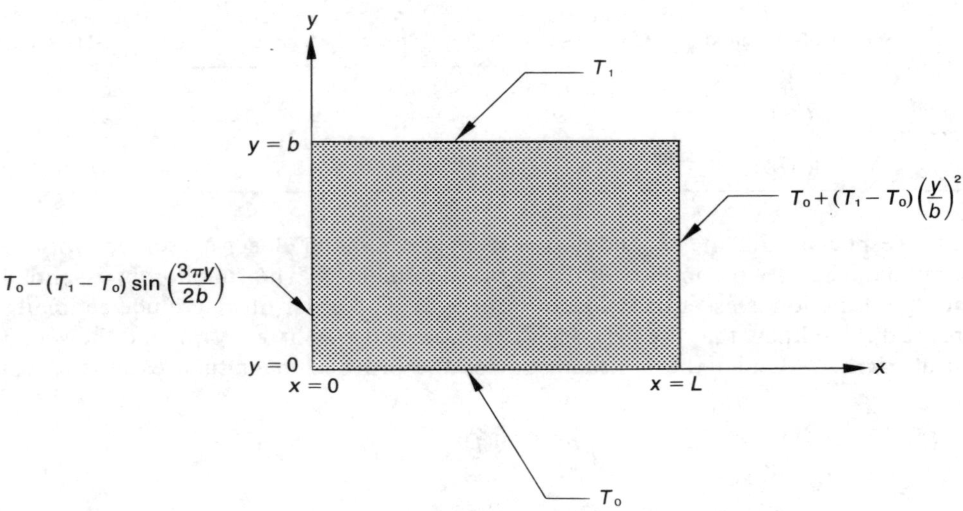

Fig. 2.10.1 Two-dimensional heat conduction process.

$$\left\{\begin{array}{l}\text{rate of heat transfer through}\\ \text{the plate per unit length}\\ \text{in the } z\text{-direction}\end{array}\right\} = \frac{kL(T_0 - T_1)}{b} \tag{2.10-2}$$

We would now like to justify our intuitive feeling that the process can be treated as a one-dimensional heat conduction problem when $L \gg b$. Provided the thermal conductivity is constant, the mathematical statement of this problem is

$$\frac{\partial^2 T}{\partial x^2} + \frac{\partial^2 T}{\partial y^2} = 0 \tag{2.10-3}$$

B.C.1 $\quad T = T_0, \quad y = 0, \quad 0 \leq x \leq L$ (2.10-4a)

B.C.2 $\quad T = T_1, \quad y = b, \quad 0 \leq x \leq L$ (2.10-4b)

B.C.3 $\quad T = T_0 - (T_1 - T_0)\sin(3\pi y/2b), \quad x = 0, \quad 0 \leq y \leq b$ (2.10-4c)

B.C.4 $\quad T = T_0 + (T_1 - T_0)(y/b)^2, \quad x = L, \quad 0 \leq y \leq b$ (2.10-4d)

Order-of-magnitude analysis is always easier to carry out in terms of dimensionless variables, thus we define

$$\Theta = (T - T_0)/(T_1 - T_0), \qquad X = x/b, \qquad Y = y/b$$
$$\beta = L/b$$

and rewrite Eqs. 2.10-3 and 2.10-4 as

$$\underset{\left(\frac{1}{\beta^2}\right)}{\frac{\partial^2 \Theta}{\partial X^2}} + \underset{(1)}{\frac{\partial^2 \Theta}{\partial Y^2}} = 0 \tag{2.10-5}$$

B.C.1′ $\quad \Theta = 0, \quad Y = 0, \quad 0 \leq X \leq \beta$ (2.10-6a)

B.C.2′ $\quad \Theta = 1, \quad Y = 1, \quad 0 \leq X \leq \beta$ (2.10-6b)

B.C.3′ $\quad \Theta = \sin(3\pi Y/2), \quad X = 0, \quad 0 \leq Y \leq 1$ (2.10-6c)

B.C.4′ $\quad \Theta = Y^2, \quad X = \beta, \quad 0 \leq Y \leq 1$ (2.10-6d)

Here we have used our standard order-of-magnitude estimates to indicate that

$$\frac{\partial^2 \Theta}{\partial X^2} = \frac{\mathbf{0}(\Theta)}{\beta^2} = \mathbf{0}\left(\frac{1}{\beta^2}\right)$$
$$\frac{\partial^2 \Theta}{\partial Y^2} = \frac{\mathbf{0}(\Theta)}{1^2} = \mathbf{0}(1)$$

For the case where $\beta \gg 1$, it is appealing (but quite incorrect) to say

$$\frac{\partial^2 \Theta}{\partial X^2} \ll \frac{\partial^2 \Theta}{\partial Y^2}, \quad \text{for } \beta \gg 1 \tag{2.10-7}$$

thus simplifying Eq. 2.10-5 to

$$\frac{d^2 \Theta}{dY^2} = 0 \tag{2.10-8}$$

which is to be solved subject to the boundary conditions

B.C.1″ $\quad \Theta = 0, \quad Y = 0$ (2.10-9a)

B.C.2″ $\quad \Theta = 1, \quad Y = 1$ (2.10-9b)

The inequality given by Eq. 2.10-7 is, of course, in contradiction to Eq. 2.10-5 which indicates that

$$\frac{\partial^2\Theta}{\partial X^2} = -\frac{\partial^2\Theta}{\partial Y^2} \tag{2.10-10}$$

Clearly $\partial^2\Theta/\partial X^2$ cannot be much, much less than $\partial^2\Theta/\partial Y^2$ if it is equal to $-\partial^2\Theta/\partial Y^2$. Remember that order-of-magnitude analysis does not distinguish positive and negative quantities, thus Eq. 2.10-10 or Eq. 2.10-5 requires

$$\frac{\partial^2\Theta}{\partial X^2} = \mathbf{0}\left(\frac{\partial^2\Theta}{\partial Y^2}\right) \tag{2.10-11}$$

At this point we might recall from Sec. 2.9 that if Θ is *essentially linear in* Y, our order-of-magnitude estimate would read

$$\left(\frac{\partial^2\Theta}{\partial Y^2}\right) \ll \mathbf{0}(1), \quad \text{when } \Theta \text{ is essentially linear in } Y$$

When $\beta \gg 1$ this is indeed plausible and we conclude that both $\partial^2\Theta/\partial X^2$ and $\partial^2\Theta/\partial Y^2$ are much, much less than one when $\beta \gg 1$. Still we cannot discard $\partial^2\Theta/\partial X^2$ to arrive at Eq. 2.10-8 and the associated one-dimensional solution. However, there is another way of attacking this problem which does lead to a satisfactory solution.

We begin our analysis of Eq. 2.10-5 by forming the indefinite integral with respect to Y to obtain

$$\left(\frac{\partial\Theta}{\partial Y}\right) = -\int_{\eta=0}^{\eta=Y}\left(\frac{\partial^2\Theta}{\partial X^2}\right) d\eta + C_1 \tag{2.10-12}$$

Here η is the dummy variable of integration, and C_1 is the constant of integration. Integrating again yields

$$\Theta = -\int_{\tau=0}^{\tau=Y}\int_{\eta=0}^{\eta=\tau}\left(\frac{\partial^2\Theta}{\partial X^2}\right) d\eta\, d\tau + C_1 Y + C_2 \tag{2.10-13}$$

where τ is the second dummy variable of integration. We now apply the boundary conditions

$$\Theta = 0, \qquad Y = 0$$

$$\Theta = 1, \qquad Y = 1$$

to evaluate the constants of integration

$$C_2 = 0$$

$$C_1 = 1 + \int_{\tau=0}^{\tau=1}\int_{\eta=0}^{\eta=\tau}\left(\frac{\partial^2\Theta}{\partial X^2}\right) d\eta\, d\tau$$

Substitution of these values into Eq. 2.10-13 leads to†

$$\Theta = Y + Y\int_{\tau=0}^{\tau=1}\int_{\eta=0}^{\eta=\tau}\left(\frac{\partial^2\Theta}{\partial X^2}\right) d\eta\, d\tau - \int_{\tau=0}^{\tau=Y}\int_{\eta=0}^{\eta=\tau}\left(\frac{\partial^2\Theta}{\partial X^2}\right) d\eta\, d\tau \tag{2.10-14}$$

Use of the mean value theorem for double integrals and our order-of-magnitude estimate for $\partial^2\Theta/\partial X^2$ finally gives us

$$\Theta = Y + \mathbf{0}\left(\frac{1}{\beta^2}\right) \tag{2.10-15}$$

For the case where $L \gg b$ or $\beta \gg 1$ this simplifies to

$$\Theta = Y \tag{2.10-16}$$

†Note that Eq. 2.10-14 is mathematically exact, and that no assumptions or approximations have been imposed on Eqs. 2.10-5 and 2.10-6.

Putting this in dimensional form gives

$$T = T_0 + (T_1 - T_0)(y/b) \tag{2.10-17}$$

from which Eq. 2.10-1 can easily be obtained.

In considering the analysis presented in this section we should remember that our recipe for estimating the order-of-magnitude of second derivatives led us to the result that

$$\frac{\partial^2 \Theta}{\partial Y^2} = \mathbf{0}(1)$$

whereas our solution for Θ given by Eq. 2.10-15 leads to

$$\frac{\partial^2 \Theta}{\partial Y^2} = \mathbf{0}\left(\frac{1}{\beta^2}\right)$$

Clearly one must remain skeptical of results obtained by order-of-magnitude analysis and comparison with experiment or a more complete theory is always in order. In this case it would be wise to solve Eq. 2.10-5 subject to Eqs. 2.10-6 for several values of β using the methods outlined in Chapter 3. Such solutions would demonstrate that the average value of the heat flux in the y-direction would be given by

$$\langle q_y \rangle = \frac{k(T_0 - T_1)}{b}\left[1 + \mathbf{0}\left(\frac{1}{\beta^2}\right)\right]$$

thus confirming that Eq. 2.10-1 is satisfactory when $\beta \gg 1$.

Some rules for order-of-magnitude analysis

(1) $0(AB) = 0(A)0(B)$
(2) $0(A + B) \leqslant 0(A) + 0(B)$
(3) Given $A + B + C = 0$, about C one can say that $C \leqslant 0(A) + 0(B)$.

Solution to design problem II

There are a number of possible solutions to this problem. For example, a sign stating "Beware, Touching this Surface May be Hazardous to Your Health" might be the least expensive solution to our problem. Placing the area off-limits to visitors is even more effective. Surrounding the tank with a wire fence, or requiring all visitors to wear asbestos gloves are also possibilities; however, we will solve this problem within the context of material presented in this chapter. This requires that we provide enough insulation so that the surface temperature will not be hazardous to one's health.

In order to specify the thickness of the insulation, we must decide on a suitable upper bound for the surface temperature. This is not an easy decision to make since we know that the temperature we "feel" depends on the material and is related to the true temperature in a complex manner. For example, we would be hesitant to touch a piece of steel at 212°F for fear of getting burned while a piece of wood at the same temperature would not appear to present this hazard. One might guess that the surface temperature of the insulation could be as high as 200°F or 300°F without presenting a hazard; however, to be on the safe side we will require the surface temperature to be essentially body temperature, i.e., 100°F. Having made this decision we are now in a position to solve for the temperature field and then specify the insulation thickness that will provide a surface temperature of 100°F. We will assume that the ambient temperature is 70°F and we will designate the thickness of the metal and the insulation as L_1 and L_2 respectively. The curvature of the tank wall will be neglected so that the problem is reduced to solving for the temperature field in a flat, composite plate.

Our governing differential equations and boundary conditions take the form

$$\frac{d^2 T_{(1)}}{dx^2} = 0, \qquad 0 \leqslant x \leqslant L_1 \tag{II-1}$$

$$\frac{d^2 T_{(2)}}{dx^2} = 0, \qquad L_1 \leqslant x \leqslant L_1 + L_2 \tag{II-2}$$

B.C.1 $$-k_1\left(\frac{dT_{(1)}}{dx}\right)=h_{\text{liq}}(T_0-T), \qquad x=0 \tag{II-3}$$

B.C.2 $$T_{(1)}=T_{(2)}, \qquad x=L_1 \tag{II-4}$$

B.C.3 $$-k_1\left(\frac{dT_{(1)}}{dx}\right)=-k_2\left(\frac{dT_{(2)}}{dx}\right), \qquad x=L_1 \tag{II-5}$$

B.C.4 $$-k_2\left(\frac{dT_{(2)}}{dx}\right)=h_{\text{air}}(T-T_a), \qquad x=L_1+L_2 \tag{II-6}$$

Here T_0 is the temperature of the fluid in the tank (800°F) and T_a is the ambient air temperature (70°F). The solution of the governing differential equations is

$$T_{(1)}=A+Bx \tag{II-7}$$

$$T_{(2)}=C+Dx \tag{II-8}$$

and the integration constants are determined by the boundary conditions

$$A=T_0+\frac{T_0-T_a}{\left[\left(\frac{h_1L_1}{k_1}\right)\left(\frac{k_1}{k_2}-1\right)-\left(\frac{h_1}{h_2}\right)\left(\frac{\Omega}{k_2}\right)-1\right]}$$

$$B=\frac{T_0-T_a}{\left[L_1\left(\frac{k_1}{k_2}-1\right)-\left(\frac{k_1}{h_2}\right)\left(\frac{\Omega}{k_2}\right)-\frac{k_1}{h_1}\right]}$$

$$C=T_a-\frac{(T_0-T_a)\left(\frac{k_1}{h_2}\right)\left(\frac{\Omega}{k_2}\right)}{\left[L_1\left(\frac{k_1}{k_2}-1\right)-\left(\frac{k_1}{h_2}\right)\left(\frac{\Omega}{k_2}\right)-\frac{k_1}{h_1}\right]}$$

$$D=\frac{(T_1-T_a)}{\left[L_1\left(1-\frac{k_2}{k_1}\right)-\left(\frac{\Omega}{h_2}\right)-\frac{k_2}{h_1}\right]}$$

Where $\Omega=k_2+h_2(L_1+L_2)$, $h_1=h_{\text{liq}}$, and $h_2=h_{\text{air}}$. If we specify the surface temperature of the insulation at $x=L_1+L_2$ as T_m we can solve for the insulation thickness, L_2.

$$L_2=L_1\left[\left(\frac{k_2}{h_2L_1}\right)\left(\frac{T_0-T_a}{T_m-T_a}\right)-\left(\frac{k_2}{k_1}\right)-\left(\frac{k_2}{h_2L_1}\right)\left(\frac{h_2}{h_1}+1\right)\right] \tag{II-9}$$

For $T_m=100$°F this expression yields $L_2=22$ in. This can represent a sizable amount of insulation; however, if we allow the surface temperature to be 150°F we find $L_2=8$ in. This still represents a significant amount of insulation; however, if insulation surface temperatures of 200°F or even 300°F were tolerable, the insulation thickness would be reduced significantly. We will explore this possibility in Chapter 4.

PROBLEMS†

II-1. Rederive Eq. II-9 using the approach given in the solution of Design Problem I.

II-2. Calculate the insulation required for $T_m=100$°F taking into account the curvature of the tank.

II-3. Neglecting the effect of curvature calculate the decrease, in Btu/day, in the energy loss from the walls of the tank if 8 in of insulation are used.

2-1. (2.1) In an engineering mechanics course the kinematics and dynamics of single particles is always studied carefully. In particular, the work done on a particle moving along a curve from $s=0$ to $s=s(t)$ is given by

$$W=\int_{\eta=0}^{\eta=s(t)}\mathbf{F}\cdot\boldsymbol{\lambda}\,d\eta$$

†Problems numbered II-1, II-2, etc. deal directly with Design Problem II, and problems marked with an asterisk (*) are concerned with the solved example problems.

Here $s(t)$ is the arc-length, $\boldsymbol{\lambda}$ is the unit tangent to the curve along which $s(t)$ is measured, $\mathbf{F}$ is the force acting on the particle, and η is the dummy variable of integration. Use the Leibnitz rule to show that the rate of work is given by

$$\frac{dW}{dt} = \mathbf{F} \cdot \mathbf{v}$$

where the velocity of the particle is given by

$$\mathbf{v} = \boldsymbol{\lambda}\left(\frac{ds}{dt}\right)$$

Hint: Be careful to remember that when $\mathbf{F}$ and $\boldsymbol{\lambda}$ appear under the integral sign they are functions of the dummy variable of integration, η, and not explicit functions of time.

2-2. Derive Eq. (b) in Table 2.2-3 both by making an energy balance on the differential volume shown in Fig. 2.2, and
(2.2)

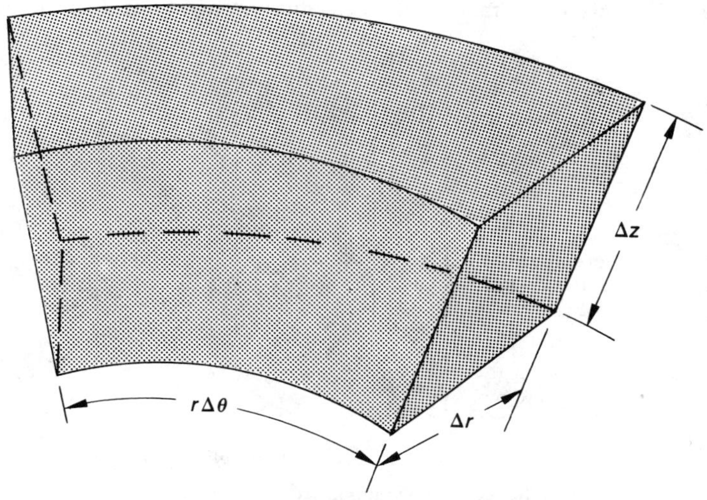

Fig. 2.2 Differential volume element in cylindrical coordinates.

by applying a transformation of variables to Eq. (a), i.e., let

$$T(r, \theta, z) = T[r(x, y), \theta(x, y), z]$$

where $r = \sqrt{x^2 + y^2}$ and $\theta = \tan^{-1}(y/x)$.

***2-3.** In Ex. 2.3-1 determine the percentage increase in the total rate of energy transfer if the plate is made of
(2.3) aluminum instead of steel.

2-4. For the system shown in Fig. 2.4 the following temperatures have been measured:
(2.3)

$$T_1 = 183°\text{F}$$
$$T_2 = 181°\text{F}$$
$$T_a = 68°\text{F}$$

$\frac{1}{4}$ in.

$T = T_2$

$T = T_1$

T_a is the ambient temperature measured far from the plate

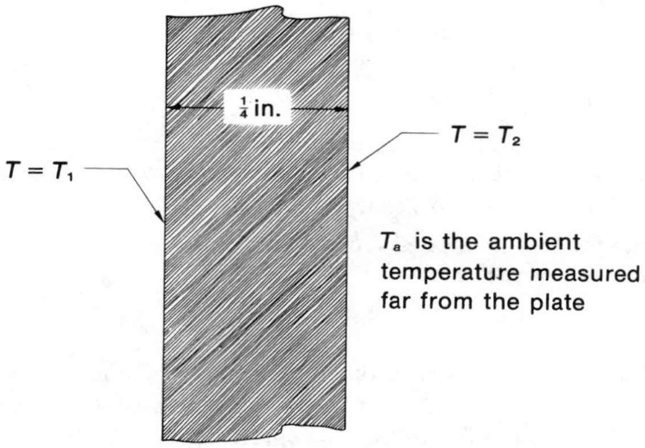

Fig. 2.4 Steady heat conduction across a flat plate.

Here T_1 represents the temperature on the inside of a ¼ in. thick steel plate, T_2 is the temperature at the interface between the plate and the air, and T_a is the ambient air temperature. Neglecting radiation, calculate the film heat transfer coefficient. Take the thermal conductivity of the plate to be 30 Btu/hrft°F. Determine the amount of insulation ($k = 0.055$ Btu/hrft°F) which must be added to the right-hand-side of the plate in order to reduce T_2 to 90°F. Assume T_1 remains constant at 183°F and that h is independent of the temperature difference, $T_2 - T_a$.

2-5. (2.3) Provide an explanation for the temperature profile in the liquid illustrated in Fig. 2.3.2 for $x > L$, i.e., why is the profile steepest at the solid–liquid interface and under what circumstances would the profile be flat far away from the plate?

2-6. (2.3) A very thin electrical heater is placed between two flat plates as shown in Fig. 2.6. The thicknesses of the plates are L_1 and L_2, and the thermal conductivities are k_1 and k_2. If the outer surfaces of the plates are maintained at a fixed temperature T_0, what is the ratio of the heat flux through plate 1 to the heat flux through plate 2?

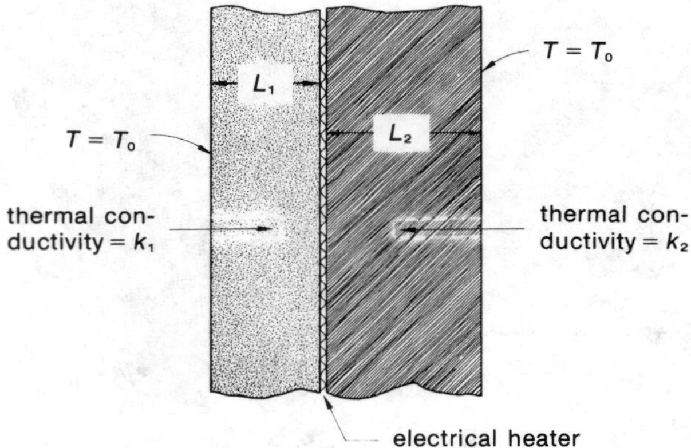

Fig. 2.6 Heat conduction from an electrical heater.

2-7. (2.3) Derive an expression for the heat flux in an infinite flat plate of thickness L with the surface temperature maintained at T_0 (for $x = 0$) and at T_1 (for $x = L$) when the thermal conductivity is given by

$$k = k_0[1 + \alpha(T - T_0)]$$

2-8. (2.3) If the thermal conductivity in Prob. 2-7 is an arbitrary function of temperature $k = k(T)$, derive an expression for the average thermal conductivity $\bar{k}$ that gives the correct heat flux when used in the equation

$$q_x = \left(\frac{\bar{k}}{L}\right)(T_0 - T_1)$$

***2-9.** (2.3) Rework Ex. 2.3-2 for the case where the heat generation is given by

$$\Phi = A\left[1 + \left(\frac{x}{L}\right)\right]$$

where $A = 24 \times 10^6$ Btu/hrft³.

2-10. (2.3) Derive an expression for the heat flux at $x = 0$ in the composite plate shown in Fig. 2.3.3 if there is a uniform heat source of strength Φ in the region $L_1 \leq x \leq L_1 + L_2$. Use the result to predict the strength of the source required to reduce the heat flux at $x = 0$ to zero.

2-11. (2.3) An infinite, flat slab of thickness b is irradiated from one side with gamma rays which are absorbed in such a way that the heat generation is given by

$$\Phi = A\, e^{-x/\ell}$$

Here A depends on the intensity of the radiation, ℓ is a material coefficient, and x is measured from the surface of the slab. If the side of the slab at $x = b$ is perfectly insulated and the natural convection film heat transfer coefficient at $x = 0$ is given as h, derive an expression for the temperature distribution in the slab. Assume that the thermal conductivity of the slab is constant and take the ambient temperature to be T_a.

4, 5, 6, 7, 10, 11, 15, 18

***2-12.** (2.4) If D_0 and D_1 in Ex. 2.4-1 are increased to 2.0 in and 2.24 in respectively, what value must D_2 take in order to keep the heat loss constant?

2-13. (2.4) For heat transfer across the pipe wall illustrated in Fig. 2.13 one can quickly determine that

$$T = T_0 - (T_0 - T_1)\frac{\ln (r/r_0)}{\ln (r_1/r_0)}$$

and that

$$(rq_r) = \frac{k(T_0 - T_1)}{\ln (r_1/r_0)}$$

Use this result to analyze the radial heat conduction process illustrated in Fig. 2.4.1, and rederive Eq. 2.4-13 following the approach given in the solution of Design Problem I.

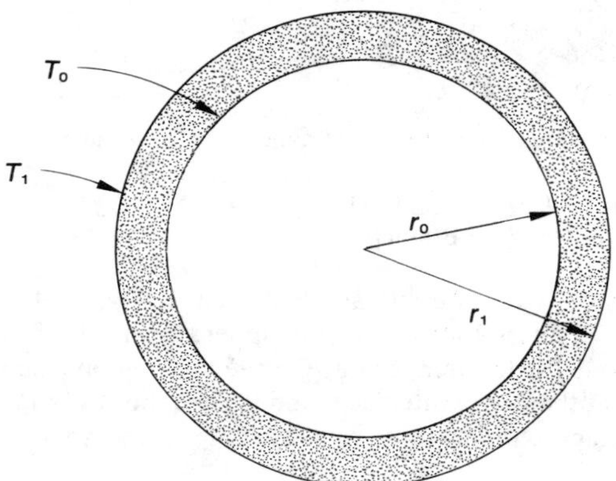

Fig. 2.13 Steady heat conduction in a pipe wall.

2-14. (2.4) Repeat Prob. 2-7 for a pipe having the inner surface at a temperature T_0 and the outer surface at a temperature T_1.

2-15. (2.4) Given a long copper wire in still air at 68°F, calculate the maximum current it can carry if the maximum temperature of the wire is not to exceed 200°F. Take the specific resistance to be 1.6×10^{-6} ohm cm and the film heat transfer coefficient to be 2.0 Btu/hr ft^2 °F. Assume the temperature in the wire is independent of θ and z. Take $D = 0.1$ in.

2-16. (2.4) Show, that for a cylinder with temperatures at r_1 and r_2 maintained at T_1 and T_2, the equation for $\dot{Q}$ in a flat slab can be used if one substitutes for the slab area A, the log-mean area for the cylinder where $A_{\ln}$ is given by

$$A_{\ln} = \frac{A_2 - A_1}{\ln (A_2/A_1)}$$

2-17. (2.4) Film heat transfer coefficients for fluids flowing through tubes can be measured by supplying heat to the tube by passing an electric current through the tube. If the outside surface is well insulated the heat flux at the inner surface is computed from voltage and current measurements. The outside surface temperature is measured, and from this the inside surface temperature can be calculated. Knowing the inner and outer radii r_i and r_o, the length of the tube L, the thermal conductivity of the tube k, the voltage E, the current I, and the "cup-mixing" temperature of the fluid T_b, derive an expression for the film heat transfer coefficient defined by

$$q_r = h(T - T_b), \qquad r = r_i$$

2-18. (2.4) In the system shown in Fig. 2.18, the rate of heat generation is 87 Btu/hr ft^3 in Region I which is perfectly insulated on the left-hand-side. Given the conditions indicated in the figure, calculate the heat flux at $x = L_1 + L_2$. *Ans*: 58 Btu/hr ft^2.

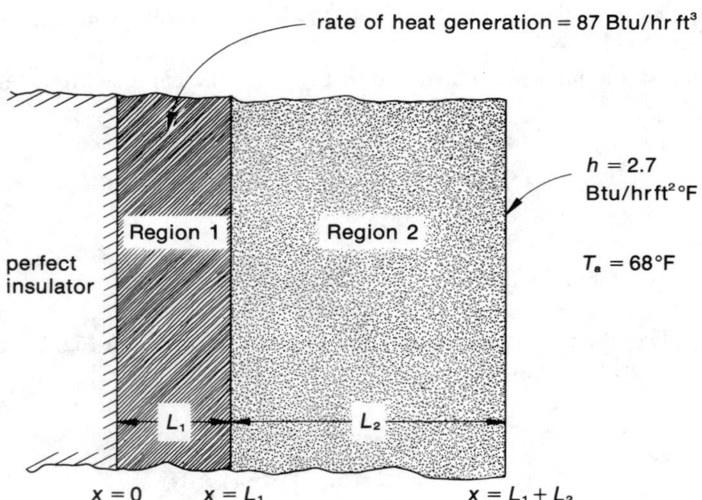

Fig. 2.18 Heat generation and conduction in a composite slab.

$L_1 = 8$ in. $\quad k_1 = 37$ Btu/hr ft °F
$L_2 = 26$ in. $\quad k_2 = 1.6$ Btu/hr ft °F

2-19. (2.5) A composite sphere consists of two materials as illustrated in Fig. 2.19. For the conditions given, derive an expression for the total rate of energy loss from the sphere using the following two methods: (a) Solve the governing differential equations for the temperature in the two regions, subject to the conditions of continuity of temperature and heat flux at the phase interface, and (b) use the result given by Eq. 2.5-9 for each region and eliminate the unknown interface temperatures as was done in the solution of Design Problem I.

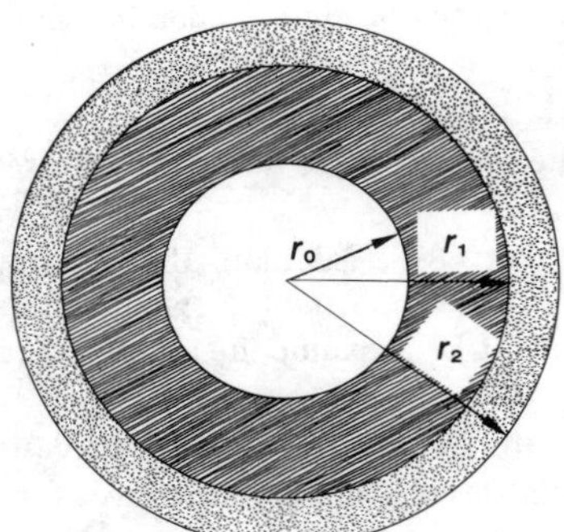

Fig. 2.19 Composite sphere.

At $r = r_0$, $\quad T = T_0$
At $r = r_2$, $\quad q_r = h(T - T_a)$
where T_a is the ambient temperature.

2-20. (2.5) Repeat Prob. 2-16 for a sphere with inner and outer radii of r_1 and r_2 to show that the area A should be replaced with the geometric mean area A_m where

$$A_m = \sqrt{A_1 A_2}$$

2-21. (2.5) Examine the problem of a critical insulation thickness discussed in Sec. 2.4 for heat transfer from a spherical surface.

2-22. (2.5) Derive an expression for the temperature at the center of a sphere having a thermal conductivity k, radius r_0, and uniform heat source Φ, with the surface temperature fixed at T_0.

2-23. Repeat Prob. 2-22 if the heat flux at $r = r_0$ is given by
(2.5)

$$q_r = h(T - T_a), \qquad r = r_0$$

2-24. A spherical nuclear reactor, 6 ft in diameter has thermal losses amounting to 100 MW. Sufficient insulation
(2.5) ($k = 0.045$ Btu/hr ft °F) must be added so that the exterior of the reactor is not hazardous to maintenance personnel. Determine the insulation thickness.

***2-25.** Determine the overall heat transfer rate for Ex. 2.6-1 if the fins are made of copper instead of steel.
(2.6)

2-26. A cylindrical steel rod (1.75 in. in diameter and 18 in. long) is connected to two steel plates maintained at 212°F
(2.6) and 32°F as shown in Fig. 2.26. If the ambient air is at 72°F and if we assume the film heat transfer coefficient is constant at 1.8 Btu/hr ft^2 °F, how does the average temperature vary along the rod?

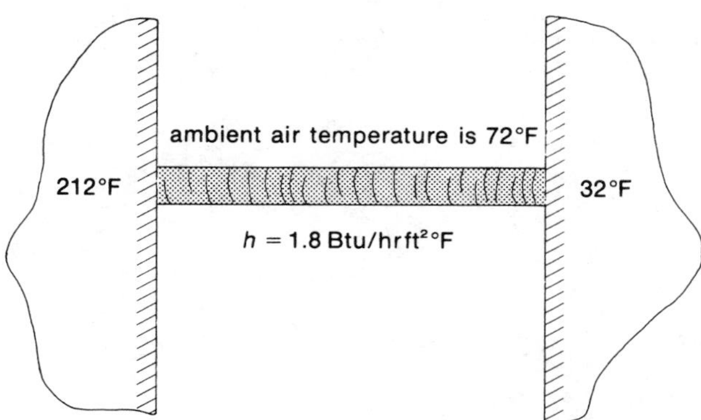

Fig. 2.26 Heat loss from a cylindrical rod.

2-27. If the rod in Prob. 2-26 is heated electrically giving rise to a uniform heat source of strength 5.6×10^4 Btu/hr ft^3, what
(2.6) is the temperature distribution?

***2-28.** Repeat the calculation presented in Ex. 2.7-1 using copper for the fin instead of steel.
(2.7)

2-29. Solve the differential equation
(2.7)

$$\frac{d^2y}{dx^2} + \lambda^2 y = 0$$

using the Frobenius method. Compare your series solution with the series representing the sine and cosine of λx.

***2-30.** Determine the fin effectiveness for the 1-in. and 3-in. fins described in Ex. 2.6-1.
(2.8)

2-31. In the analysis of steady, one-dimensional heat conduction in cylindrical coordinates (Sec. 2.4) we discarded the
(2.9) term $(1/r^2)(\partial^2 T/\partial\theta^2)$ in the heat conduction equation. For the process shown in Fig. 2.4.1, assume that the temperature variation from the bottom of the pipe to the top of the pipe is ΔT, and estimate what the order-of-magnitude of ΔT must be in order that the variation of T with θ may be neglected.

2-32. Repeat the analysis given in Sec. 2.10 for the following problem:
(2.10)

$$\frac{\partial^2 T}{\partial x^2} + \frac{\partial^2 T}{\partial y^2} = 0$$

B.C.1 $\quad T = T_0, \quad y = 0, \quad 0 \leq x \leq L$

B.C.2 $\quad T = T_1, \quad y = b, \quad 0 \leq x \leq L$

B.C.3 $\quad \dfrac{\partial T}{\partial x} = 0, \quad x = 0, \quad 0 \leq y \leq b$

B.C.4 $\quad -k\left(\dfrac{\partial T}{\partial x}\right) = h(T - T_a), \quad x = L, \quad 0 \leq y \leq b$

Here T_a is the ambient temperature which lies between T_0 and T_1. In your treatment of this problem use the boundary conditions at $x = 0$ and $x = L$ to help estimate the order-of-magnitude of $\partial^2 T/\partial x^2$. Show that this approach leads to

$$\Theta = Y + 0(N_{\mathrm{Bi}}/\beta)$$

instead of Eq. 2.10-15.

REFERENCES

1. Long, R. R., *Engineering Science Mechanics*, Prentice-Hall, Inc., Englewood Cliffs, N.J., 1963.
2. Housner, G. W., and Vreeland, T. Jr., *The Analysis of Stress and Deformation*, The Macmillan Co., New York, 1966.
3. Whitaker, S., *Introduction to Fluid Mechanics*, Prentice-Hall, Inc., Englewood Cliffs, N.J., 1968.
4. Marion, J. B., *Principles of Vector Analysis*, Academic Press, New York, 1965.
5. Lindgren, B. W., *Vector Calculus*, The Macmillan Co., New York, 1964.
6. Aris, R., *Vectors, Tensors, and the Basic Equations of Fluid Mechanics*, Prentice-Hall, Inc., Englewood Cliffs, N.J., 1962.
7. Karplus, W. J., and Soroka, W. W., *Analog Methods*, McGraw-Hill Book Co., Inc., New York, 1959.
8. Rainville, E. D., and Bedient, P. E., *Elementary Differential Equations*, Fourth Edition, The Macmillan Co., New York, 1969.
9. Ford, L. R., *Differential Equations*, McGraw-Hill Book Co., Inc., New York, 1933.
10. Birkhoff, G., *Hydrodynamics, A Study in Logic, Fact, and Similitude*, Princeton University Press, Princeton, N.J., 1960.
11. Stachiewicz, J. W., "Effect of Variation of Local Film Coefficients on Fin Performance," *Trans. ASME, Journal of Heat Transfer* **91**, 21 (1969).
12. Irey, R. K., "Errors in the One-Dimensional Fin Solution," *Trans. ASME, Journal of Heat Transfer* **90**, 175 (1968).
13. Wylie, C. R., Jr., *Advanced Engineering Mathematics*, Third Edition, McGraw-Hill Book Co., Inc., New York, 1966.

Design Problem III†

Copper pipes, carrying hot water at 180°F, are imbedded in the floor–ceiling as illustrated in Fig. III.1 in order to heat the rooms above and below. The outer diameter of the pipes is 1 in. and the resistance to heat transfer in the water and the pipe wall is negligible. If the top surface is at 60°F and the bottom surface is at 83°F, what are the average heat fluxes upwards and downwards from the hot water pipes? Take the thermal conductivity of the floor–ceiling material to be 0.42 Btu/hr ft °F.

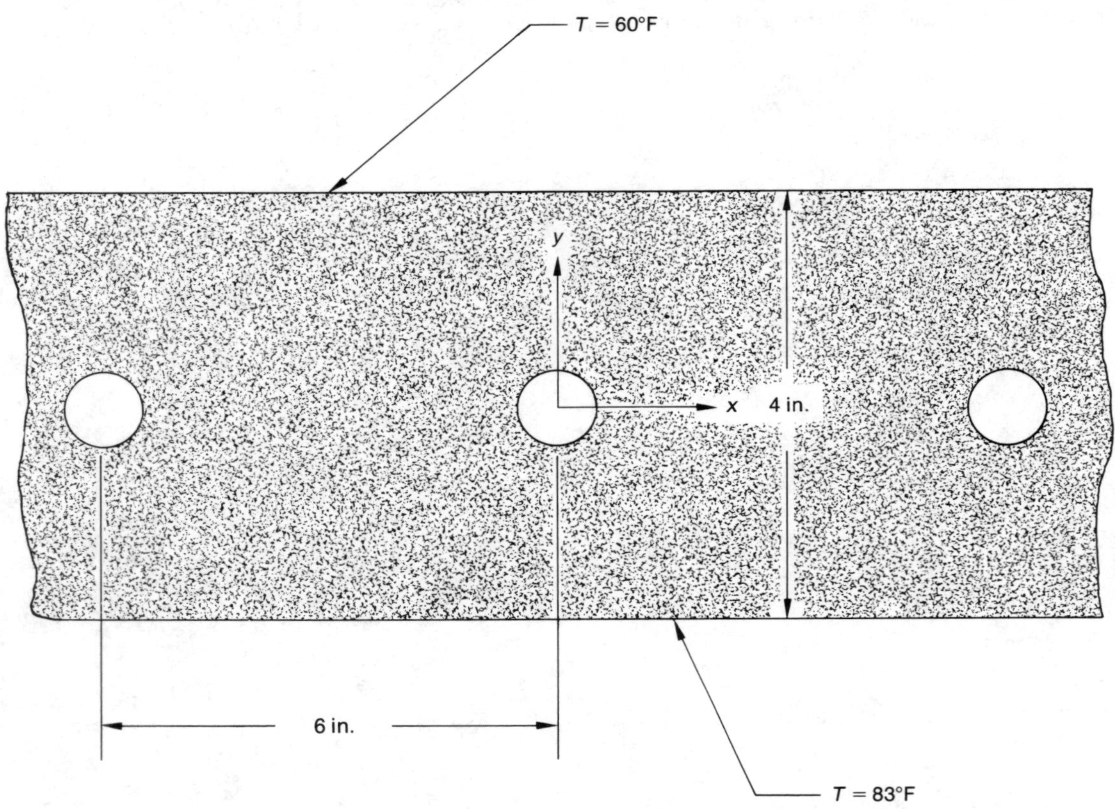

Fig. III.1 Use of hot water for heating apartments.

†This problem was suggested by Octave Levenspiel of Oregon State University.

3

Two-Dimensional, Steady Heat Conduction

In the last chapter we studied a number of one-dimensional processes, or processes that could be satisfactorily approximated with one-dimensional temperature distributions. In this chapter we will study cases where the temperature depends on two spatial variables while still imposing the steady-state condition and zero velocity.

Our objective in the previous chapter was to become familiar with a restricted form of the energy equation,

$$0 = -\int_{\mathscr{A}} \mathbf{q} \cdot \mathbf{n}\, dA + \int_{\mathscr{V}} \Phi\, dV$$

to derive the heat conduction equation,

$$0 = -\left(\frac{\partial q_x}{\partial x} + \frac{\partial q_y}{\partial y} + \frac{\partial q_z}{\partial z}\right) + \Phi$$

$$0 = -\nabla \cdot \mathbf{q} + \Phi$$

to see the need for a constitutive equation,

$$\mathbf{q} = -k\nabla T$$

in order to derive a deterministic equation governing the temperature field and therefore the interphase heat flux.

$$0 = \nabla \cdot (k\nabla T) + \Phi$$

We gained experience in formulating boundary conditions, and sketching reasonable temperature profiles.

In this chapter our objective will be much more limited for we wish only to *introduce* the student to the methods of solving the partial differential equations associated with two-dimensional steady heat conduction. A thorough understanding of partial differential equations is best obtained in a course devoted entirely to the subject; however, this chapter should prove useful to those students who wish to become familiar with, but not necessarily accomplished at, the standard methods for solving partial differential equations.

In general it is best for the undergraduate student to devote his time toward understanding the fundamental aspects of heat transfer rather than specialized mathematical methods, and for this reason all the material in this chapter can be omitted. However, those students who are planning on a thorough study of transient heat transfer should study the appropriate mathematical methods presented in this chapter before going on to Secs. 4.4 through 4.9 in Chapter 4. For an extremely brief treatment of the subject of two-dimensional heat conduction, Secs. 3.1, 3.3, and 3.5 are recommended.

3.1 Rectangular Coordinates

As an example of a two-dimensional heat conduction problem, we consider the case illustrated in Fig. 3.1.1. Here we have shown a plate with three of its sides maintained at a temperature T_0 while the fourth side at $y = L$ is maintained at a different constant temperature, T_1. The distribution of temperatures along the boundary violates the continuum postulate and leads to infinite values of the heat flux at the upper corners of the plate. In addition, the overall heat transfer rate at the top and sides of the plate is infinite. However, the temperature field determined on the basis of this type of model may still be quite representative of some real temperature field for which the temperatures along the boundaries are *nearly* constant at T_0 and T_1. If one wishes to determine the heat flux, a more realistic model which eliminates discontinuities in the temperature must be chosen.

If we assume that the thermal conductivity is constant in the region under consideration, the temperature field must satisfy

$$\frac{\partial^2 T}{\partial x^2} + \frac{\partial^2 T}{\partial y^2} = 0 \tag{3.1-1}$$

subject to the boundary conditions

B.C.1 $$T = T_0, \quad x = 0 \tag{3.1-2}$$

B.C.2 $$T = T_0, \quad y = 0 \tag{3.1-3}$$

B.C.3 $$T = T_0, \quad x = b \tag{3.1-4}$$

B.C.4 $$T = T_1, \quad y = L \tag{3.1-5}$$

In attempting to solve Eq. 3.1-1 we should keep in mind that there are an *infinite* number of solutions which satisfy the differential equation. For instance,

$$T = \text{constant}$$

$$T = A + Bx + Cy + Dxy$$

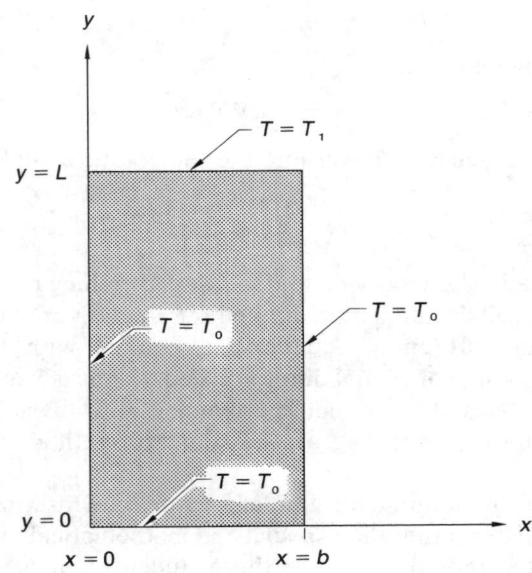

Fig. 3.1.1 Steady heat conduction in a rectangular plate.

are two solutions to Eq. 3.1-1, but neither will satisfy the boundary conditions for the problem at hand. The route to a satisfactory solution of a *partial differential equation* is much more of a "scavenger hunt" than the relatively ordered process that the student has encountered in the solution of *ordinary differential* equations. Here we will find that there is relatively little difficulty in obtaining functions which satisfy the *partial differential equation,* while the major effort in obtaining a solution centers around the problem of constructing a function which satisfies the boundary conditions.

Following the custom established in Chapter 2 we will define the following dimensionless variables:

$$\Theta = \frac{T - T_0}{T_1 - T_0}$$

$$X = x/b$$

$$Y = y/b$$

and the dimensionless parameter

$$\beta = L/b$$

so that the differential equations and the boundary conditions take the form

$$\frac{\partial^2\Theta}{\partial X^2} + \frac{\partial^2\Theta}{\partial Y^2} = 0 \tag{3.1-6}$$

B.C.1′ $\quad \Theta = 0, \quad X = 0 \qquad$ (3.1-7)

B.C.2′ $\quad \Theta = 0, \quad Y = 0 \qquad$ (3.1-8)

B.C.3′ $\quad \Theta = 0, \quad X = 1 \qquad$ (3.1-9)

B.C.4′ $\quad \Theta = 1, \quad Y = \beta \qquad$ (3.1-10)

One of the traditional techniques for attempting to find the solution to a partial differential equation is the method of *separation of variables.* In this method one assumes that the solution for Θ can be expressed in terms of separate functions of X and Y. For example,

$$\Theta = e^{-X} \cos Y$$

is a "separated" solution while

$$\Theta = \cos (XY)$$

is not. Assuming that we can separate the variables we express Θ in terms of two functions, $\mathscr{X}(X)$ and $\mathscr{Y}(Y)$,

$$\Theta = \mathscr{X}(X)\mathscr{Y}(Y) \tag{3.1-11}$$

where $\mathscr{X}(X)$ is *only* a function of X, and $\mathscr{Y}(Y)$ is *only* a function of Y. Substitution of Eq. 3.1-11 into Eq. 3.1-6 yields

$$\mathscr{Y}\frac{d^2\mathscr{X}}{dX^2} + \mathscr{X}\frac{d^2\mathscr{Y}}{dY^2} = 0 \tag{3.1-12}$$

Dividing by $\mathscr{X}\mathscr{Y}$ and rearranging yields

$$\frac{1}{\mathscr{X}}\frac{d^2\mathscr{X}}{dX^2} = -\frac{1}{\mathscr{Y}}\frac{d^2\mathscr{Y}}{dY^2} \tag{3.1-13}$$

Here we can see that the left-hand-side of Eq. 3.1-13 is *only* a function of X, whereas the right-hand-side is *only* a function of Y. This is permissible only if both sides are equal to a constant C, and we write

$$\frac{1}{\mathscr{X}}\frac{d^2\mathscr{X}}{dX^2} = -\frac{1}{\mathscr{Y}}\frac{d^2\mathscr{Y}}{dY^2} = C = \begin{cases} +\lambda^2 \\ 0 \\ -\lambda^2 \end{cases} \tag{3.1-14}$$

where λ is a real number, either positive or negative. Here we have represented the constant C in terms of three possible conditions: (1) positive ($C = +\lambda^2$), (2) zero ($C = 0$), and (3) negative ($C = -\lambda^2$). Each choice of C will lead to a different function for Θ. Our job is to find which function is capable of satisfying the boundary conditions, thus we will examine all three cases:

1. $C = 0$

Here the solution of Eqs. 3.1-14 is particularly simple and we write

$$\mathscr{X}(X) = C_1 + C_2 X$$
$$\mathscr{Y}(Y) = C_3 + C_4 Y$$

The dimensionless temperature is therefore linear in X and Y.

$$\Theta = (C_1 + C_2 X)(C_3 + C_4 Y) \tag{3.1-15}$$

Turning our attention to the boundary conditions given by Eqs. 3.1-7 through 3.1-10 we impose B.C.1′ to obtain

B.C.1′ $$0 = C_1(C_3 + C_4 Y) \tag{3.1-16}$$

Here we find that either $C_1 = 0$ or $C_3 = C_4 = 0$. The later choice would lead to a trivial solution for Θ, thus we require that C_1 be zero and our expression for Θ takes the form

$$\Theta = X(C_3 + C_4 Y) \tag{3.1-17}$$

where C_2 has been incorporated into the arbitrary constants, C_3 and C_4. Continuing on to B.C.2′ yields

B.C.2′ $$0 = X(C_3) \tag{3.1-18}$$

and we require that $C_3 = 0$ in order that the boundary condition be satisfied. Our expression for Θ now takes the form

$$\Theta = C_4 XY \tag{3.1-19}$$

Imposing the boundary condition at $X = 1$ leads to

B.C.3′ $$0 = C_4 Y \tag{3.1-20}$$

and we require that $C_4 = 0$. Our expression for Θ now takes the trivial form

$$\Theta = 0 \tag{3.1-21}$$

It satisfies the differential equation and three of the boundary conditions; however, it cannot satisfy the fourth boundary condition and we must discard it and explore the other possibilities.

2. $C = +\lambda^2$

For this condition, the first of Eqs. 3.1-14 becomes

$$\frac{d^2\mathscr{X}}{dX^2} = \lambda^2 \mathscr{X} \tag{3.1-22}$$

Assuming $\mathscr{X} = e^{mX}$ we obtain the *characteristic equation*

$$m^2 = \lambda^2 \tag{3.1-23}$$

and the solution for $\mathscr{X}$ is

$$\mathscr{X} = C_1 e^{\lambda X} + C_2 e^{-\lambda X} \tag{3.1-24}$$

The second of Eqs. 3.1-14 takes the form

$$\frac{d^2\mathscr{Y}}{dY^2} = -\lambda^2 \mathscr{Y} \tag{3.1-25}$$

thus $m = \sqrt{-\lambda^2}$ and we obtain

$$\mathscr{Y} = C_3\, e^{i\lambda Y} + C_4\, e^{-i\lambda Y} \tag{3.1-26}$$

The appearance of complex functions in the solution for a real variable is often disturbing to the student and we can eliminate this problem by noting that the most general real part of Eq. 3.1-26 is $C_3 \cos \lambda Y + C_4 \sin \lambda Y$ so that the solution for Θ takes the form

$$\Theta = (C_1\, e^{\lambda X} + C_2\, e^{-\lambda X})(C_3 \cos \lambda Y + C_4 \sin \lambda Y) \tag{3.1-27}$$

We again return to the boundary conditions given by Eqs. 3.1-7 through 3.1-10, and find that the first boundary condition leads to

B.C.1′
$$0 = (C_1 + C_2)(C_3 \cos \lambda Y + C_4 \sin \lambda Y) \tag{3.1-28}$$

This requires $C_2 = -C_1$ and our expression for Θ given by Eq. 3.1-27 is reduced to

$$\Theta = C_1(e^{\lambda X} - e^{-\lambda X})(C_3 \cos \lambda Y + C_4 \sin \lambda Y) \tag{3.1-29}$$

Imposing the second boundary condition yields

B.C.2′
$$0 = C_1(e^{\lambda X} - e^{-\lambda X})C_3 \tag{3.1-30}$$

Here we are required to set $C_3 = 0$ for satisfying B.C.2′ by setting C_1 equal to zero would reduce to solution for Θ to the trivial case, $\Theta = 0$, which we know cannot satisfy B.C.4′. With $C_3 = 0$ our solution for Θ becomes

$$\Theta = C_1(e^{\lambda X} - e^{-\lambda X}) \sin \lambda Y \tag{3.1-31}$$

where C_4 has been incorporated into the single remaining arbitrary constant, C_1. Continuing on to the third boundary condition we find

B.C.3′
$$0 = C_1(e^{\lambda} - e^{-\lambda}) \sin \lambda Y \tag{3.1-32}$$

This boundary condition can only be satisfied by $C_1 = 0$ or $e^{\lambda} = e^{-\lambda}$. The former condition leads directly to a trivial solution for Θ while the latter leads to $\lambda = 0$ which when substituted into Eq. 3.1-31 leads to

$$\Theta = 0 \tag{3.1-33}$$

Once again we have obtained a solution which satisfies the differential equation and the first three boundary conditions, but obviously cannot satisfy the fourth boundary condition. Having ruled out the first two possible solutions for Θ we go on to the third.

3. $C = -\lambda^2$

The procedure here is the same as that for $C = +\lambda^2$, and it should be fairly obvious that

$$\Theta = (C_1 \cos \lambda X + C_2 \sin \lambda X)(C_3\, e^{\lambda Y} + C_4\, e^{-\lambda Y}) \tag{3.1-34}$$

is the solution for this case. As before, we proceed to impose the boundary conditions on our solution for Θ. The first boundary condition

B.C.1′ $\qquad \Theta = 0, \qquad X = 0$

leads to

$$0 = C_1(C_3\, e^{\lambda Y} + C_4\, e^{-\lambda Y}) \tag{3.1-35}$$

It follows that $C_1 = 0$ and our general expression for Θ can be written as

$$\Theta = \sin \lambda X(C_3 e^{\lambda Y} + C_4\, e^{-\lambda Y}) \tag{3.1-36}$$

Here the constant C_2 has been included in C_3 and C_4. Imposing the second boundary condition

B.C.2′ $\qquad \Theta = 0, \qquad Y = 0$

on Eq. 3.1-36 leads to

$$0 = \sin \lambda X (C_3 + C_4) \tag{3.1-37}$$

This requires that $C_4 = -C_3$ and the resulting solution for Θ can be expressed in the form

$$\Theta = C \sin \lambda X \sinh \lambda Y \tag{3.1-38}$$

where $C = 2C_3$ is the one remaining arbitrary constant. The third boundary condition

B.C.3′ $\qquad \Theta = 0, \qquad X = 1$

leads to

$$0 = C \sin \lambda \sinh \lambda Y \tag{3.1-39}$$

which could be satisfied by either $C = 0$ or $\lambda = n\pi$ where $n = 1, 2, 3, \ldots$. The first possibility will not allow us to satisfy the last boundary condition, thus we conclude that λ takes on an infinite number of values called *eigenvalues*. We now have an infinite number of expressions for Θ:

$$\begin{aligned} &\Theta_0 = 0 \\ &\Theta_1 = C_1 \sin \pi X \sinh \pi Y \\ &\Theta_2 = C_2 \sin 2\pi X \sinh 2\pi Y \\ &\ldots\ldots\ldots\ldots\ldots\ldots \\ &\Theta_n = C_n \sin (n\pi X) \sinh (n\pi Y) \\ &\ldots\ldots\ldots\ldots\ldots\ldots \\ &\ldots\ldots\ldots\ldots\ldots\ldots \end{aligned} \tag{3.1-40}$$

all of which satisfy the differential equation and the first three boundary conditions. We can express these as

$$\Theta_n = C_n \sin (n\pi X) \sinh (n\pi Y), \qquad n = 0, 1, 2, \ldots \tag{3.1-41}$$

Here the constants $C_0, C_1, C_2 \ldots$ are all arbitrary, and need to be specified if a complete solution is to be obtained.

Going on to the fourth boundary condition

B.C.4′ $\qquad \Theta = 1, \qquad Y = \beta$

$$1 = C_n \sin (n\pi X) \sinh (n\pi\beta), \qquad n = 0, 1, 2, \ldots$$

we find ourselves in the position where the left-hand-side is a constant while the right-hand-side is a function of X. Here we are saved by the fact that the sine function is an *orthogonal function* and we can use Fourier analysis [1] to determine the values of C_n such that B.C.4′ is satisfied.

Rather than attacking B.C.4′ directly, let us consider the use of a Fourier sine series to construct a function which is equal to 1 in the region $0 \leqslant X \leqslant 1$.

$$1 = \sum_{n=0}^{\infty} A_n \sin (n\pi X), \qquad 0 \leqslant X \leqslant 1 \tag{3.1-42}$$

We can determine the coefficients A_n by multiplying Eq. 3.1-42 by $\sin (m\pi X)$ and integrating from 0 to 1. This yields

$$\int_{X=0}^{X=1} \sin (m\pi X)\, dX = A_m \int_{X=0}^{X=1} \sin^2 (m\pi X)\, dX \tag{3.1-43}$$

Here we have made use of the fact that

$$\int_{X=0}^{X=1} \sin (n\pi X) \sin (m\pi X)\, dX = 0, \qquad n \neq m \tag{3.1-44}$$

Carrying out the integrations in Eq. 3.1-43 we find

$$A_0 = 0, \qquad A_n = \frac{2[1-(-1)^n]}{n\pi}, \qquad n = 1, 2, 3, \ldots \tag{3.1-45}$$

Making use of Eq. 3.1-45 we find that Eq. 3.1-42 can be expressed as

$$1 = \left(\frac{4}{\pi}\right) \sin \pi X + \frac{4}{3\pi} \sin 3\pi X + \frac{4}{5\pi} \sin 5\pi X + \cdots \qquad 0 \leq X \leq 1$$

Partial sums from this infinite series are illustrated in Fig. 3.1.2. There we see that as successive terms are included in the sum it more closely approximates unity in the region $0 \leq X \leq 1$. Since we have been able to express the constant 1 as an infinite series of sine functions, it is obvious that B.C.4′ could indeed be satisfied if we took the solution for Θ to be the *sum* of all the solutions given by Eq. 3.1-41, thus we have infinite series which takes the form

$$\Theta = \sum_{n=0}^{\infty} C_n \sin(n\pi X) \sinh(n\pi Y) \tag{3.1-46}$$

and B.C.4′ is written as

B.C.4′

$$1 = \sum_{n=0}^{\infty} C_n \sin(n\pi X) \sinh(n\pi\beta) \tag{3.1-47}$$

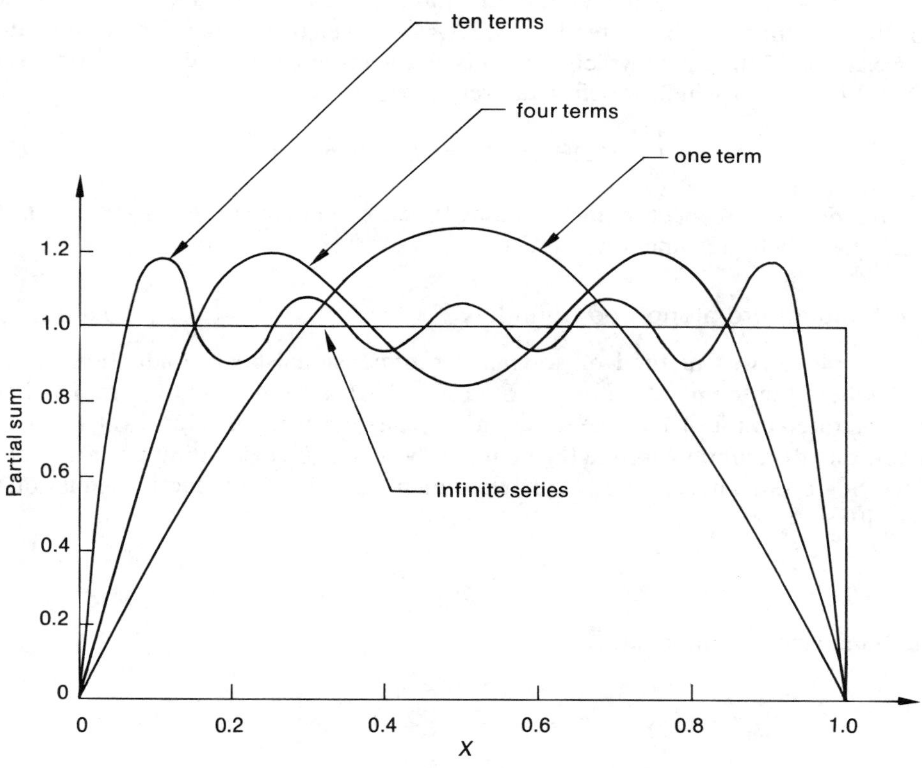

Fig. 3.1.2 Use of Fourier series to construct a function.

By Eq. 3.1-42 we can express 1 in Eq. 3.1-47 as

$$\sum_{n=0}^{\infty} A_n \sin(n\pi X) = \sum_{n=0}^{\infty} C_n \sin(n\pi X) \sinh(n\pi\beta)$$

or

$$\sum_{n=0}^{\infty} [A_n - C_n \sinh(n\pi\beta)] \sin(n\pi X) = 0$$

This requires that the coefficients C_n be given by

$$C_n = \frac{A_n}{\sinh(n\pi\beta)} = \frac{2[1-(-1)^n]}{n\pi \sinh(n\pi\beta)}, \qquad n = 1, 2, 3, \ldots \tag{3.1-48}$$

and our final solution for the dimensionless temperature field is

$$\Theta = 2 \sum_{n=1}^{\infty} \frac{[1-(-1)^n]}{n\pi \sinh(n\pi\beta)} \sin(n\pi X) \sinh(n\pi Y) \tag{3.1-49}$$

From the knowledge of Θ we can compute the heat flux anywhere in the plate, and in particular we can compute the heat flux at any point on the boundary. It should be noted that evaluation of Θ by means of the infinite series is best done on a computer, for the series need not converge rapidly, especially for values of Y close to β. Our final expression for the temperature may be obtained from Eq. 3.1-49 and is

$$T = T_0 + 2(T_1 - T_0) \sum_{n=1}^{\infty} \frac{[1-(-1)^n]}{n\pi \sinh(n\pi\beta)} \sin(n\pi X) \sinh(n\pi Y) \tag{3.1-50}$$

There are some important characteristics of this solution that deserve comment. First we should recognize that each term in Eq. 3.1-49 satisfies the partial differential equation and three of the boundary conditions (Eqs. 3.1-1 through 3.1-4). The fourth boundary condition (Eq. 3.1-5) is *not* satisfied by any *single* term in Eq. 3.1-49, but *is* satisfied by the infinite sum. Secondly, we should note that the characteristic of the sine function illustrated by Eq. 3.1-44 allowed us to quickly determine the coefficients in the infinite series. Sets of functions which have this characteristic are called orthogonal sets. In general we say that a function $\Theta_m(x)$ which satisfies the relation

$$\int_0^L w(x)\Theta_n(x)\Theta_m(x)\,dx = 0, \; n \neq m$$

is an orthogonal function with respect to the weighting function $w(x)$ in the region $0 \leq x \leq L$. In the case of the sine function, the weighting function is unity.

Nonconstant temperature along one boundary

As another example of this method of solving two-dimensional heat conduction problems we will consider the case where the temperature at $y = L$ in Fig. 3.1.1 is a function of x rather than a constant. This situation is illustrated in Fig. 3.1.3. The function $f(x)$ may take on the value T_0 at $x = 0, b$ to provide a continuous temperature distribution around the plate, or there may be discontinuities at $x = 0$ and $x = b$.

As before, we begin our analysis with the two-dimensional heat conduction equation for constant thermal conductivity

$$\frac{\partial^2 T}{\partial x^2} + \frac{\partial^2 T}{\partial y^2} = 0 \tag{3.1-51}$$

and express the boundary conditions as

B.C.1	$T = T_0,$	$x = 0$	(3.1-52)
B.C.2	$T = T_0,$	$x = b$	(3.1-53)
B.C.3	$T = T_0,$	$y = 0$	(3.1-54)
B.C.4	$T = f(x)$	$y = L$	(3.1-55)

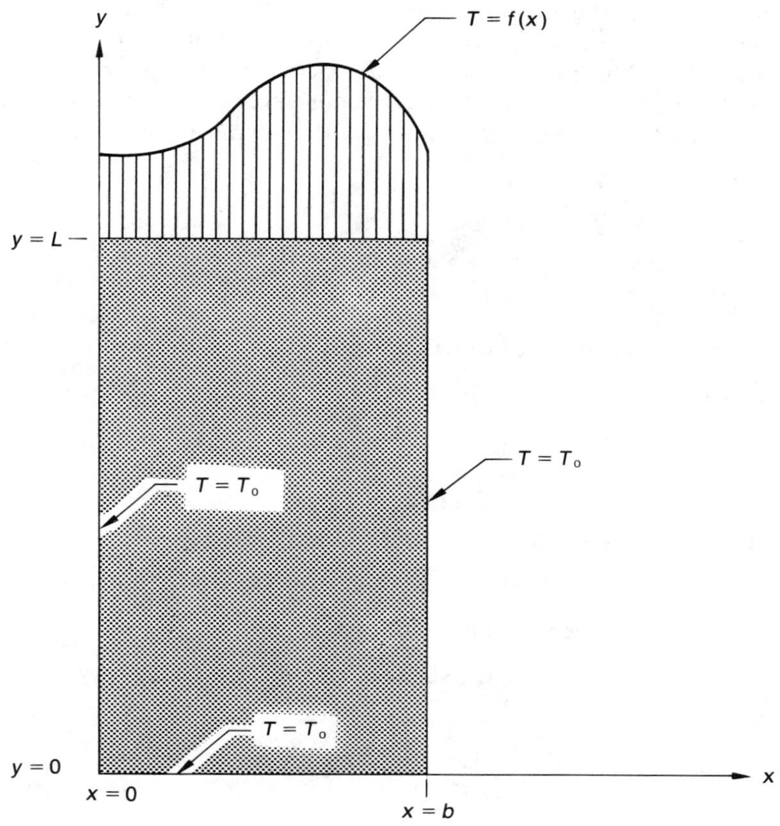

Fig. 3.1.3 Steady heat conduction in a rectangular plate with a specified temperature distribution on one edge.

In general it is advantageous to formulate problems of this type in dimensionless form with as many of the boundary conditions as possible taking on the value of zero. In this example we will leave the problem in the form given by Eqs. 3.1-51 through 3.1-55. This will lead to some minor complications, but hopefully dealing with these complications will help clarify the process of developing a solution to a partial differential equation.

Following the previous example we know that there are at least three possible solutions to Eq. 3.1-51 which we can write as

$$T_{(1)} = (C_1 + C_2 x)(C_3 + C_4 y) \tag{3.1-56}$$

$$T_{(2)} = (C_5\, e^{\lambda x} + C_6\, e^{-\lambda x})(C_7\, e^{i\lambda y} + C_8\, e^{-i\lambda y}) \tag{3.1-57}$$

$$T_{(3)} = (C_9 \cos \lambda x + C_{10} \sin \lambda x)(C_{11} \cosh \lambda y + C_{12} \sinh \lambda y) \tag{3.1-58}$$

These expressions for $T_{(1)}$, $T_{(2)}$, and $T_{(3)}$ follow directly from Eqs. 3.1-15, 3.1-27, and 3.1-34. It must be remembered that each of these expressions represents a solution of the partial differential equation but does not necessarily satisfy the boundary conditions for the problem at hand. Furthermore, we should remember that any combinations of these solutions is also a solution, i.e., $C_{(2)}T_{(2)} + C_{(3)}T_{(3)}$ is a solution to the differential equation where $C_{(2)}$ and $C_{(3)}$ are arbitrary constants.

Because we know that neither $T_{(1)}$ nor $T_{(2)}$ can satisfy the boundary condition at $y = L$, we proceed immediately to $T_{(3)}$ and see what success we have with satisfying the boundary conditions. Starting with B.C.1 we obtain

B.C.1
$$T_0 = C_9(C_{11} \cosh \lambda y + C_{12} \sinh \lambda y) \tag{3.1-59}$$

We are immediately in trouble for the left-hand-side of Eq. 3.1-59 is a constant while the right-hand-side is a function of y. Furthermore, since the hyperbolic functions are not orthogonal functions, there is no way in which we can get around this difficulty. It should become clear, perhaps with a little thought and some exploration of the other boundary conditions, that $T_{(3)}$ is not a solution which can be used to satisfy all the boundary conditions. Let us try another *solution of the differential equation* of the form

$$\begin{aligned} T_{(4)} &= T_{(1)} + T_{(3)} \\ &= (C_1 + C_2 x)(C_3 + C_4 y) \\ &\quad + (C_9 \cos \lambda x + C_{10} \sin \lambda x)(C_{11} \cosh \lambda y + C_{12} \sinh \lambda y) \end{aligned} \tag{3.1-60}$$

Application of B.C.1 now takes the form

B.C.1
$$T_0 = C_1(C_3 + C_4 y) + C_9(C_{11} \cosh \lambda y + C_{12} \sinh \lambda y) \tag{3.1-61}$$

This condition is satisfied if

$$C_4 = 0$$
$$C_9 = 0$$
$$C_1 C_3 = T_0$$

and our general solution takes the form

$$T_{(4)} = T_0 + C_2 C_3 x + C_{10} \sin \lambda x (C_{11} \cosh \lambda y + C_{12} \sinh \lambda y) \tag{3.1-62}$$

Moving on to the second boundary condition we obtain

B.C.2
$$T_0 = T_0 + C_2 C_3 b + C_{10} \sin \lambda b (C_{11} \cosh \lambda y + C_{12} \sinh \lambda y) \tag{3.1-63}$$

This condition is satisfied if†

$$C_2 \quad \text{or} \quad C_3 = 0$$
$$\lambda = n\pi/b, \qquad n = 1, 2, 3, \ldots$$

and our expression for $T_{(4)}$ becomes

$$T_{(4)} = T_0 + C_{10} \sin \left(\frac{n\pi x}{b}\right)\left[C_{11} \cosh \left(\frac{n\pi y}{b}\right) + C_{12} \sinh \left(\frac{n\pi y}{b}\right)\right], \qquad n = 1, 2, 3, \ldots \tag{3.1-64}$$

Here we see that we have an infinite number of solutions which satisfy the differential equation and the first two boundary conditions. Application of B.C.3 gives

B.C.3
$$T_0 = T_0 + C_{10} \sin \left(\frac{n\pi x}{b}\right)[C_{11}] \tag{3.1-65}$$

thus we require $C_{11} = 0$. Our expression now takes the form

$$T_{(4)} = T_0 + C_n \sin \left(\frac{n\pi x}{b}\right) \sinh\left(\frac{n\pi y}{b}\right), \qquad n = 1, 2, 3, \ldots \tag{3.1-66}$$

Here we have replaced $C_{10}C_{12}$ by C_n where $n = 0, 1, 2, \ldots$ indicating that the single remaining constant of integration in our *infinite* number of solutions can take on a different value for each one of this infinite number. Our situation at this point is that we have an infinite number of solutions all of which satisfy the *differential equation* and the *first three boundary conditions.*

Going on to the final boundary condition

B.C.4
$$f(x) = T_0 + C_n \sin \left(\frac{n\pi x}{b}\right) \sinh \left(\frac{n\pi L}{b}\right), \qquad n = 1, 2, 3, \ldots \tag{3.1-67}$$

we find that *none* of the infinite number of solutions satisfies the last boundary condition, provided of course $f(x)$ is not directly proportion to $\sin (n\pi x/b)$. We are in luck, of course, since we have available to

†Requiring C_{10} to be zero would lead to the trivial solution $T_{(4)} = T_0$ which would not satisfy all the boundary conditions.

us a method of specifying the constants C_n such that the *sum* of all our solutions can be made to satisfy B.C.4. Backing up to Eq. 3.1-66 we write

$$T_{(4)} = T_0 + \sum_{n=1}^{\infty} C_n \sin\left(\frac{n\pi x}{b}\right) \sinh\left(\frac{n\pi y}{b}\right) \tag{3.1-68}$$

where it should be clear that Eq. 3.1-68 represents a solution of the differential equation which satisfies the first three boundary conditions. The final boundary condition can now be written as

B.C.4
$$[f(x) - T_0] = \sum_{n=1}^{\infty} C_n \sin\left(\frac{n\pi x}{b}\right) \sinh\left(\frac{n\pi L}{b}\right) \tag{3.1-69}$$

We now attack the problem of determining the C_n in a more direct manner than we did in the previous example. Multiplying Eq. 3.1-69 by $\sin(m\pi x/b)$ where $m = 1, 2, 3, \ldots$ and integrating from $x = 0$ to $x = b$, we obtain

$$\int_{x=0}^{x=b} [f(x) - T_0] \sin\left(\frac{m\pi x}{b}\right) dx = C_m \sinh\left(\frac{m\pi L}{b}\right) \int_{x=0}^{x=b} \sin^2\left(\frac{m\pi x}{b}\right) dx \tag{3.1-70}$$

Here we have made use of the fact that

$$\int_{x=0}^{x=b} \sin\left(\frac{n\pi x}{b}\right) \sin\left(\frac{m\pi x}{b}\right) dx = 0, \qquad \text{for } m \neq n$$

Evaluating the integral on the right-hand-side of Eq. 3.1-70 allows us to express C_n as

$$C_n = \frac{(b/2)}{\sinh\left(\frac{n\pi L}{b}\right)} \int_{x=0}^{x=b} [f(x) - T_0] \sin\left(\frac{n\pi x}{b}\right) dx \tag{3.1-71}$$

and our expression for the temperature becomes

$$T = T_0 + \sum_{n=1}^{\infty} C_n \sin\left(\frac{n\pi x}{b}\right) \sinh\left(\frac{n\pi y}{b}\right) \tag{3.1-72}$$

In principle we have solved the problem that was originally posed, but in practice one would presumably be interested in numerical values of the temperature field or perhaps the temperature gradient normal to one of the edges of the plate. Even if a simple analytic expression exists for C_n, the evaluation of the terms in the infinite series will certainly require the programming of a digital computer. With this in mind we might suggest that it would be easier to program the computer to solve Eq. 3.1-51 directly. This approach is quite feasible and we will explore it in Sec. 3.3.

Superposition

When the temperature is not constant along more than one boundary, we encounter some difficulty and we must resort to the principle of superposition in order to obtain a solution. As an example we consider the situation illustrated in Fig. 3.1.4 and stated as follows:

$$\frac{\partial^2 T}{\partial x^2} + \frac{\partial^2 T}{\partial y^2} = 0 \tag{3.1-73}$$

B.C.1 $\qquad T = T_0, \quad x = 0 \qquad$ (3.1-74a)

B.C.2 $\qquad T = T_0 + g(y), \quad x = b \qquad$ (3.1-74b)

B.C.3 $\qquad T = T_0, \quad y = 0 \qquad$ (3.1-74c)

B.C.4 $\qquad T = T_0 + f(x), \quad y = L \qquad$ (3.1-74d)

We will simplify the statement of the problem by defining the following dimensionless variables:

$$\Theta = (T - T_0)/(T_{max} - T_0), \qquad X = x/b, \qquad Y = y/b$$

$$G(Y) = g(Yb)/(T_{max} - T_0), \qquad F(X) = f(Xb)/(T_{max} - T_0), \qquad \beta = L/b$$

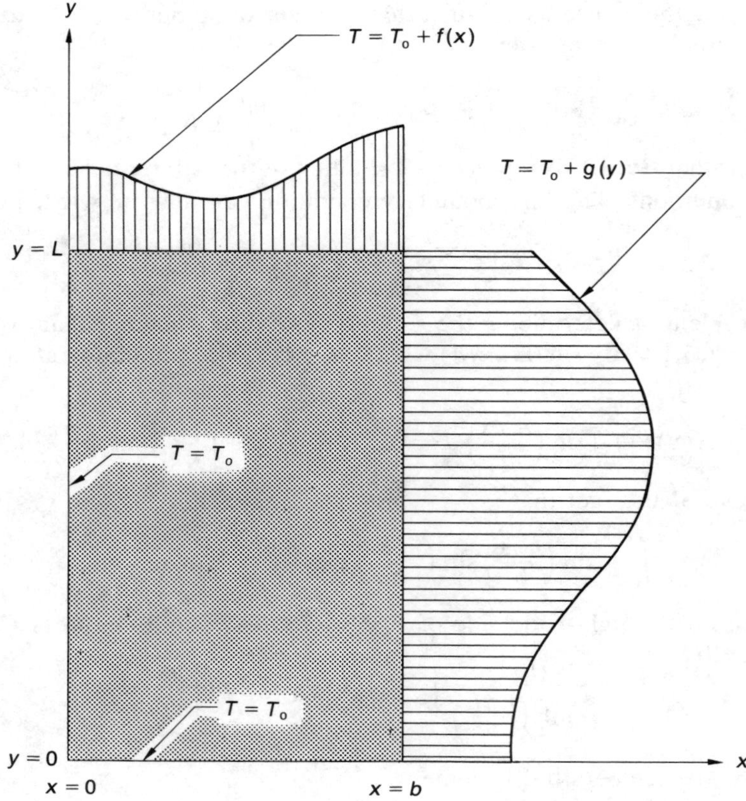

Fig. 3.1.4 Steady heat conduction in a rectangular plate with specified temperature distributions on two edges.

where T_{max} is the maximum temperature that occurs on the boundaries. Eqs. 3.1-73 and 3.1-74 now take the form

$$\frac{\partial^2\Theta}{\partial X^2}+\frac{\partial^2\Theta}{\partial Y^2}=0 \tag{3.1-75}$$

B.C.1′ $\Theta = 0, \quad X = 0$ (3.1-76a)

B.C.2′ $\Theta = G(Y), \quad X = 1$ (3.1-76b)

B.C.3′ $\Theta = 0, \quad Y = 0$ (3.1-76c)

B.C.4′ $\Theta = F(X), \quad Y = \beta$ (3.1-76d)

It should be clear from the previous discussion that we need a solution for Θ with an orthogonal function of Y in order to satisfy B.C.2′ and an orthogonal function of X to satisfy B.C.4′. Since the usual separation of variables will always provide one but not the other we must split this problem into *two* problems. We define Θ in terms of $\Theta_{(1)}$ and $\Theta_{(2)}$ as

$$\Theta = \Theta_{(1)} + \Theta_{(2)} \tag{3.1-77}$$

and specify the two problems as

Problem #1

$$\frac{\partial^2\Theta_{(1)}}{\partial X^2}+\frac{\partial^2\Theta_{(1)}}{\partial Y^2}=0 \tag{3.1-78}$$

B.C.1″ $\Theta_{(1)} = 0, \quad X = 0$ (3.1-79a)

B.C.2″ $\Theta_{(1)} = G(Y), \quad X = 1$ (3.1-79b)

B.C.3″ $\Theta_{(1)} = 0, \quad Y = 0$ (3.1-79c)

B.C.4″ $\Theta_{(1)} = 0, \quad Y = \beta$ (3.1-79d)

Problem #2

$$\frac{\partial^2 \Theta_{(2)}}{\partial X^2} + \frac{\partial^2 \Theta_{(2)}}{\partial Y^2} = 0 \tag{3.1-80}$$

B.C.1‴ $\Theta_{(2)} = 0, \quad X = 0$ (3.1-81a)

B.C.2‴ $\Theta_{(2)} = 0, \quad X = 1$ (3.1-81b)

B.C.3‴ $\Theta_{(2)} = 0, \quad Y = 0$ (3.1-81c)

B.C.4‴ $\Theta_2 = F(X), \quad Y = \beta$ (3.1-81d)

If $\Theta_{(1)}$ and $\Theta_{(2)}$ are solutions of the governing differential equation, then it is easy to show that $\Theta = \Theta_{(1)} + \Theta_{(2)}$ is also a solution by substitution of Θ into Eq. 3.1-75.

$$\frac{\partial^2 \Theta}{\partial X^2} + \frac{\partial^2 \Theta}{\partial Y^2} = \left(\frac{\partial^2 \Theta_{(1)}}{\partial X^2} + \frac{\partial^2 \Theta_{(1)}}{\partial Y^2}\right) + \left(\frac{\partial^2 \Theta_{(2)}}{\partial X^2} + \frac{\partial^2 \Theta_{(2)}}{\partial Y^2}\right) = 0 + 0 = 0 \tag{3.1-82}$$

Furthermore, inspection of the boundary conditions for $\Theta_{(1)}$ and $\Theta_{(2)}$ indicates that the sum of these two functions satisfies the original boundary conditions given by Eqs. 3.1-79.

Using this method one can reduce a very complicated problem to two, three, or four very simple problems. One must always pay strict attention to the boundary conditions when using the method of superposition, for it is in the boundary conditions that mistakes are most often made. To insure that the boundary conditions are correct one should always formally construct these conditions from the simplified solutions. In the case we have considered this is done as follows:

B.C.1′ $\Theta = \Theta_{(1)} + \Theta_{(2)} = 0 + 0 = 0, \quad X = 0$ (3.1-76a)

B.C.2′ $\Theta = \Theta_{(1)} + \Theta_{(2)} = G(Y) + 0 = G(Y), \quad X = 1$ (3.1-76b)

B.C.3′ $\Theta = \Theta_{(1)} + \Theta_{(2)} = 0 + 0 = 0, \quad Y = 0$ (3.1-76c)

B.C.4′ $\Theta = \Theta_{(1)} + \Theta_{(2)} = 0 + F(X) = F(X), \quad Y = \beta$ (3.1-76d)

This checking procedure becomes especially important when any of the boundary conditions are flux conditions.

3.2 Cylindrical Coordinates

In Chapter 2 we encountered a number of problems in cylindrical coordinates in which we assumed that the temperature was independent of θ (axially symmetric) and z. In this section we will examine a process in which the temperature depends on both r and z. Our purpose here is to give only a very brief introduction to the solution of two-dimensional heat conduction problems in cylindrical coordinates. This section should not be attempted unless the material presented in Sec. 2.7 has been studied.

As an example, we will analyze the cylindrical fin or extended heat transfer surface shown in Fig. 3.2.1. In our study of extended heat transfer surfaces in Secs. 2.6, 2.7, and 2.8 we made the realistic assumption that the temperature profile across the fin was essentially flat. In this example we will not impose that restriction, but will instead determine the temperature variation in the radial direction. Our governing equation for this heat conduction process is

$$0 = \left[\frac{1}{r}\frac{\partial}{\partial r}\left(r\frac{\partial T}{\partial r}\right) + \frac{1}{r^2}\left(\frac{\partial^2 T}{\partial \theta^2}\right) + \left(\frac{\partial^2 T}{\partial z^2}\right)\right] \tag{3.2-1}$$

provided the thermal conductivity is constant. In order to simplify our analysis somewhat we will assume that the temperature field is axially symmetric, thus

$$\frac{\partial T}{\partial \theta} = \frac{\partial^2 T}{\partial \theta^2} = 0$$

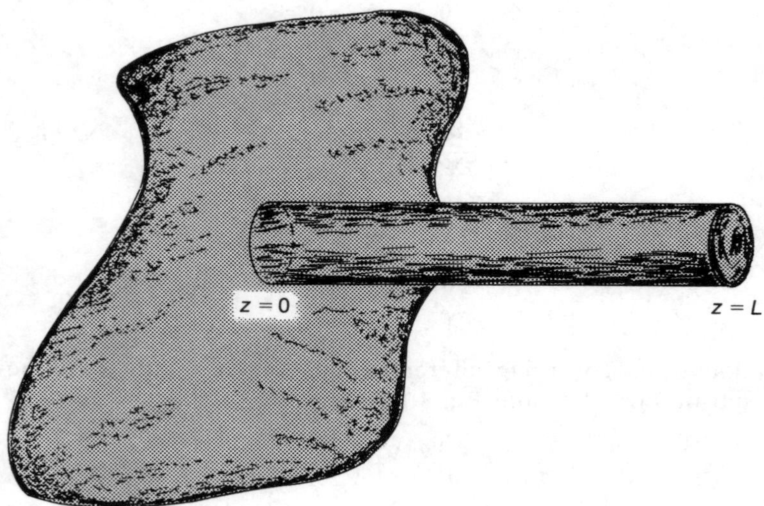

Fig. 3.2.1 A cylindrical spine or extended heat transfer surface.

and Eq. 3.2-1 takes the form

$$0=\left[\frac{1}{r}\frac{\partial}{\partial r}\left(r\frac{\partial T}{\partial r}\right)+\frac{\partial^2 T}{\partial z^2}\right] \tag{3.2-2}$$

We will further simplify our problem by specifying the boundary conditions as

B.C.1 $$T=T_0, \qquad z=0 \tag{3.2-3}$$

B.C.2 $$\frac{\partial T}{\partial z}=0, \qquad z=L \tag{3.2-4}$$

B.C.3 $$T=T_a, \qquad r=r_0 \tag{3.2-5}$$

Here we have indicated that the end of the cylinder at $z=L$ is insulated rather than imposing the flux condition as we did in Sec. 2.7 and we have specified the temperature over the surface rather than specifying the heat flux in terms of a film heat transfer coefficient. The adiabatic or insulating condition at $z=L$ is not unreasonable if $L \gg r_0$, for under those circumstances the temperature of the end of the spine is very nearly equal to the ambient temperature and a negligible amount of energy is lost through the end of the spine. Specifying the surface temperature as being equal to the ambient temperature T_a is not a very reasonable assumption, but it will reduce our algebraic effort considerably, and in this brief introduction we would like to keep things as simple as possible. From a practical point of view the problem we have posed is that of heat conduction in a spine of low thermal conductivity, or more accurately we are examining a case of large Biot number

$$N_{\mathrm{Bi}}=\left(\frac{hr_0}{k}\right)\gg 1$$

From the example in Sec. 3.1 we have learned that our analysis will be simplified (in terms of algebra not concepts) if we express the problem in dimensionless form. In terms of Θ, R, and Z we obtain

$$0=\left[\frac{1}{R}\frac{\partial}{\partial R}\left(R\frac{\partial \Theta}{\partial R}\right)+\left(\frac{\partial^2\Theta}{\partial Z^2}\right)\right] \tag{3.2-6}$$

B.C.1′ $$\Theta=1, \qquad Z=0 \tag{3.2-7}$$

B.C.2′ $$\frac{\partial\Theta}{\partial Z}=0, \qquad Z=(L/r_0) \tag{3.2-8}$$

B.C.3′ $$\Theta=0, \qquad R=1 \tag{3.2-9}$$

where

$$\Theta = (T - T_a)/(T_0 - T_a)$$
$$R = r/r_0$$
$$Z = z/r_0$$

Assuming that the variables can be separated we try for a solution of the form

$$\Theta = \mathcal{R}(R)\mathcal{Z}(Z) \tag{3.2-10}$$

Substituting Eq. 3.2-10 into Eq. 3.2-6 and rearranging gives

$$\frac{1}{\mathcal{R}}\left[\left(\frac{d^2\mathcal{R}}{dR^2}\right) + \frac{1}{R}\left(\frac{d\mathcal{R}}{dR}\right)\right] = -\frac{1}{\mathcal{Z}}\left(\frac{d^2\mathcal{Z}}{dZ^2}\right) \tag{3.2-11}$$

Since the left-hand-side is independent of Z and the right-hand-side is independent of R, both sides must be equal to a constant C. This yields

$$R^2\left(\frac{d^2\mathcal{R}}{dR^2}\right) + R\left(\frac{d\mathcal{R}}{dR}\right) - CR^2\mathcal{R} = 0 \tag{3.2-12a}$$

$$\frac{d^2\mathcal{Z}}{dZ^2} + C\mathcal{Z} = 0 \tag{3.2-12b}$$

As was the case in our study of rectangular coordinates, the constant C can be either positive, negative or zero, thus we write

$$C = \begin{cases} +\lambda^2 \\ 0 \\ -\lambda^2 \end{cases}$$

as the three possibilities of C. If we choose $C = 0$ as a possibility we find

$$\mathcal{Z}(Z) = A + BZ$$

and since $\partial\Theta/\partial Z = 0$ at $Z = L/r_0$ we require that $B = 0$. This leaves us with the trivial result

$$\mathcal{Z}(Z) = A$$

which requires that the temperature Θ be independent of Z. We discard this possibility for the present and go on to consider the case $C = +\lambda^2$. The solution to Eq. 3.2-12b takes the form

$$\mathcal{Z}(Z) = C_1 \cos(\lambda Z) + C_2 \sin(\lambda Z) \tag{3.2-13}$$

which seems like a reasonable function for the Z-dependence of Θ. For $C = +\lambda^2$ Eq. 3.2-12a takes the form

$$R^2\left(\frac{d^2\mathcal{R}}{dR^2}\right) + R\left(\frac{d\mathcal{R}}{dR}\right) - \lambda^2R^2\mathcal{R} = 0 \tag{3.2-14}$$

Going back to Sec. 2.7, we see that this is exactly the same form as Eq. 2.7-11 and its solution is therefore given by

$$\mathcal{R}(R) = C_3I_0(\lambda R) + C_4K_0(\lambda R) \tag{3.2-15}$$

This solution must be bounded for all R between zero and one, and since $K_0(\lambda R) \to \infty$ as $\lambda R \to 0$ (see Fig. 2.7.3) we require that $C_4 = 0$. Our expression for $\Theta(R, Z)$ can now be written as

$$\Theta(R, Z) = I_0(\lambda R)[C_1 \cos(\lambda Z) + C_2 \sin(\lambda Z)] \tag{3.2-16}$$

Here we have incorporated the constant of integration C_3 into the constants C_1 and C_2. Applying B.C.1′ gives

B.C.1′
$$1 = I_0(\lambda R)C_1 \tag{3.2-17}$$

This condition certainly cannot be satisfied, but before we get discouraged we should think back to the example in Sec. 3.1 and try a solution for Θ of the form

$$\Theta(R, Z) = 1 + I_0(\lambda R)[C_1 \cos(\lambda Z) + C_2 \sin(\lambda Z)] \tag{3.2-18}$$

It should be clear that this is also a solution to the differential equation since $\Theta = 1$ obviously satisfies Eq. 3.2-6. Returning now to B.C.1′ we obtain

B.C.1′
$$1 = 1 + I_0(\lambda R) C_1 \tag{3.2-19}$$

thus $C_1 = 0$ and our solution for Θ becomes

$$\Theta(R, Z) = 1 + C_2 I_0(\lambda R) \sin(\lambda Z) \tag{3.2-20}$$

Going on to the second boundary condition we obtain

B.C.2′
$$0 = -C_2 \lambda I_0(\lambda R) \cos(\lambda L / r_0) \tag{3.2-21}$$

This condition could be satisfied by $C_2 = 0$, but that would lead us to a trivial solution. Instead we choose λ to be

$$\lambda_n = \frac{(2n+1)\pi r_0}{2L}, \qquad n = 0, 1, 2, \ldots$$

thus making the right-hand-side of Eq. 3.2-21 equal to zero. We now have an infinite number of solutions for Θ which takes the form

$$\Theta(R, Z) = 1 + C_n I_0(\lambda_n R) \sin(\lambda_n Z), \qquad n = 0, 1, 2, 3, \ldots \tag{3.2-22}$$

where the constant C_2 has been replaced by C_n. Applying our final boundary condition yields

B.C.3′
$$0 = 1 + C_n I_0(\lambda_n) \sin(\lambda_n Z) \tag{3.2-23}$$

We again encounter difficulty since the right-hand-side of Eq. 3.2-23 is a function of Z and the left-hand-side is a constant; however, the orthogonal nature of the sine function will extricate us from this difficulty. Returning to Eq. 3.2-22 we write the general solution for Θ as the sum of all the individual solutions:

$$\Theta(R, Z) = 1 + \sum_{n=0}^{\infty} C_n I_0(\lambda_n R) \sin(\lambda_n Z) \tag{3.2-24}$$

so that the final boundary condition takes the form

B.C.3′
$$-1 = \sum_{n=0}^{\infty} C_n I_0(\lambda_n) \sin(\lambda_n Z) \tag{3.2-25}$$

Multiplying by $\sin(\lambda_m Z)$ and integrating from $Z = 0$ to $Z = L/r_0$ gives

$$-\int_{Z=0}^{Z=L/r_0} \sin(\lambda_m Z)\, dZ = C_m I_0(\lambda_m) \int_{Z=0}^{Z=L/r_0} \sin^2(\lambda_m Z)\, dZ \tag{3.2-26}$$

where we have made use of the fact that

$$\int_{Z=0}^{Z=L/r_0} \sin(\lambda_m Z) \sin(\lambda_n Z)\, dZ = 0, \qquad \text{for } m \neq n$$

Evaluating the integrals in Eq. 3.2-26 gives

$$C_n = -\frac{2r_0}{L\lambda_n I_0(\lambda_n)} \tag{3.2-27}$$

and our final expression for the temperature can be expressed as

$$T = T_0 - (T_0 - T_a) \sum_{n=0}^{\infty} \left[\frac{2r_0}{L\lambda_n I_0(\lambda_n)}\right] I_0(\lambda_n r / r_0) \sin(\lambda_n z / r_0) \tag{3.2-28}$$

Knowledge of the temperature will allow us to calculate the heat flux at any point in the system and thus the overall heat loss from the rod. Note that the function $I_0(\lambda_n)$ increases rapidly with increasing λ_n (see Fig. 2.7.2), thus the series converges rapidly for values of $r/r_0 \ll 1$, but converges slowly for values of $r/r_0 \sim 1$. For the latter condition

$$\frac{I_0(\lambda_n r/r_0)}{I_0(\lambda_n)} \sim 1$$

and the coefficients in the infinite series decrease only because of the increasing value of λ_n. Once again we remark that a digital computer is required to evaluate the terms in Eq. 3.2-28 and time-consuming subroutines must be used to evaluate $I_0(\lambda_n r/r_0)$ and $\sin(\lambda_n z/r_0)$. Because of this the direct numerical solution of Eq. 3.2-6 is an attractive possibility.

Nonconstant temperature on one boundary

In order to further explore the nature of Bessel functions and their use in the solution of heat conduction problems in cylindrical coordinates we will examine a slightly more complicated version of the original problem posed in this section. In this example we will allow the temperature at $Z = 0$ to be a function of r, thus our problem is stated as

$$0 = \left[\frac{1}{r}\frac{\partial}{\partial r}\left(r\frac{\partial T}{\partial r}\right) + \frac{\partial^2 T}{\partial z^2}\right] \tag{3.2-29}$$

B.C.1 $$T = T_0 - (T_0 - T_a)f(r/r_0), \qquad z = 0 \tag{3.2-30}$$

B.C.2 $$\frac{\partial T}{\partial z} = 0, \qquad z = L \tag{3.2-31}$$

B.C.3 $$T = T_a, \qquad r = r_0 \tag{3.2-32}$$

Here $f(r/r_0)$ is a dimensionless function such that $f(0) = 0$ and $f(1) = 1$, thus the temperature at $z = 0$ varies from T_0 at the center of the rod to T_a at the surface. In dimensionless form the problem is stated as

$$0 = \left[\frac{1}{R}\frac{\partial}{\partial R}\left(R\frac{\partial \Theta}{\partial R}\right) + \left(\frac{\partial^2 \Theta}{\partial Z^2}\right)\right] \tag{3.2-33}$$

B.C.1′ $$\Theta = g(R), \qquad Z = 0 \tag{3.2-34}$$

B.C.2′ $$\frac{\partial \Theta}{\partial Z} = 0, \qquad Z = L/r_0 \tag{3.2-35}$$

B.C.3′ $$\Theta = 0, \qquad R = 1 \tag{3.2-36}$$

Here we have replaced $1 - f(r/r_0)$ by $g(R)$. Once again we assume that a separable solution exists, i.e., $\Theta(R, Z) = \mathcal{R}(R)\mathcal{Z}(Z)$, and Eq. 3.2-33 can be arranged in the form

$$\frac{1}{\mathcal{R}}\left[\left(\frac{d^2\mathcal{R}}{dR^2}\right) + \frac{1}{R}\left(\frac{d\mathcal{R}}{dR}\right)\right] = -\frac{1}{\mathcal{Z}}\left(\frac{d^2\mathcal{Z}}{dZ^2}\right) = C \tag{3.2-37}$$

Here the constant C may again take on the values

$$C = \begin{cases} +\lambda^2 \\ 0 \\ -\lambda^2 \end{cases}$$

On the basis of the discussion given in the previous example we rule out the case $C = 0$ and go on to the case $C = +\lambda^2$. From our previous example we know this leads to a solution of the form

$$\Theta(R, Z) = I_0(\lambda R)[C_1 \cos(\lambda Z) + C_2 \sin(\lambda Z)] \tag{3.2-38}$$

Imposing the first boundary condition we obtain

B.C.1′ $$g(R) = I_0(\lambda R)C_1 \tag{3.2-39}$$

Unless $g(R)$ happens to be proportional to $I_0(\lambda R)$, we cannot satisfy this boundary condition. The reason for this difficulty is that the modified Bessel function $I_0(\lambda R)$ is *not* an orthogonal function, thus we cannot construct a function such as $g(R)$ in terms of an infinite series of the type $C_1 I_0(\lambda_1 R) + C_2 I_0(\lambda_2 R) + \cdots$. We must therefore find another solution to the differential equation which can be made to satisfy the boundary conditions. It should be fairly obvious that the next possibility to explore is the case $C = -\lambda^2$. This leads to

$$R^2\left(\frac{d^2\mathcal{R}}{dR^2}\right) + R\left(\frac{d\mathcal{R}}{dR}\right) + \lambda^2 R^2 \mathcal{R} = 0 \tag{3.2-40}$$

$$\frac{d^2\mathcal{Z}}{dZ^2} - \lambda^2 \mathcal{Z} = 0 \tag{3.2-41}$$

Eq. 3.2-41 is easily solved to obtain $\mathcal{Z}(Z) = C_1 e^{\lambda z} + C_2 e^{-\lambda z}$ which may be rearranged into the form

$$\mathcal{Z}(Z) = C_1 \cosh(\lambda Z) + C_2 \sinh(\lambda Z) \tag{3.2-42}$$

Turning our attention to Eq. 3.2-40 we note that it is quite similar to Eq. 3.2-14 and Eq. 2.7-11 and we should be able to obtain a solution by means of the Frobenius method. Eq. 3.2-40 is known as *Bessel's equation of order zero with parameter* λ and it has a solution of the form†

$$\mathcal{R}(R) = \sum_{n=0}^{\infty} \frac{(-1)^n (\lambda R)^{2n}}{2^{2n}(n!)^2}$$
$$= J_0(\lambda R) \tag{3.2-43}$$

A list of solutions to Bessel's equation are given in Table 3.2-1 and values of the various Bessel functions are tabulated in Appendix B. A second solution can be obtained from $J_0(\lambda R)$ by the procedure outlined in Sec. 2.7. The result is denoted by $Y_0(\lambda R)$ and is given by

$$Y_0(\lambda R) = J_0(\lambda R) \int \frac{d(\lambda R)}{\lambda R J_0^2(\lambda R)} \tag{3.2-44}$$

The general solution for $\mathcal{R}(R)$ is therefore given by

$$\mathcal{R}(R) = C_3 J_0(\lambda R) + C_4 Y_0(\lambda R) \tag{3.2-45}$$

The functions $J_0(\lambda R)$ and $Y_0(\lambda R)$ are plotted in Figs. 3.2.2 and 3.2.3 and there we see that $Y_0(\lambda R) \to -\infty$ as $\lambda R \to 0$. Thus we require that $C_4 = 0$ in order that the temperature be bounded in the region $0 \leq R \leq 1$, and our solution for Θ takes the form

$$\Theta(R, Z) = J_0(\lambda R)[C_1 \cosh(\lambda Z) + C_2 \sinh(\lambda Z)] \tag{3.2-46}$$

Beginning with the first boundary condition given by Eq. 3.2-34 we obtain

B.C.1′
$$g(R) = C_1 J_0(\lambda R) \tag{3.2-47}$$

We will ignore for the present what appears to be a difficulty in satisfying B.C.1′ and go on to the second boundary condition

B.C.2′
$$0 = J_0(\lambda R)[C_1 \lambda \sinh(\lambda L/r_0) + C_2 \lambda \cosh(\lambda L/r_0)] \tag{3.2-48}$$

This condition can be satisfied by requiring C_1 and C_2 to be related by the expression

$$C_2 = -C_1 \tanh(\lambda L/r_0) \tag{3.2-49}$$

Continuing to the third boundary condition we find

B.C.3′
$$0 = J_0(\lambda)[C_1 \cosh(\lambda Z) + C_2 \sinh(\lambda Z)] \tag{3.2-50}$$

†Reference 1, Chapter 9.

Table 3.2-1 Derivatives of Bessel Functions

$$\frac{d}{dx}[x^n J_n(x)] = x^n J_{n-1}(x) \qquad (a)$$

$$\frac{d}{dx}[x^{-n} J_n(x)] = -x^{-n} J_{n+1}(x) \qquad (b)$$

$$\frac{d}{dx}[x^n I_n(x)] = x^n I_{n-1}(x) \qquad (c)$$

$$\frac{d}{dx}[x^{-n} I_n(x)] = x^{-n} I_{n+1}(x) \qquad (d)$$

$$\frac{d}{dx}[x^n K_n(x)] = -x^n K_{n-1}(x) \qquad (e)$$

$$\frac{d}{dx}[x^{-n} K_n(x)] = -x^{-n} K_{n+1}(x) \qquad (f)$$

From Eqs. (a) through (e) we can obtain

$$\frac{d}{dx}[J_n(x)] = J_{n-1}(x) - \frac{n}{x} J_n(x) \qquad (g)$$

$$\frac{d}{dx}[I_n(x)] = I_{n-1}(x) - \frac{n}{x} I_n(x) \qquad (h)$$

$$\frac{d}{dx}[K_n(x)] = -K_{n-1}(x) - \frac{n}{x} K_n(x) \qquad (i)$$

$$\frac{d}{dx}[Y_n(x)] = Y_{n-1}(x) - \frac{n}{x} Y_n(x) \qquad (j)$$

Examination of particular power series solutions indicates that

$$\left.\begin{aligned} J_{-n}(x) &= (-1)^n J_n(x) \\ I_{-n}(x) &= I_n(x) \\ K_{-n}(x) &= K_n(x) \\ Y_{-n}(x) &= (-1)^n Y_n(x) \end{aligned}\right\} \quad n = \text{integer} \qquad (k)$$

Integration by parts or direct use of the expressions for derivatives can be used to obtain integral formulas, three of which are

$$\int x J_n^2(x)\, dx = \frac{x^2}{2}[J_n^2(x) - J_{n-1}(x) J_{n+1}(x)] \qquad (l)$$

$$\int x J_0(x)\, dx = x J_1(x) \qquad (m)$$

$$\int J_1(x)\, dx = -J_0(x) \qquad (n)$$

From the graph of $J_0(\lambda R)$ in Fig. 3.2.2 we see that $J_0(\lambda)$ can indeed take on zero values for certain values of λ. These special values of λ are called the *eigenvalues*, and the first few are given as the solution of

$$J_0(\lambda) = 0 \qquad (3.2\text{-}51)$$

and are

$$\lambda_1 = 2.4048, \qquad \lambda_2 = 5.5201, \qquad \lambda_3 = 8.6537$$

We designate the eigenvalues as λ_n and express our solution for Θ as

$$\Theta(R, Z) = C_n J_0(\lambda_n R)[\cosh(\lambda_n Z) - \tanh(\lambda_n L/r_0)\sinh(\lambda_n Z)], \qquad n = 1, 2, 3, \ldots \qquad (3.2\text{-}52)$$

Now it can be shown that $J_0(\lambda_n R)$ is an orthogonal function with respect to the weighting factor R. This means that

$$\int_{R=0}^{R=1} R J_0(\lambda_n R) J_0(\lambda_m R)\, dR = 0, \qquad m \neq n \qquad (3.2\text{-}53)$$

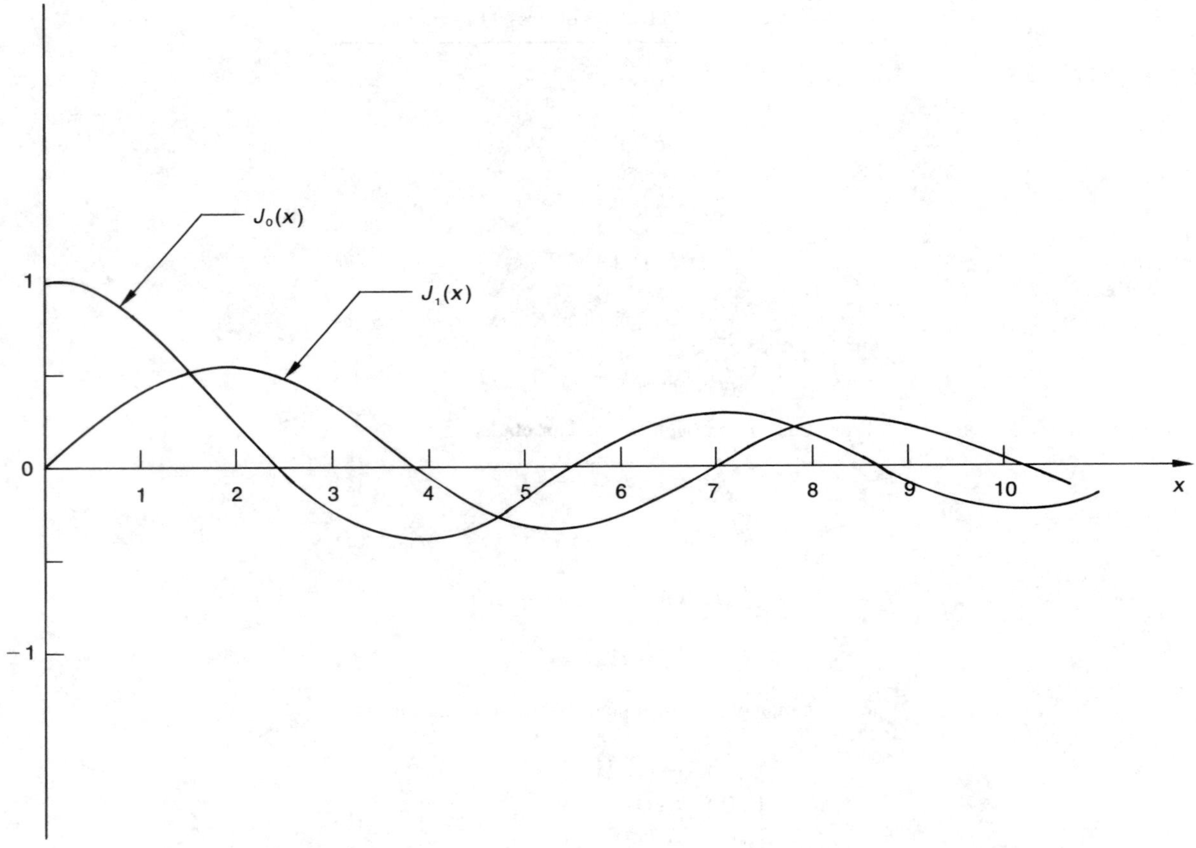

Fig. 3.2.2 Zero- and first-order Bessel functions of the first kind.

when the eigenvalues are given by Eq. 3.2-51. This means we can construct a function such as $g(R)$ with an infinite series of Bessel functions. Expressing Θ as the sum of all possible solutions yields

$$\Theta(R, Z) = \sum_{n=1}^{\infty} C_n J_0(\lambda_n R)[\cosh(\lambda_n Z) - \tanh(\lambda_n L/r_0)\sinh(\lambda_n Z)] \tag{3.2-54}$$

Returning now to B.C.1′ we write Eq. 3.2-47 as

B.C.1′
$$g(R) = \sum_{n=1}^{\infty} C_n J_0(\lambda_n R) \tag{3.2-55}$$

If we multiply by $RJ_0(\lambda_m R)$, integrate between $R = 0$ and $R = 1$, and make use of Eq. 3.2-53 we obtain

$$\int_{R=0}^{R=1} Rg(R)J_0(\lambda_m R)\, dR = C_m \int_{R=0}^{R=1} RJ_0^2(\lambda_m R)\, dR \tag{3.2-56}$$

Evaluating the integral on the right-hand-side would be a tedious job, involving the square of the power series given in Eq. 3.2-43; however, it has been done for us and the result is given by

$$\int_{R=0}^{R=1} RJ_0^2(\lambda_m R)\, dR = \left[\frac{R^2}{2}(J_0^2(\lambda_m R) + J_1^2(\lambda_m R))\right]_{R=0}^{R=1} \tag{3.2-57}$$

Other operations involving derivatives and integrals of Bessel functions are given in Table 3.2-1. The Bessel function of the first kind of order one, $J_1(\lambda R)$, and of the second kind of order one, $Y_1(\lambda R)$, are

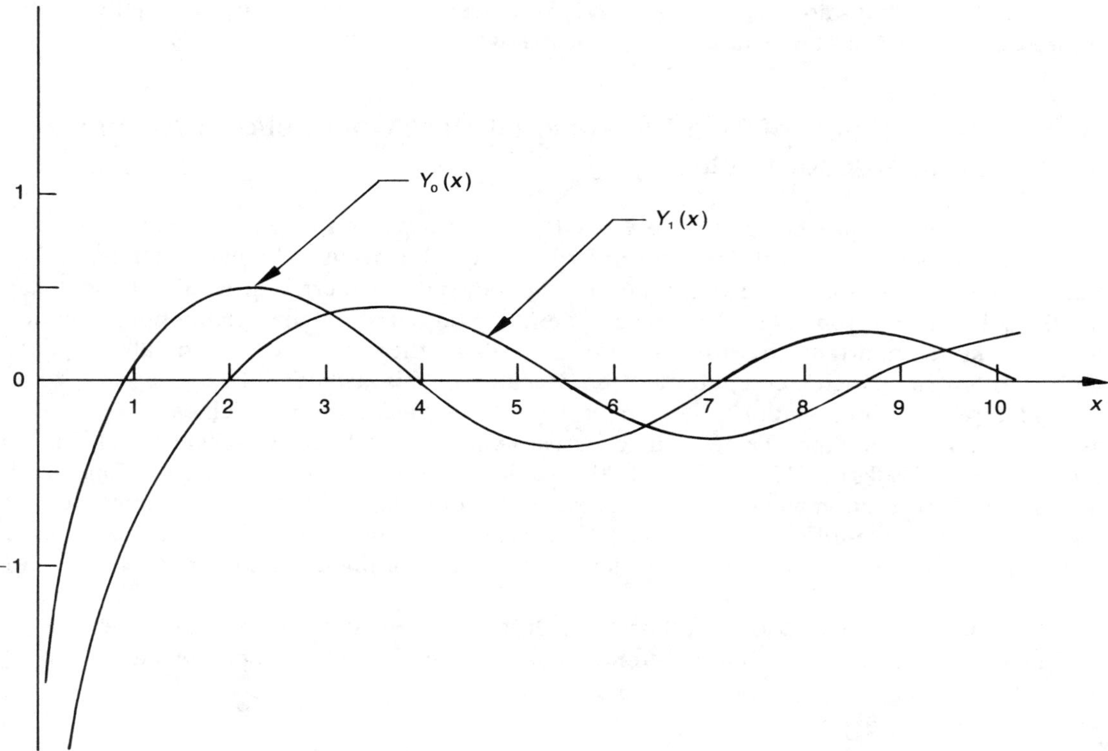

Fig. 3.2.3 Zero- and first-order Bessel functions of the second kind.

shown in Figs. 3.2.2 and 3.2.3. Evaluating the limits given in Eq. 3.2-57 yields

$$\int_{R=0}^{R=1} RJ_0^2(\lambda_m R)\, dR = [\tfrac{1}{2}(J_0^2(\lambda_m) + J_1^2(\lambda_m))] \tag{3.2-58}$$

However, $J_0(\lambda_m) = 0$ by Eq. 3.2-51, i.e., the eigenvalues are those which satisfy Eq. 3.2-51, so our expression reduces to

$$\int_{R=0}^{R=1} RJ_0^2(\lambda_m R)\, dR = \tfrac{1}{2}J_1^2(\lambda_m) \tag{3.2-59}$$

Returning to Eq. 3.2-56 we see that the constants C_n can be expressed as

$$C_n = \frac{2\displaystyle\int_{R=0}^{R=1} Rg(R)J_0(\lambda_m R)\, dR}{J_1^2(\lambda_m)} \tag{3.2-60}$$

and the temperature field is given by

$$T = T_a + (T_0 - T_a)\sum_{n=1}^{\infty} C_n J_0(\lambda_n R)[\cosh(\lambda_n Z) - \tanh(\lambda_n L/r_0)\sinh(\lambda_n Z)] \tag{3.2-61}$$

It should be clear at this point that as soon as one learns the rules and regulations for manipulating Bessel functions (just as the rules and regulations for manipulating sine and cosine functions have been learned), analytic solutions for heat conduction problems in cylindrical coordinates can be generated quite easily. But what about the problem of getting *numbers* for the temperature field or values for the heat flux or rate of heat transfer at an interface? Certainly evaluating the coefficients in Eq. 3.2-60 is no trivial task, nor is evaluation of the series in Eq. 3.2-61 easily accomplished. Tabulated values for the Bessel functions and the hyperbolic functions are readily available [2, 3]; however, their use can become quite tedious if the series representation for the temperature converges slowly.

3.3 Numerical Solution of Two-Dimensional Heat Conduction Problems in Rectangular Coordinates

We have seen in the preceding two sections that solutions for two-dimensional heat conduction problems can be generated in a fairly straightforward manner. One needs to know something of the nature of sine and cosine functions and of Bessel functions, but beyond that there is little more to be understood, provided the solutions are separable. The algebraic effort required to obtain a solution is sometimes a bit wearisome, but more important, the effort required to evaluate the infinite series generally requires that a program be written and a digital computer utilized. Because of this last step it becomes very attractive to use a finite-difference approximation of the governing differential equation which can be solved directly with the aid of a digital computer. Once again, our treatment here will be the briefest possible introduction to the subject. Entire books [4–7] are devoted to this subject and much research has been done in this area, and the purpose of this section will be to show that an enormous range of complex problems can be solved with relative ease by finite-difference approximation. We will restrict our study primarily to rectangular coordinates and discuss only two of the many methods available for obtaining solutions to finite-difference equations.

As an example of the numerical solution of a differential equation we will consider the problem illustrated in Fig. 3.1.2. The governing differential equation and boundary conditions are

$$\frac{\partial^2 T}{\partial x^2}+\frac{\partial^2 T}{\partial y^2}=0 \tag{3.3-1}$$

B.C.1 $$T=T_0, \quad x=0 \tag{3.3-2}$$

B.C.2 $$T=T_0, \quad x=b \tag{3.3-3}$$

B.C.3 $$T=T_0, \quad y=0 \tag{3.3-4}$$

B.C.4 $$T=f(x), \quad y=L \tag{3.3-5}$$

If we are going to solve Eq. 3.3-1 on a digital computer we had better put it in dimensionless form, since computers are not readily capable of carrying units. We first note that the function $f(x)$ must have the units of temperature. Furthermore, there must be some maximum or minimum value for $f(x)$ so that we could express B.C.4 as

B.C.4 $$T=T_1 g(x) \tag{3.3-6}$$

where $g(x)$ is now a dimensionless function of x. Defining the dimensionless variables as

$$\Theta=(T-T_0)/(T_1-T_0)$$
$$X=x/b$$
$$Y=y/b$$

allows us to express our problem as

$$\frac{\partial^2 \Theta}{\partial X^2}+\frac{\partial^2 \Theta}{\partial Y^2}=0 \tag{3.3-7}$$

B.C.1′ $$\Theta=0, \quad X=0 \tag{3.3-8}$$

B.C.2′ $$\Theta=0, \quad X=1 \tag{3.3-9}$$

B.C.3′ $$\Theta=0, \quad Y=0 \tag{3.3-10}$$

B.C.4′ $$\Theta=G(X), \quad Y=(L/b) \tag{3.3-11}$$

where the dimensionless function $G(X)$ is given by

$$G(X)=(T_1 g(x)-T_0)/(T_1-T_0) \tag{3.3-12}$$

The basic principle of the numerical solution of differential equations is to replace the differential equation for the continuous temperature field Θ with a finite-difference expression for the discrete temperature variable $\Theta_{i,j}$. Here the subscripts i, j have nothing to do with the index notation used in denoting vectors and tensors. These indices are simply used to denote the discrete values of Θ so that $i = 1, 2, 3, \ldots, N$ and $j = 1, 2, 3, \ldots, M$. In what follows we wish to develop expressions for the derivatives in Eq. 3.3-7 in terms of the discrete values of $\Theta_{i,j}$. For example, we will show that a reasonable approximation for $\partial^2\Theta/\partial X^2$ at the point $X = i\,\Delta X$ and $Y = j\,\Delta Y$ is given by

$$\left(\frac{\partial^2\Theta}{\partial X^2}\right)_{i,j} \sim \frac{\Theta_{i+1,j} - 2\Theta_{i,j} + \Theta_{i-1,j}}{\Delta X^2} \tag{3.3-13}$$

In order to develop a finite-difference approximation to the derivative of a function we first expand the function in a Taylor series about the point X to obtain an expression for the function at the point $X + \Delta L$.

$$\Theta(X + \Delta L, Y) = \Theta(X, Y) + \frac{\Delta L}{1!}\left(\frac{\partial\Theta}{\partial X}\right)_{X,Y} + \frac{\Delta L^2}{2!}\left(\frac{\partial^2\Theta}{\partial X^2}\right)_{X,Y} + \frac{\Delta L^3}{3!}\left(\frac{\partial^3\Theta}{\partial X^3}\right)_{X,Y} + \cdots \tag{3.3-14}$$

Here the subscript X, Y on the derivatives indicate that these derivatives are evaluated at the point X, Y. If we let ΔL take on the values $+\Delta X$ and $-\Delta X$ we obtain two expressions

$$\Theta(X + \Delta X) = \Theta(X) + \Delta X\left(\frac{\partial\Theta}{\partial X}\right)_X + \frac{\Delta X^2}{2!}\left(\frac{\partial^2\Theta}{\partial X^2}\right)_X + \frac{\Delta X^3}{3!}\left(\frac{\partial^3\Theta}{\partial X^3}\right)_X + \cdots \tag{3.3-15}$$

$$\Theta(X - \Delta X) = \Theta(X) - \Delta X\left(\frac{\partial\Theta}{\partial X}\right)_X + \frac{\Delta X^2}{2!}\left(\frac{\partial^2\Theta}{\partial X^2}\right)_X - \frac{\Delta X^3}{3!}\left(\frac{\partial^2\Theta}{\partial X^3}\right)_X + \cdots \tag{3.3-16}$$

Here we have dropped the functional dependence on Y since it is held constant. If we add Eqs. 3.3-15 and 3.3-16 we see that all the odd order derivatives will be eliminated. The result may be rearranged to obtain

$$\left(\frac{\partial^2\Theta}{\partial X^2}\right)_X = \frac{\Theta(X + \Delta X) - 2\Theta(X) + \Theta(X - \Delta X)}{\Delta X^2} - \frac{2\Delta X^2}{4!}\left(\frac{\partial^4\Theta}{\partial X^4}\right)_X + \text{higher order terms} \tag{3.3-17}$$

From Eq. 3.3-17 we can see that if ΔX and ΔY are made sufficiently small, the following expressions will be satisfactory approximations for the second derivatives:

$$\left(\frac{\partial^2\Theta}{\partial X^2}\right)_{X,Y} = \frac{\Theta(X + \Delta X, Y) - 2\Theta(X, Y) + \Theta(X - \Delta X, Y)}{\Delta X^2} \tag{3.3-18}$$

$$\left(\frac{\partial^2\Theta}{\partial Y^2}\right)_{X,Y} = \frac{\Theta(X, Y + \Delta Y) - 2\Theta(X, Y) + \Theta(X, Y - \Delta Y)}{\Delta Y^2} \tag{3.3-19}$$

These expressions, when substituted into Eq. 3.3-7, will yield an algebraic expression for the discrete values of $\Theta(X, Y)$ at each point in the network illustrated in Fig. 3.3.1. Using the nomenclature

$$X_i = i\,\Delta X, \qquad Y_j = j\,\Delta Y, \qquad \Theta_{i,j} = \Theta(X_i, Y_j)$$

the expressions for the derivatives take the form

$$\left(\frac{\partial^2\Theta}{\partial X^2}\right)_{i,j} = \frac{\Theta_{i+1,j} - 2\Theta_{i,j} + \Theta_{i-1,j}}{\Delta X^2} \tag{3.3-20}$$

$$\left(\frac{\partial^2\Theta}{\partial Y^2}\right)_{i,j} = \frac{\Theta_{i,j+1} - 2\Theta_{i,j} + \Theta_{i,j-1}}{\Delta Y^2} \tag{3.3-21}$$

and our governing differential equation becomes

$$[\Theta_{i+1,j} - 2\Theta_{i,j} + \Theta_{i-1,j}] + \left(\frac{\Delta X}{\Delta Y}\right)^2 [\Theta_{i,j+1} - 2\Theta_{i,j} + \Theta_{i,j-1}] = 0, \qquad 1 \leqslant i \leqslant N-1, \qquad 1 \leqslant j \leqslant M-1 \tag{3.3-22}$$

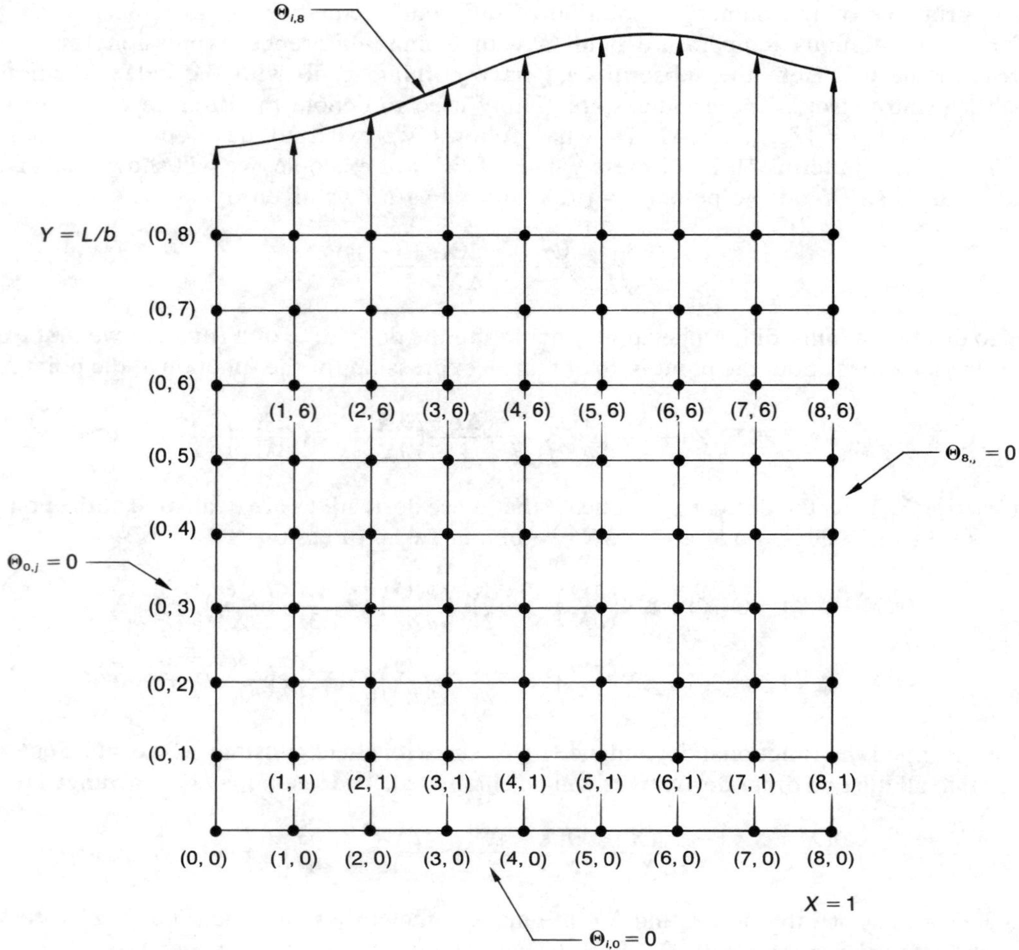

Fig. 3.3.1 Finite-difference network for two-dimensional heat conduction.

The discrete form of the boundary conditions may be expressed as

B.C.1″ $\Theta_{0,j} = 0$

B.C.2″ $\Theta_{N,j} = 0$

B.C.3″ $\Theta_{i,0} = 0$

B.C.4″ $\Theta_{i,M} = G(X_i)$

The governing differential equation has been replaced by $(N-2)(M-2)$ algebraic equations which must be solved subject to the constraints imposed by B.C.1″ through B.C.4″. We will discuss two ways of solving these equations. The first method, known as the *relaxation method*, was originally developed [8] before the use of high-speed digital computers and is primarily a hand-calculation method. Nevertheless it will be a useful method to discuss.

Relaxation method

We begin this method by assuming values for $\Theta_{i,j}$ at all the interior points in the grid work shown in Fig. 3.3.1. We designate these values by $\tilde{\Theta}_{i,j}^{(1)}$, the tilde indicating that the value is an *assumed* one and the superscript (1) indicating that it is the *first* assumed value. The governing finite-difference equation, Eq.

3.3-22, can be put in the form

$$\Theta_{i,j} = \frac{1}{2\left[1+\left(\frac{\Delta X}{\Delta Y}\right)^2\right]}\left\{\Theta_{i+1,j} + \Theta_{i-1,j} + \left(\frac{\Delta X}{\Delta Y}\right)^2 \Theta_{i,j+1} + \left(\frac{\Delta X}{\Delta Y}\right)^2 \Theta_{i,j-1}\right\} \tag{3.3-23}$$

which expresses the central or nodal value $\Theta_{i,j}$ in terms of the values at the four nearest grid points as illustrated in Fig. 3.3.2. If we have a converged solution to the finite-difference equation the nodal point value will be equal to the expression on the right-hand-side of Eq. 3.3-23. Consider now the assumed values $\tilde{\Theta}^{(1)}_{i,j}$. If these are substituted into the right-hand-side of Eq. 3.3-23 we can calculate the nodal value in terms of the *assumed* values. We will designate this value by $\Theta^{(1)}_{i,j}$, thus

$$\Theta^{(1)}_{i,j} = \frac{1}{2\left[1+\left(\frac{\Delta X}{\Delta Y}\right)^2\right]}\left\{\tilde{\Theta}^{(1)}_{i+1,j} + \tilde{\Theta}^{(1)}_{i-1,j} + \left(\frac{\Delta X}{\Delta Y}\right)^2 \tilde{\Theta}^{(1)}_{i,j+1} + \left(\frac{\Delta X}{\Delta Y}\right)^2 \tilde{\Theta}^{(1)}_{i,j-1}\right\} \tag{3.3-24}$$

In general this *calculated* value $\Theta^{(1)}_{i,j}$ will be different from the *assumed* value $\tilde{\Theta}^{(1)}_{i,j}$, and the magnitude of the difference is a measure of the extent to which the assumed values differ from the converged solution to the finite-difference equation. We can use Eq. 3.3-24 to calculate an entirely new $\Theta_{i,j}$ field, and these new values could in turn be used to recalculate the $\Theta_{i,j}$ field, etc. What is usually done is to use $\Theta^{(1)}_{i,j}$ and $\tilde{\Theta}^{(1)}_{i,j}$ to determine a *new assumed* value given by

$$\tilde{\Theta}^{(2)}_{i,j} = \tilde{\Theta}^{(1)}_{i,j} + \omega(\Theta^{(1)}_{i,j} - \tilde{\Theta}^{(1)}_{i,j}) \tag{3.3-25}$$

where ω is often called the *relaxation parameter.* If $\omega = 1$ the new assumed value is just the calculated value, while if $\omega = 0$ the new assumed value is just equal to the previous assumed value, and the net result of the calculation would leave the $\Theta_{i,j}$ field unchanged. The difference between the calculated value and the assumed value $\Theta^{(1)}_{i,j} - \tilde{\Theta}^{(1)}_{i,j}$ is termed the *residual* and in general the residual decreases with successive trial calculations. After the sum of the residuals reaches an arbitrarily small value we consider the process to have converged and the calculated value of $\Theta^{(k)}_{i,j}$ is taken to be the solution of the finite-difference equation.

The general iteration process may be specified as follows:

$$\Theta^{(k)}_{i,j} = \frac{1}{2\left[1+\left(\frac{\Delta X}{\Delta Y}\right)^2\right]}\left\{\tilde{\Theta}^{(k)}_{i+1,j} + \tilde{\Theta}^{(k)}_{i-1,j} + \left(\frac{\Delta X}{\Delta Y}\right)^2 [\tilde{\Theta}^{(k)}_{i,j+1} + \tilde{\Theta}^{(k)}_{i,j-1}]\right\} \tag{3.3-26}$$

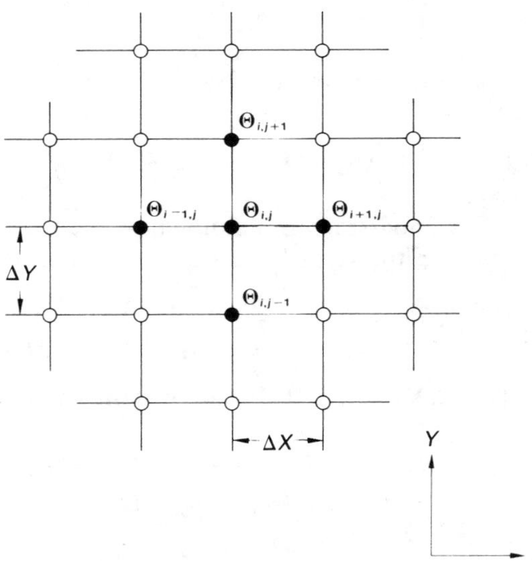

Fig. 3.3.2 Finite-difference grid network.

$$\tilde{\Theta}_{i,j}^{(k+1)} = \tilde{\Theta}_{i,j}^{(k)} + \omega[\Theta_{i,j}^{(k)} - \tilde{\Theta}_{i,j}^{(k)}] \tag{3.3-27}$$

If $0 < \omega \leq 1$ this process is called *relaxation*, while if $1 < \omega < 2$ the process is referred to as *over relaxation*. The larger the value of ω the faster the process usually converges, although in some cases the iterative scheme becomes unstable if $\omega > 1$. In carrying out the iteration procedure suggested by Eqs. 3.3-26 and 3.3-27 we must remember that the boundary conditions remain unchanged and are specified by

B.C.1″ $\Theta_{0,j}^{(k)} = 0$

B.C.2″ $\Theta_{n,j}^{(k)} = 0$

B.C.3″ $\Theta_{i,0}^{(k)} = 0$

B.C.4″ $\Theta_{i,M}^{(k)} = G(X_i)$

The relaxation method is surely the simplest method of solving a partial differential equation. The programming of a digital computer to carry out this type of computation is also relatively simple, and the outline of a program is given below.

Computer program for relaxation method

1. Specify grid size (M and N), and parameter (L/b), and the function $G(X)$.
2. Calculate the boundary values of $\Theta_{i,j}$, i.e., set $\Theta_{i,j} = 0$ along the three boundaries and use $G(X_i)$ to calculate $\Theta_{i,j}$ along the fourth boundary.
3. Generate the first set of assumed values $\tilde{\Theta}_{i,j}^{(1)}$. Setting them all equal to zero would suffice for this problem, but obviously a little thought will lead to a better first guess.
4. Use Eq. 3.3-26 at every interior point of the grid to calculate a new value of $\Theta_{i,j}$. This can be done by working row by row or column by column across the grid.
5. Use Eq. 3.3-27 to determine the new assumed values of $\Theta_{i,j}$.
6. Compare the sum of the absolute value of the residuals with some specified tolerance. If this sum is greater than the tolerance return to #4. If the sum is less than the tolerance go to #7.
7. Output results on paper or tape.

The relaxation method was originally developed for hand calculation, and the procedure outlined here is the one that one would naturally adapt for machine calculation. High-speed digital computers are well suited for the task of matrix inversion and the method of line-by-line matrix inversion is a more efficient method of solving finite-difference equations.

Matrix inversion method

In this method we once again assume that an assumed $\Theta_{i,j}$ field is available and we rearrange Eq. 3.3-22 to take the form

$$\Theta_{i-1,j} - 2\left[1 + \left(\frac{\Delta X}{\Delta Y}\right)^2\right]\Theta_{i,j} + \Theta_{i+1,j} = -\left(\frac{\Delta X}{\Delta Y}\right)^2[\tilde{\Theta}_{i,j+1} + \tilde{\Theta}_{i,j-1}] \tag{3.3-28}$$

Here the three temperatures on the left-hand-side are unknown, while the right-hand-side of Eq. 3.3-28 is considered to be known. If we designate the right-hand-side of Eq. 3.3-28 as $\tilde{D}_{i,j}$ we write

$$\Theta_{i-1,j} + B\Theta_{i,j} + \Theta_{i+1,j} = \tilde{D}_{i,j}, \qquad \begin{array}{l} i = 1, 2, 3, \ldots, N-1 \\ j = 1, 2, 3, \ldots, M-1 \end{array} \tag{3.3-29}$$

where B is a constant equal to $-2[1 + (\Delta X/\Delta Y)^2]$. If, for a constant value of j, we write Eq. 3.3-29 for all values of i we get

$$\begin{aligned} B\Theta_{1,j} + \Theta_{2,j} &= \tilde{D}_{1,j} - \Theta_{0,j} \\ \Theta_{1,j} + B\Theta_{2,j} + \Theta_{3,j} &= \tilde{D}_{2,j} \\ \Theta_{2,j} + B\Theta_{3,j} + \Theta_{4,j} &= \tilde{D}_{3,j} \\ \Theta_{N-3,j} + B\Theta_{N-2,j} + \Theta_{N-1,j} &= \tilde{D}_{N-2,j} \\ \Theta_{N-2,j} + B\Theta_{N-1,j} &= \tilde{D}_{N-1,j} - \Theta_{N,j} \end{aligned} \tag{3.3-30}$$

Here we have taken $\Theta_{0,j}$ and $\Theta_{N,j}$ over to the right-hand-side of the equation since they are known values. In matrix notation, Eq. 3.3-30 can be written as

$$\begin{bmatrix} B & 1 & & & & & \\ 1 & B & 1 & & & & \\ & 1 & B & 1 & & & \\ & & & & & & \\ & & & 1 & B & 1 & \\ & & & & 1 & B & 1 \\ & & & & & 1 & B \end{bmatrix} \begin{bmatrix} \Theta_{1,j} \\ \Theta_{2,j} \\ \\ \\ \\ \Theta_{N-2,j} \\ \Theta_{N-1,j} \end{bmatrix} = \begin{bmatrix} \tilde{D}_{1,j} - \Theta_{0,j} \\ \tilde{D}_{2,j} \\ \\ \\ \\ \tilde{D}_{N-2,j} \\ \tilde{D}_{N-1,j} - \Theta_{N-1,j} \end{bmatrix} \tag{3.3-31}$$

or in more compact form

$$[B]_j[\Theta]_j = [\tilde{D}]_j, \qquad j = 1, 2, \ldots, M-1 \tag{3.3-32}$$

Here $[B]_j$ represents a known tri-diagonal matrix, $[\Theta]_j$ represents an unknown column vector, and $[\tilde{D}]_j$ represents a known column vector. Since $[B]_j$ is known we can compute the inverse $[B]_j^{-1}$ and Eq. 3.3-32 can be solved to yield the column vector $[\Theta]_j$.

$$[\Theta]_j = [B]_j^{-1}[\tilde{D}]_j, \qquad j = 1, 2, \ldots, M-1 \tag{3.3-33}$$

This type of calculation provides us with the calculated values $\Theta_{i,j}^{(k)}$ for $i = 1, 2, \ldots, N-1$ for any given value of j. If this procedure is carried out for each value of j (i.e., line-by-line matrix inversion) we can calculate the entire field

$$\Theta_{i,j}^{(k)}, \qquad \text{for} \quad i = 1, 2, \ldots, N-1$$
$$j = 1, 2, \ldots, M-1$$

Once this is done a new assumed field is generated by the expression (Eq. 3.3-27)

$$\tilde{\Theta}_{i,j}^{(k+1)} = \tilde{\Theta}_{i,j}^{(k)} + \omega[\Theta_{i,j}^{(k)} - \tilde{\Theta}_{i,j}^{(k)}]$$

The elements of $[\tilde{D}]_j$ can now be recalculated and the entire $\Theta_{i,j}$ field can be recalculated by Eq. 3.3-33. Once the sum of the absolute values of the residuals decreases to some predetermined tolerance the iteration process is terminated and the results are printed. In general the line-by-line matrix inversion method requires more sophisticated programming, but convergence is usually more rapid and this method, or variations of it, is the standard method for solving problems of this type. Very often matrix inversion subroutines are available as part of the normal computer system, and the programming for this method is fairly straightforward. The individual steps in a computer program for line-by-line matrix inversion are essentially identical to those listed for the relaxation method.

Flux boundary conditions

As was demonstrated in Chapter 2, boundary conditions are based on the assumption that the temperature and the heat flux are continuous functions at phase interfaces. The simplest type of boundary condition occurs when the temperature is specified as it is in the example we have been considering in this section. To illustrate how flux conditions are treated in the solution of finite-difference equations we will alter the problem illustrated in Fig. 3.1.2 and instead of specifying the temperature at $y = L$ we will specify the flux, and rewrite the governing differential equation and boundary conditions (see Eqs. 3.3-7 through 3.3-11) as

$$\frac{\partial^2\Theta}{\partial X^2} + \frac{\partial^2\Theta}{\partial Y^2} = 0 \tag{3.3-34}$$

B.C.1 $$\Theta = 0, \qquad X = 0 \tag{3.3-35}$$

B.C.2 $$\Theta = 0, \qquad X = 1 \tag{3.3-36}$$

B.C.3 $$\Theta = 0, \qquad Y = 0 \tag{3.3-37}$$

B.C.4 $$\frac{\partial\Theta}{\partial Y} = \mathscr{G}(X), \qquad Y = (L/b) \tag{3.3-38}$$

As in the previous example the finite-difference form of Eq. 3.3-34 can be arranged in a form suitable for solution by either the relaxation method or the line-by-line matrix inversion method. The discrete form of the boundary conditions can be expressed as

B.C.1′ $$\Theta_{0,j} = 0 \tag{3.3-39}$$

B.C.2′ $$\Theta_{N,j} = 0 \tag{3.3-40}$$

B.C.3′ $$\Theta_{i,0} = 0 \tag{3.3-41}$$

B.C.4′ $$\Theta_{i,M} = \Theta_{i,M-1} + \Delta Y \mathscr{G}(X_i) \tag{3.3-42}$$

In going from B.C.4 to B.C.4′ we have approximated the first derivative by

$$\left(\frac{\partial \Theta}{\partial Y}\right)_{i,j+1/2} = \frac{\Theta_{i,j+1} - \Theta_j}{\Delta Y} \tag{3.3-43}$$

thus the derivative at the boundary is expressed in terms of the finite-difference approximation for the derivative at a point $\frac{1}{2}\Delta Y$ inside the boundary. The procedure in this example differs from that outlined for the previous example only to the extent that the boundary value $\Theta_{i,M}$ must be recalculated after every iteration. We begin the solution by assuming values for $\Theta_{i,j}$ at every *interior* point. These values can then be used to calculate $\Theta^{(1)}_{i,M}$

$$\Theta^{(1)}_{i,M} = \tilde{\Theta}^{(1)}_{i,M-1} + \Delta Y \mathscr{G}(X_i) \tag{3.3-44}$$

Knowing the values of $\Theta_{i,j}$ on the boundaries, either the relaxation method or the matrix inversion method can be used to recalculate the $\Theta_{i,j}$ field. A new assumed field is then generated by Eq. 3.3-27

$$\tilde{\Theta}^{(k+1)}_{i,j} = \tilde{\Theta}^{(k)}_{i,j} + \omega[\Theta^{(k)}_{i,j} - \tilde{\Theta}^{(k)}_{i,j}]$$

for every *interior* point. The boundary values at $Y = (L/b)$ can then be recalculated

$$\Theta^{(k+1)}_{i,M} = \tilde{\Theta}^{(k+1)}_{i,M-1} + \Delta Y \mathscr{G}(X_i)$$

and the process repeated until a converged solution is obtained.

The methods presented here can be applied to two-dimensional heat conduction problems in cylindrical coordinates without great difficulty and the procedure is briefly outlined in the next section. Application of the matrix inversion method is illustrated in the solution of Design Problem III, and use of the relaxation method will be illustrated in Ex. 3.3-1.

Example 3.3-1 Determination of the heat flux for a two-dimensional heat conduction process

In this example we wish to compute the average heat flux per unit depth at $y = L$ for the system illustrated in Fig. 3.3.3, and the following physical properties:

thermal conductivity of the plate:	$k = 0.27$ watt/cm°C
width of the plate:	$b = 0.70$ m
height of the plate:	$L = 0.35$ m
film heat transfer coefficient:	$h = 772$ watt/m^2°C
surface temperatures:	$T_0 = 44$°C, $T_1 = 112$°C
ambient temperature:	$T_a = 78$°C

We can express the mathematical problem as

$$\frac{\partial^2 T}{\partial x^2} + \frac{\partial^2 T}{\partial y^2} = 0 \tag{1}$$

B.C.1 $$\frac{\partial T}{\partial x} = 0, \qquad x = 0 \tag{2}$$

B.C.2 $$-k\left(\frac{\partial T}{\partial x}\right) = h(T - T_a), \qquad x = b \tag{3}$$

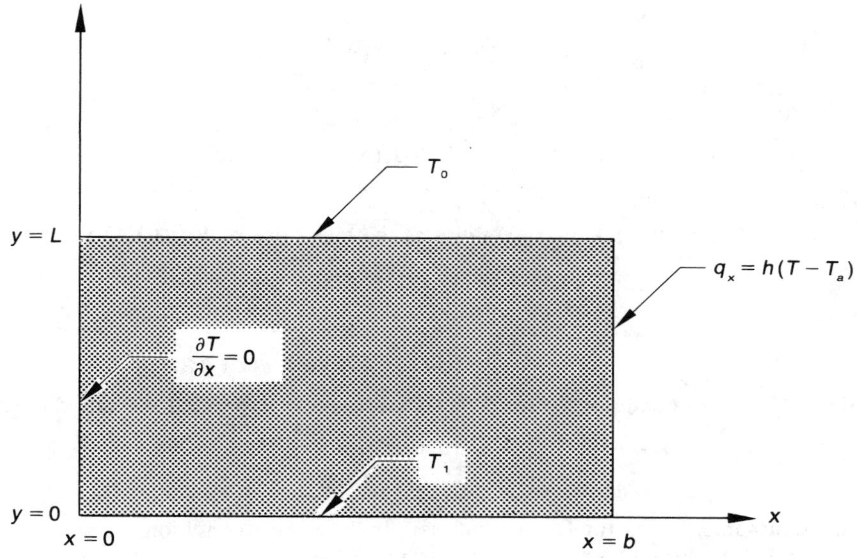

Fig. 3.3.3 Determination of the heat flux for a two-dimensional heat conduction process.

B.C.3 $$T = T_1, \qquad y = 0 \tag{4}$$

B.C.4 $$T = T_0, \qquad y = L \tag{5}$$

Since digital computers have no provision for carrying units we form the dimensionless variables

$$\Theta = (T - T_0)/(T_1 - T_0), \qquad X = x/L, \qquad Y = y/L$$

$$\Theta_a = (T_a - T_0)/(T_1 - T_0), \qquad N_{\mathrm{Bi}} = hL/k, \qquad \beta = b/L$$

and express the problem as

$$\frac{\partial^2 \Theta}{\partial X^2} + \frac{\partial^2 \Theta}{\partial Y^2} = 0 \tag{6}$$

B.C.1′ $$\frac{\partial \Theta}{\partial X} = 0, \qquad X = 0 \tag{7}$$

B.C.2′ $$-\left(\frac{\partial \Theta}{\partial X}\right) = N_{\mathrm{Bi}}(\Theta - \Theta_a), \qquad X = \beta \tag{8}$$

B.C.3′ $$\Theta = 1, \qquad Y = 0 \tag{9}$$

B.C.4′ $$\Theta = 0, \qquad Y = 1 \tag{10}$$

Since we are interested in the average heat flux at $y = L$ we express $\langle q_y \rangle$ as

$$\langle q_y \rangle|_{y=L} = \frac{1}{b}\int_0^b -k\frac{\partial T}{\partial y}\,dx \tag{11}$$

If $b \gg L$ we expect the average heat flux to be given by

$$\langle q_y \rangle = k(T_1 - T_0)/L, \qquad \text{for } b \gg L \tag{12}$$

and we can use this result to develop an expression for the dimensionless average heat flux.

$$\Phi = -\frac{1}{\beta}\int_0^1 \left(\frac{\partial \Theta}{\partial Y}\right) dX \tag{13}$$

We must now develop the appropriate finite-difference equations for Eqs. 6 through 10 and for Eq. 13. We consider a grid having N points in the X-direction and M points in the Y-direction. The finite-difference form of Eq. 6 is given by Eq. 3.3-24 as

$$\Theta_{i,j} = [\tilde{\Theta}_{i+1,j} + \tilde{\Theta}_{i-1,j} + \mathcal{R}^2(\tilde{\Theta}_{i,j+1} + \tilde{\Theta}_{i,j-1})]/2(1 + \mathcal{R}^2) \tag{14}$$

where

$$\mathcal{R} = \Delta X/\Delta Y$$
$$X_i = (i-1)\,\Delta X$$
$$Y_j = (j-1)\,\Delta Y$$
$$\Delta X = \beta/(N-1)$$
$$\Delta Y = 1/(M-1)$$

Directing our attention to the boundary conditions we make use of Eq. 3.3-43 to express B.C.1′ as

B.C.1″ $$\Theta_{1,j} = \Theta_{2,j} \tag{15}$$

and B.C.2′ as

B.C.2″ $$\Theta_{N,j} = (\Theta_{N-1,j} + \Delta X N_{\mathrm{Bi}} \Theta_a)/(1 + \Delta X N_{\mathrm{Bi}}) \tag{16}$$

The remaining boundary conditions, Eqs. 9 and 10, are easily expressed in finite-difference form as

B.C.3″ $$\Theta_{i,1} = 1 \tag{17}$$

B.C.4″ $$\Theta_{i,M} = 0 \tag{18}$$

As soon as we assume values for $\Theta_{i,j}$ we can use the boundary conditions to specify all the values on the boundaries and Eq. 14 can be used to recompute the Θ-field.

Since the dimensionless average heat flux is the quantity of interest we need to develop a finite-difference expression for Eq. 13 so that Φ can be calculated after each iteration. This allows us to see how Φ changes with each successive calculation and will indicate to us when the computation can be stopped. In Fig. 3.3.4 we have graphically illustrated the use of the trapezoidal rule to evaluate an integral. Applying this rule to Eq. 13 gives us

$$\Phi = -\frac{1}{\beta}\left[\frac{1}{2}\left(\frac{\partial \Theta}{\partial Y}\right)_{1,M} + \left(\frac{\partial \Theta}{\partial Y}\right)_{2,M} + \cdots + \frac{1}{2}\left(\frac{\partial \Theta}{\partial Y}\right)_{N,M}\right]\Delta X \tag{19}$$

Expressing the derivative as

$$\left(\frac{\partial \Theta}{\partial Y}\right)_{i,M} = \frac{\Theta_{i,M} - \Theta_{i,M-1}}{\Delta Y} \tag{20}$$

and making use of B.C.4″ allows us to express Φ as

$$\Phi = \frac{\mathcal{R}}{\beta}\left[\frac{1}{2}\Theta_{1,M-1} + \Theta_{2,M-1} + \cdots + \frac{1}{2}\Theta_{N,M-1}\right] \tag{21}$$

We are now in a position to carry out the numerical solution for the Θ-field and to calculate Φ. The physical parameters for the problem lead to

$$N_{\mathrm{Bi}} = 10, \qquad \beta = 2, \qquad \Theta_a = 0.5$$

and we will set $N = 21$ and $M = 11$ so that $\Delta X = \Delta Y = 0.1$. The flow sheet for the computer program is shown in Fig. 3.3.5 and the Fortran program is given in Fig. 3.3.6. Although the program is completed when the sum of errors is less than 0.001 or more than 200 iterations are performed, the convergence is best judged in terms of the calculated values of Φ which are given in Table 3.3-1. There we see that Φ has changed only 0.003 in the last 20 iterations and we are inclined to take the result as

$$\Phi = 1.16, \qquad \Delta X = \Delta Y = 0.1$$

In this type of calculation one always seeks to find a value of Φ which is independent of both ΔX and ΔY, and the number of iterations. Results for $\Delta X = \Delta Y = 0.05$ are shown in Table 3.3-2 and these certainly indicate that we have not found a value of Φ which is independent of the mesh size. For the smaller mesh size we take the result to be

$$\Phi = 1.20, \qquad \text{for } \Delta X = \Delta Y = 0.05$$

In order to estimate the value of Φ for $\Delta X = \Delta Y = 0$ we need to return to Eq. 3.3-15 and expand Θ in a Taylor series in Y to obtain

$$\Theta(Y + \Delta Y) = \Theta(Y) + \Delta Y\left(\frac{\partial \Theta}{\partial Y}\right) + \frac{\Delta Y^2}{2!}\left(\frac{\partial^2 \Theta}{\partial Y^2}\right) + \cdots \tag{22}$$

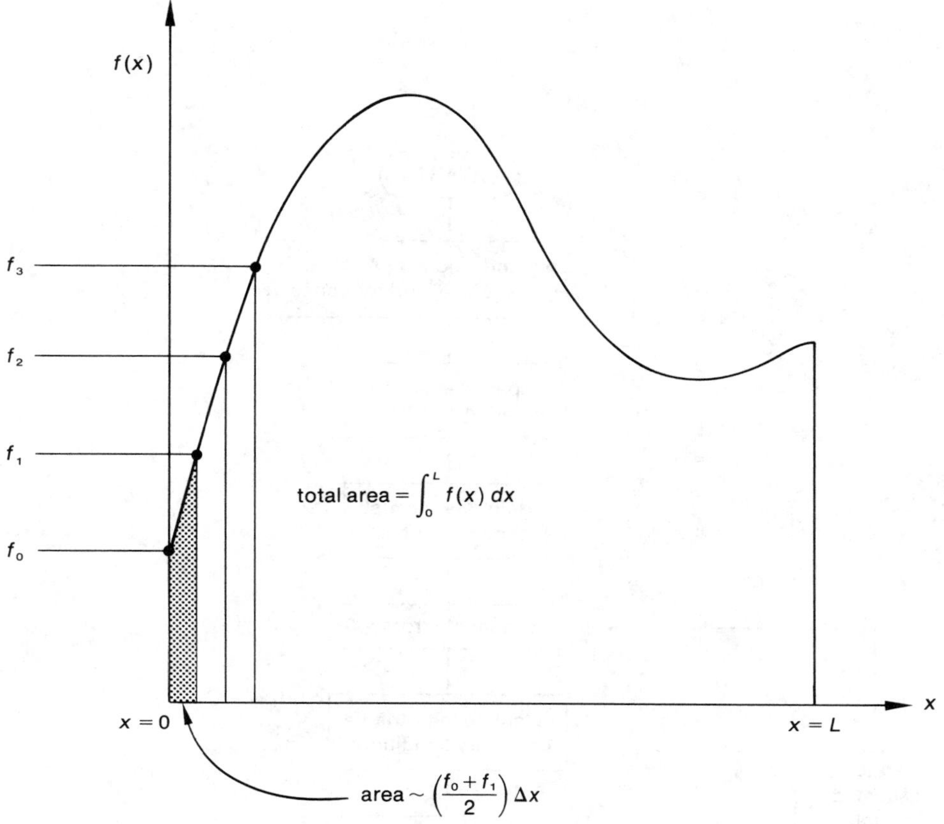

$$\text{Total area} \sim \left(\frac{f_0 + f_1}{2}\right)\Delta x + \left(\frac{f_1 + f_2}{2}\right)\Delta x + \left(\frac{f_2 + f_3}{2}\right)\Delta x + \cdots + \left(\frac{f_{n-1} + f_n}{2}\right)\Delta x$$

$$\text{Total area} \sim \left(\frac{f_0}{2} + \sum_{i=1}^{n-1} f_i + \frac{f_n}{2}\right)\Delta x$$

Fig. 3.3.4 Use of the trapezoidal rule to evaluate a one-dimensional integral.

where the derivatives are evaluated at Y. We can rearrange this result to get

$$\left(\frac{\partial \Theta}{\partial Y}\right) = \frac{\Theta(Y + \Delta Y) - \Theta(Y)}{\Delta Y} + \Delta Y\left[\frac{1}{2!}\left(\frac{\partial^2 \Theta}{\partial Y^2}\right)\right] \tag{23}$$

Comparing this result with Eq. 20 indicates that the error in the finite-difference approximation for $\partial \Theta/\partial Y$ is a linear function of ΔY, and it follows that the error in Φ is a linear function of ΔY. We can therefore plot Φ versus ΔY and extrapolate to $\Delta Y = 0$ (see Fig. 3.3.7) to obtain

$$\Phi = 1.24, \qquad \text{for } \Delta X = \Delta Y = 0$$

We now return to the definition of Φ in order to write

$$\begin{aligned}\langle q_y \rangle|_{y=L} &= \Phi k(T_1 - T_0)/L \\ &= (1.24)\left(\frac{0.27\ \text{watt}}{\text{cm}\,^\circ\text{C}}\right)(68^\circ\text{C})\left(\frac{1}{0.35\ \text{m}}\right)\left(\frac{1\ \text{m}}{100\ \text{cm}}\right) \\ &= 0.65\ \text{watt/cm}^2\end{aligned}$$

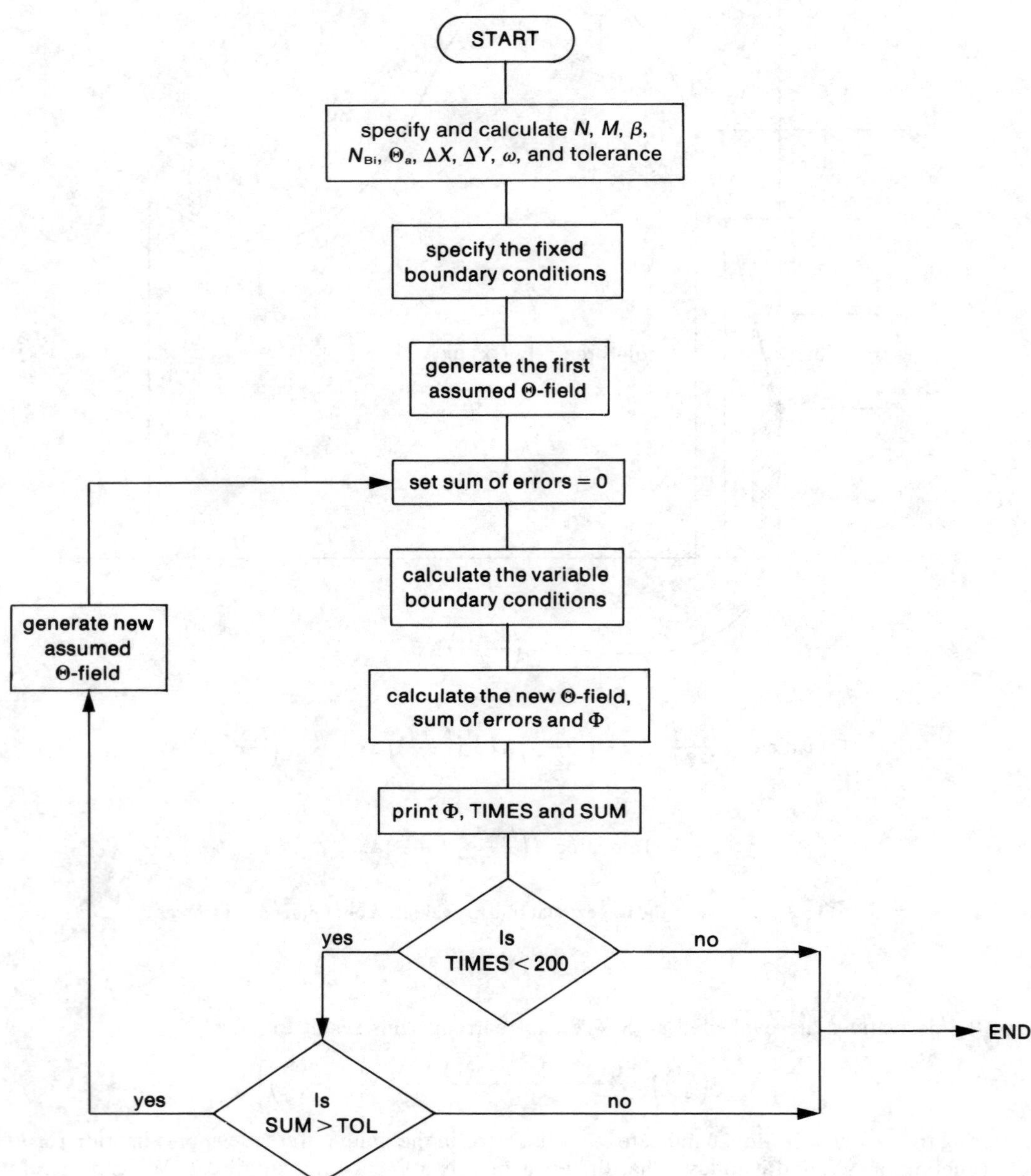

Fig. 3.3.5 Flow sheet for relaxation method.

Fortran Statements	*Comments*
DIMENSION THETA(21, 11), TA(21, 11) M = 21 N = 11	specify the size of the array for Θ = THETA and $\tilde{\Theta}$ = TA
BETA = 2.0	set β = BETA = 2.0
BIOT = 10.0	set N_{Bi} = BIOT = 10.0
TAM = 0.5	set Θ_a = TAM = 0.5
TIMES = 0.0	set number of iterations = TIMES = 0.0
TOL = 0.001	set tolerance = TOL = 0.001
OMEGA = 0.9	set ω = OMEGA = 0.9 (larger values of ω lead to instabilities for this problem)
N1 = N - 1 M1 = M - 1	set upper bounds for "do loops"
DX = BETA/N1	set ΔX = DX = 0.1
DY = 1.0/M1	set ΔY = DY = 0.1
R = DX/DY	set $\mathscr{R}$ = R = DX/DY
R2 = R*R	store R^2 for future use
WRITE(6, 1) BETA, BIOT, TAM, OMEGA, DX, DY	write pertinent parameters
1 FORMAT (6E 13.3)	specify output format
DO 100 I = 1, N THETA(I, 1) = 1.0 100 THETA(I, M) = 0.0	specify fixed boundary conditions
DO 200 J = 2, M1 DO 200 I = 2, N1 Y = (J - 1)*DY TA(I, J) = 1.0 - Y 200 THETA(I, J) = 1.0 - Y	generate first assumed field
250 SUM = 0.0	set sum of errors = SUM = 0.0
DO 300 J = 2, M1 THETA(1, J) = THETA(2, J) 300 THETA(N, J) = (THETA(N - 1, J) + DX*BIOT*TAM)/(1.0 + DX*BIOT)	calculate the variable boundary conditions
TIMES = TIMES + 1.0	calculate the number of iterations
DO 400 I = 2, N1 DO 400 J = 2, M1 THETA(I, J) = (TA(I + 1, J) + TA(I - 1, J) + R2*(TA(I, J + 1) + TA(I, J - 1)))/2.0*(1.0 + R2) 400 SUM = SUM + ABS(THETA(I, J) - TA(I, J))	calculate the new Θ-field and the error
PHI = 0.5*(THETA(1, M - 1) + THETA(N, M - 1)) DO 500 I = 2, N1 500 PHI = PHI + THETA(I, M - 1)	calculate the average dimensionless heat flux
WRITE (6, 1) PHI, TIMES, SUM	write out results
IF (TIMES.GT.200) GO TO 700	stop program
IF (SUM.LT.TOL) GO TO 700	stop program
DO 600 I = 2, N1 DO 600 J = 2, M1 600 TA(I, J) = OMEGA*THETA(I, J) + (1.0 - OMEGA)*TA(I, J)	calculate the new assumed temperature field
GO TO 250	repeat calculation
700 STOP	exit program
END	

Fig. 3.3.6 Fortran program for relaxation method.

Table 3.3-1 Results from Relaxation Calculation for $\Delta X = \Delta Y = 0.1$

Times	Φ	Sum
2	1.093	0.1938
4	1.114	0.1349
6	1.126	0.1002
8	1.134	0.0766
10	1.141	0.0594
12	1.145	0.0466
14	1.149	0.0369
16	1.152	0.0293
18	1.154	0.0235
20	1.156	0.0188
22	1.157	0.0152
24	1.158	0.0122
26	1.159	0.0099
28	1.160	0.0080
30	1.160	0.0065
32	1.161	0.0053
34	1.161	0.0043
36	1.162	0.0035
38	1.162	0.0029
40	1.162	0.0024
42	1.162	0.0019
44	1.162	0.0016
46	1.163	0.0013
48	1.163	0.0010

Table 3.3-2 Results from Relaxation Calculation for $\Delta X = \Delta Y = 0.05$

Times	Φ	Sum
10	1.126	1.7856
20	1.151	0.7880
30	1.165	0.4316
40	1.174	0.2660
50	1.180	0.1716
60	1.184	0.1112
70	1.188	0.0788
80	1.190	0.0552
90	1.192	0.0393
100	1.193	0.0280
110	1.194	0.0204
120	1.195	0.0148
130	1.196	0.0108
140	1.196	0.0080
150	1.196	0.0059
160	1.197	0.0044

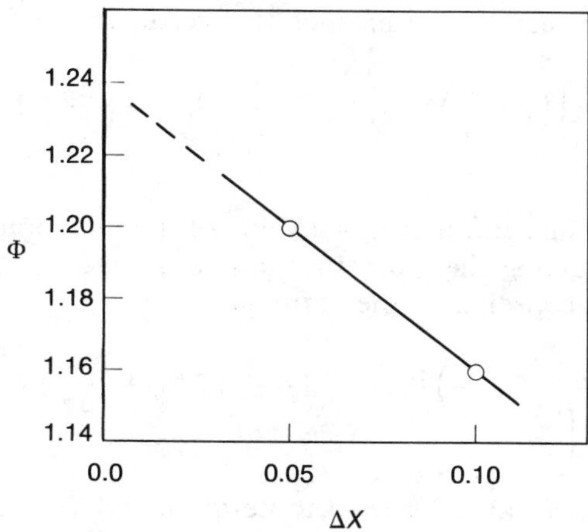

Fig. 3.3.7 Calculated values of Φ versus ΔX.

3.4 Numerical Solution of Two-Dimensional Heat Conduction Problems in Cylindrical Coordinates

The techniques used to solve problems in cylindrical coordinates are identical to those discussed in Sec. 3.3, and the objective of this section will be to simply examine the finite-difference approximate of the heat conduction equation in cylindrical coordinates. We will restrict ourselves to axially symmetric cases and write our governing differential equation as

$$\left[\frac{1}{r}\frac{\partial}{\partial r}\left(r\frac{\partial T}{\partial r}\right)+\left(\frac{\partial^2 T}{\partial z^2}\right)\right]=0 \tag{3.4-1}$$

Expanding the derivative with respect to the radial position gives

$$\left(\frac{\partial^2 T}{\partial r^2}\right)+\frac{1}{r}\left(\frac{\partial T}{\partial r}\right)+\left(\frac{\partial^2 T}{\partial z^2}\right)=0 \tag{3.4-2}$$

Designating the discrete spatial coordinates as

$$r_i = i\,\Delta r, \qquad i = 0, 1, 2, 3, \ldots$$
$$z_j = j\,\Delta z, \qquad j = 0, 1, 2, 3, \ldots$$

we write the finite-difference approximations for the derivatives as

$$\left(\frac{\partial^2 T}{\partial r^2}\right)_{r_i,z_j} \sim \frac{T_{i+1,j}-2T_{i,j}+T_{i-1,j}}{\Delta r^2} \tag{3.4-3}$$

$$\left(\frac{\partial T}{\partial r}\right)_{r_i,z_j} \sim \frac{T_{i+1,j}-T_{i-1,j}}{2\Delta r} \tag{3.4-4}$$

$$\left(\frac{\partial^2 T}{\partial z^2}\right)_{r_i,z_j} \sim \frac{T_{i,j+1}-2T_{i,j}+T_{i,j-1}}{\Delta z^2} \tag{3.4-5}$$

Substitution of Eqs. 3.4-3 through 3.4-5 into Eq. 3.4-2 yields the finite-difference approximation for the two-dimensional heat conduction equation

$$\frac{T_{i+1,j}-2T_{i,j}-T_{i-1,j}}{\Delta r^2}+\frac{T_{i+1,j}-T_{i-1,j}}{2i\,\Delta r^2}+\frac{T_{i,j+1}-2T_{i,j}+T_{i,j-1}}{\Delta z^2}=0 \tag{3.4-6}$$

If we wish to use the relaxation method we arrange this result in the form

$$T_{i,j} = \frac{1}{2\left[1+\left(\frac{\Delta r}{\Delta z}\right)^2\right]}\left\{\left(1+\frac{1}{2i}\right)T_{i+1,j}+\left(1-\frac{1}{2i}\right)T_{i-1,j}+\left(\frac{\Delta r}{\Delta z}\right)^2 T_{i,j+1}+\left(\frac{\Delta r}{\Delta z}\right)^2 T_{i,j-1}\right\} \tag{3.4-7}$$

Here we have an expression for the central or nodal value of the temperature in terms of the values at the four nearest grid points. By assuming the temperature field $\tilde{T}_{i,j}$ we can use Eq. 3.4-7 to *recalculate* the temperature at each grid point according to the formula

$$T_{i,j}^{(k)} = \frac{1}{2\left[1+\left(\frac{\Delta r}{\Delta z}\right)^2\right]}\left\{\left(1+\frac{1}{2i}\right)\tilde{T}_{i+1,j}^{(k)}+\left(1-\frac{1}{2i}\right)\tilde{T}_{i-1,j}^{(k)}+\left(\frac{\Delta r}{\Delta z}\right)^2 \tilde{T}_{i,j+1}^{(k)}+\left(\frac{\Delta r}{\Delta z}\right)^2 \tilde{T}_{i,j-1}^{(k)}\right\} \tag{3.4-8}$$

Here $T_{i,j}^{(k)}$ represents the *calculated* value for the kth iteration and $\tilde{T}_{i,j}^{(k)}$ represents the *assumed* value for the kth interation. The assumed value for the $k+1$ iteration is determined by

$$\tilde{T}_{i,j}^{(k+1)} = \tilde{T}_{i,j}^{(k)} + \omega[T_{i,j}^{(k)} - \tilde{T}_{i,j}^{(k)}] \tag{3.4-9}$$

One generally chooses ω to be as large as possible; however, the iteration scheme may be unstable for values of $\omega > 1$. If one wishes to use the matrix inversion method for solving Eq. 3.4-6 we rearrange that equation in the form

$$\left(1-\frac{1}{2i}\right)T_{i-1,j} - 2\left[1+\left(\frac{\Delta r}{\Delta z}\right)^2\right]T_{i,j} + \left(1+\frac{1}{2i}\right)T_{i+1,j} = -\left(\frac{\Delta r}{\Delta z}\right)^2[T_{i,j+1}+T_{i,j-1}] \tag{3.4-10}$$

In more compact form we could express this result as

$$A_i T_{i-1,j} + B_i T_{i,j} + C_i T_{i+1,j} = D_{i,j}, \qquad i = 1, 2, 3, \ldots, N-1 \tag{3.4-11}$$

The $N-2$ equations represented by Eq. 3.4-11 can be written in matrix form as

$$\begin{bmatrix} B_1 & C_1 & & & & \\ A_2 & B_2 & C_2 & & & \\ & A_3 & B_3 & C_3 & & \\ & & & & & \\ & & & A_{N-2} & B_{N-2} & C_{N-2} \\ & & & & A_{N-1} & B_{N-1} \end{bmatrix} \begin{bmatrix} T_{1,j} \\ T_{2,j} \\ T_{3,j} \\ \\ T_{N-2,j} \\ T_{N-1,j} \end{bmatrix} = \begin{bmatrix} \tilde{D}_{i,j} - A_1 T_{0,j} \\ \tilde{D}_{2,j} \\ \tilde{D}_{3,j} \\ \\ \tilde{D}_{N-2,j} \\ \tilde{D}_{N-1,j} - C_{N-1}T_{N,j} \end{bmatrix} \tag{3.4-12}$$

$$j = 1, 2, 3, \ldots, M-1$$

for the case where $T_{0,j}$ and $T_{N,j}$ are specified. Here $\tilde{D}_{i,j}$ indicates the value of $D_{i,j}$ determined from an assumed temperature field, i.e.,

$$\tilde{D}_{i,j} = -\left(\frac{\Delta r}{\Delta z}\right)^2[\tilde{T}_{i,j+1} + \tilde{T}_{i,j-1}] \tag{3.4-13}$$

Eq. 3.4-12 can be expressed as

$$[B]_j[T]_j = [\tilde{D}]_j, \qquad j = 1, 2, \ldots, M-1 \tag{3.4-14}$$

where $[B]_j$ represents a *known* tri-diagonal matrix, $[T]_j$ represents an *unknown* column vector, and $[\tilde{D}]_j$ represents a *known* column vector. If the inverse of $[B]_j$ can be found we can solve for the temperature vector

$$[T]_j = [B]_j^{-1}[\tilde{D}]_j, \qquad j = 1, 2, \ldots, M-1 \tag{3.4-15}$$

Carrying out this operation for all values of j yields a new set of values for the temperature field. One may then use Eq. 3.4-9 to compute a new set of assumed values and the process is repeated until the assumed and calculated values are suitably close to each other.

Boundary conditions

When the temperature or flux is specified over the boundaries, we encounter no difficulties with imposing the boundary conditions on the finite-difference equations given here. One simply follows the methods described in Sec. 3.3. Difficulty does arise however, when the region of interest includes the origin, $0 \leq r \leq r_0$, for then we need to say something about the flux or the temperature at $r = 0$. In our analytic studies of heat conduction in cylindrical coordinates we were able to obtain information about the constants of integration by simply stating†

$$T \quad \text{is finite in the region} \quad 0 \leq r \leq r_0$$

however, the finite-difference analog of the heat conduction equation cannot be treated in that manner. We instead draw upon the condition that the heat flux vector must be a continuous function, and in particular the component q_r must be continuous at $r = 0$. Keep in mind, now, that we are considering an axially symmetric process, thus the value of q_r is independent of θ. Imagine that two microscopic observers approach the centerline along opposite radii, i.e., along paths specified by $\theta = 0$ and $\theta = \pi$. The values of q_r that they measure will be designated by q_r^{I} and q_r^{II} as indicated in the sketch shown in Fig. 3.4.1. If we choose $\boldsymbol{\lambda}$ to be a unit vector pointing in the $\theta = 0$ direction these two scalar components are given by

$$q_r^{\mathrm{I}} = \mathbf{q} \cdot \boldsymbol{\lambda}|_{\theta=0}, \qquad q_r^{\mathrm{II}} = -\mathbf{q} \cdot \boldsymbol{\lambda}|_{\theta=\pi} \tag{3.4-16}$$

where $\boldsymbol{\lambda}$ is indicated in Fig. 3.4.1. Since the system is axially symmetric the values measured by observers I and II must be the same, i.e.,

$$q_r^{\mathrm{I}} = q_r^{\mathrm{II}} \tag{3.4-17}$$

When their radial position goes to zero this yields

$$\mathbf{q} \cdot \boldsymbol{\lambda} = -\mathbf{q} \cdot \boldsymbol{\lambda}, \qquad \text{at } r = 0 \tag{3.4-18}$$

and we conclude that

$$\mathbf{q} \cdot \boldsymbol{\lambda} = 0, \qquad \text{at } r = 0 \tag{3.4-19}$$

Since $\boldsymbol{\lambda}$ is pointing in the radial direction this means that

$$q_r = 0, \qquad \text{at } r = 0 \tag{3.4-20}$$

Note that Eqs. 3.4-17 and 3.4-18 are only true for axially symmetric processes, and that Eq. 3.4-19 *does not* imply that $q_z = 0$ at $r = 0$.

†See, for example, Eqs. 3.2-15 and 3.2-16.

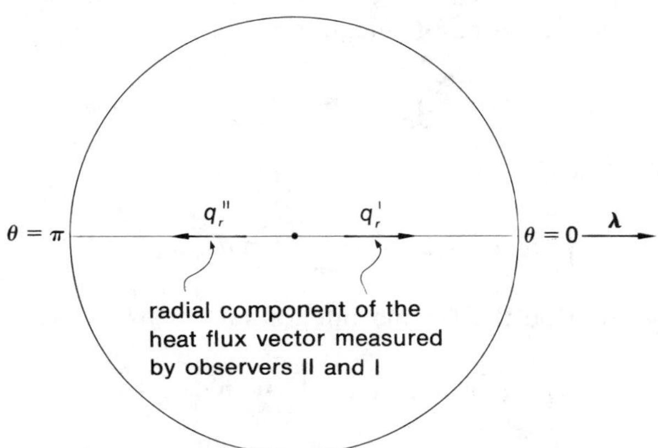

Fig. 3.4.1 Radial component of the heat flux vector for an axially symmetric temperature field.

Eq. 3.4-20 constitutes a boundary condition at $r = 0$, and imposing Fourier's law we conclude that

$$\frac{\partial T}{\partial r} = 0, \qquad r = 0 \tag{3.4-21}$$

The finite-difference approximation of Eq. 3.4-21 is

$$\left(\frac{T_{1,j} - T_{0,j}}{\Delta r}\right) = 0, \qquad r = \frac{\Delta r}{2}$$

and we express our boundary condition for the finite-difference analog as

$$\text{B.C.} \qquad T_{0,j} = T_{1,j} \tag{3.4-22}$$

Another approach to analyzing this condition at the centerline is given in Chapter 4, Sec. 4.8, and if the student is uncertain about these ideas Sec. 4.8 should be studied.

With the boundary conditions now well in hand the procedure for solving two-dimensional heat conduction problems in cylindrical coordinates follows the approach outlined in Sec. 3.3 for rectangular coordinates.

3.5 Graphical Solution for Steady, Two-Dimensional Heat Conduction

The analytical and numerical methods discussed in the previous sections have considerable appeal, because the temperature and heat flux can be determined to any desired degree of accuracy simply by evaluating an increasing number of terms in the series solutions or by using smaller values of Δx and Δy in the numerical solutions. However, there are many cases in which the uncertainties associated with the description of the real process are great enough so that only an approximate solution is warranted. Under these circumstances the graphical method described in the following paragraphs is an especially suitable technique.

For the case of steady heat conduction with no generation the energy equation reduces to

$$0 = \int_{\mathscr{A}} \mathbf{q} \cdot \mathbf{n} \, dA \tag{3.5-1}$$

For two-dimensional heat conduction this takes the form

$$\oint_C \mathbf{q} \cdot \mathbf{n} \, ds = 0 \tag{3.5-2}$$

where C represents any closed curve such as the one illustrated in Fig. 3.5.1. There we have shown the closed curve as consisting of two parts, C_1 and C_2, and lines tangent to the heat flux vector $\mathbf{q}$ have also been drawn. We can express Eq. 3.5-2 in terms of integrals along the curves, C_1 and C_2.

$$\oint_C \mathbf{q} \cdot \mathbf{n} \, ds = \int_{C_1} \mathbf{q} \cdot \mathbf{n} \, ds + \int_{C_2} \mathbf{q} \cdot \mathbf{n} \, ds = 0 \tag{3.5-3}$$

or in terms of points A and B we can write

$$\int_A^B \mathbf{q} \cdot \mathbf{n} \, ds \big|_{\text{along } C_1} + \int_B^A \mathbf{q} \cdot \mathbf{n} \, ds \big|_{\text{along } C_2} = 0 \tag{3.5-4}$$

Changing the limits of integration on the second integral allows us to express Eq. 3.5-4 as

$$\int_A^B \mathbf{q} \cdot \mathbf{n} \, ds \big|_{\text{along } C_1} = \int_A^B \mathbf{q} \cdot \mathbf{n} \, ds \big|_{\text{along } C_2} \tag{3.5-5}$$

Since Eq. 3.5-5 holds for any arbitrary curve, the integral of $\mathbf{q} \cdot \mathbf{n} \, ds$ along any curve between A and B *always has the same value*, i.e., the integral is *independent of the path*. This means that $\mathbf{q} \cdot \mathbf{n} \, ds$ is an *exact*

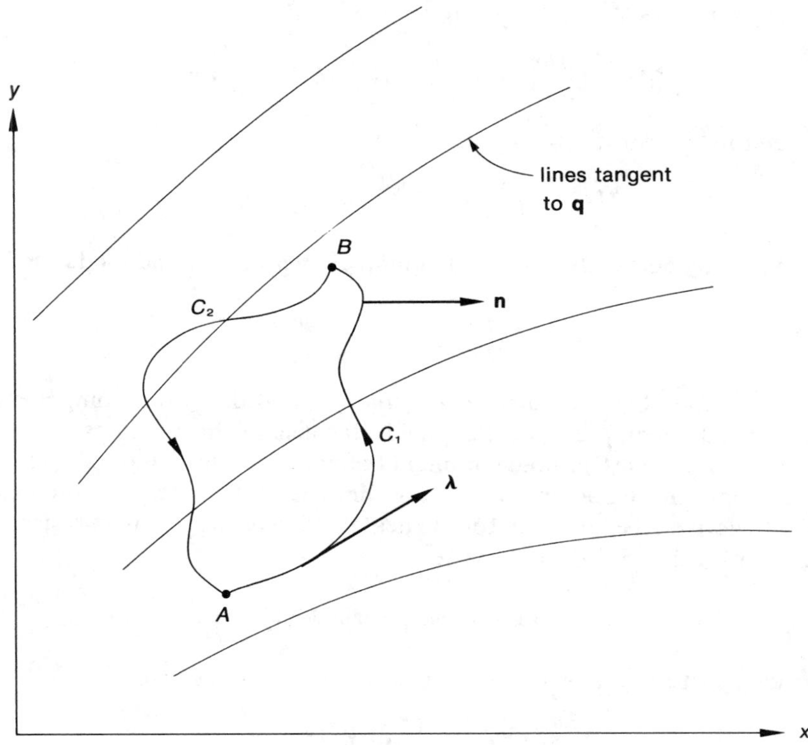

Fig. 3.5.1 Steady, two-dimensional heat conduction.

differential and may be expressed as

$$d\psi = \mathbf{q} \cdot \mathbf{n}\, ds \tag{3.5-6}$$

where the function ψ is independent of the path. Expressing ψ as a function of x and y and expanding the right-hand-side of Eq. 3.5-6 leads to

$$d\psi = \left(\frac{\partial \psi}{\partial x}\right) dx + \left(\frac{\partial \psi}{\partial y}\right) dy = q_x n_x\, ds + q_y n_y\, ds \tag{3.5-7}$$

In order to extract some useful information from Eq. 3.5-7 we need to derive expressions for n_x and n_y. This is most easily done by noting that the unit tangent shown in Fig. 3.5.1 is given by [9]

$$\boldsymbol{\lambda} = \mathbf{i}\left(\frac{dx}{ds}\right) + \mathbf{j}\left(\frac{dy}{ds}\right) \tag{3.5-8}$$

Since $\mathbf{n}$ and $\boldsymbol{\lambda}$ are orthogonal we have

$$\mathbf{n} \cdot \boldsymbol{\lambda} = n_x\left(\frac{dx}{ds}\right) + n_y\left(\frac{dy}{ds}\right) = 0 \tag{3.5-9}$$

and either

$$n_x = \frac{dy}{ds}, \qquad n_y = -\frac{dx}{ds} \tag{3.5-10}$$

or

$$n_x = -\frac{dy}{ds}, \qquad n_y = \frac{dx}{ds} \tag{3.5-11}$$

The tangent vector has been taken as pointing in the direction an observer would follow when progressing around the curve in a counterclockwise manner, thus the solution given by Eq. 3.5-10 is the correct one.

Substitution of Eq. 3.5-10 into Eq. 3.5-7 yields

$$d\psi = \left(\frac{\partial \psi}{\partial x}\right) dx + \left(\frac{\partial \psi}{\partial y}\right) dy = q_x\, dy - q_y\, dx \tag{3.5-12}$$

which can be rearranged in the form

$$\left(\frac{\partial \psi}{\partial x} + q_y\right) dx + \left(\frac{\partial \psi}{\partial y} - q_x\right) dy = 0 \tag{3.5-13}$$

Since this result is true for any curve, dx and dy are completely arbitrary and the terms in parentheses are zero. This leads to

$$q_x = \frac{\partial \psi}{\partial y}, \qquad q_y = -\frac{\partial \psi}{\partial x} \tag{3.5-14}$$

which is identical to the relation between the *stream function* and the scalar components of the velocity vector for a two-dimensional, incompressible, flow field. Because of this the lines of constant ψ shown in Fig. 3.5.1 are often called *streamlines*, although it might be more descriptive to refer to them as "adiabatic lines" since the most important characteristic of these lines is that no heat is conducted across them.

We would now like to derive an expression for the heat flowing between any two streamlines ψ_A and ψ_B. Returning to Fig. 3.5.1 and Eq. 3.5-5 we can write

$$\{\text{energy flowing across } C_1 \text{ per unit time per unit depth}\} = \int_A^B \mathbf{q} \cdot \mathbf{n}\, ds\,\Big|_{\text{along } C_1} \tag{3.5-15}$$

For a distance b orthogonal to the x–y plane we can express this result as

$$\dot{Q}_{AB} = b \int_A^B \mathbf{q} \cdot \mathbf{n}\, ds \tag{3.5-16}$$

and if we use Eq. 3.5-6 to express this result in terms of the stream function we obtain

$$\dot{Q}_{AB} = b \int_A^B \mathbf{q} \cdot \mathbf{n}\, ds = b \int_A^B d\psi = b(\psi_B - \psi_A) \tag{3.5-17}$$

This indicates that the energy per unit depth flowing between two streamlines, or two "adiabatic lines," is a constant given by

$$\{\text{energy per unit depth flowing between } \psi_A \text{ and } \psi_B\} = \frac{\dot{Q}_{AB}}{b} = \psi_B - \psi_A \tag{3.5-18}$$

This situation is illustrated in Fig. 3.5.2.

Since lines of constant ψ are tangent to $\mathbf{q}$ it is intuitively appealing that lines of constant T are orthogonal to the streamlines. Proof lies in the fact that the streamlines are tangent to ∇T by Fourier's law, and that the vector ∇T is orthogonal to the lines of constant temperature.† Thus the streamlines and the isotherms are orthogonal as indicated in Fig. 3.5.3.

In order to make use of the results we have derived, we can use Fourier's law and Eq. 3.5-14 to obtain

$$-k\frac{\partial T}{\partial x} = \frac{\partial \psi}{\partial y}, \qquad -k\frac{\partial T}{\partial y} = -\frac{\partial \psi}{\partial x} \tag{3.5-19}$$

In Fig. 3.5.3 we have constructed a new coordinate system (x', y') such that the x'-coordinate is tangent to a streamline, and the y'-coordinate is tangent to an isotherm. Expressing the first of Eqs. 3.5-19 in terms of the x', y' coordinate systems yields

$$-k\frac{\partial T}{\partial x'} = \frac{\partial \psi}{\partial y'} \tag{3.5-20}$$

†From a course in vector analysis it may be remembered that the unit normal vector $\mathbf{n}$ to a surface defined by $f(x, y, z) = C$ is given by $\mathbf{n} = \nabla f/|\nabla f|$. For example, see F. M. Stein, *An Introduction to Vector Analysis*, Sec. 2.3, Harper & Row, Pub., New York, 1963.

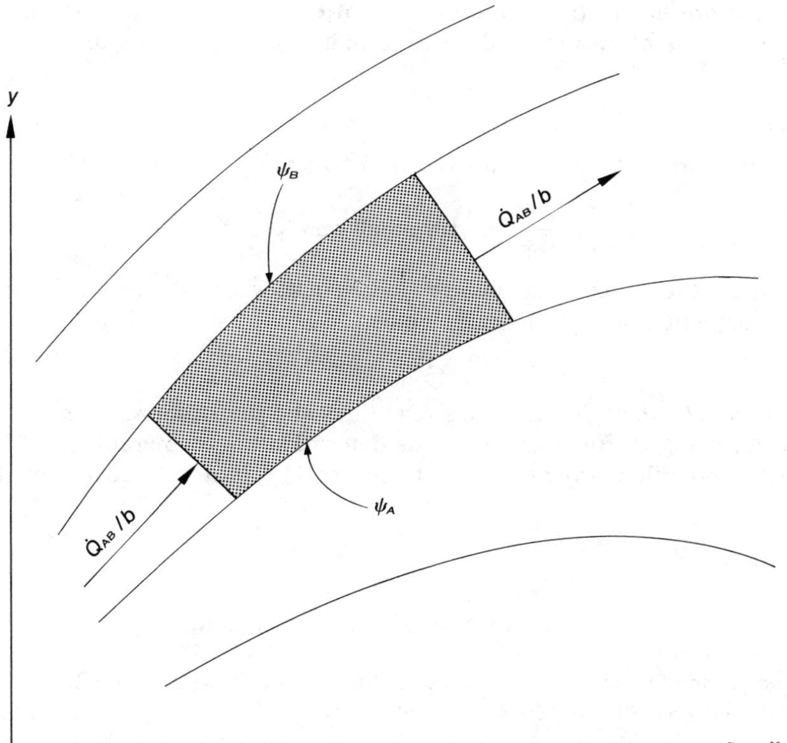

Fig. 3.5.2 Heat flow between two streamlines.

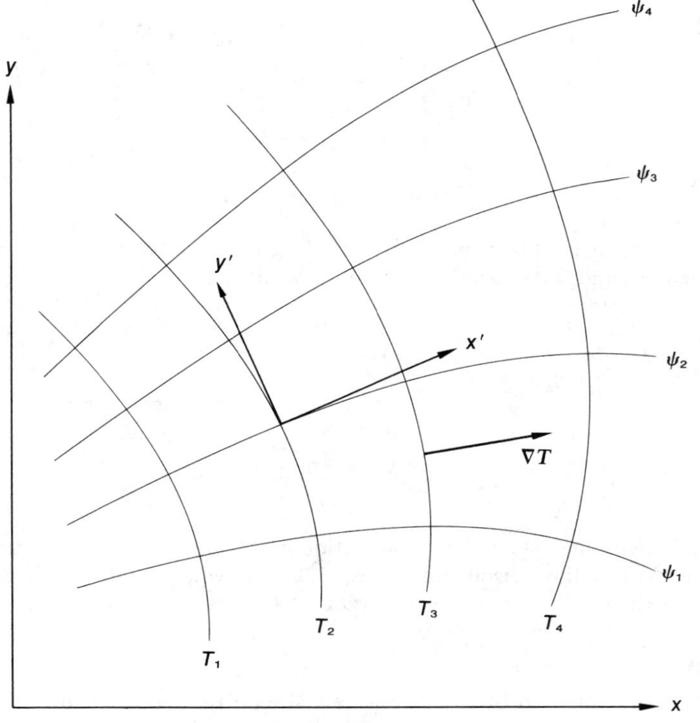

Fig. 3.5.3 Streamlines and isotherms.

Since the x'-direction is *normal* to the isotherm, x' is often replaced by n, and since the y'-direction is *tangent* to the isotherm y' is often replaced by s so that Eq. 3.5-20 takes the form

$$-k\frac{\partial T}{\partial n}=\frac{\partial \psi}{\partial s} \tag{3.5-21}$$

For small variations in n and s we can express Eq. 3.5-21 as

$$-k\frac{\Delta T}{\Delta n}=\frac{\Delta \psi}{\Delta s}, \quad \text{for small changes in } n \text{ and } s \tag{3.5-22}$$

Furthermore if we require the incremental changes to be equal, $\Delta n = \Delta s$, we obtain an expression relating the change in ψ to the change in T in a small square

$$\Delta\psi = -k\Delta T, \qquad \text{for } \Delta n = \Delta s \tag{3.5-23}$$

This relation, along with the constraint that the streamlines and the isotherms are orthogonal, can be used to graphically construct the ψ–T functions and thus determine the temperature and heat flux fields for a two-dimensional heat conduction process. Use of this method is discussed in detail in the solution of Design Problem III.

Solution to design problem III

In order to determine the desired heat fluxes for the system shown in Fig. III.1 we need to determine the temperature field which satisfies the following conditions:

$$\text{governing differential equation:} \quad \frac{\partial^2 T}{\partial x^2}+\frac{\partial^2 T}{\partial y^2}=0 \tag{III-1}$$

B.C.1 $$\frac{\partial T}{\partial x}=0, \quad x=0, \quad D/2<y\leq b/2$$
$$-b/2\leq y<-D/2 \tag{III-2}$$

B.C.2 $$T=T_1, \quad x^2+y^2=(D/2)^2 \tag{III-3}$$

B.C.3 $$T=T_2, \quad y=-b/2 \tag{III-4}$$

B.C.4 $$T=T_3, \quad y=+b/2 \tag{III-5}$$

B.C.5 $$\frac{\partial T}{\partial x}=0, \quad x=L/2 \tag{III-6}$$

Here we have chosen b to be the thickness of the slab, D to be the outer pipe diameter, and L to be the distance between pipes. For the conditions given in Fig. III.1 we have

$$b = 4 \text{ in.}$$
$$D = 1 \text{ in.}$$
$$L = 6 \text{ in.}$$
$$T_1 = 180°\text{F}$$
$$T_2 = 83°\text{F}$$
$$T_3 = 60°\text{F}$$

We wish to solve this two-dimensional heat conduction problem using both the graphical method described in Sec. 3.5 and a numerical method discussed in Sec. 3.3. This will provide an illustration of both methods in addition to providing some measure of the accuracy of the graphical method.

Graphical Solution

We begin the graphical method by defining a new stream function, ψ^*, by the equation

$$\psi^* = \psi/k \tag{III-7}$$

This allows us to write Eqs. 3.5-22 and 3.5-23 as

$$\frac{\Delta\psi^*}{\Delta s} = -\frac{\Delta T}{\Delta n}, \quad \text{for small changes in } n \text{ and } s \tag{III-8}$$

$$\Delta\psi^* = -\Delta T, \quad \text{for } \Delta n = \Delta s \tag{III-9}$$

In order to graphically construct the array of isotherms (lines of constant T) and adiabatic lines (lines of constant ψ^*) we require that these lines be orthogonal and that Eq. III-9 be satisfied. The tools required for this construction have been listed by Robertson† as a soft pencil, a good eraser, a tough piece of paper, and a ruthless pursuit of the orthogonality condition and the restriction given by Eq. III-9. Experience and a good eye are also a help. It should be noted that the author possesses neither of these latter qualities, thus the graphical construction presented here should provide a good illustration of how well a rank amateur can do with this method.

As a first approximation it was assumed that the temperature varied linearly along the symmetry line between the pipe and the upper and lower surfaces. This allowed two points on each isotherm to be fixed, and the remaining portion of the isotherm was then sketched. Orthogonal adiabatic lines were then drawn and the resulting array is shown in Fig. III.2a. The orthogonality condition is satisfied reasonably well; however, Eq. III-9 is not. We should note that between any two adiabatic lines $\Delta\psi^*$ is a constant, thus if ΔT is a constant we require that the ratio $(\Delta s/\Delta n)$ be a constant. Clearly this is not the case in Fig. III.2a. One can see that the isotherms need to be "bunched up" closer to the pipe so that we make use of the fact that $\partial T/\partial r \sim 1/r$ for one-dimensional heat conduction in cylindrical coordinates. Even though the construction shown in Fig. III.2a is not satisfactory we can use it to calculate the absolute value of the change in ψ^* between the two lines of symmetry. This is done by writing Eq. III-8 as

$$\Delta\psi^* = -\Delta T\left(\frac{\Delta s}{\Delta n}\right) \tag{III-10}$$

and estimating $(\Delta s/\Delta n)$ for the sections on the upper and lower surfaces. The sum, $\Sigma|\Delta\psi^*|$, is directly proportional to the heat flux and is listed on Fig. III.2a as 122°F for the upper surface and 76°F for the lower surface.

At this point we abandon the linear temperature variation along the symmetry line and begin work with the eraser. After considerable sketching we arrive at the condition illustrated in Fig. III.2b. There we see that the orthogonality condition is reasonably well satisfied and the constraint that $\Delta s = \Delta n$ is much more closely satisfied than it was in Fig. III.2a. In order to determine the temperatures associated with each isotherm we focus our attention on the two adiabatic lines labeled ① and ②. Since $\psi_2^* - \psi_1^* =$ constant, and since $(\Delta s/\Delta n) \sim 1$ we have from Eq. III-10 that $\Delta T =$ constant. In order that the boundary conditions be met we require that

$$8\Delta T = 180°\text{F} - 60°\text{F}$$

or

$$\Delta T = 15°\text{F}$$

This allows us to specify $\Delta\psi^*$ and determine the sums which are listed as 112°F for the upper surface and 75°F for the lower surface. There are two unsatisfactory characteristics of this solution. The first is that Δn is larger than Δs near the pipe and the second is that the boundary condition at the lower surfaces is not satisfied. Using the value of $\Delta T = 15°\text{F}$ leads to a temperature of 87°F at the lower surface. It would appear that the isotherms need to be "pushed" even closer to the pipe. More work with the eraser and more sketching leads to Fig. III.2c. The temperature difference is determined by

$$7\tfrac{1}{2}\,\Delta T = 120°\text{F}$$

thus $\Delta T = 16°\text{F}$ and the lower surface temperature is estimated to be 88°F. While we have perhaps improved the construction regarding the constraint that $\Delta s = \Delta n$ we have not yet satisfied the boundary conditions very accurately. In order to bring the graphical construction to a halt an average value of ΔT will be calculated by

$$\Delta T = \frac{1}{2}\left[\frac{120°\text{F}}{7.5} + \frac{97°\text{F}}{5.8}\right] = 16.4°\text{F}$$

Using this average value for ΔT allows us to calculate the sum of the absolute values of $\Delta\psi^*$ as 109°F for the top surface and 74°F for the bottom surface.

†Robertson, J. M., *Hydrodynamics in Theory and Application*, page 376, Prentice-Hall, Inc., Englewood Cliffs, N.J., 1965.

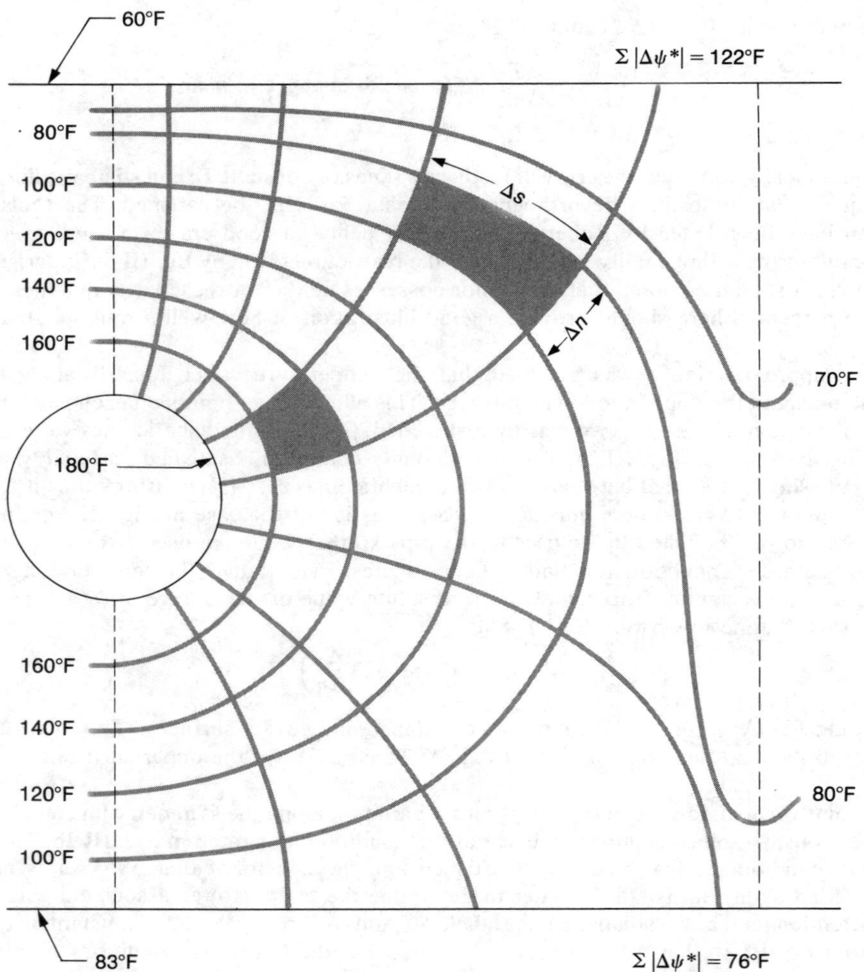

Fig. III.2a Graphical construction of isothermal and adiabatic lines.

In order to calculate the heat flux per unit width at the top and bottom surfaces we use Eq. 3.5-22 and Eq. III-7 to write

$$k|\Delta\psi^*| = k\left|\frac{\Delta T}{\Delta n}\right| \Delta s \tag{III-11}$$

The sum therefore represents the heat flux over section of surface under consideration

$$\{\text{heat flux per unit width}\} = \sum k|\Delta\psi^*| = \sum k\left|\frac{\Delta T}{\Delta n}\right| \Delta s \tag{III-12}$$

From Eq. III-12 we can determine

$$\{\text{heat flux per unit width at the top surface}\} = 0.42\frac{\text{Btu}}{\text{hr ft °F}} \times 109\text{°F} \tag{III-13a}$$

$$= 45.8\ \text{Btu/hr ft}$$

$$\{\text{heat flux per unit width at the bottom surface}\} = 0.42\frac{\text{Btu}}{\text{hr ft °F}} \times 74\text{°F} \tag{III-13b}$$

$$= 31.1\ \text{Btu/hr ft}$$

In the following paragraphs we will solve this sample problem numerically.

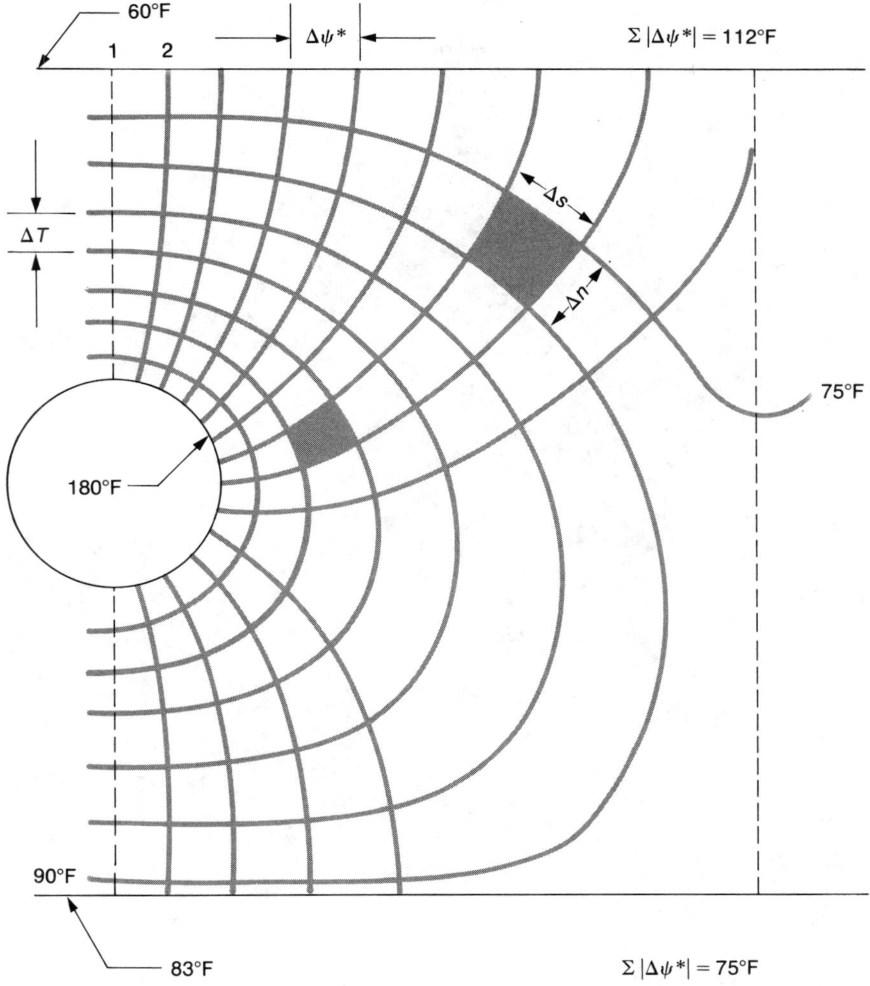

Fig. III.2b Graphical construction of isothermal and adiabatic lines.

Numerical Solution

To obtain a numerical solution we follow the development given in Section 3.3, defining dimensionless variables as

$$\Theta = \frac{T - T_3}{T_1 - T_3}$$

$$X = 2x/L, \qquad Y = 2y/L$$

and expressing Eqs. III-1 through III-6 as

$$\frac{\partial^2\Theta}{\partial X^2} + \frac{\partial^2\Theta}{\partial Y^2} = 0 \tag{III-14}$$

B.C.1′ $$\frac{\partial\Theta}{\partial X} = 0, \qquad X = 0, \quad D/L < Y \leqslant b/L$$

$$-b/L \leqslant Y < -D/L \tag{III-15}$$

B.C.2′ $$\Theta = 1, \qquad X^2 + Y^2 = (D/L)^2 \tag{III-16}$$

B.C.3′ $$\Theta = 0.1833, \qquad Y = -b/L \tag{III-17}$$

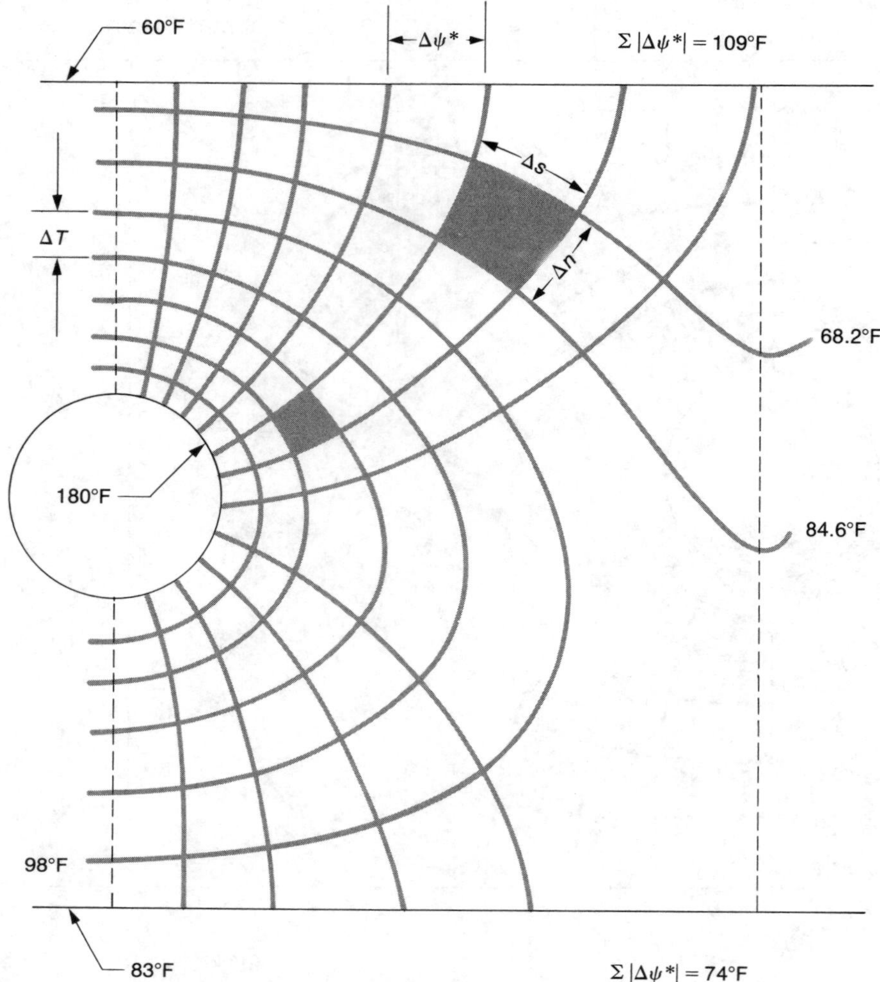

Fig. III.2c Graphical construction of isothermal and adiabatic lines.

B.C.4′
$$\Theta = 0, \qquad Y = +b/L \tag{III-18}$$

B.C.5′
$$\frac{\partial \Theta}{\partial X} = 0, \qquad X = 1 \tag{III-19}$$

We now use the finite-difference formulas given by Eqs. 3.3-18 and 3.3-19 to express Eq. III-14 as

$$(\Theta_{j,i+1} - 2\Theta_{j,i} + \Theta_{j,i-1}) + \left(\frac{\Delta X}{\Delta Y}\right)^2 (\Theta_{j+1,i} - \Theta_{j,i} + \Theta_{j-1,i}) = 0 \tag{III-20}$$

which is Eq. 3.3-22. In this example we wish to use the matrix inversion method with $\Delta X = \Delta Y$, thus we rearrange Eq. III-20 in the form

$$\Theta_{j,i-1} - 4\Theta_{j,i} + \Theta_{j,i+1} = -(\tilde{\Theta}_{j+1,i} + \tilde{\Theta}_{j-1,i}) \tag{III-21}$$

which is comparable to Eq. 3.3-28. For the particular grid illustrated in Fig. III.3a we can express the boundary conditions as

B.C.1″ & 2″
$$\Theta_{j,1} = \Theta_{j,2}, \qquad j = 2, 3, \ldots, 15$$
$$\Theta_{j,3} = 1, \qquad j = 16$$
$$\Theta_{j,4} = 1, \qquad j = 17$$

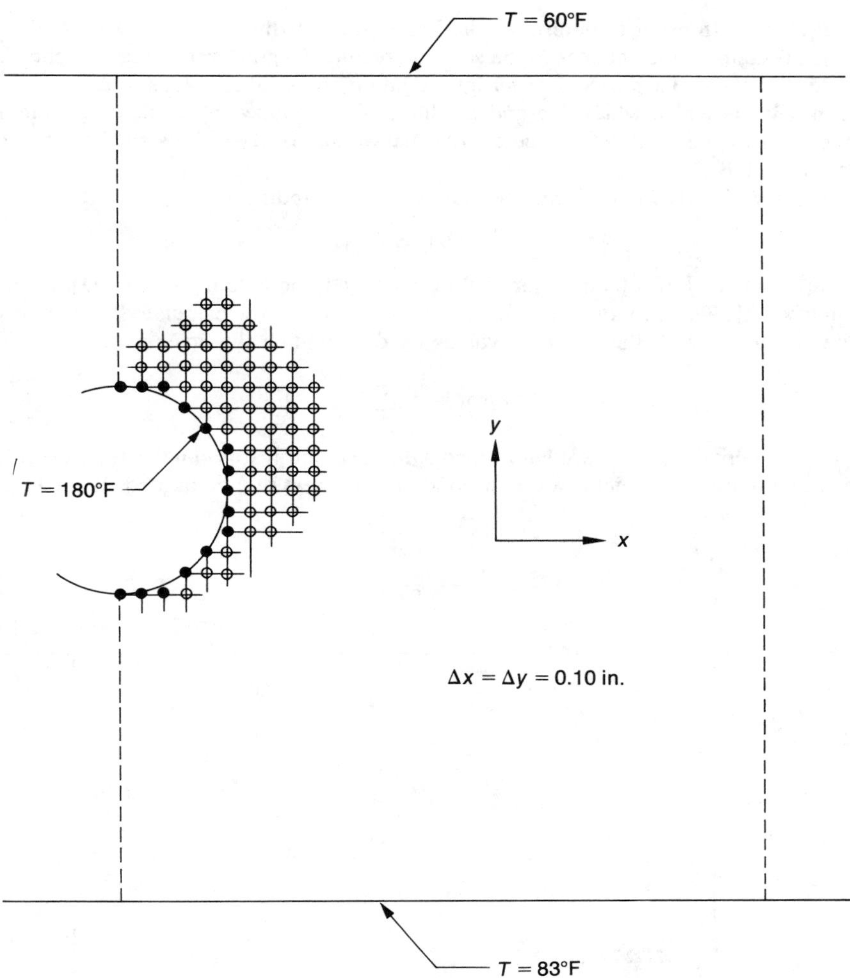

Fig. III.3a Grid for finite-difference calculation.

	$\Theta_{j,5} = 1,$	$j = 18$
	$\Theta_{j,6} = 1,$	$j = 19, 20, \ldots, 23$
	$\Theta_{j,5} = 1,$	$j = 24$
	$\Theta_{j,4} = 1,$	$j = 25$
	$\Theta_{j,3} = 1,$	$j = 26$
	$\Theta_{j,1} = \Theta_{j,2},$	$j = 27, 28, \ldots, 40$
B.C.3″	$\Theta_{1,i} = 0.1915,$	$i = 1, 2, \ldots, 31$
B.C.4″	$\Theta_{41,i} = 0.0,$	$i = 1, 2, \ldots, 31$
B.C.5″	$\Theta_{j,31} = \Theta_{j,30},$	$j = 1, 2, \ldots, 41$

Construction of the finite-difference form of the boundary conditions is straightforward except at the surface of the pipe. There we are forced to approximate the cylindrical surface in terms of the square grid points. The points which are fixed at 180°F are indicated by the solid circles in Fig. III.3a while the open circles are used to designate the interior grid points. When using a finite-difference analog of a differential equation we must always remember that there is error involved. From Eq. 3.3-17 we see that the error in the finite-difference approximation of $\partial^2\Theta/\partial X^2$ is proportional to ΔX^2, and it follows that the error in the approximation of $\partial^2\Theta/\partial Y^2$

is proportional to ΔY^2. In order to determine the importance of this error it is always advisable to change the grid size and see if appreciable changes in the solution result. If significant changes occur it means that the grid is too course for the particular problem under investigation and smaller values of ΔX and ΔY must be used. In Fig. III.3b a grid is shown in which Δx and Δy have been reduced by a factor of one-half. In addition to decreasing the error of the finite-difference approximation of Eq. III-14, this smaller grid reduces the error of the approximation of B.C.2′.

In order to solve Eq. III-21 we form the matrix as indicated in Eq. 3.3-30 and write the result as

$$[B]_j[\Theta]_j = [\tilde{D}]_j \tag{III-22}$$

for each interior value of j. If a temperature field is assumed, the column vector $[\tilde{D}]_j$ is known along with the tridiagonal matrix $[B]_j$. The equations can be solved, leading to new calculated values of $\Theta_{j,i}$. The calculated values can be compared with the assumed values by determining the error as

$$\text{error} = \sum_i \sum_j |\Theta_{j,i} - \tilde{\Theta}_{j,i}| \tag{III-23}$$

This error can be compared with a predetermined *tolerance* and if it is smaller than the tolerance the solution has converged and temperature field can be printed and the heat flux computed. If the error is larger than the

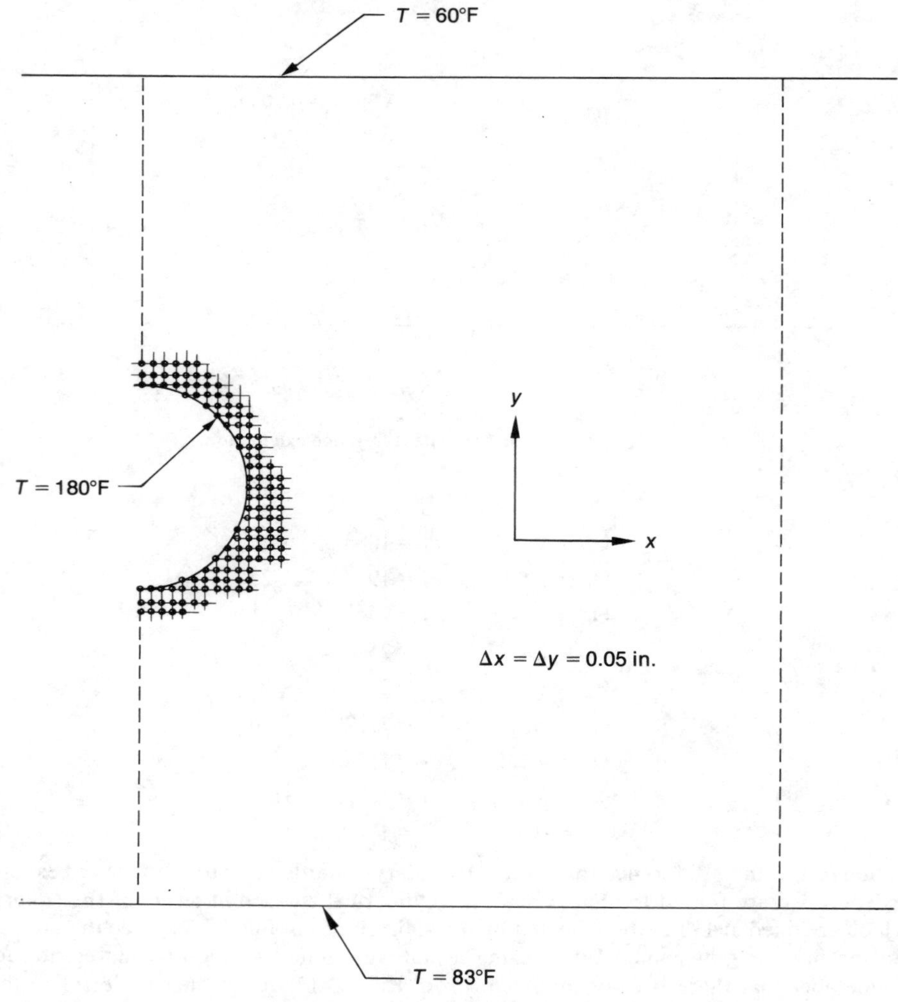

Fig. III.3b Grid for finite-difference calculation.

tolerance, new assumed values of the temperature field can be generated using Eq. 3.3-27, written here as

$$\tilde{\Theta}_{j,i}^{(k+1)} = \tilde{\Theta}_{j,i}^{(k)} + \omega[\Theta_{j,i}^{(k)} - \tilde{\Theta}_{j,i}^{(k)}] \tag{III-24}$$

and the process repeated until the error is reduced to the level specified by the tolerance.

The flow diagram for the computer program is illustrated in Fig. III.4, and the FORTRAN program is shown in Fig. III.5 for the grid illustrated in Fig. III.3a.

In solving problems of this type one must always be sure that the answer is independent of the grid size, indicating that the finite-difference equation is a reasonable approximation to the differential equation, and that the answer is independent of the tolerance, indicating that the iterative procedure has converged. In Table III-1

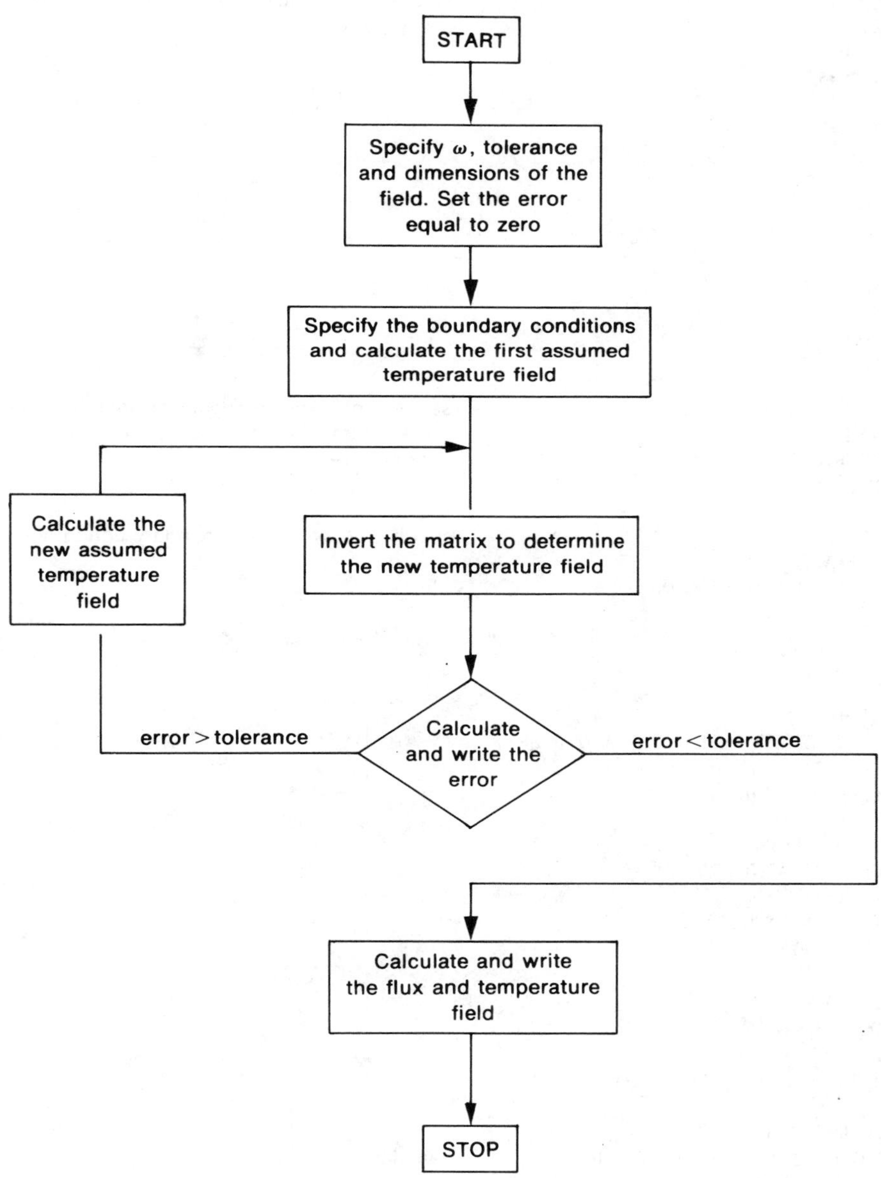

Fig. III.4 Flow diagram for computer program.

Fortran Statements	*Comments*
DIMENSION THETA (41, 31), THETA1 (41, 31), R(41), W(31), SB(31), G(31), D(31)	specify the size of the array of temperatures
TOL = 6.0	specify the tolerance
OMEGA = 1.0	specify the iteration parameter
ERROR = 0.0	set the error equal to zero
DO 100 I = 1, 31 THETA1 (1, I) = (83.0 − 60.0)/120.0 100 THETA1 (41, I) = 0.0	specify the fixed temperature boundary conditions
DO 101 J = 2, 15 101 R(J) = 2.0 R(16) = 4.0 R(17) = 5.0 R(18) = 6.0 R(19) = 7.0 R(20) = 7.0 R(21) = 7.0 R(22) = 7.0 R(23) = 7.0 R(24) = 6.0 R(25) = 5.0 R(26) = 4.0 DO 102 J = 27, 40 102 R(J) = 2.0	locate the boundary along the line of symmetry and pipe wall
DO 103 J = 2, 40 N = R(J) DO 103 I = N, 30 103 THETA1 (J, I) = 1.0	specify the fixed temperature boundary condition on the pipe wall and specify the first assumed temperature field
200 DO 201 J = 2, 40 THETA1 (J, 1) = THETA1 (J, 2) 201 THETA1 (J, 31) = THETA1 (J, 30)	specify the symmetry boundary conditions
DO 303 J = 2, 40 N = R(J) N1 = N − 1 DO 300 I = N, 30 300 D(I) = − (THETA1 (J + 1, I) + THETA1 (J − 1, I)) D(N) = D(N) − THETA1 (J, N1) D(30) = D(30) − THETA1 (J, 31) W(N) = − 4.0 SB(N) = 1.0/W(N) G(N) = D(N)/W(N) DO 301 I = N1, 30 W(I) = − 4.0 − SB(I − 1) SB(I) = 1.0/W(I) 301 G(I) = (D(I) − G(I − 1))/W(I) THETA(30) = G(30) DO 302 K = N1, 30 I = 30 + N − K 302 THETA(J, I) = G(I) − SB(I)*THETA(J, I + 1)	invert the matrix
DO 303 I = 2, 30 303 ERROR = ERROR + ABS (THETA(J, I) − THETA1 (J, I))	calculate the error

Fortran Statements

```
      WRITE (G, I) ERROR                          write error
    1 FORMAT (1HO, 2E13.4)                        output format

      IF (ERROR.LT.TOL) GO TO 500                 test error

      DO 401 J=2, 40                              calculate new assumed values for the
      DO 401 I=2, 30                              temperature field
  401 THETA1 (J, I)=THETA1 (J, I)+
      OMEGA*(THETA(J, I)-THETA1 (J, I))

      ERROR=0.0                                   set error equal to zero

      GO TO 200                                   specify new boundary values and recalculate the
                                                  temperature field

  500 TFLUX=0.0                                   set top flux equal to zero set bottom flux equal
      BFLUX=0.0                                   to zero

      DO 501 I=1, 31                              calculate the "flux" at the bottom and top
      TFLUX=(THETA1 (40, I)-THETA1 (41, I))
      *120.0+TFLUX
  501 BFLUX=(THETA1 (2, I)-THETA1 (1, I))
      *120.0+BFLUX

      WRITE (6, 1) TFLUX, BFLUX                   write the "fluxes"

      DO 502 I=1, 31                              write out the temperature field
      DO 502 J=1, 41
      TEMP=120.0*THETA1 (J, I)+60.0
  502 WRITE (6, 1) TEMP

      STOP
```

Fig. III.5 Fortran program for line-by-line matrix inversion.

we have shown the quantity $\Sigma\,|\Delta\psi^*|$, which is

$$\sum |\Delta\psi^*| = 120 \sum_i (\Theta_{40,i} - \Theta_{41,i}) \sim \int_{x=0}^{x=L/2} \left(\frac{\partial T}{\partial y}\right)_{y=b/2} dx \tag{III-25}$$

or

$$\sum |\Delta\psi^*| = 120 \sum_i (\Theta_{2,i} - \Theta_{1,i}) \sim \int_{x=0}^{x=L/2} \left(\frac{\partial T}{\partial y}\right)_{y=-b/2} dx \tag{III-26}$$

as a function of the mesh size and the tolerance, or the error as given by Eq. III-23. From those results we see that approximately 1000 iterations are required for the course grid size ($\Delta x = \Delta y = 0.10$ in.) in order to produce a result which is essentially independent of the number of iterations, or independent of the tolerance placed on the error. For the finer grid size ($\Delta x = \Delta y = 0.05$ in.) we see that somewhat more than 3000 iterations are required to obtain a converged solution. In this example our objective of obtaining a solution which is independent of both the grid size and the tolerance has not been accomplished; however, we can use the results to obtain a reasonably satisfactory estimate of the heat fluxes.

In Figs. III.6 we have plotted TFLUX and BFLUX as a function of the error, and from those figures and the tabulated values we estimate the converged values of TFLUX and BFLUX to be given by

Estimated Converged Fluxes

$\Delta x = \Delta y = 0.10$ in.	TFLUX = 126.8°F	BFLUX = 88.8°F
$\Delta x = \Delta y = 0.05$ in.	TFLUX = 122.5°F	BFLUX = 85.8°F

Table III-1 Finite-Difference Results for $\Sigma\,|\Delta\psi^*|$

$\Delta x = \Delta y = 0.10$ in.

Number of iterations	TFLUX, °F	BFLUX, °F	Error
5	882.3	713.4	12.0
22	453.0	366.3	6.0
61	275.9	224.2	3.0
122	198.2	162.9	1.5
197	161.3	127.9	0.75
275	143.9	108.6	0.375
353	135.4	98.7	0.188
431	131.1	93.7	0.094
511	129.0	91.2	0.047
589	128.0	90.0	0.023
667	127.4	89.4	0.012
745	127.2	89.0	0.0058
824	127.0	88.9	0.0029
902	127.0	88.8	0.0014
980	126.9	88.8	0.0007

Calculation time on Burroughs 6700 is 9.5 min.

$\Delta x = \Delta y = 0.05$ in.

Number of iterations	TFLUX, °F	BFLUX, °F	Error
7	1572	1271	24.0
25	838.7	678.1	12.0
94	433.2	350.3	6.0
252	265.3	215.1	3.0
500	191.4	154.6	1.5
793	156.5	121.3	0.75
1095	139.6	103.6	0.375
1399	131.2	94.6	0.188
1703	127.1	90.0	0.094
2008	125.0	87.8	0.047
2312	124.0	86.7	0.023
2616	123.5	86.1	0.012
2921	123.22	85.8	0.0058

Calculation time on Burroughs 6700 is 1 hr 54 min.

Our converged fluxes are certainly not independent of the grid size; however, the values are not very much different and we can extrapolate to $\Delta x = \Delta y = 0$ to obtain our final estimate of the fluxes. In order to carry out the extrapolation we need to know how the error in our finite-difference expression for the temperature gradient depends on Δy. Following the development given in Sec. 3.3 we can show that

$$\left(\frac{\partial T}{\partial y}\right)_{y=b/2} \sim \frac{T|_{y=b/2} - T|_{y=b/2-\Delta y}}{\Delta y} + \frac{\Delta y}{2}\left(\frac{\partial^2 T}{\partial y^2}\right)_{y=0} + \cdots \tag{III-27}$$

thus the error in our finite-difference approximation for the temperature gradient at $y = \pm b/2$ is proportional to Δy and we should extrapolate TFLUX and BFLUX as a function of Δy. This is done in Fig. III.7, and the results, TFLUX = 118.2°F and BLFUX = 82.8°F, compare quite favorably with those obtained by the graphical method and shown in Fig. III.2c. The graphical results are about 10 per cent lower than those obtained by solution of the finite-difference equations; however, we must remember that the latter results are not free from error. To obtain the heat flux per unit width we must multiply TFLUX and BFLUX by the thermal conductivity to obtain

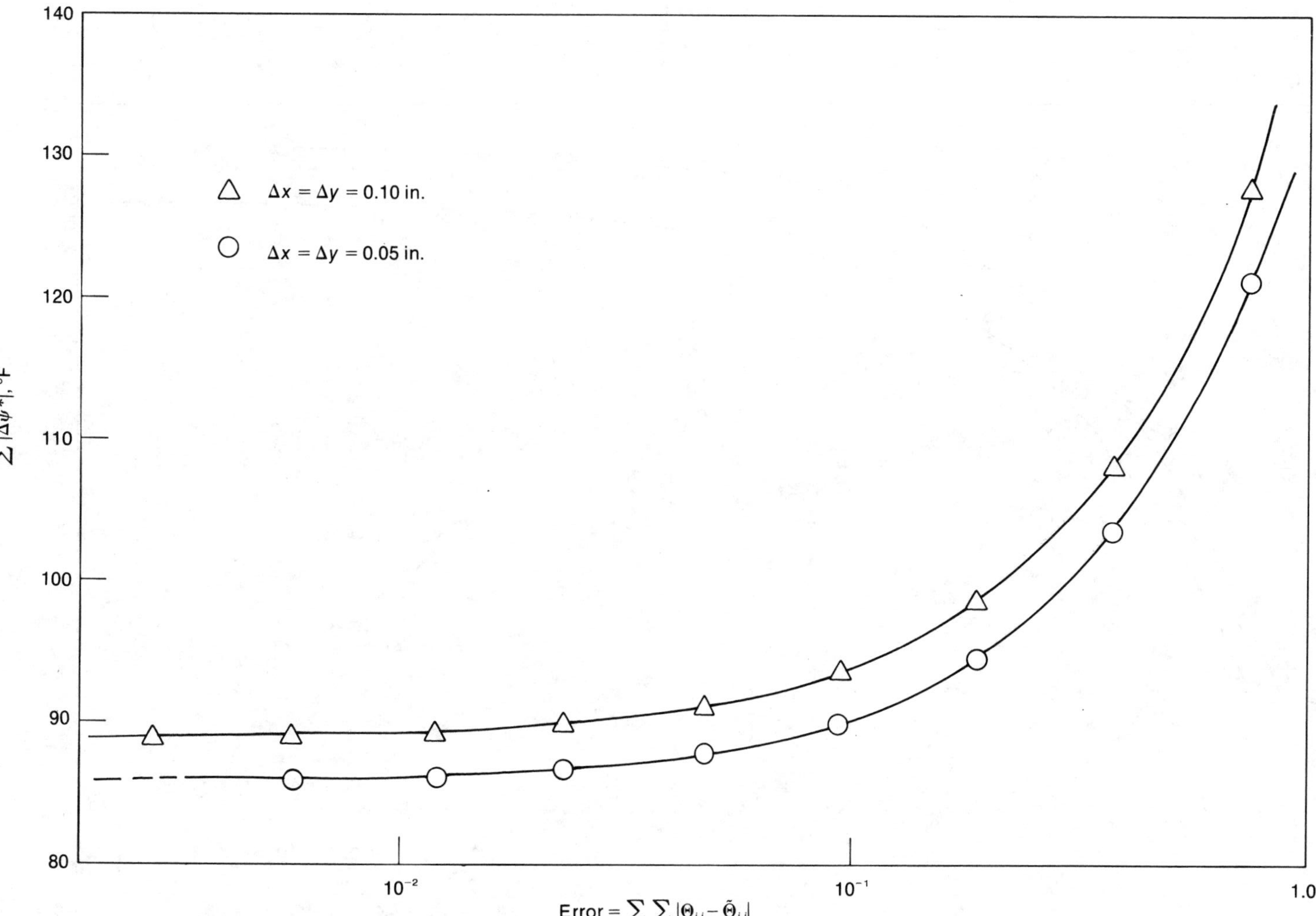

Fig. III.6a Bottom flux as a function of the error.

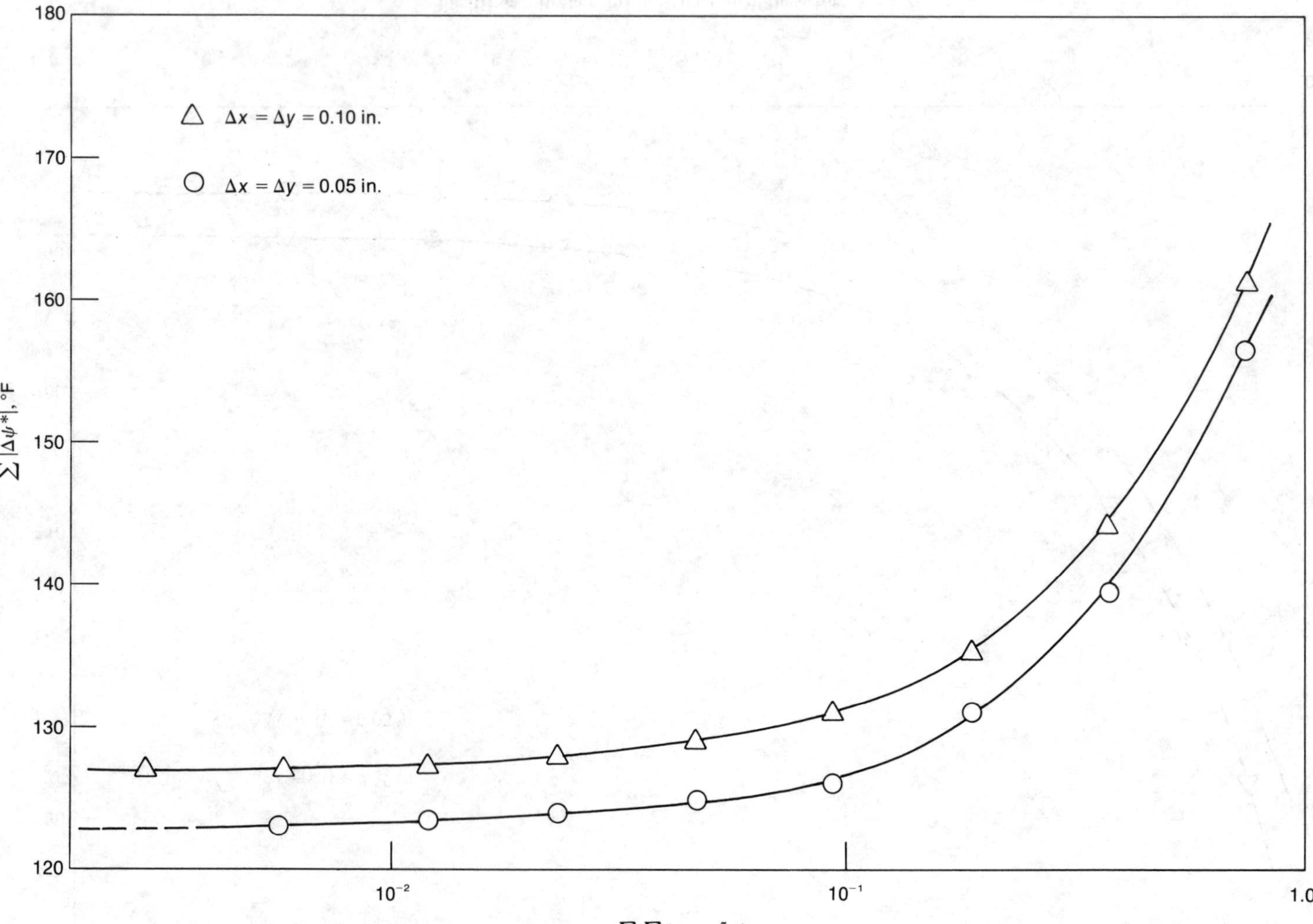

Fig. III.6b Top flux as a function of the error.

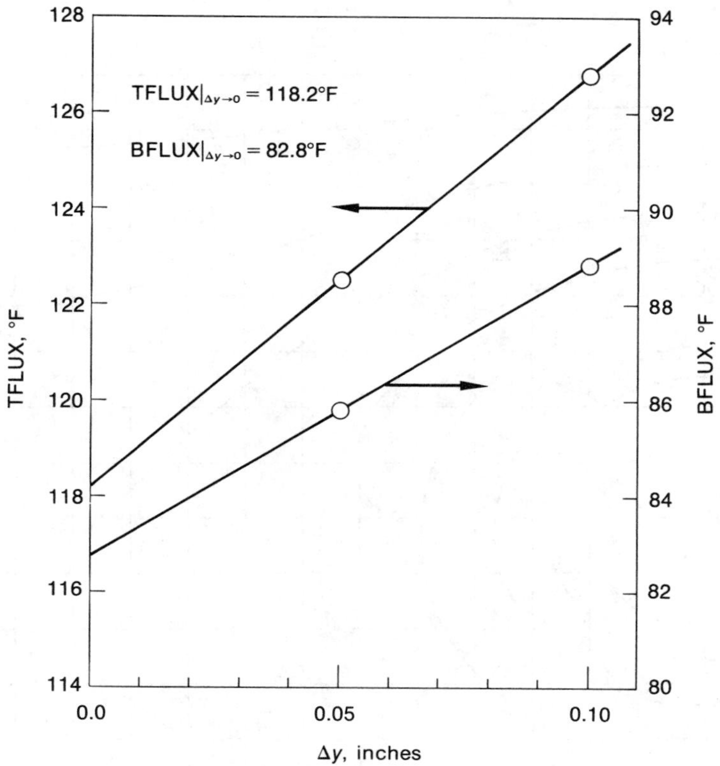

Fig. III.7 Extrapolation to zero grid size.

$$\{\text{heat flux per unit width at the bottom surface}\} = 34.8 \text{ Btu/hr ft} \qquad \text{(III-28a)}$$

$$\{\text{heat flux per unit width at the top surface}\} = 49.6 \text{ Btu/hr ft} \qquad \text{(III-28b)}$$

These results of course compare favorably with those given by Eqs. III-13 of 45.8 Btu/hr ft and 31.1 Btu/hr ft.

In order to complete our comparison between the graphical and numerical method we need to examine the isotherms determined from the numerical solution to see how closely they resemble those sketched in Fig. III.2c. In Fig. III.8 the isotherms from the numerical solution are shown, and we see reasonable agreement in regions near the specified temperatures of 60°F, 180°F, and 83°F, but rather poor agreement near the plane of symmetry between the pipes. Even though the graphical construction is poor in this region, it has only a small effect on the heat flux at the top and bottom surfaces and the agreement between the two methods of calculating the heat flux remains quite satisfactory.

PROBLEMS†

III-1. Solve Design Problem III for $\Delta x = \Delta y = 0.10$ using the relaxation method.

III-2. The rate of convergence shown in Table III-1 appears to be quite slow. This may result from the fact that the line-by-line matrix inversion was set up so that the surface temperatures of 60°F and 83°F entered into the matrix inversion only on the first and last line. If Eq. III-21 is put in the form

$$\Theta_{j-1,i} - 4\Theta_{j,i} + \Theta_{j+1,i} = -(\tilde{\Theta}_{j,i+1} + \tilde{\Theta}_{j,i-1})$$

the upper and lower surface temperatures will be included in each line, and the iterative procedure should

†Problems numbered III-1, III-2, etc. deal directly with Design Problem III, and problems marked with an asterisk (*) are concerned with the solved example problems.

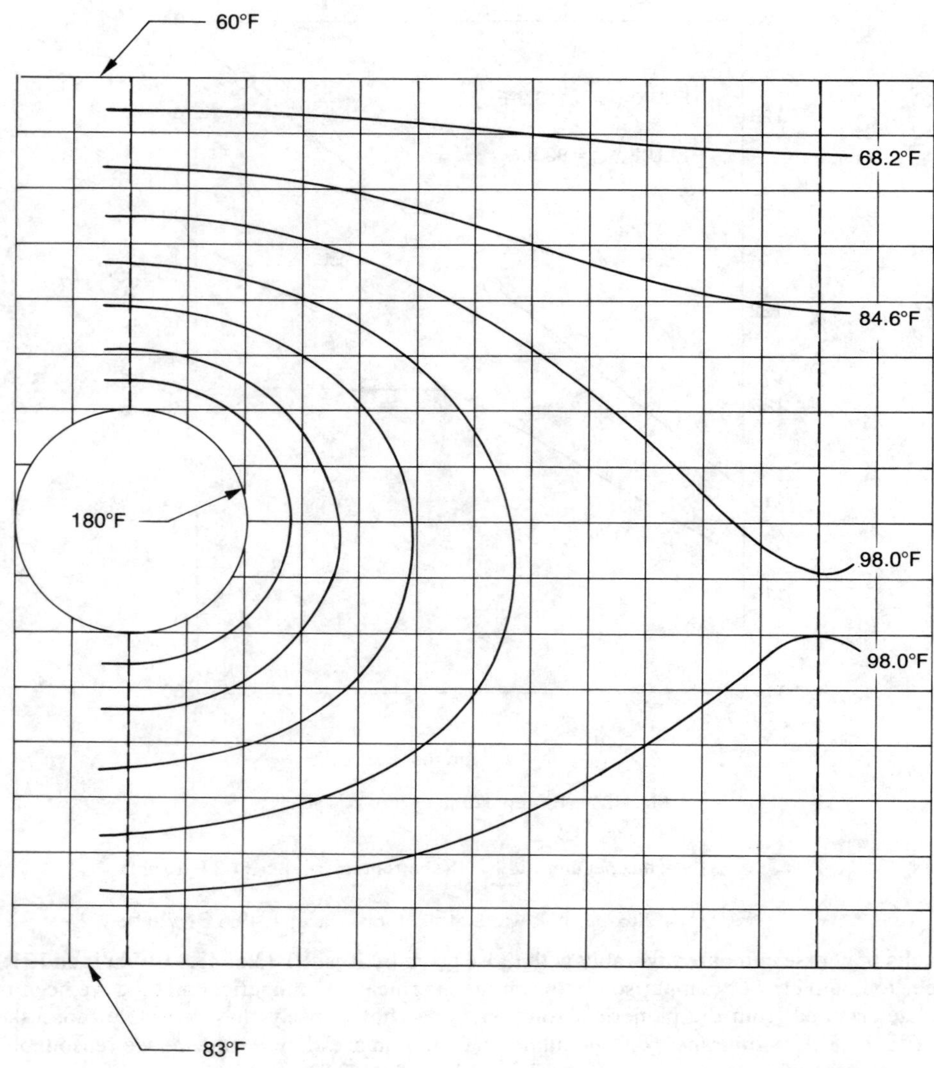

Fig. III.8 Isothermal lines from the numerical solution.

converge more rapidly. Carry out the numerical solution in this form and compare your results with those given in Table III-1 for $\Delta x = \Delta y = 0.10$ in.

III-3. Derive Eq. III-27.

III-4. Use the order-of-magnitude analysis described in Sec. 2.9 and Eqs. 3.3-17 through 3.3-22 to estimate the error in the calculated temperature field for $\Delta x = \Delta y = 0.10$ in. and $\Delta x = \Delta y = 0.05$ in.

3-1. (3.1) Solve for the temperature distribution in the rectangular plate illustrated in Fig. 3.1.1 if the boundary condition at $y = L$ is changed to a constant flux condition:

B.C.4 $$-k(\partial T/\partial y) = q_0, \qquad y = L$$

3-2. (3.1) Solve for the temperature distribution in a rectangular plate given the following boundary conditions:

B.C.1 $$T = T_0, \qquad x = 0$$

B.C.2 $$T = T_1, \qquad x = b$$

B.C.3 $$\frac{\partial T}{\partial y} = 0, \qquad y = 0$$

B.C.4 $T = T_0, \quad y = L$

3-3. (3.1) Solve for the temperature field in the rectangular plate illustrated in Fig. 3.1.3 if the temperature at $y = L$ is given by

B.C.4 $T = T_0(1 + \sin(\pi x/b)), \quad y = L$

3-4. (3.1) Use Eq. 3.1-72 to obtain an expression for the total heat flux per unit depth at the surface $y = L, 0 \leq x \leq b$.

3-5. (3.1) Use the method of superposition to set up a solution for the following problem

$$\frac{\partial^2 T}{\partial x^2} + \frac{\partial^2 T}{\partial y^2} = 0$$

B.C.1 $T = T_0, \quad x = 0$

B.C.2 $T = T_0 + (T_1 - T_0)[2(y/L) - (y/L)^2], \quad x = b$

B.C.3 $\frac{\partial T}{\partial y} = 0, \quad y = 0$

B.C.4 $T = T_1, \quad y = L$

3-6. (3.2) In the first example in Sec. 3.2 show how the solution $\Theta = 1$ results from the general solution obtained by setting $C = 0$ in Eqs. 3.2-12.

3-7. (3.2) Show how Eq. 3.2-42 is obtained from Eq. 3.2-41.

3-8. (3.2) Derive Eq. 3.2-43 using the Frobenius method described in Sec. 2.7.

3-9. (3.2) Solve for the temperature field in a cylindrical rod subject to the boundary conditions

B.C.1 $T = T_0, \quad z = 0$

B.C.2 $T = T_a, \quad z = L$

B.C.3 $T = T_a, \quad r = r_0$

3-10. (3.2) Solve for the temperature distribution in a cylindrical rod subject to the boundary conditions

B.C.1 $T = T_0 + \left(\frac{r}{r_0}\right)(T_a - T_0), \quad z = 0$

B.C.2 $T = T_a, \quad z = L$

B.C.3 $T = T_a, \quad r = r_0$

3-11. (3.2) Prove Eq. (g) in Table 3.2-1 using Eq. (a), and use Eq. (g) to prove Eq. (n).

3-12. (3.3) Use Eqs. 3.3-15 and 3.3-16 to derive an approximate expression for first derivative

$$\left(\frac{\partial \Theta}{\partial X}\right)_X = \frac{\Theta(X + \Delta X) - \Theta(X - \Delta X)}{2\Delta X}$$

3-13. (3.3) The governing differential equation for one-dimensional heat conduction with a heat source is

$$0 = \frac{d^2 T}{dx^2} + (\Phi/k)$$

If the rate of heat generation is nonlinear function of the temperature this equation must be solved numerically. Given the conditions

$$\Phi = \Phi_0 e^{-T_0/T}$$

$$T = T_0, \quad x = 0$$

$$\frac{dT}{dx} = 0, \quad x = L$$

solve for the dimensionless temperature distribution T/T_0 as a function of $X = x/L$ for $\Phi_0 L^2/kT_0 = 2.0$ using an iterative matrix inversion method.

3-14. Use the relaxation method to solve for the temperature distribution in the rectangular plate shown in Fig. 3.1.3

(3.3) given the boundary condition for $y = L$

B.C.4 $$T = T_0\left[1 + \left(\frac{x}{b}\right) - \left(\frac{x}{b}\right)^2\right], \qquad y = L$$

Choose $b/L = 0.5$.

***3-15.** Solve Ex. 3.3-1 using a line-by-line matrix inversion method.
(3.3)

3-16. Solve Prob. 3-9 numerically.
(3.4)

3-17. Solve Prob. 3-10 numerically.
(3.4)

3-18. Solve Prob. 3-3 graphically and compare the total heat flux per unit depth at the surface $y = L$ with that
(3.5) obtained from the analytic solution.

3-19. Apply the condition $\int_A \mathbf{q} \cdot \mathbf{n}\, dA = 0$ to the shaded area in Fig. 3.5.2 to prove that the energy flowing between
(3.5) two streamlines is constant.

REFERENCES

1. Wylie, C. R., Jr., *Advanced Engineering Mathematics*, Third Edition, McGraw-Hill Book Co., Inc. New York, 1960.
2. *Handbook of Mathematical Functions*, edited by M. Abramowitz and I. A. Stegun, National Bureau of Standards, Applied Mathematics Series: 55, U.S. Government Printing Office, Washington, D.C., 1964.
3. British Association Mathematical Tables, Vol. VI, Cambridge University Press, 1937.
4. Lapidus, L., *Digital Computation for Chemical Engineers*, McGraw-Hill Book Co., Inc., New York, 1962.
5. Forsythe, G. E., and Wasow, W. R., *Finite-Difference Methods for Partial Differential Equations*, John Wiley & Sons, Inc., New York, 1960.
6. Hamming, R. W., *Numerical Methods for Scientists and Engineers*, McGraw-Hill Book Co., Inc., New York, 1962.
7. Von Rosenberg, D. U., *Methods for the Numerical Solution of Partial Differential Equations*, American Elsevier Publishing Co., Inc., New York, 1969.
8. Southwell, R. V., *Relaxation Methods in Theoretical Physics*, Oxford University Press, 1946.
9. Whitaker, S., *Introduction to Fluid Mechanics*, Sec. 3.6, Prentice-Hall, Inc., Englewood Cliffs, N.J., 1968.

Design Problem IV

Our objective here is to re-examine the design problem given in Chapter 2. In that problem we were concerned with the dangerously high surface temperature of a reactor vessel. The most obvious remedy to that problem seemed to be to insulate the reactor; however, we found that the amount of insulation required to lower the surface temperature to 100°F was excessive. The question to be raised here is: What is the temperature of the skin–insulation interface? If the surface temperature of the insulation is 100°F, will the skin temperature be 100°F? Probably not, since we know from experience that different materials at the same temperature give different sensations of hotness and coldness. In this problem we are given the responsibility of examining the transient heat transfer process that occurs when a visitor puts his hand on the insulated reactor vessel, with the hope that perhaps we can tolerate higher surface temperatures and therefore less insulation.

In determining the temperature of the interface you may want to use the information given by Lathrop† that the normal skin temperature of the hand is 90°F. You are given the following information about the available insulation:

$$\rho = 80\ \text{lb}_m/\text{ft}^3, \qquad c_p = 0.2\ \text{Btu/lb}_m\,°\text{F}, \qquad k = 0.12\ \text{Btu/hr ft}\,°\text{F}$$

Information about the physical properties of skin can be found in *Physical Functions of Skin*, Oxford Press, 1964, by R. T. Tregear, or in the paper, "The Conduction of Heat to and through Skin and the Temperatures Attained Therein," *Journal of Pathology* **23**, 531 (1947) by F. C. Henriques and A. R. Maritz.

†Lathrop, T. G., "*Hypothermia*: *Killer of the Unprepared*," Mazamas Publishers, Portland, Oregon.

4

Transient Heat Conduction

In the previous chapter we examined several cases of two-dimensional heat conduction, i.e., the temperature was a function of two spatial coordinates. Our major objective there was to acquaint the student with some of the mathematical techniques that are applicable to such problems, rather than to extend our understanding of heat conduction *per se.* In this chapter we will be studying processes for which the temperature is a function of two variables (time and distance). However, our objective here is quite different from that of Chapter 3; here we will definitely be interested in understanding the physical behavior of systems under transient conditions.

As examples of important transient heat transfer process we might consider the role that a heat shield plays in the safe return of a space vehicle, or the transient heating and subsequent melting of an electrical fuse. During re-entry the enormously high temperatures on the "active" side of the heat shield must not "penetrate" through the shield, thus raising the temperature of the spacecraft to an uncomfortable level. If an electrical system is subject to a sudden increase in voltage, it is important that a fuse will burn out before any damage can be done to the equipment. In both these cases it is important that an engineer have an understanding of the nature of the transient response of these systems, and that will be the primary objective of the first three sections in this chapter. In Secs. 4.4 through 4.9 we will continue the presentation started in Chapter 3 and explore some of the more advanced mathematical techniques that can be used to analyze transient heat conduction processes.

*4.1 The Governing Equation for Transient Heat Conduction

At this point we return to the fundamental energy postulate and examine the form it takes for transient heat conduction.

$$\frac{D}{Dt}\int_{\mathcal{V}_m(t)} \rho\left(e+\frac{1}{2}v^2\right)dV = -\int_{\mathcal{A}_m(t)} \mathbf{q}\cdot\mathbf{n}\,dA + \int_{\mathcal{A}_m(t)} \mathbf{t}_{(\mathbf{n})}\cdot\mathbf{v}\,dA + \int_{\mathcal{V}_m(t)} \rho\mathbf{g}\cdot\mathbf{v}\,dV + \int_{\mathcal{V}_m(t)} \Phi\,dV \tag{4.1-1}$$

We will begin by imposing the condition that $\mathbf{v}=0$, thus restricting our analysis to constant volume systems. If the velocity is zero the material volume $\mathcal{V}_m(t)$ is *fixed* in space, the material derivative becomes a partial derivative, and Eq. 4.1-1 is simplified to

$$\frac{\partial}{\partial t}\int_{\mathcal{V}} \rho e\,dV = -\int_{\mathcal{A}} \mathbf{q}\cdot\mathbf{n}\,dA + \int_{\mathcal{V}} \Phi\,dV \tag{4.1-2}$$

Noting that the density must be constant if the material is stationary, we can interchange differentiation and integration on the left-hand-side of Eq. 3.1-2 to obtain

$$\int_{\mathcal{V}} \rho\left(\frac{\partial e}{\partial t}\right) dV = -\int_{\mathcal{A}} \mathbf{q}\cdot\mathbf{n}\, dA + \int_{\mathcal{V}} \Phi\, dV \tag{4.1-3}$$

Application of the divergence theorem to the area integral and putting all the terms under the same integral sign yields

$$\int_{\mathcal{V}} \left[\rho\left(\frac{\partial e}{\partial t}\right) + \nabla\cdot\mathbf{q} - \Phi\right] dV = 0 \tag{4.1-4}$$

Since the integrand is assumed to be a continuous function and the limits of integration are arbitrary, the integrand must be zero and we obtain

$$\rho\left(\frac{\partial e}{\partial t}\right) = -\nabla\cdot\mathbf{q} + \Phi \tag{4.1-5}$$

This result is given in Table 4.1-1 for rectangular, cylindrical, and spherical coordinates.

Table 4.1-1 The Transient Heat Conduction in Terms of the Internal Energy and Heat Flux Vector for Rectangular, Cylindrical, and Spherical Coordinates

rectangular coordinates (x, y, z, t)

$$\rho\left(\frac{\partial e}{\partial t}\right) = -\left[\left(\frac{\partial q_x}{\partial x}\right) + \left(\frac{\partial q_y}{\partial y}\right) + \left(\frac{\partial q_z}{\partial z}\right)\right] + \Phi \tag{a}$$

cylindrical coordinates (r, θ, z, t)

$$\rho\left(\frac{\partial e}{\partial t}\right) = -\left[\frac{1}{r}\frac{\partial}{\partial r}(rq_r) + \frac{1}{r}\left(\frac{\partial q_\theta}{\partial \theta}\right) + \left(\frac{\partial q_z}{\partial z}\right)\right] + \Phi \tag{b}$$

spherical coordinates (r, θ, ϕ, t)

$$\rho\left(\frac{\partial e}{\partial t}\right) = -\left[\frac{1}{r^2}\frac{\partial}{\partial r}(r^2 q_r) + \frac{1}{r\sin\theta}\frac{\partial}{\partial \theta}(q_\theta \sin\theta) + \frac{1}{r\sin\theta}\left(\frac{\partial q_\phi}{\partial \phi}\right)\right] + \Phi \tag{c}$$

In Eq. 4.1-5 we have *four* unknowns,† and only *one* equation. The number of unknowns is reduced to two by the application of Fourier's law leading to

$$\rho\left(\frac{\partial e}{\partial t}\right) = \nabla\cdot(k\nabla T) + \Phi \tag{4.1-6}$$

In order to remove the final indeterminancy we must draw upon thermodynamics and express the internal energy as a function of the temperature and density

$$e = e(T, \rho) \tag{4.1-7}$$

Note that we assume that Eq. 4.1-7 holds everywhere in time and space, i.e., we impose the assumption of "local equilibrium." Since the density is constant (this is consistent with the assumption, $\mathbf{v} = 0$) we can use Eq. 4.1-7 to obtain

$$\frac{\partial e}{\partial t} = \left(\frac{\partial e}{\partial T}\right)_\rho \left(\frac{\partial T}{\partial t}\right) \tag{4.1-8}$$

We define the constant volume (or constant density) heat capacity per unit mass as

$$c_v = \left(\frac{\partial e}{\partial T}\right)_\rho \tag{4.1-9}$$

†The source term, Φ, must be considered as a specified parameter, while e and the three components of $\mathbf{q}$ are the unknown dependent variables.

and Eq. 4.1-6 reduces to

$$\rho c_v \left(\frac{\partial T}{\partial t}\right) = \nabla \cdot (k \nabla T) + \Phi, \quad \text{constant volume processes} \tag{4.1-10}$$

It is intuitively appealing, and will be proved in Chapter 5, that for constant pressure processes Eq. 4.1-6 takes the form

$$\rho c_p \left(\frac{\partial T}{\partial t}\right) = \nabla \cdot (k \nabla T) + \Phi, \quad \text{constant pressure processes} \tag{4.1-11}$$

This result is not subject to the restriction, $\mathbf{v} = 0$; however, it does require that *convective* transport of energy be negligible compared to *conduction*. This is, of course, a satisfactory restriction for the class of problems that we wish to analyze in this chapter.

The constant *volume* heat capacity, c_v, is difficult to determine experimentally, whereas the constant *pressure* heat capacity, c_p, is relatively easy to measure and is usually the quantity found tabulated in texts and reference books. The two are related by the expression

$$c_p = c_v + \frac{T\beta^2}{\rho\kappa} \tag{4.1-12}$$

where κ and β are the compressibility and the coefficient of expansion respectively. For solids the term $T\beta^2/\rho\kappa$ is quite small relative to c_v and we can write

$$c_p \sim c_v, \quad \text{for solids} \tag{4.1-13}$$

Under these circumstances Eqs. 4.1-10 and 4.1-11 are identical. Expanded forms of Eq. 4.1-11 are listed in Table 4.1-2 for rectangular, cylindrical, and spherical coordinates.

Table 4.1-2 The Transient Heat Conduction Equation in Rectangular, Cylindrical, and Spherical Coordinates

rectangular (x, y, z, t)

$$\rho c_p \left(\frac{\partial T}{\partial t}\right) = \left[\frac{\partial}{\partial x}\left(k \frac{\partial T}{\partial x}\right) + \frac{\partial}{\partial y}\left(k \frac{\partial T}{\partial y}\right) + \frac{\partial}{\partial z}\left(k \frac{\partial T}{\partial z}\right)\right] + \Phi \tag{a}$$

cylindrical (r, θ, z, t)

$$\rho c_p \left(\frac{\partial T}{\partial t}\right) = \left[\frac{1}{r}\frac{\partial}{\partial r}\left(rk \frac{\partial T}{\partial r}\right) + \frac{1}{r^2}\frac{\partial}{\partial \theta}\left(k \frac{\partial T}{\partial \theta}\right) + \frac{\partial}{\partial z}\left(k \frac{\partial T}{\partial z}\right)\right] + \Phi \tag{b}$$

spherical (r, θ, ϕ, t)

$$\rho c_p \left(\frac{\partial T}{\partial t}\right) = \left[\frac{1}{r^2}\frac{\partial}{\partial r}\left(r^2 k \frac{\partial T}{\partial r}\right) + \frac{1}{r^2 \sin\theta}\frac{\partial}{\partial \theta}\left(k \frac{\partial T}{\partial \theta}\right) + \frac{1}{r^2 \sin\theta}\frac{\partial}{\partial \phi}\left(k \frac{\partial T}{\partial \phi}\right)\right] + \Phi \tag{c}$$

If the thermal conductivity is constant, Eq. 4.1-11 may be written as

$$\frac{\partial T}{\partial t} = \alpha \nabla^2 T + \frac{\Phi}{\rho c_p} \tag{4.1-14}$$

where α is the *thermal diffusivity* defined by

$$\alpha = \frac{k}{\rho c_p} \tag{4.1-15}$$

*4.2 Transient Heat Conduction for Bodies with Negligible Internal Resistance

We begin our analysis of transient heat conduction by examining the process that occurs when a plate at temperature T_0 is suddenly immersed in a fluid at a temperature T_1. We will assume that the dimensions of the plate in the y- and z-directions are large compared to the thickness, b, of the plate. If the thermal conductivity of the plate is "small" and the film heat transfer coefficient is "large," we can guess that the temperature profiles are similar to those illustrated in Fig. 4.2.1. There we see that the temperature disturbance at $x = 0$ propagates into the solid and the condition of symmetry is imposed at the centerline. At a time, $t = 0$, the surface temperature is suddenly raised to a value very near to T_1, and as time progresses the surface temperature approaches T_1.

If the thermal conductivity of the plate is "large" and the film heat transfer coefficient is "small," we might guess that a rather different set of temperature profiles would result such as those shown in Fig. 4.2.2. Under these circumstances the temperature in the plate is very nearly equal to the surface temperature, and the temperature in the plate is easily determined. Before doing so we should give some thought to what is meant by "small" and "large" when referring to thermal conductivities and film heat transfer coefficients. Since the units of h and k are different it should be clear that they cannot be compared with one another. Instead we should compare h with k/b and conclude that the temperature profiles illustrated in Fig. 4.2.1 are encountered when

$$h \gg k/b, \quad \text{resistance in the plate dominates the process}$$

and that the flat temperature profiles illustrated in Fig. 4.2.2 are encountered when

$$h \ll k/b, \quad \text{resistance in the film dominates the process}$$

These inequalities can be obtained by an order-of-magnitude analysis of the flux condition at $x = 0$. The analysis follows that given in Sec. 2.6 where we found that the Biot number, $N_{Bi} = hb/2k$, could be used to estimate the influence of the resistance to heat transfer in the solid phase. In terms of the Biot number we can rewrite the above inequalities as

$$N_{Bi} \gg 1, \quad \text{resistance in the plate dominates the process}$$

$$N_{Bi} \ll 1, \quad \text{resistance in the film dominates the process}$$

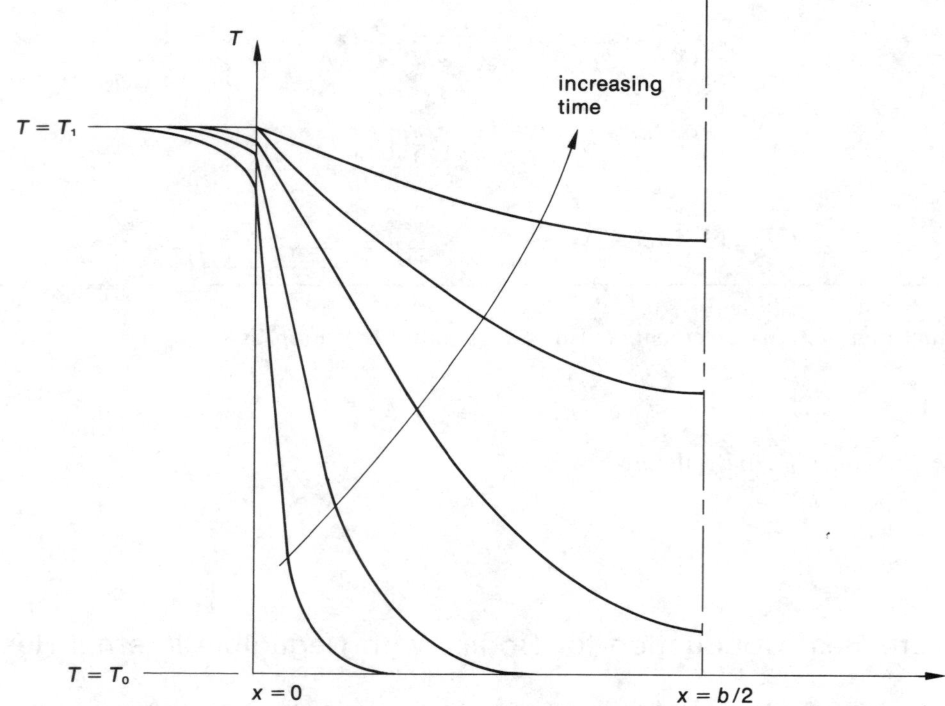

Fig. 4.2.1 Temperature profiles when the resistance to heat transfer in the plate is large.

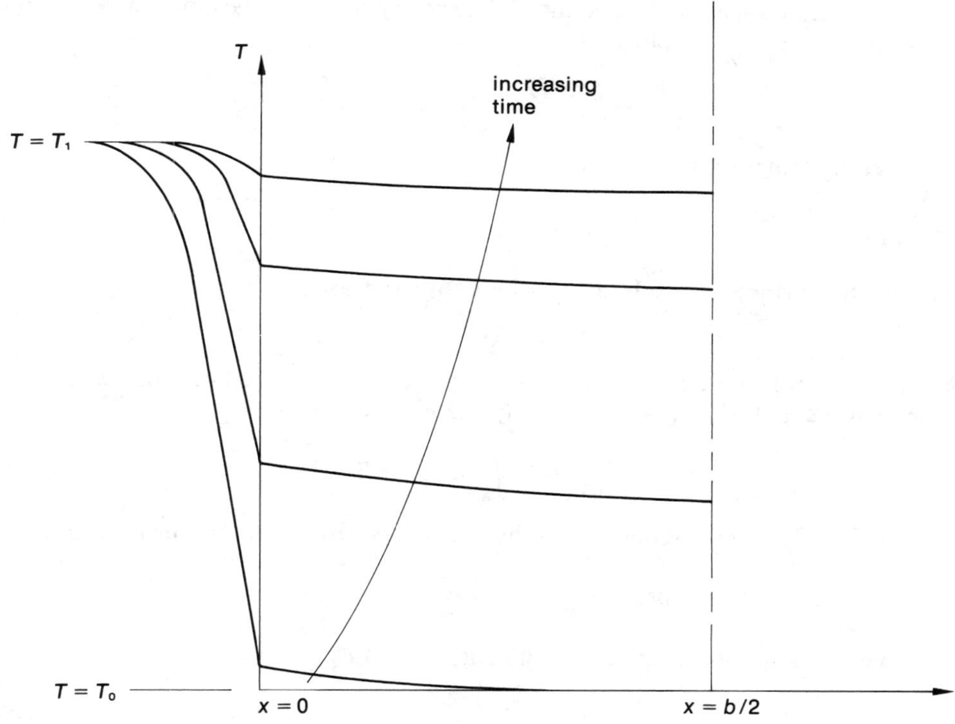

Fig. 4.2.2 Temperature profiles when the resistance to heat transfer in the plate is small.

From this qualitative discussion we conclude that if a solid body is subject to a change in its thermal environment we can neglect temperature variations within the body provided $hL/k \ll 1$, where L is an appropriate characteristic length. In the following paragraphs this type of heat transfer process is analyzed.

We consider a body of volume $\mathscr{V}$ and surface area $\mathscr{A}$ initially at a uniform temperature T_0. At a time $t = 0$ the body is immersed in a fluid at a temperature T_1, and the temperature of the body begins to approach T_1 all the while remaining essentially uniform throughout the body. Assuming that the pressure is constant, we set $\Phi = 0$ in Eq. 3.1-12 to obtain

$$\rho c_p \left(\frac{\partial T}{\partial t}\right) = \nabla \cdot (k \nabla T) \tag{4.2-1}$$

From our discussion in the previous paragraph we know that when $N_{\mathrm{Bi}} \ll 1$ the variation of the temperature within the body is small. Thinking back to the analysis of the extended surface given in Sec. 2.6, this means that the average temperature of the body, $\langle T \rangle$, is approximately equal to the temperature at the interface between the solid body and the fluid, T_i. Under these circumstances we are not interested in determining the spatial variations of the temperature within the body, but only the variation of the average temperature with time. To do this we substitute $\mathbf{q} = -k \nabla T$ into Eq. 4.2-1 and integrate over the volume of the body, $\mathscr{V}$.

$$\int_{\mathscr{V}} \rho c_p \left(\frac{\partial T}{\partial t}\right) dV = -\int_{\mathscr{V}} \nabla \cdot \mathbf{q}\, dV \tag{4.2-2}$$

Since the temperature is nearly uniform throughout the body, ρ and c_p will not be functions of the spatial coordinates and can be taken outside of the volume integral. In addition, we can use the divergence theorem on the right-hand-side of Eq. 4.2-2 to obtain

$$\rho c_p \int_{\mathscr{V}} \left(\frac{\partial T}{\partial t}\right) dV = -\int_{\mathscr{A}} \mathbf{q} \cdot \mathbf{n}\, dA \tag{4.2-3}$$

Because the limits of integration are independent of time we can interchange differentiation and integration on the left-hand-side of Eq. 4.2-3 leading to

$$\rho c_p \mathcal{V} \frac{\partial \langle T \rangle}{\partial t} = - \int_{\mathcal{A}} \mathbf{q} \cdot \mathbf{n} \, dA \tag{4.2-4}$$

Here $\langle T \rangle$ is the average temperature defined by

$$\langle T \rangle = \frac{1}{\mathcal{V}} \int_{\mathcal{V}} T \, dV$$

The heat flux at the surface of the body can be expressed as

$$\mathbf{q} \cdot \mathbf{n} = h(T_i - T_1) \tag{4.2-5}$$

where we again note that T_i is the temperature at the interface between the body and the surrounding fluid. Since $T_i \sim \langle T \rangle$ we can substitute Eq. 4.2-5 into Eq. 4.2-4 to obtain

$$\rho c_p \mathcal{V} \frac{\partial \langle T \rangle}{\partial t} = - \int_{\mathcal{A}} h(\langle T \rangle - T_1) \, dA$$

Remembering that $(\langle T \rangle - T_1)$ does not depend on the spatial coordinates allows us to simplify this result to

$$\rho c_p \mathcal{V} \frac{\partial \langle T \rangle}{\partial t} = - \langle h \rangle \mathcal{A} (\langle T \rangle - T_1) \tag{4.2-6}$$

where $\langle h \rangle$ is the average film heat transfer coefficient defined by

$$\langle h \rangle = \frac{1}{\mathcal{A}} \int_{\mathcal{A}} h \, dA$$

Following our usual procedure we define a dimensionless temperature as

$$\Theta = \frac{\langle T \rangle - T_1}{T_0 - T_1}$$

and rewrite Eq. 4.2-6 in the form

$$\frac{d\Theta}{dt} = - \left(\frac{\langle h \rangle \mathcal{A}}{\rho c_p \mathcal{V}} \right) \Theta \tag{4.2-7}$$

Here the partial derivative has been written as a total derivative since Θ depends only on time. The boundary condition for Θ is

B.C.1 $\qquad \Theta = 1, \qquad t = 0$

and the solution is

$$\Theta = e^{-(\langle h \rangle \mathcal{A} / \rho c_p \mathcal{V}) t} \tag{4.2-8}$$

Note that the quantity $\rho c_p \mathcal{V} / \langle h \rangle \mathcal{A}$ has the units of time and is often called the *time constant* for the body, something of a misnomer since the magnitude of this characteristic time depends both on the properties of the body and on motion of the surrounding fluid through the film heat transfer coefficient $\langle h \rangle$. Defining τ as the time constant

$$\tau = \rho c_p \mathcal{V} / \langle h \rangle \mathcal{A}$$

our expression for the dimensionless temperature becomes

$$\Theta = e^{-t/\tau} \tag{4.2-9}$$

Here it becomes clear that if the time constant τ is large the body responds slowly to temperature changes in the surrounding fluid, and if τ is small the response is rapid.

The rate of heat transfer between the body and the surrounding fluid is given by

$$\begin{aligned} \dot{Q} &= \langle h \rangle \mathscr{A}(\langle T \rangle - T_1) \\ &= \langle h \rangle \mathscr{A}(T_0 - T_1)\Theta \\ &= \langle h \rangle \mathscr{A}(T_0 - T_1)e^{-t/\tau} \end{aligned} \tag{4.2-10}$$

and the total heat transfer in a time t is

$$Q = \int_0^t \dot{Q}\, dt = \tau \langle h \rangle \mathscr{A}(T_0 - T_1)(1 - e^{-t/\tau}) \tag{4.2-11}$$

Substitution of the expression for τ gives

$$Q = \rho c_p \mathscr{V}(T_0 - T_1)(1 - e^{-t/\tau}) \tag{4.2-12}$$

Eqs. 4.2-9 and 4.2-10 provide simple expressions for the *maximum* rate of change of temperature of a body, and the *maximum* rate of exchange of energy of a body with the surrounding fluid. Such expressions are useful for setting *upper bounds* on response times of systems.

Example 4.2-1 Start-up-time for cooking a turkey

A cook book indicates that an 8-lb stuffed turkey should be cooked at 350°F for 3 hr and 20 min. If we define the "start-up-time" as the time required to raise the temperature to 340°F, what percentage of the total time for cooking is the start-up-time?

Estimating the film heat transfer coefficient for a turkey in an oven is not easy; however, we will assume that combined convection and radiation lead to

$$h = 2\ \text{Btu/hr ft}^2\,°\text{F}$$

We estimate the other physical properties of the turkey as

$$\begin{aligned} \rho &= 70\ \text{lb}_m/\text{ft}^3 \\ k &= 0.40\ \text{Btu/hr ft °F} \\ c_p &= 0.9\ \text{Btu/lb}_m\,°\text{F} \end{aligned}$$

We can calculate the volume to be

$$\mathscr{V} = 0.11\ \text{ft}^3$$

and estimate the surface area as

$$\mathscr{A} = 1.6\ \text{ft}^2$$

Since the characteristic length† is on the order of $\frac{1}{3}$ ft the Biot number is given by

$$N_{Bi} = \frac{hL}{k} \sim 1$$

and the analysis presented in Sec. 4.2 is perhaps applicable.

Taking the original temperature of the turkey to be 60°F we calculate the dimensionless temperature at the end of the start-up-time to be

$$\Theta = \frac{340°\text{F} - 350°\text{F}}{60°\text{F} - 350°\text{F}} = 0.0345$$

We can take the logarithm of Eq. 4.2-8 to obtain an expression for the time

$$t = -\left(\frac{\rho c_p \mathscr{V}}{\langle h \rangle \mathscr{A}}\right) \ln \Theta$$

†See Sec. 7.8 for a discussion of characteristic lengths of irregular bodies.

Substitution of the appropriate numbers leads to

$$t = \left\{ \frac{(70\ \text{lb}_m/\text{ft}^3)(0.9\ \text{Btu/lb}_m\,{}^\circ\text{F})(0.11\ \text{ft}^3)}{(2\ \text{Btu/hr}\,\text{ft}^2\,{}^\circ\text{F})(1.6\ \text{ft}^2)} \ln(0.0345) \right\}$$

or

$$t = 7.3\ \text{hr}$$

Clearly the turkey is cooked in a transient state.

*4.3 Transient Heat Conduction in a Semi-Infinite Slab

In the previous section we found that transient temperatures were easily determined when the internal resistance was negligible, i.e., $N_{\text{Bi}} \ll 1$; now we would like to consider the case where internal resistance dominates the process. Referring to Fig. 4.2.1 we would like to consider the case where $N_{\text{Bi}} \to \infty$ so that the surface temperature is instantaneously increased from T_0 to T_1. For short enough times this temperature disturbance is not propagated to the centerline at $x = b/2$ and we can approximate the process as one occurring in a semi-infinite slab.

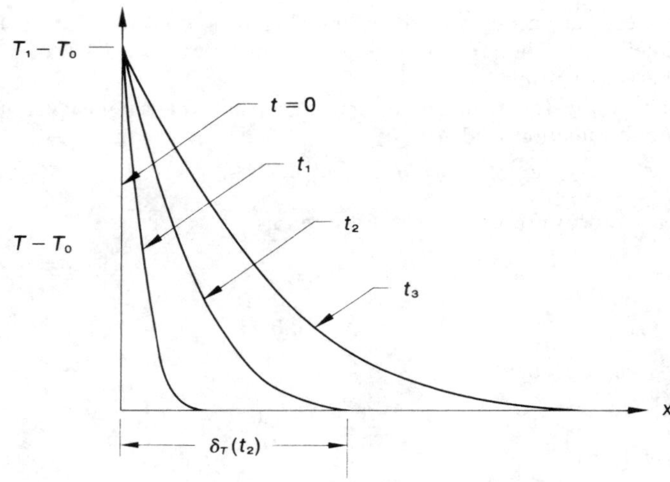

Fig. 4.3.1 Transient heat conduction in a semi-infinite slab.

A sketch of the temperature profiles that we would expect to find is given in Fig. 4.3.1. In that figure the temperature difference, $T - T_0$, is shown as being equal to $T_1 - T_0$ at $x = 0$ and $t = 0$, but equal to zero for all $x > 0$ and $t = 0$. As time progresses the temperature disturbance propagates into the slab at a rate dependent on the thermal diffusivity. The *thermal boundary layer*† $\delta_T(t)$ is defined as that distance at which the temperature difference $T - T_0$ has fallen to 1 per cent of the surface temperature difference, $T_1 - T_0$. Thus $\delta_T(t)$ locates the position at which $(T - T_0)/(T_1 - T_0) = 0.01$. Assuming that the thermal conductivity is constant and noting that T is not a function of either y or z, Eq. 4.1-11 takes the form

$$\frac{\partial T}{\partial t} = \alpha \left(\frac{\partial^2 T}{\partial x^2} \right) \tag{4.3-1}$$

which must be solved subject to the following boundary conditions‡

B.C.1 $$T = T_0, \quad t = 0, \quad 0 \leq x \leq \infty \tag{4.3-2}$$

†The subscript "T" will be used to distinguish the thermal boundary layer from the hydrodynamic boundary layer, δ_H.

‡For a detailed discussion of appropriate boundary conditions for Eq. 4.3-1, see P. M. Morse and H. Feshbach, *Methods of Theoretical Physics*, Chapter 6, McGraw-Hill Book Co., Inc., New York, 1953.

B.C.2 $\quad T = T_1, \quad t > 0, \quad x = 0$ (4.3-3)

B.C.3 $\quad T = T_0, \quad x = \infty, \quad \text{finite } t$ (4.3-4)

The first two boundary conditions are fairly obvious and indicate that the slab is initially at a uniform temperature T_0, but for all times greater than zero the surface at $x = 0$ is maintained at a constant temperature, T_1. This requires that the temperature at $x = 0$ be discontinuous in time, and we must realize that this is simply a convenient approximation to a real process in which the surface temperature is raised very rapidly to the temperature T_1. The third boundary condition simply indicates that for finite times we can always find a large enough value of x so that the temperature is not affected by the sudden increase in T at $x = 0$.

If we define a dimensionless temperature Θ as

$$\Theta = (T - T_0)/(T_1 - T_0) \tag{4.3-5}$$

the governing differential equation and boundary conditions take the form†

$$\frac{\partial \Theta}{\partial t} = \alpha\left(\frac{\partial^2 \Theta}{\partial x^2}\right) \tag{4.3-6}$$

B.C.1′ $\quad \Theta = 0, \quad t = 0, \quad 0 \leq x \leq \infty$ (4.3-7)

B.C.2′ $\quad \Theta = 1, \quad t > 0, \quad x = 0$ (4.3-8)

B.C.3′ $\quad \Theta = 0, \quad x \to \infty, \quad \text{finite } t$ (4.3-9)

Eq. 4.3-6 can be solved by the method of separation of variables discussed in Chapter 3; however, the route to a solution subject to these particular boundary conditions is rather difficult, and we will use this problem to illustrate another method of solving partial differential equations. In this method we will attempt to find a new variable $\eta(x, t)$ such that

$$\Theta(x, t) = \Theta[\eta(x, t)] \tag{4.3-10}$$

If we are successful we will be able to express T in terms of a *single independent variable* η, and thus the problem will be reduced to solving an ordinary differential equation.

We start by assuming η is of the form‡

$$\eta = a x^b t^c \tag{4.3-11}$$

The derivatives of Θ with respect to x and t are given by the chain rule, and we find

$$\frac{\partial \Theta}{\partial t} = \left(\frac{d\Theta}{d\eta}\right)\left(\frac{\partial \eta}{\partial t}\right)$$

$$\frac{\partial^2 \Theta}{\partial x^2} = \left(\frac{d^2\Theta}{d\eta^2}\right)\left(\frac{\partial \eta}{\partial x}\right)^2 + \left(\frac{d\Theta}{d\eta}\right)\left(\frac{\partial^2 \eta}{\partial x^2}\right)$$

Substitution into Eq. 4.3-6 and making use of Eq. 4.3-11 we find

$$\left(\frac{d\Theta}{d\eta}\right) a x^b c t^{c-1} = \alpha\left(\frac{d^2\Theta}{d\eta^2}\right)(abx^{b-1}t^c)^2 + \alpha\left(\frac{d\Theta}{d\eta}\right)(ab(b-1)x^{b-2}t^c) \tag{4.3-12}$$

Rearranging, we may put this equation in the form

$$\left(\frac{d^2\Theta}{d\eta^2}\right)\left[\frac{\alpha a b^2 t^{c+1}}{c x^{2-b}}\right] + \left(\frac{d\Theta}{d\eta}\right)\left[\frac{\alpha b(b-1)t}{c x^2} - 1\right] = 0 \tag{4.3-13}$$

If Eq. 4.3-13 is to be an ordinary differential equation containing coefficients which are only functions of η,

†The student may have previously encountered this *mathematical* problem in a course on fluid mechanics, for the differential equation and boundary conditions are identical to those describing the velocity field created by an infinite, flat plate being suddenly accelerated to a constant velocity. Chemical engineering students will again encounter this same *mathematical* problem in a course in mass transfer for it is the basis of the *penetration model* of mass transfer.

‡This is a "guess," but since this problem has been studied extensively elsewhere we know that it will be a successful one.

the terms in brackets must be functions of η. A little exploration will indicate that this can be accomplished for any value of b such that

$$b = -2c$$

Eq. 4.2-13 takes its simplest form if

$$b = 1, \qquad c = -\tfrac{1}{2}, \qquad a = 1/\sqrt{4\alpha}$$

which results in

$$\left(\frac{d^2\Theta}{d\eta^2}\right) + 2\eta\left(\frac{d\Theta}{d\eta}\right) = 0 \tag{4.3-14}$$

where $\eta = x/\sqrt{4\alpha t}$. In terms of the new variable η, often called the *similarity variable*, the boundary conditions are

B.C.1″ $\quad \Theta = 0, \quad \eta = \infty$ (4.3-15)

B.C.2″ $\quad \Theta = 1, \quad \eta = 0$ (4.3-16)

B.C.3″ $\quad \Theta = 0, \quad \eta \to \infty$ (4.3-17)

Here we see that the last boundary condition becomes superfluous in terms of the similarity variable, η.

The standard method of solution of equations of the type represented by Eq. 4.3-14 is to reduce the order† by the substitution

$$P = \frac{d\Theta}{d\eta}, \qquad \frac{dP}{d\eta} = \frac{d^2\Theta}{d\eta^2} \tag{4.3-18}$$

to obtain

$$\frac{dP}{d\eta} + 2\eta P = 0 \tag{4.3-19}$$

Separation of the variables and integration gives

$$\ln P = -\eta^2 + C \tag{4.3-20}$$

which can be put in the form

$$\frac{d\Theta}{d\eta} = C\,e^{-\eta^2} \tag{4.3-21}$$

where C is an arbitrary constant to be determined by the boundary conditions. We can now form the definite integral of Eq. 4.3-21 to obtain

$$\Theta(\eta) - \Theta(\eta = 0) = C\int_{\xi=0}^{\xi=\eta} e^{-\xi^2}\,d\xi \tag{4.3-22}$$

Here we have used ξ as the dummy variable of integration. By B.C.2″ we see that $\Theta|_{\eta=0} = 1$ and Eq. 4.3-22 becomes

$$\Theta = 1 + C\int_{\xi=0}^{\xi=\eta} e^{-\xi^2}\,d\xi \tag{4.3-23}$$

Application of B.C.1″ gives

B.C.1″

$$C = \frac{-1}{\displaystyle\int_0^\infty e^{-\xi^2}\,d\xi} \tag{4.3-24}$$

†This is always a useful step to make when the function itself does not appear in the differential equation. See Eq. 2.7-23 in Sec. 2.7 for another use of this method.

The definite integral here is easily evaluated and we obtain

$$C = -\frac{2}{\sqrt{\pi}}$$

The final solution for Θ is therefore

$$\Theta = 1 - \frac{2}{\sqrt{\pi}} \int_0^\eta e^{-\xi^2}\, d\xi \tag{4.3-25}$$

The latter term in this equation is known as the *error function* and is abbreviated by $\text{erf}(\eta)$. Tabulated values of the error function are given in Appendix B and the solution for Θ is plotted in Fig. 4.3.2 as a function of $\eta = x/\sqrt{4\alpha t}$. An important characteristic of this temperature profile is that $\Theta = 0.01$, or $T = T_0 + 0.01\ (T_1 - T_0)$, for $x/\sqrt{4\alpha t} = 1.8$, and we can use this fact to define a thermal boundary layer thickness $\delta_T(t)$ as

$$\delta_T(t) = 3.6\sqrt{\alpha t} \tag{4.3-26}$$

The rate at which $\delta_T(t)$ increases is a measure of the rate at which the temperature disturbance propagates into the slab.† It is important to note that the rate of propagation depends on the *square root* of both the thermal diffusivity and time.

Very often we are more interested in the heat flux at the phase interface than the temperature profile. This is given by

$$q_x|_{x=0} = -k\left(\frac{\partial T}{\partial x}\right)_{x=0}$$

†The student may remember that the hydrodynamic boundary layer for the suddenly accelerated flat plate was given by $\delta_H(t) = 3.6\sqrt{\nu t}$.

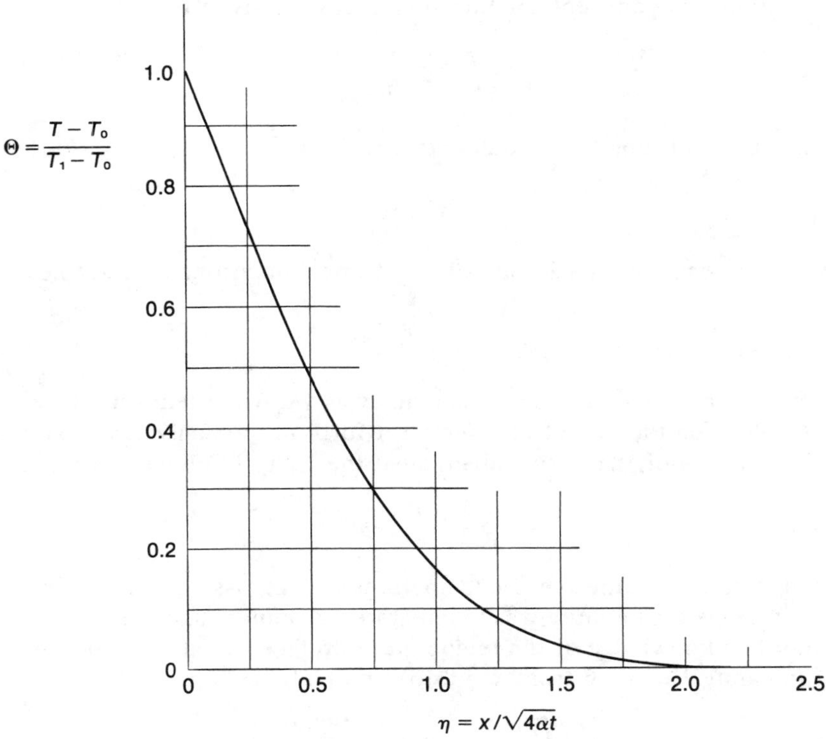

Fig. 4.3.2 Temperature profiles in a semi-infinite slab.

or in terms of the dimensionless temperature Θ and the similarity variable η we have

$$q_x|_{x=0} = -\frac{k(T_1 - T_0)}{\sqrt{4\alpha t}} \frac{d\Theta}{d\eta}\bigg|_{\eta=0} \tag{4.3-27}$$

In making use of Eq. 4.3-25 to evaluate $(d\Theta/d\eta)_{\eta=0}$ we must be sure that we correctly use the Leibnitz rule[1, 2] for differentiating an integral. This rule states that if $\phi(x)$ is given by

$$\phi(x) = \int_{y=a(x)}^{y=b(x)} f(x, y)\, dy$$

then the derivative $d\phi/dx$ is given by

$$\frac{d\phi}{dx} = \int_{y=a(x)}^{y=b(x)} \left(\frac{\partial f}{\partial x}\right) dy + f[x, b(x)]\frac{db}{dx} - f[x, a(x)]\frac{da}{dx}$$

Applying this rule to Eq. 4.3-25 we find that

$$\frac{d\Theta}{d\eta} = -\frac{2}{\sqrt{\pi}} e^{-\eta^2} \tag{4.3-28}$$

and the heat flux at $x = 0$ is

$$\{\text{heat flux at the phase interface}\} = q_x|_{x=0} = \frac{k}{\sqrt{\pi\alpha t}}(T_1 - T_0) \tag{4.3-29}$$

Note that the heat flux is infinite at $t = 0$, but falls off steadily with increasing time. We can use this derived expression for the heat flux to define a film heat transfer coefficient for the semi-infinite slab. Remembering that h is defined by an equation of the type,

$$q_x|_{x=0} = h(T_1 - T_0) \tag{4.3-30}$$

we find the film heat transfer coefficient for this simple case is given by

$$h = \frac{k}{\sqrt{\pi\alpha t}} \tag{4.3-31}$$

Noting that $\sqrt{\pi\alpha t}$ has units of length we could express h as

$$h = \frac{k}{L(t)}$$

which resembles the form encountered in our study of one-dimensional, steady heat conduction.

Approximate solution

In an effort to improve our skill at approximate analysis we will attempt to develop an approximate solution to Eq. 4.3-6 following the line of reasoning set forth in the analysis of extended surfaces. You remember that in the analysis of the fin we abandoned the idea of solving the point equation

$$\frac{\partial^2 T}{\partial x^2} + \frac{\partial^2 T}{\partial y^2} = 0$$

and instead attempted to determine the average temperature $\langle T\rangle$ across the fin. The first step in formulating an expression for the average temperature was to integrate the point equation over the cross section of the fin. With only our intuitive knowledge of the temperature profiles as indicated in Fig. 4.3.1, let us follow this procedure and integrate Eq. 4.3-6 from $x = 0$ to $x = \delta_T(t)$

$$\int_{x=0}^{x=\delta_T(t)} \left(\frac{\partial\Theta}{\partial t}\right) dx = \alpha \int_{x=0}^{x=\delta_T(t)} \left(\frac{\partial^2\Theta}{\partial x^2}\right) dx$$

Carrying out the integration on the right-hand-side leads to

$$\int_{x=0}^{x=\delta_T(t)} \left(\frac{\partial \Theta}{\partial t}\right) dx = \alpha \left[\frac{\partial \Theta}{\partial x}\bigg|_{x=\delta_T(t)} - \frac{\partial \Theta}{\partial x}\bigg|_{x=0}\right] \tag{4.3-32}$$

This does not appear to be a particularly valuable expression involving Θ, and it is not obvious where one should go from here. However, if we think back to the fin analysis, the next step to a successful solution required that we specify the nature of the temperature profile, so let us proceed along those lines.†

About Θ we know the following:

B.C.1 $$\Theta = 1, \qquad x = 0, \qquad t > 0 \tag{4.3-33}$$

A.1 $$\Theta \sim 0, \qquad x = \delta_T(t) \tag{4.3-34}$$

Here we have denoted Eq. 4.3-33 as a boundary condition (i.e., B.C.1) where as Eq. 4.3-34 is denoted as an approximation (i.e., A.1) since it is derived from our *intuitive knowledge* of the temperature profile.‡ We may further reason that if

$$\Theta = 0, \quad \text{for all } x \geqslant \delta_T(t)$$

then the derivative of Θ with respect to x at $x = \delta_T(t)$ should be zero. This is required if the heat flux is to be a continuous function at $x = \delta_T(t)$. Note how flexible we are with the continuum postulate; we allow a discontinuity in the heat flux (see Eq. 4.3-27 for $t = 0$), when it is suitable as an approximation to a real process, and when we are looking for information upon which to base our guess as to the nature of the temperature profile we require continuity and write

$$\frac{\partial \Theta}{\partial x} = 0, \qquad x = \delta_T(t) \tag{4.3-35}$$

It might also seem reasonable that all higher derivatives at $x = \delta_T(t)$ are zero, and we could write

$$\frac{\partial^n \Theta}{\partial x^n} = 0, \qquad x = \delta_T(t), \qquad n = 1, 2, 3, \ldots$$

We certainly have enough information at this point to construct a crude model of the temperature profile, for example,

$$\Theta = 1 - \frac{x}{\delta_T(t)}$$

would satisfy Eqs. 4.3-33 and 4.3-34, but not Eq. 4.3-35, while the profile

$$\Theta = 1 - 2\left(\frac{x}{\delta_T(t)}\right) + \left(\frac{x}{\delta_T(t)}\right)^2$$

would satisfy all three equations. There is another bit of information that is worthwhile considering in our attempt to construct an approximate temperature profile. This information comes directly from the differential equation, for if we realize that Θ is independent of time at $x = 0$ for all $t > 0$ we can use Eq. 4.3-6 to show that

$$\frac{\partial^2 \Theta}{\partial x^2} = 0, \qquad x = 0, \qquad t > 0 \tag{4.3-36}$$

Making use of this restriction leads to a polynomial for Θ having the form

$$\Theta = 1 - \frac{3}{2}\left(\frac{x}{\delta_T}\right) + \frac{1}{2}\left(\frac{x}{\delta_T}\right)^3 \tag{4.3-37}$$

†Remember that the key to a successful approximate analysis of beams was a shrewd guess regarding the strain field, i.e., *plane sections remain plane.*

‡Here we are dismissing the fact that we already have a solution for Θ.

It is important to realize the sources of information used in the construction of this temperature profile. Eq. 4.3-33 is a bona fide *boundary condition* which we had previously used in the solution of the differential equation. Eq. 4.3-34 is an *intuitive approximation* based mainly on the result of the exact solution; although good judgment might well have led to the same conclusion in the absence of Eqs. 4.3-25 and 4.3-26. Our next piece of information, Eq. 4.3-35, follows logically from Eq. 4.3-34 by application of the *continuum postulate.* The source of the last bit of information is entirely different from the first three, for it is derived directly from the *differential equation.* Note that, despite its appearance, Eq. 4.3-36 is *not* a boundary condition, for boundary conditions come from our intuitive knowledge of physical processes, subject to the constraints of the continuum postulate, and are *not* derivable from the governing differential equations.

Defining a new variable ξ as

$$\xi = x/\delta_T \tag{4.3-38}$$

we may rewrite Eq. 4.3-32 as

$$\int_0^1 \left(\frac{\partial \Theta}{\partial t}\right) d\xi = \frac{\alpha}{\delta_T^2}\left[\left.\frac{\partial \Theta}{\partial \xi}\right|_{\xi=1} - \left.\frac{\partial \Theta}{\partial \xi}\right|_{\xi=0}\right] \tag{4.3-39}$$

and the polynomial for Θ becomes

$$\Theta = 1 - \frac{3}{2}\xi + \frac{1}{2}\xi^3 \tag{4.3-40}$$

Substitution of Eq. 4.3-40 into Eq. 4.3-39 leads to a differential equation for the remaining undetermined parameter, $\delta_T(t)$.

$$\left(\frac{d\delta_T}{dt}\right) = \frac{4\alpha}{\delta_T} \tag{4.3-41}$$

Separating variables, integrating, and imposing the boundary condition

B.C.1 $\qquad \delta_T = 0, \qquad t = 0 \qquad$ (4.3-42)

yields

$$\delta_T(t) = \sqrt{8\alpha t}$$

$$= 2.8\sqrt{\alpha t} \tag{4.3-43}$$

While this result is not in especially good agreement with Eq. 4.3-26, the approximate solution developed here is reasonably satisfactory if all one wants is the heat flux rate at the phase interface.

$$q_x|_{x=0} = \frac{k}{\sqrt{3.56\alpha t}}(T_1 - T_0), \quad \text{approximate solution}$$

$$q_x|_{x=0} = \frac{k}{\sqrt{\pi\alpha t}}(T_1 - T_0), \quad \text{exact solution}$$

Here we see that heat flux can be determined to better than 10 per cent by means of an approximate solution. For this particular problem the approximate solution is of little value, as the exact solution is available; however, this exercise is an important one to remember, as the engineer will often encounter problems where time and money do not permit the luxury of developing exact solutions. Under these circumstances, good judgment mixed with a modest amount of mathematical skill can provide a workable solution to a complex problem.

Example 4.3-1 Escape route decision-making process

In the town of Davis, California the fire department provides a free service of inspecting homes, describing the fire hazards, and discussing escape procedures. Parents are warned that each room must have two escape routes, and children are instructed to test the temperature of their bedroom door before venturing into the hallway. If the door is hot, that escape route is abandoned and the exit is made through a window.

In this example we wish to consider whether the method of testing for the presence of dangerously hot gases in the hallway outside the bedroom is in fact a satisfactory one. We pose the problem in the following manner: Consider a rather inexpensive door having a $\frac{1}{4}$ in. thick plywood panel with a thermal diffusivity of

$$\alpha = 10^{-2}\,\text{ft}^2/\text{hr}$$

one side of which is subject to a sudden rise in temperature from 22°C to 800°C. How long will it take before this temperature disturbance can be detected on the other side of the door?

The problem we have here is a rather complex one, and some aspects of it are discussed in Design Problem IV. However, in this example we will assume that the essential features of the problem are contained in the process of transient heat transfer in a semi-infinite slab, and we seek the time required for a point $\frac{1}{4}$ in. from the surface to rise from 22°C to 27°C. The thought here is that a 5°C temperature rise is easily detectable; however, you may wish to alter this criterion after studying Design Problem IV.

Having defined a concise mathematical problem we can draw upon Eq. 4.3-25 to provide an answer. The dimensionless temperature is given by

$$\Theta = \frac{T - T_0}{T_1 - T_0} = \frac{27°\text{C} - 22°\text{C}}{800°\text{C} - 22°\text{C}} = 0.0064$$

We cannot find the appropriate value of $\eta = x/\sqrt{4\alpha t}$ from Fig. 4.3.2; however, the solution is given by

$$\Theta = 1 - \text{erf}\,(\eta)$$

where the error function is tabulated in Appendix B. For erf $(\eta) = 0.9936$ we find by interpolation that

$$\eta = x/\sqrt{4\alpha t} = 1.903$$

Setting $x = 1/48$ ft and solving for the time yields

$$t = \frac{x^2}{4\alpha(1.903)^2} = \frac{(1/48)^2\,\text{hr}}{(4)(10^{-2})(1.903)^2} = 0.003\,\text{hr}$$

More appropriately we note that the estimated time for a 5°C temperature rise is 10.8 sec, thus the danger signal is transmitted fairly rapidly for a $\frac{1}{4}$ in. thick door. Note that t depends on x^2 so that if the door is 1 in. thick the time for the signal to be transmitted is 172 sec or almost 3 min. Under these circumstances one might not detect a temperature rise at the door, and a hasty use of the primary escape route could lead a child into a blazing hallway.

4.4 Periodic Processes—The Semi-Infinite Slab

The process studied in the previous section is clearly an idealization, for surface temperatures cannot be changed instantaneously nor are there any semi-infinite slabs in the real world. Nevertheless, there are real processes where surface temperatures are rapidly raised to a nearly constant temperature, and there are real processes where the thermal boundary layer thickness $\delta_T(t)$ is small compared to the thickness of the slab for short times. Under these circumstances the idealized solution presented in Sec. 4.3 is a reasonable approximation of a real process.

Another idealization of real processes is the semi-infinite slab subject to a surface temperature which varies periodically. For example, the surface of the earth undergoes periodic variations, cooling off at night and heating up during the day. In addition to these daily variations there are yearly variations; the average surface temperature rising during the summer and lowering during the winter. The analysis of periodic processes is very often associated with the design of a control system which prevents variations in the temperature of some process from causing the process to become unstable or to operate in a undesirable manner. Although problems of this type are often quite complex, we can gain considerable insight into their nature by investigating the response of a semi-infinite slab subject to a periodic surface temperature as illustrated in Fig. 4.4.1. Since the temperature is a function of only x and t, Eq. 4.1-14 takes the form

$$\frac{\partial T}{\partial t} = \alpha \frac{\partial^2 T}{\partial x^2} \tag{4.4-1}$$

We seek a solution to this equation subject to the boundary conditions

B.C.1 $$T = T_0 + \Delta T \cos \omega t, \quad x = 0 \tag{4.4-2}$$

B.C.2 $$T = T_0, \quad x = \infty \tag{4.4-3}$$

Here $\Delta T = T_1 - T_0$ is the amplitude of the temperature variation and ω is the frequency of the variation. Following our usual procedure we define a dimensionless temperature Θ as

$$\Theta = (T - T_0)/(T_1 - T_0)$$

and express our problem as

$$\frac{\partial \Theta}{\partial t} = \alpha \frac{\partial^2 \Theta}{\partial x^2} \tag{4.4-4}$$

B.C.1′ $$\Theta = \cos \omega t, \quad x = 0 \tag{4.4-5}$$

B.C.2′ $$\Theta = 0, \quad x = \infty \tag{4.4-6}$$

We can solve Eq. 4.4-4 without resorting to the standard methods for solving partial differential equations by making a shrewd *guess* regarding the functional dependence of Θ on x and t. The essence of this guess is to assume that Θ is everywhere periodic in time with an amplitude that depends on x. Thus we guess that Θ has the form

$$\Theta(x, t) = f(x) \cos [\omega t - \theta(x)] \tag{4.4-7}$$

where $f(x)$ is the dimensionless amplitude which is unity at $x = 0$ and tends toward zero as x tends toward infinity, and $\theta(x)$ is the phase lag which is zero at $x = 0$ and tends to infinity as x tends to infinity.

Our analysis will be greatly simplified if we make use of complex variables to express a new dimensionless temperature $\tilde{\Theta}$ as

$$\tilde{\Theta}(x, t) = f(x)\, e^{i[\omega t - \theta(x)]} \tag{4.4-8}$$

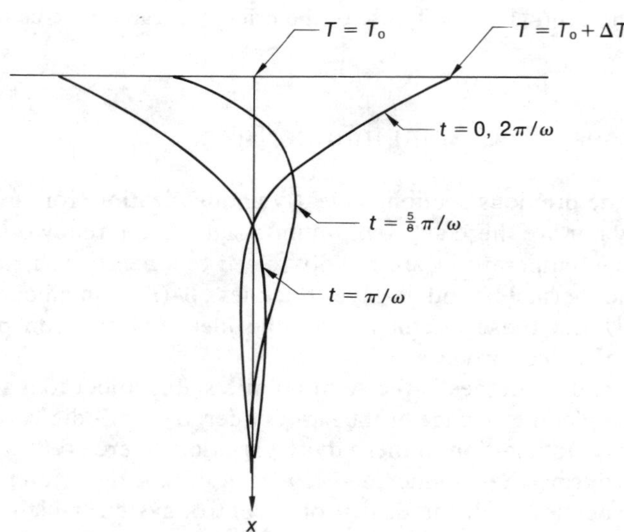

Fig. 4.4.1 Response of a semi-infinite slab to a periodic surface temperature.

The real part of $\tilde{\Theta}$ is given by Eq. 4.4-7 and is the function we seek to determine; however, the easiest route to determining Θ is to set up an *alternate problem* for $\tilde{\Theta}$ of the form

$$\frac{\partial \tilde{\Theta}}{\partial t} = \alpha \frac{\partial^2 \tilde{\Theta}}{\partial x^2} \tag{4.4-9}$$

B.C.1″ $\quad \tilde{\Theta} = e^{i\omega t}, \quad x = 0 \quad$ (4.4-10)

B.C.2″ $\quad \tilde{\Theta} = 0, \quad x = \infty \quad$ (4.4-11)

It is easy to see that the real part of $\tilde{\Theta}$ satisfies Eq. 4.4-4 subject to B.C.1′ and B.C.2′. Now we wish to rewrite Eq. 4.4-8 so that it takes the form

$$\tilde{\Theta} = g(x)\, e^{i\omega t} \tag{4.4-12}$$

where $g(x) = f(x)\, e^{-i\theta(x)}$. Substitution of Eq. 4.4-12 into Eqs. 4.4-9 through 4.4-11 yields the differential equation and boundary conditions for $g(x)$.

$$i\omega g = \alpha \frac{d^2 g}{dx^2} \tag{4.4-13}$$

B.C.1‴ $\quad g = 1, \quad x = 0 \quad$ (4.4-14)

B.C.2‴ $\quad g = 0, \quad x = \infty \quad$ (4.4-15)

In Eq. 4.4-13 we have canceled the common term $e^{i\omega t}$. A solution for $g(x)$ can be obtained by assuming a solution of the form

$$g(x) = e^{mx}$$

This quickly leads us to the result

$$g(x) = C_1\, e^{-x(1+i)\sqrt{\omega/2\alpha}} + C_2\, e^{+x(1+i)\sqrt{\omega/2\alpha}} \tag{4.4-16}$$

Application of B.C.1‴ and B.C.2‴ indicates that $C_2 = 0$ and $C_1 = 1$, so that our expression for $\tilde{\Theta}$ becomes

$$\tilde{\Theta} = e^{-x(1+i)\sqrt{\omega/2\alpha}}\, e^{i\omega t} \tag{4.4-17}$$

This can be expressed in terms of its real and imaginary parts as

$$\begin{aligned} \tilde{\Theta} = e^{-x\sqrt{\omega/2\alpha}}\{&[\cos(x\sqrt{\omega/2\alpha})\cos\omega t + \sin(x\sqrt{\omega/2\alpha})\sin\omega t] \\ &+ i[\cos(x\sqrt{\omega/2\alpha})\sin\omega t - \sin(x\sqrt{\omega/2\alpha})\cos\omega t]\} \end{aligned} \tag{4.4-18}$$

We are only interested in the real part of $\tilde{\Theta}$ which can be arranged in the form

$$\Theta = e^{-x\sqrt{\omega/2\alpha}}\{\cos[\omega t - (x\sqrt{\omega/2\alpha})]\} \tag{4.4-19}$$

Here we see that the amplitude is given by $e^{-x\sqrt{\omega/2\alpha}}$ and the phase lag by $x\sqrt{\omega/2\alpha}$, and our guess as to the function form of $\Theta(x, t)$ indicated by Eq. 4.4-7 was correct.

We can define a thermal boundary layer thickness as the depth at which the dimensionless amplitude falls to 0.01. This occurs when $x\sqrt{\omega/2\alpha} = 4.6$, thus δ_T is given by

$$\delta_T = 4.6\sqrt{2\alpha/\omega} \tag{4.4-20}$$

If we consider $\tau = \pi\omega^{-1}$ as a characteristic time for the process, the thermal boundary layer thickness takes the form

$$\delta_T = 3.7\sqrt{\alpha\tau} \tag{4.4-21}$$

As we might expect, the periodic process studied here has some interesting similarities to the transient process studied in Sec. 4.3. In both cases the depth of penetration of the temperature disturbance is proportional to the square root of the thermal diffusivity and the time.

Effect of gas-phase resistance

We can extend the previous analysis of a periodic process to include a resistance to heat transfer in the surrounding phase, thus providing a more realistic description of periodic heat transfer in a semi-infinite slab. This requires only that we alter one of the boundary conditions so that the statement of the problem becomes

$$\text{governing equation:} \quad \frac{\partial T}{\partial t} = \alpha \frac{\partial^2 T}{\partial x^2} \tag{4.4-22}$$

B.C.1 $$q_x = h(T_a - T), \qquad x = 0 \tag{4.4-23}$$

B.C.2 $$T = T_0, \qquad x = \infty \tag{4.4-24}$$

In this analysis we take the ambient air temperature to be a periodic function of time

$$T_a = T_0 + (T_1 - T_0)\cos \omega t$$

Following the analysis just given we define a dimensionless temperature

$$\Theta = (T - T_0)/(T_1 - T_0)$$

so that our problem statement becomes

$$\text{governing equation:} \quad \frac{\partial \Theta}{\partial t} = \alpha \frac{\partial^2 \Theta}{\partial x^2} \tag{4.4-25}$$

B.C.1′ $$-k\left(\frac{\partial \Theta}{\partial x}\right) = -h(\Theta - \cos \omega t), \qquad x = 0 \tag{4.4-26}$$

B.C.2′ $$\Theta = 0, \qquad x = \infty \tag{4.4-27}$$

In terms of the complex function $\tilde{\Theta}$ our problem now takes the form

$$\text{governing equation:} \quad \frac{\partial \tilde{\Theta}}{\partial t} = \alpha \left(\frac{\partial^2 \tilde{\Theta}}{\partial x^2}\right) \tag{4.4-28}$$

B.C.1″ $$-k\left(\frac{\partial \tilde{\Theta}}{\partial x}\right) + h\tilde{\Theta} = h\, e^{i\omega t} \tag{4.4-29}$$

B.C.2″ $$\tilde{\Theta} = 0, \qquad x = \infty \tag{4.4-30}$$

Use of the form for $\tilde{\Theta}$ given by Eq. 4.4-12 finally reduces our problem to that of solving the ordinary differential equation

$$i\omega g = \alpha \frac{d^2 g}{dx^2} \tag{4.4-31}$$

subject to the boundary conditions

B.C.1‴ $$-k\left(\frac{dg}{dx}\right) + hg = h, \qquad x = 0 \tag{4.4-32}$$

B.C.2‴ $$g = 0, \qquad x = \infty \tag{4.4-33}$$

The solution of this problem is relatively straightforward and is left as an exercise for the student. The final result is

$$\Theta = a\, e^{-x\sqrt{\omega/2\alpha}}\{\cos[\omega t - x\sqrt{\omega/2\alpha}] + b \sin[\omega t - x\sqrt{\omega/2\alpha}]\} \tag{4.4-34}$$

where

$$a = \left[1 + \frac{1+b}{N_{Bi}}\right]^{-1}$$

$$b = \frac{k\sqrt{\omega/2\alpha}}{h + k\sqrt{\omega/2\alpha}} = \frac{1}{N_{Bi}+1}$$

$$N_{Bi} = \left(\frac{h}{k}\right)\sqrt{\frac{2\alpha}{\omega}}, \quad \text{the Biot number}$$

Here we can see that if $N_{Bi} \to \infty$, $a = 1$ and $b = 0$, thus Eq. 4.4-19 is recovered. The amplitude of Θ still decreases exponentially with x, thus the thermal boundary layer thickness is still given by

$$\delta_T = 3.7\sqrt{\alpha\tau}$$

However, the magnitude of the amplitude is decreased by the resistance in the gas phase and is given by

$$\{\text{dimensionless amplitude at } x = 0\} = a\sqrt{1 + b^2}$$

We can now compute the surface temperature variation as

$$T(x = 0) = T_0 \pm (T_1 - T_0)a\sqrt{1 + b^2}$$

As an example consider the case where

$$\alpha = 10^{-3}\ \text{cm}^2/\text{sec} = 3.9 \times 10^{-3}\ \text{ft}^2/\text{hr}$$
$$\omega = 2\pi\ \text{rad/sec} = 1\ \text{cycle/sec}$$
$$k = 0.5\ \text{Btu/hr ft °F}$$
$$h = 5\ \text{Btu/hr ft}^2\ \text{°F}$$

These parameters lead to a Biot number given by $N_{Bi} = 4.2 \times 10^{-3}$, and the surface temperature variations are

$$T = T_0 \pm (T_1 - T_0)(4.2 \times 10^{-3})$$

Here we see that the surface temperature variations are greatly lowered when we take into account the resistance to heat transfer in the surrounding phase.

4.5 Transient Heat Conduction in Rectangular Coordinates

In the previous four sections we have discussed transient heat conduction at a level which required that only ordinary differential equations be solved. In the next five sections we will make use of some of the mathematical methods discussed in Chapter 3 to analyze in more detail some transient heat conduction processes. As was the case with Chapter 3, this material can be omitted and the student can go directly to Chapter 5 with no harmful effects.

As an example of a simple transient heat conduction problem in rectangular coordinates we will study the process illustrated in Fig. 4.5.1. The slab is taken to be infinite in the y- and z-directions so our governing differential equation takes the form

$$\left(\frac{\partial T}{\partial t}\right) = \alpha\left(\frac{\partial^2 T}{\partial x^2}\right) \tag{4.5-1}$$

We seek a solution to this equation which satisfies the boundary conditions

B.C.1 $\qquad T = T_0, \quad t = 0, \quad -\frac{b}{2} \leq x \leq +\frac{b}{2} \qquad$ (4.5-2)

B.C.2 $\qquad T = T_1, \quad x = \pm b/2, \quad t > 0 \qquad$ (4.5-3)

Our first boundary condition specifies the temperature distribution at some initial time, arbitrarily taken to be zero, and is often referred to as an *initial condition* rather than a *boundary condition.* Our second boundary condition is in fact two boundary conditions and it could be replaced by a boundary condition specifying the temperature at one surface

$$T = T_1, \quad x = b/2, \quad t > 0 \tag{4.5-4}$$

and a symmetry condition

$$\frac{\partial T}{\partial x} = 0, \quad x = 0, \quad t > 0 \tag{4.5-5}$$

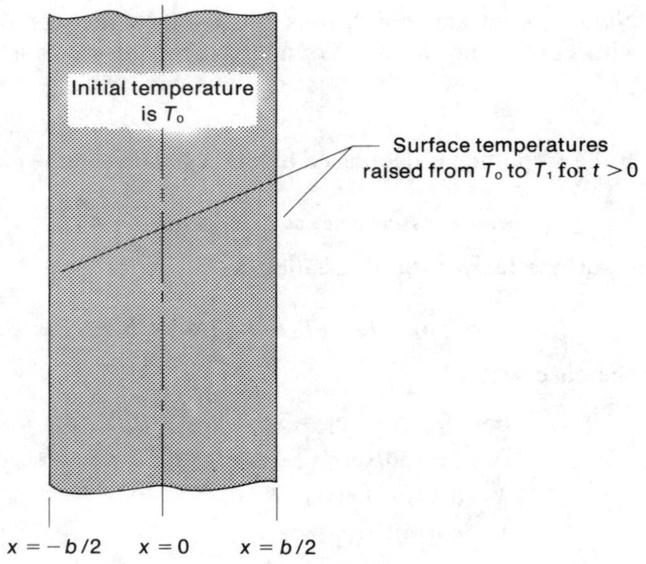

Fig. 4.5.1 Transient heat transfer in a finite slab.

Eqs. 4.5-4 and 4.5-5 logically follow from Eq. 4.5-3 *and* Eq. 4.5-1 which is symmetric in the variable x. We have used the symmetry condition in other studies (see Eq. 2.6-3); however, this time we will continue the analysis using B.C.2 instead of Eqs. 4.5-4 and 4.5-5.

It will be advantageous to work with dimensionless quantities, so we will restate the problem as

$$\frac{\partial \Theta}{\partial t^*} = \frac{\partial^2 \Theta}{\partial X^2} \tag{4.5-6}$$

B.C.1′ $\quad \Theta = 1, \quad t^* = 0, \quad -1 \leq X \leq +1 \quad$ (4.5-7)

B.C.2′ $\quad \Theta = 0, \quad t^* > 0, \quad X = \pm 1 \quad$ (4.5-8)

where

$$\Theta = (T - T_1)/(T_0 - T_1)$$
$$X = 2x/b$$
$$t^* = 4t\alpha/b^2$$

We follow the procedure introduced in Chapter 3 and assume that the solution can be represented as†

$$\Theta = \mathcal{T}(t^*)\mathcal{X}(X) \tag{4.5-9}$$

Substitution of Eq. 4.5-9 into Eq. 4.5-6 and rearranging yields

$$\frac{1}{\mathcal{T}}\frac{d\mathcal{T}}{dt^*} = \frac{1}{\mathcal{X}}\left(\frac{d^2\mathcal{X}}{dX^2}\right) = C \tag{4.5-10}$$

Since the left-hand-side may only be a function of t^*, while the right-hand-side may only be a function of X, it is necessary that both sides be equal to a constant. This constant may be positive, negative or zero, so we express C as

$$C = \begin{cases} +\lambda^2 \\ 0 \\ -\lambda^2 \end{cases}$$

†We must always remember that this is a *guess* regarding the nature of the solution.

If $C = 0$ the dimensionless temperature is independent of time, so we immediately discard this possibility and explore the other two. Setting $C = +\lambda^2$ we find

$$\frac{d\mathcal{T}}{dt^*} = \lambda^2 \mathcal{T} \tag{4.5-11}$$

which integrates to

$$\mathcal{T}(t^*) = C_1 \, e^{\lambda^2 t^*} \tag{4.5-12}$$

This solution requires that the temperature be unbounded as $t^* \to \infty$, so we dismiss it as a possible solution and go to the case $C = -\lambda^2$. For this condition the time dependence of the solution becomes

$$\mathcal{T}(t^*) = C_1 \, e^{-\lambda^2 t^*} \tag{4.5-13}$$

while the solution for $\mathcal{X}(X)$ takes the form

$$\mathcal{X}(X) = C_2 \cos \lambda X + C_3 \sin \lambda X \tag{4.5-14}$$

The dimensionless temperature may now be represented as

$$\Theta(X, t^*) = e^{-\lambda^2 t^*}[C_2 \cos(\lambda X) + C_3 \sin(\lambda X)] \tag{4.5-15}$$

where the constant C_1 has been incorporated in the constants C_2 and C_3. If we now impose B.C.2′ we obtain

B.C.2′
$$0 = e^{-\lambda^2 t^*}[C_2 \cos(\pm\lambda) + C_3 \sin(\pm\lambda)] \tag{4.5-16}$$

Since the cosine is an *even* function, i.e.,

$$\cos(x) = \cos(-x)$$

we wish to retain the $\cos(\lambda X)$ portion of the solution for Θ. We can do this by requiring

$$C_3 = 0$$

$$\lambda = \frac{\pi}{2}, \frac{3\pi}{2}, \frac{5}{2}\pi, \text{ etc.}$$

thus the solution for Θ takes the form

$$\Theta = C_n \, e^{-\lambda_n^2 t^*} \cos(\lambda_n X), \qquad n = 0, 1, 2, 3, \ldots \tag{4.5-17}$$

where

$$\lambda_n = \left(\frac{2n+1}{2}\right)\pi \tag{4.5-18}$$

Here we have an infinite number of solutions for Θ, all of which satisfy the differential equation and the two conditions represented by B.C.2′. We express the solution for Θ as the sum of all possible solutions

$$\Theta = \sum_{n=0}^{\infty} C_n \, e^{-\lambda_n^2 t^*} \cos(\lambda_n X) \tag{4.5-19}$$

and apply B.C.1′ to obtain

B.C.1′
$$1 = \sum_{n=0}^{\infty} C_n \cos(\lambda_n X) \tag{4.5-20}$$

From previous experience we know that the constants C_n can be chosen in such a way that the right-hand-side of Eq. 4.5-20 is just equal to unity in the region $-1 \leq X \leq +1$. Multiplying Eq. 4.5-20 by $\cos(\lambda_m X)$ and integrating between -1 and $+1$ yields

$$\int_{X=-1}^{X=+1} \cos(\lambda_m X)\, dX = C_m \int_{X=-1}^{X=+1} \cos^2(\lambda_m X)\, dX \tag{4.5-21}$$

Here we have used the fact that

$$\int_{X=-1}^{X=+1} \cos(\lambda_n X)\cos(\lambda_m X)\, dX = 0, \qquad \text{for } \lambda_m \neq \lambda_n$$

provided the eigenvalues are given by Eq. 4.5-18. Carrying out the integrations in Eq. 4.5-21 gives us an expression for C_n.

$$C_n = (-1)^n \left(\frac{2}{\lambda_n}\right)$$

Our final expression for the temperature can now be written as

$$T = T_1 + (T_0 - T_1) \sum_{n=0}^{\infty} \frac{[2(-1)^n]\, e^{-\lambda_n^2 4\alpha t/b^2}}{\lambda_n} \cos(2\lambda_n x/b) \tag{4.5-22}$$

A complete picture of the temperature field as a function of x and t requires the use of a digital computer to evaluate the terms in the series. The dimensionless centerline temperature is given in Fig. 4.5.2 for the case where

$$N_{\text{Bi}}^{-1} = k/hb = 0$$

as a function of the dimensionless time, $4\alpha t/b^2$. The heat flux at the interface $x = b/2$ takes a fairly simple form

$$q_x|_{x=b/2} = -k\left(\frac{\partial T}{\partial x}\right)_{x=b/2} = \frac{4k}{b}(T_0 - T_1) \sum_{n=0}^{\infty} e^{-\lambda_n^2 4\alpha t/b^2} \tag{4.5-23}$$

and the total heat transferred from the plate to the surrounding fluid after a time t is given by

$$Q(t) = 2A \int_{\xi=0}^{\xi=t} \left(\frac{4k}{b}\right)(T_0 - T_1) \sum_{n=0}^{\infty} e^{-\lambda_n^2 4\alpha\xi/b^2}\, d\xi \tag{4.5-24}$$

Evaluating the integral and rearranging the terms gives

$$Q(t) = 2Ab\rho c_p (T_0 - T_1) \sum_{n=0}^{\infty} (1 - e^{-\lambda_n^2 4\alpha t/b^2})/\lambda_n^2 \tag{4.5-25}$$

There is still some computing to be done in order to determine $Q(t)$, although for long times the series can be simplified. Noting that $Ab\rho c_p(T_o - T_1)$ represents the maximum amount of energy that can be transferred from the plate we can express $Q(t)$ as

$$Q(t) = 2Q_\infty \sum_{n=0}^{\infty} (1 - e^{-\lambda_n^2 4\alpha t/b^2})/\lambda_n^2 \tag{4.5-26}$$

Since $Q(t) \to Q_\infty$ as $t \to \infty$ it is clear that

$$\sum_{n=0}^{\infty} \lambda_n^{-2} = \tfrac{1}{2}$$

allowing us to write Eq. 4.5-26 as

$$Q(t) = Q_\infty \left[1 - 2\sum_{n=0}^{\infty} (e^{-\lambda_n^2 4\alpha t/b^2})/\lambda_n^2\right] \tag{4.5-27}$$

For values of $4\alpha t/b^2 > \frac{1}{2}$ the series coverges rapidly and a good approximation for $Q(t)$ is

$$Q(t) \sim Q_\infty \left[1 - \left(\frac{8}{\pi^2}\right) e^{-\pi^2 \alpha t/b^2}\right] \tag{4.5-28}$$

Clearly Eq. 4.5-28 does not apply when $t \to 0$ for the term in the brackets does not go to zero. However, if one is concerned with the time required for a flat plate to reach equilibrium with its surroundings, Eq. 4.5-28 could be used.

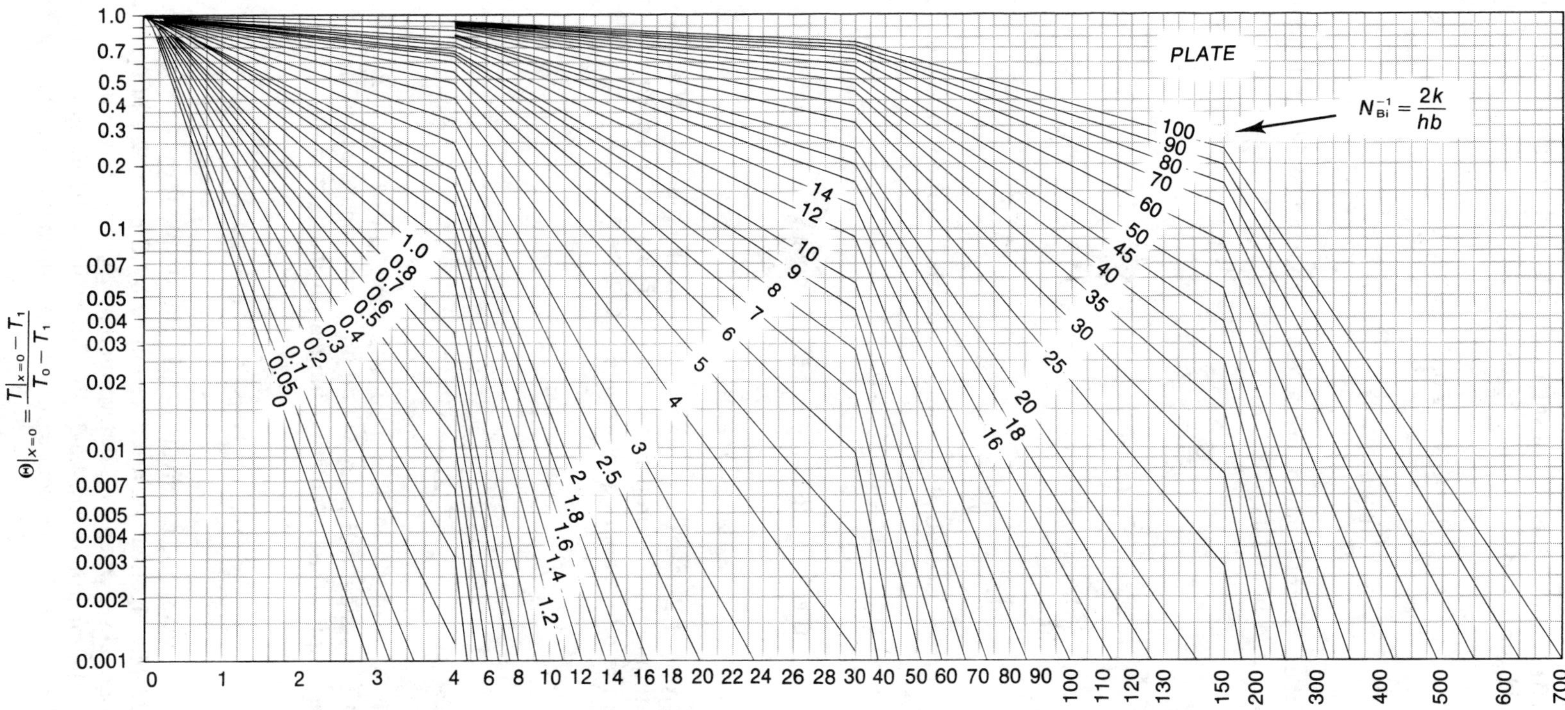

Fig. 4.5.2 Heisler chart for the centerline temperature of an infinite flat plate. (Reproduced from M. P. Heisler, *Trans ASME* **69**, 227 (1947).)

Finite resistance in the fluid phase surrounding an infinite slab

The obvious extension of this analysis is to consider a flux boundary condition at $x = \pm b/2$. Under these circumstances we would replace B.C.2 (Eq. 4.5-3) with

B.C.2a $$-k\left(\frac{\partial T}{\partial x}\right) = h(T - T_1), \qquad x = \frac{b}{2} \tag{4.5-29a}$$

B.C.2b $$-k\left(\frac{\partial T}{\partial x}\right) = h(T_1 - T), \qquad x = \frac{-b}{2} \tag{4.5-29b}$$

where T_1 is now taken to be the ambient temperature of the surrounding fluid. In dimensionless form our governing differential equation and boundary conditions are

$$\frac{\partial \Theta}{\partial t^*} = \frac{\partial^2 \Theta}{\partial X^2}$$

B.C.1 $$\Theta = 1, \qquad t^* = 0, \qquad -1 \leqslant X \leqslant +1$$

B.C.2a $$-\left(\frac{\partial \Theta}{\partial X}\right) = \tfrac{1}{2} N_{\mathrm{Bi}} \Theta, \qquad X = +1, \qquad t^* > 0$$

B.C.2b $$-\left(\frac{\partial \Theta}{\partial X}\right) = -\tfrac{1}{2} N_{\mathrm{Bi}} \Theta, \qquad X = -1, \qquad t^* > 0$$

Following the analysis in the previous example we know that the solution must take the form

$$\Theta = C e^{-\lambda^2 t^*} \cos(\lambda X) \tag{4.5-30}$$

Application of B.C.2a gives

B.C.2a $$C e^{-\lambda^2 t^*} \lambda \sin(\lambda) = \tfrac{1}{2} N_{\mathrm{Bi}} C e^{-\lambda^2 t} \cos(\lambda) \tag{4.5-31}$$

Solving for λ yields

$$\lambda_n \sin(\lambda_n) = \tfrac{1}{2} N_{\mathrm{Bi}} \cos(\lambda_n) \tag{4.5-32}$$

where λ_n represents the nth root of Eq. 4.5-32. The roots have been tabulated [3] elsewhere; however, we can proceed satisfactorily without them. In preparation for satisfying B.C.1 we express Θ as the sum of all possible solutions satisfying the differential equation and B.C.2.

$$\Theta = \sum_{n=0}^{\infty} C_n e^{-\lambda_n^2 t^*} \cos(\lambda_n X) \tag{4.5-33}$$

Applying B.C.1

B.C.1 $$1 = \sum_{n=0}^{\infty} C_n \cos(\lambda_n X) \tag{4.5-34}$$

we are again confronted with the problem of determining the constants C_n in such a way that the infinite number of terms on the right-hand-side of Eq. 4.5-34 add up to one regardless of the value of X provided $-1 \leqslant X \leqslant +1$. In previous examples this calculation hinged on the fact that

$$\int_{X=-1}^{X=+1} \cos(\lambda_n X) \cos(\lambda_m X)\, dX = 0 \tag{4.5-35}$$

for $\lambda_m \neq \lambda_n$. This is easy to prove when the eigenvalues take the simple form $\lambda_n = n\pi$ or $\lambda_n = (2n+1)\pi/2$, but what of the case at hand? The eigenvalues are determined by Eq. 4.5-32 and it is not at all clear that $\cos(\lambda_n X)$ represents an orthogonal set when λ_n is determined by Eq. 4.5-32. At this stage the easiest course of action is to simply examine the integral in Eq. 4.5-35; however, it should be apparent that a general study of orthogonal functions is in order if one wants to become proficient at solving partial differential equations.

Proceeding with the problem at hand we multiply Eq. 4.5-34 by $\cos(\lambda_m X)$ and integrate from $X = -1$ to $X = +1$.

$$\int_{X=-1}^{X=+1} \cos(\lambda_m X)\, dX = \sum_{n=0}^{\infty} C_n \int_{X=-1}^{X=+1} \cos(\lambda_n X) \cos(\lambda_m X)\, dX \tag{4.5-36}$$

The integral on the left-hand-side presents no difficulty and turning our attention to the integral on the right-hand-side we write

$$\int_{X=-1}^{X=+1} \cos(\lambda_n X) \cos(\lambda_m X)\, dX = \left[\frac{\sin(\lambda_n - \lambda_m)X}{2(\lambda_n - \lambda_m)} + \frac{\sin(\lambda_n + \lambda_m)X}{2(\lambda_n + \lambda_m)}\right]_{-1}^{+1} \tag{4.5-37}$$

provided $\lambda_m \neq \lambda_n$. Substituting the limits of integration and making use of the fact that $\sin(x) = \sin(-x)$ we obtain

$$\int_{X=-1}^{X=+1} \cos(\lambda_n X) \cos(\lambda_m X)\, dX = \frac{\sin(\lambda_n - \lambda_m)}{(\lambda_n - \lambda_m)} + \frac{\sin(\lambda_n + \lambda_m)}{(\lambda_n + \lambda_m)} \tag{4.5-38}$$

Using the standard expressions for the sine of the sum and difference of two angles we can arrange this expression in the form

$$\int_{X=-1}^{X=+1} \cos(\lambda_n X) \cos(\lambda_m X)\, dX = \frac{2}{\lambda_n^2 - \lambda_m^2} [\lambda_n \sin(\lambda_n) \cos(\lambda_m) - \lambda_m \sin \lambda_m \cos \lambda_n] \tag{4.5-39}$$

If we now make use of Eq. 4.5-32 in the right-hand-side of Eq. 4.5-39 we find

$$\int_{X=-1}^{X=+1} \cos(\lambda_n X) \cos(\lambda_m X)\, dX = \frac{2}{\lambda_n^2 - \lambda_m^2} [\tfrac{1}{2} N_{Bi} \cos(\lambda_n) \cos(\lambda_m) - \tfrac{1}{2} N_{Bi} \cos(\lambda_m) \cos(\lambda_n)] = 0, \quad n \neq m \tag{4.5-40}$$

thus we have proved Eq. 4.5-35 for the case where the eigenvalues are given by Eq. 4.5-32. Returning now to Eq. 4.5-36 we express the constants C_n as

$$C_n = \frac{\displaystyle\int_{X=-1}^{X=+1} \cos(\lambda_n X)\, dX}{\displaystyle\int_{X=-1}^{X=+1} \cos^2(\lambda_n X)\, dX}$$

Evaluation of the integrals gives

$$C_n = \frac{2 \sin(\lambda_n)}{\lambda_n + \sin(\lambda_n) \cos(\lambda_n)} \tag{4.5-41}$$

and our final expression for the temperature is

$$T = T_1 + (T_0 - T_1) \sum_{n=0}^{\infty} \left[\frac{2 \sin(\lambda_n)}{\lambda_n + \sin(\lambda_n) \cos(\lambda_n)}\right] e^{-\lambda_n^2 4\alpha t/b^2} \cos(2\lambda_n x/b) \tag{4.5-42}$$

For a given value of N_{Bi}, the eigenvalues can be determined by Eq. 4.5-32 and the terms in the infinite series evaluated. The results [4] of such a calculation for the centerline temperature are shown in Fig. 4.5.2.

Response of a flat plate to an instantaneous heat source

As an example of the response of a flat plate to an instantaneous heat source we will consider the following problem:

$$\text{governing equation:} \quad \frac{\partial T}{\partial t} = \alpha \left(\frac{\partial^2 T}{\partial x^2}\right) + \Phi/\rho c_p \tag{4.5-43}$$

B.C.1 $\quad T = T_0, \quad t = 0, \quad -\frac{b}{2} \leq x \leq \frac{b}{2} \quad$ (4.5-44)

B.C.2 $\quad T = T_0, \quad t > 0, \quad x = \pm b/2 \quad$ (4.5-45)

These equations represent a process in which a flat plate, infinite in the y- and z-directions, is subjected to a uniform heat source of strength Φ at some initial time $t=0$. The plate is initially at a uniform temperature T_0 and the surfaces of the plate are held constant at this temperature.

We begin by putting our problem in dimensionless form, and invoking the symmetry condition at $x=0$, we obtain

$$\frac{\partial \Theta}{\partial t^*}=\frac{\partial^2 \Theta}{\partial X^2}+[\Phi b^2/k(T_1-T_0)] \tag{4.5-46}$$

B.C.1 $\quad \Theta=0, \quad t^*=0, \quad 0\leq X\leq \frac{1}{2}$ (4.5-47)

B.C.2 $\quad \Theta=0, \quad X=\frac{1}{2}, \quad t^*>0$ (4.5-48)

B.C.3 $\quad \dfrac{\partial \Theta}{\partial X}=0, \quad X=0, \quad t^*\geq 0$ (4.5-49)

where

$$\Theta=(T-T_0)/(T_1-T_0)$$
$$X=x/b$$
$$t^*=t\alpha/b^2$$

Here T_1 is the maximum centerline temperature which can be determined by solving the steady-state problem

$$0=\frac{\partial^2 \Theta_\infty}{\partial X^2}+\Phi^* \tag{4.5-50}$$

B.C.2 $\quad \Theta_\infty=0, \quad X=\frac{1}{2}$ (4.5-51)

B.C.3 $\quad \dfrac{\partial \Theta_\infty}{\partial X}=0, \quad X=0$ (4.5-52)

Here we have replaced $\Phi b^2/k(T_1-T_0)$ with the dimensionless heat generation term, Φ^*, and the subscript ∞ has been added to the dimensionless temperature as a reminder that this is the temperature for $t^*\to\infty$. The solution for Eqs. 4.5-50 through 4.5-52 is straightforward yielding

$$\Theta_\infty=\frac{\Phi^*}{8}(1-4X^2) \tag{4.5-53}$$

The definition of Θ_∞ requires that it be equal to 1 for $X=0$, thus

$$\Phi^*=8 \tag{4.5-54}$$

and the maximum temperature T_1 is given by

$$T_1=T_0+\left(\frac{\Phi b^2}{8k}\right) \tag{4.5-55}$$

Our governing differential equation now takes the form

$$\frac{\partial \Theta}{\partial t}=\left(\frac{\partial^2 \Theta}{\partial X^2}\right)+8 \tag{4.5-56}$$

and if we assume the variables are separable, substitute $\mathcal{T}(t^*)\mathcal{X}(X)$ for Θ and rearrange in the usual manner we obtain

$$\frac{1}{\mathcal{T}}\left(\frac{d\mathcal{T}}{dt^*}\right)=\frac{1}{\mathcal{X}}\left(\frac{d^2\mathcal{X}}{dX^2}\right)+\frac{8}{\mathcal{T}\mathcal{X}} \tag{4.5-57}$$

Here we encounter difficulty for we cannot arrange our governing differential equation so that the left-hand-side is only a function of t^* and the right-hand-side is only a function of X. However, there is a way out of this difficulty that is a fairly standard method. It requires that we *define* a new *auxiliary solution* according to

$$\{\text{complete solution}\}=\{\text{auxiliary solution}\}+\{\text{steady-state solution}\}$$

Symbolically we write this as

$$\Theta(X, t^*) = \Theta_a(X, t^*) + \Theta_\infty(X) \tag{4.5-58}$$

Substitution into Eq. 4.5-56, and using Eqs. 4.5-53 and 4.5-54 yields

$$\frac{\partial \Theta_a}{\partial t^*} = \left(\frac{\partial^2 \Theta_a}{\partial X^2}\right) \tag{4.5-59}$$

Examining the boundary conditions we find that Θ_a must satisfy

B.C.1′ $$\Theta_a = -(1 - 4X^2), \qquad t^* = 0, \qquad 0 \leq X \leq \tfrac{1}{2} \tag{4.5-60}$$

B.C.2′ $$\Theta_a = 0, \qquad X = \tfrac{1}{2}, \qquad t^* \geq 0 \tag{4.5-61}$$

B.C.3′ $$\frac{\partial \Theta_a}{\partial X} = 0, \qquad X = 0, \qquad t^* \geq 0 \tag{4.5-62}$$

Obviously the auxiliary solution Θ_a will be amenable to analysis by separation of variables, and we substitute $\mathcal{T}(t^*)\mathcal{X}(X)$ for Θ_a to obtain

$$\frac{1}{\mathcal{T}}\left(\frac{\partial \mathcal{T}}{dt^*}\right) = \frac{1}{\mathcal{X}}\left(\frac{d^2\mathcal{X}}{dX^2}\right) = C = \begin{cases} +\lambda^2 \\ 0 \\ -\lambda^2 \end{cases} \tag{4.5-63}$$

Here we have indicated the three possible conditions on the constant C. The choice of zero would lead to a solution independent of time, while the choice of $+\lambda^2$ leads to an unbounded time dependence. We are left with only the possibility that $C = -\lambda^2$ and this yields a solution of the form

$$\Theta_a = e^{-\lambda^2 t^*}[C_1 \cos(\lambda X) + C_2 \sin(\lambda X)] \tag{4.5-64}$$

Application of B.C.3′

B.C.3′ $$0 = e^{-\lambda^2 t^*}[-C_1\lambda \sin(0) + C_2\lambda \cos(0)] \tag{4.5-65}$$

leads to the conclusion that $C_2 = 0$, while B.C.2′

B.C.2′ $$0 = e^{-\lambda^2 t^*}[C_1 \cos(\lambda/2)] \tag{4.5-66}$$

provides the eigenvalues

$$\lambda_n = (2n + 1)\pi, \qquad n = 0, 1, 2, 3, \ldots \tag{4.5-67}$$

Obviously a Fourier series is going to be required to satisfy B.C.1′ and so we express our solution at this point as

$$\Theta_a = \sum_{n=0}^{\infty} C_n e^{-\lambda_n^2 t^*} \cos(\lambda_n X) \tag{4.5-68}$$

Applying B.C.1′

B.C.1 $$-(1 - 4X^2) = \sum_{n=0}^{\infty} C_n \cos(\lambda_n X) \tag{4.5-69}$$

indicates that the constants C_n must be those of a Fourier cosine series for the function $-(1 - 4X^2)$. This is done, as before, by multiplying Eq. 4.5-69 by $\cos(\lambda_m X)$ and integrating between $X = 0$ and $X = \frac{1}{2}$ to obtain

$$-\int_{X=0}^{X=1/2} (1 - 4X^2) \cos(\lambda_m X)\, dX = C_m \int_{X=0}^{X=1/2} \cos^2(\lambda_m X)\, dX \tag{4.5-70}$$

Evaluating the integrals provides an expression for C_n

$$C_n = -32(-1)^n/\lambda_n^3 \tag{4.5-71}$$

and our final expression for the auxiliary solution is

$$\Theta_a = -32 \sum_{n=0}^{\infty} \left[\frac{(-1)^n}{\lambda_n^3}\right] e^{-\lambda_n^2 t^*} \cos(\lambda_n X) \tag{4.5-72}$$

When this result is added to the steady-state solution we obtain for the temperature

$$\Theta = (1-4X^2) - \frac{32}{\pi^3}\sum_{n=0}^{\infty}\left[\frac{(-1)^n}{(2n-1)^3}\right] e^{-\lambda_n^2 t^*} \cos(\lambda_n X) \tag{4.5-73}$$

Remembering that T_1 is given by Eq. 4.5-55 we can express the temperature T as

$$T = T_0 + \left(\frac{\Phi b^2}{8k}\right)\left\{\left[1-4\left(\frac{x}{b}\right)^2\right] - \frac{32}{\pi^3}\sum_{n=0}^{\infty}\left[\frac{(-1)^n}{(2n+1)^3}\right] e^{-\lambda_n^2 \alpha t/b^2} \cos(\lambda_n x/b)\right\} \tag{4.5-74}$$

where $\lambda_n = (2n+1)\pi$. This result can be used to compute the heat flux at the surface of the plate and the time required to attain steady-state conditions. In the former case one must evaluate a series of exponential terms, but for the latter the first term in the series will usually give a sufficiently accurate answer.

4.6 Transient Heat Conduction in Cylindrical Coordinates

In this section we will extend the type of analysis presented in Sec. 4.5 to cylindrical coordinates. The analysis will be more complex because Bessel functions are more difficult to deal with than the sine and cosine functions used in the previous section. We will restrict our study to a single example, encouraging the interested student to go elsewhere [5, 6] for more thorough treatments.

Consider the infinitely long, cylindrical rod shown in Fig. 4.6.1. The temperature will be independent of θ and z and the appropriate form of the transient heat conduction equation is

$$\left(\frac{\partial T}{\partial t}\right) = \alpha\left[\frac{1}{r}\frac{\partial}{\partial r}\left(r\frac{\partial T}{\partial r}\right)\right] \tag{4.6-1}$$

The boundary conditions take the form

B.C.1 $\quad T = T_0, \quad t = 0, \quad 0 \leq r \leq r_0$ (4.6-2)

B.C.2 $\quad T = T_1, \quad r = r_0, \quad t > 0$ (4.6-3)

B.C.3 $\quad T$ is finite for $0 \leq r \leq r_0$ (4.6-4)

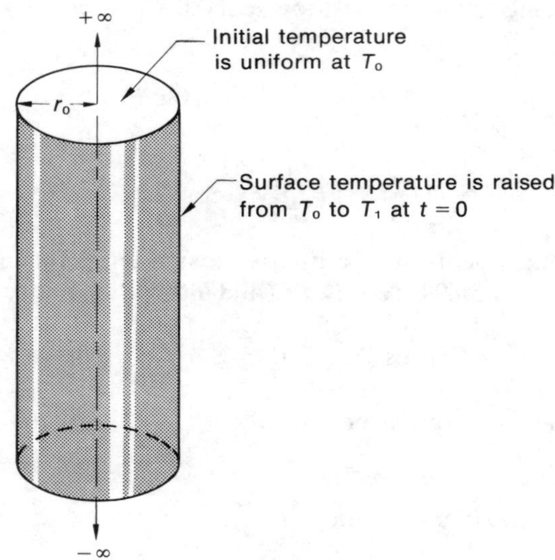

Fig. 4.6.1 Cylindrical rod subject to a sudden increase in the surface temperature.

Remember that B.C.1 may often be referred to as an *initial condition*, and that B.C.3 is really not a boundary condition, but a constraint imposed on the temperature field. Similar constraints are to be found on the velocity† in the analysis of laminar flow in pipes, and on the stress [7] in the analysis of torsion in solid shafts.

Following our usual practice we define the dimensionless variables

$$\Theta = (T - T_1)/(T_0 - T_1)$$
$$R = r/r_0$$
$$t^* = t\alpha/r_0^2$$

so that the differential equation and boundary conditions take the form

$$\frac{\partial \Theta}{\partial t^*} = \left(\frac{\partial^2 \Theta}{\partial R^2}\right) + \frac{1}{R}\left(\frac{\partial \Theta}{\partial R}\right) \tag{4.6-5}$$

B.C.1′ $\quad \Theta = 1, \quad t^* = 0, \quad 0 \leq R \leq 1 \qquad$ (4.6-6)

B.C.2′ $\quad \Theta = 0, \quad R = 1, \quad t^* > 0 \qquad$ (4.6-7)

B.C.3′ $\quad \Theta$ is finite for $0 \leq R \leq 1 \qquad$ (4.6-8)

Assuming that separation of variables will work, we substitute $\mathcal{T}(t^*)\mathcal{R}(R)$ for Θ in Eq. 4.6-5 and rearrange to obtain

$$\frac{1}{\mathcal{T}}\frac{d\mathcal{T}}{dt^*} = \frac{1}{\mathcal{R}}\left[\left(\frac{d^2\mathcal{R}}{dR^2}\right) + \frac{1}{R}\left(\frac{d\mathcal{R}}{dR}\right)\right] = C \tag{4.6-9}$$

The constant C may be positive, negative, or zero, but it should be obvious that positive values lead to unbounded time dependence and a zero valve leads to a trivial case. We are left with only the possibility that C is negative, i.e., $C = -\lambda^2$. Making this substitution quickly leads to

$$R^2\left(\frac{d^2\mathcal{R}}{dR^2}\right) + R\left(\frac{d\mathcal{R}}{dR}\right) + \lambda^2 R^2 \mathcal{R} = 0 \tag{4.6-10}$$

$$\left(\frac{d\mathcal{T}}{dt^*}\right) + \lambda^2 \mathcal{T} = 0 \tag{4.6-11}$$

Eq. 4.6-10 is identical to Eq. 3.2-40 and we know the solution to be

$$\mathcal{R}(R) = C_1 J_0(\lambda R) + C_2 Y_0(\lambda R) \tag{4.6-12}$$

The solution for $\mathcal{T}$ is easily obtained

$$\mathcal{T}(t^*) = C_3\, e^{-\lambda^2 t^*} \tag{4.6-13}$$

and our general expression for the dimensionless temperature takes the form

$$\Theta(R, t^*) = e^{-\lambda^2 t^*}[C_1 J_0(\lambda R) + C_2 Y_0(\lambda R)] \tag{4.6-14}$$

where the constant C_3 has been incorporated into the constants C_1 and C_2. Referring to B.C.3′ and Fig. 3.2.3 which shows that $Y_0(x) \to -\infty$ as $x \to 0$, we require that $C_2 = 0$, and our solution for Θ becomes

$$\Theta = C_1\, e^{-\lambda^2 t^*} J_0(\lambda R) \tag{4.6-15}$$

Application of B.C.2′ yields

B.C.2′ $\quad 0 = C_1\, e^{-\lambda^2 t^*} J_0(\lambda) \qquad$ (4.6-16)

Setting C_1 would lead to a trivial solution, thus we require that

$$J_0(\lambda) = 0 \tag{4.6-17}$$

†See Reference 2, Sec. 2.8.

There are an infinite number of roots, or eigenvalues (see Fig. 3.2.2) which satisfy Eq. 4.6-17, thus we have an infinite number of solutions of the form

$$\Theta_n = C_n\, e^{-\lambda_n^2 t^*} J_0(\lambda_n R), \qquad n = 0, 1, 2, \ldots \tag{4.6-18}$$

where the λ_n are solutions of Eq. 4.6-17. The sum of all these solutions will also be a solution which satisfies the differential equation and B.C.2′ and B.C.3′ so we can express Θ as

$$\Theta = \sum_{n=0}^{\infty} C_n\, e^{-\lambda_n^2 t^*} J_0(\lambda_n R) \tag{4.6-19}$$

Application of B.C.1′ leads to

$$\text{B.C.1}' \qquad 1 = \sum_{n=0}^{\infty} C_n J_0(\lambda_n R) \tag{4.6-20}$$

and we are confronted with the problem of constructing a function (in this case a constant = 1.0) in terms of an infinite series of Bessel functions. We can do this since the functions $J_0(\lambda_n R)$ form an orthogonal set with respect to the weight function R, thus

$$\int_{R=0}^{R=1} R J_0(\lambda_n R) J_0(\lambda_m R)\, dR = 0, \qquad \lambda_n \neq \lambda_m \tag{4.6-21}$$

when the eigenvalues λ_n are given by Eq. 4.6-17. Multiplying Eq. 4.6-20 by $RJ_0(\lambda_m R)$, integrating from $R = 0$ to $R = 1$, and making use of Eq. 4.6-21 yields an expression for C_m

$$C_m = \frac{\displaystyle\int_{R=0}^{R=1} R J_0(\lambda_m R)\, dR}{\displaystyle\int_{R=0}^{R=1} R J_0^2(\lambda_m R)\, dR} \tag{4.6-22}$$

We can use the results given in Table 3.2-1 or make direct use of Eq. 3.2-59 to evaluate the integral in the denominator of Eq. 4.6-22 to obtain

$$\int_{R=0}^{R=1} R J_0^2(\lambda_m R)\, dR = \tfrac{1}{2} J_1^2(\lambda_m) \tag{4.6-23}$$

The integral in the numerator is given by Eq. (m) in Table 3.2-1 and we write

$$\int_{R=0}^{R=1} R J_0(\lambda_m R)\, dR = \left(\frac{R}{\lambda_n^2}\right) J_1(\lambda_m R)\Big]_{R=0}^{R=1} = J_1(\lambda_m)/\lambda_m \tag{4.6-24}$$

Substitution of the results into Eq. 4.6-22, which is then substituted into Eq. 4.6-19 yields our final solution for Θ

$$\Theta = 2 \sum_{n=0}^{\infty} \frac{e^{-\lambda_n^2 t^*} J_0(\lambda_n R)}{\lambda_n J_1(\lambda_n)} \tag{4.6-25}$$

From this result we can obtain an expression for the temperature in terms of r and t

$$T = T_1 + 2(T_0 - T_1) \sum_{n=0}^{\infty} \frac{e^{-\lambda_n^2 \alpha t / r_0^2} J_0(\lambda_n r / r_0)}{\lambda_n J_1(\lambda_n)} \tag{4.6-26}$$

As we have found in previous studies, considerable computational effort must be expended before values for the temperature can be obtained from either Eq. 4.6-25 or Eq. 4.6-26. Much of this work has been done for us, and some of the results are shown in Fig. 4.6.2 where the dimensionless centerline temperature $\Theta(R = 0)$ is shown as a function of the dimensionless time $\alpha t/r_0^2$. The result we have obtained here is for $N_{\text{Bi}}^{-1} = 0$; the solution for the flux boundary condition will be left as an exercise for the student.

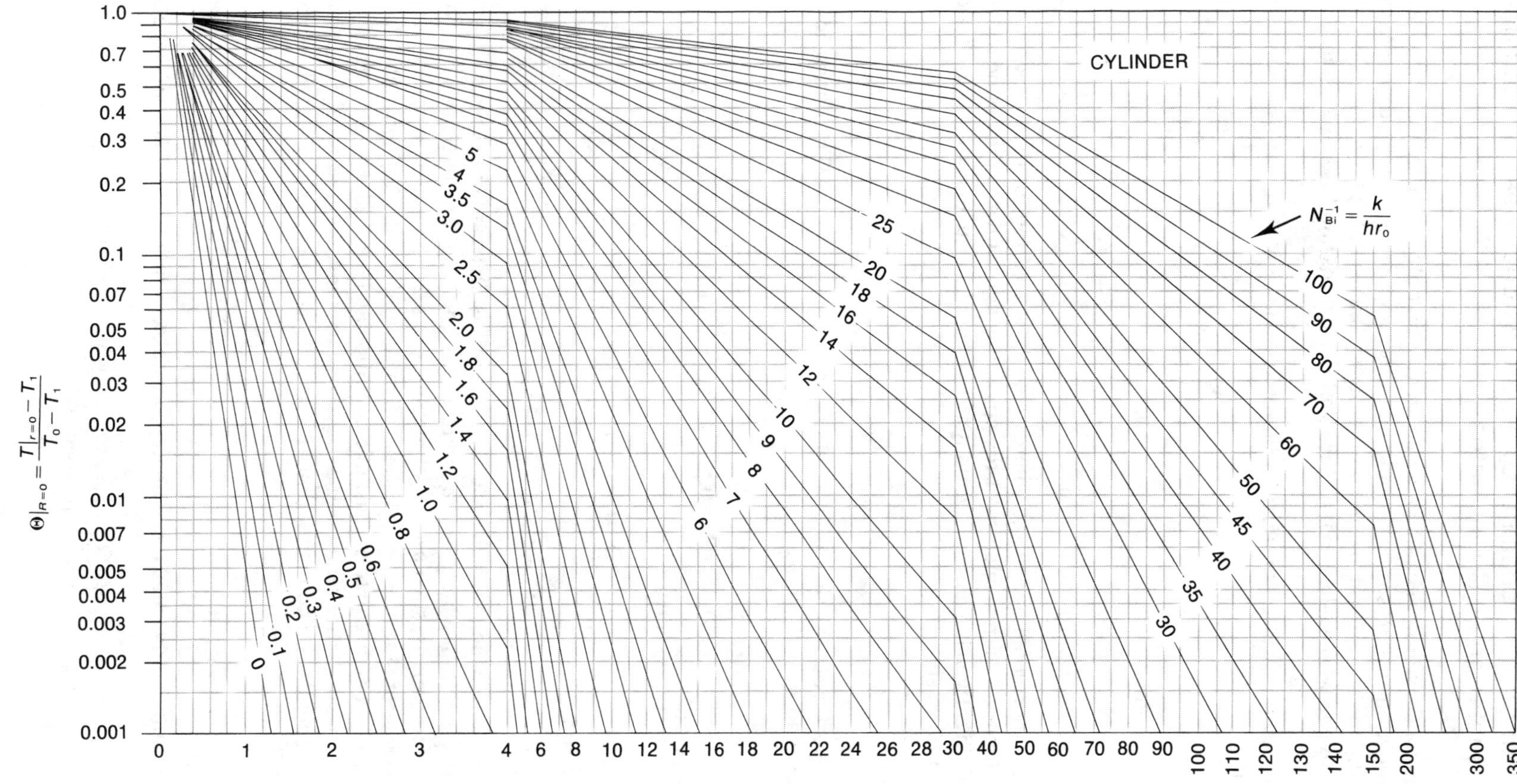

Fig. 4.6.2 Heisler chart for the centerline temperature for an infinitely long cylinder. (Reproduced from M. P. Heisler, *Trans ASME* **69**, 227 (1947).)

4.7 Numerical Solution of Transient, One-Dimensional Heat Conduction Problems in Rectangular Coordinates

In the previous examples given in Sec. 4.5 and 4.6, we saw that obtaining an analytical expression for the temperature as a function of one space variable and time was not especially difficult. In each case, however, the final result took the form of an infinite series and significant computational effort was obviously required by anyone who wished to turn the symbolic expression for the temperature into a real number.

Our objective in this section will be to obtain a numerical solution of the transient, one-dimensional heat conduction equation

$$\frac{\partial T}{\partial t} = \alpha\left(\frac{\partial^2 T}{\partial x^2}\right) \tag{4.7-1}$$

subject to the boundary conditions

B.C.1 $\quad T = T_0, \quad t = 0, \quad -b/2 \leq x \leq +b/2 \quad$ (4.7-2)

B.C.2 $\quad T = T_1, \quad t > 0, \quad x = \pm b/2 \quad$ (4.7-3)

This problem was previously studied in Sec. 4.5 where an analytic solution for the temperature was given. Here we will formulate finite-difference analogs of the governing equation and the boundary conditions so that they may be solved directly using a digital computer. Following our usual convention we consider the dimensionless form of Eq. 4.7-1

$$\frac{\partial \Theta}{\partial t^*} = \left(\frac{\partial^2 \Theta}{\partial X^2}\right) \tag{4.7-4}$$

since digital computers work conveniently with numbers and not dimensions. The dimensionless form of the boundary conditions can be written as

B.C.1′ $\quad \Theta = 1, \quad t^* = 0, \quad -1 \leq X \leq +1 \quad$ (4.7-5)

B.C.2′ $\quad \Theta = 0, \quad t^* > 0, \quad X = \pm 1 \quad$ (4.7-6)

Our discrete time steps are represented by

$$t_j^* = j\,\Delta t^*, \qquad j = 0, 1, 2, \ldots \tag{4.7-7}$$

and the discrete spatial steps by

$$X_i = i\,\Delta X, \qquad i = 0, 1, 2, \ldots \tag{4.7-8}$$

The time–space grid work with which we will concern ourselves is illustrated in Fig. 4.7.1. In this example we have assumed that the region in which we are interested is bounded; however, this type of analysis is easily applied to unbounded regions, such as that studied in Sec. 4.2. There are two predominate methods of solving the finite-difference analog of Eq. 4.7-4; the *explicit method* and the *implicit method.* The former is an especially easy method, but may lead to an unstable condition and has limits on the size of the time step, Δt^*, that may be taken, while the latter requires the use of a matrix inversion routine, but can utilize larger time steps and thereby economize on computer time. In the following paragraphs we will use both of these methods to solve Eq. 4.7-4.

Explicit method

If the time step Δt^* is sufficiently small a reasonably satisfactory finite-difference analog can be written as

$$\left(\frac{\partial \Theta}{\partial t^*}\right)_{X,t^*+(\Delta t^*/2)} \sim \left(\frac{\partial^2 \Theta}{\partial X^2}\right)_{X,t^*} \tag{4.7-9}$$

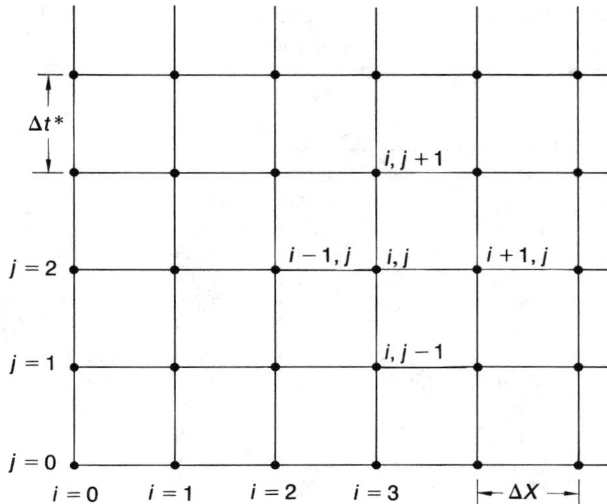

Fig. 4.7.1 Time–space grid.

Here we propose to evaluate the time derivative at the time $t^*+(\Delta t^*/2)$ while the spatial derivative is evaluated at an earlier time, t^*. Substituting the appropriate finite-difference approximations for the derivatives gives

$$\frac{\Theta_{i,j+1}-\Theta_{i,j}}{\Delta t^*}=\frac{\Theta_{i+1,j}-2\Theta_{i,j}+\Theta_{i-1,j}}{\Delta X^2} \tag{4.7-10}$$

This may be rearranged to give an expression for $\Theta_{i,j+1}$, the value of the temperature at the new discrete time step, t^*_{j+1}.

$$\Theta_{i,j+1}=\Theta_{i,j}+\left(\frac{\Delta t^*}{\Delta X^2}\right)[\Theta_{i+1,j}-2\Theta_{i,j}+\Theta_{i,-1,j}] \tag{4.7-11}$$

Here we see that the temperature at the point X_i and at the *new* time t^*_{j+1} is completely determined by the values of the temperature at the *old* time t^*_j. Very often this approach is referred to as a *marching technique* for one does indeed march forward in time computing the new temperature values in terms of previously computed or specified values. An important restriction in the use of Eq. 4.7-11 is that the value of $\Delta t^*/\Delta X^2$ may not exceed a value of $\frac{1}{2}$ or else the procedure will become unstable [8] and the results from the solution of the finite-difference equation will fluctuate considerably about the true solution of the differential equation (Eq. 4.7-4). The explicit method provides such a simple method of solution that one can readily obtain solutions using a desk calculator. As an example of the use of Eq. 4.7-11 we will obtain temperature profiles for the transient process illustrated in Fig. 4.5.1. In Table 4.7-1 we have tabulated the calculated values for ΔX of 0.2 and for Δt^* of 0.004, and the exact values determined by the equation

$$\Theta_{i,j}=\frac{4}{\pi}\sum_{n=0}^{\infty}\frac{(-1)^n}{(2n+1)}\exp\left[-(2n+1)^2\left(\frac{\pi}{2}\right)^2 n\ \Delta t^*\right]\cos\left[\frac{(2n+1)\pi i\ \Delta X}{2}\right] \tag{4.7-12}$$

Eq. 4.7-12 is obtained from Eqs. 4.5-18 and 4.5-19 and the expression for C_n. In Table 4.7-1 the first row of values for $\Theta_{i,j}$ are all 1.0 in accordance with the boundary condition given by Eq. 4.7-5. After the first time step, $t^*=\Delta t^*$, the value of Θ at $X=\pm 1$ is set equal to zero in accordance with the boundary condition given by Eq. 4.7-6. After several time steps the agreement between the finite-difference approximation and the exact solution becomes quite good.

Table 4.7-1 Comparison of Values of $\Theta_{i,j}$ Determined by the Explicit Finite-Difference Method and Values Determined by the Exact Series Solution†

t^* \ X	−1.0	−0.8	−0.6	−0.4	−0.2	0.0	+0.2	+0.4	+0.6	+0.8	+1.0
0	1.000 (1.000)	1.000 (1.000)	1.000 (1.000)	1.000 (1.000)	1.000 (1.000)	1.000 (1.000)	1.000 (1.000)	1.000 (1.000)	1.000 (1.000)	1.000 (1.000)	1.000 (1.000)
0.004	0.000 (0.000)	1.000 (0.975)	1.000 (1.000)	1.000 (1.000)	1.000 (1.000)	1.000 (1.000)	1.000 (1.000)	1.000 (1.000)	1.000 (1.000)	1.000 (0.975)	1.000 (0.000)
0.008	0.000 (0.000)	0.900 (0.886)	1.000 (0.998)	1.000 (1.000)	1.000 (1.000)	1.000 (1.000)	1.000 (1.000)	1.000 (1.000)	1.000 (0.998)	0.900 (0.886)	0.000 (0.000)
0.012	0.000 (0.000)	0.820 (0.803)	0.990 (0.990)	1.000 (1.000)	1.000 (1.000)	1.000 (1.000)	1.000 (1.000)	1.000 (1.000)	0.990 (0.990)	0.820 (0.803)	0.000 (0.000)
0.016	0.000 (0.000)	0.755 (0.736)	0.974 (0.975)	0.999 (0.999)	1.000 (1.000)	1.000 (1.000)	1.000 (1.000)	0.999 (0.999)	0.974 (0.975)	0.755 (0.736)	0.000 (0.000)
0.020	0.000 (0.000)	0.701 (0.683)	0.955 (0.954)	0.997 (0.997)	1.000 (1.000)	1.000 (1.000)	1.000 (1.000)	0.997 (0.997)	0.955 (0.954)	0.701 (0.683)	0.000 0.000
0.024	0.000 (0.000)	0.657 (0.638)	0.934 (0.932)	0.993 (0.994)	1.000 (1.000)	1.000 (1.000)	1.000 (1.000)	0.993 (0.994)	0.934 (0.932)	0.657 (0.638)	0.000 (0.000)

†Values for the series solution are given in parentheses.

Implicit method

If we return to Eq. 4.7-9, and perhaps decide that a better finite-difference approximation to the differential equation would be given by

$$\left(\frac{\partial \Theta}{\partial t^*}\right)_{X,t^*+(\Delta t^*/2)} = \left(\frac{\partial^2 \Theta}{\partial X^2}\right)_{X,t^*+(\Delta t^*/2)} \tag{4.7-13}$$

we obtain

$$\frac{\Theta_{i,j+1} - \Theta_{i,j}}{\Delta t^*} = \frac{1}{2}\left[\frac{\Theta_{i+1,j+1} - 2\Theta_{i,j+1} + \Theta_{i-1,j+1}}{\Delta X^2} + \frac{\Theta_{i+1,j} - 2\Theta_{i,j} + \Theta_{i-1,j}}{\Delta X^2}\right] \tag{4.7-14}$$

This can be rearranged in the form

$$\Theta_{i-1,j+1} - 2\left(1 + \frac{\Delta X^2}{\Delta t^*}\right)\Theta_{i,j+1} + \Theta_{i+1,j+1} = -\left\{\Theta_{i+1,j} - 2\left(1 - \frac{\Delta X^2}{\Delta t^*}\right)\Theta_{i,j} + \Theta_{i-1,j}\right\} \tag{4.7-15}$$

Here we see that each term on the right-hand-side has a subscript j while the terms on the left-hand-side all have the subscript $j+1$. Thus the unknown temperatures at the new times are on the left, and the *known* temperatures at the old times are on the right. We can write Eq. 4.7-15 in the form

$$\Theta_{i-1,j+1} + B\Theta_{i,j+1} + \Theta_{i+1,j+1} = D_{i,j}, \qquad i = 0, 1, 2, \ldots \tag{4.7-16}$$

where $D_{i,j}$ is *known* and B is a constant. If we return to Chapter 3, Sec. 3.3 and examine Eq. 3.3-29 we see that Eq. 4.7-16 is of the same form and thus is amenable to analysis by matrix inversion. Writing Eq. 4.7-16 for all values of i gives

$$\begin{aligned}
B\Theta_{1,j+1} + \Theta_{2,j+1} &= D_{1,j} - \Theta_{0,j+1} \\
\Theta_{1,j+1} + B\Theta_{2,j+1} + \Theta_{3,j+1} &= D_{2,j} \\
\Theta_{2,j+1} + B\Theta_{3,j+1} + \Theta_{4,j+1} &= D_{3,j} \\
\cdots\cdots\cdots\cdots\cdots & \\
\Theta_{N-3,j+1} + B\Theta_{N-2,j+1} + \Theta_{N-1,j+1} &= D_{N-2,j} \\
\Theta_{N-2,j+1} + B\Theta_{N-1,j+1} &= D_{N+1,j} - \Theta_{N,j+1}
\end{aligned} \tag{4.7-17}$$

Here we have taken the boundary values, $\Theta_{0,j+1}$ and $\Theta_{N,j+1}$, over to the right-hand-side with the knowledge that they will be specified in terms of the temperature boundary condition given by Eq. 4.7-6. Following the development in Sec. 3.3 we write Eqs. 4.7-17 in matrix form

$$\begin{bmatrix} B & 1 & & & & & \\ 1 & B & 1 & & & & \\ & 1 & B & 1 & & & \\ \cdot & \cdot & \cdot & \cdot & \cdot & \cdot & \cdot \\ & & & 1 & B & 1 & \\ & & & & 1 & B & 1 \\ & & & & & 1 & B \end{bmatrix} \begin{bmatrix} \Theta_{1,j} \\ \Theta_{2,j} \\ \Theta_{3,j} \\ \cdot \\ \cdot \\ \cdot \\ \cdot \\ \Theta_{N-3,j} \\ \Theta_{N-2,j} \\ \Theta_{N-1,j} \end{bmatrix} = \begin{bmatrix} D_{1,j} - \Theta_{0,j} \\ D_{2,j} \\ D_{3,j} \\ \cdot \\ \cdot \\ \cdot \\ \cdot \\ D_{N-3,j} \\ D_{N-2,j} \\ D_{N-1,j} - \Theta_{N,j} \end{bmatrix} \tag{4.7-18}$$

and then in more compact notation

$$[A][\Theta]_{j+1} = [D]_j \tag{4.7-19}$$

Here $[A]$ represents a *known* tri-diagonal matrix, $[\Theta]$ represents an *unknown* column vector, and $[D]$ a *known* column vector.† Since the matrix $[A]$ is known, we can compute the inverse $[A]^{-1}$, provided it exists, and Eq. 4.7-19 can be solved to yield the column vector $[\Theta]$. Multiplication of Eq. 4.7-19 by $[A]^{-1}$ gives

$$[A]^{-1}[A][\Theta]_{j+1} = [A]^{-1}[D]_j \tag{4.7-20}$$

But $[A]^{-1}[A]$ is the unit matrix $[U]$ so that

$$[A]^{-1}[A][\Theta]_{j+1} = [U][\Theta]_{j+1} = [\Theta]_{j+1}$$

and $[\Theta]$ is given by

$$[\Theta]_{j+1} = [A]^{-1}[D]_j \tag{4.7-21}$$

Standard techniques [9] are available for developing the inverse of a matrix, and inversion subroutines are usually available at any computer center. Eq. 4.7-21 indicates that the new values of Θ at t^*_{j+1} can be computed from the old values of Θ at t^*_j for all values of X_i except at the boundaries where Θ is specified.

We can see that the implicit method very definitely involves a more complex computational scheme; however, the results are generally more accurate for a given value of $\Delta t^*/\Delta X^2$ and the method is completely stable.‡ Results from the implicit method are compared with the exact solution in Fig. 4.7.2 for $\Delta t^* = 0.02$ and $\Delta X = 0.2$, and we can see that better agreement with the exact solution is obtained by using the implicit method. The reason for this is simply that Eq. 4.7-13 is a better finite-difference approximate to Eq. 4.7-4 than Eq. 4.7-9.

4.8 Flux Boundary Conditions for Finite-Difference Equations

To illustrate the use of flux boundary conditions with the explicit and implicit we will alter the problem described by Eqs. 4.7-1 through 4.7-3 and consider a process described by

$$\frac{\partial T}{\partial t} = \alpha \left(\frac{\partial^2 T}{\partial x^2} \right) \tag{4.8-1}$$

B.C.1 $$T = T_0, \qquad t = 0, \qquad -\frac{b}{2} \leqslant x \leqslant +\frac{b}{2} \tag{4.8-2}$$

†Note that the word *vector* here is used in the linear algebra sense, not in the mechanical sense where a vector is a *first-order tensor.*

‡See Reference 8.

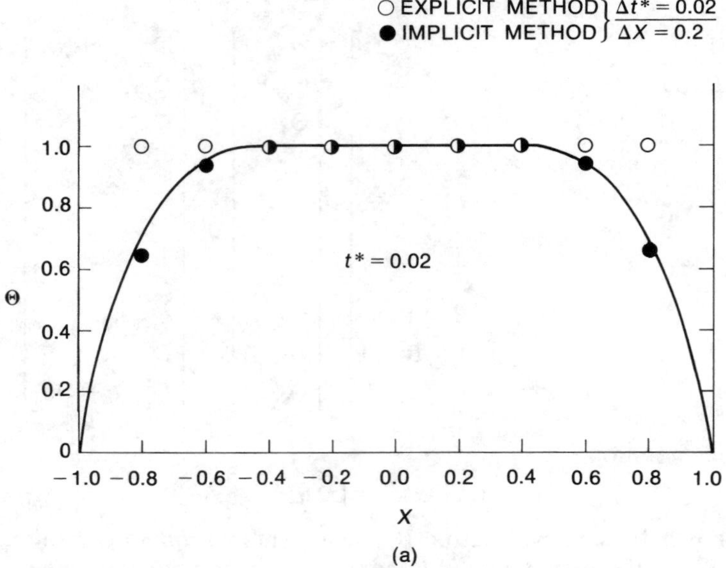

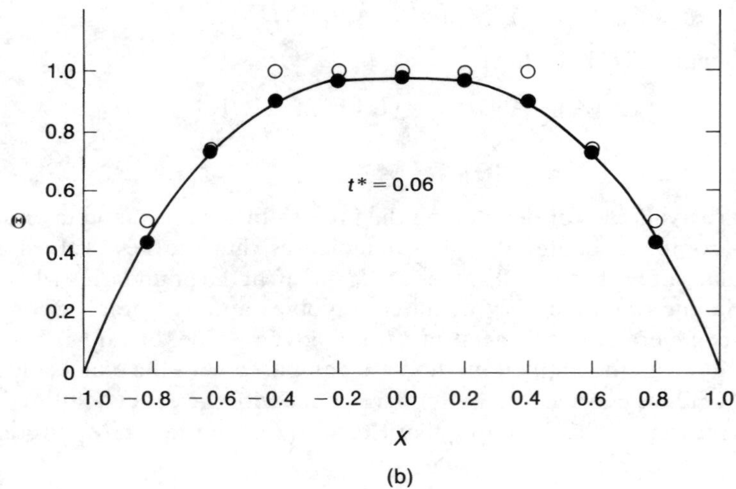

Fig. 4.7.2a–b Comparison of numerical results with the exact solution for Θ.

B.C.2 $$T = T_1, \qquad t > 0, \qquad x = -b/2 \tag{4.8-3}$$

B.C.3 $$-k\left(\frac{\partial T}{\partial x}\right) = h(T - T_1), \qquad t > 0, \qquad x = +b/2 \tag{4.8-4}$$

Eqs. 4.8-1 through 4.8-4 describe a process whereby one surface of a slab is subject to an instantaneous change in temperature from T_0 to T_1, while the other surface is suddenly brought in contact with a fluid at a temperature T_1. This type of situation might occur when a plate is immersed in a liquid at $t = 0$ in such a way that the film heat transfer coefficient on one side of the plate was exceptionally large, thus causing the temperature at the surface to change very rapidly to the fluid temperature. In terms of the dimensionless

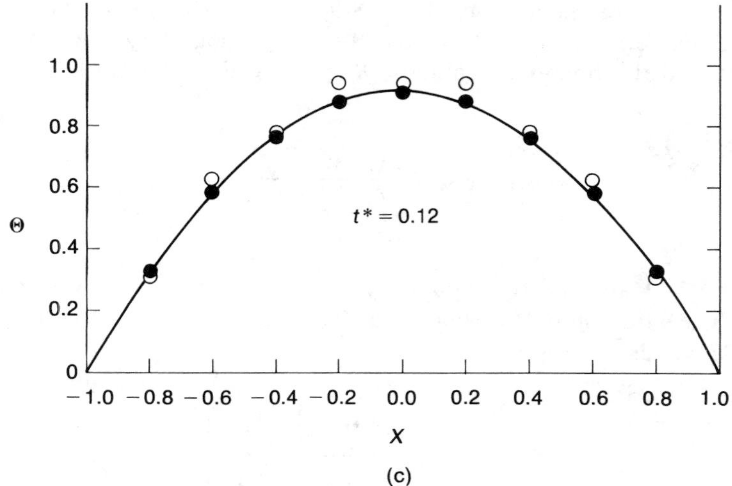

Fig. 4.7.2c Comparison of numerical results with exact solution for Θ.

variables

$$\Theta = \frac{T - T_1}{T_0 - T_1}, \qquad X = 2x/b, \qquad t^* = 4t\alpha/b, \qquad N_{Bi} = \frac{hb}{k}$$

our process is described by

$$\frac{\partial \Theta}{\partial t^*} = \left(\frac{\partial^2 \Theta}{\partial X^2}\right) \tag{4.8-5}$$

B.C.1′ $$\Theta = 1, \qquad t^* = 0, \qquad -1 \leqslant X \leqslant +1 \tag{4.8-6}$$

B.C.2′ $$\Theta = 0, \qquad t^* > 0, \qquad X = -1 \tag{4.8-7}$$

B.C.3′ $$-\left(\frac{\partial \Theta}{\partial X}\right) = \frac{1}{2} N_{Bi}\Theta, \qquad t^* > 0, \qquad X = +1 \tag{4.8-8}$$

Explicit method

The finite-difference form of Eq. 4.8-5 is given by Eq. 4.7-11; the finite-difference form of the initial condition is given by

B.C.1″ $$\Theta_{i,0} = 1, \qquad i = 0, 1, 2, \ldots, N-1, N \tag{4.8-9}$$

the second boundary condition is written as

B.C.2″ $$\Theta_{0,j} = 0, \qquad j = 1, 2, 3, \ldots \tag{4.8-10}$$

and the finite-difference form of the flux boundary condition can be expressed as

B.C.3″ $$-\left(\frac{\Theta_{N,j} - \Theta_{N-1,j}}{\Delta X}\right) = \frac{1}{2} N_{Bi} \left(\frac{\Theta_{N,j} + \Theta_{N-1,j}}{2}\right), \qquad j = 1, 2, 3, \ldots \tag{4.8-11}$$

Here we have been forced to approximate the derivative of Θ at $X = 1.0 - \frac{1}{2}\Delta X$, and since the left-hand-side of Eq. 4.8-8 has been evaluated at $1.0 - \frac{1}{2}\Delta X$ we have chosen to evaluate the right-hand-side at this point. If ΔX is made small enough Eq. 4.8-11 should be a suitable approximation of Eq. 4.8-8. We can rearrange Eq. 4.8-11 to obtain an expression for the boundary value of the dimensionless temperature

$$\Theta_{N,j} = \Theta_{N-1,j} \left[\frac{\left(1.0 - \frac{\Delta X}{4} N_{Bi}\right)}{\left(1.0 + \frac{\Delta X}{4} N_{Bi}\right)}\right] \tag{4.8-12}$$

Since all the values of $\Theta_{i,0}$ are specified by Eq. 4.8-9, we can use Eq. 4.7-11 to calculate the interior values of Θ at the new time, i.e., $\Theta_{1,1}$, $\Theta_{2,1,\ldots}$ $\Theta_{N-2,1}$ and $\Theta_{N-1,1}$. The boundary value at $X=-1$ is specified by Eq. 4.8-10, i.e., $\Theta_{0,1}=0$, and the boundary value at $X=+1$ is given by Eq. 4.8-12

$$\Theta_{N,1}=\Theta_{N-1,1}\left[\frac{\left(1.0-\frac{\Delta X}{4}N_{Bi}\right)}{\left(1.0+\frac{\Delta X}{4}N_{Bi}\right)}\right] \tag{4.8-13}$$

Thus by means of Eq. 4.7-11 and the two boundary conditions at $X=\pm 1$ we can calculate the entire temperature field at each new time step. If we choose $\Delta X=0.2$ and $\Delta t^*=0.004$ and specify the Biot number as $N_{Bi}=10.0$, Eq. 4.8-13 yields

$$\begin{aligned}\Theta_{N,1}&=1.000\left[\frac{\left(1.0-\left(\frac{0.2}{4.0}\right)10\right)}{\left(1.0-\left(\frac{0.2}{4.0}\right)10\right)}\right]\\&=0.333\end{aligned} \tag{4.8-14}$$

At the next time step this calculation is repeated to yield

$$\begin{aligned}\Theta_{N,2}&=0.933(\tfrac{1}{3})\\&=0.311\end{aligned} \tag{4.8-15}$$

Values calculated by Eq. 4.7-11 and the boundary conditions are shown in Table 4.8-1. There we see that the surface temperature at $X=-1$ has been decreased from 1.000 to 0.0 in the first time step in accordance with Eq. 4.8-10, while the surface temperature at $X=+1$ is progressing more slowly from one to zero owing to the resistance to heat transfer at that surface.

Table 4.8-1 Tabulated Values of $\Theta_{i,j}$ Determined by the Explicit Method for a Flux Boundary Condition with $N_{Bi}=10$

t^* \ X	−1.0	−0.8	−0.6	−0.4	−0.2	0.0	+0.2	+0.4	+0.6	+0.8	+1.0
0.000	1.000	1.000	1.000	1.000	1.000	1.000	1.000	1.000	1.000	1.000	1.000
0.004	0.000	1.000	1.000	1.000	1.000	1.000	1.000	1.000	1.000	1.000	(0.333)
0.008	0.000	0.900	1.000	1.000	1.000	1.000	1.000	1.000	1.000	0.933	(0.311)
0.012	0.000	0.820	0.990	1.000	1.000	1.000	1.000	1.000	0.993	0.878	(0.293)
0.016	0.000	0.755	0.974	0.999	1.000	1.000	1.000	0.999	0.982	0.831	(0.277)
0.020	0.000	0.701	0.955	0.997	1.000	1.000	1.000	0.998	0.969	0.791	(0.264)

Implicit method

In using the implicit or matrix inversion method we still make use of the boundary conditions as expressed by Eqs. 4.8-9 through 4.8-12; however, the finite-difference form of Eq. 4.8-5 is now given by Eq. 4.7-16. In writing out Eq. 4.7-16 for all values of i we use Eq. 4.8-10 to specify $\Theta_{0,j}$ and Eq. 4.8-12 to eliminate $\Theta_{N,j}$ from the very last finite-difference equation. Under these circumstances Eq. 4.7-17 takes the form

$$
\begin{aligned}
B\,\Theta_{1,j+1} + \Theta_{2,j+1} &= D_{1,j} - \Theta_{0,j+1} \\
\Theta_{1,j+1} + B\,\Theta_{2,j+1} + \Theta_{3,j+1} &= D_{2,j} \\
\Theta_{2,j+1} + B\,\Theta_{3,j+1} + \Theta_{4,j+1} &= D_{3,j} \\
\cdots\cdots\cdots\cdots\cdots\cdots \\
\Theta_{N-3,j+1} + B\,\Theta_{N-2,j+1} + \Theta_{N-1,j+1} &= D_{N-2,j} \\
\Theta_{N-2,j+1} + \left\{ B + \left[\frac{\left(1.0 - \frac{\Delta X}{4} N_{\mathrm{Bi}}\right)}{\left(1.0 + \frac{\Delta X}{4} N_{\mathrm{Bi}}\right)} \right] \right\} \Theta_{N-1,j+1} &= D_{N-1,j}
\end{aligned}
\tag{4.8-16}
$$

From this point one simply follows the same steps given by Eqs. 4.7-18 through 4.7-21 in the previous section. Note that in the matrix inversion method the surface temperature $\Theta_{N,j}$ need never be calculated unless it is desired.

Following the discussion in Sec. 4.7 one might guess that the implicit method represents the more satisfactory approach to this problem, and indeed this is so. Not only is the finite-difference form of the differential equation a better approximation, but the boundary conditions are imposed on the solution at each time step. In the explicit method the boundary conditions are always one time step behind the calculation of the temperature field. This can be seen in Table 4.8-1 where the interior values of Θ at $t^* = 0.004$ are completely unaffected by the boundary conditions, while the values presented in Table 4.8-2 for the implicit method show a definite change after the first time step. In a sense, the temperature field calculated by the explicit method *lags* behind the boundary conditions, thus small time steps are required in order to obtain a satisfactory solution.

Table 4.8-2 Tabulated Values of $\Theta_{i,j}$ Determined by the Implicit Matrix Inversion Method for a Flux Boundary Condition with $N_{\mathrm{Bi}} = 10$

t^* \ X	−1.0	−0.8	−0.6	−0.4	−0.2	0.0	+0.2	+0.4	+0.6	+0.8	+1.0
0.000	1.000	1.000	1.000	1.000	1.000	1.000	1.000	1.000	1.000	1.000	1.000
0.004	0.000	0.909	0.996	1.000	1.000	1.000	1.000	1.000	0.999	0.969	(0.323)
0.008	0.000	0.834	0.985	0.999	1.000	1.000	1.000	1.000	0.993	0.912	(0.304)
0.012	0.000	0.771	0.969	0.997	1.000	1.000	1.000	0.999	0.984	0.863	(0.288)
0.016	0.000	0.718	0.951	0.994	0.999	1.000	1.000	0.997	0.973	0.820	(0.274)
0.020	0.000	0.673	0.932	0.990	0.999	1.000	0.999	0.994	0.959	0.783	(0.261)

4.9 Numerical Solution of Transient, One-Dimensional Heat Conduction Problems in Cylindrical Coordinates

Here we wish only to present the finite-difference forms for the transient heat conduction equation in cylindrical coordinates. The methods of solution are identical to those discussed previously for rectangular coordinates. Since we plan only to illustrate the form that the finite-difference equations take, and not to discuss their solution, we will not bother to put the governing differential equation in dimensionless form and simply begin with

$$
\begin{aligned}
\frac{\partial T}{\partial t} &= \alpha\left[\frac{1}{r}\frac{\partial}{\partial r}\left(r\frac{\partial T}{\partial r}\right)\right] \\
&= \alpha\left[\left(\frac{\partial^2 T}{\partial r^2}\right) + \frac{1}{r}\left(\frac{\partial T}{\partial r}\right)\right]
\end{aligned}
\tag{4.9-1}
$$

Explicit method

In the explicit formulation the spatial derivatives on the right-hand-side are evaluated at t_j while the time derivative is evaluated at $t_{j+1/2}$ or at $t_j + (\Delta t/2)$. The spatial derivatives take the form

$$\left(\frac{\partial^2 T}{\partial r^2}\right)_{r_i,t_j} \sim \frac{T_{i+1,j} - 2T_{i,j} + T_{i-1,j}}{\Delta r^2}$$
$$\frac{1}{r}\left(\frac{\partial T}{\partial r}\right)_{r_i,t_j} \sim \frac{T_{i+1,j} - T_{i-1,j}}{(r_i)(2\Delta r)} \tag{4.9-2}$$

and the time derivative is written as

$$\left(\frac{\partial T}{\partial t}\right)_{r_i,t_{j+1/2}} = \frac{T_{i,j+1} - T_{i,j}}{\Delta t} \tag{4.9-3}$$

Note that the left-hand-side is evaluated at a different time than the right-hand-side, our obvious hope being that if Δt is made small enough this will provide a satisfactory approximation. Substituting Eqs. 4.9-2 and 4.9-3 into Eq. 4.9-1 and solving for $T_{i,j+1}$ we obtain

$$T_{i,j+1} = T_{i,j} + \alpha\left(\frac{\Delta t}{\Delta r^2}\right)\left[T_{i+1,j}\left(1+\frac{1}{2i}\right) - 2T_{i,j} + T_{i-1,j}\left(1-\frac{1}{2i}\right)\right]$$
$$i = 1, 2, 3, \ldots, N-1 \tag{4.9-4}$$

Here we have replaced r_i with $i\,\Delta r$ since

$$r_i = i\,\Delta r, \qquad i = 0, 1, 2, \ldots \tag{4.9-5}$$

Note that in Eq. 4.9-4 the index i never takes on the value $i = 0$ thus the terms $(1 + 1/2i)$ and $(1 - 1/2i)$ cause no difficulty, but what about the temperature at the centerline $T_{0,j}$? We need this temperature if we are to use Eq. 4.9-4 to calculate some evolving temperature field. In our analytic studies of heat conduction in cylindrical coordinates for regions of the type $0 \leq r \leq r_0$ we were able to determine constants of integration by simply specifying (see Secs. 4.6 and 3.2) that

$$T \quad \text{is finite in the region} \quad 0 \leq r \leq r_0$$

however, the finite-difference analog of the transient heat conduction equation cannot be treated that simply and we must explore the temperature field around the origin. Very often in situations such as this we can extract some useful information by applying the macroscopic balance to the region in question. To do this we return to Eq. 4.1-2 and rewrite it here as

$$\frac{\partial}{\partial t}\int_{\mathcal{V}} \rho e\, dV = -\int_{\mathcal{A}} \mathbf{q}\cdot\mathbf{n}\, dA + \int_{\mathcal{V}} \Phi\, dV \tag{4.9-6}$$

Application of Eq. 4.9-6 to the cylindrical element shown in Fig. 4.9.1 and letting $r \to 0$ and $\Delta z \to 0$ will provide the information we seek. For the region in question we express the volume integrals in terms of averages as

$$\int_{\mathcal{V}} \rho e\, dV = \langle \rho c_p (T - T_0)\rangle \mathcal{V} \tag{4.9-7}$$

$$\int_{\mathcal{V}} \Phi\, dV = \langle \Phi \rangle \mathcal{V} \tag{4.9-8}$$

Noting that $\mathcal{V} = \pi r^2\,\Delta z$, we substitute Eqs. 4.9-7 and 4.9-8 into Eq. 4.9-6 and rearrange to obtain

$$\int_{\mathcal{A}} \mathbf{q}\cdot\mathbf{n}\, dA = -\left[\frac{\partial}{\partial t}(\langle \rho c_p (T - T_0)\rangle)\right]\pi r^2\,\Delta z + \langle \Phi \rangle \pi r^2\,\Delta z \tag{4.9-9}$$

The left-hand-side of Eq. 4.9-9 can be expressed as

$$\int_{\mathcal{A}} \mathbf{q}\cdot\mathbf{n}\, dA = 2\Delta z \pi r \langle q_r\rangle|_r + (\langle q_z\rangle|_{z+\Delta z} - \langle q_z\rangle|_z)\pi r^2 \tag{4.9-10}$$

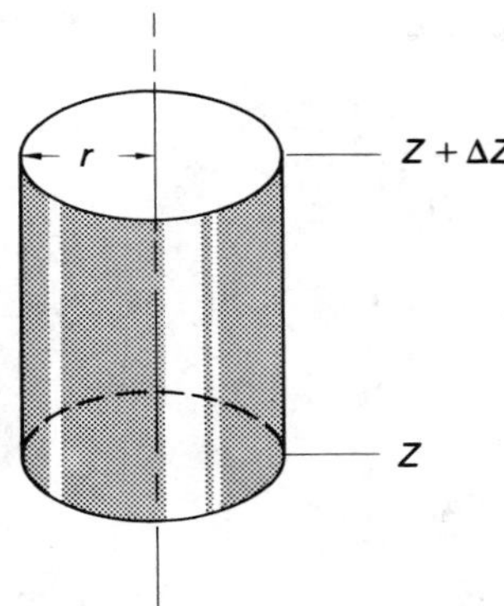

Fig. 4.9.1 Application of the macroscopic thermal energy equation to a differential cylindrical element.

Note that in Eq. 4.9-10 the angular brackets ⟨ ⟩ indicate averages over *surfaces* while in Eq. 4.9-9 they indicate *volume* averages. Substitution of Eq. 4.9-10 into Eq. 4.9-9, division by $2\pi r\,\Delta z$, and rearrangement yields

$$\langle q_r\rangle|_r = -\left[\frac{\langle q_z\rangle|_{z+\Delta z} - \langle q_z\rangle|_z}{\Delta z}\right]\frac{r}{2} - \left[\frac{\partial}{\partial t}(\langle\rho c_p(T-T_0)\rangle)\right]\frac{r}{2} + \langle\Phi\rangle\frac{r}{2} \tag{4.9-11}$$

Letting $\Delta z \to 0$ and $r \to 0$ gives us the value of q_r at the centerline, thus

$$q_r = 0, \qquad \text{at } r = 0 \tag{4.9-12}$$

which immediately leads to

$$\frac{\partial T}{\partial r} = 0, \qquad \text{at } r = 0 \tag{4.9-13}$$

The finite-difference analog of Eq. 4.9-13 is

$$\left(\frac{\partial T}{\partial r}\right)_{r=\Delta r/2} \sim \frac{T_{1,j} - T_{0,1}}{\Delta r} \tag{4.9-14}$$

thus the centerline temperature $T_{0,j}$ can be taken to be equal to the temperature at the first interior point $T_{1,j}$.

$$T_{0,j} = T_{1,j} \tag{4.9-15}$$

The point to be understood here is that for transient problems $0 \leq r \leq r_0$ the boundary condition at the centerline is a *flux* condition, and the implicit method of calculation follows the procedure given for rectangular coordinates in Sec. 4.8. If the region under consideration does not include the centerline the boundary condition may either result from the temperature being specified or the flux being specified.

Implicit method

In this approach we attempt to improve on the *explicit* method by evaluating both sides of Eq. 4.9-1 at the same time. Instead of Eqs. 4.9-2 we now write

$$\left(\frac{\partial^2 T}{\partial r^2}\right)_{r_i,t_{j+1/2}} \sim \frac{1}{2}\left\{\left[\frac{T_{i+1,j+1} - 2T_{i,j+1} + T_{i-1,j+1}}{\Delta r^2}\right] + \left[\frac{T_{i+1,j} - 2T_{i,j} + T_{i-1,j}}{\Delta r^2}\right]\right\}$$

$$\frac{1}{r}\left(\frac{\partial T}{\partial r}\right)_{r_i,t_{j+1/2}} \sim \frac{1}{2r_i}\left\{\left[\frac{T_{i+1,j+1} - T_{i-1,j+1}}{2\Delta r}\right] + \left[\frac{T_{i+1,j} - T_{i-1,j}}{2\Delta r}\right]\right\} \tag{4.9-16}$$

We evaluate the time derivative as indicated in Eq. 4.9-3 and substitute these expressions into Eq. 4.9-1 to obtain

$$\left(1+\frac{1}{2i}\right)T_{i+1,j+1}-2\left(1+\frac{2\Delta r^2}{\alpha\,\Delta t^*}\right)T_{i,j+1}+\left(1-\frac{1}{2i}\right)T_{i-1,j+1}$$

$$=-\left\{\left(1+\frac{1}{2i}\right)T_{i+1,j}-2\left(1-\frac{2\Delta r^2}{\alpha\,\Delta t^*}\right)T_{i,j}+\left(1-\frac{1}{2i}\right)T_{i-1,j}\right\} \tag{4.9-17}$$

$$i=1,2,3,\ldots,N-1$$

Letting

$$A_i=\left(1+\frac{1}{2i}\right)$$

$$B_i=-2\left(1+\frac{2\Delta r^2}{\alpha\,\Delta t^*}\right)$$

$$C_i=\left(1-\frac{1}{2i}\right)$$

$$D_{i,j}=-\left\{\left(1+\frac{1}{2i}\right)T_{i+1,j}-2\left(1-\frac{2\Delta r^2}{\alpha\,\Delta t^*}\right)T_{i,j}+\left(1-\frac{1}{2i}\right)T_{i-1,j}\right\}$$

We can write the $N-1$ equations given by Eq. 4.9-17 as

$$\begin{bmatrix} B_1 & C_1 & & & & \\ A_2 & B_2 & C_2 & & & \\ & A_3 & B_3 & C_3 & & \\ & \cdot & \cdot & \cdot & & \\ & & \cdot & \cdot & \cdot & \\ & & & A_{N-2} & B_{N-2} & C_{N-2} \\ & & & & A_{N-1} & B_{N-1} \end{bmatrix} \begin{bmatrix} T_{1,j+1} \\ T_{2,j+1} \\ T_{3,j+1} \\ \cdot \\ \cdot \\ T_{N-2,j+1} \\ T_{N-1,j+1} \end{bmatrix} = \begin{bmatrix} D_{1,j}-A_1T_{0,j} \\ D_{2,j} \\ D_{3,j} \\ \cdot \\ \cdot \\ D_{N-2,j} \\ D_{N-1,j}-C_{N-1}T_{N,j} \end{bmatrix} \tag{4.9-18}$$

In compact notation we write

$$[B][T]_{j+1}=[D]_j \tag{4.9-19}$$

where $[B]$ is a *known* tri-diagonal matrix, $[T]_{j+1}$ is the *unknown* column vector composed of the temperatures at the new time t_{j+1}, and $[D]_j$ is a *known* column vector made up of terms evaluated at the old time, t_j. As was pointed out in the previous section, the explicit method involves more complex programming but has the advantage of being more accurate and absolutely stable.

Solution to design problem IV

As a first step in attacking this problem we should sketch the temperature field that we expect to find for this transient heat transfer process. This has been done in Fig. IV.1a. It is not at all clear on the basis of intuition how the interface temperature T_i will vary with time. Solution of the transient problem illustrated if Fig. IV.1a could be accomplished by numerical methods without great difficulty; however, an analytic solution would require some effort. The time and expense required by either method is not justified in this case and we must seek an approximate solution.

In constructing an approximate solution we first assume that the temperature of the insulation is initially uniform at a value of T_1. Secondly, we assume that the temperature field in the insulation and in the hand can be approximated by a linear temperature profile and two thermal boundary layers, δ_1 and δ_2, as illustrated in Fig. IV.1b. Under these conditions the temperature field is given by

$$T=T_i-\left(\frac{x}{\delta_1}\right)(T_1-T_i),\qquad -\delta_1\leq x\leq 0$$

$$T=T_i+\left(\frac{x}{\delta_2}\right)(T_0-T_i),\qquad 0\leq x\leq \delta_2$$

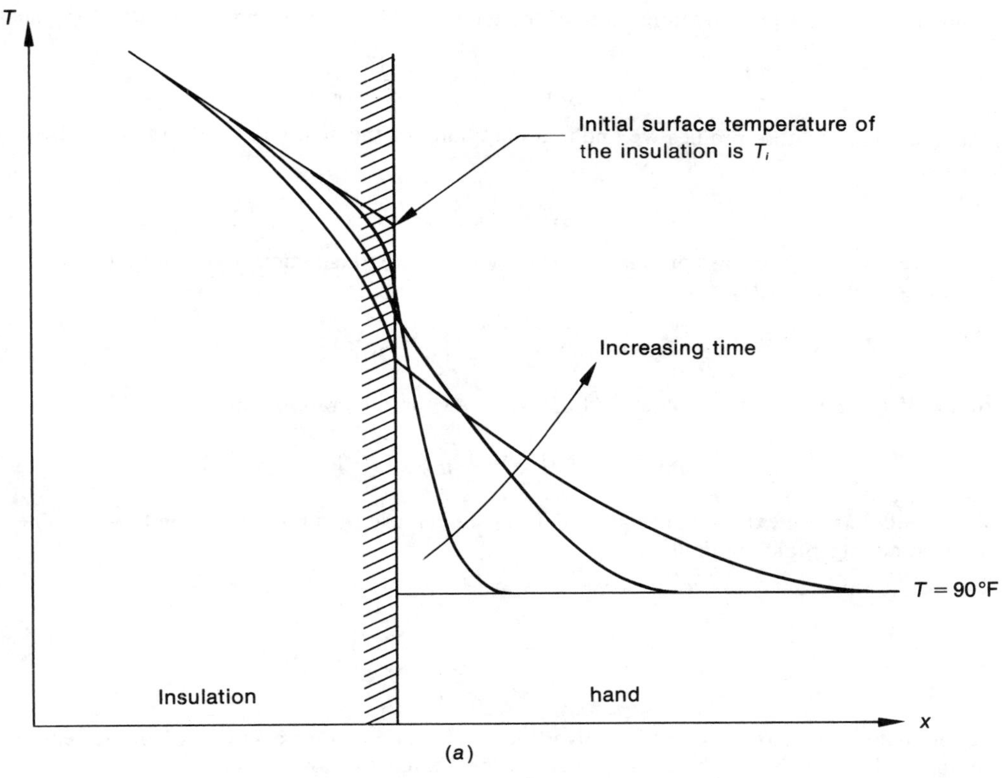

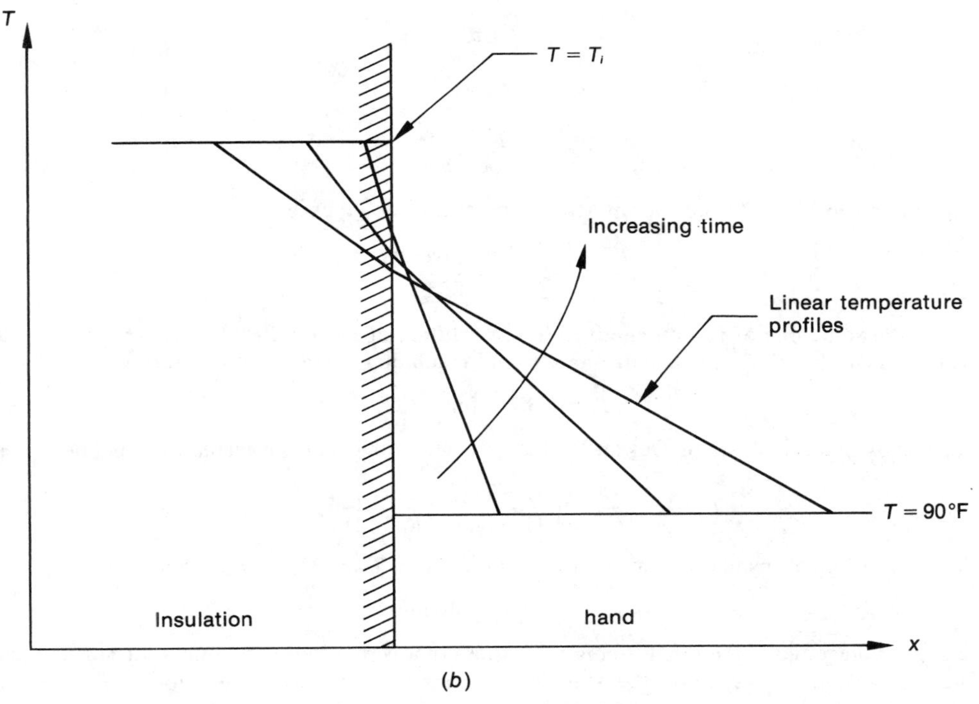

Fig. IV.1 Temperature profiles at the skin–insulation interface.

These temperature profiles require continuity of the temperature at $x = 0$, and continuity of the heat flux gives us

$$-k_1\left(\frac{\partial T}{\partial x}\right)_{x=0^-} = -k_2\left(\frac{\partial T}{\partial x}\right)_{x=0^+}$$

Using the linear temperature profiles we find that continuity of the heat flux yields a relation between the two boundary layers.

$$\left(\frac{\delta_1}{\delta_2}\right) = -\left(\frac{k_1}{k_2}\right)\left(\frac{T_1 - T_i}{T_0 - T_i}\right)$$

Since there are no energy sources or sinks the energy lost by the insulation is gained by the hand, and we can write an energy balance in the form

$$\int_{x=-\delta_1}^{x=0} \rho_1 c_{p_1}(T_1 - T)\,dx = \int_{x=0}^{x=\delta_2} \rho_2 c_{p_2}(T - T_0)\,dx$$

Substitution of the temperature profiles and carrying out the integration yields

$$\rho_1 c_{p_1}(T_1 - T_i)\left(\frac{\delta_1}{2}\right) = -\rho_2 c_{p_2}(T_0 - T_i)\left(\frac{\delta_2}{2}\right)$$

Since we already have an expression relating δ_1 to δ_2 we can use the above equation to determine T_i which is given, after some algebraic manipulation, by

$$T_i = \frac{T_1 + T_0\left(\frac{k_2}{k_1}\right)\sqrt{\frac{\alpha_1}{\alpha_2}}}{1 + \left(\frac{k_2}{k_1}\right)\sqrt{\frac{\alpha_1}{\alpha_2}}}$$

Here we see that our approximate solution gives an interface temperature which is independent of time. If we take the physical properties of the average hand to be similar to those of water we find

$$k_2 = 0.35 \text{ Btu/hr ft °F}$$

$$\rho_2 = 62 \text{ lb}_m/\text{ft}^3$$

$$c_{p_2} = 1 \text{ Btu/lb}_m \text{ °F}$$

and the quantity

$$\left(\frac{k_2}{k_1}\right)\sqrt{\frac{\alpha_1}{\alpha_2}}$$

can be calculated to be 3.33, and the interface temperature is given by

$$T_i = \frac{T_1 + 3.33T_0}{4.33}$$

If we follow the same line of reasoning given in the solution of Design Problem II we would require T_i to be 100°F. Taking T_0 to be 90°F this leads to an original insulation surface temperature of

$$T_1 = 133\text{°F} \quad \text{for} \quad T_i = 100\text{°F}$$

From our steady-state analysis of Design Problem II, we know that the insulation thickness is given by

$$L_2 = L_1\left(\frac{k_2}{h_2 L_1}\right)\left(\frac{T_0 - T_a}{T_1 - T_a}\right) - \left(\frac{k_2}{k_1}\right) - \left(\frac{k_2}{h_2 L_1}\right)\left(\frac{h_2}{h_1}\right) + 1$$

where T_1 is the original insulation surface temperature. For $T_1 = 133$°F we obtain

$$L_2 = 10 \text{ in.}$$

This is a significant reduction in the insulation thickness that is required to maintain the surface temperature at 100°F, i.e., $L_2 = 24$ in. If we allow the skin–insulation interface temperature to be as high as 150°F, the steady-state insulation surface temperature becomes 250°F, and the insulation thickness is reduced to $L_2 = 2.8$ in. Thus it would seem reasonable to add 3 in. of insulation to our reactor vessel.

PROBLEMS†

IV-1. Improve the solution given for Design Problem IV by choosing temperature profiles which require that the heat flux be continuous at $x = -\delta_1$ and $+\delta_2$.

IV-2. Solve Design Problem IV using an explicit numerical method to solve the governing differential equations. Be careful in formulating the finite-difference form of the flux condition at the interface.

***4-1.** (4.2) After 3 hr 20 min of cooking, what is the average temperature of the turkey described in Ex. 4.2-1?

4-2. (4.2) If a body of volume $\mathscr{V}$ and surface area $\mathscr{A}$ is immersed in a fluid, the temperature of which is given by

$$T_f = T_0 + (T_1 - T_0)\cos \omega t$$

what is the temperature of the body if there is negligible resistance to heat transfer in the body. Take the value of the film heat transfer coefficient to be h: Hint: Assume a solution of the form

$$\langle T\rangle = T_0 + A\cos(\omega t - \theta)$$

where A is the unknown amplitude of the temperature variation in the body and θ is the unknown phase lag of the temperature variation.

4-3. (4.2) In the process described in Sec. 4.2 we assumed that the ambient temperature T_a was constant. If the value of $\rho c_p \mathscr{V}$ for the body is *not* small compared to the value of $\rho c_p \mathscr{V}$ for the surrounding fluid, the ambient temperature will change with time. Extend the analysis presented in Sec. 4.2 to the case where a body initially at a temperature T_0 is immersed in a tank of fluid initially at a temperature T_f. Take the Biot number to be much less than one, and derive an expression for the temperature of the body given that $\rho c_p \mathscr{V}$ for the body is η_b and $\rho c_p \mathscr{V}$ for the surrounding fluid is η_f. Show that your result reduces to Eq. 4.2-8 when $(\eta_b/\eta_f) \to 0$. If the solid body is steel and the surrounding fluid is water, what is the ratio of volumes, $\mathscr{V}_b/\mathscr{V}_f$, required in order that Eq. 4.2-8 be a reasonable approximation? Assume that the fluid is well mixed.

4-4. (4.2) Develop an order-of-magnitude analysis of Eq. 4.2-5 in order to show that one can assume a uniform temperature in the solid when $N_{Bi} \ll 1$.

4-5. (4.2) A small diameter wire is heated to 400°F and then exposed to a 68°F environment through a film heat transfer coefficient of 0.80 Btu/hr ft²°F. Determine the time required to cool the wire to 100°F.

Given:
1. The wire is very long
2. $D = 0.003$ in.
3. $k = 180$ Btu/hr ft °F
4. $\rho = 480\ \text{lb}_m/\text{ft}^3$
5. $c_p = 0.083\ \text{Btu/lb}_m\,°\text{F}$

***4-6.** (4.3) In Ex. 4.3-1 we found that a 1 in. thick door would respond slowly to a change in the surface temperature. If a 1 in. thick aluminum disk is inserted in the door, how long will it take to detect a fire on the opposite side of the door?

***4-7.** (4.3) Use the approximate solution for the temperature field in a semi-infinite slab to solve Ex. 4.3-1.

4-8. (4.3) In Ex. 4.3-1 it was suggested that a 5°C temperature rise was detectable by touch. Take the thermal conductivity of the $\frac{1}{4}$ in. thick plywood panel to be $k = 0.07$ Btu/hr ft °F, and use the result of the solution of Design Problem IV to reestimate the response time. Assume that a 5°C rise in the *interface temperature* is detectable by touch. The first question to be answered here is what is the temperature of the wood–hand interface when the wood is at 22°C. Then one must decide to what temperature the wood must be raised in order to give a 5°C increase in the wood–hand interface temperature. Keep in mind that the semi-infinite slab approximation becomes less and less accurate as the dimensionless temperature, $\Theta = (T - T_0)/(T_1 - T_0)$, increases.

4-9. (4.3) Develop approximate solutions for transient heat conduction in a semi-infinite slab using the following sets of conditions on Θ:

(*a*) $\Theta = 1, x = 0$
$\Theta = 0, x = \delta_T(t)$

†Problems numbered IV-1 and IV-2 deal directly with Design Problem IV, and problems marked with an asterisk (*) are concerned with the solved example problems.

(b) $\Theta = 1, x = 0$
$\Theta = 0, x = \delta_T(t)$
$\frac{\partial \Theta}{\partial x} = 0, x = \delta_T(t)$
$\frac{\partial^2 \Theta}{\partial x^2} = 0, x = \delta_T(t)$

Use the results to calculate the heat flux at $x = 0$ and compare your calculation with the exact solution.

$$q_x|_{x=0} = \frac{k}{\sqrt{\pi \alpha t}}(T_1 - T_0)$$

4-10. (4.3) If a flat plate of thickness b and infinite in the y- and z-directions is suddenly subjected to a heat source of strength Φ, the temperature in the plate will rise until some steady state is obtained. If the surfaces of the plate are held constant at T_0 during this process, the mathematical statement of the process is

$$\text{governing differential equation: } \frac{\partial T}{\partial t} = \alpha\left(\frac{\partial^2 T}{\partial x^2}\right) - \Phi/\rho c_p$$

B.C.1 $\quad T = T_0, \quad t = 0, \quad -\frac{b}{2} \leqslant x \leqslant +\frac{b}{2}$

B.C.2 $\quad T = T_0, \quad x = +b/2, \quad t \geqslant 0$

B.C.3 $\quad T = T_0, \quad x = -b/2, \quad t \geqslant 0$

This problem can be solved exactly (see Sec. 4.5); however, to improve your skill at approximate analysis you are asked to develop an approximate solution for the temperature as a function of x and t. Hint: Solve the steady-state problem ($t \to \infty$) to help you in guessing the shape of the temperature profile.

4-11. (4.3) In Sec. 4.3 the transient heat conduction in a semi-infinite slab was analyzed using a similarity transformation to reduce the governing partial differential equation to an ordinary differential equation. If the heat flux at $x = 0$ is suddenly raised from zero to q_0, the problem appears to be more complex; however, the results of Sec. 4.3 can be used if the governing differential equation for the temperature is differentiated with respect to x to obtain a differential equation for q_x. Solve this equation subject to a boundary condition of the type

B.C.1 $\quad q_x = 0, \quad t = 0, \quad x \geqslant 0$

B.C.2 $\quad q_x = q_0, \quad x = 0, \quad t > 0$

B.C.3 $\quad q_x = 0, \quad x = \infty, \quad t > 0$

***4-12.** (4.4) Estimate the thermal diffusivity of the earth and use the result given in Sec. 4.4 to calculate the depth of penetration of the daily and yearly temperature variations at the earth's surface.

4-13. (4.4) A slab of thickness $2b$ has its surfaces at $x = \pm b$ maintained at a constant temperature T_0. A uniformly distributed heat source within the slab varies with time according to the relation

$$\Phi = A \cos \omega t$$

where A is the amplitude of the variation. In this case Φ represents a source part of the time and a sink part of the time. Derive an expression for the temperature field.

4-14. (4.5) Show how Eq. 4.5-14 is obtained from Eq. 4.5-10.

4-15. (4.5) Rework the problem posed by Eqs. 4.5-1, 4.5-2, and 4.5-3 using a dimensionless temperature defined by $\Theta = (T - T_0)/(T_1 - T_0)$ instead of the definition used in the text.

4-16. (4.5) Prove Eq. 4.5-34 when $\lambda_n = (2n + 1)\pi/2$.

4-17. (4.5) Repeat the problem posed by Eqs. 4.5-41 through 4.5-43 if a flux condition is used at the surface of the plate, i.e.,

B.C.2 $\quad q_x = h(T - T_0), \quad x = +b/2, \quad t > 0$

$\quad q_x = h(T_0 - T), \quad x = -b/2, \quad t > 0$

4-18. (4.5) Consider a flat plate, infinite in the y- and z-directions, which is initially at a uniform temperature T_0. At a time $t = 0$ the surface $x = 0$ is suddenly raised to a new temperature T_1 while the surface at $x = b$ is maintained at the initial temperature T_0. Derive an expression for the temperature as a function of x and t.

4-19. (4.5) Outline the solution of Eq. 4.5-1 subject to the boundary conditions given by Eqs. 4.5-4 and 4.5-5 rather than the boundary condition (Eq. 4.5-2) used in the text.

***4-20.** (4.5) In Ex. 4.3-1 we treated a door panel as a semi-infinite slab in order to estimate the inside surface temperature as a function of time. As another approximation to the process described in Ex. 4.3-1 we could assume that the surface was insulated so that the mathematical problem becomes

$$\left(\frac{\partial T}{\partial t}\right) = \alpha\left(\frac{\partial^2 T}{\partial x^2}\right)$$

B.C.1 $\quad T = T_0, \quad t = 0, \quad 0 \leqslant x \leqslant d$

B.C.2 $\quad T = T_1, \quad x = d, \quad t > 0$

B.C.3 $\quad \dfrac{\partial T}{\partial x} = 0, \quad x = 0, \quad t > 0$

This problem has been solved as part of a more general case and the dimensionless temperature at $x = 0$ is available in the Heisler Chart given in Fig. 4.5.2. Use those calculated results to predict the response time for the case where the inside of the door is assumed to be insulated. Be careful in translating the problem posed here to the one presented in Fig. 4.5.2.

4-21. (4.6) A hollow cylinder with inner radius r_1 and outer radius r_2 is initially at a uniform temperature T_0. At a time $t = 0$ the inner surface is suddenly raised to a temperature T_1 while the outer surface is subject to a flux condition given by

$$\mathbf{q}\cdot\mathbf{n} = h(T - T_0), \qquad r = r_2$$

Solve for the temperature as a function of r and t.

4-22. (4.6) Rework the problem described by Eqs. 4.6-1 through 4.6-4 using a flux boundary condition at $r = r_0$, i.e.,

B.C.2 $\quad q_r = h(T - T_1), \qquad r = r_0$

***4-23.** (4.6) A polymer fiber is extruded from a die at 550°F into a 68°F environment. The velocity of the fiber is 2.5 ft/sec and the average film heat transfer coefficient is 9.0 Btu/hr ft °F. Given the following properties of the fiber

1. diameter = 0.002 in.
2. thermal conductivity = 0.11 kcal/m hr °C
3. density = 68 lb_m/ft^3
4. heat capacity = 0.7 Btu/lb_m °F

use the Heisler Chart given in Fig. 4.6.2 to determine the time required for the centerline temperature to reach 150°F. If the fiber can be wound at this temperature, determine the distance from the die to the wind-up mechanism.

4-24. (4.7) Solve Prob. 4-10 using: (a) the explicit marching method, and (b) the matrix inversion method. Compare your result with the exact solution given in Sec. 4.5.

4-25. (4.7) Solve Prob. 4-18 using: (a) the explicit marching method, and (b) the matrix inversion method.

4-26. (4.8) Do Prob. IV-2 using the matrix inversion method.

4-27. (4.8) Solve Prob. 4-17 using: (a) the explicit marching method, and (b) the implicit matrix inversion method.

4-28. (4.9) Solve Prob. 4-22 using: (a) the explicit marching technique, and (b) the implicit matrix inversion method.

4-29. (4.9) Solve Prob. 4-21 using: (a) the explicit marching technique, and (b) the implicit matrix inversion method.

4-30. (4.9) Prove Eq. 4.9-12 by simply requiring the heat flux vector be a continuous function. Imagine what happens to q_r as one approaches the centerline along oppositely directed radii when the process is axially symmetric.

REFERENCES

1. Sokolnikoff, I. S., and Sokolnikoff, E. S., *Higher Mathematics for Engineers and Physicists*, Second Edition, McGraw-Hill Book Co., Inc., New York, 1941.
2. Whitaker, S., *Introduction to Fluid Mechanics*, Prentice-Hall, Inc., Englewood Cliffs, N.J., 1968.
3. Carslaw, H. S., and Jaeger J. C., *Conduction of Heat in Solids*, Oxford Press, 1957.
4. Heisler, M. P., "Temperature Charts for Induction Heating and Constant Temperature Heating," *Trans. ASME* **69**, 227 (1947).
5. Churchill, R. V., *Fourier Series and Boundary Value Problems*, McGraw-Hill Book Co., Inc., New York, 1941.
6. Wylie, C. R., Jr., *Advanced Engineering Mathematics*, Third Edition, McGraw-Hill Book Co., Inc., New York, 1966.
7. Whitaker, S., "Some Comments on the Torsion Problem," unpublished notes, University of California, Davis, 1968.
8. Forsythe, G. E., and Wasow, W. R., *Finite-Difference Methods for Partial Differential Equations*, John Wiley & Sons, Inc., New York, 1960.
9. Lapidus, L., *Digital Computation for Chemical Engineers*, McGraw-Hill Book Co., Inc., New York, 1962.

Design Problem V

The power consumption of the average U.S. citizen is becoming a problem of increasing concern owing to the air and thermal pollution caused by power plants and the destruction of our wild rivers by hydroelectric dams. In certain portions of the country airconditioning of homes is a major cause of increased power consumption, while home heating units have always contributed to the air pollution problem in the Midwest and the East.

The pollution caused by our heating and cooling needs can be reduced by increased insulation of homes and office buildings; however, windows represent a difficulty for they are not easily insulated and often the window area of a home or office building is responsible for a major portion of the heat exchanged with the outside environment.† The restricted use of windows is undesirable, for according to Masten,‡ "A man's ideals are only as great as the view from his kitchen window." One method of reducing this heat exchange is to use a double window as illustrated below. The two plates of glass are 1/4 in. thick and have a thermal conductivity of about 0.4 Btu/hrft°F. The window is 3 feet high and the air gap between the two plates of glass is 1/8 inch. For representative values of the outside and inside film heat transfer coefficients

$$h_o = 5\ \text{Btu/hr ft}^\circ\text{F}, \qquad h_1 = 0.5\ \text{Btu/hr ft}^\circ\text{F}$$

we want to know how much the overall heat transfer rate is reduced relative to a single window.

The effect of direct sunlight impinging upon the window is to be neglected in this problem; however, infrared radiant energy transport between the two glass plates should be taken into account.

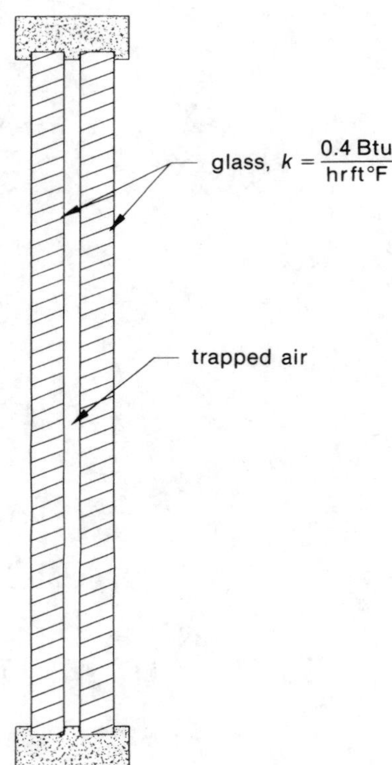

Fig. V.1 Double window.

†J. L. Threlkeld, *Thermal Environmental Engineering*, Sec. 16.2, Prentice-Hall, Inc., Englewood Cliff, N.J., 1970.
‡Ric Masten, *Windows*, Star King School for the Ministry Publications, 2441 Le Conte Ave., Berkeley, Calif., 1970.

5

The Basic Equations of Momentum and Energy Transfer

In the first four chapters we considered both steady and transient heat conduction for a variety of important processes. Throughout our analysis of these problems we encountered flux boundary conditions which we often specified in terms of a *film heat transfer coefficient*. Outside of the definition

$$\mathbf{q} \cdot \mathbf{n} \equiv h(T - T_a)$$

and some qualitative comments we know very little about the parameter h, except that it is enormously helpful in calculating interphase heat transfer rates. If we are going to advance to the point of predicting, measuring, and correlating film heat transfer coefficients, we shall need to develop a much more thorough understanding of the fundamental energy postulate and how it can be used to attack convective heat transfer problems. For example, if we add insulation to a steam pipe we know the heat loss will be reduced as will the surface temperature. In our analysis of problems of this type we have not considered how the film heat transfer coefficient might be affected by the lowering of the surface temperature. If the dominant mechanism of heat transfer in the fluid phase is *free convection*, lowering the surface temperature reduces the driving force for fluid motion and the film heat transfer coefficient becomes smaller. But what if *forced convection* is the dominant mechanism? Will the film heat transfer coefficient be affected by the lowering of the surface temperature?

If we are to answer questions of this type we must certainly understand the factors which affect the film heat transfer coefficient, and the purpose of this chapter is to lay the groundwork for an understanding of convective heat transfer. To do so we must briefly review material that has already been studied in courses in fluid mechanics, solid mechanics, and thermodynamics.

Summary of Section 5.1

The study of the kinematics of point functions leads us to an expression for the *total time derivative*

$$\frac{dS}{dt} = \frac{\partial S}{\partial t} + \mathbf{w} \cdot \nabla S \qquad (5.1\text{-}6)$$

where $\mathbf{w}$ is the velocity of the point at which S is evaluated. For the case where $\mathbf{w} = \mathbf{v}$ we obtain an expression for the *material derivative*

$$\frac{DS}{Dt} = \frac{\partial S}{\partial t} + \mathbf{v} \cdot \nabla S \qquad (5.1\text{-}8)$$

Extending our study to the time derivatives of volume integrals leads to the *general transport theorem*

$$\frac{d}{dt}\int_{\mathcal{V}_a(t)} S\,dV = \int_{\mathcal{V}_a(t)} \left(\frac{\partial S}{\partial t}\right) dV + \int_{\mathcal{A}_a(t)} S\,\mathbf{w}\cdot\mathbf{n}\,dA \tag{5.1-21}$$

Here $\mathcal{V}_a(t)$ represents an arbitrary volume, moving and deforming in space, and $\mathbf{w}$ is the velocity of the surface of this volume. For the case where $\mathbf{w} = \mathbf{v}$ the arbitrary volume becomes a *material volume* and Eq. 5.1-21 reduces to the *Reynolds transport theorem*

$$\frac{D}{Dt}\int_{\mathcal{V}_m(t)} S\,dV = \int_{\mathcal{V}_m(t)} \left(\frac{\partial S}{\partial t}\right) dV + \int_{\mathcal{A}_m(t)} S\,\mathbf{v}\cdot\mathbf{n}\,dA \tag{5.1-22}$$

The principle of conservation of mass can be stated as

$$\frac{D}{Dt}\int_{\mathcal{V}_m(t)} \rho\,dV = 0 \tag{5.1-25}$$

and the Reynolds transport theorem and divergence theorem can be used to obtain the *continuity equation*

$$\frac{\partial\rho}{\partial t} + \nabla\cdot(\rho\mathbf{v}) = 0 \tag{5.1-27}$$

This result is then used in conjunction with Eq. 5.1-22 to derive the *special form* of the Reynolds transport theorem

$$\frac{D}{Dt}\int_{\mathcal{V}_m(t)} \rho\,\mathcal{S}\,dV = \int_{\mathcal{V}_m(t)} \rho\left(\frac{D\mathcal{S}}{Dt}\right) dV \tag{5.1-31}$$

*5.1 Kinematics

In order to carefully analyze systems in which fluid motion is taking place we must understand some concepts of kinematics. Our discussion here will be concerned with the time derivatives of point functions, and time derivatives of volume integrals when the limits of integration are functions of time.

Consider an observer moving through space at a velocity $\mathbf{w}$ which may be different than the fluid velocity $\mathbf{v}$. This observer is continuously measuring some property of the fluid designated by S. For the present think of S as being some scalar such as the temperature, density, x-component of the velocity vector, etc. We would like to know the meaning of time rate of change of S as measured by our observer. We designate this derivative as dS/dt and call it the *total time derivative.* It is given by

$$\frac{dS}{dt} = \lim_{\Delta t\to 0}\left[\frac{S|_{t+\Delta t} - S|_t}{\Delta t}\right] \tag{5.1-1}$$

In the general case S depends on x, y, z, and t, i.e.,

$$S = S(x, y, z, t)$$

and in the case under consideration we must remember that the spatial coordinates at which the function is measured depend on time. Thus we express Eq. 5.1-1 as

$$\frac{dS}{dt} = \frac{d}{dt}\{S[x(t), y(t), z(t), t]\} \tag{5.1-2}$$

Using the chain rule for differentiation[1] we can write

$$\frac{dS}{dt} = \left(\frac{dS}{dx}\right)_{y,z,t}\left(\frac{dx}{dt}\right) + \left(\frac{dS}{dy}\right)_{x,z,t}\left(\frac{dy}{dt}\right) + \left(\frac{dS}{dz}\right)_{x,y,t}\left(\frac{dz}{dt}\right) + \left(\frac{dS}{dt}\right)_{x,y,z} \tag{5.1-3}$$

If we remember that the *partial derivative* refers to that derivative taken with all other independent variables held constant we write Eq. 5.1-3 as

$$\frac{dS}{dt} = \left(\frac{\partial S}{\partial x}\right)\left(\frac{dx}{dt}\right) + \left(\frac{\partial S}{\partial y}\right)\left(\frac{dy}{dt}\right) + \left(\frac{\partial S}{\partial z}\right)\left(\frac{dz}{dt}\right) + \left(\frac{\partial S}{\partial t}\right) \tag{5.1-4}$$

We interpret dx/dt as the time rate of change of the x-coordinate position of our observer, i.e., dx/dt is the x-component of the velocity, $\mathbf{w}$, of our observer. Thus

$$w_x = \frac{dx}{dt}$$

$$w_y = \frac{dy}{dt}$$

$$w_z = \frac{dz}{dt}$$

and Eq. 5.1-4 becomes

$$\frac{dS}{dt} = \left(\frac{\partial S}{\partial t}\right) + w_x\left(\frac{\partial S}{\partial x}\right) + w_y\left(\frac{\partial S}{\partial y}\right) + w_z\left(\frac{\partial S}{\partial z}\right) \tag{5.1-5}$$

In vector notation this becomes

$$\frac{dS}{dt} = \left(\frac{\partial S}{\partial t}\right) + \mathbf{w}\cdot\nabla S \tag{5.1-6}$$

and in index notation we express this result as

$$\frac{dS}{dt} = \frac{\partial S}{\partial t} + w_i\left(\frac{\partial S}{\partial x_i}\right) \tag{5.1-7}$$

Here the repeated indices are summed from 1 to 3 in accordance with the summation convention [2]. If our observer moves *with the fluid*, i.e., $\mathbf{w} = \mathbf{v}$ the time derivative is called the *material derivative* and is denoted by

$$\frac{DS}{Dt} = \frac{\partial S}{\partial t} + \mathbf{v}\cdot\nabla S \tag{5.1-8}$$

If our observer fixes himself in space, $\mathbf{w} = 0$, and the *total time derivative* is simply equal to the partial time derivative

$$\frac{dS}{dt} = \frac{\partial S}{\partial t}, \qquad \text{for } \mathbf{w} = 0 \tag{5.1-9}$$

Now we wish to consider the total time derivative of the volume integral of S over the region $\mathscr{V}_a(t)$. Here $\mathscr{V}_a(t)$ represents an *arbitrary* (hence the subscript a) volume moving through space in some specified manner. The time derivative we seek is given by

$$\frac{d}{dt}\int_{\mathscr{V}_a(t)} S\,dV = \lim_{\Delta t\to 0}\left\{\frac{\left[\int_{\mathscr{V}_a(t+\Delta t)} S(t+\Delta t)\,dV - \int_{\mathscr{V}_a(t)} S(t)\,dV\right]}{\Delta t}\right\} \tag{5.1-10}$$

To visualize the process under consideration we must think of a volume, such as a sphere, moving through space so that the velocity of each point on the surface of the volume is given by $\mathbf{w}$. The velocity $\mathbf{w}$ may be a function of the spatial coordinates (if the volume is deforming) and time (if the volume is accelerating or decelerating). At every instant of time some quantity, denoted by S, is measured throughout the region occupied by the volume $\mathscr{V}_a(t)$. The volume integral can then be evaluated at each point in time and the time derivative obtained by Eq. 5.1-10.

In Fig. 5.1.1 we have shown a volume at the times t and $t+\Delta t$ as it moves and deforms in space. During the time interval Δt the volume sweeps out a "new" region designated by $V_{\mathrm{II}}(\Delta t)$ and leaves behind an "old" region designated by $V_{\mathrm{I}}(\Delta t)$. Clearly we can express the volume $\mathscr{V}_a(t+\Delta t)$ as

$$\mathscr{V}_a(t+\Delta t) = \mathscr{V}_a(t) + V_{\mathrm{II}}(\Delta t) - V_{\mathrm{I}}(\Delta t) \tag{5.1-11}$$

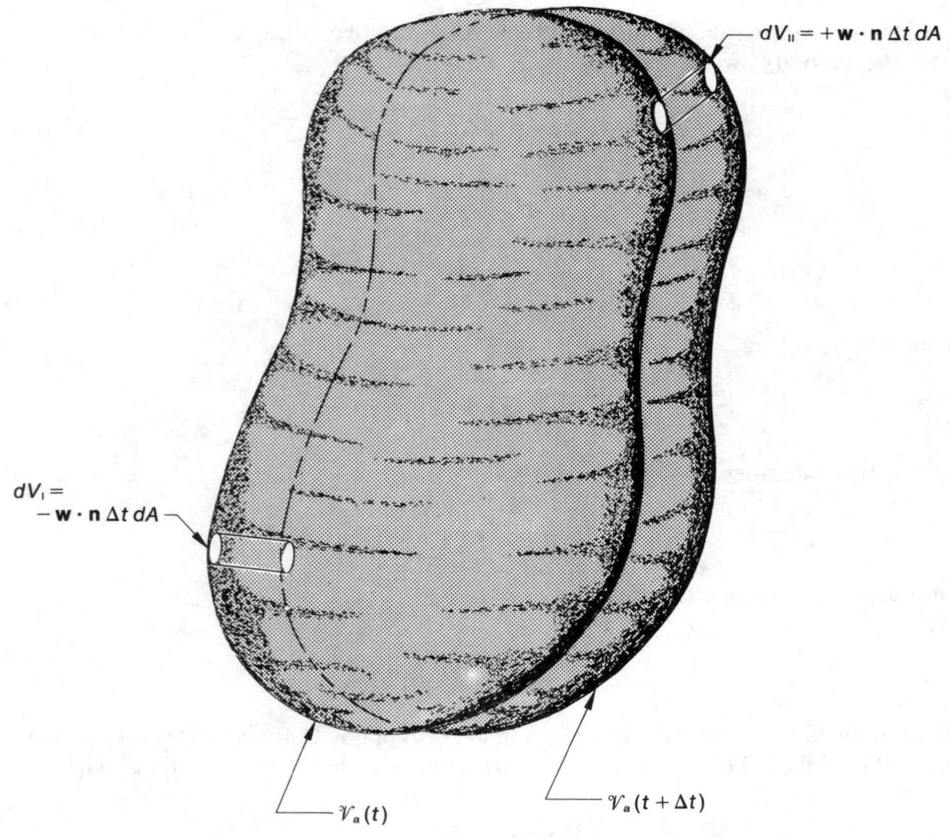

Fig. 5.1.1 A moving volume $\mathscr{V}_a(t)$.

so that the integral of $S(t+\Delta t)$ in Eq. 5.1-10 can be put in the form

$$\int_{\mathscr{V}_a(t+\Delta t)} S(t+\Delta t)\,dV = \int_{\mathscr{V}_a(t)} S(t+\Delta t)\,dV + \int_{V_{II}(\Delta t)} S(t+\Delta t)\,dV_{II} - \int_{V_I(\Delta t)} S(t+\Delta t)\,dV_I \tag{5.1-12}$$

Substitution of Eq. 5.1-12 into Eq. 5.1-10 leads to

$$\frac{d}{dt}\int_{\mathscr{V}_a(t)} S\,dV = \lim_{\Delta t\to 0}\left\{\frac{\displaystyle\int_{\mathscr{V}_a(t)} S(t+\Delta t)\,dV - \int_{\mathscr{V}_a(t)} S(t)\,dV}{\Delta t}\right\} + \lim_{\Delta t\to 0}\left\{\frac{\displaystyle\int_{V_{II}(\Delta t)} S(t+\Delta t)\,dV_{II} - \int_{V_I(\Delta t)} S(t+\Delta t)\,dV_I}{\Delta t}\right\} \tag{5.1-13}$$

In treating the first term on the right-hand-side of Eq. 5.1-13 we note that limits of integration are the same so that the two terms can be combined to give

$$\lim_{\Delta t\to 0}\left\{\frac{\displaystyle\int_{\mathscr{V}_a(t)} S(t+\Delta t)\,dV - \int_{\mathscr{V}_a(t)} S(t)\,dV}{\Delta t}\right\} = \lim_{\Delta t\to 0}\left\{\frac{1}{\Delta t}\int_{\mathscr{V}_a(t)} [S(t+\Delta t) - S(t)]\,dV\right\} \tag{5.1-14}$$

Since the limits of integration are independent of Δt the limit can be taken inside the integral sign so that Eq. 5.1-14 takes the form

$$\lim_{\Delta t\to 0}\left\{\frac{\displaystyle\int_{\mathscr{V}_a(t)} S(t+\Delta t)\,dV - \int_{V_a(t)} S(t)\,dV}{\Delta t}\right\} = \int_{\mathscr{V}_a(t)} \lim_{\Delta t\to 0}\left[\frac{S(t+\Delta t) - S(t)}{\Delta t}\right] \tag{5.1-15}$$

Here we must recognize that $S(t+\Delta t)$ and $S(t)$ are evaluated at the *same point in space* so that the integrand on the right-hand-side of Eq. 5.1-15 is the partial derivative and Eq. 5.1-15 takes the form

$$\lim_{\Delta\to 0}\left\{\frac{\int_{\mathscr{V}_a(t)} S(t+\Delta t)\,dV - \int_{\mathscr{V}_a(t)} S(t)\,dV}{\Delta t}\right\} = \int_{\mathscr{V}_a(t)} \frac{\partial S}{\partial t}\,dV \tag{5.1-16}$$

We can now return to Eq. 5.1-13 and express the time rate of change of the volume integral as

$$\frac{d}{dt}\int_{\mathscr{V}_a(t)} S\,dV = \int_{\mathscr{V}_a(t)} \left(\frac{\partial S}{\partial t}\right) dV + \lim_{\Delta t\to 0}\left\{\frac{\int_{V_{\mathrm{II}}(\Delta t)} S(t+\Delta t)\,dV_{\mathrm{II}} - \int_{V_{\mathrm{I}}(\Delta t)} S(t+\Delta t)\,dV_{\mathrm{I}}}{\Delta t}\right\} \tag{5.1-17}$$

From Fig. 5.1.1 we note that the differential volume elements of the "new" and "old" regions can be expressed as†

$$dV_{\mathrm{II}} = +\,\mathbf{w}\cdot\mathbf{n}\,\Delta t\,dA_{\mathrm{II}} \tag{5.1-18}$$

$$dV_{\mathrm{I}} = -\,\mathbf{w}\cdot\mathbf{n}\,\Delta t\,dA_{\mathrm{I}} \tag{5.1-19}$$

Use of Eqs. 5.1-18 and 5.1-19 allows us to express the volume integrals as area integrals, thus leading to

$$\frac{d}{dt}\int_{\mathscr{V}_a(t)} S\,dV = \int_{\mathscr{V}_a(t)} \left(\frac{\partial S}{\partial t}\right) dV + \lim_{\Delta t\to 0}\left\{\frac{\int_{A_{\mathrm{II}}} S(t+\Delta t)\,\mathbf{w}\cdot\mathbf{n}\,\Delta t\,dA_{\mathrm{II}} + \int_{A_{\mathrm{I}}} S(t+\Delta t)\,\mathbf{w}\cdot\mathbf{n}\,\Delta t\,dA_{\mathrm{I}}}{\Delta t}\right\} \tag{5.1-20}$$

On the right-hand-side of Eq. 5.1-20 we can cancel Δt in the numerator and denominator and note that

$$A_{\mathrm{II}} + A_{\mathrm{I}} \to \mathscr{A}_a(t) \quad \text{as} \quad \Delta t \to 0$$

so that Eq. 5.1-20 takes the form

$$\frac{d}{dt}\int_{\mathscr{V}_a(t)} S\,dV = \int_{\mathscr{V}_a(t)} \left(\frac{\partial S}{\partial t}\right) dV + \int_{\mathscr{A}_a(t)} S\,\mathbf{w}\cdot\mathbf{n}\,dA \tag{5.1-21}$$

This is known as the *general transport theorem*. A more rigorous derivation is given by Slattery [3]. If we let our arbitrary volume $\mathscr{V}_a(t)$ move *with the fluid*, the velocity $\mathbf{w}$ is equal to the fluid velocity $\mathbf{v}$, the volume $\mathscr{V}_a(t)$ becomes a *material volume* designated by $\mathscr{V}_m(t)$, and the total derivative becomes the material derivative. Under these circumstances Eq. 5.1-21 takes the form

$$\frac{D}{Dt}\int_{\mathscr{V}_m(t)} S\,dV = \int_{\mathscr{V}_m(t)} \left(\frac{\partial S}{\partial t}\right) dV + \int_{\mathscr{A}_m(t)} S\,\mathbf{v}\cdot\mathbf{n}\,dA \tag{5.1-22}$$

and is called the *Reynolds transport theorem*.

Conservation of mass

The principle of conservation of mass can be stated as

$$\{\text{the mass of a body}\} = \text{constant} \tag{5.1-23}$$

or in the rate form

$$\{\text{time rate of change of the mass of a body}\} = 0 \tag{5.1-24}$$

Using the language of calculus we express Eq. 5.1-24 as

$$\frac{D}{Dt}\int_{\mathscr{V}_m(t)} \rho\,dV = 0 \tag{5.1-25}$$

†See Reference 2, Sec. 3.4 for a detailed discussion of this point.

Application of the Reynolds transport theorem and the divergence theorem leads to

$$\frac{D}{Dt}\int_{\mathscr{V}_m(t)} \rho\, dV = \int_{\mathscr{V}_m(t)} \left[\frac{\partial \rho}{\partial t} + \nabla \cdot (\rho \mathbf{v})\right] dV = 0 \tag{5.1-26}$$

Since the limits of integration are arbitrary and ρ and $\mathbf{v}$ are assumed to be continuous functions with continuous derivatives, the integrand in the second integral must be zero and we obtain the continuity equation

$$\frac{\partial \rho}{\partial t} + \nabla \cdot (\rho \mathbf{v}) = 0 \tag{5.1-27}$$

This expression represents the differential or point form of the principle of conservation of mass and is given in expanded form in Table 5.1-1 for rectangular, cylindrical, and spherical coordinates.

Table 5.1-1 Continuity Equation

rectangular coordinates (x, y, z)

$$\frac{\partial \rho}{\partial t} + \frac{\partial}{\partial x}(\rho v_x) + \frac{\partial}{\partial y}(\rho v_y) + \frac{\partial}{\partial z}(\rho v_z) = 0 \tag{a}$$

cylindrical coordinates (r, θ, z)

$$\frac{\partial \rho}{\partial t} + \frac{1}{r}\frac{\partial}{\partial r}(\rho r v_r) + \frac{1}{r}\frac{\partial}{\partial \theta}(\rho v_\theta) + \frac{\partial}{\partial z}(\rho v_z) = 0 \tag{b}$$

spherical coordinates (r, θ, ϕ)

$$\frac{\partial \rho}{\partial t} + \frac{1}{r^2}\frac{\partial}{\partial r}(\rho r^2 v_r) + \frac{1}{r \sin\theta}\frac{\partial}{\partial \theta}(\rho v_\theta \sin\theta) + \frac{1}{r \sin\theta}\frac{\partial}{\partial \phi}(\rho v_\phi) = 0 \tag{c}$$

The continuity equation can also be used to derive a modified form of the Reynolds transport theorem which we will find especially useful. If the function S in Eq. 5.1-21 is replaced by a new function $\rho\mathscr{S}$, and the divergence theorem is used to change the area integral to a volume integral we obtain

$$\frac{D}{Dt}\int_{\mathscr{V}_m(t)} \rho\mathscr{S}\, dV = \int_{\mathscr{V}_m(t)} \left[\frac{\partial}{\partial t}(\rho\mathscr{S}) + \nabla \cdot (\rho\mathscr{S}\mathbf{v})\right] dV \tag{5.1-28}$$

Carrying out the differentiation and regrouping the terms allows us to express the right-hand-side in the form

$$\frac{D}{Dt}\int_{\mathscr{V}_m(t)} \rho\mathscr{S}\, dV = \int_{\mathscr{V}_m(t)} \left\{\rho\left(\frac{\partial \mathscr{S}}{\partial t}\right) + \rho\mathbf{v}\cdot\nabla\mathscr{S} + \mathscr{S}\left[\frac{\partial \rho}{\partial t} + \nabla \cdot (\rho\mathbf{v})\right]\right\} dV \tag{5.1-29}$$

The term in brackets is zero by Eq. 5.1-27, and if we remember that the material derivative of $\mathscr{S}$ is given by

$$\frac{D\mathscr{S}}{Dt} = \frac{\partial \mathscr{S}}{\partial t} + \mathbf{v}\cdot\nabla\mathscr{S} \tag{5.1-30}$$

we can write

$$\frac{D}{Dt}\int_{\mathscr{V}_m(t)} \rho\mathscr{S}\, dV = \int_{\mathscr{V}_m(t)} \rho\left(\frac{D\mathscr{S}}{Dt}\right) dV \tag{5.1-31}$$

This will be referred to as the *special form* of the Reynolds transport theorem.

Summary of Section 5.2

The linear momentum principle, or Euler's first law of mechanics, can be expressed as

$$\underbrace{\frac{D}{Dt}\int_{\mathcal{V}_m(t)} \rho \mathbf{v}\, dV}_{\substack{\text{time rate}\\ \text{of change}\\ \text{of linear}\\ \text{momentum}}} = \underbrace{\int_{\mathcal{V}_m(t)} \rho \mathbf{g}\, dV}_{\substack{\text{body}\\ \text{force}}} + \underbrace{\int_{\mathcal{A}_m(t)} \mathbf{t}_{(\mathbf{n})}\, dA}_{\substack{\text{surface}\\ \text{force}}} \tag{5.2-3}$$

while Euler's second law, the angular momentum principle, takes the form

$$\underbrace{\frac{D}{Dt}\int_{\mathcal{V}_m(t)} \mathbf{r}\times\rho \mathbf{v}\, dV}_{\substack{\text{time rate of}\\ \text{change of}\\ \text{angular}\\ \text{momentum}}} = \underbrace{\int_{\mathcal{V}_m(t)} \mathbf{r}\times\rho \mathbf{g}\, dV}_{\substack{\text{torque owing}\\ \text{to body}\\ \text{forces}}} + \underbrace{\int_{\mathcal{A}_m(t)} \mathbf{r}\times\mathbf{t}_{(\mathbf{n})}\, dA}_{\substack{\text{torque owing}\\ \text{to surface}\\ \text{forces}}} \tag{5.2-11}$$

Using the special form of the Reynolds transport theorem, the divergence theorem, and the stress vector–stress tensor relation, we can derive Cauchy's first and second equations

$$\rho\frac{D\mathbf{v}}{Dt} = \rho\mathbf{g} + \nabla\cdot\mathbf{T} \tag{5.2-10}$$

$$\mathbf{T} = \mathbf{T}^{T} \quad \text{or} \quad T_{ij} = T_{ji} \tag{5.2-12}$$

The first of these is often referred to as the stress equations of motion, while the second simply denotes that the stress tensor is symmetric. In terms of the viscous stress tensor Eq. 5.2-10 takes the form

$$\rho\frac{D\mathbf{v}}{Dt} = -\nabla p + \rho\mathbf{g} + \nabla\cdot\boldsymbol{\tau} \tag{5.2-25}$$

where $\boldsymbol{\tau}$ is a symmetric tensor. For a constant viscosity Newtonian fluid and incompressible flow Eq. 5.2-25 leads to the Navier–Stokes equations.

$$\rho\left(\frac{\partial \mathbf{v}}{\partial t} + \mathbf{v}\cdot\nabla\mathbf{v}\right) = -\nabla p + \rho\mathbf{g} + \mu\nabla^2\mathbf{v} \tag{5.2-22}$$

*5.2 The Laws of Mechanics

In the analysis of a continuous medium there are two laws of mechanics [4], the *linear* momentum principle (Euler's first law of mechanics) and the *angular* momentum principle (Euler's second law of mechanics). These may be stated as

$$\{\text{the time rate of change of } \textit{linear} \text{ momentum of a body}\} = \{\text{the } \textit{force} \text{ acting on the body}\} \tag{5.2-1}$$

$$\{\text{the time rate of change of } \textit{angular} \text{ momentum of a body}\} = \{\text{the } \textit{torque} \text{ acting on the body}\} \tag{5.2-2}$$

It must be remembered that for a continuum these two laws stand as separate fundamental postulates. This is probably contrary to what the student has encountered in earlier physics or dynamics courses; however, the problems encountered in those courses generally did not deal explicitly with shear forces and consequently a somewhat simpler point of view could be followed.†

†See *Essays in the History of Mechanics*, Chap. V, "Whence the Law of Moment of Momentum," by C. Truesdell, Springer-Verlag New York Inc., 1968.

The symbolic form of Eq. 5.2-1 is

$$\frac{D}{Dt}\int_{\mathscr{V}_m(t)} \rho \mathbf{v}\, dV = \int_{\mathscr{V}_m(t)} \rho \mathbf{g}\, dV + \int_{\mathscr{A}_m(t)} \mathbf{t}_{(\mathbf{n})}\, dA \tag{5.2-3}$$

Here we have split the force acting on the body into body forces ($\rho\mathbf{g}$ represents the body force per unit volume) and surface forces. The term $\mathbf{t}_{(\mathbf{n})}$ represents the surface force per unit area, and is called the *stress vector.* The stress vector can be represented in terms of the stress tensor by the expression

$$\mathbf{t}_{(\mathbf{n})} = \mathbf{T} \cdot \mathbf{n} \tag{5.2-4}$$

where $\mathbf{n}$ is the outwardly directed unit normal to the volume $\mathscr{V}_m(t)$. In matrix form this expression is written as

$$\begin{bmatrix} t_x \\ t_y \\ t_z \end{bmatrix} = \begin{bmatrix} T_{xx} & T_{yx} & T_{zx} \\ T_{xy} & T_{yy} & T_{zy} \\ T_{xz} & T_{yz} & T_{zz} \end{bmatrix} \begin{bmatrix} n_x \\ n_y \\ n_z \end{bmatrix} \tag{5.2-5}$$

We can look upon the stress matrix shown in Eq. 5.2-5 as the matrix which maps the normal vector $\mathbf{n}$ into the stress vector $\mathbf{t}_{(\mathbf{n})}$. In this sense the stress matrix completely determines the state of stress for if we know the components of this matrix we can compute the stress vector for any arbitrary surface designated by $\mathbf{n}$. In addition to mapping $\mathbf{n}$ into $\mathbf{t}_{(\mathbf{n})}$ the scalar components of the stress matrix must satisfy the law of transformation for tensors, and because of this we refer to $\mathbf{T}$ as the stress *tensor.* In index notation Eqs. 5.2-4 and 5.2-5 take the form

$$t_{(\mathbf{n})i} = T_{ji} n_j \tag{5.2-6}$$

Substitution of Eq. 5.2-4 into Eq. 5.2-3 yields

$$\frac{D}{Dt}\int_{\mathscr{V}_m(t)} \rho \mathbf{v}\, dV = \int_{\mathscr{V}_m(t)} \rho \mathbf{g}\, dV + \int_{\mathscr{A}_m(t)} \mathbf{T} \cdot \mathbf{n}\, dA \tag{5.2-7}$$

Application of the special form of the Reynolds transport theorem allows us to put the time derivative inside the integral

$$\int_{\mathscr{V}_m(t)} \rho \frac{D\mathbf{v}}{Dt}\, dV = \int_{\mathscr{V}_m(t)} \rho \mathbf{g}\, dV + \int_{\mathscr{A}_m(t)} \mathbf{T} \cdot \mathbf{n}\, dA \tag{5.2-8}$$

The area integral on the right-hand-side can be converted to a volume integral via the divergence theorem for a tensor† and we can put all the terms under the same integral sign to obtain

$$\int_{\mathscr{V}_m(t)} \left[\rho \frac{D\mathbf{v}}{Dt} - \rho \mathbf{g} - \nabla \cdot \mathbf{T}\right] dV = 0 \tag{5.2-9}$$

Since the limits of integration are arbitrary and the integrand is assumed to be continuous, we conclude that the integrand is identically zero and the *stress equations of motion* result.

$$\rho \frac{D\mathbf{v}}{Dt} = \rho \mathbf{g} + \nabla \cdot \mathbf{T} \tag{5.2-10}$$

Moving on to the angular momentum principle we express Eq. 5.2-2 as

$$\frac{D}{Dt}\int_{\mathscr{V}_m(t)} (\mathbf{r} \times \rho \mathbf{v})\, dV = \int_{\mathscr{V}_m(t)} (\mathbf{r} \times \rho \mathbf{g})\, dV + \int_{\mathscr{A}_m(t)} \mathbf{r} \times \mathbf{t}_{(\mathbf{n})}\, dA \tag{5.2-11}$$

If we attack the angular momentum principle in the same manner as we have done with the linear momentum principle we could prove that the stress tensor $\mathbf{T}$ is symmetric; however, a rigorous proof [2, 3]

†See Reference 2, Prob. 4-15 or Reference 3, page 659.

is rather long and tedious, and we will only note here that the *point equation* which results from Eq. 5.2-11 is

$$\mathbf{T} = \mathbf{T}^{\mathrm{T}} \tag{5.2-12}$$

This means that the stress matrix is equal to its transpose, thus

$$\begin{bmatrix} T_{xx} & T_{yx} & T_{zx} \\ T_{xy} & T_{yy} & T_{zy} \\ T_{xz} & T_{yz} & T_{zz} \end{bmatrix} = \begin{bmatrix} T_{xx} & T_{xy} & T_{xz} \\ T_{yx} & T_{yy} & T_{yz} \\ T_{zx} & T_{zy} & T_{zz} \end{bmatrix} \tag{5.2-13}$$

In terms of the individual scalar components we can write,

$$T_{xy} = T_{yx}, \qquad T_{yz} = T_{zy}, \qquad T_{zx} = T_{xz} \tag{5.2-14}$$

and in index notation we express this result as

$$T_{ij} = T_{ji} \tag{5.2-15}$$

On the basis of Eq. 5.2-15 we see that there are only six distinct components of the stress tensor, and if we refer to Eqs. 5.1-27 and 5.2-10 we see that we have *ten* unknowns: ρ, v_x, v_y, v_z, T_{xx}, T_{yy}, T_{zz}, T_{xy}, T_{yz}, T_{zx}, and only *four* equations. Clearly we need a *constitutive equation* for the stress tensor if we are to develop a set of determinate equations. We begin by expressing the total stress tensor in terms of the thermodynamic pressure, p, and the viscous stress tensor, $\boldsymbol{\tau}$.

$$\mathbf{T} = -p\mathbf{U} + \boldsymbol{\tau} \tag{5.2-16}$$

Here $\mathbf{U}$ is the unit tensor, the scalar components of which are given by

$$\{\text{scalar components of the unit tensor}\} = \begin{bmatrix} 1 & 0 & 0 \\ 0 & 1 & 0 \\ 0 & 0 & 1 \end{bmatrix} \tag{5.2-17}$$

The tensor $\mathbf{U}$ has the property that,

$$\mathbf{a} \cdot \mathbf{U} = \mathbf{U} \cdot \mathbf{a} = \mathbf{a} \tag{5.2-18}$$

thus $-p\mathbf{U}$ represents an isotropic stress. Substitution of Eq. 5.2-16 into Eq. 5.2-10 yields the viscous stress equations of motion.

$$\rho\left(\frac{\partial \mathbf{v}}{\partial t} + \mathbf{v} \cdot \nabla \mathbf{v}\right) = -\nabla p + \rho \mathbf{g} + \nabla \cdot \boldsymbol{\tau} \tag{5.2-19}$$

Here we have expanded the material derivative and noted that $\nabla \cdot (p\mathbf{U}) = \nabla p$. The scalar components of Eq. 5.2-19 are listed in Table 5.2-1 for rectangular, cylindrical, and spherical coordinates.

For Newtonian fluids the viscous stress tensor is represented as

$$\boldsymbol{\tau} = \mu(\nabla \mathbf{v} + \nabla \mathbf{v}^{\mathrm{T}}) + \mathbf{U}\left(\kappa - \frac{2}{3}\mu\right)\nabla \cdot \mathbf{v} \tag{5.2-20}$$

or in index notation†

$$\tau_{ij} = \mu\left(\frac{\partial v_i}{\partial x_j} + \frac{\partial v_j}{\partial x_i}\right) + \delta_{ij}\left(\kappa - \frac{2}{3}\mu\right)\frac{\partial v_k}{\partial x_k} \tag{5.2-21}$$

Here μ is the coefficient of shear viscosity and κ is the coefficient of bulk viscosity. If we substitute Eq. 5.2-20 into Eq. 5.2-19 and require that the flow be incompressible and the coefficient of viscosity, μ, to be constant, we obtain the well-known Navier–Stokes equations.

$$\rho\left(\frac{\partial \mathbf{v}}{\partial t} + \mathbf{v} \cdot \nabla \mathbf{v}\right) = -\nabla p + \rho \mathbf{g} + \mu \nabla^2 \mathbf{v} \tag{5.2-22}$$

†Here δ_{ij} represents the Kroneker delta which has the property that $\delta_{ij} = 1$ when $i = j$, and $\delta_{ij} = 0$ when $i \neq j$. Note that Eq. 5.2-21 is valid only in rectangular, Cartesian coordinates.

Table 5.2-1 Viscous Stress Equations of Motion

Rectangular Coordinates (x, y, z)

x-Direction

$$\rho\left(\frac{\partial v_x}{\partial t} + v_x\frac{\partial v_x}{\partial x} + v_y\frac{\partial v_x}{\partial y} + v_z\frac{\partial v_x}{\partial z}\right) = -\frac{\partial p}{\partial x} + \rho g_x + \left(\frac{\partial \tau_{xx}}{\partial x} + \frac{\partial \tau_{yx}}{\partial y} + \frac{\partial \tau_{zx}}{\partial z}\right) \quad (a)$$

y-Direction

$$\rho\left(\frac{\partial v_y}{\partial t} + v_x\frac{\partial v_y}{\partial x} + v_y\frac{\partial v_y}{\partial y} + v_z\frac{\partial v_y}{\partial z}\right) = -\frac{\partial p}{\partial y} + \rho g_y + \left(\frac{\partial \tau_{xy}}{\partial x} + \frac{\partial \tau_{yy}}{\partial y} + \frac{\partial \tau_{zy}}{\partial z}\right) \quad (b)$$

z-Direction

$$\rho\left(\frac{\partial v_z}{\partial t} + v_x\frac{\partial v_z}{\partial x} + v_y\frac{\partial v_z}{\partial y} + v_z\frac{\partial v_z}{\partial z}\right) = -\frac{\partial p}{\partial z} + \rho g_z + \left(\frac{\partial \tau_{xz}}{\partial x} + \frac{\partial \tau_{yz}}{\partial y} + \frac{\partial \tau_{zz}}{\partial z}\right) \quad (c)$$

Cylindrical Coordinates (r, θ, z)

r-Direction

$$\rho\left(\frac{\partial v_r}{\partial t} + v_r\frac{\partial v_r}{\partial r} + \frac{v_\theta}{r}\frac{\partial v_r}{\partial \theta} - \frac{v_\theta^2}{r} + v_z\frac{\partial v_r}{\partial z}\right) = -\frac{\partial p}{\partial r} + \rho g_r + \left[\frac{1}{r}\frac{\partial}{\partial r}(r\tau_{rr}) + \frac{1}{r}\frac{\partial \tau_{\theta r}}{\partial \theta} - \frac{\tau_{\theta\theta}}{r} + \frac{\partial \tau_{zr}}{\partial z}\right] \quad (d)$$

θ-Direction

$$\rho\left(\frac{\partial v_\theta}{\partial t} + v_r\frac{\partial v_\theta}{\partial r} + \frac{v_\theta}{r}\frac{\partial v_\theta}{\partial \theta} + \frac{v_r v_\theta}{r} + v_z\frac{\partial v_\theta}{\partial z}\right) = -\frac{1}{r}\frac{\partial p}{\partial \theta} + \rho g_\theta + \left[\frac{1}{r^2}\frac{\partial}{\partial r}(r^2\tau_{r\theta}) + \frac{1}{r}\frac{\partial \tau_{\theta\theta}}{\partial \theta} + \frac{\partial \tau_{z\theta}}{\partial z}\right] \quad (e)$$

z-Direction

$$\rho\left(\frac{\partial v_z}{\partial t} + v_r\frac{\partial v_z}{\partial r} + \frac{v_\theta}{r}\frac{\partial v_z}{\partial \theta} + v_z\frac{\partial v_z}{\partial z}\right) = -\frac{\partial p}{\partial z} + \rho g_z + \left[\frac{1}{r}\frac{\partial}{\partial r}(r\tau_{rz}) + \frac{1}{r}\frac{\partial \tau_{\theta z}}{\partial \theta} + \frac{\partial \tau_{zz}}{\partial z}\right] \quad (f)$$

Spherical Coordinates (r, θ, ϕ)

r-Direction

$$\rho\left(\frac{\partial v_r}{\partial t} + v_r\frac{\partial v_r}{\partial r} + \frac{v_\theta}{r}\frac{\partial v_r}{\partial \theta} + \frac{v_\phi}{r\sin\theta}\frac{\partial v_r}{\partial \phi} - \frac{v_\theta^2 + v_\phi^2}{r}\right) = -\frac{\partial p}{\partial r}$$
$$+ \rho g_r + \left[\frac{1}{r^2}\frac{\partial}{\partial r}(r^2\tau_{rr}) + \frac{1}{r\sin\theta}\frac{\partial}{\partial \theta}(\tau_{\theta r}\sin\theta) + \frac{1}{r\sin\theta}\frac{\partial \tau_{\phi r}}{\partial \phi} - \frac{\tau_{\theta\theta} - \tau_{\phi\phi}}{r}\right] \quad (g)$$

θ-Direction

$$\rho\left(\frac{\partial v_\theta}{\partial t} + v_r\frac{\partial v_\theta}{\partial r} + \frac{v_\theta}{r}\frac{\partial v_\theta}{\partial \theta} + \frac{v_\phi}{r\sin\theta}\frac{\partial v_\theta}{\partial \phi} + \frac{v_r v_\theta}{r} - \frac{v_\phi^2\cot\theta}{r}\right)$$
$$= -\frac{1}{r}\frac{\partial p}{\partial \theta} + \rho g_\theta + \left[\frac{1}{r^2}\frac{\partial}{\partial r}(r^2\tau_{r\theta}) + \frac{1}{r\sin\theta}\frac{\partial}{\partial \theta}(\tau_{\theta\theta}\sin\theta) + \frac{1}{r\sin\theta}\frac{\partial \tau_{\phi\theta}}{\partial \phi} + \frac{\tau_{r\theta}}{r} - \frac{\tau_{\phi\phi}\cot\theta}{r}\right] \quad (h)$$

ϕ-Direction

$$\rho\left(\frac{\partial v_\phi}{\partial t} + v_r\frac{\partial v_\phi}{\partial r} + \frac{v_\theta}{\partial r}\frac{\partial v_\phi}{\partial \theta} + \frac{v_\phi}{r\sin\theta}\frac{\partial v_\phi}{\partial \phi} + \frac{v_\phi v_r}{r} + \frac{v_\theta v_\phi\cot\theta}{r}\right)$$
$$= -\frac{1}{r\sin\theta}\frac{\partial p}{\partial \phi} + \rho g_\phi + \left[\frac{1}{r^2}\frac{\partial}{\partial r}(r^2\tau_{r\phi}) + \frac{1}{r}\frac{\partial \tau_{\theta\phi}}{\partial \theta} + \frac{1}{r\sin\theta}\frac{\partial \tau_{\phi\phi}}{\partial \phi} + \frac{\tau_{r\phi}}{r} + \frac{2\tau_{\theta\phi}\cot\theta}{r}\right] \quad (i)$$

The scalar components of Eq. 5.2-22 are listed in Table 5.2-2 for rectangular, cylindrical, and spherical coordinates. There are many other types of fluids besides Newtonian fluids; however, the study of such fluids is properly taken up in a course in fluid mechanics or rheology. For our studies in heat transfer it will be sufficient to consider only Newtonian fluids; however, the student must keep in mind that there are many important heat transfer problems involved in the processing of polymers which are highly nonlinear and usually have elastic characteristics, i.e., they are *visco-elastic* fluids. Our review of the laws of

Table 5.2-2a The Equations of Motion for Constant μ and ρ in Rectangular Coordinates (x, y, z)

x-Direction

$$\rho\left(\frac{\partial v_x}{\partial t}+v_x\frac{\partial v_x}{\partial x}+v_y\frac{\partial v_x}{\partial y}+v_z\frac{\partial v_x}{\partial z}\right)=-\frac{\partial p}{\partial x}+\rho g_x+\mu\left(\frac{\partial^2 v_x}{\partial x^2}+\frac{\partial^2 v_x}{\partial y^2}+\frac{\partial^2 v_x}{\partial z^2}\right) \quad (a)$$

y-Direction

$$\rho\left(\frac{\partial v_y}{\partial t}+v_x\frac{\partial v_y}{\partial x}+v_y\frac{\partial v_y}{\partial y}+v_z\frac{\partial v_y}{\partial z}\right)=-\frac{\partial p}{\partial y}+\rho g_y+\mu\left(\frac{\partial^2 v_y}{\partial x^2}+\frac{\partial^2 v_y}{\partial y^2}+\frac{\partial^2 v_y}{\partial z^2}\right) \quad (b)$$

z-Direction

$$\rho\left(\frac{\partial v_z}{\partial t}+v_x\frac{\partial v_z}{\partial x}+v_y\frac{\partial v_z}{\partial y}+v_z\frac{\partial v_z}{\partial z}\right)=-\frac{\partial p}{\partial z}+\rho g_z+\mu\left(\frac{\partial^2 v_z}{\partial x^2}+\frac{\partial^2 v_z}{\partial y^2}+\frac{\partial^2 v_z}{\partial z^2}\right) \quad (c)$$

Table 5.2-2b The Equations of Motion for Constant μ and ρ in Cylindrical Coordinates (r, θ, z)

r-Direction

$$\rho\left(\frac{\partial v_r}{\partial t}+v_r\frac{\partial v_r}{\partial r}+\frac{v_\theta}{r}\frac{\partial v_r}{\partial \theta}-\frac{v_\theta^2}{r}+v_z\frac{\partial v_r}{\partial z}\right)=-\frac{\partial p}{\partial r}+\rho g_r+\mu\left[\frac{\partial}{\partial r}\left(\frac{1}{r}\frac{\partial}{\partial r}(r v_r)\right)+\frac{1}{r^2}\frac{\partial^2 v_r}{\partial \theta^2}-\frac{2}{r^2}\frac{\partial v_\theta}{\partial \theta}+\frac{\partial^2 v_r}{\partial z^2}\right] \quad (a)$$

θ-Direction

$$\rho\left(\frac{\partial v_\theta}{\partial t}+v_r\frac{\partial v_\theta}{\partial r}+\frac{v_\theta}{r}\frac{\partial v_\theta}{\partial \theta}+\frac{v_r v_\theta}{r}+v_z\frac{\partial v_\theta}{\partial z}\right)=-\frac{1}{r}\frac{\partial p}{\partial \theta}+\rho g_\theta+\mu\left[\frac{\partial}{\partial r}\left(\frac{1}{r}\frac{\partial}{\partial r}(r v_\theta)\right)+\frac{1}{r^2}\frac{\partial^2 v_\theta}{\partial \theta^2}+\frac{2}{r^2}\frac{\partial v_r}{\partial \theta}+\frac{\partial^2 v_\theta}{\partial z^2}\right] \quad (b)$$

z-Direction

$$\rho\left(\frac{\partial v_z}{\partial t}+v_r\frac{\partial v_z}{\partial r}+\frac{v_\theta}{r}\frac{\partial v_z}{\partial \theta}+v_z\frac{\partial v_z}{\partial z}\right)=-\frac{\partial p}{\partial z}+\rho g_z+\mu\left[\frac{1}{r}\frac{\partial}{\partial r}\left(r\frac{\partial v_z}{\partial r}\right)+\frac{1}{r^2}\frac{\partial^2 v_z}{\partial \theta^2}+\frac{\partial^2 v_z}{\partial z^2}\right] \quad (c)$$

Table 5.2-2c The Equations of Motion Constant μ and ρ in Spherical Coordinates (r, θ, ϕ)†

r-Direction

$$\rho\left(\frac{\partial v_r}{\partial t}+v_r\frac{\partial v_r}{\partial r}+\frac{v_\theta}{r}\frac{\partial v_r}{\partial \theta}+\frac{v_\phi}{r\sin\theta}\frac{\partial v_r}{\partial \phi}-\frac{v_\theta^2-v_\phi^2}{r}\right)=-\frac{\partial p}{\partial r}+\rho g_r+\mu\left(\nabla^2 v_r-\frac{2v_r}{r^2}-\frac{2}{r^2}\frac{\partial v_\theta}{\partial \theta}-\frac{2v_\theta\cot\theta}{r^2}-\frac{2}{r^2\sin\theta}\frac{\partial v_\phi}{\partial \phi}\right) \quad (a)$$

θ-Direction

$$\rho\left(\frac{\partial v_\theta}{\partial t}+v_r\frac{\partial v_\theta}{\partial r}+\frac{v_\theta}{r}\frac{\partial v_\theta}{\partial \theta}+\frac{v_\phi}{r\sin\theta}\frac{\partial v_\theta}{\partial \phi}+\frac{v_r v_\theta}{r}-\frac{v_\phi^2\cot\theta}{r}\right)=-\frac{1}{r}\frac{\partial p}{\partial \theta}+\rho g_\theta+\mu\left(\nabla^2 v_\theta+\frac{2}{r^2}\frac{\partial v_r}{\partial \theta}-\frac{v_\theta}{r^2\sin^2\theta}-\frac{2\cos\theta}{r^2\sin^2\theta}\frac{\partial v_\phi}{\partial \phi}\right) \quad (b)$$

ϕ-Direction

$$\rho\left(\frac{\partial v_\phi}{\partial t}+v_r\frac{\partial v_\phi}{\partial r}+\frac{v_\theta}{r}\frac{\partial v_\phi}{\partial \theta}+\frac{v_\phi}{r\sin\theta}\frac{\partial v_\phi}{\partial \phi}+\frac{v_\phi v_r}{r}+\frac{v_\theta v_\phi}{r}\cot\theta\right)=-\frac{1}{r\sin\theta}\frac{\partial p}{\partial \phi}+\rho g_\phi+\mu\left(\nabla^2 v_\phi-\frac{v_\phi}{r^2\sin^2\theta}+\frac{2}{r^2\sin\theta}\frac{\partial v_r}{\partial \phi}+\frac{2\cos\theta}{r^2\sin^2\theta}\frac{\partial v_\theta}{\partial \phi}\right) \quad (c)$$

†For spherical coordinates the Laplacian is

$$\nabla^2=\frac{1}{r^2}\frac{\partial}{\partial r}\left(r^2\frac{\partial}{\partial r}\right)+\frac{1}{r^2\sin\theta}\frac{\partial}{\partial \theta}\left(\sin\theta\frac{\partial}{\partial \theta}\right)+\frac{1}{r^2\sin^2\theta}\left(\frac{\partial^2}{\partial \phi^2}\right)$$

mechanics and the principle of conservation of mass is now complete and we turn our attention to a detailed analysis of the fundamental energy principle.

Summary of Section 5.3

The fundamental energy postulate is stated as

$$\frac{D}{Dt}\int_{\mathscr{V}_m(t)} \rho\left(e+\frac{1}{2}v^2\right) dV = -\int_{\mathscr{A}_m(t)} \mathbf{q}\cdot\mathbf{n}\, dA \quad \text{rate of heat transfer to the body}$$

time rate of change of internal and kinetic energy of the body

$$+\int_{\mathscr{A}_m(t)} \mathbf{t}_{(\mathbf{n})}\cdot\mathbf{v}\, dA \quad \text{rate of surface work done on the body}$$

$$+\int_{\mathscr{V}_m(t)} \rho\mathbf{g}\cdot\mathbf{v}\, dV \quad \text{rate of work owing to body forces}$$

$$+\int_{\mathscr{V}_m(t)} \Phi\, dV \quad \text{rate of energy absorbed or emitted owing to electromagnetic radiation} \tag{5.3-1}$$

Note that Eq. 5.3-1 represents what is traditionally known as the first law of thermodynamics, but in addition we have incorporated the principle of *local equilibrium*. Thus the internal energy per unit mass, e, is assumed to be a function of time and space and specified in terms of the *local thermodynamic state*. The differential form of Eq. 5.3-1 will be referred to as *total energy equation* and it is given by

$$\rho\frac{D}{Dt}\left(e+\frac{1}{2}v^2\right) = -\nabla\cdot\mathbf{q}+\nabla\cdot(\mathbf{T}\cdot\mathbf{v})+\rho\mathbf{g}\cdot\mathbf{v}+\Phi \tag{5.3-6}$$

If the velocity and pressure are known from a solution of the equations of motion and if Φ is specified, we can represent the heat flux vector by Fourier's law and express the internal energy in terms of temperature and pressure to obtain an equation for the temperature field. However, Eq. 5.3-6 is not the most convenient form of the energy equation for determining the temperature, and in Sec. 5.4 we will derive the more useful *thermal energy equation.*

*5.3 The Energy Principle

We begin with the complete form of the energy principle discussed in Sec. 2.1.

$$\frac{D}{Dt}\int_{\mathscr{V}_m(t)} \rho\left(e+\frac{1}{2}v^2\right) dV = -\int_{\mathscr{A}_m(t)} \mathbf{q}\cdot\mathbf{n}\, dA + \int_{\mathscr{A}_m(t)} \mathbf{t}_{(\mathbf{n})}\cdot\mathbf{v}\, dA + \int_{\mathscr{V}_m(t)} \rho\mathbf{g}\cdot\mathbf{v}\, dV + \int_{\mathscr{V}_m(t)} \Phi\, dV \tag{5.3-1}$$

Our objective here is to derive a differential form of Eq. 5.3-1, and in doing so we will begin with the term on the left-hand-side and work toward the right. Application of the special form of the Reynolds transport theorem gives

$$\frac{D}{Dt}\int_{\mathscr{V}_m(t)} \rho\left(e+\frac{1}{2}v^2\right) dV = \int_{\mathscr{V}_m(t)} \rho\frac{D}{Dt}\left(e+\frac{1}{2}v^2\right) dV \tag{5.3-2}$$

Use of the divergence theorem on the first term on the right-hand-side of Eq. 5.3-1 leads to

$$-\int_{\mathscr{A}_m(t)} \mathbf{q}\cdot\mathbf{n}\, dA = -\int_{\mathscr{V}_m(t)} \nabla\cdot\mathbf{q}\, dV \tag{5.3-3}$$

The next term requires that we express the stress vector as $\mathbf{t}_{(\mathbf{n})} = \mathbf{T}\cdot\mathbf{n}$ and apply the divergence theorem to obtain

$$\int_{\mathscr{A}_m(t)} \mathbf{t}_{(\mathbf{n})} \cdot \mathbf{v}\, dA = \int_{\mathscr{V}_m(t)} \nabla \cdot (\mathbf{T} \cdot \mathbf{v})\, dV \tag{5.3-4}$$

Substitution of Eqs. 5.3-2 through 5.3-4 into Eq. 5.3-1 and placing all the terms under the same integral sign yields

$$\int_{\mathscr{V}_m(t)} \left[\rho \frac{D}{Dt}\left(e + \frac{1}{2}v^2\right) + \nabla \cdot \mathbf{q} - \nabla \cdot (\mathbf{T} \cdot \mathbf{v}) - \rho \mathbf{g} \cdot \mathbf{v} - \Phi\right] dV = 0 \tag{5.3-5}$$

Since the limits of integration are arbitrary and the integrand is assumed to be continuous, the integrand must be identically equal to zero. Thus our governing differential equations for fluid motion and energy transport are

$$\rho \frac{D}{Dt}\left(e + \frac{1}{2}v^2\right) = -\nabla \cdot \mathbf{q} + \nabla \cdot (\mathbf{T} \cdot \mathbf{v}) + \rho \mathbf{g} \cdot \mathbf{v} + \Phi, \quad \text{energy} \tag{5.3-6}$$

$$\rho \frac{D\mathbf{v}}{Dt} = \rho \mathbf{g} + \nabla \cdot \mathbf{T}, \quad \text{momentum} \tag{5.3-7}$$

$$\frac{\partial \rho}{\partial t} + \nabla \cdot (\rho \mathbf{v}) = 0, \quad \text{mass} \tag{5.3-8}$$

These three equations, along with some thermodynamic information, and a constitutive equation for $\mathbf{q}$, are sufficient to specific temperature and velocity fields from which the desired interphase heat transfer rates can be determined.

Example 5.3-1 Heat transferred to an expanding gas

In this example we wish to consider the process illustrated in Fig. 5.3.1. The gas is initially at a temperature of 100°C, a volume of 1 liter, and a pressure of 2 atmospheres. Heat is transferred to the gas by the bunsen burner and carried away by the coolant. The rate of the heat transfer from the gas to the coolant is given by

$$\begin{Bmatrix} \text{rate of heat transfer} \\ \text{from the gas} \\ \text{to the coolant} \end{Bmatrix} = UA(T - T_0)$$

where T is the gas temperature, T_0 is the coolant temperature (10°C), and the product UA is given as

$$UA = 1.2 \text{ cal/sec °C}$$

At the initial condition the rate at which the bunsen burner supplies energy to the gas is just equal to the rate at which energy is transferred from the gas to the coolant, thus

$$\dot{Q}_{\text{bb}}^{(1)} = UA(T_1 - T_0), \quad \text{initial condition}$$

where $T_1 = 100$°C and $T_0 = 10$°C. We would like to know to what level $\dot{Q}_{\text{bb}}$ must be raised in order that the gas (at a constant pressure of 2 atmospheres) will double in volume.

We begin our analysis with Eq. 5.3-6, and have as our first objective putting this equation in a form encountered by the student in a thermodynamics course. The gravity vector can be expressed as the gradient of a scalar

$$\mathbf{g} = -\nabla \phi \tag{1}$$

where ϕ is referred to as the gravitational potential energy function. Substitution of Eq. 1 into Eq. 5.3-6 leads to

$$\rho \frac{D}{Dt}\left(e + \frac{1}{2}v^2\right) = -\nabla \cdot \mathbf{q} + \nabla \cdot (\mathbf{T} \cdot \mathbf{v}) - \rho \mathbf{v} \cdot \nabla \phi + \Phi \tag{2}$$

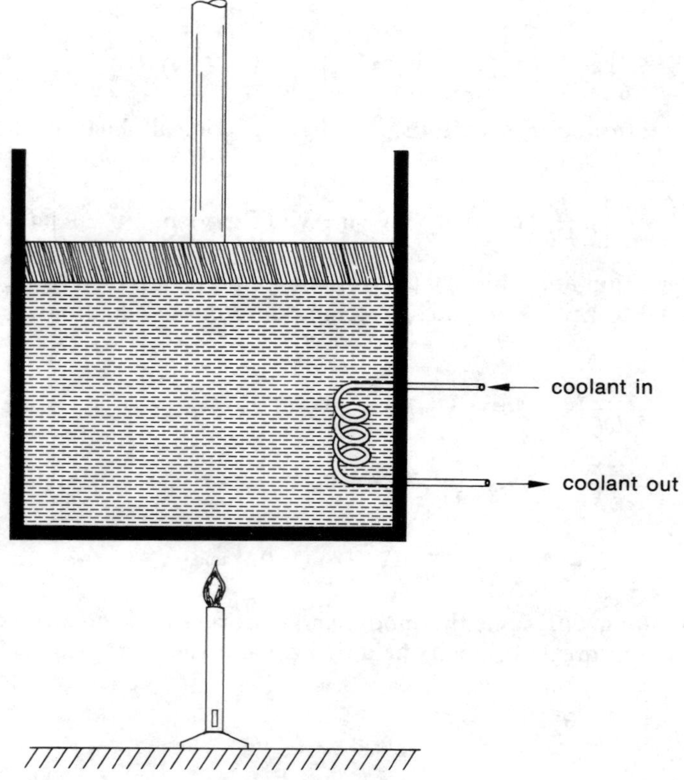

Fig. 5.3.1 Energy analysis of a closed system.

Noting that the material derivative of ϕ is given by

$$\frac{D\phi}{Dt} = \frac{\partial \phi}{\partial t} + \mathbf{v} \cdot \nabla \phi \tag{3}$$

we have

$$\rho \mathbf{v} \cdot \nabla \phi = \rho \frac{D\phi}{Dt} \tag{4}$$

since ϕ is not a function of time and $\partial \phi / \partial t = 0$. Substitution of Eq. 4 into Eq. 2 gives us

$$\rho \frac{D}{Dt}\left(e + \frac{1}{2} v^2 + \phi\right) = -\nabla \cdot \mathbf{q} + \nabla \cdot (\mathbf{T} \cdot \mathbf{v}) + \Phi \tag{5}$$

Here $e + \frac{1}{2}v^2 + \phi$ represents the sum of the *internal* plus *kinetic* plus *potential* energy per unit mass. Since we are dealing with a closed system in our analysis of the process shown in Fig. 5.3.1 we are interested in changes associated with a material volume and we integrate Eq. 5 over $\mathscr{V}_m(t)$ to obtain

$$\int_{\mathscr{V}_m(t)} \rho \frac{D}{Dt}\left(e + \frac{1}{2} + \phi\right) dV = -\int_{\mathscr{V}_m(t)} \nabla \cdot \mathbf{q} \, dV + \int_{\mathscr{V}_m(t)} \nabla \cdot (\mathbf{T} \cdot \mathbf{v}) \, dV \tag{6}$$

Here we have dropped the source term since it is zero in our example. The special form of the Reynolds transport theorem, the divergence theorem, and the stress vector–stress tensor relationship can all be used to put this in the form

$$\frac{D}{Dt} \int_{\mathscr{V}_m(t)} \rho \left(e + \frac{1}{2} v^2 + \phi\right) dV = -\int_{\mathscr{A}_m(t)} \mathbf{q} \cdot \mathbf{n} \, dA + \int_{\mathscr{A}_m(t)} \mathbf{t}_{(\mathbf{n})} \cdot \mathbf{v} \, dA \tag{7}$$

In the nomenclature often used in thermodynamics this could be written as

$$\dot{U} + \dot{KE} + \dot{PE} = \dot{Q} + \int_{\mathscr{A}_m(t)} \mathbf{t}_{(\mathbf{n})} \cdot \mathbf{v} \, dA \tag{8}$$

where U, KE, and PE represent the total internal, kinetic, and potential energy respectively. If we express the stress vector in terms of the thermodynamic pressure and the viscous stress tensor

$$\mathbf{t}_{(\mathbf{n})} = -p\mathbf{n} + \mathbf{n} \cdot \boldsymbol{\tau} \tag{9}$$

and note that $\mathbf{v} = 0$ everywhere on $\mathscr{A}_m(t)$ except on the surface of the piston, Eq. 8 takes the form

$$\dot{U} + \dot{KE} + \dot{PE} = \dot{Q} - \int_{A_{\text{piston}}} p\mathbf{v} \cdot \mathbf{n} \, dA + \int_{A_{\text{piston}}} \mathbf{v} \cdot \boldsymbol{\tau} \, \mathbf{n} \, dA \tag{10}$$

Provided the pressure is constant over the surface of the piston we can write

$$\dot{U} + \dot{KE} + \dot{PE} = \dot{Q} - p \int_{A_{\text{piston}}} \mathbf{v} \cdot \mathbf{n} \, dA + \int_{A_{\text{piston}}} \mathbf{v} \cdot \boldsymbol{\tau} \cdot \mathbf{n} \, dA \tag{11}$$

Noting that

$$\int_{A_{\text{piston}}} \mathbf{v} \cdot \mathbf{n} \, dA = \frac{dV}{dt} \tag{12}$$

where V now represents the volume of the system, we can express Eq. 11 as

$$\dot{U} + \dot{KE} + \dot{PE} = \dot{Q} - p\left(\frac{dV}{dt}\right) \tag{13}$$

Here we have neglected viscous effects at the surface of the piston; it will be left as an exercise for the student to show under what circumstances this is a reasonable assumption.

Application of Eq. 13 to the final steady state of our system will lead us to an expression for the rate at which the bunsen burner must supply energy to the gas; however, it may be helpful to connect Eq. 13 to the form of the first law of thermodynamics that the student has undoubtedly encountered in previous courses. If we integrate Eq. 13 from t_1 to t_2, noting that

$$\int_{t_1}^{t_2} p\left(\frac{dV}{dt}\right) dt = \int_{V_1}^{V_2} p \, dV \tag{14}$$

we obtain

$$\Delta U + \Delta KE + \Delta PE = Q - \int_{V_1}^{V_2} p \, dV \tag{15}$$

Here the symbol Δ is used to denote the difference between state 2 and state 1, i.e.,

$$\Delta U = U_2 - U_1 \tag{16}$$

and Q represents the total heat transferred to the system as it progressed from state 1 to state 2. The connection between Eq. 5.3-6, previous studies in thermodynamics, and Eq. 15 should be clear; however, the latter equation is not particularly suitable for the analysis of our particular problem, and we will return to Eq. 13. At the final steady state each term in Eq. 13 is zero and in particular

$$\dot{Q} = \dot{Q}_{\text{bb}}^{(2)} - UA(T_2 - T_0) = 0 \tag{17}$$

Making use of the ideal gas law

$$pV = n\mathscr{R}T \tag{18}$$

and the fact that the pressure is constant leads us to

$$T_2 = \left(\frac{V_2}{V_1}\right) T_1 \tag{19}$$

Substitution of this result into Eq. 17 leads to

$$\dot{Q}_{\text{bb}}^{(2)} = UA\left[\left(\frac{V_2}{V_1}\right) T_1 - T_0\right] \tag{20}$$

Making use of the initial conditions we find that

$$\dot{Q}_{bb}^{(1)} = \left(\frac{1.2\ \text{cal}}{\text{sec}\ ^\circ\text{C}}\right)(373.16^\circ\text{K} - 283.16^\circ\text{K})$$
$$= 108\ \text{cal/sec}$$

whereas Eq. 19 gives us

$$Q_{bb}^{(2)} = \left(\frac{1.2\ \text{cal}}{\text{sec}\ ^\circ\text{C}}\right)[2(373.16^\circ\text{K}) - 283.16^\circ\text{K}]$$
$$= 556\ \text{cal/sec}$$

Thus we find that the rate of heat transfer from the bunsen burner to the gas must be increased by a factor of 5.1 in order to double the volume.

In the previous example we attacked a heat transfer problem using the total energy equation, Eq. 5.3-6. In addition to solving the heat transfer problem we used the example as a vehicle to show that previously used forms of the first law of thermodynamics were derivable from Eq. 5.3-6. In actual fact we could solve all convective heat transfer problems using Eq. 5.3-6, just as we solved steady and transient heat conduction problems using special forms of that equation. However, the total energy equation is a cumbersome tool and from it we wish to extract the *thermal energy equation.* This will be done in the next section.

Summary of Section 5.4

In this section we begin with the total energy equation

$$\rho \frac{D}{Dt}\left(e + \frac{1}{2}v^2\right) = -\nabla \cdot \mathbf{q} + \nabla \cdot (\mathbf{T} \cdot \mathbf{v}) + \rho \mathbf{g} \cdot \mathbf{v} + \Phi \tag{5.4-1}$$

and the stress equations of motion

$$\rho \frac{D\mathbf{v}}{Dt} = \rho \mathbf{g} + \nabla \cdot \mathbf{T} \tag{5.4-7}$$

Forming the scalar product between the velocity vector, $\mathbf{v}$, and Eq. 5.4-7 eventually leads to the mechanical energy equation

$$\rho \frac{D}{Dt}\left(\frac{1}{2}v^2\right) = \rho \mathbf{g} \cdot \mathbf{v} + \nabla \cdot (\mathbf{T} \cdot \mathbf{v}) - \nabla \mathbf{v} : \mathbf{T} \tag{5.4-13}$$

If we subtract this result from Eq. 5.4-1 we remove *most* of the mechanical energy terms from the total energy equation to arrive at

$$\rho \frac{De}{Dt} = -\nabla \cdot \mathbf{q} + \nabla \mathbf{v} : \mathbf{T} + \Phi \tag{5.4-14}$$

This result is appropriately referred to as the thermal energy equation. By using the following relations

$$\mathbf{T} = -p\mathbf{U} + \boldsymbol{\tau} \tag{5.4-15}$$

$$\mathbf{q} = -k\nabla T \tag{5.4-20}$$

$$e = e(T, \rho) \tag{5.4-24}$$

we can derive special forms of Eq. 5.4-14 for constant density and constant pressure processes. For a constant density process the thermal energy equation takes the form

$$\rho c_v \frac{DT}{Dt} = \nabla \cdot (k\nabla T) + \nabla \mathbf{v} : \boldsymbol{\tau} + \Phi, \quad \text{constant density process} \tag{5.4-28}$$

where $\nabla \mathbf{v} : \boldsymbol{\tau}$ represents the viscous dissipation. For a constant pressure process we obtain an equally simple form given by

$$\rho c_p \frac{DT}{Dt} = \nabla \cdot (k\nabla T) + \nabla \mathbf{v} : \boldsymbol{\tau} + \Phi, \quad \text{constant pressure process} \tag{5.4-41}$$

Most real processes are neither constant density nor constant pressure, and the appropriate form of the thermal energy equation for a general flow process is given in Sec. 5.5.

*5.4 The Thermal Energy Equation

In the previous section we derived the differential form of the first law of thermodynamics, incorporating the principle of local thermodynamic equilibrium in order to obtain

$$\rho \frac{D}{Dt}\left(e + \frac{1}{2}v^2\right) = -\nabla \cdot \mathbf{q} + \nabla \cdot (\mathbf{T} \cdot \mathbf{v}) + \rho \mathbf{g} \cdot \mathbf{v} + \Phi \tag{5.4-1}$$

For the case where $\mathbf{v} = 0$ and the process is steady Eq. 5.4-1 reduces to

$$0 = -\nabla \cdot \mathbf{q} + \Phi, \quad \text{steady heat conduction} \tag{5.4-2}$$

Making use of Fourier's law, $\mathbf{q} = -k\nabla T$, we can express Eq. 5.4-2 as

$$0 = k\nabla^2 T + \Phi, \quad \text{steady heat conduction with a constant thermal conductivity} \tag{5.4-3}$$

provided the thermal conductivity is constant. These two equations were presented in Chapter 2, and served as the starting point for the analysis of a wide variety of important heat conduction processes.

If we expand the left-hand-side of Eq. 5.4-1 according to Eq. 5.1-8 we obtain

$$\rho \frac{\partial}{\partial t}\left(e + \frac{1}{2}v^2\right) + \mathbf{v} \cdot \nabla \left(e + \frac{1}{2}v^2\right) = -\nabla \cdot \mathbf{q} + \nabla \cdot (\mathbf{T} \cdot \mathbf{v}) + \rho \mathbf{g} \cdot \mathbf{v} + \Phi \tag{5.4-4}$$

and if we impose the restriction that $\mathbf{v} = 0$ our general equation reduces to

$$\rho \frac{\partial e}{\partial t} = -\nabla \cdot \mathbf{q} + \Phi \tag{5.4-5}$$

This result was presented in Chapter 4 where transient heat conduction was studied. For the case where $c_p \sim c_v$ we could express Eq. 5.4-5 as

$$\frac{\partial T}{\partial t} = \alpha \nabla^2 T + \Phi/\rho c_p \tag{5.4-6}$$

where α is the thermal diffusivity defined by Eq. 4.1-15. This equation provided the basis for the analysis of a number of transient heat conduction processes described in Chapter 4.

We would now like to apply Eq. 5.4-1 to the analysis of processes for which the velocity, $\mathbf{v}$, is not equal to zero. It should be clear that if we can use the laws of mechanics to determine the velocity field, then we can in turn calculate the kinetic energy term in Eq. 5.4-1, $\rho D(\frac{1}{2}v^2)/Dt$, the rate of work term, $\nabla \cdot (\mathbf{T} \cdot \mathbf{v})$, and the rate at which body forces do work, $\rho \mathbf{g} \cdot \mathbf{v}$. With these terms specified we are left with the problem of determining e, $\mathbf{q}$, and Φ; however, we have already confronted that problem in Chapters 2 and 4. Although we can analyze *convective transport processes* using Eq. 5.4-1, there is a more suitable form of this equation which we will derive in the following paragraphs. It is known as the *thermal energy equation.*

We begin our development with the stress equations of motion

$$\rho \frac{D\mathbf{v}}{Dt} = \rho \mathbf{g} + \nabla \cdot \mathbf{T} \tag{5.4-7}$$

which were derived in Sec. 5.2. If we form the dot product of Eq. 5.4-7 with the velocity $\mathbf{v}$ we obtain

$$\rho \mathbf{v} \cdot \frac{D\mathbf{v}}{Dt} = \rho \mathbf{g} \cdot \mathbf{v} + \mathbf{v} \cdot (\nabla \cdot \mathbf{T}) \tag{5.4-8}$$

We should remember that each term in Eq. 5.4-7 has the units of (force/unit volume) and is a *vector* equation. Multiplication by the velocity, i.e., forming the dot product with $\mathbf{v}$, gives rise to a *scalar* equation, each term having units of (force–distance/unit time–unit volume) or (energy/unit time–unit volume). Thus Eq. 5.4-8 is an *energy* equation obtained directly from the laws of mechanics and is appropriately called the *mechanical energy equation.*

The mechanical energy equation is a useful tool for solving certain fluid flow problems; however, our objective here is to use it to simplify the total energy equation by extracting the thermal energy equation from Eq. 5.4-1. We first note that the left-hand-side of Eq. 5.4-8 can be expressed as

$$\rho\mathbf{v}\cdot\frac{D\mathbf{v}}{Dt}=\rho\frac{D}{Dt}\left(\frac{1}{2}\mathbf{v}\cdot\mathbf{v}\right)=\rho\frac{D}{Dt}\left(\frac{1}{2}v^2\right) \tag{5.4-9}$$

The gravitational work term needs no analysis, and moving on to the term $\mathbf{v}\cdot(\nabla\cdot\mathbf{T})$ we make use of index notation to write

$$\nabla\cdot(\mathbf{v}\cdot\mathbf{T})=\frac{\partial}{\partial x_j}(v_iT_{ij})=\left(\frac{\partial v_i}{\partial x_j}\right)T_{ij}+v_i\left(\frac{\partial T_{ij}}{\partial x_j}\right) \tag{5.4-10}$$

We should recognize the last term in Eq. 5.4-10 as the term of interest and we rearrange this result to obtain

$$v_i\left(\frac{\partial T_{ij}}{\partial x_j}\right)=\frac{\partial}{\partial x_j}(v_iT_{ij})-\left(\frac{\partial v_i}{\partial x_j}\right)T_{ij},\quad\text{index notation} \tag{5.4-11}$$

or

$$\mathbf{v}\cdot(\nabla\cdot\mathbf{T})=\nabla\cdot(\mathbf{v}\cdot\mathbf{T})-\nabla\mathbf{v}:\mathbf{T},\quad\text{Gibbs notation} \tag{5.4-12}$$

Note that the "double dot" notation used in Eq. 5.4-12 is a logical extension of a dot product notation, each dot indicating a summation or a pair of repeated indices. If we substitute Eqs. 5.4-12 and 5.4-9 into Eq. 5.4-8 we obtain

$$\rho\frac{D}{Dt}\left(\frac{1}{2}v^2\right)=\rho\mathbf{g}\cdot\mathbf{v}+\nabla\cdot(\mathbf{v}\cdot\mathbf{T})-\nabla\mathbf{v}:\mathbf{T},\quad\text{mechanical energy equation} \tag{5.4-13}$$

If this is now subtracted from the *total energy equation*, Eq. 5.4-1, we obtain our objective, the *thermal energy equation.*

$$\rho\frac{De}{Dt}=-\nabla\cdot\mathbf{q}+\nabla\mathbf{v}:\mathbf{T}+\Phi,\quad\text{thermal energy equation} \tag{5.4-14}$$

One should keep in mind that combined energy and momentum transport processes can be analyzed using either Eqs. 5.3-6, 5.3-7, and 5.3-8, or one can use Eq. 5.4-14 along with Eqs. 5.3-7 and 5.3-8. Either combination gives a complete description of the physical process; however, the thermal energy equation is considerably easier to use than the total energy equation.

We can extend our analysis of Eq. 5.4-14 and gain some insight into the physical significance of the term $\nabla\mathbf{v}:\mathbf{T}$ if we express the total stress tensor $\mathbf{T}$ in terms of the thermodynamic pressure p and the viscous stress tensor $\boldsymbol{\tau}$.

$$\mathbf{T}=-p\mathbf{U}+\boldsymbol{\tau} \tag{5.4-15}$$

Here $\mathbf{U}$ represents the unit tensor, its scalar components being given in terms of the Kronecker delta. Making use of Eq. 5.4-15 and switching to index notation we write

$$\nabla\mathbf{v}:\mathbf{T}=\left(\frac{\partial v_i}{\partial x_j}\right)T_{ij}=\left(\frac{\partial v_i}{\partial x_j}\right)[-p\delta_{ij}+\tau_{ij}] \tag{5.4-16}$$

By writing out the double sum and remembering that $\delta_{ij}=1$ if $i=j$ and $\delta_{ij}=0$ if $i\neq j$ we can show

$$\left(\frac{\partial v_i}{\partial x_j}\right)\delta_{ij}=\left(\frac{\partial v_i}{\partial x_i}\right) \tag{5.4-17}$$

Thus Eq. 5.4-16 reduces to

$$\nabla \mathbf{v} : \mathbf{T} = -p \nabla \cdot \mathbf{v} + \nabla \mathbf{v} : \boldsymbol{\tau} \tag{5.4-18}$$

and substitution into Eq. 5.4-14 yields the final form of the thermal energy equation

$\rho \dfrac{De}{Dt} =$	$-\nabla \cdot \mathbf{q}$	$-p \nabla \cdot \mathbf{v}$ $+$	$\nabla \mathbf{v} : \boldsymbol{\tau}$ $+$	Φ	
↑	↑	↑	↑	↑	
time rate of change of internal energy per unit volume	net heat flux of energy per unit volume	rate of reversible work per unit volume	rate of irreversible work per unit volume	rate of heat generation per unit volume owing to electromagnetic effects	(5.4-19)

The expanded forms of Eq. 5.4-19 are listed in Table 5.4-1 for rectangular, cylindrical, and spherical coordinates, and the dissipation term $\nabla \mathbf{v} : \boldsymbol{\tau}$ is given in expanded form for an incompressible Newtonian fluid† in Table 5.4-2. The term $-p \nabla \cdot \mathbf{v}$ is called the reversible work since it can take on either positive or negative values and is the type of work that can be completely recovered in a device such as that shown in Fig. 5.3.1 provided the process is reversible. The term $\nabla \mathbf{v} : \boldsymbol{\tau}$ is called irreversible work since it is always positive regardless of the processes. This can be seen by examining Table 5.4-2 where we see that $\nabla \mathbf{v} : \boldsymbol{\tau}$ is

†The term "incompressible fluid" is a misnomer for the condition whereby the flow of a fluid is adequately approximated by the incompressible form of the equations of motion. There are no incompressible fluids.

Table 5.4-1 The Thermal Energy Equation

rectangular coordinates (x, y, z)

$$\rho\left(\frac{\partial e}{\partial t} + v_x \frac{\partial e}{\partial x} + v_y \frac{\partial e}{\partial y} + v_z \frac{\partial e}{\partial z}\right) = -\left(\frac{\partial q_x}{\partial x} + \frac{\partial q_y}{\partial y} + \frac{\partial q_z}{\partial z}\right) - p\left(\frac{\partial v_x}{\partial x} + \frac{\partial v_y}{\partial y} + \frac{\partial v_z}{\partial z}\right) + \nabla \mathbf{v} : \boldsymbol{\tau} + \Phi \tag{a}$$

cylindrical coordinates (r, θ, z)

$$\rho\left(\frac{\partial e}{\partial t} + v_r \frac{\partial e}{\partial r} + \frac{v_\theta}{r} \frac{\partial e}{\partial \theta} + v_z \frac{\partial e}{\partial z}\right) = -\left[\frac{1}{r}\frac{\partial}{\partial r}(r q_r) + \frac{1}{r}\left(\frac{\partial q_\theta}{\partial \theta}\right) + \left(\frac{\partial q_z}{\partial z}\right)\right] - p\left[\frac{\partial v_r}{\partial r} + \frac{v_r}{r} + \frac{1}{r}\left(\frac{\partial v_\theta}{\partial \theta}\right) + \frac{\partial v_z}{\partial z}\right] + \nabla \mathbf{v} : \boldsymbol{\tau} + \Phi \tag{b}$$

spherical coordinates (r, θ, ϕ)

$$\rho\left(\frac{\partial e}{\partial t} + v_r \frac{\partial e}{\partial r} + \frac{v_\theta}{r} \frac{\partial e}{\partial \theta} + \frac{v_\phi}{r \sin\theta} \frac{\partial e}{\partial \phi}\right) = -\left[\frac{1}{r^2}\frac{\partial}{\partial r}(r^2 q_r) + \frac{1}{r \sin\theta}\frac{\partial}{\partial \theta}(q_\theta \sin\theta) + \frac{1}{r \sin\theta}\left(\frac{\partial q_\phi}{\partial \phi}\right)\right] - p\left[\left(\frac{\partial v_r}{\partial r}\right) + \frac{2 v_r}{r} + \frac{1}{r \sin\theta}\frac{\partial}{\partial \theta}(v_\theta \sin\theta) \frac{1}{r \sin\theta}\left(\frac{\partial v_\phi}{\partial \phi}\right)\right] + \nabla \mathbf{v} : \boldsymbol{\tau} + \Phi \tag{c}$$

Table 5.4-2 The Viscous Dissipation Function $\nabla \mathbf{v} : \boldsymbol{\tau}$ for Newtonian Fluids

rectangular coordinates (x, y, z)

$$\nabla \mathbf{v} : \boldsymbol{\tau} = 2\mu\left[\left(\frac{\partial v_x}{\partial x}\right)^2 + \left(\frac{\partial v_y}{\partial y}\right)^2 + \left(\frac{\partial v_z}{\partial z}\right)^2\right] + \mu\left[\left(\frac{\partial v_y}{\partial x} + \frac{\partial v_x}{\partial y}\right)^2 + \left(\frac{\partial v_z}{\partial y} + \frac{\partial v_y}{\partial z}\right)^2 + \left(\frac{\partial v_z}{\partial x} + \frac{\partial v_x}{\partial z}\right)^2\right] \tag{a}$$

cylindrical coordinates (r, θ, z)

$$\nabla \mathbf{v} : \boldsymbol{\tau} = 2\mu\left[\left(\frac{\partial v_r}{\partial r}\right)^2 + \left(\frac{1}{r}\frac{\partial v_\theta}{\partial \theta} + \frac{v_r}{r}\right)^2 + \left(\frac{\partial v_z}{\partial z}\right)^2\right] + \mu\left[r\frac{\partial}{\partial r}\left(\frac{v_\theta}{r}\right) + \frac{1}{r}\left(\frac{\partial v_r}{\partial \theta}\right)\right]^2 + \mu\left[\frac{1}{r}\left(\frac{\partial v_z}{\partial \theta}\right) + \left(\frac{\partial v_\theta}{\partial z}\right)\right]^2 + \mu\left(\frac{\partial v_r}{\partial z} + \frac{\partial v_z}{\partial r}\right)^2 \tag{b}$$

spherical coordinates (r, θ, ϕ)

$$\nabla \mathbf{v} : \boldsymbol{\tau} = 2\mu\left[\left(\frac{\partial v_r}{\partial r}\right)^2 + \left(\frac{1}{r}\frac{\partial v_\theta}{\partial \theta} + \frac{v_r}{r}\right)^2 + \left(\frac{1}{r \sin\theta}\frac{\partial v_\phi}{\partial \phi} + \frac{v_r}{r} + \frac{v_\theta \cot\theta}{r}\right)^2\right] + \mu\left[r\frac{\partial}{\partial r}\left(\frac{v_\theta}{r}\right) + \frac{1}{r}\frac{\partial v_r}{\partial \theta}\right]^2 + \mu\left[\frac{1}{r \sin\theta}\frac{\partial v_r}{\partial \phi} + r\frac{\partial}{\partial r}\left(\frac{v_\phi}{r}\right)\right]^2 + \mu\left[\frac{\sin\theta}{r}\frac{\partial}{\partial \theta}\left(\frac{v_\phi}{\sin\theta}\right) + \frac{1}{r \sin\theta}\frac{\partial v_\theta}{\partial \phi}\right]^2 \tag{c}$$

composed entirely of squared terms. This term is generally referred to as the viscous dissipation and is encountered in the analysis of turbulent flow systems as the *friction loss* or *minor loss* terms in the mechanical energy balance.

Our analysis of the fundamental energy postulate is not yet complete for Eq. 5.4-19 contains four unknowns† (e, q_x, q_y, q_z) and thus represents an indeterminate description of energy transport. Our difficulties are reduced to some extent if we introduce the *linear constitutive equation* for energy transport‡

$$\mathbf{q} = -k\nabla T, \quad \text{Fouriers law} \tag{5.4-20}$$

leading to

$$\rho\frac{De}{Dt} = \nabla\cdot(k\nabla T) - p\nabla\cdot\mathbf{v} + \nabla\mathbf{v}:\boldsymbol{\tau} + \Phi \tag{5.4-21}$$

There are two types of processes for which Eq. 5.4-21 takes a relatively simple form, and we will examine these in the following paragraphs.

Constant volume processes

When the volume, and therefore the density, is constant, the continuity equation takes the form,

$$\nabla\cdot\mathbf{v} = 0 \tag{5.4-22}$$

and Eq. 5.4-21 reduces to

$$\rho\frac{De}{Dt} = \nabla\cdot(k\nabla T) + \nabla\mathbf{v}:\boldsymbol{\tau} + \Phi \tag{5.4-23}$$

Using a thermal equation of state, we can express the internal energy as a function of temperature and density.

$$e = e(T, \rho) \tag{5.4-24}$$

The chain rule allows us to write the material derivative of e as

$$\frac{De}{Dt} = \left(\frac{\partial e}{\partial T}\right)_\rho \frac{DT}{Dt} + \left(\frac{\partial e}{\partial \rho}\right)_T \frac{D\rho}{Dt} \tag{5.4-25}$$

Taking ρ to be a constant, and remembering that the constant volume (or density) heat capacity is given by

$$c_v = \left(\frac{\partial e}{\partial T}\right)_v = \left(\frac{\partial e}{\partial T}\right)_\rho \tag{5.4-26}$$

†The source term Φ must be specified, p, $\mathbf{v}$, and $\boldsymbol{\tau}$ are determined by the laws of mechanics, and ρ must be determined by an equation of state.

‡The scalar components of Eq. 5.4-20 are listed for rectangular, cylindrical, and spherical coordinates in Table 5.4-3.

Table 5.4-3 Scalar Components of Fouriers Law

rectangular coordinates (x, y, z)				
	$q_x = -\frac{\partial T}{\partial x}$	$q_y = -k\frac{\partial T}{\partial y}$	$q_z = -k\frac{\partial T}{\partial z}$	(*a*)
cylindrical coordinates (r, θ, z)				
	$q_r = -k\frac{\partial T}{\partial r}$	$q_\theta = -k\frac{1}{r}\frac{\partial T}{\partial \theta}$	$q_z = -k\frac{\partial T}{\partial z}$	(*b*)
spherical coordinates (r, θ, ϕ)				
	$q_r = -k\frac{\partial T}{\partial r}$	$q_\theta = -k\frac{1}{r}\frac{\partial T}{\partial \theta}$	$q_\phi = -k\frac{1}{r\sin\theta}\frac{\partial T}{\partial \phi}$	(*c*)

we can express Eq. 5.4-25 as

$$\frac{De}{Dt} = c_v \frac{DT}{Dt} \tag{5.4-27}$$

Substitution of Eq. 5.4-27 into Eq. 5.4-23 leads to

$$\rho c_v \frac{DT}{Dt} = \nabla \cdot (k \nabla T) + \nabla \mathbf{v} : \boldsymbol{\tau} + \Phi, \quad \text{thermal energy equation for constant density processes} \tag{5.4-28}$$

The constant volume and constant pressure heat capacities are related by

$$c_p = c_v + T\beta^2/\rho\kappa \tag{5.4-29}$$

where β is the coefficient of thermal expansion and κ is the compressibility

$$\beta = -\frac{1}{\rho}\left(\frac{\partial \rho}{\partial T}\right)_p \tag{5.4-30}$$

$$\kappa = \frac{1}{\rho}\left(\frac{\partial \rho}{\partial p}\right)_T \tag{5.4-31}$$

In Table 5.4-4 values of c_p and $T\beta^2/\rho\kappa$ are shown for several liquids and solids at room temperature. From these results we can conclude that

$$c_v \sim c_p, \quad \text{for solids} \tag{5.4-32}$$

however, making this approximation for liquids is another matter. The values of c_p and c_v for water differ by about $\frac{1}{2}$ per cent while the difference for a petroleum oil is nearly 25 per cent.

Table 5.4-4 Values of c_p and $T\beta^2/\rho\kappa$ at Room Temperature

Substance	c_p, cal/g-°C	$T\beta^2/\rho\kappa$, cal/g-°C
Ethyl alcohol	0.56	0.06
Carbon tetrachloride	0.20	0.03
Mercury	0.03	0.005
SAE 30 oil	~0.4	0.096
Water	1.0	0.005
Copper	0.094	0.0015
Steel	0.12	1.3×10^{-6}
Concrete	0.2	6.0×10^{-5}

Constant pressure processes

There are a large variety of heat transfer processes which can be reasonably approximated as constant pressure processes. Air flowing past an automobile radiator is a common example, and any free-convection process takes place at essentially constant pressure. Many forced-convection processes for gases flowing in closed conduits can be treated as constant pressure processes owing to the relatively low pressure drops that occur in such systems.

We begin the analysis by noting that the continuity equation, Eq. 5.1-27, can be expressed in the form

$$\frac{D\rho}{Dt} + \rho \nabla \cdot \mathbf{v} = 0 \tag{5.4-33}$$

Using this result allows us to write Eq. 5.4-21 as

$$\rho \frac{De}{Dt} = \nabla \cdot (k \nabla T) + \frac{p}{\rho}\frac{D\rho}{Dt} + \nabla \mathbf{v} : \boldsymbol{\tau} + \Phi \tag{5.4-34}$$

Since the pressure is taken to be constant we can express the third term in Eq. 5.4-34 as

$$\frac{p}{\rho}\frac{D\rho}{Dt} = -p\rho\frac{D}{Dt}\left(\frac{1}{\rho}\right) = -\rho\frac{D}{Dt}\left(\frac{p}{\rho}\right) \tag{5.4-35}$$

Substitution of Eq. 5.4-35 into Eq. 5.4-34 and rearranging quickly leads to

$$\rho\frac{D}{Dt}(e + p/\rho) = \nabla \cdot (k\nabla T) + \nabla \mathbf{v} : \boldsymbol{\tau} + \Phi \tag{5.4-36}$$

The quantity $e + p/\rho$ is the enthalpy per unit mass and we will express it as

$$h = e + p/\rho \tag{5.4-37}$$

with the hope that there will be no confusion between the enthalpy and the film heat transfer coefficient. Eq. 5.4-36 now takes the form

$$\rho\frac{Dh}{Dt} = \nabla \cdot (k\nabla T) + \nabla \mathbf{v} : \boldsymbol{\tau} + \Phi \tag{5.4-38}$$

Representing the enthalpy in terms of temperature and pressure, and using the chain rule leads to

$$\frac{Dh}{Dt} = \left(\frac{\partial h}{\partial T}\right)_p \frac{DT}{Dt} + \left(\frac{\partial h}{\partial p}\right)_T \frac{Dp}{Dt} \tag{5.4-39}$$

Since the pressure is constant this reduces to

$$\frac{Dh}{Dt} = \left(\frac{\partial h}{\partial T}\right)_p \frac{DT}{Dt} = c_p \frac{DT}{Dt}, \quad \text{for constant pressure processes} \tag{5.4-40}$$

and Eq. 5.4-38 can be expressed as

$$\rho c_p \frac{DT}{Dt} = \nabla \cdot (k\nabla T) + \nabla \mathbf{v} : \boldsymbol{\tau} + \Phi, \quad \text{the thermal energy equation for constant pressure processes} \tag{5.4-41}$$

Here we see that Eq. 5.4-41 is identical to Eq. 5.4-28 with c_p replacing c_v in the latter equation.

Summary of Section 5.5

In this section we examine the thermal energy equation for a flow which is neither constant density nor constant pressure. We begin the analysis using the general form of the thermal energy equation

$$\rho\frac{De}{Dt} = \nabla \cdot (k\nabla T) - p\nabla \cdot \mathbf{v} + \nabla \mathbf{v} : \boldsymbol{\tau} + \Phi \tag{5.4-21}$$

With the help of some thermodynamic relations and a bit of algebra we obtain

$$\rho c_p \frac{DT}{Dt} = \nabla \cdot (k\nabla T) + T\beta\frac{Dp}{Dt} + \nabla \mathbf{v} : \boldsymbol{\tau} + \Phi \tag{5.5-10}$$

It is important to derive a form of Eq. 5.4-21 that contains the constant pressure heat capacity, c_p, since it is relatively easy to determine experimentally, whereas c_v is essentially impossible to measure except for gases.

The term $T\beta(Dp/Dt)$ represents compression and expansion work and may be either positive (compression) or negative (expansion). The viscous dissipation, $\nabla \mathbf{v} : \boldsymbol{\tau}$, is always positive, and the electromagnetic radiation and electrical heating term, Φ, represents both the emission (negative) and absorption (positive) of energy. The magnitude of the work terms in Eq. 5.5-10 is analyzed in this section and it is shown that for many practical processes these terms can be neglected. In addition, the thermal conductivity can often be treated as a constant and Eq. 5.5-10 simplifies to

$$\rho c_p \left(\frac{\partial T}{\partial t} + \mathbf{v} \cdot \nabla T\right) = k\nabla^2 T + \Phi \tag{5.5-12}$$

It is this form of the thermal energy equation that is used most often in the remainder of this text.

*5.5 The Thermal Energy Equation for General Flow Processes

In the preceding section we have analyzed the thermal energy equation for two special cases: constant density and constant pressure. The derived results are reasonable approximations to many real processes; however, it is necessary to explore the thermal energy equation further in order to gain some insight into the nature of these approximations.

We begin with the general form of the thermal energy equation

$$\rho \frac{De}{Dt} = -\nabla \cdot \mathbf{q} - p\nabla \cdot \mathbf{v} + \nabla \mathbf{v} : \boldsymbol{\tau} + \Phi \tag{5.5-1}$$

and use the definition of the enthalpy per unit mass, $h = e + p/\rho$, to express the internal energy as

$$e = h - p/\rho \tag{5.5-2}$$

Substitution of this expression for the internal energy into Eq. 5.5-1 leads to

$$\rho \frac{Dh}{Dt} - \rho \frac{D}{Dt}\left(\frac{p}{\rho}\right) = -\nabla \cdot \mathbf{q} - p\nabla \cdot \mathbf{v} + \nabla \mathbf{v} : \boldsymbol{\tau} + \Phi \tag{5.5-3}$$

Carrying out the differentiation of p/ρ and rearranging will give us

$$\rho \frac{Dh}{Dt} = -\nabla \cdot \mathbf{q} + \rho\left[\frac{1}{\rho}\left(\frac{Dp}{Dt}\right) - \frac{p}{\rho^2}\left(\frac{D\rho}{Dt}\right) - \frac{p}{\rho^2}(\rho \nabla \cdot \mathbf{v})\right] + \nabla \mathbf{v} : \boldsymbol{\tau} + \Phi$$

$$= -\nabla \cdot \mathbf{q} + \frac{Dp}{Dt} - \frac{p}{\rho}\left[\frac{D\rho}{Dt} + \rho \nabla \cdot \mathbf{v}\right] + \nabla \mathbf{v} : \boldsymbol{\tau} + \Phi \tag{5.5-4}$$

Referring to Eq. 5.4-33 we see that the continuity equation requires that the term in brackets be zero, and the thermal energy equation is simplified to

$$\rho \frac{Dh}{Dt} = -\nabla \cdot \mathbf{q} + \frac{Dp}{Dt} + \nabla \mathbf{v} : \boldsymbol{\tau} + \Phi \tag{5.5-5}$$

We choose the enthalpy to be a function of the temperature and pressure, and use the chain rule to write

$$\left(\frac{Dh}{Dt}\right) = \left(\frac{\partial h}{\partial T}\right)_p \frac{DT}{Dt} + \left(\frac{\partial h}{\partial p}\right)_T \frac{Dp}{Dt} \tag{5.5-6}$$

Following the type of analysis presented in any thermodynamics text† we can express the derivative of the enthalpy with respect to pressure as

$$\left(\frac{\partial h}{\partial p}\right)_T = \frac{1}{\rho}(1 - T\beta) \tag{5.5-7}$$

where β is the coefficient of thermal expansion given by

$$\beta = -\frac{1}{\rho}\left(\frac{\partial \rho}{\partial T}\right)_p \tag{5.5-8}$$

Substitution of Eqs. 5.5-7 and 5.5-6 into Eq. 5.5-5 leads to

$$\rho \left(\frac{\partial h}{\partial T}\right)_p \frac{DT}{Dt} = -\nabla \cdot \mathbf{q} + T\beta \frac{Dp}{Dt} + \nabla \mathbf{v} : \boldsymbol{\tau} + \Phi \tag{5.5-9}$$

Substitution of the relations

$$c_p = \left(\frac{\partial h}{\partial T}\right)_p$$

$$\mathbf{q} = -k\nabla T$$

†See, for example, J. M. Smith and H. C. Van Ness, *Introduction to Chemical Engineering Thermodynamics*, third edition, page 175, McGraw-Hill Book Co., Inc., New York, 1959.

leads to the final form of the thermal energy equation for a general flow process

$$\rho c_p \frac{DT}{Dt} = \nabla \cdot (k\nabla T) + T\beta \frac{Dp}{Dt} + \nabla \mathbf{v} : \boldsymbol{\tau} + \Phi \tag{5.5-10}$$

Expanded forms of Eq. 5.5-10 are given in Table 5.5-1 for rectangular, cylindrical, and spherical coordinates.

Table 5.5-1 The Thermal Energy Equation

rectangular coordinates (x, y, z)

$$\rho c_p \left(\frac{\partial T}{\partial t} + v_x \frac{\partial T}{\partial x} + v_y \frac{\partial T}{\partial y} + v_z \frac{\partial T}{\partial z}\right) = \frac{\partial}{\partial x}\left(k\frac{\partial T}{\partial x}\right) + \frac{\partial}{\partial y}\left(k\frac{\partial T}{\partial y}\right) + \frac{\partial}{\partial z}\left(k\frac{\partial T}{\partial z}\right) + T\beta\frac{Dp}{Dt} + \nabla \mathbf{v} : \boldsymbol{\tau} + \Phi \tag{a}$$

cylindrical coordinates (r, θ, z)

$$\rho c_p \left(\frac{\partial T}{\partial t} + v_r \frac{\partial T}{\partial r} + \frac{v_\theta}{r}\frac{\partial T}{\partial \theta} + v_z \frac{\partial T}{\partial z}\right) = \frac{1}{r}\frac{\partial}{\partial r}\left(rk\frac{\partial T}{\partial r}\right) + \frac{1}{r}\frac{\partial}{\partial \theta}\left(\frac{k}{r}\frac{\partial T}{\partial \theta}\right) + \frac{\partial}{\partial z}\left(k\frac{\partial T}{\partial z}\right) + T\beta\frac{Dp}{Dt} + \nabla \mathbf{v} : \boldsymbol{\tau} + \Phi \tag{b}$$

spherical coordinates (r, θ, ϕ)

$$\rho c_p \left(\frac{\partial T}{\partial t} + v_r \frac{\partial T}{\partial r} + \frac{v_\theta}{r}\frac{\partial T}{\partial \theta} + \frac{v_\phi}{r \sin\theta}\frac{\partial T}{\partial \phi}\right) = \frac{1}{r^2}\frac{\partial}{\partial r}\left(r^2 k\frac{\partial T}{\partial r}\right) + \frac{1}{r\sin\theta}\frac{\partial}{\partial \theta}\left(\frac{k\sin\theta}{r}\frac{\partial T}{\partial \theta}\right)$$
$$+ \frac{1}{r\sin\theta}\frac{\partial}{\partial \phi}\left(\frac{k}{r\sin\theta}\frac{\partial T}{\partial \phi}\right) + T\beta\frac{Dp}{Dt} + \nabla \mathbf{v} : \boldsymbol{\tau} + \Phi \tag{c}$$

Before going on to the applications of Eq. 5.5-10 to convective heat transfer processes, we need to consider the three source terms: $T\beta Dp/Dt$, $\nabla \mathbf{v} : \boldsymbol{\tau}$, and Φ, to see under what conditions they may be important.†

Electromagnetic radiation

The source term Φ represents energy emitted or absorbed owing to electromagnetic effects. For electrical heating this term is given by

$$\Phi = j^2\sigma$$

where j represents the magnitude of the electron flux vector (amperes per square centimeter) and σ is the specific resistance (ohm cm). Electrical heating effects can be small or large depending on the nature of the problem. Nonzero values of Φ can also result from the absorption and emission of photons, i.e., thermal radiation, and this process may become extremely important at high temperatures. Certainly Φ would be an important term for the energy transport process taking place in a flame or plasma.

Viscous dissipation—laminar flow in a tube

To develop an appreciation for the nature of the visous dissipation term, $\nabla \mathbf{v} : \boldsymbol{\tau}$, let us consider the process of laminar flow in a tube. From Table 5.4-2 we find that

$$\nabla \mathbf{v} : \boldsymbol{\tau} = \mu\left(\frac{\partial v_z}{\partial r}\right)^2, \quad \text{for steady, one-dimensional laminar flow in a tube}$$

and an order-of-magnitude estimate of $\nabla \mathbf{v} : \boldsymbol{\tau}$ can be expressed as

$$\nabla \mathbf{v} : \boldsymbol{\tau} = \mathbf{0}(32\mu\langle v_z\rangle^2/D^2)$$

Referring to Eq. 5.5-10 we see that the time rate of change of temperature owing to viscous dissipation can be estimated as

†This subject is treated in Ex. 7.5-1 for turbulent flows.

$$\frac{DT}{Dt} = 0(\nabla \mathbf{v} : \boldsymbol{\tau}/\rho c_p) = 0(32\mu \langle v_z \rangle^2/\rho c_p D^2)$$

Since we are considering a steady, one-dimensional flow, the material derivative takes the form,

$$\frac{DT}{Dt} = v_z \frac{\partial T}{\partial z}$$

and an order-of-magnitude estimate of the temperature gradient owing to viscous dissipation is

$$\left(\frac{\partial T}{\partial z}\right)_{\text{viscous dissipation}} = 0(32\mu\langle v_z\rangle/\rho c_p D^2)$$

In terms of the Reynolds number this can be expressed as

$$\left(\frac{\partial T}{\partial z}\right)_{\text{viscous dissipation}} = 0(30 N_{\text{Re}} \nu^2/c_p D^3)$$

For *air* at room temperature and atmospheric pressure we could assume the following values as being representative:

$$N_{\text{Re}} \sim 10^3$$
$$\nu \sim 0.2 \text{ cm}^2/\text{sec}$$
$$D \sim 1 \text{ cm}$$
$$c_p \sim 0.2 \text{ cal/g-°C}$$

and the temperature gradient *owing to viscous dissipation* is estimated to be

$$\left(\frac{\partial T}{\partial z}\right)_{\text{viscous dissipation}} = 0(1.5 \times 10^{-4}\,°\text{C/cm}), \quad \text{for air}$$

This is a rather small temperature gradient relative to the kinds of gradients one encounters in typical heat transfer processes, thus viscous dissipation can be neglected for gas flows except under unusual circumstances.†

For *water* at room temperature we could take the following values as being representative:

$$N_{\text{Re}} \sim 10^3$$
$$\nu \sim 10^{-2} \text{ cm}^2/\text{sec}$$
$$D \sim 1 \text{ cm}$$
$$c_p \sim 1 \text{ cal/g-°C}$$

and the temperature gradient *owing to viscous dissipation* is estimated to be

$$\left(\frac{\partial T}{\partial z}\right)_{\text{viscous dissipation}} = 0(6 \times 10^{-8}\,°\text{C/cm}), \quad \text{for water}$$

Once again the temperature gradient is very small and viscous dissipation can be neglected for water and similar fluids.

For a *petroleum oil* at room temperature we consider the following values:

$$N_{\text{Re}} \sim 10^3$$
$$\nu \sim 10 \text{ cm}^2/\text{sec}$$
$$D \sim 1 \text{ cm}$$
$$c_p \sim 0.5 \text{ cal/g-°C}$$

and find the temperature gradient to be

$$\left(\frac{\partial T}{\partial z}\right)_{\text{viscous dissipation}} = 0(0.15\ °\text{C/cm}), \quad \text{for oil}$$

Here we see that a temperature rise of about 150°C could occur over a distance of 1000 cm or 30 ft. Under

†The "aerodynamic heating" that occurs in high-speed flight is an obvious example.

certain circumstances this could be an important effect, and we should keep in mind that viscous dissipation can cause significant temperature gradients if viscous oils are forced through small conduits at high Reynolds numbers. Note that if the tube diameter is 1 in. instead of 1 cm the temperature rise is decreased from 150°C to 9°C for a 30-ft section of pipe. Clearly for large diameter pipes this effect is negligible even for very viscous oils.

Reversible work—laminar flow in a tube

We will refer to the source term, $T\beta Dp/Dt$, as the reversible work term since it can be either positive or negative depending on whether the fluid is being compressed or expanded. As in the previous analysis of viscous dissipation we will consider the case of laminar flow in a tube in order to estimate the importance of this effect. The time rate of change of temperature *owing to the reversible work* can be estimated from Eq. 5.5-10 as

$$\frac{DT}{Dt} = \mathbf{0}\left(T\beta \frac{Dp}{Dt} \bigg/ \rho c_p\right)$$

and since we are considering a steady, one-dimensional flow for which

$$\frac{DT}{Dt} = v_z \frac{\partial T}{\partial z}, \qquad \frac{Dp}{Dt} = v_z \frac{\partial p}{\partial z}$$

this order-of-magnitude estimate reduces to

$$\left(\frac{\partial T}{\partial z}\right)_{\text{reversible work}} = \mathbf{0}\left[\left(\frac{T\beta}{\rho c_p}\right)\left(\frac{\partial p}{\partial z}\right)\right]$$

Since the pressure gradient for laminar flow is given by

$$\left(\frac{\partial p}{\partial z}\right) = -\frac{32\mu\langle v_z\rangle}{D^2}$$

our order-of-magnitude estimate for the temperature gradient can be written as

$$\left(\frac{\partial T}{\partial z}\right)_{\text{reversible work}} = \mathbf{0}\left[32T\beta\left(\frac{N_{\text{Re}}\nu^2}{c_p D^3}\right)\right]$$

Comparing this result with our expression for the temperature gradient owing to viscous dissipation allows us to express our order-of-magnitude estimate as

$$\left(\frac{\partial T}{\partial z}\right)_{\text{reversible work}} = \mathbf{0}\left[32T\beta\left(\frac{\partial T}{\partial z}\right)_{\text{viscous dissipation}}\right]$$

Although our order-of-magnitude analysis does not take into account the sign of the terms, we should note that for pipe flow the reversible work term gives rise to a decrease in the temperature, whereas viscous dissipation gives rise to an increase. Our only task now is to estimate $32T\beta$ for air, water, and a petroleum oil.

If we treat air as an ideal gas $\beta = 1/T$ we find that the temperature gradient owing to reversible work is given by

$$\left(\frac{\partial T}{\partial z}\right)_{\text{reversible work}} = \mathbf{0}\,(1.5\times 10^{-4}\,°\text{C/cm}), \quad \text{for air}$$

Once again this effect is quite small; however, at very high flow rates, say $N_{\text{Re}} \sim 10^6$, reversible work can lead to appreciable temperature gradients for gas flows.†

For *liquids* the coefficient of thermal expansion is given by

$$\beta = \mathbf{0}\,(10^{-3}\,°\text{C}^{-1}), \quad \text{for liquids}$$

†The order-of-magnitude analysis for turbulent flows is given in Ex. 7.5-1.

thus $32T\beta \sim 10$ at room temperature and the temperature gradient owing to reversible work is given by

$$\left(\frac{\partial T}{\partial z}\right)_{\text{reversible work}} = \mathbf{0}\left[10\left(\frac{\partial T}{\partial z}\right)_{\text{viscous dissipation}}\right], \quad \text{for liquids}$$

For *water* this leads to

$$\left(\frac{\partial T}{\partial z}\right)_{\text{reversible work}} = \mathbf{0}\,(2\times 10^{-8}\,^\circ\text{C/cm}), \quad \text{for water}$$

and for a *petroleum oil* we find

$$\left(\frac{\partial T}{\partial z}\right)_{\text{reversible work}} = \mathbf{0}\,(5\times 10^{-2}\,^\circ\text{C/cm}), \quad \text{for oil}$$

Here we see a potential 5°C decrease in the temperature over a distance of 100 cm or 3 ft. Once again we should point out that if the diameter is increased from 1 cm to 1 in. the temperature change is reduced from 5°C to 0.3°C.

In the previous paragraphs we have discussed the source terms, $T\beta Dp/Dt$, $\nabla\mathbf{v}:\boldsymbol{\tau}$, and Φ, in the thermal energy equation. For most convective heat transfer processes of practical interest the reversible work and the viscous dissipation are small enough to be neglected, and Eq. 5.5-10 reduces to

$$\rho c_p \frac{DT}{Dt} = \nabla\cdot(k\nabla T) + \Phi, \quad \text{negligible viscous dissipation and reversible work} \tag{5.5-11}$$

In addition it is often an excellent assumption to take the thermal conductivity to be a constant so that Eq. 5.5-11 reduces to

$$\rho c_p\left(\frac{\partial T}{\partial t} + \mathbf{v}\cdot\nabla T\right) = k\nabla^2 T + \Phi, \quad \text{negligible viscous dissipation and reversible work with a constant thermal conductivity} \tag{5.5-12}$$

We will use this form of the thermal energy equation, along with the Navier–Stokes equations and the continuity equation, to analyze a variety of convective heat transfer processes.

*5.6 Dimensional Analysis for Forced-Convection Heat Transfer

Before going on to the application of Eq. 5.5-12 to the problem of heat transfer in a laminar boundary layer, it will be helpful to develop the *dimensionless form* of these equations. In general, dimensional analysis is used in the planning and interpretation of experiments, although the results presented in this section will be of some value in the theoretical developments presented in Sec. 5.7. The analysis presented here will be restricted to incompressible flows and constant physical properties. In Sec. 5.10 we will extend this treatment and analyze flows for which the density is a function of the temperature, and in Chapter 7 we will consider the case where the viscosity is a function of temperature. This piecemeal approach to the dimensional analysis of the governing equations for energy and momentum transfer has the obvious drawback that the complete picture is not laid out once and for all. On the other hand, it has the advantage that the important aspects of the analysis are presented as they occur in our exploration of heat transfer phenomena.

If we examine the expanded form of Eq. 5.5-12

$$\rho c_p\left[\frac{\partial T}{\partial t} + v_x\left(\frac{\partial T}{\partial x}\right) + v_y\left(\frac{\partial T}{\partial y}\right) + v_z\left(\frac{\partial T}{\partial z}\right)\right] = k\left[\left(\frac{\partial^2 T}{\partial x^2}\right) + \left(\frac{\partial^2 T}{\partial y^2}\right) + \left(\frac{\partial^2 T}{\partial z^2}\right)\right] + \Phi \tag{5.6-1}$$

it should be clear that the temperature may be a function of

1. the independent variables (x, y, z, t)
2. the parameters that occur in the differential equation $(\rho,\ c_p,\ k,\ \Phi,\ v_x,\ v_y,\ v_z)$

in addition to any parameters that occur in the boundary conditions. If one is capable of developing an analytic solution for the temperature field the dependence on these variables and parameters is clearly established. For example, in Sec. 4.4 we studied the problem of a semi-infinite slab subject to periodic ambient temperature variations and found that the temperature was given by

$$T = T_0 + (T_1 - T_0)a\, e^{-x\sqrt{\omega/2\alpha}} \left\{ \cos\left[\omega t - x\sqrt{\frac{\omega}{2\alpha}}\right] + b \sin\left[\omega t - x\sqrt{\frac{\omega}{2\alpha}}\right] \right.$$

where

$$a = \left[1 + \frac{1+b}{N_{\text{Bi}}}\right]^{-1}$$

$$b = \frac{k\sqrt{\omega/2\alpha}}{h + k\sqrt{\omega/2\alpha}}$$

$$N_{\text{Bi}} = \left(\frac{h}{k}\right)\sqrt{\frac{2\alpha}{\omega}}$$

Here the dependence of the temperature on the independent variables (x, t), the single parameter that occurs in the differential equation (α), and the parameters that appear in the boundary conditions (ω, k, h, T_1, T_0), is clearly established. Note that the dependence on the parameters in the differential equation has been simplified by grouping ρ, c_p, and k into a single parameter, α.

Now we should ask the question, what does one do if an analytic solution is not available? Is one forced to perform experiments hoping to deduce the functional dependence of the temperature on the eight quantities, x, t, α, ω, k, h, T_1, and T_0? Such an experimental program would seem impossible; however, with the aid of dimensional analysis it becomes quite a plausible program.

Let us return now to the governing differential equations and write them in the form

$$\frac{\partial T}{\partial t} + \mathbf{v}\cdot\nabla T = \alpha\nabla^2 T + (\Phi/\rho c_p), \quad \text{thermal energy equation} \tag{5.6-2}$$

$$\frac{\partial \mathbf{v}}{\partial t} + \mathbf{v}\cdot\nabla\mathbf{v} = -\frac{1}{\rho}\nabla p + \mathbf{g} + \nu\nabla^2\mathbf{v}, \quad \text{Navier–Stokes equations} \tag{5.6-3}$$

$$\nabla\cdot\mathbf{v} = 0, \quad \text{continuity equation} \tag{5.6-4}$$

We assume that for any given process of forced-convection heat transfer there is:

1. a characteristic temperature difference, $T_1 - T_0$
2. a characteristic velocity, u_0
3. a characteristic length, L

Beginning first with the thermal energy equation we note that it can be written as

$$\frac{\partial}{\partial t}(T - T_0) + \mathbf{v}\cdot\nabla(T - T_0) = \alpha\nabla^2(T - T_0) + (\Phi/\rho c_p)$$

and we then divide each term in the equation by $u_0(T_1 - T_0)/L$. Here we can think of L/u_0 as being a scaling factor for time and $T_1 - T_0$ as a scaling factor for the temperature difference, $T - T_0$. The dimensionless thermal energy equation takes the form†

$$\frac{\partial\Theta}{\partial t^*} + \mathbf{U}\cdot\nabla\Theta = \left(\frac{\alpha}{u_0 L}\right)\nabla^2\Theta + \Phi^* \tag{5.6-5}$$

†In general, dimensionless variables will be represented by either capital letters or denoted by an asterisk*. The symbols ∇ and ∇^2 are used to represent *both* the dimensional and dimensionless forms of these operators.

where

$$\Theta = \frac{T - T_0}{T_1 - T_0}, \quad \text{a dimensionless temperature}$$

$$\mathbf{U} = \mathbf{v}/u_0, \quad \text{a dimensionless velocity vector}$$

$$t^* = tu_0/L, \quad \text{a dimensionless time}$$

$$\nabla = L\nabla, \quad \text{a dimensionless vector operator}$$

$$\nabla^2 = L^2\nabla^2, \quad \text{a dimensionless scalar operator}$$

$$\Phi^* = \frac{\Phi L}{\rho c_p u_0(T_1 - T_0)}, \quad \text{a dimensionless source term}$$

In Eq. 5.6-5 we have used the same symbol for the dimensionless and dimensional "del" and Laplacian operators, since no other suitable symbols are available and the addition of an asterisk would make for some cumbersome notation. The term (α/u_0L) is generally written as

$$\frac{\alpha}{u_0L} = \left(\frac{\alpha}{\nu}\right)\left(\frac{\nu}{u_0L}\right) = N_{\text{Pr}}^{-1}\, N_{\text{Re}}^{-1}$$

so that the final form of the dimensionless thermal energy equation is

$$\frac{\partial \Theta}{\partial t^*} + \mathbf{U}\cdot\nabla\Theta = \frac{1}{N_{\text{Pr}}N_{\text{Re}}}\nabla^2\Theta + \Phi^* \tag{5.6-6}$$

The Prandtl number, N_{Pr}, is an important dimensionless parameter which always appears in the analysis of convective heat transfer processes. It is the ratio of the kinematic viscosity to the thermal diffusivity, and it has a very definite physical significance.

If we refer back to Eqs. 5.6-2 and 5.6-3 we can rewrite them as

$$\frac{\partial T}{\partial t} + \mathbf{v}\cdot\nabla T = \alpha\nabla^2 T + \Omega_T, \quad \text{energy transport}$$

$$\frac{\partial \mathbf{v}}{\partial t} + \mathbf{v}\cdot\nabla\mathbf{v} = \nu\nabla^2\mathbf{v} + \mathbf{\Omega}_M, \quad \text{momentum transport}$$

Here Ω_T represents a thermal energy source given by $\Phi/\rho c_p$, and $\mathbf{\Omega}_M$ represents a momentum source given by $-\nabla p/\rho + \mathbf{g}$. When written in this form the equations appear to be quite similar, and we can think of ν, the kinematic viscosity, as being a *momentum diffusivity* coefficient which plays the same role in momentum transport processes as α, the *thermal diffusivity*, plays in energy transport processes. Thus the Prandtl number, ν/α may be looked upon as the ratio of the momentum diffusivity to the thermal diffusivity; however, we must always keep in mind that momentum is a *vector* quantity and energy is a *scalar* quantity, thus the two transport processes are inherently different.

Continuing with our dimensional analysis of the governing differential equations, we begin our analysis of the Navier–Stokes equations by expressing the gravitational vector as the gradient of a scalar

$$\mathbf{g} = -\nabla\phi$$

where ϕ is the gravitational potential energy function. Remembering that the density is a constant, and noting that $\nabla p = \nabla(p - p_0)$ if p_0 is a constant, we can write Eq. 5.6-3 as

$$\frac{\partial \mathbf{v}}{\partial t} + \mathbf{v}\cdot\nabla\mathbf{v} = -\nabla\left(\frac{p - p_0}{\rho}\right) - \nabla\phi + \nu\nabla^2\mathbf{v} \tag{5.6-7}$$

Multiplying each term in Eq. 5.6-7 by L/u_0^2 gives

$$\frac{\partial \mathbf{U}}{\partial t^*} + \mathbf{U}\cdot\nabla\mathbf{U} = -\nabla\left[\left(\frac{p - p_0}{\rho u_0^2}\right) + \frac{\phi}{u_0^2}\right] + \frac{1}{N_{\text{Re}}}\nabla^2\mathbf{U} \tag{5.6-8}$$

where the del operator, ∇, and the Laplacian, ∇^2, are dimensionless. The term in brackets is defined as the dimensionless piezometric pressure,

$$\mathcal{P} = \frac{p - p_0}{\rho u_0^2} + \frac{\phi}{u_0^2}$$

and the final form of the dimensionless Navier–Stokes equations is

$$\frac{\partial \mathbf{U}}{\partial t^*} + \mathbf{U} \cdot \nabla \mathbf{U} = -\nabla \mathcal{P} + \frac{1}{N_{\text{Re}}} \nabla^2 \mathbf{U} \tag{5.6-9}$$

Moving on to the continuity equation we quickly find the dimensionless form to be

$$\nabla \cdot \mathbf{U} = 0 \tag{5.6-10}$$

With the dimensionless forms of the governing differential equations (Eqs. 5.6-6, 5.6-9, and 5.6-10) at our disposal we are in a position to make statements about the functional dependence of **U** and Θ. From Eqs. 5.6-9 and 5.6-10 we conclude that the functional dependence of **U** and $\mathcal{P}$, the two *dependent* variables in the equations of motion, be represented as†

$$\mathbf{U} = \mathbf{U}(X, Y, Z, t^*, N_{\text{Re}}, N_{\text{BC}}^{\text{I}}) \tag{5.6-11}$$

$$\mathcal{P} = \mathcal{P}(X, Y, Z, t^*, N_{\text{Re}}, N_{\text{BC}}^{\text{I}}) \tag{5.6-12}$$

Here N_{BC}^{I} represents all the *dimensionless* parameters appearing in the boundary conditions for the velocity and pressure. Turning our attention to Eq. 5.6-6 we express the functional dependence of Θ as

$$\Theta = \Theta(X, Y, Z, t^*, (N_{\text{Pr}} N_{\text{Re}}), \mathbf{U}, \Phi^*, N_{\text{BC}}^{\text{II}}) \tag{5.6-13}$$

where $N_{\text{BC}}^{\text{II}}$ represents all the *dimensionless* parameters appearing in the boundary conditions for the temperature. On the basis of the functional dependence of **U** given by Eq. 5.6-11 we can simplify Eq. 5.6-13 to obtain

$$\Theta = \Theta(X, Y, Z, t^*, N_{\text{Pr}}, N_{\text{Re}}, \Phi^*, N_{\text{BC}}^{\text{I}}, N_{\text{BC}}^{\text{II}}) \tag{5.6-14}$$

Note that the temperature field depends on *both* the dimensionless parameters appearing in the boundary conditions for the temperature, $N_{\text{BC}}^{\text{II}}$, *and* the dimensionless parameters appearing in the boundary conditions for the velocity, N_{BC}^{I}.

In the analysis of experiments and the correlation of experimental data, we are most often interested in the heat flux at a phase interface, or more specifically the film heat transfer coefficient. The two are related by the definition

$$\mathbf{q} \cdot \mathbf{n} = h(T_i - T_a), \quad \text{at an interface} \tag{5.6-15}$$

where **n** is the unit normal to the interface,‡ T_i is the temperature at the interface, and T_a is some suitable ambient temperature. In terms of Fouriers law this takes the form

$$-k\nabla T \cdot \mathbf{n} = h(T_i - T_a), \quad \text{at an interface} \tag{5.6-16}$$

Putting Eq. 5.6-16 in dimensionless form gives

$$-\nabla\Theta \cdot \mathbf{n} = \left(\frac{hL}{k}\right)\Theta_i, \quad \text{at an interface} \tag{5.6-17}$$

Here ∇ represents the dimensionless vector operator, $\Theta = (T - T_a)/(T_1 - T_a)$, and Θ_i is the dimensionless temperature at the interface. The dimensionless group (hL/k) is the Nusselt number and can be represented as

$$N_{\text{Nu}} = \left(\frac{hL}{k}\right) = -\frac{\nabla\Theta \cdot \mathbf{n}}{\Theta_i} \tag{5.6-18}$$

†Here X, Y, and Z are the dimensionless spatial coordinates.

‡Note that **n** is directed *into* the phase having the temperature T_a.

thus N_{Nu} has the same functional dependence as Θ and we can write

$$N_{\mathrm{Nu}} = N_{\mathrm{Nu}}(X, Y, Z, t^*, N_{\mathrm{Pr}}, N_{\mathrm{Re}}, \Phi^*, N_{\mathrm{BC}}^{\mathrm{I}}, N_{\mathrm{BC}}^{\mathrm{II}}) \tag{5.6-19}$$

Very often Nusselt numbers are determined in terms of area averaged film heat transfer coefficients, thus the dependence on X, Y, and Z vanishes. In addition, if the process is steady and there is no heat generation the functional dependence reduces to

$$N_{\mathrm{Nu,av}} = N_{\mathrm{Nu,av}}(N_{\mathrm{Pr}}, N_{\mathrm{Re}}, N_{\mathrm{BC}}^{\mathrm{I}}, N_{\mathrm{BC}}^{\mathrm{II}}) \tag{5.6-20}$$

Since the dimensionless parameters describing the boundary conditions are different for each process this functional dependence is often shortened to

$$N_{\mathrm{Nu}} = N_{\mathrm{Nu}}(N_{\mathrm{Pr}}, N_{\mathrm{Re}}) \tag{5.6-21}$$

with the dependence of the parameters appearing in the boundary conditions understood. This functional representation is convenient, but one must be constantly on guard to *remember the dependence on the dimensionless parameters appearing in the boundary operations.*

Example 5.6-1 Dimensional analysis for a finned tube

In a modern petroleum refinery the use of water for cooling process streams is avoided as much as possible. Any water that enters a refinery is likely to become contaminated, thus limiting the use of water can reduce pollution problems and minimize the cost of water treatment plants. In order to cool process streams without using or misusing local water supplies, air can be used instead. Process streams are passed through finned tubes and propellors are used to blow air past the tubes at the proper rate.

A precise knowledge of the heat transfer rates is required for the design of such units, and experimental studies are necessary in order to determine the effect of tube geometry and air flow rates on the film heat transfer coefficient. For the tube illustrated in Fig. 5.6.1 we would like to specify the parameters on which h depends. Our experimental program would consist of heating the inside of the tube with an electrical heater so that the total heat transfer rate would be specified. In addition we would arrange the experiment so that all the

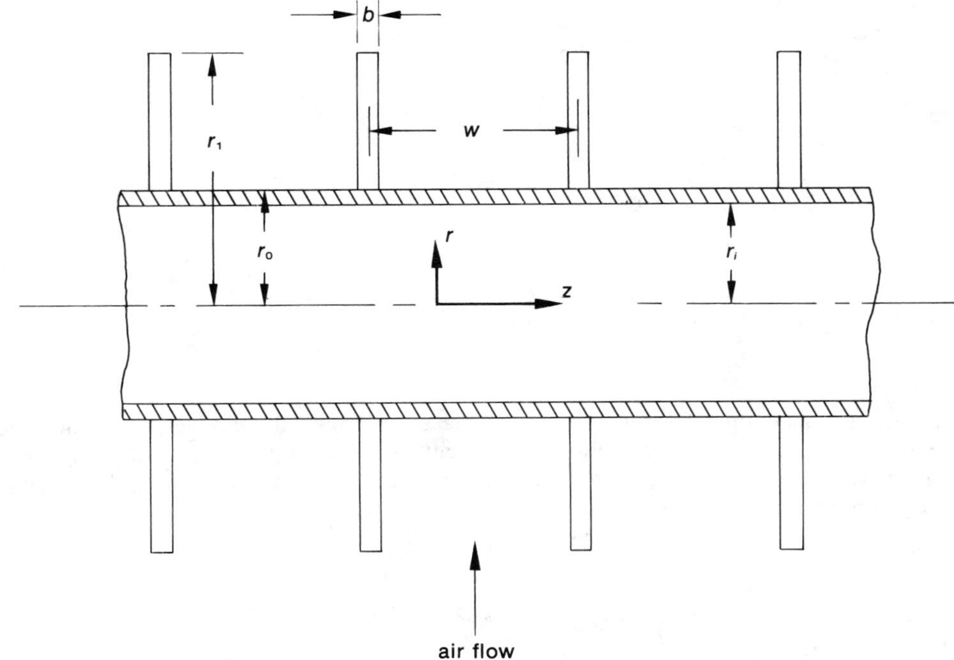

Fig. 5.6.1 Finned tube for use in an air-cooled heat exchanger.

resistance to heat transfer is in the gas phase.† This means that the fins and tube wall are at some uniform temperature, T_0.

In performing a dimensional analysis we assume that the physical properties of the air are constant and the flow is incompressible so that the governing differential equations take the form

$$\frac{\partial T}{\partial t} + \mathbf{v} \cdot \nabla T = \alpha \nabla^2 T \tag{1}$$

$$\frac{\partial \mathbf{v}}{\partial t} + \mathbf{v} \cdot \nabla \mathbf{v} = -\frac{1}{\rho} \nabla p + \mathbf{g} + \nu \nabla^2 \mathbf{v} \tag{2}$$

$$\nabla \cdot \mathbf{v} = 0 \tag{3}$$

The boundary conditions are represented in cylindrical coordinates as

B.C.1 $\quad T = T_a, \quad r = \infty \quad (4)$

B.C.2 $\quad v_r = u_0 \cos \theta, \quad r = \infty \quad (5)$

B.C.3 $\quad v_\theta = u_0 \sin \theta$ and $v_z = 0 \quad r = \infty \quad (6)$

B.C.4 $\quad \mathbf{v} = 0, \quad a(r, z, r_0, r_1, b, w) = 0 \quad (7)$

B.C.5 $\quad T = T_0, \quad a(r, z, r_0, r_1, b, w) = 0 \quad (8)$

Here we have designated the surface of the finned tube as $a(r, z, r_0, r_1, b, w) = 0$ where it should be clear that the *parameters* r_0, r_1, b, and w are required to locate the surface. We could be more explicit and locate the position of the surface as

$$r = r_0, \quad \frac{b}{2} < z < w - \frac{b}{2}$$

$$r = r_0, \quad w + \frac{b}{2} < z < 2w - \frac{b}{2}$$

$$r = r_0, \quad -w + \frac{b}{2} < z < -\frac{b}{2}$$

etc.

$$z = \pm \frac{b}{2}, \quad r_0 \leqslant r \leqslant r_1$$

$$z = w \pm \frac{b}{2}, \quad r_0 \leqslant r \leqslant r_1$$

$$z = -w \pm \frac{b}{2}, \quad r_0 \leqslant r \leqslant r_1$$

etc.

$$r = r_1, \quad -\frac{b}{2} < z < +\frac{b}{2}$$

$$r = r_1, \quad w - \frac{b}{2} < z < w + \frac{b}{2}$$

$$r = r_1, \quad -w - \frac{b}{2} < z < -w + \frac{b}{2}$$

etc.

Our task is now to make Eqs. 1 through 8 dimensionless. We take the characteristic length to be r_0, the characteristic time as r_0/u_0, and the characteristic temperature difference as $T_0 - T_a$. Following the development given by Eqs. 5.6-2 through 5.6-10 we arrive at the dimensionless form of the governing differential equations and boundary conditions

$$\frac{\partial \Theta}{\partial t^*} + \mathbf{U} \cdot \nabla \Theta = \frac{1}{N_{\text{Re}} N_{\text{Pr}}} \nabla^2 \Theta \tag{9}$$

$$\frac{\partial \mathbf{U}}{\partial t^*} + \mathbf{U} \cdot \nabla \mathbf{U} = -\nabla \mathscr{P} + \frac{1}{N_{\text{Re}}} \nabla^2 \mathbf{U} \tag{10}$$

†The more general case where the resistance to heat transfer in the solid phase is important will be left as a problem for the student.

$$\nabla \cdot \mathbf{U} = 0 \tag{11}$$

B.C.1′ $\Theta = 0, \qquad R = \infty$ (12)

B.C.2′ $U_r = \cos\theta, \qquad R = \infty$ (13)

B.C.3′ $U_\theta = \sin\theta$ and $U_z = 0, \qquad R = \infty$

B.C.4′ $\mathbf{U} = 0, \qquad \mathscr{A}(R, Z, \beta, \gamma, \eta) = 0$ (14)

B.C.5′ $\Theta = 1, \qquad \mathscr{A}(R, Z, \beta, \gamma, \eta) = 0$ (15)

Here we have used $\mathscr{A}(R, Z, \beta, \gamma, \eta) = 0$ to designate the position of the surface of the finned tube where

$$\beta = \frac{r_1}{r_0}$$

$$\gamma = \frac{b}{r_0}$$

$$\eta = \frac{w}{r_0}$$

The parameters, β, γ, and η, result from expressing the dimensionless surface position as

$$R = 1, \qquad \frac{1}{2}\left(\frac{b}{r_0}\right) < Z < \left(\frac{w}{r_0}\right) - \frac{1}{2}\left(\frac{b}{r_0}\right)$$

$$R = 1, \qquad \left(\frac{w}{r_0}\right) + \frac{1}{2}\left(\frac{b}{r_0}\right) < Z < 2\left(\frac{w}{r_0}\right) - \frac{1}{2}\left(\frac{b}{r_0}\right)$$

etc.

$$Z = \pm\frac{1}{2}\left(\frac{b}{r_0}\right), \qquad 1 \leq R \leq \left(\frac{r_1}{r_0}\right)$$

$$Z = \left(\frac{w}{r_0}\right) \pm \frac{1}{2}\left(\frac{b}{r_0}\right), \qquad 1 \leq R \leq \left(\frac{r_1}{r_0}\right)$$

$$Z = -\left(\frac{w}{r_0}\right) \pm \frac{1}{2}\left(\frac{b}{r_0}\right), \qquad 1 \leq R \leq \left(\frac{r_1}{r_0}\right)$$

etc.

$$R = \left(\frac{r_1}{r_0}\right), \qquad -\frac{1}{2}\left(\frac{b}{r_0}\right) < Z < +\frac{1}{2}\left(\frac{b}{r_0}\right)$$

$$R = \left(\frac{r_1}{r_0}\right), \qquad \left(\frac{w}{r_0}\right) - \frac{1}{2}\left(\frac{b}{r_0}\right) < Z < \left(\frac{w}{r_0}\right) + \frac{1}{2}\left(\frac{b}{r_0}\right)$$

$$R = \left(\frac{r_1}{r_0}\right), \qquad -\left(\frac{w}{r_0}\right) - \frac{1}{2}\left(\frac{b}{r_0}\right) < Z < -\left(\frac{w}{r_0}\right) + \frac{1}{2}\left(\frac{b}{r_0}\right)$$

etc.

From Eqs. 10, 11 and B.C.2′, B.C.3′, and B.C.4′ we know that the function dependence of $\mathbf{U}$ is given by

$$\mathbf{U} = \mathbf{U}(R, \theta, Z, t^*, N_{Re}, \beta, \gamma, \eta) \tag{16}$$

Here R, θ, Z, t^* are the dimensionless independent variables; N_{Re} is the single parameter appearing in the differential equations; and β, γ, η are the parameters appearing in the boundary conditions. In Eq. 5.6-11 these latter parameters are denoted by N^{I}_{BC}. From Eqs. 9, 12, and 15 we have

$$\Theta = \Theta(R, \theta, Z, t^*, N_{Pr}N_{Re}, \mathbf{U}, \beta, \gamma, \eta) \tag{17}$$

and taking into account the functional dependence of $\mathbf{U}$ leads to

$$\Theta = \Theta(R, \theta, Z, t^*, N_{Re}, N_{Pr}, \beta, \gamma, \eta) \tag{18}$$

From here our analysis follows that given by Eqs. 5.6-15 through 5.6-20 which leads to

$$N_{\mathrm{Nu,av}} = N_{\mathrm{Nu,av}}(N_{\mathrm{Pr}}, N_{\mathrm{Re}}, \beta, \gamma, \eta) \tag{19}$$

We should be careful to point out that average film heat transfer coefficient would be *defined* by

$$h_{\mathrm{av}} = \dot{Q}/A(T_0 - T_a)$$

where A is the total surface area.

In our experimental studies N_{Pr} will be constant, thus we cannot determine the functional dependence of the Nusselt number on the Prandtl number. The functional dependence of the Reynolds number can be determined by varying the air velocity, and we are left with the problem of determining the dependence of β, γ, and η. This requires the construction of several different geometries and we would want to give careful thought to this part of the experiment before deciding on the values of β, γ, and η to be tested.

In the previous example we have demonstrated how one can determine the functional dependence of the Nusselt number and therefore the functional dependence of the film heat transfer coefficient. We must always remember that

$$h = kN_{\mathrm{Nu}}/L \tag{5.6-22}$$

thus a correlation for the Nusselt number provides a means of determining h, the film heat transfer coefficient. In Ex. 5.6-1 we learned that the functional dependence for the Nusselt number was given by

$$N_{\mathrm{Nu,av}} = N_{\mathrm{Nu,av}}(N_{\mathrm{Pr}}, N_{\mathrm{Re}}, \beta, \gamma, \eta)$$

however, this result *does not* tell us how important the functional dependence may be. For example, one might guess that the Nusselt number is not a strong function of w/r_0 for large values of this parameter. However, for small values of w/r_0 we might expect $N_{\mathrm{Nu,av}}$ to be very sensitive to the value of this parameter. We will consider this matter further in Sec. 5.9.

Summary of Section 5.7

In this section we wish to apply the equations of motion and the thermal energy equation to the laminar flow past a flat plate illustrated in Fig. 5.7.1. We begin with the governing differential equations which are the x- and y-direction equations of motion, the continuity equation for an incompressible flow, and the simplified form of the thermal energy equation; all for a steady flow.

$$\rho\left(v_x\frac{\partial v_x}{\partial x} + v_y\frac{\partial v_x}{\partial y}\right) = -\frac{\partial p}{\partial x} + \rho g_x + \mu\left(\frac{\partial^2 v_x}{\partial x^2} + \frac{\partial^2 v_x}{\partial y^2}\right) \tag{5.7-1}$$

$$\rho\left(v_x\frac{\partial v_y}{\partial x} + v_y\frac{\partial v_y}{\partial y}\right) = -\frac{\partial p}{\partial y} + \rho g_y + \mu\left(\frac{\partial^2 v_y}{\partial x^2} + \frac{\partial^2 v_y}{\partial y^2}\right) \tag{5.7-2}$$

$$\frac{\partial v_x}{\partial x} + \frac{\partial v_y}{\partial y} = 0 \tag{5.7-3}$$

$$\rho c_p\left(v_x\frac{\partial T}{\partial x} + v_y\frac{\partial T}{\partial y}\right) = k\left(\frac{\partial^2 T}{\partial x^2} + \frac{\partial^2 T}{\partial y^2}\right) \tag{5.7-4}$$

For the case where $\partial p/\partial x = 0$ outside of the boundary layer, i.e., $y > \delta_H$, we can use order-of-magnitude analysis to simplify these equations to

$$\rho\left(v_x\frac{\partial v_x}{\partial x} + v_y\frac{\partial v_x}{\partial y}\right) = \mu\left(\frac{\partial^2 v_x}{\partial y^2}\right)$$

$$\frac{\partial v_x}{\partial x} + \frac{\partial v_y}{\partial y} = 0$$

$$\rho c_p\left(v_x\frac{\partial T}{\partial x} + v_y\frac{\partial T}{\partial y}\right) = k\left(\frac{\partial^2 T}{\partial y^2}\right)$$

provided the plate is long enough so that the restriction, $\delta_H \ll L$, is satisfied. These equations are often referred

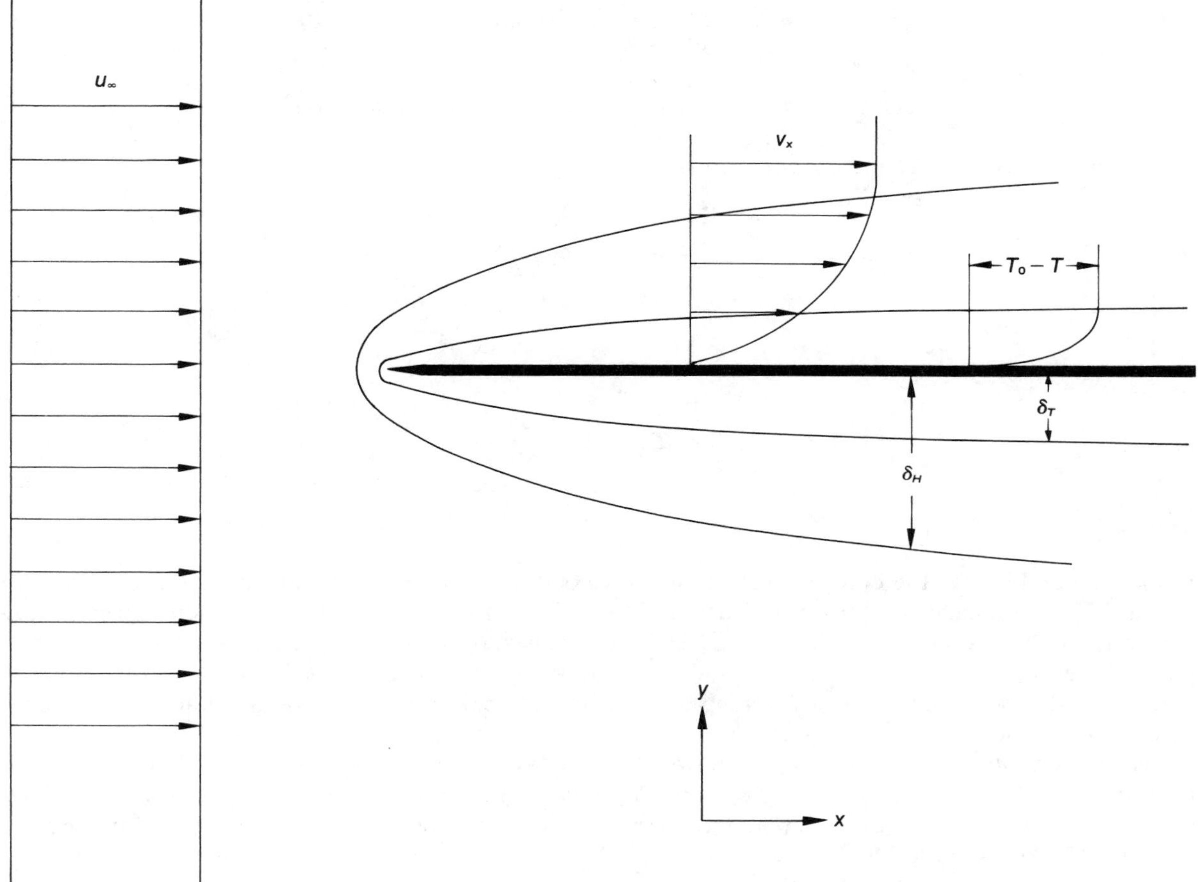

Fig. 5.7.1 Velocity and temperature profiles in a laminar boundary layer.

to as the *Prandtl boundary layer equations*, and the dimensionless forms are given by Eqs. 5.7-28 through 5.7-30. In Sec. 5.8 an exact solution is presented for the velocity and temperature field, and in Sec. 5.9 approximate solutions are developed.

*5.7 The Momentum and Energy Equations for Laminar Boundary Layer Flow

With the governing differential equations now at our disposal we are in a position to attack the problem of heat transfer in a laminar boundary layer. This process is illustrated in Fig. 5.7.1; the temperature profile being for the case where a hot plate is cooled by the flowing fluid. This process is a highly idealized version of the types of processes that are actually encountered in practice, i.e., the plate is taken to be very thin with a sharp leading edge, and the temperature of the plate is taken to be constant. Such a situation is not likely to occur in practice, but it is not a bad approximation of what can occur and there is much to be learned from the analysis of this special case. We begin by assuming the flow to be purely two-dimensional, steady, and incompressible so that the governing equations take the form

$$\rho\left(v_x\frac{\partial v_x}{\partial x}+v_y\frac{\partial v_x}{\partial y}\right)=-\left(\frac{\partial p}{\partial x}\right)+\rho g_x+\mu\left(\frac{\partial^2 v_x}{\partial x^2}+\frac{\partial^2 v_x}{\partial y^2}\right),\quad x\text{-direction momentum equation}\tag{5.7-1}$$

$$\rho\left(v_x\frac{\partial v_y}{\partial x}+v_y\frac{\partial v_y}{\partial y}\right)=-\left(\frac{\partial p}{\partial y}\right)+\rho g_y+\mu\left(\frac{\partial^2 v_y}{\partial x^2}+\frac{\partial^2 v_y}{\partial y^2}\right),\quad y\text{-direction momentum equation}\tag{5.7-2}$$

$$\frac{\partial v_x}{\partial x}+\frac{\partial v_y}{\partial y}=0, \quad \text{continuity equation} \tag{5.7-3}$$

$$\rho c_p\left(v_x\frac{\partial T}{\partial x}+v_y\frac{\partial T}{\partial y}\right)=k\left(\frac{\partial^2 T}{\partial x^2}+\frac{\partial^2 T}{\partial y^2}\right), \quad \text{thermal energy equation} \tag{5.7-4}$$

and we will specify the boundary conditions to be

B.C.1 $$v_x=u_\infty, \quad v_y=0, \quad x\to-\infty \tag{5.7-5}$$

B.C.2 $$v_x=u_\infty, \quad y\to\pm\infty \tag{5.7-6}$$

B.C.3 $$v_x=v_y=0, \quad y=0, \quad x>0 \tag{5.7-7}$$

B.C.4 $$p=p_\infty, \quad x\to-\infty \tag{5.7-8}$$

B.C.5 $$p=p_\infty, \quad y\to\pm\infty, \quad x>0 \tag{5.7-9}$$

B.C.6 $$T=T_\infty, \quad x\to-\infty \tag{5.7-10}$$

B.C.7 $$T=T_\infty, \quad y\to\pm\infty \tag{5.7-11}$$

B.C.8 $$T=T_0, \quad y=0, \quad x>0 \tag{5.7-12}$$

Here u_∞, p_∞, and T_∞ are the constant values of the velocity, pressure, and temperature far removed from the plate. The boundary conditions indicate that far removed from the plate the velocity, pressure, and temperature fields are uniform. The velocity and temperature profiles illustrated in Fig. 5.7.1 indicate that changes in the velocity and temperature fields occur in a region near the plate designated as the boundary layer. The hydrodynamic boundary layer is shown as being thicker than the thermal boundary layer for this is usually (but not always) the case.

Clearly the problem is a complex one; however, the governing equations can be simplified by means of an order-of-magnitude analysis which leads to the *boundary layer equations.* An exact solution of these equations is presented in Sec. 5.8 and an approximate solution is developed and compared with experimental data in Sec. 5.9.

Order-of-magnitude analysis†

In analyzing the order-of-magnitude of the terms in Eqs. 5.7-1 through 5.7-4 it will be helpful to work in terms of dimensionless variables defined by

$$\begin{aligned}
U_x &= v_x/u_\infty\\
U_y &= v_y/u_\infty\\
\mathcal{P} &= (p-p_\infty)/\rho u_\infty^2+\phi/u_\infty^2\\
X &= x/L\\
Y &= y/L\\
\Delta_H &= \delta_H/L\\
\Delta_T &= \delta_T/L\\
N_{\mathrm{Re},L} &= \rho u_\infty L/\mu\\
N_{\mathrm{Pr}} &= \mu c_p/k=\nu/\alpha\\
\Theta &= (T-T_0)/(T_\infty-T_0)
\end{aligned}$$

Here L represents the length of the plate. Putting the governing equations in dimensionless form by multiplying and dividing by the appropriate parameters (i.e., ρ, u_∞, c_p, μ, L, and T_0-T_∞) we obtain

$$\underset{(1)\ (1)}{U_x\left(\frac{\partial U_x}{\partial X}\right)}+\underset{(\Delta_H)\left(\frac{1}{\Delta_H}\right)}{U_y\left(\frac{\partial U_x}{\partial Y}\right)}=-\left(\frac{\partial\mathcal{P}}{\partial X}\right)+\frac{1}{N_{\mathrm{Re},L}}\left(\underset{(1)}{\frac{\partial^2 U_x}{\partial X^2}}+\underset{\left(\frac{1}{\Delta_H^2}\right)}{\frac{\partial^2 U_x}{\partial Y^2}}\right) \tag{5.7-13}$$

†See Sec. 2.9.

$$\overset{(1)}{U_x}\overset{(\Delta_H)}{\left(\frac{\partial U_y}{\partial X}\right)}+\overset{(\Delta_H)}{U_y}\overset{(1)}{\left(\frac{\partial U_y}{\partial Y}\right)}=-\overset{(\Delta_H)}{\left(\frac{\partial \mathcal{P}}{\partial Y}\right)}+\frac{1}{N_{\mathrm{Re},L}}\overset{\left(\frac{1}{\Delta_H}\right)}{\left(\frac{\partial^2 U_y}{\partial X^2}+\frac{\partial^2 U_y}{\partial Y^2}\right)} \tag{5.7-14}$$

$$\overset{(1)}{\left(\frac{\partial U_x}{\partial X}\right)}+\overset{(1)}{\left(\frac{\partial U_y}{\partial Y}\right)}=0 \tag{5.7-15}$$

$$\overset{(1)}{U_x}\overset{(1)}{\left(\frac{\partial \Theta}{\partial X}\right)}+\overset{(\Delta_H)}{U_y}\overset{\left(\frac{1}{\Delta_T}\right)}{\left(\frac{\partial \Theta}{\partial Y}\right)}=\frac{1}{N_{\mathrm{Re},L}N_{\mathrm{pr}}}\left(\overset{(1)}{\frac{\partial^2 \Theta}{\partial X^2}}+\overset{\left(\frac{1}{\Delta_T^2}\right)}{\frac{\partial^2 \Theta}{\partial Y^2}}\right) \tag{5.7-16}$$

Our order-of-magnitude analysis begins by noting that U_x lies between 0 and 1, thus

$$U_x=\mathbf{0}(1) \tag{5.7-17}$$

Since the dimensionless distance X also lies between 0 and 1 we estimate the order-of-magnitude of the derivative $\partial U_x/\partial X$ to be

$$\frac{\partial U_x}{\partial X}=\frac{\mathbf{0}(U_x)}{\mathbf{0}(X)}=\mathbf{0}(1) \tag{5.7-18}$$

It follows from the continuity equation that

$$\frac{\partial U_y}{\partial Y}=\mathbf{0}(1) \tag{5.7-19}$$

which in turn gives us an order-of-magnitude estimate for U_y

$$\begin{aligned} U_y&=\mathbf{0}\left(\frac{\partial U_y}{\partial Y}\right)\mathbf{0}(Y) \\ &=\mathbf{0}(1)\mathbf{0}(\Delta_H) \\ &=\mathbf{0}(\Delta_H) \end{aligned} \tag{5.7-20}$$

In obtaining this result we are making use of the fact that significant variations in the velocity take place in the boundary layer, thus significant variations in U_y take place over the distance Δ_H. Noting that the order-of-magnitude estimate of the second derivatives takes the form

$$\left(\frac{\partial^2 U_x}{\partial X^2}\right)=\frac{\mathbf{0}(U_x)}{\mathbf{0}(X)^2}=1 \tag{5.7-21}$$

$$\frac{\partial^2 U_x}{\partial Y^2}=\frac{\mathbf{0}(U_x)}{\mathbf{0}(Y)^2}=\frac{1}{\Delta_H^2} \tag{5.7-22}$$

we obtain the order-of-magnitude estimates shown in parentheses over the individual terms in Eqs. 5.7-13 through 5.7-15. Attacking the energy equation in the same manner, we begin with

$$\Theta=\mathbf{0}(1) \tag{5.7-23}$$

and quickly conclude that

$$\frac{\partial \Theta}{\partial X}=\mathbf{0}(1),\qquad \frac{\partial \Theta}{\partial Y}=\mathbf{0}\left(\frac{1}{\Delta_T}\right),\qquad \frac{\partial^2 \Theta}{\partial X^2}=\mathbf{0}(1),\qquad \frac{\partial^2 \Theta}{\partial Y^2}=\mathbf{0}\left(\frac{1}{\Delta_T^2}\right) \tag{5.7-24}$$

These order-of-magnitude estimates are listed in parentheses over the individual terms in Eq. 5.7-16.

From experimental observations [5] we know that for many practical conditions the boundary layer thickness δ_H is much smaller than the length of the plate L, thus $\Delta_H \ll 1$ and certain terms in Eqs. 5.7-13 and 5.7-14 become large compared to others, i.e.,

$$\frac{\partial^2 U_x}{\partial Y^2} \gg \frac{\partial^2 U_x}{\partial X^2} \quad \text{and} \quad \frac{\partial^2 U_y}{\partial Y^2} \gg \frac{\partial^2 U_y}{\partial X^2}$$

If we assume that small causes lead to small effects (not always a good assumption) we drop the small terms in these equations to obtain

$$\begin{array}{l} (1)\quad(1)\qquad(\Delta_H)\left(\frac{1}{\Delta_H}\right)\qquad\qquad\qquad\qquad\left(\frac{1}{\Delta_H^2}\right) \\ U_x\left(\frac{\partial U_x}{\partial X}\right)+U_y\left(\frac{\partial U_x}{\partial Y}\right)=-\left(\frac{\partial \mathcal{P}}{\partial X}\right)+\frac{1}{N_{\mathrm{Re},L}}\left(\frac{\partial^2 U_x}{\partial Y^2}\right)\end{array} \tag{5.7-25}$$

$$\begin{array}{l} (1)\quad(\Delta_H)\qquad(\Delta_H)\quad(1)\qquad\qquad\qquad\qquad\left(\frac{1}{\Delta_H}\right) \\ U_x\left(\frac{\partial U_y}{\partial X}\right)+U_Y\left(\frac{\partial U_y}{\partial Y}\right)=-\left(\frac{\partial \mathcal{P}}{\partial Y}\right)+\frac{1}{N_{\mathrm{Re},L}}\left(\frac{\partial^2 U_y}{\partial Y^2}\right)\end{array} \tag{5.7-26}$$

Comparing Eqs. 5.7-25 and 5.7-26 we see that the individual terms in the y-direction momentum equation are smaller by a factor of Δ_H than the comparable terms in the x-direction momentum equation. If Δ_H is much smaller than one, i.e.,

$$\delta_H \ll L$$

the pressure gradient in the y-direction $\partial\mathcal{P}/\partial Y$ is small compared to the terms in Eq. 5.7-25. This means that we can neglect the pressure variation across the boundary layer and express Eq. 5.7-25 as

$$U_x\left(\frac{\partial U_x}{\partial X}\right)+U_y\left(\frac{\partial U_x}{\partial Y}\right)=-\left(\frac{d\mathcal{P}}{dX}\right)+\frac{1}{N_{\mathrm{Re},L}}\left(\frac{\partial^2 U_x}{\partial Y^2}\right) \tag{5.7-27}$$

We could perhaps reinforce this point of view by considering the *possibility* that there are regions within the boundary layer where viscous affects predominate and regions where inertial effects predominate. *If this were the case,* then in regions where viscous effects predominate we can use Eqs. 5.7-25 and 5.7-26 to write

$$\left(\frac{\partial P}{\partial X}\right)=\mathbf{0}\left(\frac{1}{N_{\mathrm{Re},L}\,\Delta_H^2}\right),\ \left(\frac{\partial P}{\partial Y}\right)=\mathbf{0}\left(\frac{\Delta_H}{N_{\mathrm{Re},L}\,\Delta_H^2}\right),\quad \text{viscous effects predominate}$$

and in regions where inertial effects predominate we can write

$$\left(\frac{\partial P}{\partial X}\right)=\mathbf{0}(1),\ \left(\frac{\partial P}{\partial Y}\right)=\mathbf{0}(\Delta_H),\quad \text{inertial effects predominate}$$

From this it is clear that

$$\left(\frac{\partial P}{\partial Y}\right)=\mathbf{0}\left[\Delta_H\left(\frac{\partial P}{\partial X}\right)\right]$$

and when $\Delta_H \ll 1$ we can write

$$\left(\frac{\partial P}{\partial Y}\right)\ll\mathbf{0}\left(\frac{\partial P}{\partial X}\right)$$

which leads to our previously stated conclusion that

$$\left(\frac{\partial P}{\partial X}\right)=\left(\frac{dP}{dX}\right)$$

Outside the boundary layer, $y > \delta_H$, the velocity U_x is assumed to be constant and the pressure is equal to the ambient pressure, p_∞.

$$p = p_\infty, \qquad y > \delta_H$$

This means that $\mathcal{P}$ is constant outside the boundary layer, and since the order-of-magnitude analysis indicates negligible variation in $\mathcal{P}$ across the boundary later, i.e., $\partial\mathcal{P}/\partial X = d\mathcal{P}/dX$, we conclude that

$$\frac{d\mathcal{P}}{dX}=0, \qquad 0 \leq y \leq \delta_H$$

Under these circumstances our governing equations for momentum and energy transport in a laminar boundary layer reduce to

$$U_x\left(\frac{\partial U_x}{\partial X}\right)+U_y\left(\frac{\partial U_x}{\partial Y}\right)=\frac{1}{N_{\mathrm{Re},L}}\left(\frac{\partial^2 U_x}{\partial Y^2}\right) \tag{5.7-28}$$

$$\frac{\partial U_x}{\partial X}+\frac{\partial U_Y}{\partial Y}=0 \tag{5.7-29}$$

$$U_x\left(\frac{\partial \Theta}{\partial X}\right)+U_y\left(\frac{\partial \Theta}{\partial Y}\right)=\frac{1}{N_{\mathrm{Re},L}N_{\mathrm{Pr}}}\left(\frac{\partial^2 \Theta}{\partial Y^2}\right) \tag{5.7-30}$$

These equations are often known as the Prandtl boundary layer equations. In the energy equation we have dropped the term $\partial^2\Theta/\partial X^2$ in accordance with the order-of-magnitude estimates given by Eqs. 5.7-24. The dimensionless form of the boundary conditions given by Eqs. 5.7-5 through 5.7-12 is

B.C.1′ $\qquad U_x = 1, \qquad X = 0 \qquad$ (5.7-31)

B.C.2′ $\qquad U_x = 1, \qquad Y = \pm\infty \qquad$ (5.7-32)

B.C.3′ $\qquad U_x = U_y = 0, \qquad Y = 0, \qquad X > 0 \qquad$ (5.7-33)

B.C.4′ $\qquad \Theta = 1, \qquad X = 0 \qquad$ (5.7-34)

B.C.5′ $\qquad \Theta = 1, \qquad Y = \pm\infty \qquad$ (5.7-35)

B.C.6′ $\qquad \Theta = 0, \qquad Y = 0, \qquad X > 0 \qquad$ (5.7-36)

Here we should note that the boundary conditions previously expressed at $x \to -\infty$ have now been imposed at $x = 0$. The reason for this is that in going from Eqs. 5.7-1 through 5.7-4 to Eqs. 5.7-28 through 5.7-30 we have changed from *elliptic* equations to *parabolic* equations.† The former are capable of accounting for disturbances (caused by the plate) propagating upstream, i.e., in the negative x-direction, while the latter are not. Because of this the boundary conditions for the parabolic equations must be placed at the leading edge of the plate in order that the mathematical problem be well posed. Note that because we have assumed that viscosity and density are independent of temperature, the equation of motion (Eq. 5.7-28) and the energy equation (Eq. 5.7-30) are uncoupled to the extent that the velocity field is entirely independent of the temperature field. If we were to take into account the temperature dependence of μ and ρ we would have a more realistic mathematical model of the flow process and the governing equations for U_x and U_y would be considerably more complex, in addition to being coupled with the energy equation. Because of this independence we can solve Eqs. 5.7-28 and 5.7-29 for the two components of velocity before going to the solution of Eq. 5.7-30.

Summary of Section 5.8

In this section we begin with the Prandtl boundary layer equations in dimensionless form

$$U_x\left(\frac{\partial U_x}{\partial X}\right)+U_y\left(\frac{\partial U_x}{\partial Y}\right)=\frac{1}{N_{\mathrm{Re},L}}\left(\frac{\partial U_x}{\partial Y^2}\right) \tag{5.7-28}$$

$$\frac{\partial U_x}{\partial X}+\frac{\partial U_y}{\partial Y}=0 \tag{5.7-29}$$

$$U_x\left(\frac{\partial \Theta}{\partial X}\right)+U_y\left(\frac{\partial \Theta}{\partial Y}\right)=\frac{1}{N_{\mathrm{Re},L}N_{\mathrm{Pr}}}\left(\frac{\partial^2 \Theta}{\partial Y^2}\right) \tag{5.7-30}$$

make use of the stream function

$$U_x=\frac{\partial \Psi}{\partial Y}, \qquad U_y=\frac{\partial \Psi}{\partial X} \tag{5.8-1}$$

†See P. M. Morse and H. Feshbach, *Methods of Theoretical Physics*, Chap. 6, McGraw-Hill Book Co., Inc., New York, 1953.

and a similarity transformation to reduce Eqs. 5.7-28 through 5.7-30 to

$$f''' + \tfrac{1}{2}ff'' = 0 \qquad (5.8\text{-}15)$$

$$\Theta'' + \tfrac{1}{2}N_{Pr}f\Theta' = 0 \qquad (5.8\text{-}20)$$

Here the primes (′) represent differentiation with respect to the transformation variable

$$\eta = Y\sqrt{N_{Re,L}/X}$$

These *ordinary* differential equations have been solved numerically and the results can be used to predict heat transfer rates or film heat transfer coefficients and Nusselt numbers. The results are accurately represented by the following three equations:

$$N_{Nu,av} = 0.664N_{Re,L}^{1/2}N_{Pr}^{1/3}, \qquad 0.6 \leq N_{Pr} \leq 10 \qquad (5.8\text{-}28)$$

$$N_{Nu,av} = 0.678N_{Re,L}^{1/2}N_{Pr}^{1/3}, \qquad N_{Pr} \to \infty \qquad (5.8\text{-}29)$$

$$N_{Nu,av} = 1.03N_{Re,L}^{1/2}N_{Pr}^{1/2}, \qquad N_{Pr} \to 0 \qquad (5.8\text{-}30)$$

In each case the Nusselt number is defined as

$$N_{Nu,av} = \frac{h_{av}L}{k}$$

where L is the length of the plate.

5.8 Exact Solution of the Laminar Boundary Layer Equations†

The exact solution of Eqs. 5.7-28 and 5.7-29 is obtained by first transforming the equations to an ordinary differential equation. This is accomplished in the same way that the transient heat conduction equation in Sec. 4.3 is transformed to an ordinary equation. The first step in obtaining the transformed equation is to represent U_x and U_y in terms of a stream function Ψ

$$U_x = \frac{\partial \Psi}{\partial Y}, \qquad U_y = -\frac{\partial \Psi}{\partial X} \qquad (5.8\text{-}1)$$

so that the continuity equation is satisfied and Eq. 5.7-28 takes the form

$$\frac{\partial \Psi}{\partial Y}\left(\frac{\partial^2 \Psi}{\partial X\, \partial Y}\right) - \frac{\partial \Psi}{\partial X}\left(\frac{\partial^2 \Psi}{\partial Y^2}\right) = \frac{1}{N_{Re,L}}\left(\frac{\partial^3 \Psi}{\partial Y^3}\right) \qquad (5.8\text{-}2)$$

If we try (as we did in Sec. 4.3) for a solution of the form

$$\Psi(X, Y) = \Psi[\eta(X, Y)] \qquad (5.8\text{-}3)$$

where

$$\eta = aX^bY^c \qquad (5.8\text{-}4)$$

we encounter difficulties, for there is no choice of a, b, and c which will allow Eq. 5.8-2 to be transformed to an ordinary differential equation. If we persist in our hunt for a solution and try a function of the form

$$\Psi[X, Y] = g(X)f[\eta(X, Y)] \qquad (5.8\text{-}5)$$

where η is again given by Eq. 5.8-4, we obtain

$$N_{Re,L}\left\{-ff''\left[\frac{dg}{dX}a^{-1}X^{-b}\right] + (f')^2\left[\frac{dg}{dX}a^{-1}X^{-b} + ga^{-1}bX^{-(b+1)}\right]\right\} = f''' \qquad (5.8\text{-}6)$$

Here the primes indicate differentiation with respect to η, and we have chosen $c = 1$ in Eq. 5.8-4. In order that this transformation be a satisfactory one we require that the terms in brackets must be functions of η

†It is strongly recommended that Sec. 4.3 be studied before this section is undertaken.

alone. The simplest way in which this could be accomplished is for these terms to be constant. With the hope that this is possible we set

$$N_{\mathrm{Re},L}\left[\left(\frac{dg}{dX}\right)a^{-1}X^{-b}\right]=C_1 \tag{5.8-7}$$

$$N_{\mathrm{Re},L}\left[\left(\frac{dg}{dX}\right)a^{-1}X^{-b}+ga^{-1}bX^{-(b+1)}\right]=C_2 \tag{5.8-8}$$

Substitution of Eq. 5.8-7 into Eq. 5.8-8 leads to

$$N_{\mathrm{Re},L}[ga^{-1}bX^{-(b+1)}]=C_2-C_1 \tag{5.8-9}$$

and the function $g(X)$ can be expressed as

$$g(X)=\frac{a(C_2-C_1)X^{(b+1)}}{bN_{\mathrm{Re},L}} \tag{5.8-10}$$

Integration of Eq. 5.8-7 also leads to an expression for $g(X)$ which is given by

$$g(X)=\frac{aC_1X^{(b+1)}}{(b+1)N_{\mathrm{Re},L}}+C_3 \tag{5.8-11}$$

where C_3 is the constant of integration. Comparison of Eqs. 5.8-10 and 5.8-11 indicates that

$$C_3=0 \tag{5.8-12}$$

$$\frac{C_2-C_1}{b}=\frac{C_1}{b+1} \tag{5.8-13}$$

From this we see that a successful transformation has been developed, i.e., Eq. 5.8-6 is an ordinary differential equation with constant coefficients, provided C_1 and C_2 are related by

$$C_2=C_1\left(\frac{2b+1}{b+1}\right) \tag{5.8-14}$$

For convenience we choose $b=-\frac{1}{2}$ so that $C_2=0$. Traditionally the term $2aC_1$ is chosen to be $\sqrt{N_{\mathrm{Re},L}}$ so that

$$\eta=Y\sqrt{N_{\mathrm{Re},L}/X}$$

$$g(X)=\sqrt{X/N_{\mathrm{Re},L}}$$

With these choices our governing equation, Eq. 5.8-6, reduces to

$$f'''+\tfrac{1}{2}ff''=0 \tag{5.8-15}$$

Some questions can be asked about this development: (1) After finding that the form suggested by Eq. 5.8-4 was unsatisfactory why was Eq. 5.8-5 tried? (2) Why is the term $2aC_1$ taken to be $\sqrt{N_{\mathrm{Re},L}}$? Why not zero or ten? (3) Why was the coefficient b set equal to $\frac{1}{2}$? Why not 1.0? A hasty set of answers to these questions would be: (1) Qualitative arguments [6] can be put forth in favor of the form of Eq. 5.8-5, but in the final analysis that form is used because it has been found to work. (2) Any nonzero constant would do. The choice of $\sqrt{N_{\mathrm{Re},L}}$ simply puts the final equation in a relatively neat form. Setting this term equal to zero would require that $g(X)$ be a constant and Eq. 5.8-5 would reduce to Eq. 5.8-3, which we already know is an unsatisfactory expression. (3) Setting the coefficient of b equal to $-\frac{1}{2}$ yields a simpler differential equation for $f(\eta)$ since it eliminates the term $(f')^2$.

To complete our formulation of this problem we must supply some boundary conditions to go along with Eq. 5.8-15. Expressing the components of the velocity as

$$U_x=\frac{\partial\Psi}{\partial Y}=g(X)f'\left(\frac{\partial\eta}{\partial Y}\right) \tag{5.8-16}$$

$$=f'$$

$$U_y = -\frac{\partial \Psi}{\partial X} = -\left(\frac{dg}{dX}\right) f(\eta) - g(X) f' \frac{\partial \eta}{\partial X}$$
$$= [\eta f'(\eta) - f(\eta)]/2\sqrt{X N_{\mathrm{Re},L}} \qquad (5.8\text{-}17)$$

the boundary conditions B.C.1′, B.C.2′, and B.C.3′ take the form

B.C.1″ $\qquad f' = 1, \quad \eta = \infty \qquad$ (5.8-18a)

B.C.2″ $\qquad f = f' = 0, \quad \eta = 0 \qquad$ (5.8-18b)

B.C.3″ $\qquad f' = 1, \quad \eta = \infty \qquad$ (5.8-18c)

Here we see that B.C.3″ is the same as B.C.1″, and we should remember that the same situation occurred when we used a similarity transformation in Sec. 4.3. Eq. 5.8-15 has been solved numerically by Howarth [7] subject to the boundary conditions given by Eqs. 5.8-18 and the results are listed in Table 5.8-1. These results can be used to specify the components of the velocity in Eq. 5.7-30, thus allowing us to solve for the dimensionless temperature field. In addition they can be used to deduce that the hydrodynamic boundary layer thickness, i.e., the point at which $v_x = 0.99 u_\infty$, occurs at $\eta = 4.9$ or $\delta_H = 4.9\sqrt{\nu x / u_\infty}$.

Directing our attention to Eq. 5.7-30, the boundary layer form of the thermal energy equation, we *assume* that a similarity transform exists for Θ and write

$$\Theta(X, Y) = \Theta[\eta(X, Y)] \qquad (5.8\text{-}19)$$

where $\eta(X, Y)$ is given by

$$\eta = Y\sqrt{\frac{N_{\mathrm{Re},L}}{X}}$$

Substituting Eqs. 5.8-16 and 5.8-17 for U_x and U_y into Eq. 5.7-30 and evaluating the derivatives on the basis of Eq. 5.8-19 yields

$$\left(\frac{d^2\Theta}{d\eta^2}\right) + \frac{1}{2} N_{\mathrm{Pr}} f(n) \left(\frac{d\Theta}{d\eta}\right) = 0 \qquad (5.8\text{-}20)$$

Here we see that our assumption that Θ could be expressed in terms of a single variable η was satisfactory and the partial differential equation (Eq. 5.7-30) could be transformed to an ordinary differential equation.

Examination of the boundary conditions for Θ (Eqs. 5.7-34 through 5.7-36) leads us to the following set of conditions:

B.C.4″ $\qquad \Theta = 1, \quad X = 0, \quad 0 \leqslant Y \leqslant \infty \qquad$ (5.8-21a)

B.C.5″ $\qquad \Theta = 0, \quad Y = 0, \quad X > 0 \qquad$ (5.8-21b)

B.C.6″ $\qquad \Theta = 1, \quad Y = \infty, \quad X > 0 \qquad$ (5.8-21c)

In terms of the transformation variable η these boundary conditions take the form

B.C.4‴ $\qquad \Theta = 1, \quad \eta = \infty \qquad$ (5.8-22a)

B.C.5‴ $\qquad \Theta = 0, \quad \eta = 0 \qquad$ (5.8-22b)

B.C.6‴ $\qquad \Theta = 1, \quad \eta = \infty \qquad$ (5.8-22c)

Once again we see that boundary conditions are satisfactorily expressed in terms of η and the one boundary condition becomes superfluous in terms of the transformation variable. We can solve Eq. 5.8-20 by first reducing the order

$$P = \frac{d\Theta}{d\eta}, \qquad \frac{dP}{d\eta} = \frac{d^2\Theta}{d\eta^2}$$

leading to

$$\frac{dP}{d\eta} + \frac{1}{2} N_{\mathrm{Pr}} f P = 0 \qquad (5.8\text{-}23)$$

Table 5.8-1 Results for Exact Solution for Laminar Boundary Layer

$\eta = y\sqrt{\frac{u_\infty}{\nu x}}$	f	$f' = \frac{v_x}{u_\infty}$	f''	$\eta = y\sqrt{\frac{u_\infty}{\nu x}}$	f	$f' = \frac{v_x}{u_\infty}$	f''
0	0	0	0.33206	4.4	2.69238	0.97587	0.03897
0.2	0.00664	0.06641	0.33199	4.6	2.88826	0.98269	0.02948
0.4	0.02656	0.13277	0.33147	4.8	3.08534	0.98779	0.02187
0.6	0.05974	0.19894	0.33008	5.0	3.28329	0.99155	0.01591
0.8	0.10611	0.26471	0.32739	5.2	3.48189	0.99425	0.01134
1.0	0.16557	0.32979	0.32301	5.4	3.68094	0.99616	0.00793
1.2	0.23795	0.39378	0.31659	5.6	3.88031	0.99748	0.00543
1.4	0.32298	0.45627	0.30787	5.8	4.07990	0.99838	0.00365
1.6	0.42032	0.51676	0.29667	6.0	4.27964	0.99898	0.00240
1.8	0.52952	0.57477	0.28293	6.2	4.47948	0.99937	0.00155
2.0	0.65003	0.62977	0.26675	6.4	4.67938	0.99961	0.00098
2.2	0.78120	0.68132	0.24835	6.6	4.87931	0.99977	0.00061
2.4	0.92230	0.72899	0.22809	6.8	5.07928	0.99987	0.00037
2.6	1.07252	0.77246	0.20646	7.0	5.27926	0.99992	0.00022
2.8	1.23099	0.81152	0.18401	7.2	5.47925	0.99996	0.00013
3.0	1.39682	0.84605	0.16136	7.4	5.67924	0.99998	0.00007
3.2	1.56911	0.87609	0.13913	7.6	5.87924	0.99999	0.00004
3.4	1.74696	0.90177	0.11788	7.8	6.07923	1.00000	0.00002
3.6	1.92954	0.92333	0.09809	8.0	6.27923	1.00000	0.00001
3.8	2.11605	0.94112	0.08013	8.2	6.47923	1.00000	0.00001
4.0	2.30576	0.95552	0.06424	8.4	6.67923	1.00000	0.00000
4.2	2.49806	0.96696	0.05052	8.6	6.87923	1.00000	0.00000
				8.8	7.07923	1.00000	0.00000

Separation of variables and integration leads to

$$\ln\left[\frac{P(\eta)}{P(\eta=0)}\right] = -\int_{\xi=0}^{\xi=\eta} \frac{1}{2} N_{Pr} f(\xi)\, d\xi \tag{5.8-24}$$

which can be expressed in terms of Θ as

$$\frac{d\Theta}{d\eta} = \left(\frac{d\Theta}{d\eta}\right)_{\eta=0} \exp\left[-\int_{\xi=0}^{\xi=\eta} \frac{1}{2} N_{Pr} f(\xi)\, d\xi\right] \tag{5.8-25}$$

Integration with respect to η yields

$$\Theta(\eta) = \Theta(\eta=0) + \left(\frac{d\Theta}{d\eta}\right)_{\eta=0} \int_{\zeta=0}^{\zeta=\eta} \exp\left[-\int_{\xi=0}^{\xi=\zeta} \frac{1}{2} N_{Pr} f(\xi)\, d\xi\right] d\zeta \tag{5.8-26}$$

Here ξ and ζ are dummy variables of integration. Applying B.C.5‴ and B.C.6‴ yields

B.C.5‴ $$\Theta(\eta = 0) = 0$$

B.C.6‴ $$\left(\frac{d\Theta}{d\eta}\right)_{\eta=0} = \frac{1}{\displaystyle\int_{\zeta=0}^{\zeta=\infty} \exp\left[-\int_{\xi=0}^{\xi=\zeta} \frac{1}{2} N_{Pr} f(\xi)\, d\xi\right] d\zeta}$$

and our final expression for the dimensionless temperature Θ in a laminar boundary layer becomes

$$\Theta(\eta) = \frac{\displaystyle\int_{\zeta=0}^{\zeta=\eta} \exp\left[-\frac{1}{2} N_{Pr} \int_{\xi=0}^{\xi=\zeta} f(\xi)\, d\xi\right] d\zeta}{\displaystyle\int_{\zeta=0}^{\zeta=\infty} \exp\left[-\frac{1}{2} N_{Pr} \int_{\xi=0}^{\xi=\zeta} f(\xi)\, d\xi\right] d\zeta} \tag{5.8-27}$$

With the values of $f(\eta)$ available from Table 5.8-1, the integrals in Eq. 5.8-27 can be evaluated for specified values of the Prandtl number. This has been done [8] and the results for several values of N_{Pr} are shown in Fig. 5.8.1. A more detailed examination of the results will show that for $N_{\mathrm{Pr}} = 1.0$ the thermal boundary layer (i.e., the distance at which $\Theta = 0.01$) is just equal to the hydrodynamic boundary layer. For $N_{\mathrm{Pr}} = 0.7$, a value representative of most gases at standard conditions, the thermal boundary layer lies outside the hydrodynamic boundary layer, while for $N_{\mathrm{Pr}} > 3$ the thermal boundary layer is well inside the hydrodynamic boundary layer. Since the Prandtl number is simply the ratio of the kinematic viscosity to the thermal diffusivity, $N_{\mathrm{Pr}} = \nu/\alpha$, or the ratio of the *momentum diffusivity* to the *thermal diffusivity*, we should expect that when $\nu \gg \alpha$ the hydrodynamic boundary layer thickness would be much larger than the thermal boundary layer thickness. To clarify this point it might be helpful to remember that the thermal boundary layer thickness for transient heat transfer to a semi-infinite slab was given as

$$\delta_T = 3.6\sqrt{\alpha t}$$

in Sec. 4.3, while the hydrodynamic boundary layer thickness for the suddenly accelerated flat plate† was

$$\delta_H = 3.6\sqrt{\nu t}$$

Here we see that the ratio of the hydrodynamic to the thermal boundary layer thickness is just the square root of the Prandtl number.

$$(\delta_H/\delta_T) = \sqrt{\nu/\alpha} = N_{\mathrm{Pr}}^{1/2}$$

The solution for Θ given by Eq. 5.8-27 can be used to calculate the heat flux and thus an average Nusselt number. For Prandtl numbers near one Schlichting [6] suggests that the results are accurately represented by

$$N_{\mathrm{Nu,av}} = 0.664 N_{\mathrm{Re},L}^{1/2} N_{\mathrm{Pr}}^{1/3}, \qquad 0.6 \leq N_{\mathrm{Pr}} \leq 10 \tag{5.8-28}$$

In the limit as $N_{\mathrm{Pr}} \to \infty$ the result is only slightly different.

$$N_{\mathrm{Nu,av}} = 0.678 N_{\mathrm{Re},L}^{1/2} N_{\mathrm{Pr}}^{1/3}, \qquad N_{\mathrm{Pr}} \to \infty \tag{5.8-29}$$

For very small Prandtl numbers (i.e., less than equal to 10^{-2}) the limiting solution for $N_{\mathrm{Pr}} \to 0$ should be useful

$$N_{\mathrm{Nu,av}} = 1.03 N_{\mathrm{Re},L}^{1/2} N_{\mathrm{Pr}}^{1/2}, \qquad N_{\mathrm{Pr}} \to 0 \tag{5.8-30}$$

These results are certainly nice to have available; however, with only a small amount of effort we can develop approximate solutions for both the temperature and velocity profiles which are quite satisfactory.

†See Reference 2, Sec. 11.2.

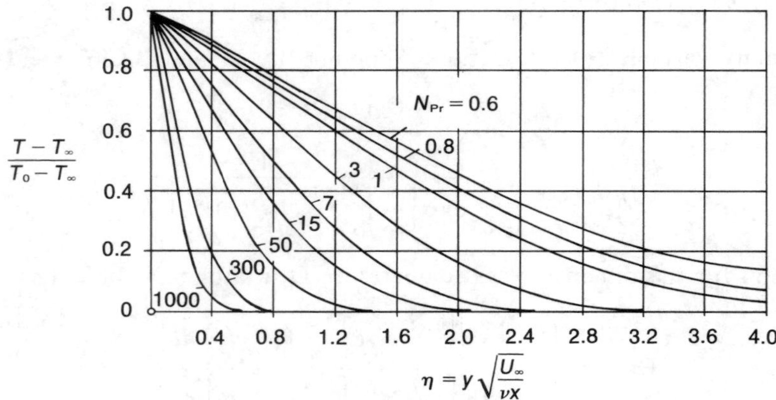

Fig. 5.8.1 Temperature profiles in a laminar boundary layer.

Not only will this provide us with simple expressions for the velocity and temperature fields, but in the course of developing an approximate solution we will be forced to think very carefully about the physical process under investigation.

Summary of Section 5.9

In this section we continue our analysis of Prandtl boundary equations. We begin with the governing equations

$$v_x \frac{\partial v_x}{\partial x} + v_y \frac{\partial v_x}{\partial y} = \nu \left(\frac{\partial^2 v_x}{\partial y^2}\right) \tag{5.9-1}$$

$$\frac{\partial v_x}{\partial x} + \frac{\partial v_y}{\partial y} = 0 \tag{5.9-2}$$

$$v_x \frac{\partial T}{\partial x} + v_y \frac{\partial T}{\partial y} = \alpha \left(\frac{\partial^2 T}{\partial y^2}\right) \tag{5.9-3}$$

and develop an approximate solution for the velocity field of the form

$$v_x = u_\infty \left[\frac{3}{2}\left(\frac{y}{\delta_H}\right) - \frac{1}{2}\left(\frac{y}{\delta_H}\right)^3\right] \tag{5.9-10}$$

$$v_y = \frac{3u_\infty}{4}\left(\frac{d\delta_H}{dx}\right)\left[\left(\frac{y}{\delta_H}\right)^2 - \frac{1}{2}\left(\frac{y}{\delta_H}\right)^4\right] \tag{5.9-13}$$

where the *hydrodynamic* boundary layer thickness is given by

$$\delta_H = 4.64\sqrt{\nu x / u_\infty} \tag{5.9-17}$$

The velocity field can be substituted into Eq. 5.9-3 and for $N_{\rm Pr} \geqslant 1$ we obtain an approximate solution for the temperature field

$$T = T_0 + (T_\infty - T_0)\left[\frac{3}{2}\left(\frac{y}{\delta_T}\right) - \frac{1}{2}\left(\frac{y}{\delta_T}\right)^3\right] \tag{5.9-25}$$

where the *thermal* boundary layer thickness is given by

$$\delta_T = 4.64 N_{{\rm Re},x}^{-1/2} N_{\rm Pr}^{-1/3} x \tag{5.9-35}$$

The approximate temperature field can be used to calculate heat transfer rates, film heat transfer coefficients, and the average Nusselt number which is given by

$$N_{\rm Nu,av} = 0.646 N_{{\rm Re},L}^{1/2} N_{\rm Pr}^{1/3}, \qquad 1 \leqslant N_{\rm Pr} \tag{5.9-52}$$

This result is in excellent agreement with the exact solution given by Eqs. 5.8-28 and 5.8-29, and compares quite favorably with experimental data as illustrated in Fig. 5.9.3.

*5.9 Approximate Solution of the Laminar Boundary Layer Equations

In Sec. 5.7 we found that the governing differential equations for heat transfer to a fluid flowing past a thin, flat plate could be simplified to

$$v_x \frac{\partial v_x}{\partial x} + v_y \frac{\partial v_x}{\partial y} = \nu \left(\frac{\partial^2 v_x}{\partial y^2}\right) \tag{5.9-1}$$

$$\frac{\partial v_x}{\partial x} + \frac{\partial v_y}{\partial y} = 0 \tag{5.9-2}$$

$$v_x \frac{\partial T}{\partial x} + v_y \frac{\partial T}{\partial y} = \alpha \left(\frac{\partial^2 T}{\partial y^2}\right) \tag{5.9-3}$$

provided δ_H and δ_T are small compared to the length of the plate, L. These equations are comparable to the *dimensionless* equations given by Eqs. 5.7-28 through 5.7-30.

The velocity field

In order to solve for the temperature field we must first determine v_x and v_y by solving Eqs. 5.9-1 and 5.9-2. Our attack on this problem is motivated by our knowledge that the boundary condition given by Eq. 5.7-6

$$v_x = u_\infty, \qquad y = \infty \tag{5.7-6}$$

can be replaced by the approximation

A.1 $$v_x = u_\infty, \quad y = \delta_H, \quad \text{an intuitive approximation} \tag{5.9-4}$$

Under these circumstances we can proceed to develop an approximate solution for v_x and v_y in the region $0 \leq y \leq \delta_H$ by integrating the momentum equation from $y = 0$ to $y = \delta_H$.

$$\int_0^{\delta_H} \left(v_x \frac{\partial v_x}{\partial x} + v_y \frac{\partial v_x}{\partial y} \right) dy = \nu \int_0^{\delta_H} \left(\frac{\partial^2 v_x}{\partial y^2} \right) dy \tag{5.9-5}$$

Our procedure here is identical to that followed in the analysis of the rectangular fin in Sec. 2.6,† and the analysis of transient heat transfer in a semi-infinite slab given in Sec. 4.3.‡ As in both of those studies, our next step is to specify v_x and v_y in terms of the unknown parameter, δ_H.

In addition to the approximation given by Eq. 5.9-4 we can use a boundary condition based on the principle that the velocity is continuous:

B.C.1 $$v_x = 0, \qquad y = 0, \quad \text{continuity of velocity} \tag{5.9-6}$$

According to our picture of the velocity field illustrated in Fig. 5.6.1 the velocity v_x is constant for $y > \delta_H$, thus the derivative $\partial v_x / \partial y$ is zero for $y > \delta_H$. It seems reasonable to require that the derivative of v_x be continuous in the neighborhood of $y = \delta_H$, thus we write

A.2 $$\frac{\partial v_x}{\partial y} = 0, \qquad y = \delta_H, \quad \text{follows logically from our picture of the velocity field} \tag{5.9-7}$$

Another bit of information about the velocity field can be obtained directly from Eq. 5.9-1. Noting that $v_x = v_y = 0$ at $y = 0$ we see that Eq. 5.9-1 requires that

DE.1 $$\frac{\partial^2 v_x}{\partial y^2} = 0, \qquad y = 0, \quad \text{from the differential equation} \tag{5.9-8}$$

On the basis of Eqs. 5.9-4, 5.9-6, 5.9-7, and 5.9-8 we can express v_x as a polynomial in (y/δ_H),

$$v_x = a + b\left(\frac{y}{\delta_H}\right) + c\left(\frac{y}{\delta_H}\right)^2 + d\left(\frac{y}{\delta_H}\right)^3 \tag{5.9-9}$$

and solve for the constants to find

$$v_x = u_\infty \left[\frac{3}{2}\left(\frac{y}{\delta_H}\right) - \frac{1}{2}\left(\frac{y}{\delta_H}\right)^3 \right] \tag{5.9-10}$$

We should note that the information used to construct this velocity profile came from several sources. Eqs. 5.9-4 and 5.9-7 are based on our picture of the velocity field and should be considered as *approximations*, while Eq. 5.9-6 results from the "no slip" requirement and should be thought of as a bona fide *boundary condition.* The condition given by Eq. 5.9-8 is derived directly from the *differential equation*, and it must not be thought of as a boundary condition. For an exact solution, such as that given in Sec. 5.8, Eq. 5.9-8 is completely superfluous; however, when developing approximate solutions of the equations of motion any and all information about the velocity field should be used.

To determine v_y we can integrate the continuity equation to obtain

$$v_y = v_y|_{y=0} - \int_0^y \left(\frac{\partial v_x}{\partial x} \right) dy \tag{5.9-11}$$

†See the equation preceding Eq. 2.6-7 for the step analogous to Eq. 5.9-5.

‡See the equation preceding Eq. 4.3-32 for the step analogous to Eq. 5.9-5.

Imposing the "no slip" boundary condition

B.C.2 $$v_y = 0, \qquad y = 0 \tag{5.9-12}$$

and making use of Eq. 5.9-10 to obtain an expression for $\partial v_x/\partial x$, we can perform the integration in Eq. 5.9-11 to obtain

$$v_y = \frac{3u_\infty}{4}\left(\frac{d\delta_H}{dx}\right)\left[\left(\frac{y}{\delta_H}\right)^2 - \frac{1}{2}\left(\frac{y}{\delta_H}\right)^4\right] \tag{5.9-13}$$

We now return to Eq. 5.9-5 and note that the right-hand-side can be easily integrated and condition A.2 imposed to yield

$$\int_0^{\delta_H}\left(v_x\frac{\partial v_x}{\partial x} + v_y\frac{\partial v_y}{\partial y}\right)dy = -\nu\frac{\partial v_x}{\partial y}\bigg|_{y=0} \tag{5.9-14}$$

Substituting Eqs. 5.9-10 and 5.9-13 for v_x and v_y into Eq. 5.9-14 and performing the integration leads to

$$\frac{39}{280}\left(\frac{d\delta_H}{dx}\right) = \frac{3\nu}{2u_\infty\delta_H} \tag{5.9-15}$$

Separating variables, integrating, and applying the boundary condition

$$\delta_H = 0, \qquad x = 0 \tag{5.9-16}$$

leads to an expression for the boundary layer thickness

$$\delta_H = 4.64\sqrt{\nu x/u_\infty} \tag{5.9-17}$$

Eqs. 5.9-10, 5.9-13, and 5.9-17 completely determine the velocity field which can now be used in Eq. 5.9-3. Before going on to the solution of the thermal energy equation it would be of interest to compare the result obtained in this analysis with the exact solution described in Sec. 5.8. In Fig. 5.9.1 we have shown the dimensionless velocity $U_x = v_x/u_\infty$ as a function of $y\sqrt{u_\infty/\nu x}$ and there we see excellent agreement between the exact and approximate solutions.

Example 5.9-1 Further consideration of the dimensional analysis of a finned tube

In Ex. 5.6-1 we performed a dimensional analysis for the finned tube shown in Fig. 5.6.1. For the case where all of the resistance to heat transfer is in the gas phase, $N_{Bi} \ll 1$, we found that the average Nusselt number was a function of five dimensionless parameters

$$N_{Nu,av} = N_{Nu,av}(N_{Pr}, N_{Re}, \beta, \gamma, \eta)$$

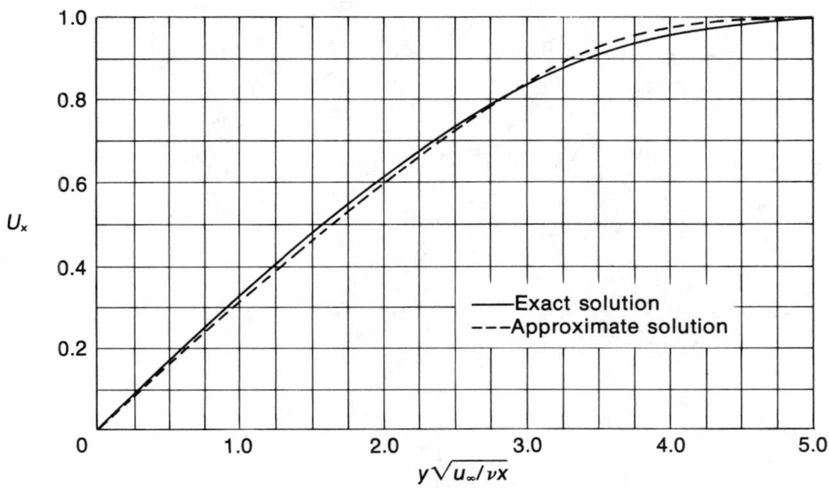

Fig. 5.9.1 Velocity profile in a laminar boundary layer on a flat plate.

where

$$\beta = r_1/r_0$$
$$\gamma = b/r_0$$
$$\eta = w/r_0$$

We need not determine the functional dependence of N_{Pr} since we have in mind using only air in our cooling system. The functional dependence of N_{Re} is easily determined by carrying out experiments for a wide range of air velocities; however, determining the functional dependence of β, γ, and η requires the construction of several different geometric configurations. Before entering into such an experimental program, one would always like to determine under what circumstances the functional dependence of β, γ, and η may be important.

To begin with, it seems quite plausible that the thickness of the fin would be unimportant provided it was small compared to the distance between the fins, i.e., $b \ll w$. This leads us to conclude that the Nusselt number is independent of γ provided $\gamma \ll \eta$. Such information is certainly of importance when planning an experimental program. At this point we should keep in mind that we are considering a case where the surface temperature is fixed at T_0, and a more realistic model would require that we consider the resistance to heat transfer in the fin. Under these circumstances decreasing the fin thickness would create a change in the surface temperature leading to a lower heat transfer rate and a lower measured value of the average film heat transfer coefficient. The dimensional analysis for the general case is offered as a problem at the end of this chapter.

In considering the effect that w, the fin spacing, has on the average heat transfer coefficient, we might come to the conclusion that the average heat transfer coefficient would be independent of w provided w was large enough so that the temperature and velocity fields around each fin are *not* influenced by the other fins. In this example we will concern ourselves with the velocity field which is sketched in Fig. 5.9.2. Certainly the velocity field is a complex one; however, we could get an *estimate* of the maximum boundary layer thickness by calculating δ_H for a flat plate of length $2r_1$. Referring to Eq. 5.9-17 we have

$$\delta_H = 4.64\sqrt{2\nu r_1/u_\infty}$$

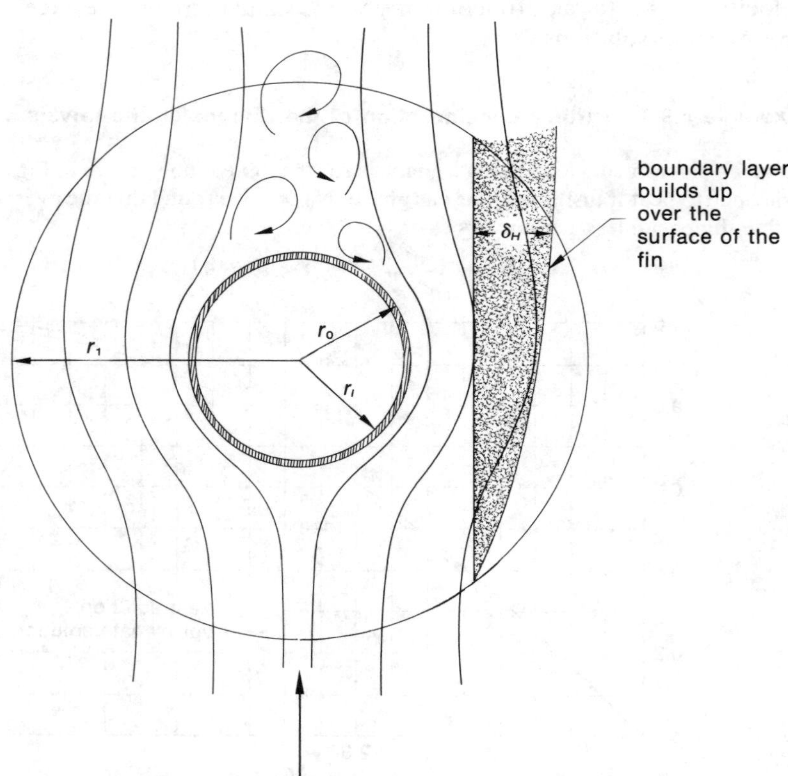

Fig. 5.9.2 Boundary layer formation on a circular fin.

Normally we define the Reynolds number for flow past a cylinder as

$$N_{\rm Re} = u_\infty D/\nu = 2u_\infty r_0/\nu$$

so that

$$\left(\frac{\delta_H}{r_0}\right) = 9.28\sqrt{\beta/N_{\rm Re}}$$

If $2\delta_H < w$ we expect the flow field around each fin to be independent of w. In terms of the above expression for δ_H we find that the Nusselt number should be independent of $\eta = w/r_0$ provided

$$\eta > 18\sqrt{\beta/N_{\rm Re}}$$

To summarize our thoughts about the functional dependence of the Nusselt number we note that

$$N_{\rm Nu,av} = N_{\rm Nu,av}(N_{\rm Pr}, N_{\rm Re}, \beta)$$

provided $\gamma \ll \eta$ and $18\sqrt{\beta/N_{\rm Re}} < \eta$. If these restrictions are satisfied, as they often are, the experimental program is greatly simplified for we need only vary the air velocity and the fin radius to completely determine the functional dependence of the Nusselt number.

The temperature field

In developing an approximate solution for the temperature we follow the analysis given in the previous paragraphs and given earlier in Secs. 2.6 and 4.3. Starting with the governing differential equation, Eq. 5.9-3, we integrate over the region $0 \leq y \leq \delta_T$ to obtain

$$\int_0^{\delta_T}\left(v_x\frac{\partial T}{\partial x} + v_y\frac{\partial T}{\partial y}\right)dy = \alpha\left[\frac{\partial T}{\partial y}\bigg|_{y=\delta_T} - \frac{\partial T}{\partial y}\bigg|_{y=0}\right] \tag{5.9-18}$$

Once again this result is of no use to us unless we can generate a suitable description for T as a function of y and δ_T. To do this we write down as much information as possible about the temperature profile. On the basis of B.C.8 in Sec. 5.7 (constant plate temperature) we write

B.C.1 $\quad T = T_0, \quad y = 0, \quad$ a boundary condition (5.9-19)

and the assumption that significant variations in the temperature are confined to the region $0 \leq y \leq \delta_T$ leads us to

A.1 $\quad T = T_\infty, \quad y = \delta_T, \quad$ based on the assumption that a well-defined thermal boundary layer exists (5.9-20)

Since T is constant for $y > \delta_T$, the derivative of T with respect to y must be zero, thus $q_y = 0$ for $y > \delta_T$. Since the heat flux is continuous it follows that $q_y = 0$ at $y = \delta_T$ and we can obtain

A.2 $\quad \dfrac{\partial T}{\partial y} = 0, \quad y = \delta_T, \quad$ continuity of heat flux (5.9-21)

Noting that

$$v_x = v_y = 0, \qquad y = 0 \tag{5.9-22}$$

we can infer from the governing differential equation that

DE.1 $\quad \dfrac{\partial^2 T}{\partial y^2} = 0, \quad y = 0, \quad$ from the differential equation (5.9-23)

Expressing T as a polynomial in (y/δ_T)

$$T = a + b\left(\frac{y}{\delta_T}\right) + c\left(\frac{y}{\delta_T}\right)^2 + d\left(\frac{y}{\delta_T}\right)^3 \tag{5.9-24}$$

and making use of Eqs. 5.9-19, 5.9-20, 5.9-21, and 5.9-23 leads to

$$T = T_0 + (T_\infty - T_0)\left[\frac{3}{2}\left(\frac{y}{\delta_T}\right) - \frac{1}{2}\left(\frac{y}{\delta_T}\right)^3\right] \tag{5.9-25}$$

Here we see that the y-dependence of T is similar to that of v_x given in Eq. 5.9-10.

We now return to Eq. 5.9-18 and substitute Eqs. 5.9-10, 5.9-13, and 5.9-25 for v_x, v_y, and T to obtain

$$u_\infty(T_\infty - T_0)\int_0^{\delta_T}\left\{\left[\frac{3}{2}\left(\frac{y}{\delta_H}\right)-\frac{1}{2}\left(\frac{y}{\delta_H}\right)^3\right]\left[-\frac{3}{2}\left(\frac{y}{\delta_T}\right)+\frac{3}{2}\left(\frac{y}{\delta_T}\right)^3\right]\frac{1}{\delta_T}\left(\frac{d\delta_T}{dx}\right) + \frac{3}{4}\left(\frac{d\delta_H}{dx}\right)\left[\left(\frac{y}{\delta_H}\right)^2-\frac{1}{2}\left(\frac{y}{\delta_H}\right)^4\right]\left[\frac{3}{2}-\frac{3}{2}\left(\frac{y}{\delta_T}\right)^2\right]\left(\frac{1}{\delta_T}\right)\right\}dy = -\frac{3(T_\infty - T_0)\alpha}{2\delta_T} \tag{5.9-26}$$

Note that in writing Eq. 5.9-26 we are assuming that $\delta_T \leq \delta_H$ for Eqs. 5.9-10 and 5.9-13 are only valid in the region $0 \leq y \leq \delta_H$. After some algebraic manipulation Eq. 5.9-26 can be put in the form

$$\int_0^{\delta_T}\left\{\left[-\frac{3}{2}\left(\frac{y}{\delta_T}\right)^2\mathcal{R}+\frac{3}{2}\left(\frac{y}{\delta_T}\right)^4\mathcal{R}+\frac{1}{2}\left(\frac{y}{\delta_T}\right)^4\mathcal{R}^3-\frac{1}{2}\left(\frac{y}{\delta_T}\right)^6\mathcal{R}^3\right]\frac{d\delta_T}{dx} + \frac{3}{4}\left[\left(\frac{y}{\delta_T}\right)^2\mathcal{R}^2-\left(\frac{y}{\delta_T}\right)^4\mathcal{R}^2-\frac{1}{2}\left(\frac{y}{\delta_T}\right)^4\mathcal{R}^4+\frac{1}{2}\left(\frac{y}{\delta_T}\right)^6\mathcal{R}^4\right]\frac{d\delta_H}{dx}\right\}dy = -\frac{\alpha}{u_\infty} \tag{5.9-27}$$

Here $\mathcal{R}$ is the ratio of the thermal boundary layer thickness to the hydrodynamic boundary layer thickness, $\mathcal{R} = \delta_T/\delta_H$. Integration and simplification of the terms leads to

$$\left[-\frac{1}{5}\mathcal{R}+\frac{1}{35}\mathcal{R}^3\right]\frac{d\delta_T}{dx}+\frac{3}{4}\left[\frac{2}{15}\mathcal{R}^2-\frac{1}{35}\mathcal{R}^4\right]\frac{d\delta_H}{dx} = -\frac{\alpha}{u_\infty\delta_T} \tag{5.9-28}$$

Eq. 5.9-28 can be looked upon as a first-order, nonlinear, ordinary differential equation for δ_T which must be solved subject to the single boundary condition

$$\text{B.C.1} \qquad \delta_T = 0, \qquad x = 0 \tag{5.9-29}$$

Under ordinary circumstances the solution of Eq. 5.9-28 would require numerical methods; however, our problem becomes quite simple if we assume that $\mathcal{R}$ is *independent* of x, i.e., the x-dependence of δ_T is identical to that of δ_H. In actual fact we know this to be true from the exact analysis given in Sec. 5.8, but even in the absence of that development, it would not be unreasonable to assume that $\mathcal{R}$ is independent of x or is a weak function of x. Under these circumstances we can write

$$\frac{d\delta_H}{dx} = \frac{1}{\mathcal{R}}\frac{d\delta_T}{dx} \tag{5.9-30}$$

and Eq. 5.9-28 is simplified to

$$\left[\frac{1}{10}\mathcal{R}-\frac{1}{140}\mathcal{R}^3\right]\frac{d\delta_T}{dx} = \frac{\alpha}{u_\infty\delta_T} \tag{5.9-31}$$

Here the term in brackets is constant so that we can separate variables, integrate, and impose B.C.1 to obtain

$$\left[\frac{1}{10}\mathcal{R}-\frac{1}{140}\mathcal{R}^3\right]\delta_T^2 = 2\alpha x/u_\infty \tag{5.9-32}$$

Substituting $\mathcal{R}\delta_H$ for δ_T allows us to write Eq. 5.9-32 as

$$\mathcal{R}^3 - \frac{1}{14}\mathcal{R}^5 = 20\alpha x/u_\infty\delta_H^2 \tag{5.9-33}$$

We can now draw upon our previous analysis of the flow field to express δ_H as

$$\delta_H = 4.64\sqrt{\nu x/u_\infty}$$

and write Eq. 5.9-33 in the form

$$\mathcal{R}^3 - \frac{1}{14}\mathcal{R}^5 = \frac{20}{(4.64)^2}\left(\frac{\alpha}{\nu}\right) = 0.93 N_{\text{Pr}}^{-1} \tag{5.9-34}$$

Here we see that as the Prandtl number becomes large (viscous oils) the ratio of the thermal boundary layer thickness to the hydrodynamic boundary layer thickness becomes small, i.e.,

$$\frac{\delta_T}{\delta_H} \to 0, \quad \text{as} \quad N_{\text{Pr}} \to \infty$$

For a Prandtl number of one we can use Eqs. 5.9-34 to find that

$$\delta_T = \delta_H, \quad \text{for } N_{\text{Pr}} = 1$$

For most gases at standard conditions the Prandtl number is about 0.7 and Eq. 5.9-34 would predict

$$\delta_T \sim 1.13\delta_H, \quad \text{for } N_{\text{Pr}} = 0.7$$

We must remember that our analysis was based on the assumption that $\delta_T \leqslant \delta_H$; nevertheless, Eq. 5.9-34 does correctly predict that the thermal boundary layer thickness for $N_{\text{Pr}} = 0.7$ is about 13 per cent larger than the hydrodynamic boundary layer thickness.

A reasonable approximation to Eq. 5.9-34 is

$$\mathscr{R} = N_{\text{Pr}}^{-1/3}, \quad \text{for } N_{\text{Pr}} \geqslant 0.7 \tag{5.9-35}$$

which leads to a thermal boundary layer thickness given by

$$\delta_T = 4.64 \left(\frac{x\nu}{u_\infty}\right)^{1/2} N_{\text{Pr}}^{-1/3} = 4.64 N_{\text{Re},x}^{-1/2} N_{\text{Pr}}^{-1/3} x \tag{5.9-36}$$

We can use this result, along with the temperature profile, to determine the heat flux at the surface of the plate.

$$q_y|_{y=0} = -k \frac{\partial T}{\partial y}\bigg|_{y=0} \tag{5.9-37}$$

Substituting Eq. 5.9-25 leads to

$$q_y|_{y=0} = -3k(T_\infty - T_0)/2\delta_T \tag{5.9-38}$$

and use of Eq. 5.9-36 yields

$$q_y|_{y=0} = \frac{-3k(T_\infty - T_0) N_{\text{Re},x}^{1/2} N_{\text{Pr}}^{1/3}}{2(4.64)x} \tag{5.9-39}$$

We should note that Eq. 5.9-39 predicts that the heat flux goes to infinity as $x \to 0$, thus we can conclude that Eq. 5.9-39 is not valid near the leading edge of the plate. It is in this region that the inequality

$$\frac{\partial^2 T}{\partial x^2} \ll \frac{\partial^2 T}{\partial y^2} \tag{5.9-40}$$

does not hold, thus the simplified form of the thermal energy equation given by Eq. 5.9-3 is not valid.

After developing an approximate solution to any problem it is always wise to try to determine the region in which the solution is valid. We can do this by examining the inequality listed above. From Eq. 5.9-25 we can obtain

$$\frac{\partial^2 T}{\partial x^2} = (T_\infty - T_0) \left\{ \frac{3}{2}\left(\frac{y}{\delta_T}\right) \left[\frac{2}{\delta_T^2}\left(\frac{d\delta_T}{dx}\right)^2 - \frac{1}{\delta_T}\left(\frac{d^2\delta_T}{dx^2}\right)\right] - \frac{1}{2}\left(\frac{y}{\delta_T}\right)^3 \left[\frac{12}{\delta_T^2}\left(\frac{d\delta_T}{dx}\right)^2 - \frac{3}{\delta_T}\left(\frac{d^2\delta_T}{dx^2}\right)\right]\right\} \tag{5.9-41}$$

$$\left(\frac{\partial^2 T}{\partial y^2}\right) = -3(T_\infty - T_0)\left(\frac{y}{\delta_T}\right)\left(\frac{1}{\delta_T^2}\right) \tag{5.9-42}$$

Combining Eqs. 5.9-41 and 5.9-42 and evaluating the derivatives at the center of the boundary layer, i.e., at

$y = 0.5\delta_T$, leads to

$$\frac{\left(\frac{\partial^2 T}{\partial x^2}\right)_{y=0.5\delta_T}}{\left(\frac{\partial^2 T}{\partial y^2}\right)_{y=0.5\delta_T}} = -\frac{1}{2}\left(\frac{d\delta_T}{dx}\right)^2 + \frac{9}{24}\delta_T\left(\frac{d^2\delta_T}{dx^2}\right) \tag{5.9-43}$$

In order to satisfy the inequality given by Eq. 5.9-40 we require

$$\left|-\frac{1}{2}\left(\frac{d\delta_T}{dx}\right)^2 + \frac{9}{24}\delta_T\left(\frac{d^2\delta_T}{dx^2}\right)\right| \ll 1 \tag{5.9-44}$$

Making use of Eq. 5.9-36 we find that this leads to

$$x \gg \left(\frac{21}{96}\right)(4.64)^2\left(\frac{\nu}{u_\infty}\right)N_{\text{Pr}}^{-2/3} \tag{5.9-45}$$

or in terms of the length Reynolds number we expect our boundary layer analysis to be satisfactory only if

$$N_{\text{Re},x} \gg 5N_{\text{Pr}}^{-2/3} \tag{5.9-46}$$

From this we conclude that if $N_{\text{Re},x}$ is on the order of 10^3 or larger, our analysis should provide reasonably satisfactory results for $N_{\text{Pr}} \geqslant 0.7$.

The film heat transfer coefficient

We should remember that at the beginning of this chapter one of our objectives was to learn something of the film heat transfer coefficient. Having determinined the temperature field and the heat flux, we are now in a position to derive an expression for the film heat transfer coefficient which is defined by the relation

$$q_y|_{y=0} \equiv h_{\text{loc}}(T_0 - T_\infty) \tag{5.9-47}$$

We should note that temperature difference used in this definition is chosen so that the film heat transfer coefficient will be a positive quantity. Substituting Eq. 5.9-39 into Eq. 5.9-47 leads to

$$h_{\text{loc}} = 0.323\left(\frac{k}{x}\right)N_{\text{Re},x}^{1/2}N_{\text{Pr}}^{1/3} = 0.323\,k\left(\frac{u_\infty}{\nu x}\right)^{1/2}\left(\frac{\nu}{\alpha}\right)^{1/3} \tag{5.9-48}$$

Since we are generally interested in the total rate of heat transfer between the plate and the flowing fluid, it is useful to know the average film heat transfer coefficient which is given by

$$h_{\text{av}} = \frac{1}{L}\int_0^L h_{\text{loc}}\,dx \tag{5.9-49}$$

Substitution of h_{loc} from Eq. 5.9-48 gives

$$h_{\text{av}} = 0.646\left(\frac{k}{L}\right)N_{\text{Re},L}^{1/2}N_{\text{Pr}}^{1/3} \tag{5.9-50}$$

Generally, calculated and experimentally determined film heat transfer coefficients are tabulated and correlated in terms of the dimensionless group N_{Nu} known as the Nusselt number which is defined as

$$N_{\text{Nu}} = hL/k \tag{5.9-51}$$

Here L is a characteristic length which is the length of the flat plate for the case under study. The local and average Nusselt numbers are given by

$$N_{\text{Nu,loc}} = 0.323N_{\text{Re},L}^{1/2}N_{\text{Pr}}^{1/3}X^{-1/2} \tag{5.9-52}$$

$$N_{\text{Nu,av}} = 0.646N_{\text{Re},L}^{1/2}N_{\text{Pr}}^{1/3} \tag{5.9-53}$$

where $X = x/L$. One of the useful aspects of the approximate solution that we have developed here is that the temperature field is represented by a simple polynomial and the results are easily used to calculate heat fluxes, film heat transfer coefficients, and Nusselt numbers.

Comparing Eq. 5.9-53 with Eqs. 5.8-28 and 5.8-29 indicates excellent agreement with the exact solution for Prandtl numbers ranging from 0.6 to ∞. Our analysis was clearly invalid for very small Prandtl numbers, and it will be left as an exercise for the student to develop an approximate solution for the limiting case $N_{\rm Pr} \rightarrow 0$.

While the agreement between the exact solution and the approximate solution is encouraging, the important comparison is between theory and experiment, and in Fig. 5.9.3 we show experimental data for air compared with the theoretical calculations. The agreement is excellent for length Reynolds numbers less than 2×10^5; above that value the boundary layer becomes turbulent and the Nusselt number (the dimensionless film heat transfer coefficient) begins to increase rapidly. In Chapters 6 and 7 we will study the effect of turbulence on heat transfer rates, and for the present we can conclude that our initial effort at calculating forced-convection heat transfer rates has been quite successful.

Example 5.9-2 Approximate analysis of the heat transfer rate for a finned tube

In an earlier discussion we conceded that the heat transfer rates for the finned tube shown in Fig. 5.6.1 should be studied experimentally. The dimensional analysis given in Ex. 5.6-1 and the additional information developed in Ex. 5.9-1 indicated that the Nusselt number dependence was given by

$$N_{\rm Nu,av} = N_{\rm Nu,av}(N_{\rm Pr}, N_{\rm Re}, \beta)$$

provided $\gamma \ll \eta$ and $\eta > 18\sqrt{\beta/N_{\rm Re}}$. Remember that γ, β, and η are the geometrical parameters given by

$$\gamma = b/r_0, \qquad \beta = r_1/r_0, \qquad \eta = w/r_0$$

Experimental determination of the Nusselt number dependence on $N_{\rm Re}$ and β will require that we vary the air velocity and fin radius; however, before plunging into a costly experimental study it would be wise to develop an approximate solution for the heat transfer rate. Because of the complexity of the flow field illustrated in Fig. 5.9.2, it seems likely that we will be restricted to a very crude approximation for the velocity and temperature fields. Nevertheless, an analytic solution will be of considerable help in planning an experimental program.

In order to simplify the process under consideration we construct the hypothetical flow field illustrated in Fig. 5.9.4. Here we have straightened out the streamlines and assumed that a boundary layer type of flow exists in the wake of the cylinder. This will certainly overestimate the heat transfer rate in the wake region; however, the analysis should give us the proper order-of-magnitude for the total heat transfer rate and should give a general indication of the functional dependence of $N_{\rm Nu}$ on $N_{\rm Pr}$, $N_{\rm Re}$, and β.

Given the velocity field shown in Fig. 5.9.4 we can use the approximate solution for the temperature field in a laminar boundary layer given by Eqs. 5.9-25 and 5.9-36.

$$T = T_0 + (T_\infty - T_0)\left[\frac{3}{2}\left(\frac{y}{\delta_T}\right) - \frac{1}{2}\left(\frac{y}{\delta_T}\right)^3\right]$$

$$\delta_T = 4.64\left(\frac{x\nu}{u_\infty}\right)^{1/2} N_{\rm Pr}^{-1/3}$$

Here x represents the distance from the leading edge of the fin. The heat flux at any point on the fin is given by

$$q_y = -k\left.\frac{\partial T}{\partial y}\right|_{y=0} = \frac{3k(T_0 - T_\infty)}{2\delta_T}$$

Forming the integral of q_y over the surface of the fin yields the total heat transfer rate for one side.

$$\dot{Q} = \int_A q_y \, dA = 2\int_{z=0}^{z=r_0}\int_{x=0}^{x=\sqrt{r_1^2-z^2}-\sqrt{r_0^2-z^2}} q_y \, dx \, dz + \int_{z=r_0}^{z=r_1}\int_{x=0}^{x=2\sqrt{r_1^2-z^2}} q_y \, dx \, dz$$

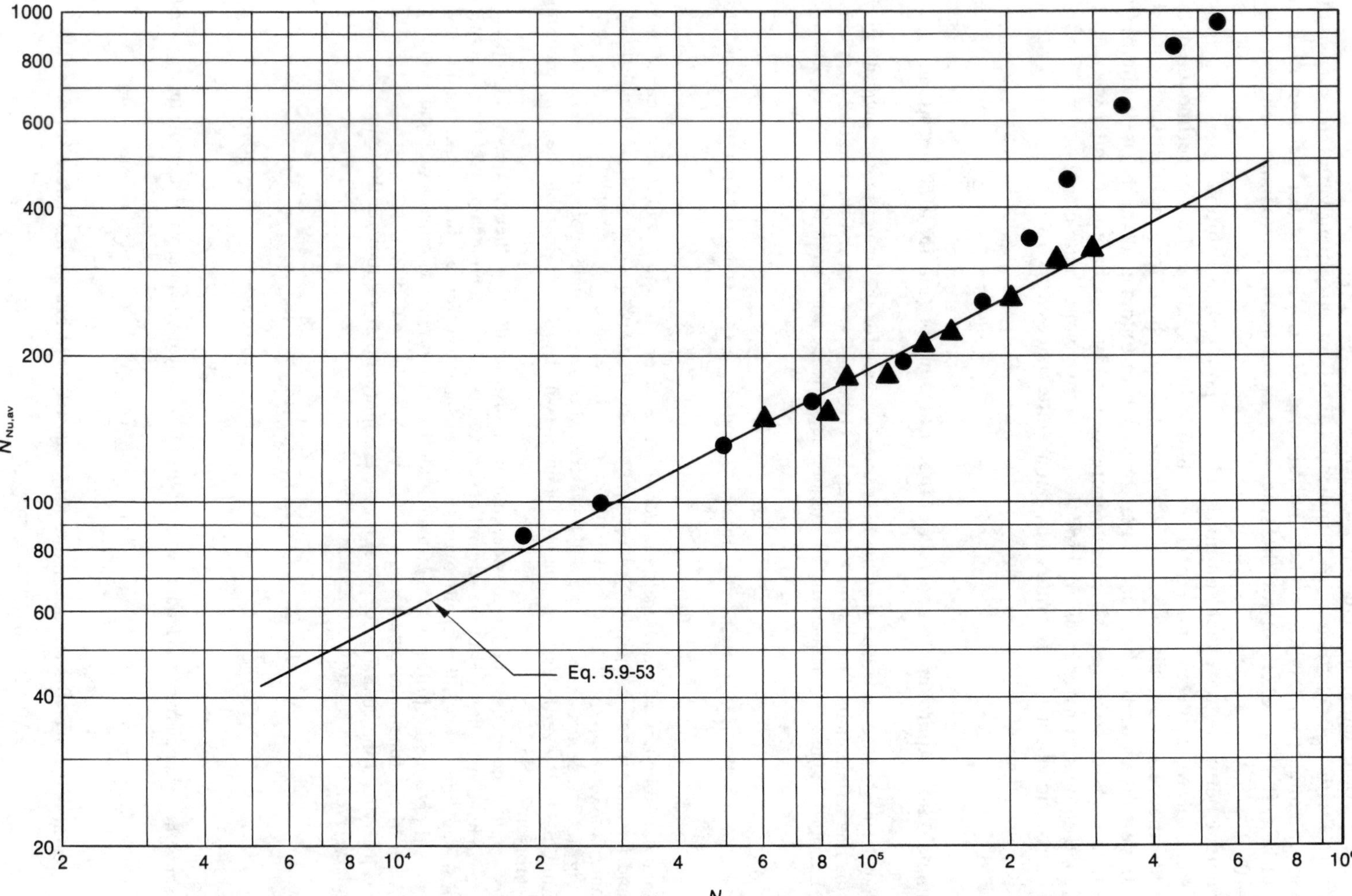

Fig. 5.9.3 Comparison of theory and experiment for the flow of air past a flat plate.

▲ A. Edwards and B. N. Furber, "The Influence of Free Steam Turbulence on Heat Transfer by Convection from an Isolated Region of a Plane Surface in Parallel Air Flow," *Proc. Inst. Mech. Engrs.* (*London*) **170**, 941 (1956).

● Experimental data from G. V. Parmelee and R. G. Huebscher, "Heat Transfer by Forced Convection Along a Smooth Flat Surface," *Heating, Piping and Air Conditioning* **19**, No. 8, 115 (1947).

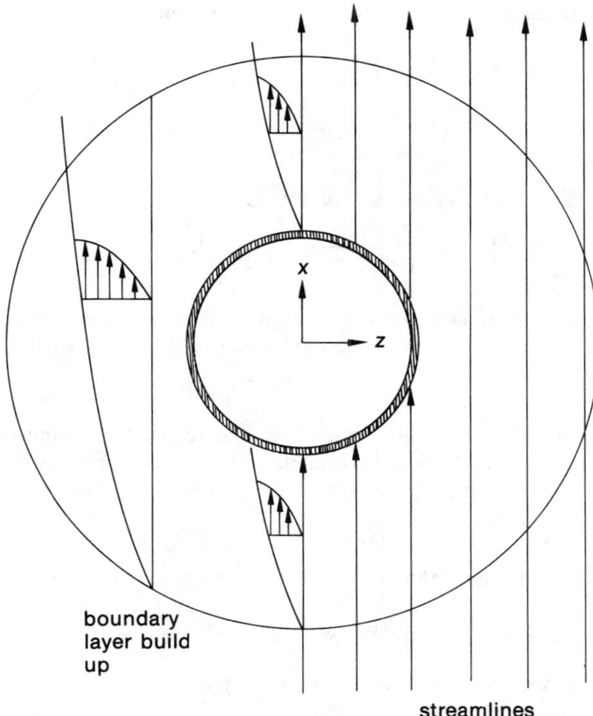

Fig. 5.9.4 Hypothetical flow field around a cylindrical fin.

Here one must remember that x is the distance measured along individual streamlines, while z is the distance measured from the center to the outer edge of the fin where $z = r_1$. The first term in the expression for $\dot{Q}$ represents the heat transfer rate in region bounded by $z = 0$ and $z = r_0$, and according to the model the rate in front of the tube is just equal to the rate in the wake of the tube. The second term in the expression for $\dot{Q}$ represents the heat transfer rate in the region bounded by $z = r_0$ and $z = r_1$. In that region the length of the individual streamlines is given by $2\sqrt{r_1^2 - z^2}$. Substitution of the expression for q_y and δ_T leads to

$$\dot{Q} = \left\{\frac{3k(T_0 - T_\infty)N_{\mathrm{Pr}}^{1/3}}{2(4.64)(\nu/u_\infty)^{1/2}}\right\}\left\{2\int_{z=0}^{z=r_0}\int_{x=0}^{x=\sqrt{r_1^2-z^2}-\sqrt{r_0^2-z^2}} x^{-1/2}\,dx\,dz + \int_{z=r_0}^{z=r_1}\int_{x=0}^{x=2\sqrt{r_1^2-z^2}} x^{-1/2}\,dx\,dz\right\}$$

Carrying out the integration with respect to x leads to

$$\dot{Q} = \left\{\frac{3k(T_0 - T_\infty)N_{\mathrm{Pr}}^{1/3}}{4.64(\nu/u_\infty)^{1/2}}\right\}\left\{2\int_{z=0}^{z=r_o}\left(\sqrt{r_1^2 - z^2} - \sqrt{r_0^2 - z^2}\right)^{1/2} dz + \int_{z=0}^{z=r_1}\left(2\sqrt{r_1^2 - z^2}\right)^{1/2} dz\right\}$$

Remembering that $\beta = r_1/r_0$ and defining $Z = z/r_0$ we can put this result in dimensionless form

$$\dot{Q} = \left\{\frac{3k(T_0 - T_\infty)N_{\mathrm{Pr}}^{1/3}N_{\mathrm{Re}}^{1/2}r_0}{4.64\sqrt{2}}\right\}\left\{2\int_{Z=0}^{Z=1}\left(\sqrt{\beta^2 - Z^2} - \sqrt{1 - Z^2}\right)^{1/2} dZ + \int_{Z=0}^{Z=\beta}\left(2\sqrt{\beta^2 - Z^2}\right)^{1/2} dZ\right\}$$

where $N_{\mathrm{Re}} = u_\infty 2r_0/\nu$. We now *define* the average film heat transfer coefficient by

$$\dot{Q} = h_{\mathrm{av}}A(T_0 - T_\infty)$$

where the area of the fin is given by

$$A = \frac{1}{2}\pi(r_1^2 - r_0^2)$$

Comparing this with our derived expression for $\dot{Q}$ leads to

$$h_{\mathrm{av}}\left(\frac{\pi}{2}\right)(r_1^2 - r_0^2)(T_0 - T_\infty) = \left\{\frac{3k(T_0 - T)N_{\mathrm{Pr}}^{1/3}N_{\mathrm{Re}}^{1/2}r_0}{4.64\sqrt{2}}\right\}\Omega$$

where Ω represents the integrals. Defining the average Nusselt number

$$N_{\text{Nu,av}} = \frac{h_{\text{av}} 2 r_0}{k}$$

eventually leads to the expression

$$N_{\text{Nu,av}} = 0.58 N_{\text{Re}}^{1/2} N_{\text{Pr}}^{1/3} \mathcal{F}(\beta)$$

where the geometrical effects are accounted for by $\mathcal{F}(\beta)$

$$\mathcal{F}(\beta) = \frac{1}{\beta^2 - 1}\left\{2\int_{Z=0}^{Z=1} \left(\sqrt{\beta^2 - Z^2} - \sqrt{1 - Z^2}\right)^{1/2} dZ + \int_{Z=1}^{Z=\beta} \left(2\sqrt{\beta^2 - Z^2}\right)^{1/2} dZ\right\}$$

The function $\mathcal{F}(\beta)$ has to be evaluated numerically and the results are shown in Fig. 5.9.5. We can represent $\mathcal{F}(\beta)$ with surprising accuracy with $1.25/\sqrt{\beta - 1}$ so that our final expression for the average Nusselt number is

$$N_{\text{Nu,av}} = 0.72 N_{\text{Re}}^{1/2} N_{\text{Pr}}^{1/3} (\beta - 1)^{-1/2}$$

In the absence of experimental data one could use this result to estimate the average film heat transfer coefficient for a cylindrical fin. In addition, this result serves as an excellent guide for correlating experimental data. One would certainly be inclined to correlate data with an expression of the form

$$N_{\text{Nu,av}} = a N_{\text{Re}}^{b} N_{\text{Pr}}^{c} (\beta - 1)^{d}$$

where a, b, c, and d are to be determined from the experimental results.

Very small and very large Prandtl numbers

Although our previous analysis was restricted to the case where $\delta_H > \delta_T$, we can draw upon Eq. 5.9-34 and our intuition to conclude that

$$\frac{\delta_H}{\delta_T} \sim N_{\text{Pr}}^{1/3} \tag{5.9-54}$$

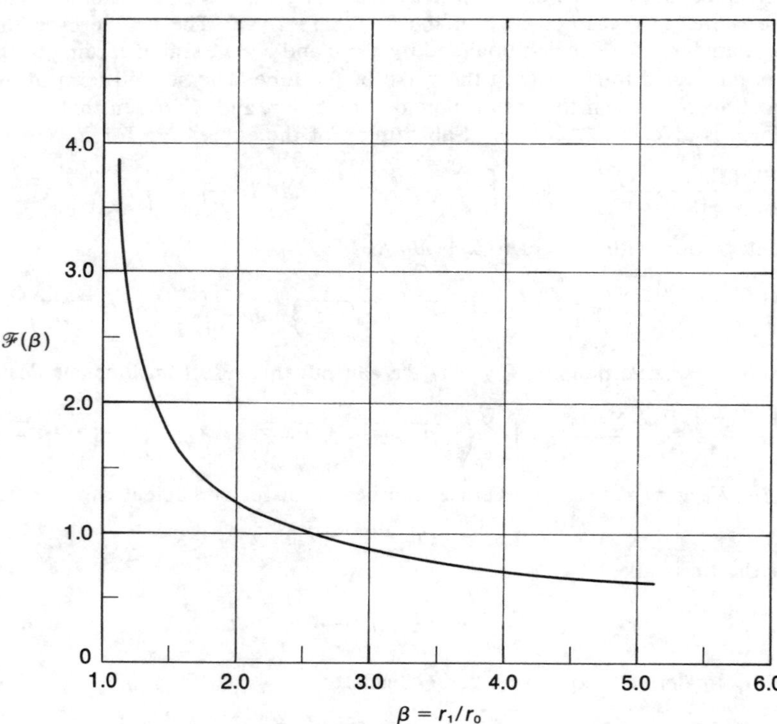

Fig. 5.9.5 Functional dependence of the Nusselt number on r_1/r_0.

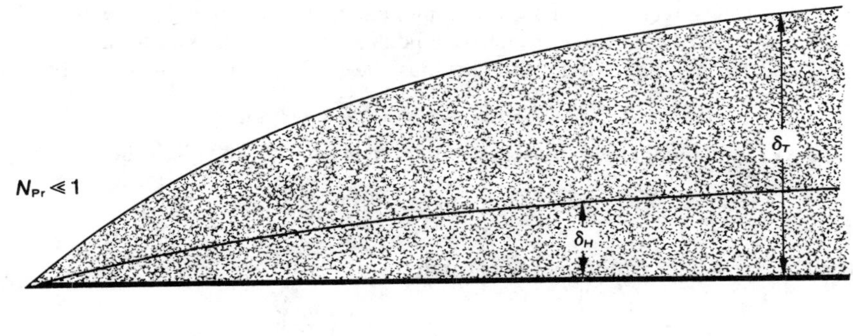

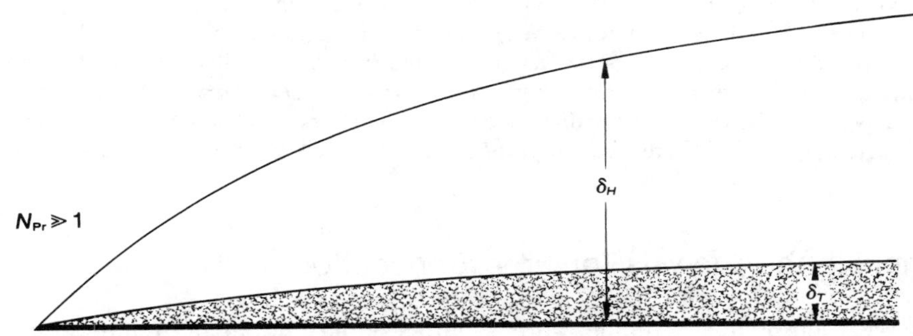

Fig. 5.9.6 Thermal and hydrodynamic (momentum) boundary layers for small and large Prandtl numbers.

Remember that the Prandtl number is simply the ratio of the *momentum diffusivity*, ν, to the *thermal diffusivity*, α,

$$N_{\mathrm{Pr}} = \nu/\alpha \tag{5.9-55}$$

thus we would expect the *momentum boundary layer thickness*, δ_H, to be larger than the *thermal boundary layer thickness*, δ_T, when the Prandtl number is greater than one. Conversely, when $\alpha > \nu$ we would expect the thermal boundary layer thickness to be larger, i.e., $\delta_T > \delta_H$. These ideas are illustrated in Fig. 5.9.6.

Prandtl numbers much less than one are encountered only with liquid metals where

$$N_{\mathrm{Pr}} \sim 10^{-2}, \quad \text{for liquid metals}$$

and for the limiting case of $N_{\mathrm{Pr}} \rightarrow 0$ one can use Eq. 5.8-27 to show that

$$N_{\mathrm{Nu,av}} = 1.03 N_{\mathrm{Re},L}^{1/2} N_{\mathrm{Pr}}^{1/2}, \quad \text{for } N_{\mathrm{Pr}} \rightarrow 0 \tag{5.9-56}$$

Prandtl numbers much larger than one are usually encountered with viscous oils. For $N_{\mathrm{Pr}} \gg 1$ the thermal boundary layer is confined to a region very near the solid surface and one need only know the velocity profile in this region in order to solve the thermal energy equation. Because of the simplified nature of the thermal energy equation for large Prandtl number it is possible to solve a variety of more complex boundary layer heat transfer problems for this condition [9].

Summary of Section 5.10

In this section we analyze the continuity equation, the equations of motion, and the thermal energy equation for flows which are caused by buoyancy forces. Such flows are complex because the thermal energy equation and the equations of motion are coupled, for it is the temperature field which causes the density variations which in turn cause the flow which influences the temperature field.

The analysis of the governing equations is complicated by the coupling of the thermal energy equation and the equations of motion; however, aside from that difficulty the treatment is quite similar to that presented in Sec. 5.6 and we find that the average Nusselt number has the following functional dependence

$$N_{\mathrm{Nu,av}} = \mathscr{F}(N_{\mathrm{Pr}}, N_{\mathrm{Gr}}, \boldsymbol{\lambda}, N^{\mathrm{I}}_{\mathrm{BC}}, N^{\mathrm{II}}_{\mathrm{BC}}) \tag{5.10-34}$$

Here N_{Pr} is the Prandtl number previously encountered in Sec. 5.6, and N_{Gr} is the Grashof number given by

$$N_{\mathrm{Gr}} = \frac{\beta(T_0 - T_\infty)gL^3}{\nu^2} \tag{5.10-28}$$

where β is the coefficient of thermal expansion

$$\beta = -\frac{1}{\rho}\left(\frac{\partial \rho}{\partial T}\right)_p \tag{5.10-23}$$

The Grashof number essentially replaces the Reynolds number for free-convection flows, for when N_{Gr} is large the free-convection currents are large and when $N_{\mathrm{Gr}} \to 0$ the fluid motion ceases.

The parameter $\boldsymbol{\lambda}$ is the unit vector representing the orientation of the system relative to the direction of the gravitational force. It should be clear that a liquid heated from below will undergo a different type of fluid motion than a liquid heated from above, thus there is an important dependence of the Nusselt number on $\boldsymbol{\lambda}$. The parameters $N^{\mathrm{I}}_{\mathrm{BC}}$ and $N^{\mathrm{II}}_{\mathrm{BC}}$ represent the dimensionless parameters which appear in the boundary conditions for the velocity and temperature fields respectively, and as always these parameters are the ones most easily overlooked.

*5.10 Dimensional Analysis for Free Convection

If we immerse a flat plate at a temperature T_0 into a pool of liquid at a temperature T_∞ where $T_0 > T_\infty$, free or "natural" convection currents are set up such as those illustrated in Fig. 5.10.1. If the temperature difference $T_0 - T_\infty$ is large the currents are large and as $(T_0 - T_\infty) \to 0$ the fluid motion disappears. Clearly, the motion is caused by the density variations, and we must take into account the temperature dependence of the density if we are to analyze natural convection phenomena. The development presented here will be an extension of that given in Sec. 5.6 where we assumed that the density was constant; however, we will retain the simplification that all other physical properties besides the density are constant.

In order to allow for variations in the density we must re-examine all the governing differential equations. We begin with the continuity equation which must be written as

$$\frac{\partial \rho}{\partial t} + \nabla \cdot (\rho \mathbf{v}) = 0 \tag{5.10-1}$$

In our analysis of the equations of motion we return to Eq. 5.2-19

$$\rho\left(\frac{\partial \mathbf{v}}{\partial t} + \mathbf{v} \cdot \nabla \mathbf{v}\right) = -\nabla p + \rho \mathbf{g} + \nabla \cdot \boldsymbol{\tau} \tag{5.10-2}$$

and note that it is not restricted to incompressible flows. Considering only Newtonian fluids we express the viscous stress tensor as

$$\boldsymbol{\tau} = \mu(\nabla \mathbf{v} + \nabla \mathbf{v}^{\mathrm{T}}) + \mathbf{U}(\kappa - \tfrac{2}{3}\mu)\nabla \cdot \mathbf{v} \tag{5.10-3}$$

and substitute it into Eq. 5.10-2 to obtain

$$\rho\left(\frac{\partial \mathbf{v}}{\partial t} + \mathbf{v} \cdot \nabla \mathbf{v}\right) = -\nabla p + \rho \mathbf{g} + \mu \nabla^2 \mathbf{v} + (\kappa + \tfrac{1}{3}\mu)\nabla(\nabla \cdot \mathbf{v}) \tag{5.10-4}$$

Here we have taken the shear and bulk coefficients of viscosity, μ and κ, to be constant. Eq. 5.10-4 is a satisfactory form of the equations of motion for our study, and now we need only choose an appropriate form of the thermal energy equation in order to complete our formulation of the governing differential equations. We return to Eq. 5.5-10 and neglect viscous dissipation and reversible work and take the thermal conductivity to be constant so that the thermal energy equation takes the form

$$\rho c_p \left(\frac{\partial T}{\partial t} + \mathbf{v} \cdot \nabla T \right) = k \nabla^2 T + \Phi \tag{5.10-5}$$

We have already simplified our analysis of this phenomenon by assuming that only the density is a function of temperature, while all other properties are constant; however, we need to make one more simplification if we are to be able to proceed in a reasonably efficient manner. We write the density as

$$\rho = \rho_\infty + \tilde{\rho} \tag{5.10-6}$$

where ρ_∞ is the density at the temperature T_∞, and *assume*

$$\tilde{\rho} \ll \rho_\infty \tag{5.10-7}$$

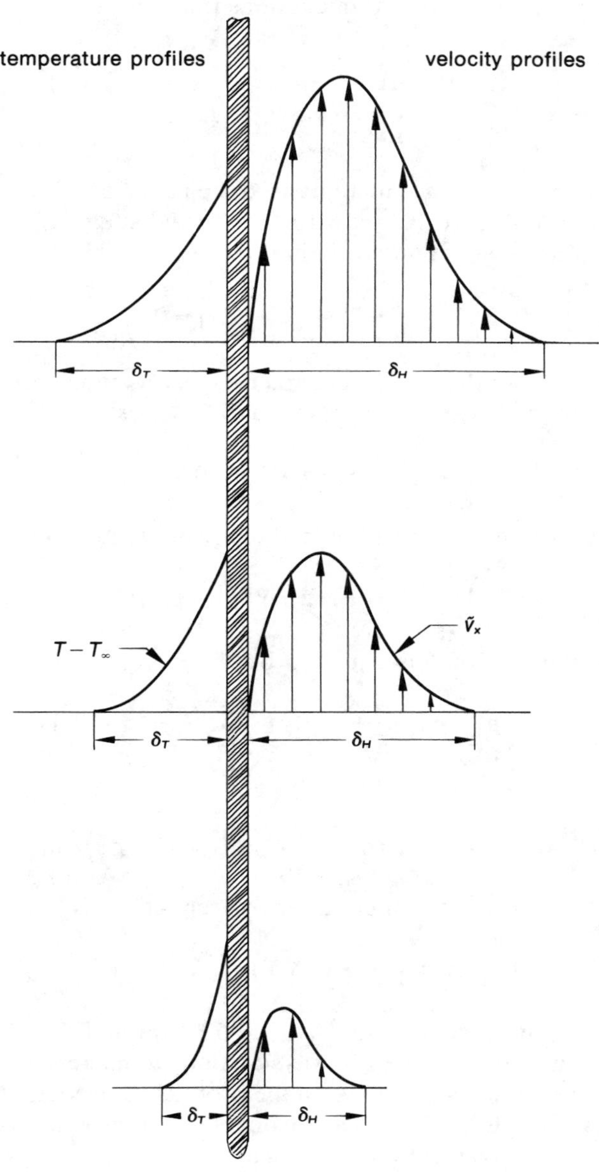

Fig. 5.10.1 Velocity and temperature profiles for free convection around a heated vertical flat plate.

This means that we are restricting our analysis to processes in which the density variation is small. We can also express the velocity and pressure fields in the same way

$$\mathbf{v} = \mathbf{v}_\infty + \tilde{\mathbf{v}} \tag{5.10-8}$$

$$p = p_\infty + \tilde{p} \tag{5.10-9}$$

Here $\mathbf{v}_\infty$ and p_∞ represent the velocity and pressure fields when the temperature is everywhere equal to T_∞. Since we are dealing with a system in which the fluid motion is caused entirely by the buoyancy effect, it follows that

$$\mathbf{v}_\infty = 0 \tag{5.10-10}$$

$$\nabla p_\infty = \rho_\infty \mathbf{g} \tag{5.10-11}$$

In addition, the quantities $\tilde{\rho}$, $\tilde{\mathbf{v}}$, and $\tilde{p}$ can be thought of as functions of the temperature difference, $T_0 - T_\infty$ such that

$$\left.\begin{matrix}\tilde{\rho}\\ \tilde{\mathbf{v}}\\ \tilde{p}\end{matrix}\right\} \to 0, \quad \text{as } (T_0 - T_\infty) \to 0$$

Before attempting to put the governing equations in dimensionless form, we wish to make use of the condition expressed by Eqs. 5.10-7, 5.10-10, and 5.10-11 to see what kind of simplifications we can make.

Beginning with the continuity equation we write

$$\frac{\partial \tilde{\rho}}{\partial t} + \nabla \cdot [(\rho_\infty + \tilde{\rho})\tilde{\mathbf{v}}] = 0 \tag{5.10-12}$$

Here we have made use of the fact that ρ_∞ is a constant so that its time derivative is zero. On the basis of the inequality expressed by Eq. 5.10-7 we express Eq. 5.10-12 as†

$$\frac{\partial \tilde{\rho}}{\partial t} + \rho_\infty \nabla \cdot \tilde{\mathbf{v}} = 0 \tag{5.10-13}$$

Substitution of Eqs. 5.10-6, 5.10-8, and 5.10-9 into the equations of motion, Eq. 5.10-4, yields

$$(\rho_\infty + \tilde{\rho})\left(\frac{\partial \tilde{\mathbf{v}}}{\partial t} + \tilde{\mathbf{v}} \cdot \nabla \tilde{\mathbf{v}}\right) = -\nabla p_\infty + \rho_\infty \mathbf{g} - \nabla \tilde{p} + \tilde{\rho}\mathbf{g} + \mu \nabla^2 \tilde{\mathbf{v}} + \left(\kappa + \frac{1}{3}\mu\right)\nabla(\nabla \cdot \tilde{\mathbf{v}}) \tag{5.10-14}$$

We approximate the left-hand-side of this equation by

$$(\rho_\infty + \tilde{\rho})\left(\frac{\partial \tilde{\mathbf{v}}}{\partial t} + \tilde{\mathbf{v}} \cdot \nabla \tilde{\mathbf{v}}\right) \sim \rho_\infty \left(\frac{\partial \tilde{\mathbf{v}}}{\partial t} + \tilde{\mathbf{v}} \cdot \nabla \tilde{\mathbf{v}}\right) \tag{5.10-15}$$

since $\rho_\infty \gg \tilde{\rho}$, and note that $-\nabla p_\infty + \rho_\infty \mathbf{g} = 0$ to obtain

$$\rho_\infty \left(\frac{\partial \tilde{\mathbf{v}}}{\partial t} + \tilde{\mathbf{v}} \cdot \nabla \tilde{\mathbf{v}}\right) = -\nabla \tilde{p} + \tilde{\rho}\mathbf{g} + \mu \nabla^2 \tilde{\mathbf{v}} + (\kappa + \tfrac{1}{3}\mu)\nabla(\nabla \cdot \tilde{\mathbf{v}}) \tag{5.10-16}$$

Similar arguments lead us to express the thermal energy equation as

$$\rho_\infty c_p \left(\frac{\partial T}{\partial t} + \tilde{\mathbf{v}} \cdot \nabla T\right) = k \nabla^2 T + \Phi \tag{5.10-17}$$

One can easily appreciate, by glancing at Eqs. 5.10-13, 5.10-16, and 5.10-17, that our problem is still a difficult one. Under such circumstances one is always anxious to make simplifying assumptions provided the essential elements of the problem are not lost in the process. Considerable simplification is obtained if we restrict the analysis to *steady* flows. This is a reasonable restriction to make since we will generally be interested in steady-state natural convection phenomena.

†Here we require that $\rho_\infty \nabla \cdot \tilde{\mathbf{v}} \gg \nabla \cdot (\tilde{\rho}\tilde{\mathbf{v}})$.

Under these circumstances the continuity equation takes the form†

$$\nabla \cdot \tilde{\mathbf{v}} = 0, \quad \text{for steady flows} \tag{5.10-18}$$

which allows us to simplify the equations of motion and the thermal energy equation to

$$\rho_\infty(\tilde{\mathbf{v}} \cdot \nabla \tilde{\mathbf{v}}) = -\nabla \tilde{p} + \tilde{\rho}\,\mathbf{g} + \mu \nabla^2 \tilde{\mathbf{v}}, \quad \text{for steady flows} \tag{5.10-19}$$

$$\tilde{\mathbf{v}} \cdot \nabla T = \alpha \nabla^2 T + (\Phi/\rho_\infty c_p), \quad \text{for steady flows} \tag{5.10-20}$$

Our problem now is considerably simpler and we are ready to put the equations in dimensionless form.

We begin, as usual, by specifying a characteristic length L, and a characteristic time L/u_0. Presumably a characteristic length, such as the length of the plate in Fig. 5.10.1 will always be available to us, but what do we use for a characteristic velocity? Since the fluid motion is generated by the buoyancy effect there is no characteristic velocity in the sense that we have become accustomed to in our analysis of forced-convection flow processes; however, the quantity (ν/L) has the same units as the velocity and we can use this term to make our equations dimensionless. Starting with the continuity equation we multiply by L (to make ∇ dimensionless) and divide by ν/L (to make $\tilde{\mathbf{v}}$ dimensionless) to obtain

$$\nabla \cdot \tilde{\mathbf{U}} = 0 \tag{5.10-21}$$

where

$$\tilde{\mathbf{U}} = (\tilde{\mathbf{v}}L/\nu), \quad \text{a dimensionless velocity}$$

$$\nabla = L\nabla, \quad \text{a dimensionless "del" operator}$$

Going on to the equations of motion we divide by $\rho_\infty(\nu/L)^2$ and multiply by L to obtain

$$\tilde{\mathbf{U}} \cdot \nabla \tilde{\mathbf{U}} = -\nabla \tilde{P} + \left(\frac{\tilde{\rho}\,\mathbf{g}L^3}{\rho_\infty \nu^2}\right) + \nabla^2 \tilde{\mathbf{U}} \tag{5.10-22}$$

where

$$\tilde{P} = \left[\frac{\tilde{p} - p_0}{\rho_\infty(\nu/L)^2}\right]$$

The coefficient of thermal expansion, β, may be defined as

$$\beta = -\frac{1}{\rho}\left(\frac{\partial \rho}{\partial T}\right)_p \tag{5.10-23}$$

although the student is probably more familiar with the definition given in a thermodynamics text

$$\beta = +\frac{1}{V}\left(\frac{\partial V}{\partial T}\right)_p$$

As given in Eq. 5.10-23, the coefficient of thermal expansion defines the variation of density with temperature at a *constant* pressure, and is certainly a suitable parameter for describing density variations in natural convection processes where pressure variations are generally small. On the basis of the inequality $\tilde{\rho} \ll \rho_\infty$ we can write Eq. 5.10-23 as

$$\beta = -\frac{1}{\rho_\infty}\left(\frac{\partial \tilde{\rho}}{\partial T}\right)_p \tag{5.10-24}$$

If we assume the β is essentially constant for the range of pressures and temperatures encountered in any given free-convection process we can integrate Eq. 5.10-24 (remembering that $\tilde{\rho} = 0$ when $(T_0 - T_\infty) = 0$) to obtain

$$\tilde{\rho} = -\rho_\infty \beta \Theta (T_0 - T_\infty) \tag{5.10-25}$$

†Strictly speaking, Eq. 5.10-1 reduces to

$$\nabla \cdot \tilde{\mathbf{v}} = -\frac{\tilde{\mathbf{v}} \cdot \nabla(\tilde{\rho}/\rho_\infty)}{[1 + (\tilde{\rho}/\rho_\infty)]} \sim 0$$

i.e., the product of $\tilde{\mathbf{v}}$ and $\nabla(\tilde{\rho}/\rho_\infty)$ is taken to be vanishingly small.

where the dimensionless temperature is given by

$$\Theta = (T - T_\infty)/(T_0 - T_\infty) \tag{5.10-26}$$

Substituting Eq. 5.10-25 into Eq. 5.10-22 and expressing $\mathbf{g}$ in terms of the magnitude g and the direction $\boldsymbol{\lambda}$ we obtain

$$\tilde{\mathbf{U}} \cdot \nabla \tilde{\mathbf{U}} = -\nabla \tilde{P} - \left[\frac{\beta(T_0 - T_\infty)gL^3}{\nu^2}\right]\Theta\boldsymbol{\lambda} + \nabla^2 \tilde{\mathbf{U}} \tag{5.10-27}$$

The term in brackets is the Grashof number which we write as

$$N_{\mathrm{Gr}} = \frac{\beta(T_0 - T_\infty)gL^3}{\nu^2} \tag{5.10-28}$$

and the final form of the dimensionless equations of motion is

$$\tilde{\mathbf{U}} \cdot \nabla \tilde{\mathbf{U}} = -\nabla \tilde{P} - N_{\mathrm{Gr}}\Theta\boldsymbol{\lambda} + \nabla^2 \tilde{\mathbf{U}} \tag{5.10-29}$$

In treating the thermal energy equation we first replace T by $T - T_\infty$, and then divide each term in Eq. 5.10-20 by $(T_0 - T_\infty)\nu/L^2$ to obtain the dimensionless form

$$\tilde{\mathbf{U}} \cdot \nabla \Theta = \frac{1}{N_{\mathrm{Pr}}} \nabla^2 \Theta + \Phi^* \tag{5.10-30}$$

where

$$\Phi^* = \frac{\Phi L^2}{\mu c_p (T_0 - T_\infty)}$$

Examining Eqs. 5.10-29 and 5.10-30 we see that the equations of motion and the thermal energy equation are *coupled* as we no doubt understood simply by intuition.

Referring to Eq. 5.10-30 we express the functional dependence of Θ as

$$\Theta = \Theta(X, Y, Z, N_{\mathrm{Pr}}, \Phi^*, \tilde{\mathbf{U}}, N_{\mathrm{BC}}^{\mathrm{II}}) \tag{5.10-31}$$

where $N_{\mathrm{BC}}^{\mathrm{II}}$ represents all the dimensionless parameters occurring in the boundary conditions for the temperature field. Since the functional dependence of $\tilde{\mathbf{U}}$ is given by†

$$\tilde{\mathbf{U}} = \tilde{\mathbf{U}}(X, Y, Z, N_{\mathrm{Gr}}, \Theta, \boldsymbol{\lambda}, N_{\mathrm{BC}}^{\mathrm{I}}) \tag{5.10-32}$$

we can express Eq. 5.10-31 as

$$\Theta = \Theta(X, Y, Z, N_{\mathrm{Pr}}, N_{\mathrm{Gr}}, \boldsymbol{\lambda}, \Phi^*, N_{\mathrm{BC}}^{\mathrm{I}}, N_{\mathrm{BC}}^{\mathrm{II}}) \tag{5.10-33}$$

Here $N_{\mathrm{BC}}^{\mathrm{I}}$ represents all the dimensionless parameters occurring in the boundary conditions for the velocity field. Following the discussion in Sec. 5.6 between Eqs. 5.6-14 and 5.6-20 we express the functional dependence of some average Nusselt number as

$$N_{\mathrm{Nu,av}} = N_{\mathrm{Nu,av}}(N_{\mathrm{Pr}}, N_{\mathrm{Gr}}, \boldsymbol{\lambda}, N_{\mathrm{BC}}^{\mathrm{I}}, N_{\mathrm{BC}}^{\mathrm{II}}) \tag{5.10-34}$$

when there is no heat generation. Very often one finds this result listed as

$$N_{\mathrm{Nu,av}} = N_{\mathrm{Nu,av}}(N_{\mathrm{Pr}}, N_{\mathrm{Gr}}) \tag{5.10-35}$$

where the dependence on the boundary condition parameters and $\boldsymbol{\lambda}$ being understood. The form given by Eq. 5.10-34 is certainly preferable since the dimensionless parameters appearing in the boundary conditions are the easiest to overlook. In the next section we will analyze one simple type of free-convection process, and we will see that our final expression for the Nusselt number will involve the Prandtl and Grashof numbers as predicted by Eq. 5.10-34.

†Note that the functional dependence of $\tilde{P}$ is identical to that of $\tilde{\mathbf{U}}$.

Summary of Section 5.11

In this section a boundary layer analysis of the flow illustrated in Fig. 5.10.1 is performed. The approach is quite similar to the treatment given in Sec. 5.8 for forced-convection boundary layer flows. Order-of-magnitude analysis is used to simplify Eqs. 5.10-18, 5.10-19, and 5.10-20 leading to

$$\frac{\partial \tilde{v}_x}{\partial x} + \frac{\partial \tilde{v}_y}{\partial y} = 0 \tag{5.11-13}$$

$$\tilde{v}_x \left(\frac{\partial \tilde{v}_x}{\partial x}\right) + \tilde{v}_y \left(\frac{\partial \tilde{v}_x}{\partial y}\right) = -\left(\frac{\tilde{\rho}}{\rho_\infty}\right) g + \nu \left(\frac{\partial^2 \tilde{v}_x}{\partial y^2}\right) \tag{5.11-14}$$

$$\tilde{v}_x \left(\frac{\partial T}{\partial x}\right) + \tilde{v}_y \left(\frac{\partial T}{\partial y}\right) = \alpha \left(\frac{\partial^2 T}{\partial y^2}\right) \tag{5.11-15}$$

The momentum and energy equations are coupled through the temperature dependence of the density

$$\tilde{\rho} = -\rho_\infty \beta (T - T_\infty)$$

where T_∞ is the temperature of the fluid far removed from the plate, and ρ_∞ is the density of the fluid at T_∞. A similarity transformation exists which allows the mass, momentum, and energy equations to be expressed as

$$f''' + 3ff'' - 2(f')^2 + \Theta = 0 \tag{5.11-22}$$

$$\Theta'' + 3N_{\mathrm{Pr}}\Theta' = 0 \tag{5.11-23}$$

Solutions of these equations are in good agreement with experimental data as illustrated in Figs. 5.11.3 and 5.11.4. Results for the average Nusselt number obtained from Eqs. 5.11-22 and 5.11-23 can be expressed in the form

$$N_{\mathrm{Nu,av}} = C(N_{\mathrm{Gr}} N_{\mathrm{Pr}})^{1/4} \tag{5.11-29}$$

where the coefficient C depends on the Prandtl number. Several values of C as a function of N_{Pr} are listed here:

C	N_{Pr}
0	0
0.242	0.01
0.516	0.72
0.535	1.0
0.620	10
0.653	100

and more values are given in Table 5.11-1. Experimental values of the Nusselt number are compared with Eq. 5.11-29 in Fig. 5.11.5. For values of $N_{\mathrm{Gr}} < 10^3$ (remember that $N_{\mathrm{Pr}} \sim 1$ for air) the data are not in agreement with Eq. 5.11-29 because the boundary layer approximations are no longer valid, while at large values of the Grashof number, $N_{\mathrm{Gr}} > 10^9$, turbulence sets in and the heat transfer rates are higher than those predicted by laminar boundary layer theory.

5.11 Boundary Layer Analysis of Free Convection

In this section we will study the free-convection phenomenon illustrated in Fig. 5.10.1. The type of flow shown there is essentially the free-convection analog of the laminar boundary layer heat transfer process studied in Secs. 5.7, 5.8, and 5.9. One might imagine that the process is susceptible to the type of approximate analysis described in Sec. 5.9; however, it is very difficult to choose satisfactory velocity profiles because of the coupling between the velocity and temperature fields, and we will confine our treatment to the type of exact analysis given in Sec. 5.8. This is unfortunate for there is much to be learned by the development of approximate solutions and the interested reader is referred to the work of Braun and Heighway[10].

We begin with a statement of the governing equations presented in Sec. 5.10 and a set of boundary conditions which hopefully represent a reasonable picture of the real process.

$$\nabla \cdot \tilde{\mathbf{v}} = 0, \quad \text{continuity equation} \tag{5.11-1}$$

$$\rho_\infty \tilde{\mathbf{v}} \cdot \nabla \tilde{\mathbf{v}} = -\nabla \tilde{p} + \tilde{\rho}\,\mathbf{g} + \mu \nabla^2 \tilde{\mathbf{v}}, \quad \text{equations of motion} \tag{5.11-2}$$

$$\tilde{\mathbf{v}} \cdot \nabla T = \alpha \nabla^2 T, \quad \text{thermal energy equation} \tag{5.11-3}$$

Here we have dropped the transient terms, $\rho_\infty(\partial \mathbf{v}/\partial t)$ and $\partial T/\partial t$, thus our analysis is restricted to steady processes. Note that we have retained the tildes ($\sim$) on $\mathbf{v}$, p, and ρ as a reminder that these terms all tend to zero as the temperature difference $(T_0 - T_\infty)$ goes to zero, i.e.,

$$\left.\begin{matrix} \tilde{\mathbf{v}} \\ \tilde{p} \\ \tilde{\rho} \end{matrix}\right\} \to 0, \quad \text{as } (T_0 - T_\infty) \to 0$$

We specify the boundary conditions for a heated plate immersed in a infinite fluid as

B.C.1 $\quad \tilde{\mathbf{v}} = 0, \quad x \to -\infty$

B.C.2 $\quad \tilde{\mathbf{v}} = 0, \quad y \to \pm\infty$

B.C.3 $\quad \tilde{\mathbf{v}} = 0, \quad y = 0, \quad x > 0$

B.C.4 $\quad T = T_\infty, \quad x \to -\infty$

B.C.5 $\quad T = T_\infty, \quad y \to \pm\infty$

B.C.6 $\quad T = T_0, \quad y = 0, \quad x > 0$

Solution of Eqs. 5.11-1 through 5.11-3 is a tedious task although it can be accomplished with the use of finite-difference equations and a digital computer. However, with the "picture" of the velocity and temperature fields shown in Fig. 5.10.1, we are naturally led to try for a boundary layer solution. Considering the plate to be infinite in the z-direction we assume that T is independent of z and $v_z = 0$ so that the expanded forms of the governing equations are

$$\underset{\left(\frac{u_0}{L}\right)}{\frac{\partial \tilde{v}_y}{\partial y}} + \underset{\left(\frac{u_0}{L}\right)}{\frac{\partial \tilde{v}_x}{\partial x}} = 0 \tag{5.11-4}$$

$$\rho_\infty \left(\underset{\left(\frac{\delta_H}{L} u_0\right)}{\tilde{v}_y} \underset{\left(\frac{u_0}{L}\right)}{\frac{\partial \tilde{v}_y}{\partial y}} + \underset{(u_0)}{\tilde{v}_x} \underset{\left(\frac{\delta_H u_0}{L}\right)}{\frac{\partial \tilde{v}_y}{\partial x}} \right) = -\frac{\partial \tilde{p}}{\partial y} + \mu \left(\underset{\left(\frac{u_0}{\delta_H L}\right)}{\frac{\partial^2 \tilde{v}_y}{\partial y^2}} + \underset{\left(\frac{u_0 \delta_H}{L^3}\right)}{\frac{\partial^2 \tilde{v}_y}{\partial x^2}} \right) \tag{5.11-5}$$

$$\rho_\infty \left(\underset{\left(\frac{\delta_H u_0}{L}\right)}{\tilde{v}_y} \underset{\left(\frac{u_0}{\delta_H}\right)}{\frac{\partial \tilde{v}_x}{\partial y}} + \underset{(u_0)}{\tilde{v}_x} \underset{\left(\frac{u_0}{L}\right)}{\frac{\partial \tilde{v}_x}{\partial x}} \right) = -\frac{\partial \tilde{p}}{\partial x} - \tilde{\rho} g + \mu \left(\underset{\left(\frac{u_0}{\delta_H^2}\right)}{\frac{\partial^2 \tilde{v}_x}{\partial y^2}} + \underset{\left(\frac{u_0}{L^2}\right)}{\frac{\partial^2 \tilde{v}_x}{\partial x^2}} \right) \tag{5.11-6}$$

$$\underset{\left(\frac{\delta_H u_0}{L}\right)}{\tilde{v}_y} \underset{\left(\frac{T_1 - T_0}{\delta_T}\right)}{\frac{\partial T}{\partial y}} + \underset{(u_0)}{\tilde{v}_x} \underset{\left(\frac{T_1 - T_0}{L}\right)}{\frac{\partial T}{\partial x}} = \alpha \left(\underset{\left(\frac{T_1 - T_0}{\delta_T^2}\right)}{\frac{\partial^2 T}{\partial y^2}} + \underset{\left(\frac{T_1 - T_0}{L^2}\right)}{\frac{\partial^2 T}{\partial x^2}} \right) \tag{5.11-7}$$

If we choose the length of the plate to be L, and designate the order-of-magnitude of $\tilde{v}_x$ and $\tilde{v}_y$ as

$$\tilde{v}_x = \mathbf{0}(u_0) \tag{5.11-8}$$

then the order-of-magnitude of $\partial \tilde{v}_x/\partial x$ is given by†

$$\frac{\partial \tilde{v}_x}{\partial x} = \mathbf{0}\left(\frac{u_0}{L}\right) \tag{5.11-9}$$

It follows then that both terms in the continuity equation are of the order-of-magnitude of (u_0/L), as is indicated over the terms in Eq. 5.11-4. By the same type of reasoning that led us to Eq. 5.11-9 we conclude that

$$\frac{\partial \tilde{v}_y}{\partial y} = \frac{\mathbf{0}(\tilde{v}_y)}{\delta_H} \tag{5.11-10}$$

But since the order-of-magnitude of $\partial \tilde{v}_y/\partial y$ by the continuity equation is (u_0/L) we obtain

$$\tilde{v}_y = \mathbf{0}\left[\left(\frac{\delta_H}{L}\right) u_0\right] \tag{5.11-11}$$

With order-of-magnitude estimates available for $\tilde{v}_y$ and $\tilde{v}_x$ and characteristic lengths in the y- and x-directions of δ_H and L we obtain the order-of-magnitude estimates for the individual terms in the equations of motion listed in parentheses over each term. If we restrict our study to boundary layer flows we are dealing with processes for which

$$\delta_H \ll L \quad \text{and} \quad \delta_T \ll L$$

Under these circumstances the spatial derivatives with respect to x are small compared to the derivatives with respect to y.

$$\frac{\partial^2 \tilde{v}_y}{\partial y^2} \gg \frac{\partial^2 \tilde{v}_y}{\partial x^2}, \qquad \frac{\partial^2 \tilde{v}_x}{\partial y^2} \gg \frac{\partial^2 \tilde{v}_x}{\partial x^2}, \qquad \frac{\partial^2 T}{\partial y^2} \gg \frac{\partial^2 T}{\partial x^2}$$

If we assume that "small causes lead to small effects" we can neglect these derivatives. Further simplification results if we note that each term in Eq. 5.11-5 is smaller by a factor of δ_H/L than the comparable term in Eq. 5.10-6. This means that

$$\left(\frac{\partial \tilde{p}}{\partial y}\right) \ll \frac{\partial \tilde{p}}{\partial x}$$

but we know that $\partial \tilde{p}/\partial x = 0$ outside the boundary layer, thus the pressure gradient in the x-direction is negligible and we write

$$\frac{\partial \tilde{p}}{\partial x} = 0, \qquad 0 \leq x \leq \delta_H \tag{5.11-12}$$

Remember from Sec. 5.10 that the total pressure is given by

$$p = p_\infty + \tilde{p}$$

where p_∞ represents the hydrostatic pressure, and $\tilde{p}$ represents variations in the pressure field owing to the natural convection process.

On the basis of the order-of-magnitude arguments given here our governing differential equations reduce to

$$\frac{\partial \tilde{v}_y}{\partial y} + \frac{\partial \tilde{v}_x}{\partial x} = 0 \tag{5.11-13}$$

$$\tilde{v}_y\left(\frac{\partial v_x}{\partial y}\right) + \tilde{v}_x\left(\frac{\partial \tilde{v}_x}{\partial x}\right) = -\left(\frac{\tilde{\rho}}{\rho_\infty}\right) g + \nu\left(\frac{\partial^2 \tilde{v}_z}{\partial y^2}\right) \tag{5.11-14}$$

$$\tilde{v}_y\left(\frac{\partial T}{\partial y}\right) + \tilde{v}_x\left(\frac{\partial T}{\partial x}\right) = \alpha\left(\frac{\partial^2 T}{\partial y^2}\right) \tag{5.11-15}$$

†See Sec. 2.9 for a detailed discussion of order-of-magnitude analysis and Sec. 5.7 for an application.

We can use Eq. 5.10-25 to express $\tilde{\rho}$ as

$$\tilde{\rho} = -\rho_\infty \beta (T - T_\infty)$$

and use a stream function to represent the velocity components,

$$\tilde{v}_x = \frac{\partial \psi}{\partial y}, \qquad \tilde{v}_y = -\frac{\partial \psi}{\partial x}$$

so that Eqs. 5.11-13 through 5.11-15 can be expressed as

$$\frac{\partial \psi}{\partial y}\frac{\partial^2 \psi}{\partial x \partial y} - \frac{\partial \psi}{\partial x}\frac{\partial^2 \psi}{\partial y^2} = \beta g \Theta (T_0 - T_\infty) + \nu \left(\frac{\partial^3 \psi}{\partial y^3}\right) \tag{5.11-16}$$

$$\frac{\partial \psi}{\partial y}\frac{\partial \Theta}{\partial y} - \frac{\partial \psi}{\partial x}\frac{\partial \Theta}{\partial x} = \alpha \frac{\partial^2 \Theta}{\partial y^2} \tag{5.11-17}$$

Here we have used a dimensionless temperature defined by

$$\Theta = \frac{T - T_\infty}{T_0 - T_\infty} \tag{5.11-18}$$

Following the procedure discussed in some detail in Sec. 5.8 we use a similarity transform to express the stream function as

$$\psi = 4\nu a x^{3/4} f(\eta) \tag{5.11-19}$$

where the similarity variable is given by

$$\eta = ay/x^{1/4} \tag{5.11-20}$$

The parameter, a, is given by the expression

$$a = \left[\frac{\beta g (T_0 - T_\infty)}{4\nu^2}\right]^{1/4} \tag{5.11-21}$$

Use of Eqs. 5.11-19 and 5.11-20 allows us to transform the momentum and energy equations to ordinary differential equations yielding

$$f''' + 3ff'' - 2(f')^2 + \Theta = 0 \tag{5.11-22}$$

$$\Theta'' + 3N_{\text{Pr}} f \Theta' = 0 \tag{5.11-23}$$

where the prime (′) refers to differentiation with respect to η.

The boundary conditions listed after Eq. 5.11-3 transform to

B.C.1′ $$f = f' = 0, \quad \Theta = 1, \quad \text{at } \eta = 0 \tag{5.11-24}$$

B.C.2′ $$f' = \Theta = 0, \quad \text{at } \eta \to \infty \tag{5.11-25}$$

Eqs. 5.11-22 and 5.11-23 have been solved subject to the boundary conditions given by Eqs. 5.11-24 and 5.11-25 using numerical methods such as those described in Secs. 3.3 and 4.7. The results for the temperature field obtained by Ostrach [11] are illustrated in Fig. 5.11.1. There the transformation variable, η, has been expressed as

$$\eta = \left(\frac{y}{x}\right)\left[\frac{\beta g (T_0 - T_\infty) x^3}{4\nu^2}\right]^{1/4} = \left(\frac{y}{x}\right)\left(\frac{N_{\text{Gr},x}}{4}\right)^{1/4} \tag{5.11-26}$$

As we would expect, the thermal boundary layer thickness decreases with increasing Prandtl number, and inspection of the dimensionless velocity profiles shown in Fig. 5.11.2 indicates that

$$\frac{\delta_T}{\delta_H} \to 0, \quad \text{as } N_{\text{Pr}} \to \infty$$

Ostrach has compared his theoretical results with the work of Schmidt and Beckman [12] for air, and the

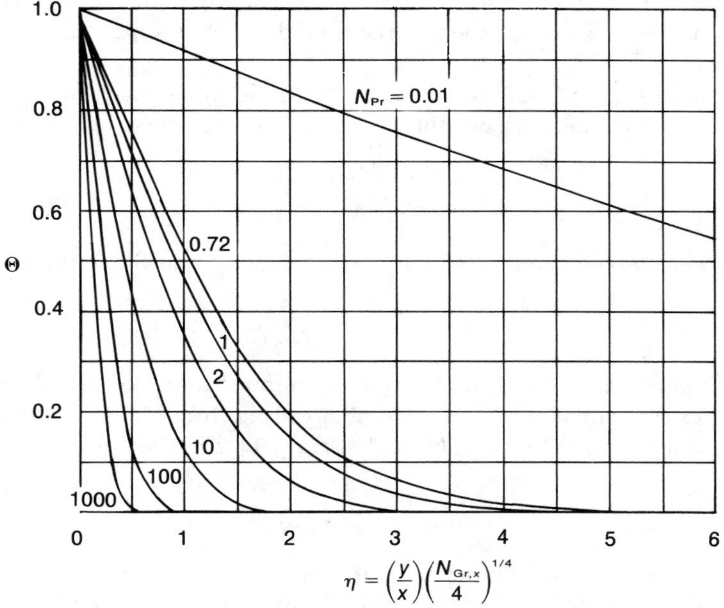

Fig. 5.11.1 Dimensionless temperature profiles for laminar free convection on a vertical plate.

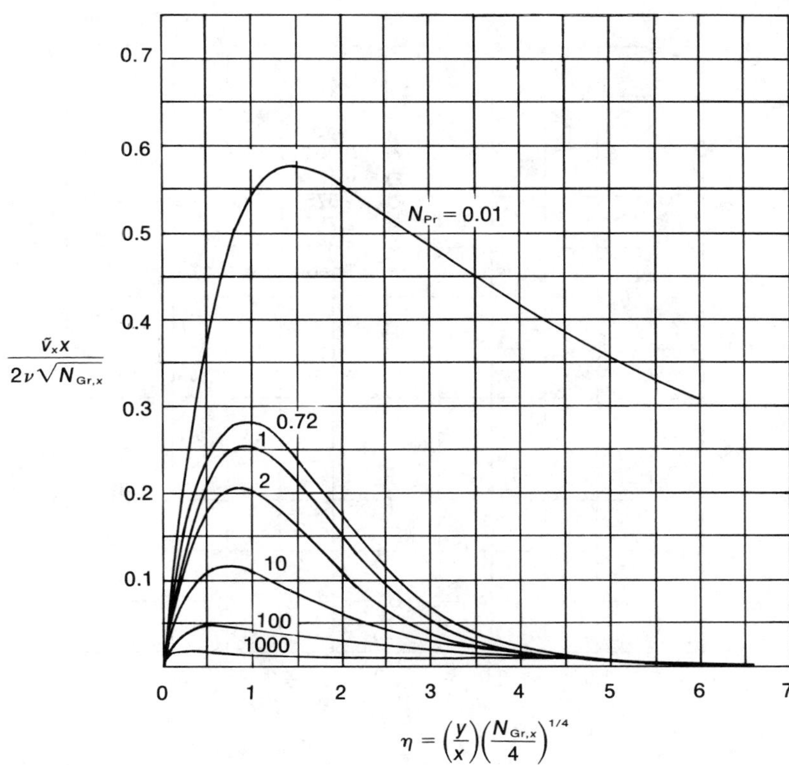

Fig. 5.11.2 Dimensionless velocity profiles for laminar free convection on a vertical plate.

results are shown in Figs. 5.11.3 and 5.11.4. The agreement is quite good; however, we should not expect this type of agreement for small values of x where the boundary layer approximations given by Eq. 5.11-11 are not valid.

LeFevre [13] has solved Eqs. 5.11-22 and 5.11-23 for the limiting cases of very small and very large Prandtl numbers and finds that the Nusselt numbers, $h_{av}L/k$, are given by

$$N_{Nu,av} = 0.80 N_{Gr}^{1/4} N_{Pr}^{1/2}, \quad \text{for } N_{Pr} \to 0 \tag{5.11-27}$$

$$N_{Nu,av} = 0.67 N_{Gr}^{1/4} N_{Pr}^{1/4}, \quad \text{for } N_{Pr} \to \infty \tag{5.11-28}$$

A number of other workers have solved Eqs. 5.11-22 and 5.11-23 and Schlichting† has represented their results in the form

$$N_{Nu,av} = C(N_{Gr} N_{Pr})^{1/4} \tag{5.11-29}$$

where the coefficient is given as a function of Prandtl number in Table 5.11-1. There we see that the coefficient varies about 25 per cent as the Prandtl number ranges from 0.72 to ∞; however, larger variations are encountered for the low Prandtl numbers. Note that Eq. 5.11-27 indicates that the coefficient C is given by

$$C = 0.80 N_{Pr}^{1/4}, \quad \text{for } N_{Pr} \to 0 \tag{5.11-30}$$

and thus goes to zero as the Prandtl number goes to zero.

These results are compared with the experimental data of Saunders [14] in Fig. 5.11.5, and there we see excellent agreement for the intermediate values of $N_{Gr}N_{Pr}$ and less satisfactory agreement for both small and large values of $N_{Gr}N_{Pr}$. The explanation for these results is that the boundary layer approximations

†See Chapter XII in Reference 6.

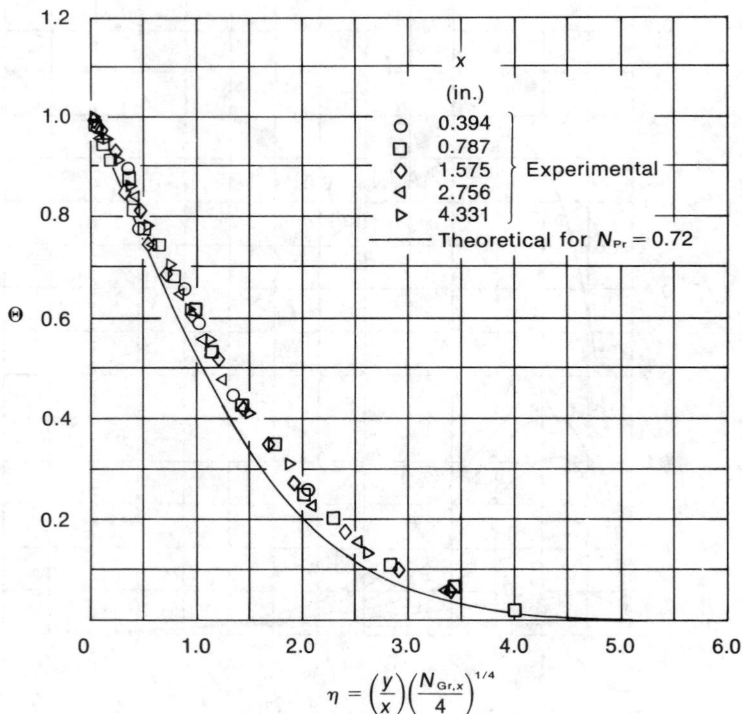

Fig. 5.11.3 Comparison of experimental and theoretical dimensionless temperature profiles for air in laminar free convection on a vertical plate.

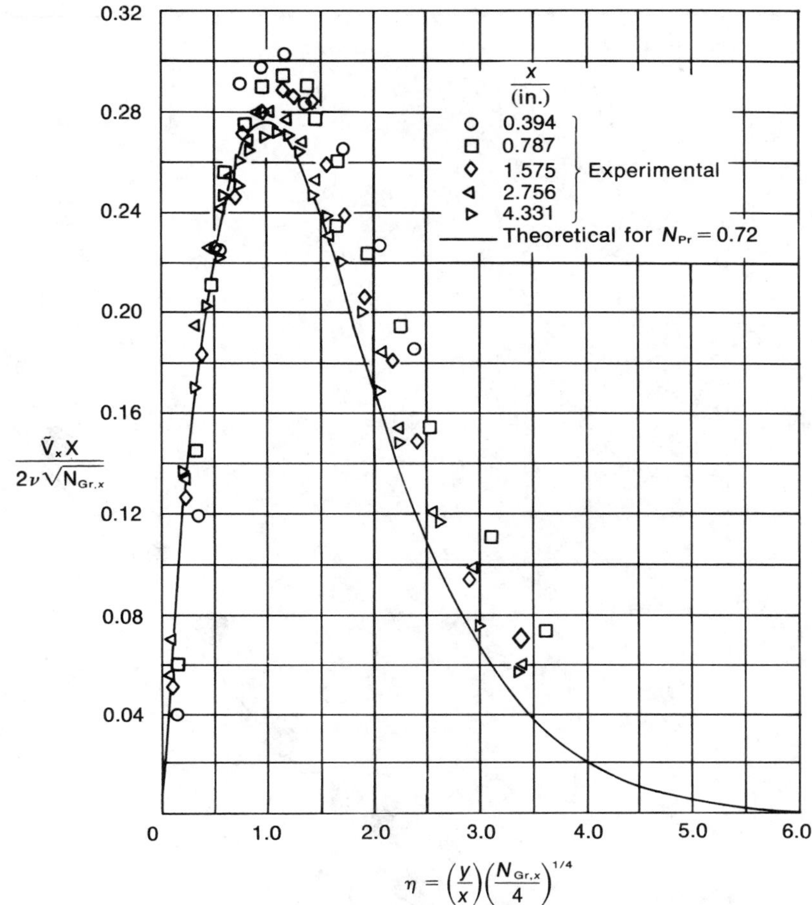

Fig. 5.11.4 Comparison of experimental and theoretical dimensionless velocity profiles for air in laminar free convection on a vertical plate.

Table 5.11-1 Coefficient in Eq. 5.11-29 for Heat Transfer for Laminar Free Convection on a Vertical Plate

N_{Pr}	0	0.003	0.008	0.01	0.02	0.03	0.72	0.73	1	2	10	100	1000	∞
C	0	0.182	0.228	0.242	0.280	0.305	0.516	0.518	0.535	0.568	0.620	0.653	0.665	0.670

given by Eq. 5.11-11 are not valid for values of $N_{Gr}N_{Pr}$ less than 10^3, and for values of $N_{Gr}N_{Pr}$ greater than 10^9 an increasingly large portion of the boundary layer is turbulent and the heat transfer rate is naturally increased. These results are similar in nature to those presented in Fig. 5.9.3 for the forced-convection boundary layer heat transfer process.

The analysis of forced convection presented in Secs. 5.7, 5.8, and 5.9 and of free convection in this section represent two relatively simple heat transfer processes. When the boundary layer assumptions were valid we were capable of predicting the Nusselt number and therefore the heat transfer rate with some degree of accuracy. If we are to be successful in our study of heat transfer we must be able to deal with a wide range of forced- and free-convection processes, many of which are not susceptible to mathematical analysis because of the complex form of the governing differential equations or because the flow is turbulent. In the next chapter we will briefly examine turbulent momentum and energy transport and in Chapter 7 we will set up methods for analyzing more complex processes.

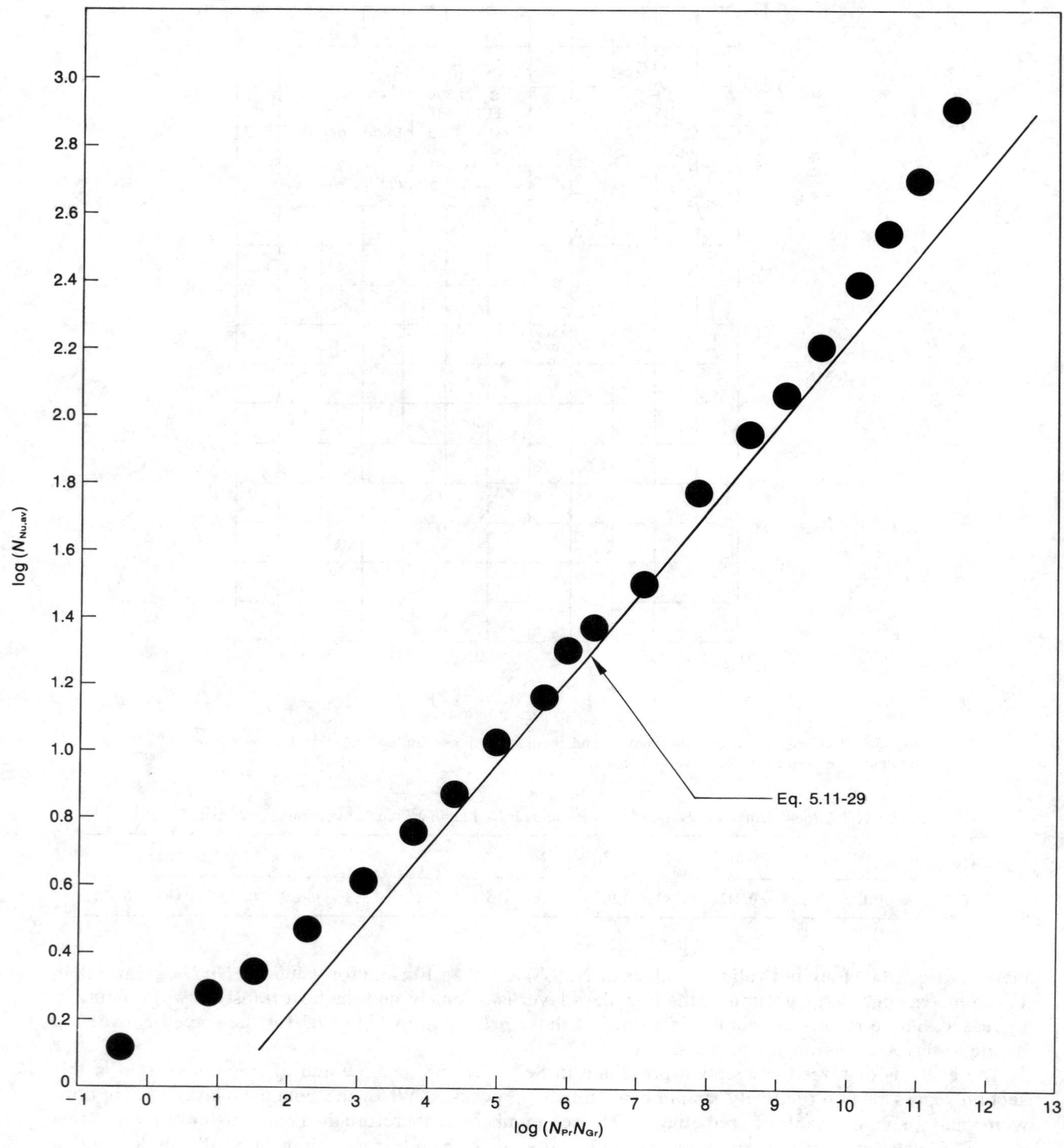

Fig. 5.11.5 Comparison of theory and experiment for free convection from vertical flat plates.

● Experimental data taken from O. A. Saunders, "The Effect of Pressure Upon Free Convection in Air," *Proc. Roy Soc*, **A157**, 278 (1936).

Solution to design problem V

Our first step in the analysis of this process is to sketch the velocity field that we expect to occur. This is shown in Fig. V.2 where we have indicated that the air will descend at the cold surface and rise at the hot surface as illustrated by the streamlines and the velocity profile. We have assumed that the flow is laminar and this is an assumption that we should consider more carefully in the course of our analysis.

If we neglect the complex process that occurs at the top and bottom of the air gap, we can restrict the velocity field by

$$\tilde{v}_y = \tilde{v}_z = 0, \qquad \tilde{v}_x = \tilde{v}_x(y) \tag{V-1}$$

Under these circumstances the thermal energy and linear momentum equations take the form

$$\tilde{v}_x \frac{\partial T}{\partial x} = \alpha\left(\frac{\partial^2 T}{\partial x^2} + \frac{\partial^2 T}{\partial y^2}\right) \tag{V-2}$$

$$0 = -\frac{\partial \tilde{p}}{\partial x} - \tilde{\rho} g + \mu\left(\frac{\partial^2 \tilde{v}_x}{\partial y^2}\right) \tag{V-3}$$

$$0 = -\frac{\partial \tilde{p}}{\partial y} \tag{V-4}$$

Here we have used the nomenclature given in Secs. 5.10 and 5.11. Since $\tilde{p}$ is not a function of y, the pressure gradient, $\partial\tilde{p}/\partial x$, must also be independent of y. This means that $\partial\tilde{p}/\partial x$ takes on the same value near the hot surface where the fluid is rising as it does near the cold surface where the fluid is descending. It seems clear then that $\partial\tilde{p}/\partial x$ must be zero. Furthermore, it should be relatively appealing to neglect conduction in the y-direction, i.e.,

$$\frac{\partial^2 T}{\partial x^2} \ll \frac{\partial^2 T}{\partial y^2} \tag{V-5}$$

Under these circumstances our governing differential equations take the form

$$\tilde{v}_x\left(\frac{\partial T}{\partial x}\right) = \alpha\left(\frac{\partial^2 T}{\partial y^2}\right), \qquad \text{energy transport} \tag{V-6}$$

$$0 = -\tilde{\rho} g + \mu\left(\frac{\partial^2 \tilde{v}_x}{\partial y^2}\right), \qquad \text{momentum transport} \tag{V-7}$$

Remember that $\tilde{\rho}$ is a function of the temperature so that the above equations represent a set of coupled, partial differential equations which may be rather difficult to solve. It does not seem likely that a boundary layer type solution could be developed for this process, and quite possibly a computer solution would be required if we were to demand a complete solution of Eqs. V-6 and V-7. Experimental studies of heat transfer for free convection in confined spaces have been carried out† and these results could be used to help us solve this problem. However, before plunging into any problem an engineer should ask the question: "Is there a special case or a limiting condition for which a simple solution exists?" If there is, one should always examine the solution to the special case with the idea that it will provide insight into the problem and perhaps provide a lower or upper bound for the complete solution.

If we examine the energy transport equation given by Eq. V-6, we see immediately that the temperature profile is easily determined if the convective transport is sufficiently small. To determine what is "sufficiently small," we follow the procedure presented in Sec. 2.10 and integrate Eq. V-6 twice to obtain

$$T = C_1 y + C_2 + \int_{\tau=0}^{\tau=y} \int_{\eta=0}^{\eta=\tau} \left(\frac{\tilde{v}_x}{\alpha}\right)\left(\frac{\partial T}{\partial x}\right) d\eta\, d\tau \tag{V-8}$$

†See, for example, Eckert, E. R. G. and R. M. Drake, Jr., *Analysis of Heat Transfer,* page 537, McGraw-Hill Book Co., N.Y., 1972.

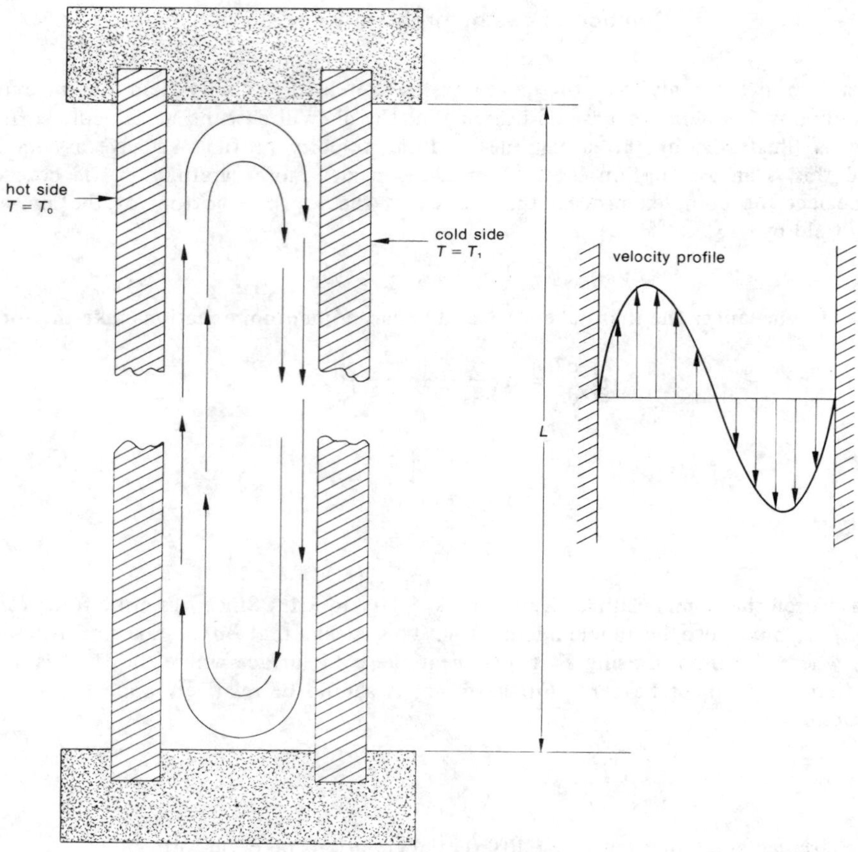

Fig. V.2 Velocity profile in a double window.

We choose a coordinate system so that the boundary conditions for the temperature can be expressed as

B.C.1 $$T = T_\alpha, \qquad y = 0 \tag{V-9a}$$

B.C.2 $$T = T_\beta, \qquad y = b \tag{V-9b}$$

Use of these boundary conditions with Eq. V-8 allows us to evaluate the constants of integration and express the temperature in the air gap as

$$T = T_a + (T_\beta - T_\alpha)\left(\frac{y}{b}\right) + \int_{\tau=0}^{\tau=y}\int_{\eta=0}^{\eta=\tau}\left(\frac{\tilde{v}_x}{\alpha}\right)\left(\frac{\partial T}{\partial x}\right)d\eta d\tau - \left(\frac{y}{b}\right)\int_{\tau=0}^{\tau=b}\int_{\eta=0}^{\eta=\tau}\left(\frac{\tilde{v}_x}{\alpha}\right)\left(\frac{\partial T}{\partial x}\right)d\eta d\tau \tag{V-10}$$

Here we can see that the first two terms on the right-hand side of Eq. V-10 represent the linear temperature profile associated with one-dimensional heat conduction. The integrals in Eq. V-10 can be estimated using order of magnitude analysis leading to

$$\int_{\tau=0}^{\tau=y}\int_{\eta=0}^{\eta=\tau}\left(\frac{\tilde{v}_x}{\alpha}\right)\left(\frac{\partial T}{\partial x}\right)d\eta d\tau - \left(\frac{y}{b}\right)\int_{\tau=0}^{\tau=b}\int_{\eta=0}^{\eta=\tau}\left(\frac{\tilde{v}_x}{\alpha}\right)\left(\frac{\partial T}{\partial x}\right)d\eta d\tau$$

$$= \mathbf{0}\left\{\left(\frac{\tilde{v}_x}{\alpha}\right)\left(\frac{\partial T}{\partial x}\right)b^2\left[\left(\frac{y}{b}\right)^2 - \left(\frac{y}{b}\right)\right]\right\} \tag{V-11}$$

Here it should be clear that we can neglect convective transport relative to conductive transport when the following constraint is satisfied

$$T_\beta - T_a \gg \left(\frac{\tilde{v}_x}{\alpha}\right)\left(\frac{\partial T}{\partial x}\right)b^2 \tag{V-12}$$

A plausible estimate of the temperature gradient is

$$\frac{\partial T}{\partial x} = \mathbf{0}\left(\frac{T_a - T_\beta}{L}\right) \tag{V-13}$$

where L is the height of the double window. Use of Eq. V-13 in Eq. V-12 leads to the restriction

$$1 \gg \left(\frac{\tilde{v}_x b^2}{\alpha L}\right) \tag{V-14}$$

In order that this constraint be useful, we need an estimate of $\tilde{v}_x$ which we obtain from Eq. V-7 as

$$\tilde{v}_x = \mathbf{0}\left(\frac{\tilde{\rho} g b^2}{\mu}\right) \tag{V-15}$$

We can now follow the development given in Sec. 5.10 to estimate $\tilde{\rho}$ as

$$\tilde{\rho} = \mathbf{0}[\rho\beta(T_a - T_\beta)] \tag{V-16}$$

where ρ represents the average density. Use of this result in Eq. V-15 leads to an estimate of the free convection velocity given by

$$\tilde{v}_x = \mathbf{0}\left[\frac{\rho\beta(T_a - T_\beta)gb^2}{\mu}\right] \tag{V-17}$$

This result can now be used in the restriction given by Eq. V-14 and arranged as

$$1 \gg \left[\frac{\beta g(T_a - T_\beta)b^3}{\nu^2}\right]\left(\frac{\nu}{\alpha}\right)\left(\frac{b}{L}\right) \tag{V-18}$$

or in terms of the Grashof and Prandtl numbers we have

$$1 \gg N_{\text{Gr}} N_{\text{Pr}} \left(\frac{b}{L}\right) \tag{B-19}$$

When this restriction is satisfied the conductive heat flux is given by

$$q_{\text{cond}} = \frac{k_{\text{air}}}{b}(T_\alpha - T_\beta) \tag{V-20}$$

In order to determine the radiant energy heat flux we exclude the case of direct sunlight impinging on the window. This means that the radiation is in the infrared region and the glass is therefore opaque to the radiation. We further assume that the glass behaves as a black body with respect to infrared radiation so that all incident radiation is absorbed and the rate of emission of energy is given by the Stefan-Boltzmann law. Under these circumstances the radiant energy heat flux between the two glass plates is given by

$$q^{\text{rad}} = \sigma(T_\alpha^4 - T_\beta^4) \tag{V-21}$$

and from our discussion in Sec. 1.4 we know that the flux can be expressed as

$$q^{\text{rad}} = 4\sigma T_{\text{av}}^3 (T_\alpha - T_\beta) \tag{V-22}$$

The total heat flux in the air gap is designated as q_1 and we add Eqs. V-20 and V-22 to determine this flux as

$$q_1 = \left(\frac{k_{\text{air}}}{b} + 4\sigma T_{\text{av}}^3\right)(T_a - T_\beta) \tag{V-23}$$

In order to express this result in terms of the outside and inside air temperatures, T_0 and T_1, we follow the method illustrated in the solution of Design Problem I to eliminate the unknown interfacial temperatures and solve for the heat flux to obtain

$$q_1 = \frac{T_0 - T_1}{\dfrac{1}{h_0} + \dfrac{d}{k} + \dfrac{b}{k_{air}}\left(\dfrac{1}{1 + 4\sigma T_{av}^3 b/k_{air}}\right) + \dfrac{d}{k} + \dfrac{1}{h_1}} \qquad \text{(V-24)}$$

Here d is the thickness of the glass plate and k is the thermal conductivity of the glass. The outside and inside film heat transfer coefficients have been designated by h_0 and h_1, and the heat flux across a single-pane window is given by

$$q_0 = \frac{T_0 - T_1}{\dfrac{1}{h_0} + \dfrac{k}{d} + \dfrac{1}{h_1}} \qquad \text{(V-25)}$$

Given these two results we can determine the ratio q_1/q_0 for various values of the parameters involved, but before doing so it is important to note from Eq. V-24 that q_1 is independent of the thickness of the air gap, b, when this distance is sufficiently large. To be more precise, we note that q_1 is independent of b when

$$4\sigma T_{av}^3 b/k_{air} \gg 1 \qquad \text{(V-26)}$$

Under these circumstances, radiation in the air gap dominates and increasing b no longer reduces the heat flux. For the particular case under consideration we take the average temperature to be 530°R so that the term on the left-hand side of Eq. V-26 is

$$4\sigma T_{av}^3 b/k_{air} = \frac{4(1.71 \times 10^{-9}\,\text{Btu/hr ft}^2\,{}^\circ\text{R}^4)(530^\circ\text{R})^3(0.126\text{ in})}{(0.015\,\text{Btu/hr ft}\,{}^\circ\text{R})(12\text{ in/ft})}$$

$$= 7.07$$

Here we can see that radiation clearly dominates the energy transport between the two glass plates.

For the conditions given in the problem statement we can use Eq. V-25 to obtain the following expression for q_0

$$q_0 = \frac{(T_0 - T_1)\,\text{Btu/hr ft}^2\,{}^\circ\text{F}}{\underset{\substack{\uparrow \\ \text{outside} \\ \text{resistance}}}{0.2} + \underset{\substack{\uparrow \\ \text{resistance} \\ \text{of glass}}}{0.052} + \underset{\substack{\uparrow \\ \text{inside} \\ \text{resistance}}}{2.0}}$$

while use of Eq. V-24 leads to

$$q_1 = \frac{(T_0 - T_1)\,\text{Btu/hr ft}^2\,{}^\circ F}{\underset{\substack{\uparrow \\ \text{outside} \\ \text{resistance}}}{0.2} + \underset{\substack{\uparrow \\ \text{resistance} \\ \text{of glass}}}{0.052} + \underset{\substack{\uparrow \\ \text{resistance} \\ \text{of air gap}}}{0.087} + \underset{\substack{\uparrow \\ \text{resistance} \\ \text{of glass}}}{0.052} + \underset{\substack{\uparrow \\ \text{inside} \\ \text{resistance}}}{2.0}}$$

Here we can see that it is the resistance at the inside surface of the window that dominates the heat transfer process, and the air gap is of little value in reducing the heat flux. The ratio of q_1 to q_0 is given by

$$\frac{q_1}{q_0} = 0.94$$

indicating that the double window causes a 6% reduction in the heat flux. In order to determine the largest possible reduction that can occur, we examine the case where h_0 and h_1 become arbitrarily large so that the resistance to heat transfer is entirely in the glass plates and the air gap. This condition leads to

$$\left(\frac{q_1}{q_0}\right) = 0.27, \qquad \text{for } h_0,\ h_1 \to \infty$$

and we see that a 73% reduction in the heat flux is possible under extreme conditions.

We should be careful to point out that our analysis indicated that radiant energy transport between the two glass plates represents an important contribution to the heat flux; however, we *neglected* this mechanism in our treatment of the energy transfer between the window and the inside and outside environments. Clearly a more thorough analysis is required before we can make a reliable judgment concerning the efficacy of double windows.

PROBLEMS†

V-1. If the gap between the glass plates were filled with a low viscosity oil, would the effect of convective transport be increased or decreased?

V-2. If $T_0 - T_1 = 40°F$, will the restriction associated with negligible convective transport be satisfied?

V-3. In Prob. I-3 of Chapter 1 it was suggested that convective transport could be neglected in the region between the window and the storm window. Was that a reasonable suggestion?

5-1. (5.1) Show how the continuity equation given by Eq. 5.1-27 can be put in the form

$$\frac{D\rho}{Dt} + \rho \nabla \cdot \mathbf{v} = 0$$

5-2. (5.1) Prove that the general transport theorem takes the form

$$\frac{d}{dt}\int_{\mathscr{V}_a(t)} S\, dV = \int_{\mathscr{V}_a(t)} \left(\frac{dS}{dt}\right) dV$$

when $\mathbf{w}$ is independent of the spatial coordinates.

5-3. (5.2) Prove that the stress vector $\mathbf{t}_{(\mathbf{n})}$ can be represented in terms of the stress tensor $\mathbf{T}$ (see Eq. 5.2-6) by applying the linear momentum principle to a vanishingly small tetrahedron. The stress vector for the coordinate planes should be expressed as

$$\mathbf{t}_{(\mathbf{i})} = \mathbf{i}\, T_{xx} + \mathbf{j}\, T_{xy} + \mathbf{k}\, T_{xz}$$

for example.

5-4. (5.2) Given the divergence theorem for a vector,

$$\int_{V} \nabla \cdot \mathbf{f}\, dV = \int_{\mathscr{A}} \mathbf{f} \cdot \mathbf{n}\, dA$$

derive the divergence theorem for a symmetric tensor,

$$\int_{V} \nabla \cdot \mathbf{F}\, dV = \int_{\mathscr{A}} \mathbf{F} \cdot \mathbf{n}\, dA$$

by letting $\mathbf{f} = \mathbf{b} \cdot \mathbf{F}$ where $\mathbf{b}$ is an arbitrary constant vector. Index notation may be useful in order to express $\nabla \cdot \mathbf{f}$ as

$$\nabla \cdot \mathbf{f} = \frac{\partial f_i}{\partial x_i} = \frac{\partial}{\partial x_i}[b_j F_{ji}]$$

Remember that a symmetric tensor has the property that

$$\mathbf{F} \cdot \mathbf{n} = \mathbf{n} \cdot \mathbf{F} \qquad \text{or} \qquad F_{ij} n_j = n_j F_{ji}$$

5-5. (5.2) Derive Eq. 5.2-22 from Eqs. 5.2-19 and 5.2-20.

***5-6.** In Ex. 5.3-1 we found that the rate of heat transfer from the bunsen burner to the gas had to be increased by a factor of 5.1 in order to double the volume of the gas. If we assume that the heat transferred to the gas is instantaneously changed from $\dot{Q}_{bb}^{(1)}$ to $\dot{Q}_{bb}^{(2)}$, how long will it take in order for the volume to reach 99 per cent of the final value of 2 liters? Treat the gas as ideal so that $c_v = 3\mathscr{R}/2$ and $c_p = 5\mathscr{R}/2$.

***5-7.** (5.3) Viscous effects are often neglected in the thermodynamic analysis of systems of the type shown in Fig. 5.3.1 by arguing that the compression or expansion takes place "very slowly." For a cylinder of length L containing a gas at a temperature T, develop a criterion which can be used to determine what is meant by "very slowly." Assume that the ideal gas law can be used so that the pressure is given by

$$p = \rho R T$$

†Problems numbered V-1, V-2, etc. deal directly with Design Problem V, and problems marked with an asterisk (*) are concerned with the solved example problems.

where $R = \mathcal{R}/(\text{molecular weight})$ and $\mathcal{R}$ is the universal gas constant. It will be convenient to note that

$$c^2 = \gamma RT$$

where c is the velocity of sound and γ is the ratio of specific heats, c_p/c_v.

If the gas in the cylinder is air at standard conditions we know that

$$c \sim 1100 \text{ ft/sec}$$
$$\gamma \sim 1.4$$
$$\mu/\rho \sim \kappa/\rho \sim 2\times 10^{-4} \text{ ft}^2/\text{sec}$$

For a cylinder 1 ft in length containing air, what is the maximum velocity of the piston which will lead to negligible viscous effects? Hint: Use the material in Sec. 2.9 to estimate the derivative of the velocity.

5-8. (5.4) Prove that $(\nabla\mathbf{v}):\mathbf{U} = \nabla\cdot\mathbf{v}$ by writing out the terms on the left-hand-side of Eq. 5.4-17 and showing that they are equal to the terms on the right-hand-side.

5-9. (5.5) The reversible work term given in Eq. 5.5-10 gives rise to a cooling effect for laminar flow in a tube. Give a qualitative explanation of this effect.

5-10. (5.5) For turbulent flow in pipes the time-averaged pressure gradient and viscous dissipation can be represented as

$$\left(\frac{\partial \bar{p}}{\partial z}\right) = -\frac{1}{2}\rho\langle \bar{v}_z\rangle^2(L/D)f$$

$$\nabla\mathbf{v}:\boldsymbol{\tau} = \frac{1}{2}\rho\langle \bar{v}_z\rangle^2(\langle \bar{v}_z\rangle/D)f$$

where f is the Darcy–Weisbach friction factor. If the pipes are hydraulically smooth the friction factor is given by

$$f = 0.316 N_{\text{Re}}^{-1/4}$$

where

$$N_{\text{Re}} = \rho\langle \bar{v}_z\rangle D/\mu$$

Use this information to estimate the temperature gradient owing to the effect of reversible work and viscous dissipation in turbulent flow. Present results for air, water, and a petroleum oil as was done in Sec. 5.5.

***5-11.** (5.6) Finned tubes such as the one shown in Fig. 5.6.1 are rarely used under circumstances where the surface temperature is a constant, T_0, as was the case for the analysis presented in Ex. 5.6-1. It is much more reasonable to assume that the temperature at the inside of the tube is some specified value, i.e.,

$$T = T_0, \qquad r = r_i$$

Given this condition, perform a dimensional analysis to show that the *overall* Nusselt number depends on two additional parameters, r_i/r_0 and k_g/k_s, in addition to the parameters given in Ex. 5.6-1. The *overall* Nusselt number is defined as

$$N_{\text{Nu}} = UL/k$$

where U is given by

$$U = \dot{Q}/A(T_0 - T_a)$$

In this analysis you must take into account the governing differential equations for the solid phase and carefully apply the conditions of continuity of temperature and heat flux at the phase interface.

5-12. (5.6) If the characteristic velocity is taken to be ν/L, where L is the characteristic length, the dimensionless form of the equations of motion for incompressible flow is

$$\frac{\partial \mathbf{U}}{\partial t^*} + \mathbf{U}\cdot\nabla\mathbf{U} = -\nabla\mathcal{P} + \nabla^2\mathbf{U}$$

where $t^* = t\nu/L^2$, $\mathbf{U} = \mathbf{v}L/\nu$, etc. For flow in a pipe we know that $\mathbf{U}$ depends on the Reynolds number; however, no Reynolds number appears in the dimensionless form of the equations of motion. Explain this apparent contradiction.

5-13. (5.7) Derive a criterion which can be used to determine under what circumstances viscous dissipation must be taken into account in the laminar boundary layer analysis. Do this by including this viscous dissipation term in Eq. 5.7-4 and repeating the order-of-magnitude analysis given in Sec. 5.7.

5-14. (5.7) By examining Eqs. 5.7-28 and 5.7-30 and the boundary conditions for U_x and Θ, prove that $\Theta = U_x$ when $N_{Pr} = 1$.

5-15. (5.8) Derive Eq. 5.8-20 using the similarity transform indicated in the text.

5-16. (5.9) Air at 72°F and 1 atm ($\nu = 0.16\ cm^2/sec$) flows past a flat plate with a uniform free stream velocity of 3 ft/sec. What is the boundary layer thickness at a point 5 in. from the leading edge? If the plate is 8 ft long and 3 ft wide, what is the drag force on one side of the plate?

5-17. (5.9) If the temperature of the plate described in Prob. 5-16 is 68°F, what is the total rate of heat transfer from the air to one side of the plate?

5-18. (5.9) Determine under what conditions, i.e., what value of $N_{Re,x}$, the boundary layer approximation, $\partial^2 U_x/\partial Y^2 \gg \partial^2 U_x/\partial X^2$, is valid.

***5-19.** (5.9) In Ex. 5.9-1 we concluded that the Nusselt number would be independent of the parameter η provided $\eta > 18\sqrt{\beta/N_{Re}}$. Our argument was based on the fact that the velocity field around a single fin would not be influenced by the presence of other fins provided the above restriction on $\eta = w/r_0$ was met. Our treatment of the problem was somewhat misleading for it is the *temperature field*, not the velocity field, which governs the heat transfer rate. Determine the restriction that must be placed on the parameter η in order that the temperature field around a single fin not be influenced by the presence of other fins. Consider the case for air, $N_{Pr} = 0.72$, and for liquids, $N_{Pr} > 1$.

***5-20.** (5.9) Use the analysis presented in Ex. 5.9-2 to determine the average film heat transfer coefficient for the conditions listed below and compare your result with the values given in Table 1.3-1.

air velocity:	8 ft/sec
air temperature:	62°F
pipe diameter:	1 in.
fin diameter:	2 in.
fin thickness:	$\frac{1}{16}$ in.

If the fin temperature is uniform at 112°F, what is the total rate of heat transfer for the fin? What air velocity is required to double this rate of heat transfer assuming that the fin temperature remains fixed at 112°F? If the air velocity is held constant at 8 ft/sec, how much must the fin diameter be increased in order to double the total heat transfer rate? Assume again that the fin temperature is uniform at 112°F and remember that *both* the film heat transfer coefficient *and* the surface area for heat transfer are functions of $\beta = r_1/r_0$. Note that the assumption of a uniform fin temperature may not be reasonable; the analysis given in Sec. 2.7 could be used to check this point.

5-21. (5.9) Derive an expression for the boundary layer thickness if the velocity profile is given by

$$v_x = u_\infty \sin(\pi y/2\delta_H)$$

5-22. (5.9) In Sec. 5.9 the analysis was restricted to cases for which $\delta_T \leq \delta_H$, yet good agreement with the exact solution was obtained for Prandtl numbers less than 1.0 for which $\delta_T > \delta_H$. Why is this?

5-23. (5.9) Liquid metals have Prandtl numbers in the range of 0.003 to 0.03, thus the laminar boundary layer analysis presented in Sec. 5.9 is not valid for liquid metals. Develop an approximate theory of liquid metal heat transfer in laminar boundary layers by analyzing the limiting case $N_{Pr} \to 0$. Hint: Take advantage of the fact that $\delta_T/\delta_H \to \infty$ as $N_{Pr} \to 0$.

5-24. (5.9) Rework the boundary layer analysis given in Sec. 5.9 to include the following conditions on the temperature and velocity fields

1. $\dfrac{\partial^2 T}{\partial y^2} = 0, \qquad y = \delta_T$
2. $\dfrac{\partial^2 v_x}{\partial y^2} = 0, \qquad y = \delta_H$

in addition to the conditions given in the text. Compare your calculated value for the average Nusselt number with the exact and approximate solutions given in the text.

5-25. (5.9) A cold fluid is flowing between two infinitely wide parallel plates as shown in Fig. 5.25. At $x = 0$, the temperature of the plates is suddenly changed from T_0 to T_1 and a thermal boundary layer is generated as illustrated. Assuming that the velocity field is unaffected by the heat transfer process, derive an expression for the local Nusselt number, $N_{Nu,loc} = h_{loc}b/k$, for the region where $\delta_T \leq b/2$. The velocity profile in the lower half of the

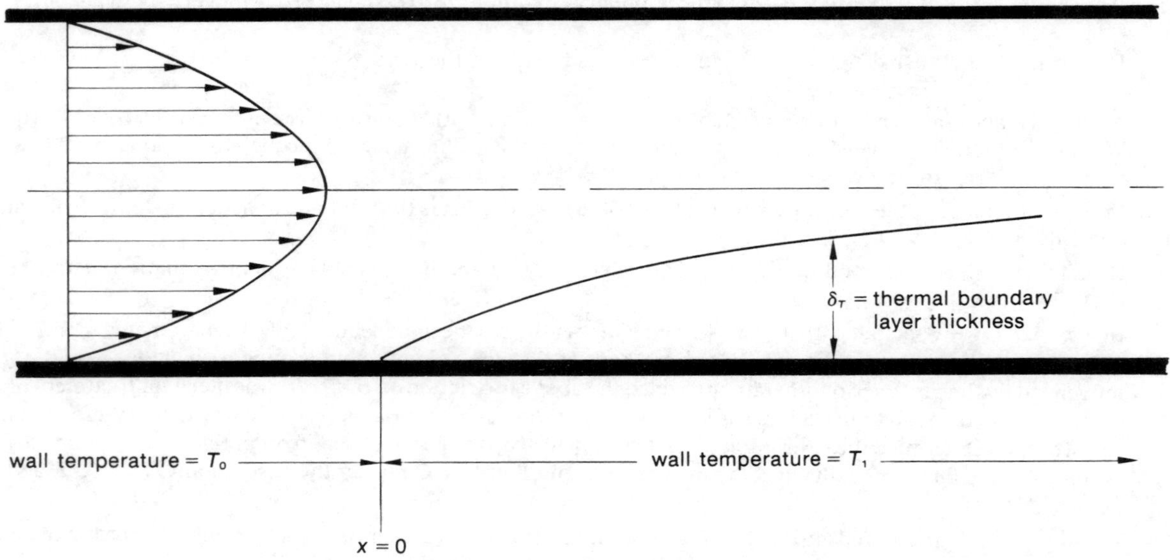

Fig. 5.25 Heat transfer in the entrance region of a rectangular channel

channel is given by

$$v_x = 6\langle v_x\rangle\left[\left(\frac{y}{b}\right) - \left(\frac{y}{b}\right)^2\right]$$

5-26. (5.10) Mountaineers who climb on the glaciated peaks of the Northwest are always careful to set up their high camps in an area which is protected from the "night wind" which can often develop into a rather stiff breeze even when the daytime weather is quite balmy. Explain why this wind occurs and whether it blows up or down the mountainside.

5-27. (5.10) Give a qualitative description of the type of flow that is generated if the plate shown in Fig. 5.10.1 is inclined at an angle of 45° to the vertical.

5-28. (5.10) If the Grashof number is considered to be the equivalent of a Reynolds number for free-convection flows, what is the characteristic velocity for such flows? For a vertical plate, 3 ft high, at a temperature of 172°F in contact with air at 68°F, what is the magnitude of the characteristic velocity?

5-29. (5.11) Show that Eq. 5.11-19 can be obtained from the more general relation

$$\psi = g(x)f(\eta), \qquad \eta = ax^b y^c$$

Hint: Follow the procedure outlined in Sec. 5.8.

5-30. (5.11) A vertical plate, 1 ft high, with a surface temperature of 89°F is placed in a large enclosure containing atmospheric air at 70°F. Find the average film heat transfer coefficient. If the plate is 2 ft wide and both sides are exposed to the air, what is the total rate of heat loss from the plate?

REFERENCES

1. Stein, S. K., *Calculus in the First Three Dimensions*, McGraw-Hill Book Co., Inc., New York, 1967.
2. Whitaker, S., *Introduction to Fluid Mechanics*, Prentice-Hall, Inc., Englewood Cliffs, N.J., 1968.
3. Slattery, J., *Momentum, Energy, and Mass Transfer in Continua*, McGraw-Hill Book Co., Inc., New York, 1972.
4. Truesdell, C., "A Program Toward Rediscovering the Rational Mechanics of the Age of Reason," *Arch. Hist. Exact Sci.* **1**, 31 (1961).
5. Shapiro, A. H., *Shape and Flow: The Fluid Dynamics of Drag*, Anchor Books, Doubleday & Co., Inc., Garden City, New York, 1961.
6. Schlichting, H., *Boundary Layer Theory*, Sixth Edition, McGraw-Hill Book Co., Inc., New York, 1968.
7. Howarth, L., "On the Solution of the Laminar Boundary Layer Equations," *Proc. Roy. Soc. London* **A164**, 155 (1957).
8. Eckert, E., and Drewitz, O., "The Heat Transfer to a Plate in Flow at High Speed," *NACA Tech. Memo 1045*, 1943.
9. Acrivos, A., "Solution of the Laminar Boundary Layer Energy Equation at High Prandtl Numbers," *Physics of Fluids* **3**, 657 (1960).
10. Braun, W. H., and Heighway, J. E., "An Integral Method for Free Convection Flows at High and Low Prandtl Numbers," *NASA Tech. Note D-292*, 1960.
11. Ostrach, S., "An Analysis of Laminar Free Convection Flow and Heat Transfer about a Flat Plate Parallel to the Direction of the Generating Body Force," *NACA Rept. 1111*, 1953.
12. Schmidt, E., and Beckmann, W., "Das Temperatur-und-Geschwindigkeitsfeld vor einter Warme abgebenden senkrechter Platte bei naturlicher Konvektion," *Tech. Mech. u. Thermodynamik*, Bd. 1, Nr. **11**, 391 (1930).
13. LeFevre, E. J., "Laminar Free Convection from a Vertical Plane Surface," *Heat Div. Paper 113*, Dept. Sci. and Ind. Res., Mech. Engr. Lab (Gt. Britain), Aug. 1956.
14. Saunders, O. A., "The Effect of Pressure Upon Free Convection in Air," *Proc. Roy. Soc. London* **A157**, 278 (1936).

Design Problem VI

A nuclear power plant is to be constructed on the banks of the Wazoo River which will serve as a source of cooling water and a sink for the "waste heat" from the plant. Disposal of the waste heat represents a serious problem during the summer months when the mean temperature of the Wazoo is 78°F and the average stream discharge is reduced to 18 000 ft^3/sec. The amount of energy to be disposed of is 1.66×10^{11} Btu/day in the form of 2200 ft^3/sec of cooling water having a 14°F temperature rise over the ambient river temperature. In the design of the waste heat disposal system we are required to restrict the surface area of the river which is heated to temperatures greater than 82°F to one acre or less. During the summer months the average depth of the Wazoo River is 20 ft and the average width is 600 ft. A recommendation regarding the disposal system is required.

6
Turbulent Flow

In the preceding chapter we studied two convective heat transfer processes, and we were able to develop analytical solutions for the temperature field which allowed us to calculate interphase heat transfer rates. Comparison of our calculations with experimental results indicated that the analysis was reasonably successful; however, there were two situations for which we could not accurately calculate the heat transfer rate. For both forced and free convection the boundary layer equations are not valid for sufficiently short plates, and we would have to solve the more general form of the transport equations in order to accurately determine the temperature field. At the other extreme of very long plates, we found poor agreement between theory and experiment because of the onset of turbulence.

The transport equations take on an exceedingly complex form for turbulent flow, and under such conditions an engineer must resort to the use of experimental results in order to determine interphase heat transfer rates. In this chapter we will examine the time-averaged form of the transport equations, conceding immediately that the detailed time history of the velocity and temperature fields is beyond our grasp. In Chapter 7 we will develop the macroscopic balance forms of the transport equations with the idea in mind that if we cannot solve the differential transport equations, the best alternative is to try for approximate solutions using the macroscopic balances† and experimental data. We have already had some experience in developing approximate solutions by means of the macroscopic balances (although they were not referred to as such) in Secs. 2.6, 4.3, and 5.9 and we will simply formalize these methods in Chapter 7.

*6.1 Time Averages

Since we plan to derive time-averaged or time-smoothed forms of the transport equations we need to make some definite statements about time averages. We *define* the time average of some function S at a time t as

$$\bar{S}(t) \equiv \frac{1}{2\Delta t} \int_{\eta=t-\Delta t}^{\eta=t+\Delta t} S(\eta)\, d\eta \tag{6.1-1}$$

where η is the dummy variable of integration. The time interval Δt is arbitrary, but in general we would hope that Δt could be made large enough so that $\bar{S}(t)$ is independent of Δt. The dependence of $\bar{S}$ on Δt is

†The word *equation* will be used as much as possible in reference to the point form of the transport equations, while the word *balance* will be used in reference to the macroscopic form of the transport equations.

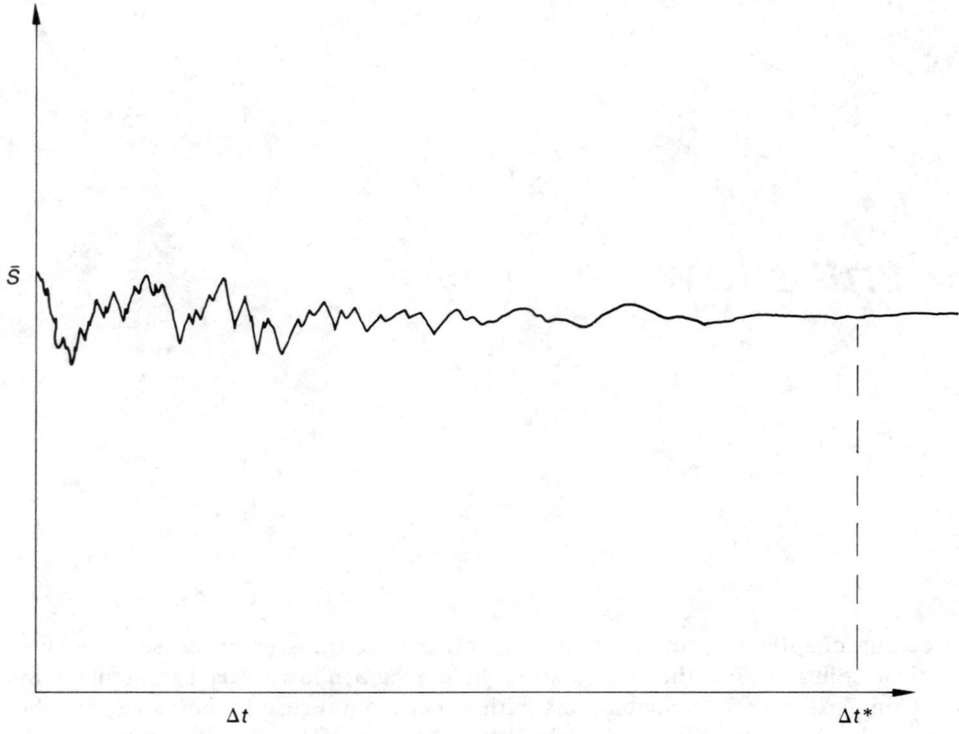

Fig. 6.1.1 Effect of Δt on the time-averaged value of S.

illustrated in Fig. 6.1.1 where Δt^* depends on the nature of the function S. In addition, we will require that all time-averaged functions, such as $\bar{\mathbf{v}}$, and $\bar{T}$, vary only slowly with time so that the *time average of the time average is equal to the time average.* By this we mean that

$$\bar{\bar{S}} = \bar{S} \tag{6.1-2}$$

This condition is satisfied if significant variations in $\bar{S}(t)$ occur over time intervals which are large compared to Δt.

Both the velocity and the temperature can be expressed in terms of the time averages ($\bar{\mathbf{v}}$, $\bar{T}$) and the fluctuations ($\mathbf{v}'$, T') by the relations

$$\mathbf{v} = \bar{\mathbf{v}} + \mathbf{v}' \tag{6.1-3}$$

$$T = \bar{T} + T' \tag{6.1-4}$$

If the restriction indicated by Eq. 6.1-2 is satisfied we have

$$\bar{\bar{\mathbf{v}}} = \bar{\mathbf{v}}$$

$$\bar{\bar{T}} = \bar{T}$$

and it follows by time averaging Eqs. 6.1-3 and 6.1-4 that the time averages of the fluctuations are zero.

$$\overline{\mathbf{v}'} = 0 \tag{6.1-5}$$

$$\overline{T'} = 0 \tag{6.1-6}$$

However, the square of the fluctuation is always positive and the ratios

$$\frac{\sqrt{\overline{(v_x')^2}}}{\bar{v}_x}, \quad \frac{\sqrt{\overline{(v_y')^2}}}{\bar{v}_x}, \quad \frac{\sqrt{\overline{(v_z')^2}}}{\bar{v}_x}$$

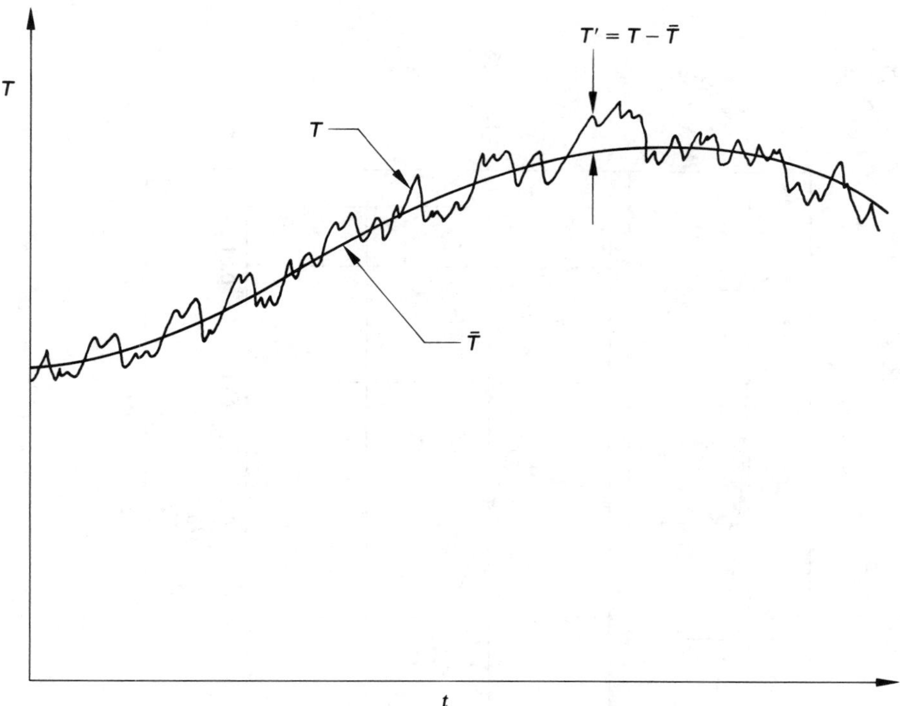

Fig. 6.1.2 The temperature at a fixed point in a turbulent stream.

are convenient measures of the *intensity of turbulence.* These quantities, which are often referred to as the fractional intensity of turbulence, have been measured in the turbulent boundary layer on a flat plate by Klebanoff [1] and the results are shown in Fig. 6.1.3. The data were taken for a length Reynolds number of 4.2×10^6 and indicate that the fluctuating components of the velocity are small compared to the free stream velocity, u_∞. However, the *local* time-averaged velocity, $\bar{v}_x$, shown in Fig. 6.1.4 tends to zero as $y/\delta_H \to 0$,

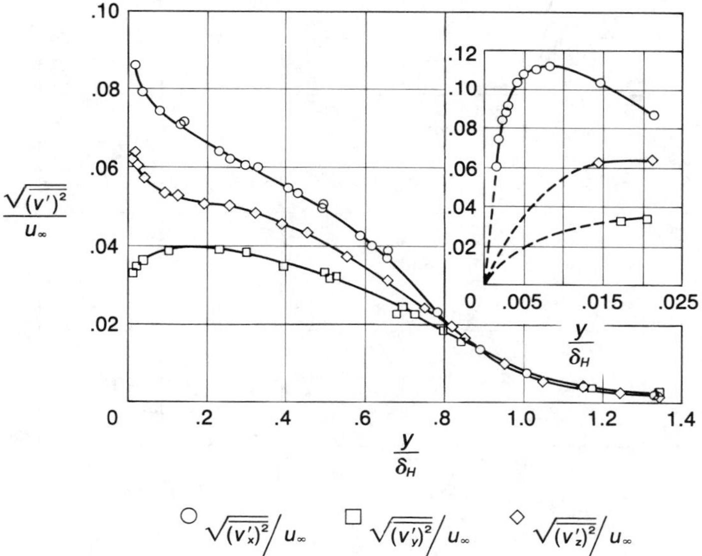

Fig. 6.1.3 Distribution of intensities in a turbulent boundary layer.

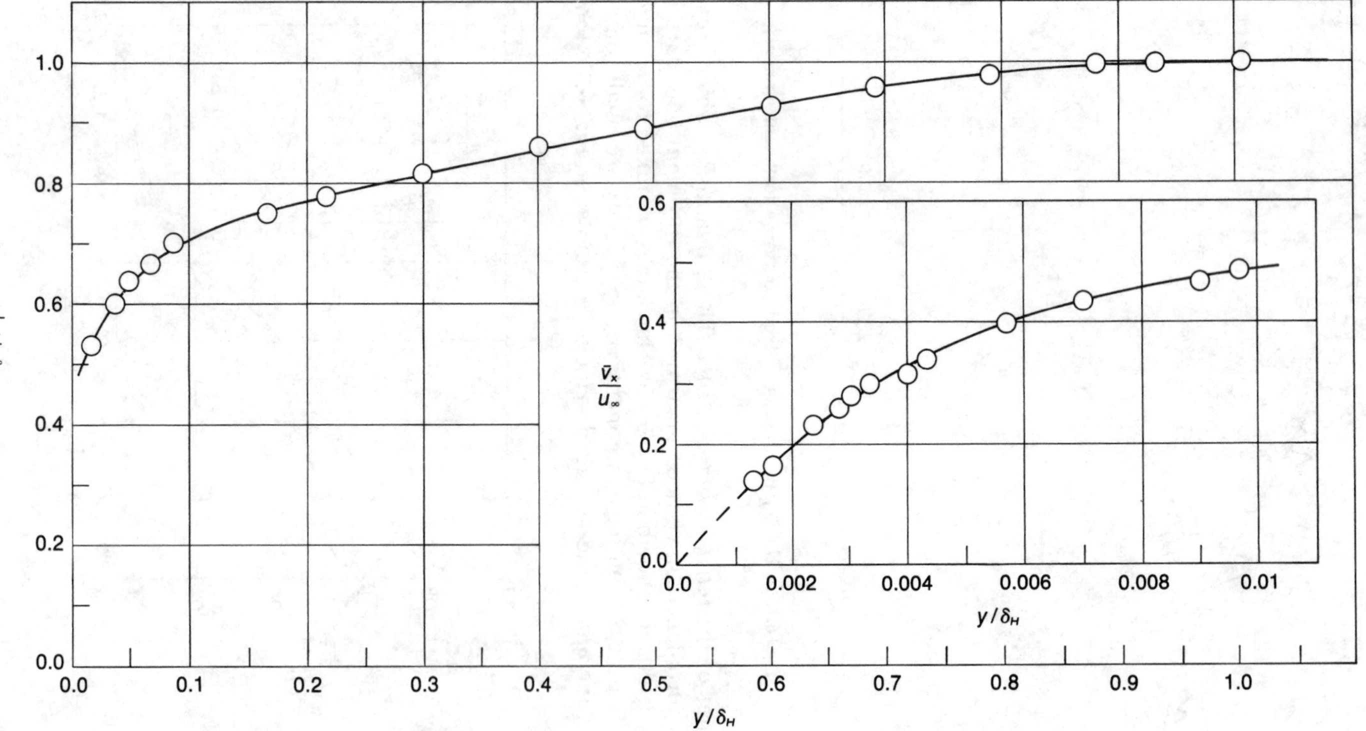

Fig. 6.1.4 Time-averaged velocity distribution in a turbulent boundary layer.

and in a region very near the wall the turbulent fluctuations become comparable in magnitude to that of the local time-averaged velocity. From Figs. 6.1.3 and 6.1.4 we can conclude that

$$\sqrt{\overline{(v_x')^2}} = 0(\bar{v}_x), \quad \text{for } y/\delta_H \sim 0.005$$

while the magnitudes of v_y' and v_z' are smaller than $\bar{v}_x$ by about a factor of ten.

The measurements of Klebanoff indicate that turbulent eddies are capable of penetrating very close to solid surfaces. Recent visual observations by Corino and Brodkey[2] for pipe flow have shown that the region near the wall is periodically disturbed by fluid elements which penetrate into the region from positions further removed from the wall, in addition to being disturbed by the periodic ejection of fluid elements from the wall region. Corino and Brodkey indicate that the ejections and the resulting fluctuations are the most important feature of the flow field in the wall region, and are believed to be a factor in the generation and maintenance of turbulence. In our discussion of turbulent heat transfer we will assume that the temperature fluctuations, T', follow much the same pattern as the velocity fluctuations.

Example 6.1-1 Evaluation of the local intensity in a turbulent boundary layer

Given air ($\nu = 0.16\ \text{cm}^2/\text{sec}$) flowing past a flat plate at 50 ft/sec, determine the distance from the solid surface at which the intensity $\sqrt{\overline{(v_x')^2}}/u_\infty$ is a maximum and determine the value of the *local intensity* at this point. We shall take the length Reynolds number to be 4.2×10^6 so that the data shown in Figs. 6.1.3 and 6.1.4 can be used.

The boundary layer thickness for a turbulent boundary layer on a flat plate can be represented with reasonable accuracy by the expression

$$\delta_H = 0.37 x N_{\text{Re},x}^{-1/5}, \qquad \text{turbulent boundary layer thickness}$$

where $N_{\text{Re},x} = u_\infty x/\nu$.

Given that $N_{\text{Re},x} = 4.2 \times 10^6$ we can determine x for our case to be

$$\begin{aligned} x &= \left(\frac{\nu}{u_\infty}\right)(4.2 \times 10^6) \\ &= \left(\frac{0.16\ \text{cm}^2/\text{sec}}{50\ \text{ft/sec}}\right)\left(\frac{\text{in.}}{2.54\ \text{cm}}\right)\left(\frac{\text{ft}}{12\ \text{in.}}\right)(4.2 \times 10^6) \\ &= 441\ \text{cm} \end{aligned}$$

The boundary layer thickness is now given by

$$\begin{aligned} \delta_H &= (0.37)(441\ \text{cm})(4.2 \times 10^6)^{-1/5} \\ &= 7.73\ \text{cm} \end{aligned}$$

From Fig. 6.1.3 we can see that the maximum value of the intensity occurs at $y/\delta_H = 0.008$, thus the distance from the solid surface at which the intensity is a maximum is given by

$$\begin{aligned} y &= (0.008)(7.73\ \text{cm}) \\ &= 0.062\ \text{cm} \end{aligned}$$

Here we see that the maximum turbulent fluctuations occur at about two hundredths of an inch from the solid surface. For water we would find this point to be even closer to the wall, and determining the exact value will be left as an exercise for the student.

Referring to Figs. 6.1.3 and 6.1.4 we find that

$$\sqrt{\overline{(v_x')^2}}/u_\infty = 0.11, \qquad \bar{v}_x/u_\infty = 0.46, \qquad \text{at } y/\delta_H = 0.008$$

thus the *local intensity* is given by

$$\sqrt{\overline{(v_x')^2}}/\bar{v}_x = 0.24, \qquad \text{at } y/\delta_H = 0.008$$

Here we see that the magnitude of v_x' is about 25 per cent of the local value of the time-averaged velocity, $\bar{v}_x$. Since both v_x' and $\bar{v}_x$ tend to zero as $y \to 0$ we can expect the turbulent fluctuations to be significant throughout the entire region, $0 \leq y/\delta_H \leq 0.008$. For example, at $y/\delta_H = 0.0025$ or $y = 0.019$ cm we see that

$$\sqrt{\overline{(v_x')^2}}/u_\infty = 0.08, \qquad \bar{v}_x/u_\infty = 0.23$$

and the local intensity takes on the even larger value of

$$\sqrt{\overline{(v_x')^2}}/\bar{v}_x = 0.34, \qquad \text{at } y/\delta_H = 0.0025$$

From these calculations we see that turbulent eddies can penetrate very close to solid surfaces, and that the magnitude of the turbulent fluctuations can be comparable to the time-averaged velocity.

*6.2 Time-Averaged Form of the Transport Equations

In this section we will develop the time-averaged form of the continuity equation, the thermal energy equation, and the equations of motion, all for incompressible flows. The analysis of flows for which there is a variation in the density will be left as an exercise for the student.

Continuity equation

For incompressible flows the continuity equation can be expressed as

$$\nabla \cdot \mathbf{v} = 0 \tag{6.2-1}$$

and the time-averaged form is

$$\frac{1}{2\Delta t} \int_{\eta=t-\Delta t}^{\eta=t+\Delta t} \nabla \cdot \mathbf{v} \, d\eta = 0 \tag{6.2-2}$$

Since the limits of integration are not functions of x, y, or z, we can interchange differentiation and integration to obtain

$$\frac{1}{2\Delta t} \int_{\eta=t-\Delta t}^{\eta=t+\Delta t} \nabla \cdot \mathbf{v} \, d\eta = \nabla \cdot \left[\frac{1}{2\Delta t} \int_{\eta=t-\Delta t}^{\eta=t+\Delta t} \mathbf{v} \, d\eta \right] = \nabla \cdot \bar{\mathbf{v}} = 0 \tag{6.2-3}$$

Thus we find that the time-averaged form of the continuity equation is identical to the original form.

Thermal energy equation

Referring to Eq. 5.5-10 we write the thermal energy equation as

$$\rho c_p \left(\frac{\partial T}{\partial t} + \mathbf{v} \cdot \nabla T \right) = k \nabla^2 T + \Phi \tag{6.2-4}$$

where Φ is now used to represent the reversible work, the viscous dissipation, and the heat generation owing to electromagnetic effects, and we have taken the thermal conductivity to be constant. We will further restrict our analysis to processes for which c_p can be considered constant, and write the time-averaged form of Eq. 6.2-4 as

$$\rho c_p \left[\frac{1}{2\Delta t} \int_{\eta=t-\Delta t}^{\eta=t+\Delta t} \left(\frac{\partial T}{\partial \eta} \right) d\eta + \frac{1}{2\Delta t} \int_{\eta=t-\Delta t}^{\eta=t+\Delta t} (\mathbf{v} \cdot \nabla T) \, d\eta \right] = k \left[\frac{1}{2\Delta t} \int_{\eta=t-\Delta t}^{\eta=t+\Delta t} \nabla^2 T \, d\eta \right] + \bar{\Phi} \tag{6.2-5}$$

The explicit time-averaged form of the source term, Φ, will be more complex than we have indicated here if this term is the result of viscous dissipation or reversible work; however, the detailed analysis of this term will be left as an exercise for the student.

Beginning with the first term on the right-hand-side of Eq. 6.2-5 we interchange differentiation and integration to obtain

$$\frac{1}{2\Delta t}\int_{\eta=t-\Delta t}^{\eta=t+\Delta t} \nabla^2 T\, d\eta = \nabla^2\left[\frac{1}{2\Delta t}\int_{\eta=t-\Delta t}^{\eta=t+\Delta t} T\, d\eta\right] = \nabla^2 \bar{T} \tag{6.2-6}$$

Moving on to the convective transport term we express the velocity and temperature as $\mathbf{v} = \bar{\mathbf{v}} + \mathbf{v}'$ and $\bar{T} + T'$ and write

$$\frac{1}{2\Delta t}\int_{\eta=t-\Delta t}^{\eta=t+\Delta t} (\mathbf{v}\cdot\nabla T)\, d\eta = \frac{1}{2\Delta t}\int_{\eta=t-\Delta t}^{\eta=t+\Delta t} (\bar{\mathbf{v}}\cdot\nabla\bar{T} + \bar{\mathbf{v}}\cdot\nabla T' + \mathbf{v}'\cdot\nabla\bar{T} + \mathbf{v}'\cdot\nabla T')\, d\eta \tag{6.2-7}$$

Examining the four individual terms on the right-hand-side of Eq. 6.2-7 we obtain for the first term

$$\frac{1}{2\Delta t}\int_{\eta=t-\Delta t}^{\eta=t+\Delta t} \bar{\mathbf{v}}\cdot\nabla\bar{T}\, d\eta = \bar{\mathbf{v}}\cdot\nabla\bar{T} \tag{6.2-8a}$$

Here it is assumed, in accordance with Eq. 6.1-2, that $\bar{\mathbf{v}}$ and $\bar{T}$ undergo negligible variation during the time, $2\Delta t$. The second and third terms are zero since $\overline{T'}$ and $\overline{\mathbf{v}'}$ are zero as indicated in Eqs. 6.1-5 and 6.1-6,

$$\frac{1}{2\Delta t}\int_{\eta=t-\Delta t}^{\eta=t+\Delta t} \bar{\mathbf{v}}\cdot\nabla T'\, d\eta = \bar{\mathbf{v}}\cdot\nabla\left[\frac{1}{2\Delta t}\int_{\eta=t-\Delta t}^{\eta=t+\Delta t} T'\, d\eta\right] = 0 \tag{6.2-8b}$$

$$\frac{1}{2\Delta t}\int_{\eta=t-\Delta t}^{\eta=t+\Delta t} \mathbf{v}'\cdot\nabla\bar{T}\, d\eta = \left[\frac{1}{2\Delta t}\int_{\eta=t-\Delta t}^{\eta=t+\Delta t} \mathbf{v}'\, d\eta\right]\cdot\nabla\bar{T} = 0 \tag{6.2-8c}$$

and the fourth term is simply expressed as

$$\frac{1}{2\Delta t}\int_{\eta=t-\Delta t}^{\eta=t+\Delta t} \mathbf{v}'\cdot\nabla T'\, d\eta = \overline{\mathbf{v}'\cdot\nabla T'} \tag{6.2-8d}$$

Substitution of Eqs. 6.2-6 and 6.2-8 into Eq. 6.2-5, and making use of the fact that $\mathbf{v}'\cdot\nabla T' = \nabla\cdot(\mathbf{v}'T')$ for incompressible flows we obtain

$$\rho c_p\left[\frac{1}{2\Delta t}\int_{\eta=t-\Delta t}^{\eta=t+\Delta t}\left(\frac{\partial T}{\partial \eta}\right) d\eta\right] + \rho c_p\bar{\mathbf{v}}\cdot\nabla\bar{T} + \rho c_p\nabla\cdot\overline{(\mathbf{v}'T')} = k\nabla^2\bar{T} + \bar{\Phi} \tag{6.2-9}$$

The first term on the left-hand-side is easiest to treat by first evaluating the integral to show that the *average of the derivative* is given by

$$\overline{\left(\frac{\partial T}{\partial t}\right)} = \frac{1}{2\Delta t}[T(t+\Delta t) - T(t-\Delta t)] \tag{6.2-10}$$

and then examine the *derivative of the average*

$$\left(\frac{\partial \bar{T}}{\partial t}\right) = \frac{\partial}{\partial t}\left[\frac{1}{2\Delta t}\int_{\eta=t-\Delta t}^{\eta=t+\Delta t} T(\eta)\, d\eta\right] \tag{6.2-11}$$

Here we must be careful to note that the integrand is a function of the dummy variable of integration, η, while the limits of integration are indeed functions of time. Differentiation of the integral is accomplished by use of the Leibnitz rule [3] giving us

$$\left(\frac{\partial \bar{T}}{\partial t}\right) = \frac{1}{2\Delta t}[T(t+\Delta t) - T(t-\Delta t)] \tag{6.2-12}$$

Here we have used the relations

$$\frac{\partial}{\partial t}(t+\Delta t) = \frac{\partial}{\partial t}(t-\Delta t) = 1$$

$$\frac{\partial T(\eta)}{\partial t} = 0$$

Comparing Eqs. 6.2-10 and 6.2-12, we see that the average of the derivative is equal to the derivative of the average [4],

$$\overline{\left(\frac{\partial T}{\partial t}\right)} = \frac{\partial \bar{T}}{\partial t}$$

and Eq. 6.2-9 can be written as

$$\rho c_p \left(\frac{\partial \bar{T}}{\partial t} + \bar{\mathbf{v}} \cdot \nabla \bar{T}\right) = k \nabla^2 \bar{T} - \nabla \cdot (\rho c_p \overline{T' \mathbf{v}'}) + \bar{\Phi} \tag{6.2-13}$$

Here we see that the time-averaged form of the thermal energy equation differs from the original form only in the term $\nabla \cdot (\rho c_p \overline{T' \mathbf{v}'})$. We define $(\rho c_p \overline{T' \mathbf{v}'})$ as the turbulent energy flux vector and write

$$\bar{\mathbf{q}}^{(t)} = (\rho c_p \overline{T' \mathbf{v}'}) \tag{6.2-14}$$

where the quantity $\bar{\mathbf{q}}^{(t)}$ represents the energy transported by the fluctuating velocity field. The time-averaged conduction term can be expressed as

$$k \nabla^2 \bar{T} = -\nabla \cdot \bar{\mathbf{q}} \tag{6.2-15}$$

thus we may rewrite Eq. 6.2-13 in the form

$$\rho c_p \left(\frac{\partial \bar{T}}{\partial t} + \bar{\mathbf{v}} \cdot \nabla \bar{T}\right) = -\nabla \cdot [\bar{\mathbf{q}} + \bar{\mathbf{q}}^{(t)}] + \bar{\Phi} \tag{6.2-16}$$

This in turn may be expressed as

$$\rho c_p \left(\frac{\partial \bar{T}}{\partial t} + \bar{\mathbf{v}} \cdot \nabla \bar{T}\right) = -\nabla \cdot \bar{\mathbf{q}}^{(T)} + \bar{\Phi} \tag{6.2-17}$$

where $\bar{\mathbf{q}}^{(T)}$ is the *total* heat flux vector.

$$\bar{\mathbf{q}}^{(T)} = \bar{\mathbf{q}} + \bar{\mathbf{q}}^{(t)} \tag{6.2-18}$$

At this point we see that the time-averaged form of the thermal energy equation is *identical* to the original form provided we interpret the velocity and temperature as time averages and the heat flux vector as the sum of the time-averaged heat flux plus the turbulent heat flux.

Equations of motion

The analysis of the equations of motion for incompressible flow and constant physical properties begins with the viscous stress equations of motion

$$\rho \left(\frac{\partial \mathbf{v}}{\partial t} + \mathbf{v} \cdot \nabla \mathbf{v}\right) = -\nabla p + \rho \mathbf{g} + \nabla \cdot \boldsymbol{\tau} \tag{6.2-19}$$

The development is essentially identical to that given for the thermal energy equation and it will be left as an exercise for the student. In summary, our time-averaged equations are

Continuity equation

$$\nabla \cdot \bar{\mathbf{v}} = 0 \tag{6.2-20}$$

Thermal energy equation

$$\rho c_p \left(\frac{\partial \bar{T}}{\partial t} + \bar{\mathbf{v}} \cdot \nabla \bar{T}\right) = k \nabla^2 \bar{T} - \nabla \cdot (\rho c_p \overline{\mathbf{v}' T'}) + \bar{\Phi} \tag{6.2-21}$$

Equations of motion

$$\rho \left(\frac{\partial \bar{\mathbf{v}}}{\partial t} + \bar{\mathbf{v}} \cdot \nabla \bar{\mathbf{v}}\right) = -\nabla \bar{p} + \rho \mathbf{g} + \nabla \cdot \bar{\boldsymbol{\tau}} - \nabla \cdot (\overline{\rho \mathbf{v}' \mathbf{v}'}) \tag{6.2-22}$$

Table 6.2-1 Related Terms for Laminar and Turbulent Flow

Laminar flow	*Turbulent flow*
$\mathbf{v}$	$\bar{\mathbf{v}}$
T	$\bar{T}$
p	$\bar{p}$
$\boldsymbol{\tau}$	$\bar{\boldsymbol{\tau}}^{(T)} = \bar{\boldsymbol{\tau}} - \rho\overline{\mathbf{v}'\mathbf{v}'}$
$\mathbf{q}$	$\bar{\mathbf{q}}^{(T)} = \bar{\mathbf{q}} + \rho c_p \overline{\mathbf{v}'T'}$
Φ	$\bar{\Phi}$

It is convenient to remember that the original transport equations are applicable to the analysis of turbulent flows provided the terms are interpreted as listed in Table 6.2-1.

Our difficulty in analyzing heat and momentum transfer is that there are no suitable constitutive equations for $\bar{\mathbf{q}}^{(t)}$ and $\bar{\boldsymbol{\tau}}^{(t)}$ where the latter is called the turbulent stress tensor and is given by

$$\bar{\boldsymbol{\tau}}^{(t)} = -\rho\overline{\mathbf{v}'\mathbf{v}'} \tag{6.2-23}$$

If there were generally valid expressions for $\bar{\mathbf{q}}^{(t)}$ and $\bar{\boldsymbol{\tau}}^{(t)}$ of the type

$$\bar{\mathbf{q}}^{(t)} = \mathbf{f}(\nabla\bar{T}) \tag{6.2-24a}$$

$$\bar{\boldsymbol{\tau}}^{(t)} = \mathbf{G}(\nabla\bar{\mathbf{v}}) \tag{6.2-24b}$$

we could solve turbulent flow problems in just the same manner as we solved laminar flow problems. However, there are no unique functional relationships between the turbulent heat flux vector and the gradient of the average temperature, or the turbulent stress tensor and the gradient of the average velocity. For this reason the analysis of turbulent flow phenomena is primarily an experimental problem, although many theories have been presented for special cases.

Example 6.2-1 The time average of the time average

An important step in the development of the time-averaged mass, momentum, and energy equations was the assumption that $\bar{\bar{T}} = \bar{T}$ and $\bar{\bar{\mathbf{v}}} = \bar{\mathbf{v}}$. In order to gain some insight into the nature of this assumption we propose a crude representation of the temperature–time curve shown in Fig. 6.1.2 of the form

$$T = T_0(1 + bt + ct^2) + A\cos\omega t$$

Here $A\cos\omega t$ represents the turbulent fluctuations, the term bt gives rise to a linear variation of the temperature with time, and the term ct^2 represents a parabolic dependence on time. Our objective is to calculate the time average, $\bar{T}$, and the time average of the time average, $\bar{\bar{T}}$, at $t = 0$. Clearly the representation for T is unrealistic for large times, but we can learn something from examining this temperature–time dependence for short times, i.e., $t = 0$. We take the coefficients b, c, and ω to be

$$b = 0.2\ \text{sec}^{-1}$$
$$c = 0.07\ \text{sec}^{-2}$$
$$\omega = 75\ \text{sec}^{-1}$$

so that our case is one of a high-frequency fluctuation imposed on a fairly rapidly changing temperature field, i.e., the value of the temperature will double in 5 sec.

In order to eliminate $A\cos\omega t$ by time averaging we must integrate over a time period of one cycle, $2\pi/\omega$, and we wish to know if this time period is small enough so that $\bar{\bar{T}} = \bar{T}$. Forming the time average yields

$$\bar{T} = \frac{1}{2\Delta t}\int_{\eta=t-\Delta t}^{\eta=t+\Delta t} T_0(1 + b\eta + c\eta^2)\,d\eta + \frac{1}{2\Delta t}\int_{\eta=t-\Delta t}^{\eta=t+\Delta t} A\cos\omega\eta\,d\eta$$

or

$$\bar{T} = \frac{T_0}{2\Delta t}\left[\eta + \frac{1}{2}b\eta^2 + \frac{1}{3}c\eta^3\right]_{\eta=t-\Delta t}^{\eta=t+\Delta t} + \frac{A}{2\Delta t\omega}\left[\sin\omega\eta\right]_{\eta=t-\Delta t}^{\eta=t+\Delta t}$$

We can see that the second term is zero for $\Delta t = \pi/\omega$ if we remember that $\sin(\omega t + \pi) = \sin(\omega t - \pi)$, and the limits may be imposed on the first term to yield

$$\bar{T} = T_0(1 + bt + ct^2 + \tfrac{1}{3}c\Delta t^2)$$

Note at this point that it is the nonlinear dependence on time that causes the time average to be a function of the averaging time, Δt. Repeating the integration to determine the average of the average gives us,

$$\bar{\bar{T}} = T_0(1 + bt + ct^2 + \tfrac{2}{3}c\Delta t^2)$$

and at time equal to zero we have

$$\bar{T} = T_0(1 + \tfrac{1}{3}c\Delta t^2),$$

$$\text{for } t = 0$$

$$\bar{\bar{T}} = T_0(1 + \tfrac{2}{3}c\Delta t^2),$$

Using $c = 0.07\ \text{sec}^{-2}$ and $\Delta t = \pi/\omega = 0.042$ sec we find that $\bar{T}$ and $\bar{\bar{T}}$ are essentially equal:

$$\bar{T} = T_0\,(1.001)$$

$$\bar{\bar{T}} = T_0\,(1.002)$$

*6.3 Turbulent Momentum and Energy Transport

Turbulent flows can occur under many different circumstances. In Chapter 5 we encountered turbulent boundary layer flows for both forced and free convection. Flows in closed conduits and open channels may be either laminar or turbulent depending on the Reynolds number and other factors; the flow in the wake of an immersed body is generally turbulent; the periodic growth and escape of bubbles during boiling gives rise to a turbulent motion; and the condensation of vapors on a vertical surface can give rise to a turbulent falling liquid film if the flow rate is large enough. Although the structure of the turbulence (i.e., the nature of the $\mathbf{v}'$ field) varies greatly for these different processes, there are some common characteristics that can be assigned to all turbulent fields. In each case we find that large velocity gradients cause intense turbulence (i.e., large values of $\overline{\mathbf{v}'\,\mathbf{v}'}$), the intensity tends toward zero at solid surfaces where $\mathbf{v}'$ must go toward zero, and in the absence of large velocity gradients viscous effects tend to reduce the intensity. Rather than attempt to survey the various types of turbulent flow, we will restrict our discussion to turbulent flow in a tube. Since the main features of most turbulent flows can be brought out by this example, and since turbulent flow in tubes is a rather important subject, it is not unreasonable to restrict our discussion to this single example. However, the student must realize that we will have just scratched the surface of the subject of turbulence.

When the flow is laminar and one-dimensional the velocity profile in a tube is

$$v_z = v_{z,\max}\left[1 - \left(\frac{r}{r_0}\right)^2\right] \tag{6.3-1}$$

This result is obtained directly from the special form that the Navier–Stokes equations take for one-dimensional steady, laminar flow. If we had a constitutive equation relating the turbulent stress $\bar{\tau}_{rz}^{(t)}$ to the velocity gradient $(\partial\bar{v}_z/\partial r)$ we could solve the time-averaged equations of motion to determine $\bar{v}_z$ as a function of r. Since this constitutive equation is not available, experiments are in order, and the results of experimental studies indicate that the time-averaged velocity is fairly accurately described by the expression

$$\bar{v}_z = \bar{v}_{z,\max}\left(1 - \frac{r}{r_0}\right)^{1/7} \tag{6.3-2}$$

While Eq. 6.3-2 is in good agreement with experimental data, it cannot be used to predict the shear stress at the tube wall, because the derivative of $\bar{v}_z$ with respect to r tends to infinity as $r \to r_0$. Eqs. 6.3-1 and 6.3-2 are shown in Fig. 6.3.1. There we see that the turbulent velocity profile is much more flat over the central region of the tube and the gradient at the wall is much larger than for laminar flow. In the central region of the tube, the velocity fluctuations are large and the turbulent stress is much larger than the time-averaged viscous stress, i.e.,

$$\bar{\boldsymbol{\tau}}^{(t)} \gg \bar{\boldsymbol{\tau}}, \quad \text{in the core}$$

As we approach the wall $\mathbf{v}$ and $\mathbf{v}'$ tend toward zero and it is necessary that in some region near the wall the time-averaged viscous stresses must become dominant, i.e.,

$$\bar{\boldsymbol{\tau}} \gg \bar{\boldsymbol{\tau}}^{(t)}, \quad \text{near the wall}$$

It follows that there must be a *transition* region where turbulent and viscous stresses are comparable, thus the region outside the core can be arbitrarily divided into two regions as shown in Fig. 6.3.2.

If we examine the viscous stress equations of motion listed in Table 5.2-1 subject to the restrictions

1. $\bar{v}_r = \bar{v}_\theta = 0$, i.e., the time-averaged flow is one-dimensional
2. $\dfrac{\partial \bar{v}_z}{\partial z} = 0$, follows logically from assumption 1 and the time-averaged continuity equation

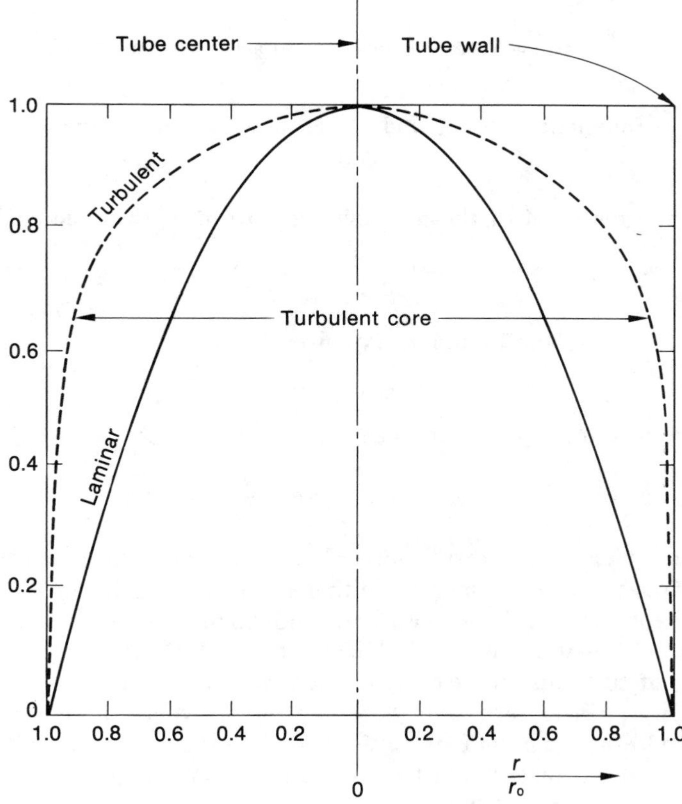

Fig. 6.3.1 Laminar and turbulent velocity profiles in a tube.

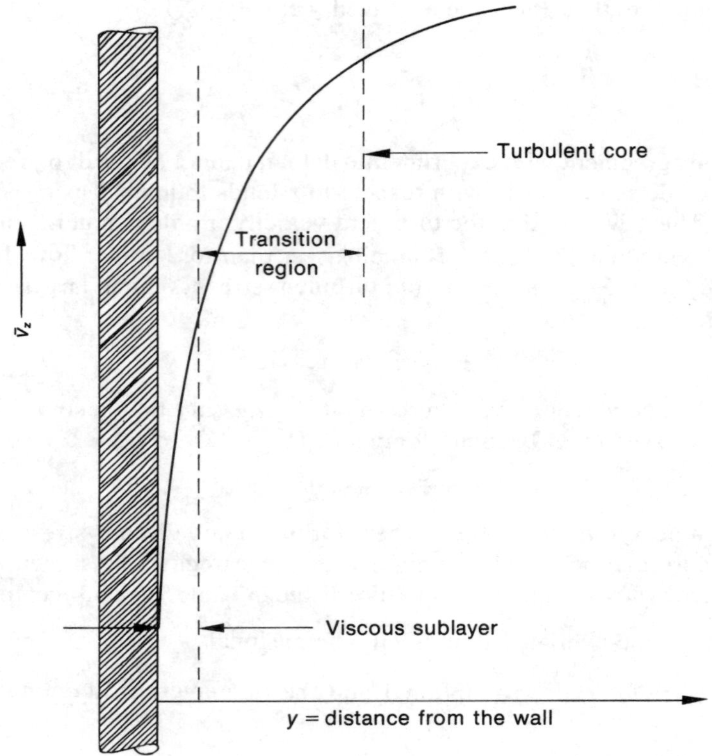

Fig. 6.3.2 Viscous sublayer and transition region in a tube.

3. $\bar{\tau}_{\theta z}^{(T)}$, $\bar{\tau}_{zz}^{(T)}$, and $\bar{\tau}_{zr}^{(T)}$ are independent of θ and z, i.e., flow is axially symmetric and one-dimensional
4. $g_z = 0$

we can deduce that the z-component of the time-averaged form of these equations takes the form

$$-\frac{\Delta \bar{p}}{L} = \frac{1}{r}\frac{d}{dr}(r\bar{\tau}_{rz}^{(T)}) \tag{6.3-3}$$

Integration of Eq. 6.3-3 subject to the boundary condition

B.C. $\bar{\tau}_{rz}^{(T)}$ is finite for $0 \leqslant r \leqslant r_0$ (6.3-4)

yields an equation for the total time-averaged shear stress

$$\bar{\tau}_{rz}^{(T)} = \bar{\tau}_{rz} + \bar{\tau}_{rz}^{(t)} = -\left(\frac{\Delta \bar{p}}{L}\right)\frac{r}{2} \tag{6.3-5}$$

Here we see that the total shear stress distribution is immediately determined by measurement of the pressure gradient $-(\Delta \bar{p}/L)$, and if we can measure either $\bar{\tau}_{rz}$ or $\bar{\tau}_{rz}^{(t)}$ we can completely determine the shear stress distribution. Such measurements have been made and illustrative results are shown in Fig. 6.3.3, and the variation of intensity is shown in Fig. 6.3.4. Measurements by Laufer [5] indicate that the intensity $\sqrt{\overline{(v_z')^2}}/\langle \bar{v}_z \rangle$ is on the order of 10^{-2}, thus in the core region $v_z' \ll \bar{v}_z$. However, as one approaches the wall the local time-averaged velocity goes to zero, and there is a region where the magnitude of the fluctuating components is comparable to the magnitude of $\bar{v}_z$. We find from these two figures that the turbulent shear stress predominates in the core region and falls to zero at the wall. We also find that the maximum intensity occurs quite near the wall, and we conclude that the turbulence is generated near the wall where the velocity gradient is large. The intensity tends to zero as we approach the wall because $\mathbf{v}'$, and thus $\rho\overline{\mathbf{v}'\mathbf{v}'}$,

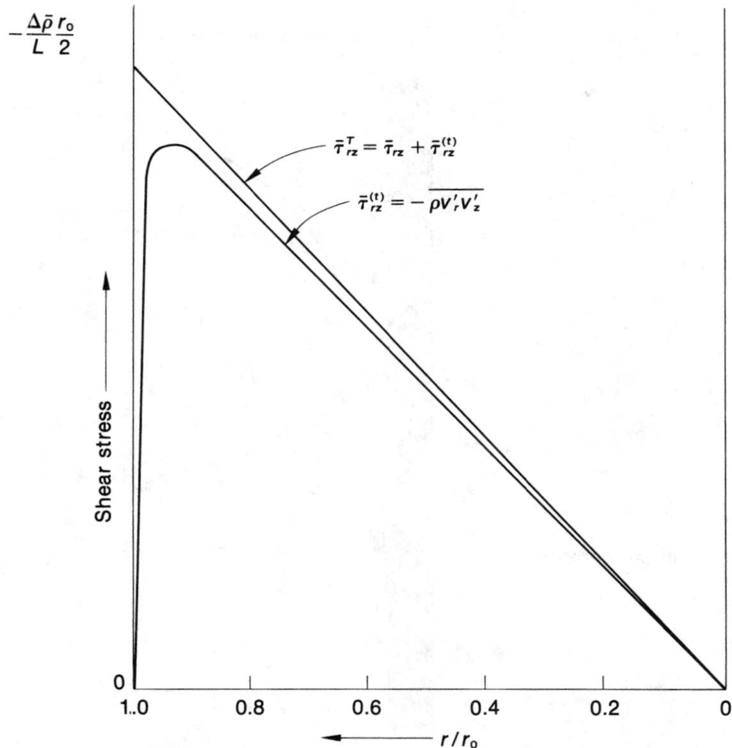

Fig. 6.3.3 Total shear stress and turbulent shear stress for flow in a tube.

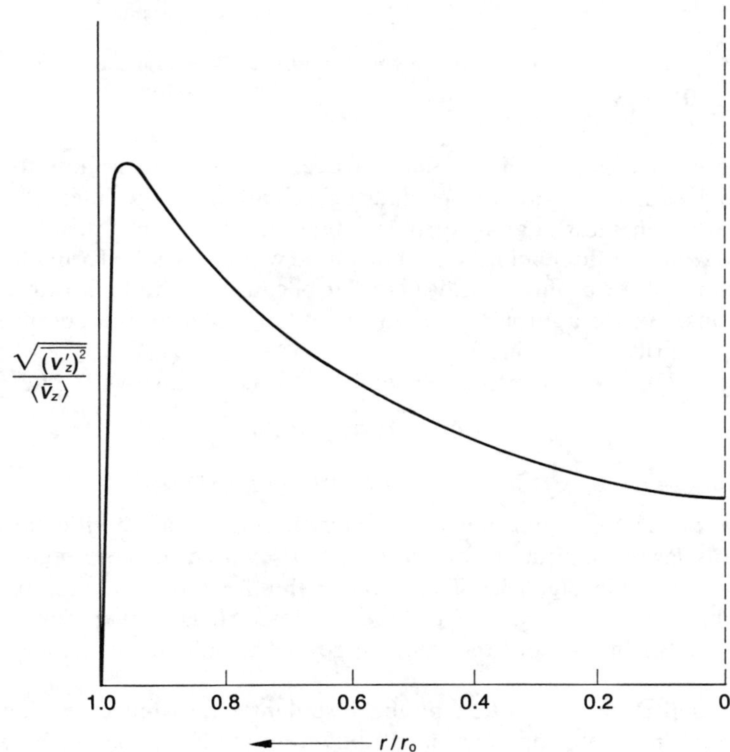

Fig. 6.3.4 Variation of intensity of turbulence with radial position.

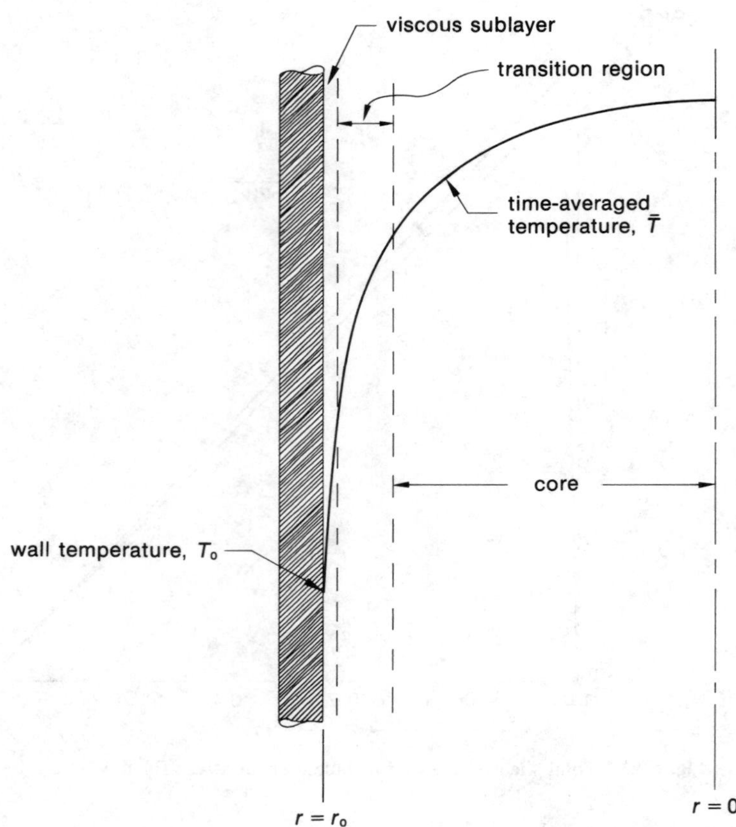

Fig. 6.3.5 Temperature profile for turbulent flow in a tube.

must tend to zero as we approach a solid surface. In the core region the generating force (shear deformation) decreases and viscous forces cause a reduction in the intensity.

With only this meager knowledge of turbulent flow in tubes at our disposal, one might guess that the temperature profile for a hot fluid being cooled in a tube would take the form illustrated in Fig. 6.3.5. In the core region the temperature profile is relatively flat because of the high rate of energy transport by the turbulent fluctuations. As we approach the wall $\bar{\mathbf{q}}^{(t)}$ tends to zero and energy is transported across the viscous sublayer primarily by conduction.

In terms of the radial component of the total heat flux vector, we would express these ideas as

$$\bar{q}_r^{(t)} \gg \bar{q}_r, \quad \text{in the core region}$$

$$\bar{q}_r^{(t)} \ll \bar{q}_r, \quad \text{in the viscous sublayer}$$

However, this is *not* true for liquid metals, as their thermal conductivities are so large that conductive transport is generally larger than the turbulent transport even in the core region. This is illustrated by the temperature profiles shown in Fig. 6.4.3. There we see that for $N_{\mathrm{Pr}} = 4$ the temperature profile in the core is nearly flat indicating a very high rate of turbulent transport. However, for a liquid metal ($N_{\mathrm{Pr}} = 0.024$) conduction predominates throughout the entire tube and a significant temperature gradient exists in the core region.

An interesting qualitative description of the turbulent stress tensor $\bar{\boldsymbol{\tau}}^{(t)}$ and the turbulent heat flux vector $\bar{\mathbf{q}}^{(t)}$ can be obtained by proposing constitutive equations similar to Newton's law of viscosity†

†Here $\nabla \mathbf{v}^{T}$ represents the transpose of $\nabla \mathbf{v}$, and Eq. 6.3-6 is only valid for an incompressible flow.

$$\boldsymbol{\tau} = \mu(\nabla \mathbf{v} + \nabla \mathbf{v}^{\mathrm{T}}) \tag{6.3-6}$$

and Fourier's law of heat conduction

$$\mathbf{q} = -k\nabla T \tag{6.3-7}$$

We should remember that the *material coefficients*, μ and k, depend on the local thermodynamic state and are intimately related to the molecular structure of the fluid.

By analogy we might be encouraged to express the associated turbulent quantities as

$$\bar{\boldsymbol{\tau}}^{(t)} = \mu^{(t)}(\nabla \bar{\mathbf{v}} + \nabla \bar{\mathbf{v}}^{\mathrm{T}}) \tag{6.3-8}$$

where $\mu^{(t)}$ is the turbulent or *eddy* viscosity, and

$$\bar{\mathbf{q}}^{(t)} = -k^{(t)}\nabla \bar{T} \tag{6.3-9}$$

where $k^{(t)}$ is the turbulent thermal conductivity. With these definitions we can express the total time-averaged stress tensor and total time-averaged heat flux vector as

$$\bar{\boldsymbol{\tau}}^{(T)} = (\mu + \mu^{(t)})(\nabla \bar{\mathbf{v}} + \nabla \bar{\mathbf{v}}^{\mathrm{T}}) \tag{6.3-10}$$

$$\bar{\mathbf{q}}^{(T)} = -(k + k^{(t)})\nabla \bar{T} \tag{6.3-11}$$

These eddy or turbulent transport coefficients are rather difficult to work with for they are not functions of the *thermodynamic state*; rather they are functions of the *mechanical state* of the system (i.e., the intensity and structure of the turbulence). A relatively simple approach to developing expressions for $\mu^{(t)}$ and $k^{(t)}$ is to make use of the Prandtl mixing length theory [6] which is presented in the following section. The arguments used in the development of this theory are not precise; however, its presentation should enhance the student's qualitative understanding of turbulent transport phenomena. A more precise understanding of turbulent transport coefficients can only be gained by an examination of current research on the subject.

Example 6.3-1 Bulk and averaged temperature for turbulent flow

In the analysis of heat transfer for flow in closed conduits we will encounter a temperature known as the *bulk temperature* which is defined as

$$\bar{T}_b \equiv \frac{\int_A \bar{T}\bar{v}_z \, dA}{\int_A \bar{v}_z \, dA}$$

where A is the cross-sectional area of the conduit. Sometimes this temperature is referred to as the "mixing-cup" temperature, for it is the temperature one would measure if the fluid issuing from a pipe were collected in a cup and thoroughly mixed. We can also define an area-averaged temperature in a closed conduit by the expression

$$\langle \bar{T} \rangle \equiv \frac{\int_A \bar{T} \, dA}{\int_A dA}$$

In this example we will take the velocity profile to be given by Eq. 6.3-2 which we write as

$$\bar{v}_z = u_0 \left(1 - \frac{r}{r_0}\right)^{1/7}$$

where u_0 is the velocity at the center of the tube. We will assume that the temperature profile is similar to the velocity profile, thus leading to

$$\frac{\bar{T} - T_w}{T_0 - T_w} = \left(1 - \frac{r}{r_0}\right)^{1/7}$$

Here $\bar{T}$ is the time-averaged temperature, T_w is the temperature at the wall, and T_0 is the temperature at the centerline. This choice of velocity and temperature profiles can be used to express the bulk temperature as

$$\bar{T}_b = \frac{2\pi \int_0^{r_0} \left[T_w + (T_0 - T_w)\left(1 - \frac{r}{r_0}\right)^{1/7}\right]\left[u_0\left(1 - \frac{r}{r_0}\right)^{1/7}\right] r\,dr}{2\pi \int_0^{r_0} u_0\left(1 - \frac{r}{r_0}\right)^{1/7} r\,dr}$$

We can cancel $2\pi u_0$ so that this expression is simplified to

$$\bar{t} = \frac{\int_0^{r_0} \left[T_w + \Delta T\left(1 - \frac{r}{r_0}\right)^{1/7}\right]\left(1 - \frac{r}{r_0}\right)^{1/7} r\,dr}{\int_0^{r_0} \left(1 - \frac{r}{r_0}\right)^{1/7} r\,dr}$$

where $\Delta T = T_0 - T_w$. The integrals may be evaluated by standard methods leading to

$$\bar{T}_b = T_w + (T_0 - T_w)(0.83)$$

This can be written as

$$\bar{T}_b = T_0 - 0.17(T_0 - T_w)$$

indicating that the bulk temperature is very nearly equal to the centerline temperature, T_0, provided $(T_0 - T_w) < T_0$.

It will be interesting to compare this result for $\bar{T}_b$ with the value for the area-averaged temperature which is given by

$$\langle \bar{T} \rangle = \frac{2\pi \int_0^{r_0} \left[T_w + (T_0 - T_w)\left(1 - \frac{r}{r_0}\right)^{1/7}\right] r\,dr}{2\pi \int_0^{r_0} r\,dr}$$

Evaluating the integral and rearranging the result leads to

$$\langle \bar{T} \rangle = T_0 - 0.18(T_0 - T_w)$$

Here we see that the bulk temperature and the area-averaged temperature are almost identical, $\bar{T}_b \sim \langle \bar{T} \rangle$; however, this occurs because the temperature profile is very nearly flat, and we should expect to find a different result when this is not the case.

6.4 Turbulent Transport Coefficients

In this section we will develop a qualitative theory for the turbulent viscosity, $\mu^{(t)}$, and the turbulent thermal conductivity, $k^{(t)}$. Consider the steady (on the average), one-dimensional flow illustrated in Fig. 6.4.1, and assume that discrete "lumps" or "eddies" or "particles" of fluid can move from one position to another and still retain their momentum during this motion. Such a picture is certainly an oversimplification for viscous effects will alter the momentum of a fluid particle as it moves from one region to another. Nevertheless, if a particle moves from a high-velocity region to a low-velocity region we expect it to arrive with a velocity component that is greater than the local velocity. Put another way, we assume there is some distance over which a turbulent eddy can maintain its momentum, and we refer to this distance as the *hydrodynamic mixing length.*

In Fig. 6.4.1 we have illustrated two fluid particles exchanging places in the flow field. The particles are separated by a distance ℓ_H and their velocities can be related using the first term of a Taylor series expansion for $\bar{v}_x$ to obtain

$$\bar{v}_x\big|_{y+\ell_H} = \bar{v}_x\big|_y + \ell_H\left(\frac{\partial \bar{v}_x}{\partial y}\right) \tag{6.4-1}$$

Imagine now that we are measuring the velocity continuously at the position, y. Before the exchange takes place the measured velocity is $\bar{v}_x(y)$, immediately after the exchange the velocity increases to $\bar{v}_x(y + \ell_H)$,

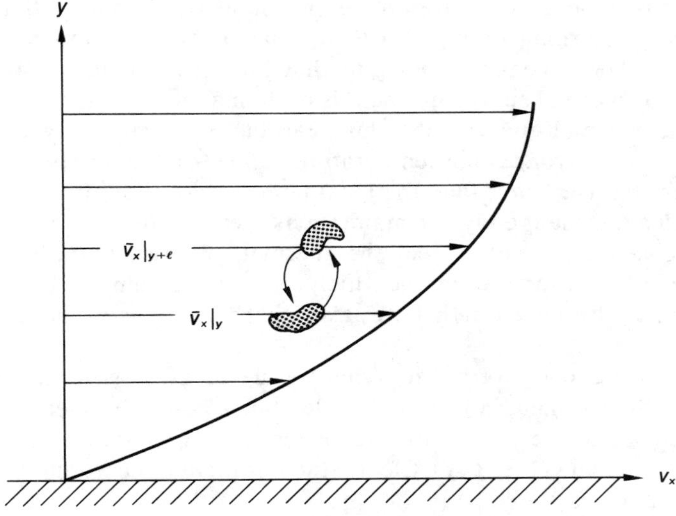

Fig. 6.4.1 The turbulent transport process.

and a short time after that the velocity again returns to its original value, $\bar{v}_x(y)$. Clearly the turbulent velocity component v'_x is related to the difference and we write

$$v'_x = \mathbf{0}\,(\bar{v}_x|_{y+\ell_H} - \bar{v}_x|_y) = \mathbf{0}\left[\ell_H\left(\frac{\partial \bar{v}_x}{\partial y}\right)\right] \tag{6.4-2}$$

From the discussion in Sec. 6.2 one can easily show that the turbulent velocity field, $\mathbf{v}'$, must obey the continuity equation, which for an incompressible flow takes the form

$$\nabla \cdot \mathbf{v}' = 0 \tag{6.4-3}$$

Considering the expanded form

$$\frac{\partial v'_x}{\partial x} + \frac{\partial v'_y}{\partial y} + \frac{\partial v'_z}{\partial z} = 0 \tag{6.4-4}$$

we note that the order-of-magnitudes of v'_x, v'_y, and v'_z should be the same if the scale of the turbulence is comparable in the x-, y-, and z-directions. This leads to the conclusion that

$$v'_y = \mathbf{0}(v'_x) \quad \text{and} \quad v'_z = \mathbf{0}(v'_x) \tag{6.4-5}$$

The results shown in Fig. 6.1.3 confirm this point of view, and we use Eqs. 6.4-5 and 6.4-2 to express v'_y as

$$v'_y = \mathbf{0}\left[\ell_H\left(\frac{\partial \bar{v}_x}{\partial y}\right)\right] \tag{6.4-6}$$

From Eq. 6.2-23 we note that the component of the turbulent stress $\bar{\tau}^{(t)}_{yx}$, i.e., the turbulent stress (force per unit area) acting on the y-surface in the x-direction, is given by

$$\bar{\tau}^{(t)}_{yx} = -\rho\overline{v'_y v'_x} \tag{6.4-7}$$

and we can use Eqs. 6.4-2 and 6.4-6 to express the order-of-magnitude of $\bar{\tau}^{(t)}_{yx}$ as

$$\bar{\tau}^{(t)}_{yx} = -\rho\overline{v'_y v'_x} = \mathbf{0}\left[\rho\ell_H^2\left(\frac{\partial \bar{v}_x}{\partial y}\right)^2\right] \tag{6.4-8}$$

Note that our analysis has given us more than the order-of-magnitude; it has also suggested a functional form for the turbulent stress.

We now turn our attention to the turbulent energy flux in the y-direction. From Eq. 6.2-8 we take this to be

$$\bar{q}_y^{(t)} = -\rho c_p \overline{T' v'_y} \tag{6.4-9}$$

and our task at this point is to develop appropriate expressions for T' and v'_y that are consistent with the energy transport process. Returning to Fig. 6.4.1 we imagine that a temperature profile exists in the y-direction and is given by $\bar{T}(y)$. We further imagine that particles of fluid can move from one position to another and still retain their thermal energy during this motion. Once again this is an oversimplification for conduction will alter the thermal energy of a fluid particle as it moves from one region to another. Nevertheless, if a particle moves from a high-temperature region to a low-temperature region we expect it to arrive with a temperature that is greater than the local temperature. Put another way, we assume there is some distance over which a turbulent eddy can maintain its thermal energy, and we refer to this distance as the *thermal mixing length*. We do not expect the thermal mixing length, ℓ_T, to be the same as the hydrodynamic mixing length, ℓ_H, for the rate at which the particle gains or loses momentum because of viscous effects may be quite different from the rate at which it gains or loses thermal energy because of heat conduction.

Referring once again to Fig. 6.4.1 we imagine that we are measuring the temperature continuously at some position, y. Before the exchange of fluid particles takes place the measured temperature is $\bar{T}(y)$, immediately after the exchange the temperature changes to $\bar{T}(y+\ell_T)$, and a short time after that the temperature returns to its original value, $\bar{T}(y)$. Clearly the turbulent temperature fluctuation is related to the difference and we express T' as

$$T' = \mathbf{0}(\bar{T}|_{y+\ell_T} - \bar{T}|_y) = \mathbf{0}\left[\ell_T\left(\frac{\partial \bar{T}}{\partial y}\right)\right] \tag{6.4-10}$$

Here we have again used the first term of a Taylor series expansion to express the temperature as

$$\bar{T}|_{y+\ell_T} = \bar{T}|_y + \ell_T\left(\frac{\partial \bar{T}}{\partial y}\right)$$

The turbulent velocity component, v'_y, in the expression for $\bar{q}_y^{(t)}$ is the velocity associated with the thermal energy transport process, thus Eq. 6.4-6 is modified to give

$$v'_y = \mathbf{0}\left[\ell_T\left(\frac{\partial \bar{v}_x}{\partial y}\right)\right], \quad \text{for turbulent thermal energy transport} \tag{6.4-11}$$

Substitution of Eqs. 6.4-11 and 6.4-10 into Eq. 6.4-9 yields an expression for the turbulent energy flux

$$\bar{q}_y^{(t)} = \mathbf{0}\left[\rho c_p \ell_T^2\left(\frac{\partial \bar{v}_x}{\partial y}\right)\left(\frac{\partial \bar{T}}{\partial y}\right)\right] \tag{6.4-12}$$

Once again our analysis has given us an order-of-magnitude estimate of $\bar{q}_y^{(t)}$ in addition to suggesting a function form for the turbulent energy flux.

If we think about the exchange of fluid particles in a temperature field we quickly come to the conclusion that energy must be transported down the temperature gradient, i.e.,

$$\bar{q}_y^{(t)} \propto -\left(\frac{\partial \bar{T}}{\partial y}\right)$$

Furthermore, the direction of the flow of energy will not be changed when the sign of the velocity gradient changes, thus we are led to express Eq. 6.4-12 as

$$\bar{q}_y^{(t)} = -\rho c_p \ell_T^2\left|\frac{\partial \bar{v}_x}{\partial y}\right|\left(\frac{\partial \bar{T}}{\partial y}\right) \tag{6.4-13}$$

Similar arguments for the case of momentum transport lead us to write Eq. 6.4-8 as

$$\bar{\tau}_{yx}^{(t)} = \rho \ell_H^2\left|\frac{\partial \bar{v}_x}{\partial y}\right|\left(\frac{\partial \bar{v}_x}{\partial y}\right) \tag{6.4-14}$$

Note that all of the slack generated by our crude treatment of this problem is conveniently taken up in the mixing length, for we will use ℓ_H and ℓ_T as correlating variables choosing the magnitude and functional dependence to be anything that accurately represents experimental measurements. It should be clear that ℓ

must approach zero in the region of solid surfaces where $\bar{\tau}_{yx}^{(t)}$ and $\bar{q}_y^{(t)}$ both must go to zero. Furthermore, it should be clear that the undetermined parameter ℓ can only vaguely resemble the mixing length as it is depicted in Fig. 6.4.1.

The general tensor forms of Eqs. 6.4-13 and 6.4-14 are†

$$\bar{\mathbf{q}}^{(t)} = -c_p(2\rho\ell_T^2\sqrt{2\mathbf{d}:\mathbf{d}})\nabla\bar{T} \tag{6.4-15}$$

$$\bar{\boldsymbol{\tau}}^{(t)} = (2\rho\ell_H^2\sqrt{2\mathbf{d}:\mathbf{d}})\mathbf{d} \tag{6.4-16}$$

which leads to expressions for the eddy viscosity and eddy thermal conductivity of

$$k^{(t)} = \rho c_p\ell_T^2\sqrt{2\mathbf{d}:\mathbf{d}} \tag{6.4-17}$$

$$\mu^{(t)} = \rho\ell_H^2\sqrt{2\mathbf{d}:\mathbf{d}} \tag{6.4-18}$$

If we consider the two mixing lengths to be the same, our development implies that

$$\frac{\mu^{(t)}/\rho}{k^{(t)}/\rho c_p} = \frac{\nu^{(t)}}{\alpha^{(t)}} = 1, \quad \text{for } \ell_T = \ell_H \tag{6.4-19}$$

Experimental results [7] indicate that this is approximately true for turbulent flow in pipes where values of $\nu^{(t)}/\alpha^{(t)}$ are near unity, provided the Prandtl number is on the order of 1.0. Thinking back to the problem of forced convection in a laminar boundary layer (Sec. 5.8) we remember that for $N_{\mathrm{Pr}} = 1.0$ the dimensionless velocity and temperature profiles were identical, and for that case it could be said that *momentum and energy transport were analogous.* However, one must keep in mind that the laminar boundary layer equations represent a very special form of the equations of motion, and in general, the transport of a vector quantity (momentum) is not likely to be analogous to the transport of a scalar quantity (energy).

Qualitative comments on the mixing length

In order to help clarify the mechanism of energy and momentum transport illustrated in Fig. 6.4.1 we need to think about the history of a "fluid particle" as it moves about in the turbulent field. In doing so we must remember that there are no fluid particles, that a fluid moves and deforms continuously in time and space, and that our "picture" of a turbulent field consisting of such particles is simply a device to provide a reference point for our discussion.

Consider the case of a fluid particle having a very low thermal conductivity, i.e., the case where $k \to 0$. Such a particle would exchange energy *very slowly* with its surroundings and the distance it would travel before losing a significant portion of its energy would be large, i.e., the thermal mixing length would be *large* for a fluid particle with a *small* thermal conductivity. If we think awhile about the opposite case of a fluid particle having a very *large* thermal conductivity we should conclude that its mixing length would be *small.*

We can express these ideas in a somewhat more quantitative manner if we apply the thermal energy equation‡ to our fluid particle.

$$\frac{DT}{Dt} = \alpha\nabla^2 T \tag{6.4-20}$$

We can use the ideas developed in Sec. 2.9 to express the order-of-magnitude of $\nabla^2 T$ for our hypothetical particle as

$$\nabla^2 T = \mathbf{0}\left(\frac{T_{\text{particle}} - T_{\text{surroundings}}}{L^2}\right) \tag{6.4-21}$$

where L is a characteristic length for the particle, i.e.,

$$\{\text{volume of the particle}\} \sim L^3$$

†Here $\mathbf{d}$ represents the rate of strain tensor and is given by

$$\mathbf{d} = \tfrac{1}{2}(\nabla\mathbf{v} + \nabla\mathbf{v}^T)$$

‡See Eq. 5.5-12.

We can use Eq. 6.4-21 to write the thermal energy equation as

$$\frac{DT}{Dt} = \mathbf{0}\left(\frac{\alpha\,\Delta T}{L^2}\right) \tag{6.4-22}$$

Here we see that the time rate of change of temperature of the fluid particle should *increase* with *increasing* thermal diffusivity, α. This means that a *large* thermal diffusivity gives rise to a *small* thermal mixing length, ℓ_T. In a casual manner we could express this result as

$$\ell_T \sim \frac{1}{\alpha} \tag{6.4-23}$$

By Eq. 6.4-23 we simply mean that the mixing length should be *small* when α is *large*, and that ℓ_T should be *large* when α is *small*.

Let us now turn our attention to the velocity of a fluid particle and consider the case of a fluid particle having a very low viscosity, i.e., the case where $\mu \to 0$. Such a particle would exchange momentum *very slowly* with its surroundings and the distance it would travel before losing a significant portion of its momentum would be large, i.e., the hydrodynamic mixing length would be *large* for a fluid particle with a *small* viscosity.† If we think awhile about the opposite case of a fluid particle having a very *large* viscosity we should conclude that its hydrodynamic mixing length should be *small* for the large viscous forces will quickly cause it to lose its momentum to the surroundings.

If we attempt to describe these ideas in a more quantitative manner by using the equations of motion

$$\frac{D\mathbf{v}}{Dt} = -\frac{1}{\rho}\nabla p + \mathbf{g} + \nu\nabla^2\mathbf{v} \tag{6.4-24}$$

we follow our previous treatment of the thermal energy equation and write

$$\frac{D\mathbf{v}}{Dt} = \mathbf{0}\left(-\frac{1}{\rho}\nabla p + \mathbf{g}\right) + \mathbf{0}\left(\frac{\nu\Delta\mathbf{v}}{L^2}\right) \tag{6.4-25}$$

where $\Delta\mathbf{v}$ is given by

$$\Delta\mathbf{v} = \mathbf{v}_{\text{particle}} - \mathbf{v}_{\text{surroundings}} \tag{6.4-26}$$

Our arguments are hindered at this point by the term, $-(1/\rho)\nabla p + \mathbf{g}$; nevertheless, we will follow the arguments given for Eq. 6.4-22 and conclude that the hydrodynamic mixing length could be expressed as

$$\ell_H \sim \frac{1}{\nu} \tag{6.4-27}$$

Once again we state that Eq. 6.4-27 simply means that the mixing length should be *small* when ν is *large*, and that ℓ_H should be large when ν is *small*.

Combining Eqs. 6.4-23 and 6.4-27 yields

$$\frac{\ell_T}{\ell_H} \sim N_{\text{Pr}} \tag{6.4-28}$$

indicating that the thermal mixing length should be larger than the hydrodynamic mixing length when $N_{\text{Pr}} \gg 1$, and for liquid metals ($N_{\text{Pr}} = 10^{-2}$ to 10^{-3}) we should expect that $\ell_T \ll \ell_H$. We should note once again that Eq. 6.4-28 provides only an *indication* of the functional dependence, and from dimensional analysis we can quickly conclude that the functional dependence of ℓ_T/ℓ_H should be of the form

$$\frac{\ell_T}{\ell_H} = \mathcal{F}(N_{\text{Pr}}, N_{\text{Re}}, X, Y, Z) \tag{6.4-29}$$

provided the physical properties of the fluid are independent of temperature. The qualitative development presented here tells only that the functional dependence of N_{Pr} in Eq. 6.4-29 is such that ℓ_T/ℓ_H *increases* with *increasing* Prandtl number.

†Note that this argument is not at all valid if the particle is heading toward a solid surface.

From Eqs. 6.4-17 and 6.4-18 we can obtain

$$\left(\frac{\ell_T}{\ell_H}\right)^2 = \frac{k^{(t)}/\rho c_P}{\mu^{(t)}/\rho} = \frac{\alpha^{(t)}}{\nu^{(t)}} \sim N_{\text{Pr}}^2 \tag{6.4-30}$$

Jenkins [8] has analyzed this process in some detail for an isotropic turbulent field and his results are presented in Fig. 6.4.2. There we see that the ratio $\alpha^{(t)}/\nu^{(t)}$ does indeed *increase* with *increasing* Prandtl number. The dependence on the Reynolds number suggested by Eq. 6.4-29 appears in Jenkins calculations as a dependence on the ratio of the turbulent kinematic viscosity to the molecular kinematic viscosity, $\nu^{(t)}/\nu$.

It would be nice at this point to see if these qualitative ideas about turbulent transport are consistent with experimental observation. In Fig. 6.4.3 we have shown three temperature profiles for turbulent pipe flow. The profiles are quite different and we can explain the difference using Eq. 6.4-30 to express the turbulent thermal conductivity as

$$k^{(t)} \sim N_{\text{Pr}}^2 \rho c_P \nu^{(t)} \tag{6.4-31}$$

This result can also be expressed as

$$\frac{k^{(t)}}{k} \sim N_{\text{Pr}}^3 \frac{\nu^{(t)}}{\nu} \tag{6.4-32}$$

For Reynolds numbers on the order of 40000 we expect† $\nu^{(t)}/\nu \sim 100$ in the core region (see Figs. 6.3.1 and 6.3.5), and we can use Eq. 6.4-32 to conclude

$$k^{(t)} \gg k, \quad \text{for } N_{\text{Pr}} = 4.0$$
$$k^{(t)} > k, \quad \text{for } N_{\text{Pr}} = 0.7$$
$$k^{(t)} \ll k, \quad \text{for } N_{\text{Pr}} = 0.024$$

†See Reference 4, page 208.

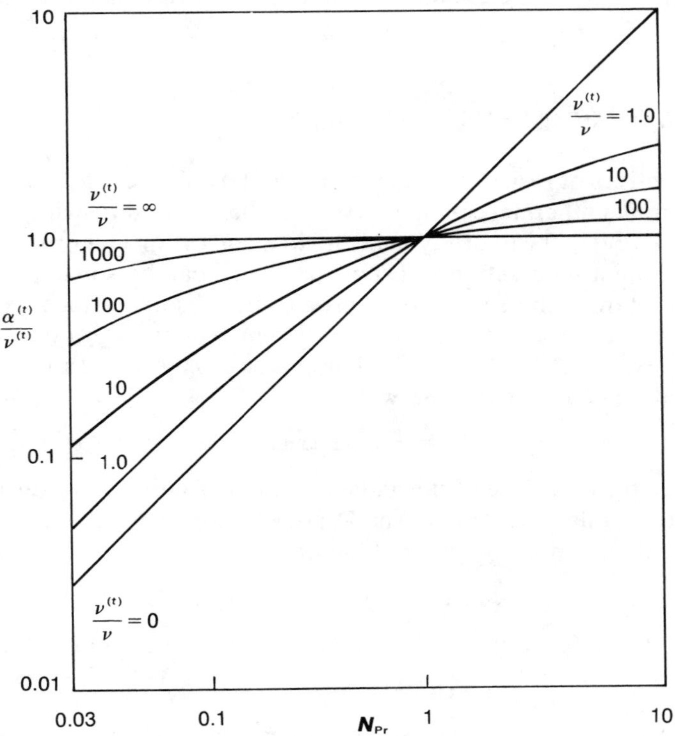

Fig. 6.4.2 Effect of Prandtl number on the ratio $\alpha^{(t)}/\nu^{(t)}$.

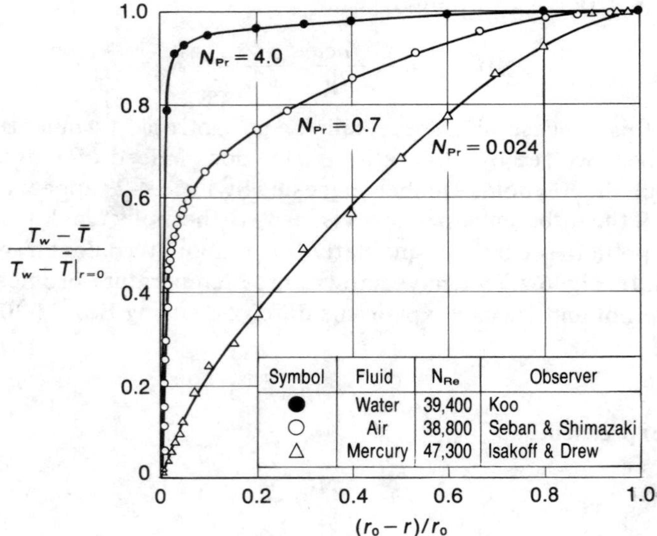

Fig. 6.4.3 Experimental temperature profiles. (Adapted from W. H. McAdams, *Heat Transmission*, McGraw-Hill Book Co., Inc., New York, 1954.)

For $N_{Pr} = 4$ the temperature profile is nearly flat in the core region, and this is to be expected since $k^{(t)} \gg k$. For mercury, $N_{Pr} = 0.024$ and Eq. 6.4-32 indicates that turbulence should have little effect on the temperature profile, and the experimentally determined temperature profile shown in Fig. 6.4.3 indicates that indeed this is true.

We conclude that our crude picture of a turbulent field has some connection with reality, but we must always remember that at best it is only a simplified picture of the complex process of turbulent energy and momentum transport.

6.5 Hydrodynamic Mixing Length Theory

One of the major objectives of research on the subject of turbulence is to be able to predict the turbulent viscosity, $\mu^{(t)}$, and the turbulent thermal conductivity $k^{(t)}$. In this section we will restrict our discussion to the estimation of $\mu^{(t)}$ or alternatively the hydrodynamic mixing length, ℓ_H. Our objective will *not* be to provide the tools with which turbulent momentum transport problems can be solved, but simply to enhance our qualitative understanding of the turbulent transport process near a solid surface. To this end we will examine a mixing length theory and experimental data for turbulent pipe flow.

The simplest possible expression for the mixing length was proposed by Prandtl [6] who suggested that ℓ_H be a linear function of the distance from the wall

$$\ell_H = \kappa_1 y, \quad \text{Prandtl's model} \tag{6.5-1}$$

where y is measured from the wall. Use of this model leads to unsatisfactory results [9]. By considering an oscillating flow parallel to an infinite flat plate, van Driest [10] concluded that near a solid surface Prandtl's mixing length should be modified by a damping factor of the form $[1-\exp(-\kappa_2 y)]$. This leads to

$$\ell_H = \kappa_1(1 - e^{-\kappa_2 y})y, \quad \text{van Driest's modification} \tag{6.5-2}$$

The arguments leading to this form are rather crude; however, the limiting form of Eq. 6.5-2

$$\ell_H \rightarrow \kappa_1 \kappa_2 y^2, \quad y \rightarrow 0 \tag{6.5-3}$$

is similar to that obtained by Sternberg [11] by means of a more rigorous analysis.

In order to use a mixing length theory to calculate the velocity distribution we return to Eq. 6.3-5 and express $\bar{\tau}_{rz}^{(t)}$ in terms of Eq. 6.4-14 to obtain

$$\mu\left(\frac{d\bar{v}_z}{dr}\right)+\rho\ell_H^2\left|\frac{d\bar{v}_z}{dr}\right|\left(\frac{d\bar{v}_z}{dr}\right)=-\left(\frac{\Delta\bar{P}}{L}\right)\frac{r}{2} \tag{6.5-4}$$

Letting y be the distance measured from the wall we note that

$$r=r_0-y \quad \text{and} \quad \frac{d}{dr}=-\frac{d}{dy}$$

so that Eq. 6.5-4 can be expressed as

$$\mu\left(\frac{d\bar{v}_z}{dy}\right)+\rho\ell_H^2\left(\frac{d\bar{v}_z}{dy}\right)^2=\left(\frac{\Delta\bar{P}}{L}\right)\frac{r_0}{2}\left(1-\frac{y}{r_0}\right) \tag{6.5-5}$$

Here we have made use of the fact that $(d\bar{v}_z/dy)$ is always positive so the absolute value sign can be dropped. If we restrict our analysis to the region $(y/r_0)\ll 1$ we can simplify Eq. 6.5-5 to obtain

$$\mu\left(\frac{d\bar{v}_z}{dy}\right)+\rho\ell_H^2\left(\frac{d\bar{v}_z}{dy}\right)^2=\left(\frac{\Delta\bar{P}r_0}{2L}\right) \tag{6.5-6}$$

This simplification will make our analysis a great deal easier without losing any essential information, for we are primarily interested in the velocity profile near the wall. Noting that $\sqrt{\Delta\bar{P}r_0/2\rho L}$ has the units of velocity and that ν has the units of length times velocity, we can define a dimensionless velocity, v^+, as

$$v^+=\bar{v}_z/\sqrt{\Delta\bar{P}r_0/2\rho L} \tag{6.5-7}$$

and a dimensionless length, y^+, as

$$y^+=y\sqrt{\Delta\bar{P}r_0/2\rho L}\Big/\nu \tag{6.5-8}$$

In terms of v^+ and y^+ Eq. 6.5-6 takes the form

$$\left(\frac{dv^+}{dy^+}\right)+\ell_H^2\left(\frac{\Delta\bar{P}r_0}{2\nu^2\rho L}\right)\left(\frac{dv^+}{dy^+}\right)^2=1 \tag{6.5-9}$$

Substitution of van Driest's expression for ℓ_H leads to

$$\left(\frac{dv^+}{dy^+}\right)+(\kappa_1 y^+)^2(1-e^{-\kappa_2^* y^+})^2\left(\frac{dv^+}{dy^+}\right)^2=1 \tag{6.5-10}$$

where κ_2^* is the dimensionless version of κ_2 given by

$$\kappa_2^*=\kappa_2\nu\Big/\sqrt{\Delta\bar{P}r_0/2\rho L}$$

We can solve the quadratic equation, Eq. 6.5-10, for dv^+/dy^+ to obtain

$$\left(\frac{dv^+}{dy^+}\right)=\frac{-1\pm\sqrt{1+4(\kappa_1 y^+)^2(1-e^{-\kappa_2^* y^+})^2}}{2(\kappa_1 y^+)^2(1-e^{-\kappa_2^* y^+})^2} \tag{6.5-11}$$

Only the positive root is physically reasonable and we can rearrange this root in the form†

$$\left(\frac{dv^+}{dy^+}\right)=\frac{2}{1+\sqrt{1+4(\kappa_1 y^+)^2(1-e^{-\kappa_2^* y^+})^2}} \tag{6.5-12}$$

Imposing the boundary condition

B.C. $\qquad v^+=0, \qquad y^+=0$ $\qquad$ (6.5-13)

and integrating leads to

$$v^+=\int_0^{y^+}\frac{2\,dy^+}{1+\sqrt{1+4(\kappa_1 y^+)^2(1-e^{-\kappa_2^* y^+})^2}} \tag{6.5-14}$$

†Choose the positive root and multiply the numerator and denominator by $[1+\sqrt{1+4(\kappa_1 y^+)^2(1-e^{-\kappa_2^* y^+})^2}]$.

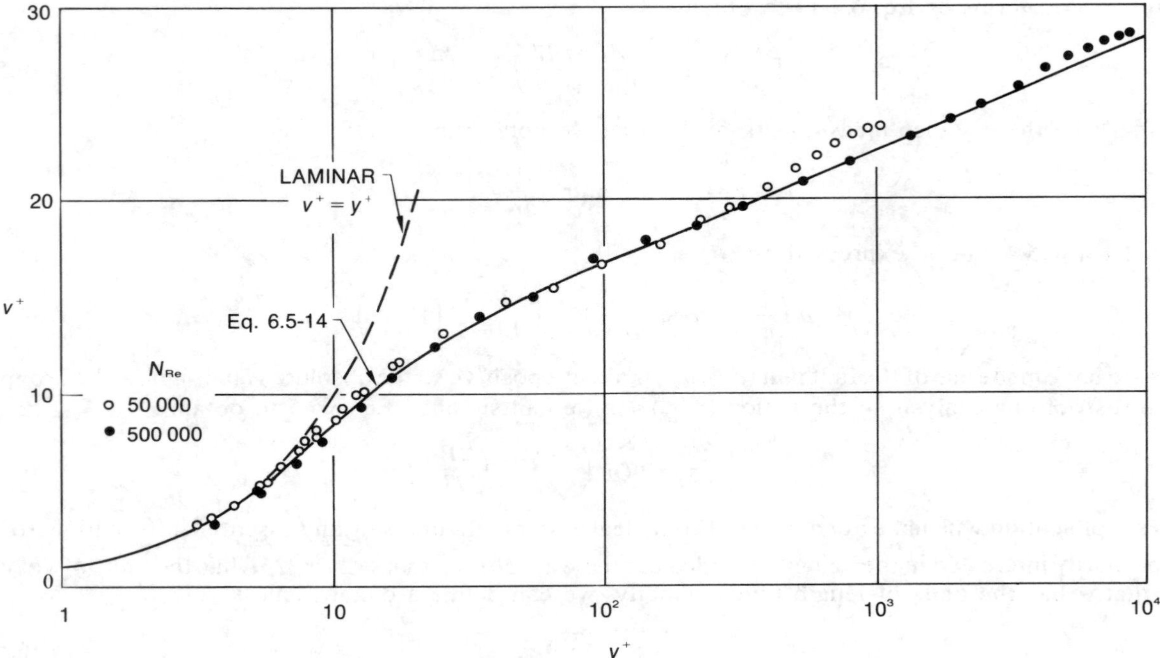

Fig. 6.5.1 Comparison of van Driest's mixing length theory with the experimental data of Laufer.

Van Driest has evaluated this integral numerically for $\kappa_1 = 0.4$ and $\kappa_2^* = 0.04$, and compared the result with the experimental data of Laufer[12] for Reynolds numbers of 5×10^4 and 5×10^5. The agreement shown in Fig. 6.5.1 is certainly encouraging, but one must always remember that with two adjustable parameters even a very crude theory can be made to fit the data[13]. The dashed curve in Fig. 6.5.1 represents the solution of Eq. 5.6-14 for $\kappa_1 = 0$ (or $l_H = 0$) which gives

$$v^+ = y^+, \quad \text{for laminar flow} \tag{6.5-15}$$

From these results we can conclude that viscous forces predominate for $y^+ < 10$, and this region is often referred to as the viscous sublayer:

$$0 < y^+ < 10, \quad \text{viscous sublayer}$$

Solution to design problem VI

A possible method of disposing of the waste heat is simply to run a pipe to the center of the river and deposit the hot water from the plant at that point. In the language of sanitary engineers we will leave our waste product "untreated" and dispose of it with a suitably placed outfall as illustrated in Fig. VI.1. The Reynolds number for the river is given by

$$N_{Re} = \frac{\rho \langle v_x \rangle D_h}{\mu}, \tag{VI-1}$$

where D_h is the hydraulic diameter and takes the form

$$D_h = 4 \left\{ \frac{\text{cross-sectional area}}{\text{wetted perimeter}} \right\} = \frac{4Wd}{W + 2d} \tag{VI-2}$$

for a rectangular channel of width W and depth d. The Reynolds number can now be computed as

$$N_{Re} = 1.1 \times 10^7 \tag{VI-3}$$

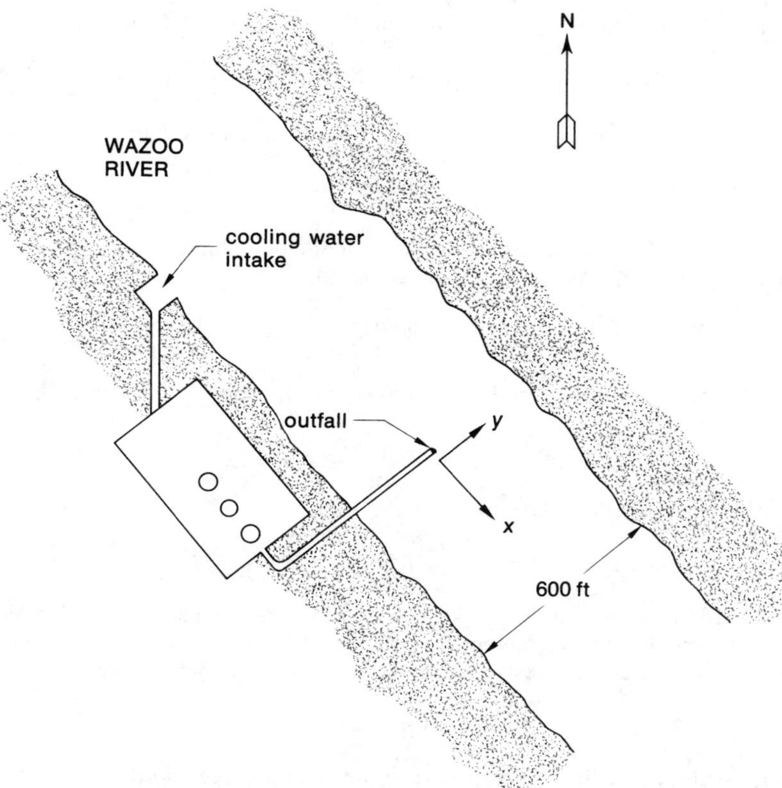

Fig. VI.1 Outfall for waste heat disposal in the Wazoo River.

and we conclude that the river is in turbulent flow. The governing equation was given in Sec. 6.2 as

$$\rho c_p\left(\frac{\partial \bar{T}}{\partial t}+\bar{\mathbf{v}}\cdot\nabla\bar{T}\right)=-\nabla\cdot\bar{\mathbf{q}}^{(T)} \tag{VI-4}$$

where the source term $\bar{\Phi}$ has been dropped for this problem. Assuming the process to be steady and the flow to be one-dimensional, Eq. VI-4 reduces to

$$\rho c_p\bar{v}_x\left(\frac{\partial \bar{T}}{\partial x}\right)=-\nabla\cdot\bar{\mathbf{q}}^{(T)} \tag{VI-5}$$

If we describe the turbulent transport in terms of an eddy thermal conductivity as outlined in Sec. 6.3 we obtain†

$$\rho c_p\bar{v}_x\left(\frac{\partial \bar{T}}{\partial x}\right)=(k+k^{(t)})\left(\frac{\partial^2\bar{T}}{\partial x^2}+\frac{\partial^2\bar{T}}{\partial y^2}+\frac{\partial^2\bar{T}}{\partial z^2}\right) \tag{VI-6}$$

where $k^{(t)}$ has been taken to be constant. Solution of this equation to determine the temperature as a function of x, y, and z would be desirable; however, such a solution would require a considerable mathematical effort. Instead we will be content with determining the average temperature defined by

$$\bar{T}_{\text{av}}=\frac{1}{d}\int_{z=0}^{z=d}\bar{T}\,dz \tag{VI-7}$$

where d is the depth of the river. If the velocity profile in the river is flat we can write

$$\bar{v}_x=\langle\bar{v}_x\rangle=\frac{\text{volumetric flow rate}}{\text{cross-sectional area}} \tag{VI-8}$$

†This form for $\bar{\mathbf{q}}^{(T)}$ requires that the turbulent transport be isotropic and homogeneous, a situation not confirmed by experimental observations.

Substituting Eq. VI-8 into Eq. VI-6 and performing the integration indicated in Eq. VI-7 yields

$$\rho c_p \langle \bar{v}_x \rangle \left(\frac{\partial \bar{T}_{av}}{\partial x} \right) = (k + k^{(t)}) \left(\frac{\partial^2 \bar{T}_{av}}{\partial x^2} + \frac{\partial^2 \bar{T}_{av}}{\partial y^2} + \frac{1}{d} \frac{\partial \bar{T}}{\partial z}\bigg|_{z=d} - \frac{1}{d} \frac{\partial \bar{T}}{\partial z}\bigg|_{z=0} \right) \tag{VI-9}$$

It is reasonable to assume that the river bottom is essentially an insulating surface, thus

$$\frac{\partial \bar{T}}{\partial z}\bigg|_{z=0} = 0 \tag{VI-10}$$

In addition it is reasonable to assume that the eddy thermal conductivity is large compared to the molecular thermal conductivity, $k \ll k^{(t)}$, and Eq. VI-9 simplifies to

$$\rho c_p \langle \bar{v}_x \rangle \left(\frac{\partial \bar{T}_{av}}{\partial x} \right) = k^{(t)} \left(\frac{\partial^2 \bar{T}_{av}}{\partial x^2} + \frac{\partial^2 \bar{T}_{av}}{\partial y^2} + \frac{1}{d} \frac{\partial \bar{T}}{\partial z}\bigg|_{z=d} \right) \tag{VI-11}$$

Under almost all practical circumstances the convective transport will be large compared to the turbulent transport in the x-direction

$$\rho c_p \langle \bar{v}_x \rangle \left(\frac{\partial \bar{T}_{av}}{\partial x} \right) \gg k^{(t)} \left(\frac{\partial^2 \bar{T}_{av}}{\partial x^2} \right) \tag{VI-12}$$

and we can further simplify Eq. VI-11 to

$$\rho c_p \langle \bar{v}_x \rangle \left(\frac{\partial \bar{T}_{av}}{\partial x} \right) = k^{(t)} \left(\frac{\partial^2 \bar{T}_{av}}{\partial y^2} + \frac{1}{d} \frac{\partial \bar{T}}{\partial z}\bigg|_{z=d} \right) \tag{VI-13}$$

Although we have greatly simplified Eq. VI-4 by making a series of reasonable assumptions, and by limiting our objective to determining the average temperature $\bar{T}_{av}$ rather than $\bar{T}$, we can simplify our problem still further if we are content with a conservative estimate of the effect of our thermal outfall.

The term

$$k^{(t)} \left(\frac{\partial \bar{T}}{\partial z} \right)_{z=d}$$

in Eq. VI-13 represents the flux of energy between the river surface and the atmosphere. Radiation from the noonday sun or to a clear night sky, or a high wind can cause this term to be of considerable importance. If we neglect these mechanisms and set this term equal to zero, Eq. VI-13 reduces to

$$\rho c_p \langle \bar{v}_x \rangle \left(\frac{\partial \bar{T}_{av}}{\partial x} \right) = k^{(t)} \left(\frac{\partial^2 \bar{T}_{av}}{\partial y^2} \right) \tag{VI-14}$$

and we will obtain a conservative estimate of the effect of our waste disposal system. At this point our model of the process has been reduced to that of pure turbulent mixing, and knowledge of the eddy thermal conductivity is of prime importance.

It will be helpful to put Eq. VI-14 in dimensionless form by defining the following variables

$$\Theta = \frac{\bar{T}_{av} - T_0}{\Delta T_{rise}}, \qquad \text{dimensionless temperature}$$

$$X = x k^{(t)} / \rho c_p d^2 \langle \bar{v}_x \rangle, \qquad \text{dimensionless longitudinal distance}$$

$$Y = y/d, \qquad \text{dimensionless lateral distance}$$

where ΔT_{rise} represents the temperature rise of the cooling water as it passes through the plant, and T_0 is the ambient river temperature. In terms of these dimensionless variables we can write Eq. VI-14 as

$$\frac{\partial \Theta}{\partial X} = \frac{\partial^2 \Theta}{\partial Y^2} \tag{VI-15}$$

Specification of appropriate boundary conditions at $x = 0$ remains a difficult problem. To be accurate we should construct a boundary condition which would describe the *convection* of thermal energy into the stream by the hot cooling water. If the flow of cooling water is small compared to the stream flow we can neglect the flow at the outfall and simply treat the problem as a source of thermal energy at $x = 0$ having a strength of 1.66×10^{11} Btu/day. In addition to treating the outfall as a point source we can simplify the boundary conditions by assuming that the thermal disturbance from the point source is not influenced by the river banks, i.e., for mathematical simplicity we take the river as being infinitely wide and write

B.C. $\qquad \Theta \to 0, \qquad Y \to \pm\infty \qquad$ (VI-16)

If we designate the strength of our source as $\dot{Q}$ we require that this be equal to the thermal energy convected across any plane downstream of the source

$$\dot{Q} = \int_{-\infty}^{+\infty} \rho c_p \langle v_x \rangle d(\bar{T}_{av} - T_0)\, dy \tag{VI-17}$$

Here we see that the process we are analyzing is simply one of convection downstream with lateral mixing due to the turbulent motion. No thermal energy is lost from the river. This of course cannot be an accurate picture of the real process for eventually the waste heat will be transferred to the atmosphere via radiation, conduction, and convection (i.e., evaporation). However, in the region near the outfall our analysis will be a reasonable approximation and in any event it will provide us with an upper bound on the average temperature, $\bar{T}_{av}$. Putting Eq. VI-17 in dimensionless form yields

$$\dot{\mathcal{Q}} = \int_{-\infty}^{+\infty} \Theta \, dY \tag{VI-18}$$

where $\dot{\mathcal{Q}}$ is the dimensionless source given by

$$\dot{\mathcal{Q}} = \dot{Q}/\rho c_p \langle \bar{v}_x \rangle \Delta T_{\text{rise}}\, d^2 \tag{VI-19}$$

We now seek a solution to Eq. VI-15 which satisfies the boundary condition given by Eq. VI-16 and the constraint given by Eq. VI-18. This is accomplished by recognizing that

$$\Theta = \frac{C}{\sqrt{X}} e^{-Y^2/4X} \tag{VI-20}$$

is a solution† of the differential equation which satisfies the boundary condition for $Y \to \pm\infty$. Imposing the restriction given by Eq. VI-18 allows us to specify the constant C,

$$\dot{\mathcal{Q}} = \frac{C}{\sqrt{X}} \int_{-\infty}^{+\infty} e^{-Y^2/4X} dY = 2C\sqrt{\pi} \tag{VI-21}$$

and our expression for the dimensionless temperature becomes

$$\Theta = \frac{\dot{\mathcal{Q}}}{2\sqrt{\pi X}} e^{-Y^2/4X} \tag{VI-22}$$

We can now define some critical dimensionless temperature, Θ_c, which is used to define the region of thermal pollution. In our present problem

$$\Theta_c = \frac{\bar{T}_{av,c} - T_0}{\Delta T_{\text{rise}}} = \frac{82°\text{F} - 78°\text{F}}{14°\text{F}} = 0.286$$

We wish to find the area contained within the isotherm defined by Θ_c. The coordinates (X_c, Y_c) of this isotherm are given implicitly by the expression

$$\Theta_c = \frac{\dot{\mathcal{Q}}}{2\sqrt{\pi X_c}} e^{-Y_c^2/4X_c} \tag{VI-23}$$

and illustrated in Fig. VI.2. Solving Eq. VI-23 for Y_c we obtain

$$Y_c = 2X_c^{1/2}\left\{\ln\left[\frac{\dot{\mathcal{Q}}}{2\Theta_c\sqrt{\pi X_c}}\right]\right\}^{1/2} \tag{VI-24}$$

The area of the thermally polluted region, or the region bounded by Θ_c, is given by

$$A = 2\int_{\eta=0}^{\eta=\ell} y_c \, d\eta \tag{VI-25}$$

where ℓ is the distance downstream at which $y_c = 0$.

In terms of the dimensionless variables

$$A = \frac{2\rho c_p d^3 \langle \bar{v}_x \rangle}{k^{(t)}} \int_{\eta=0}^{\eta=L} Y_c \, d\eta \tag{VI-26}$$

†See J. Crank, *The Mathematics of Diffusion*, p. 11, Oxford Press, London, 1956.

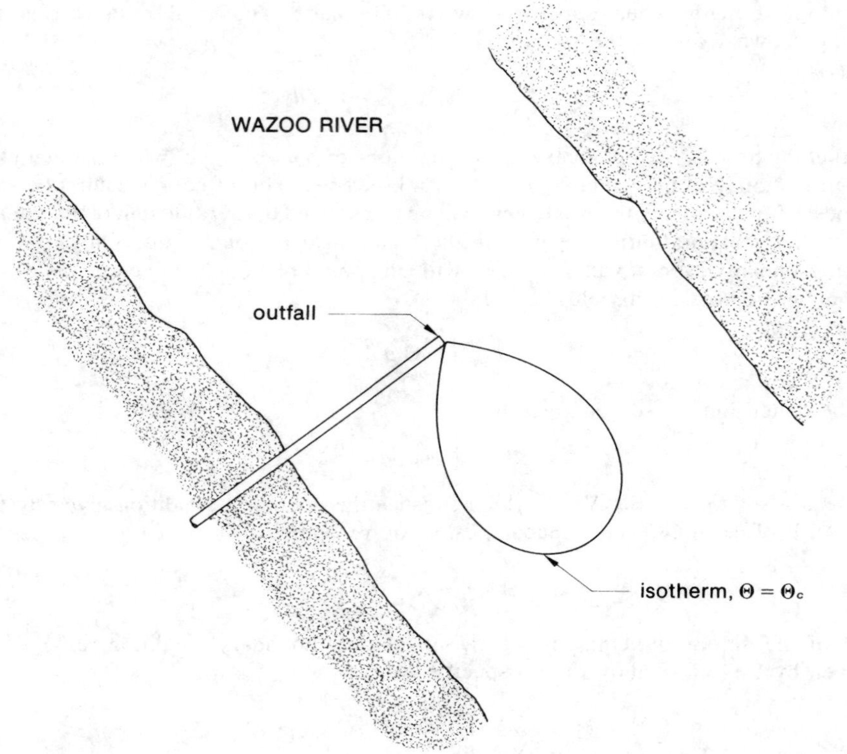

Fig. VI.2 Region of thermal pollution.

where η is now the dimensionless dummy variable of integration. Substitution of Eq. VI-24 into Eq. VI-26 gives us our expression for the area

$$A = \frac{2\rho c_p d^3\langle \bar{v}_x \rangle}{k^{(t)}} \int_{\eta=0}^{\eta=L} 2\eta^{1/2} \left\{ \ln \left[\frac{\dot{\mathcal{Q}}}{2\Theta_c \sqrt{\pi\eta}} \right] \right\}^{1/2} d\eta \qquad \text{(VI-27)}$$

We can simplify this equation somewhat by defining a new variable

$$\xi = 2\Theta_c \sqrt{\pi\eta} / \dot{\mathcal{Q}} \qquad \text{(VI-28)}$$

and noting that L is given by

$$L = (\dot{\mathcal{Q}} / 2\sqrt{\pi}\Theta_c)^2 \qquad \text{(VI-29)}$$

After some algebraic manipulations we obtain

$$A = \left\{ \frac{Q_p^3 W^2}{Q_R^2 d\alpha^{(t)} \Theta_c^3} \right\} \left\{ \frac{1}{\pi^{3/2}} \int_0^1 \xi^2 \left[\ln \left(\frac{1}{\xi} \right) \right]^{1/2} d\xi \right\} \qquad \text{(VI-30)}$$

Here Q_p is the volumetric flow rate of cooling water in the plant, Q_R is the volumetric flow rate in the river, W is the width of the river; and $\alpha^{(t)} = k^{(t)}/\rho c_p$.

The definite integral in Eq. VI-30 has been evaluated† and the area can be expressed as

$$A = 0.03 \left\{ \frac{Q_p^3 W^2}{Q_R^2 d\alpha^{(t)} \Theta_c^3} \right\} \qquad \text{(VI-31)}$$

†See J. E. Edinger and E. M. Polk, Jr., "Initial Mixing of Thermal Discharges into a Uniform Current," Report No. 1, Dept. of Environmental & Water Resources Engineering, Vanderbilt University, Oct. 1969.

All of the terms in this expression are known except for the eddy thermal diffusivity, $\alpha^{(t)}$. Experimental determinations of $\alpha^{(t)}$ are not so numerous as those available for closed conduit and boundary layer flows; however, some information is available† and we can estimate $\alpha^{(t)}$ from the correlation

$$\alpha^{(t)} = \beta d \sqrt{\tau_0/\rho} \tag{V-32}$$

where the coefficient β ranges from 0.2 for straight laboratory flumes to 0.7 for natural streams and rivers. Secondary currents caused by bends in the river could give rise to substantially larger values of β. The "shear velocity," $\sqrt{\tau_0/\rho}$, can be determined by application of the macroscopic momentum balance and the Manning formula for the friction factor‡

$$\sqrt{\tau_0/\rho} = \frac{Q_R}{Wd}\sqrt{\frac{116n^2}{8R_h^{1/3}}} \tag{VI-33}$$

Here n is the Manning number and R_h is the hydraulic radius. For streams and rivers n is on the order of $0.03\ \text{ft}^{1/6}$. We can substitute Eq. VI-33 into Eq. VI-32 to obtain

$$\alpha^{(t)} = \frac{3.8\beta Q_R}{W}\left(\frac{n^2}{R_h^{1/3}}\right)^{1/2} \tag{VI-34}$$

and incorporate this result into Eq. VI-31 in order to express the area as

$$A = \frac{0.008}{\beta}\left(\frac{Q_p W}{Q_R \Theta_c}\right)^3 \left(\frac{R_h^{1/3}}{n^2 d^2}\right)^{1/2} \tag{VI-35}$$

Taking β to be 0.5 and substituting the values for the other terms in Eq. VI-35 gives us the area in which the temperature rise will be 4°F,

$$A = 740\,000\ \text{ft}^2$$

This is of course much larger than the allowed one acre, which is equal to 43 500 ft^2, and our proposed design of a single outfall is not satisfactory.

Examining Eq. VI-35 we see that the area depends on the cube of the source strength, i.e., it is proportional to Q_p^3. If we dispose of the waste heat by means of N outfalls the area, A_N, of thermally polluted water will be given by

$$A_N = \frac{1}{N^2} A_1 \tag{VI-36}$$

where A_1 is the area for a single outfall. In order to meet the restriction of 43000 ft^2 we need to place five outfalls across the river, thus giving us 29 700 ft^2 of thermally polluted water. However, before we can settle on this as a final solution we must be sure that the outfalls do not influence each other so that Eq. VI-16 is satisfied and our mathematical analysis is correct. In order to estimate the influence of one outfall on another let us calculate the maximum spread of the thermal "wake" for a value of $\Theta_c = 0.1$. We can use Eq. VI-24 to express $Y_{0.1}$ as

$$Y_{0.1} = 2X^{1/2}\left\{\ln\left[\frac{5\dot{\mathcal{Q}}}{\sqrt{\pi X}}\right]\right\}^{1/2} \tag{VI-37}$$

The maximum value of $Y_{0.1}$ occurs at a value of X which is determined by

$$\ln\left[\frac{5\dot{\mathcal{Q}}}{\sqrt{\pi X}}\right] = \frac{1}{2}, \qquad \text{for } Y = 0.1 \tag{VI-38}$$

Thus we obtain

$$X = (5\dot{\mathcal{Q}}/\sqrt{\pi})^2/2.72, \qquad \text{for maximum } Y_{0.1}$$

Substituting this result into Eq. VI-37 yields

$$Y_{0.1} = \left(\frac{5\dot{\mathcal{Q}}}{\sqrt{\pi}}\right)\sqrt{\frac{2}{2.72}} \tag{VI-39}$$

†See, for example, N. Yotsukura and E. D. Cobb, "Transverse Diffusion of Solutes in Natural Streams," U.S. Geological Survey Paper 582-C, 1972.

‡See Reference 4, Chapter 9.

Since $\dot{\mathcal{Q}} = (Q_p W / Q_R d)$ and $Y = y/d$, we can express this last result as

$$y_{0.1} = (2.4)\left(\frac{Q_p}{Q_R}\right) W \tag{VI-40}$$

In calculating Q_p we must remember that we are considering placing five outfalls across the river, thus the value of Q_p that goes into Eq. VI-40 is one-fifth of 2200 ft³/sec. Calculating $y_{0.1}$ yields

$$y_{0.1} = 35 \text{ ft}$$

This means that our five outfalls should be placed 70 ft apart in order for our mathematical analysis to be reasonably accurate.

PROBLEMS†

VI-1. Show that Eq. VI-20 is a solution for Eq. VI-15.

VI-2. Redesign the thermal outfall system so that the surface area of the river which is heated to temperatures greater than 80°F is one acre or less.

***6-1.** (6.1) Repeat the analysis given in Ex. 6.1-1 for water at 70°F flowing past a flat plate at 35 ft/sec.

6-2. (6.2) Derive Eq. 6.2-22 from Eq. 6.2-19.

6-3. (6.2) Show that the time-averaged form of the complete continuity equation is given by

$$\frac{\partial \bar{\rho}}{\partial t} + \nabla \cdot (\bar{\rho}\bar{\mathbf{v}}) = -\nabla \cdot \overline{(\rho' \mathbf{v}')}$$

6-4. (6.2) Determine the form of the time-averaged thermal energy equation when density fluctuations are taken into account. Take the heat capacity and the thermal conductivity to be constant, but express ρ as

$$\rho = \bar{\rho} + \rho'$$

Can the result be expressed in the form

$$\bar{\rho} c_p \left(\frac{\partial \bar{T}}{\partial t} + \bar{\mathbf{v}} \cdot \nabla \bar{T}\right) = -\nabla \cdot \bar{\mathbf{q}}^{(T)} + \Phi$$

if

$$\bar{\rho}\left(\frac{\partial \bar{T}}{\partial t}\right) \gg \rho' \left(\frac{\partial T'}{\partial t}\right)?$$

6-5. (6.2) Determine the form of the time-averaged viscous dissipation function. See Table 5.4-2 for $\nabla \mathbf{v} : \boldsymbol{\tau}$ in rectangular coordinates.

6-6. (6.2) Show that $k\nabla^2 \bar{T} = -\nabla \cdot \bar{\mathbf{q}}$ when the thermal conductivity is constant.

6-7. (6.2) Show that the time-averaged viscous stress for an incompressible flow is given by

$$\bar{\boldsymbol{\tau}} = \mu(\nabla \bar{\mathbf{v}} + \nabla \bar{\mathbf{v}}^T)$$

***6-8.** (6.2) The function S has a time dependence given by

$$S = S_0 + A_1 \cos \omega_1 t + A_2 \cos \omega_2 t$$

where ω_2 represents a high frequency comparable to the turbulent fluctuations shown in Fig. 6.1.2, and ω_1 is a low frequency comparable to the slow variation of $\bar{T}$ with time indicated in Fig. 6.1.2. In order to effectively average out the turbulent fluctuations we require that

$$2\Delta t \gg \omega_2^{-1}$$

If $\bar{\bar{S}}$ is to be within 1 per cent of $\bar{S}$, what is the restriction on ω_1?

†Problems numbered VI-1 and VI-2 deal directly with Design Problem VI, and problems marked with an asterisk (*) are concerned with the solved example problems.

6-9. (6.3) Starting with the complete time-averaged stress equations of motion, use the four restrictions given in the text to derive Eq. 6.3-3.

***6-10.** (6.3) Repeat the analysis given in Ex. 6.3-1 for the case where the temperature is given by

$$\bar{T} = T_w + (T_0 - T_w)\left[1 - \left(\frac{r}{r_0}\right)^2\right]$$

6-11. (6.4) Prove that the turbulent velocity field, $\mathbf{v}'$, must satisfy the equation

$$\nabla \cdot \mathbf{v}' = 0$$

if the flow is incompressible.

6-12. (6.5) In Fig. 6.12 we have shown two infinite flat plates with the lower plate fixed and the upper plate moving in an oscillatory motion. Let the distance between the plates go to infinity, $L \to \infty$, and solve the equation of motion for v_x,

$$\frac{\partial v_x}{\partial t} = \nu \frac{\partial^2 v_x}{\partial y^2}$$

using the method described in Sec. 4.4. Discuss van Driest's "damping factor" for the hydrodynamic mixing length in terms of your result.

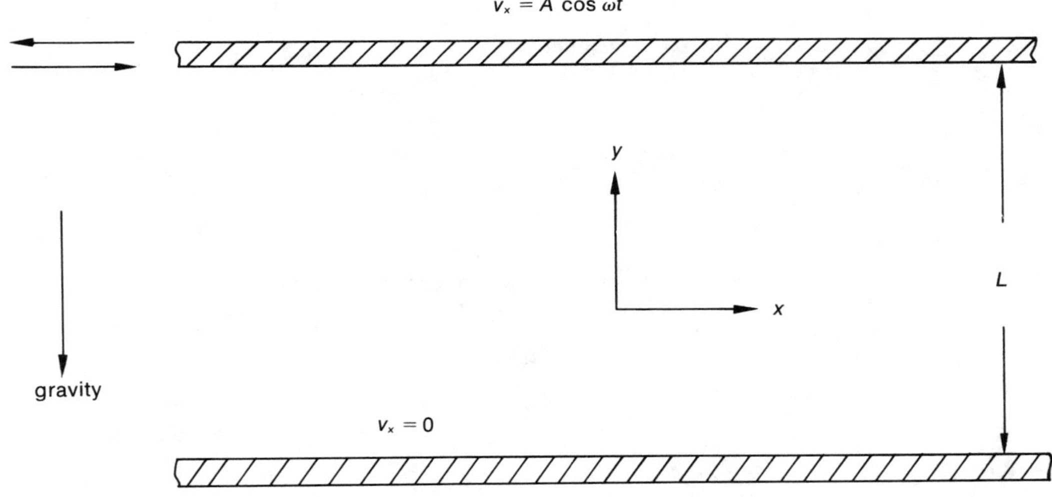

Fig. 6.12 Oscillating parallel plates.

REFERENCES

1. Klebanoff, P. S., "Characteristics of Turbulence in a Boundary Layer with Zero Pressure Gradient," *NACA Report 1247*, 1955.
2. Corino, E. R., and Brodkey, R. S., "A Visual Investigation of the Wall Region in Turbulent Flow," *J. Fluid Mech.* **37**, 1 (1969).
3. Wylie, C. R., Jr., *Advanced Engineering Mathematics*, Third Edition, McGraw-Hill Book Co., Inc., New York, 1966.
4. Whitaker, S., *Introduction to Fluid Mechanics*, Prentice-Hall, Inc., Englewood Cliffs, N.J., 1968.
5. Laufer, J., "The Structure of Turbulence in Fully Developed Pipe Flow," *NACA Report 1174*, 1954.
6. Prandtl, L., "Investigations on Turbulent Flow," *ZAMM* **5**, 136 (1925).
7. Rohsenow, W. M., and Choi, H., *Heat, Mass, and Momentum Transfer*, Prentice-Hall, Inc., Englewood Cliffs, N.J., 1961.
8. Jenkins, R., "Variation of the Eddy Conductivity with Prandtl Number and Its Use in Prediction of Turbulent Heat Transfer Coefficients," *Heat Transfer and Fluid Mechanics Institute*, Stanford University Press, 1951.
9. Slattery, J. C., *Momentum, Energy, and Mass Transfer in Continua*, McGraw-Hill Book Co., Inc., New York, 1972.
10. Van Driest, E. R., "On Turbulent Flow Near a Wall," *J. Aero. Sci.* **23**, 1007 (1956).
11. Sternberg, J., "A Theory for the Viscous Sublayer of a Turbulent Flow," *J. Fluid Mech.* **13**, 241 (1961).
12. Laufer, J., "The Structure of Turbulence in Fully Developed Pipe Flow," *NACA Tech. Note 2954*, 1953.
13. Whitaker, S., *Solutions Manual for Introduction to Fluid Mechanics*, Prentice-Hall, Inc., Englewood Cliffs, N.J., 1968.

Design Problem VII

A feed stream to a distillation column consists of 20 000 gals/day of a light oil, and is fed to the column through a 6-in. I.D. pipeline as illustrated in Fig. VII.1. The temperature of the feed is usually 80°F; however, under some circumstances the feed is available at temperatures as low as 74°F. You are asked to explore the possibility of using a double-pipe heat exchanger, shown in Fig. VII.1, as an auxiliary heater for the feed stream. There is available for heating the oil 7000 gals/day of water at 200°F. The necessary physical properties of the system are

Oil (~80°F)	*Water* (~200°F)	*Pipe*
$\rho = 53\ \text{lb}_m/\text{ft}^3$	$\rho = 61\ \text{lb}_m/\text{ft}^3$	I.D. = 6.0 in.
$c_p = 0.46\ \text{Btu/lb}_m\,°\text{F}$	$c_p = 1.0\ \text{Btu/lb}_m\,°\text{F}$	O.D. = 6.62 in.
$\mu = 150$ centipoises	$\mu = 0.7\ \text{lb}_m/\text{hr ft}$	$k = 26$ Btu/hr ft °F
$k = 0.11$ Btu/hr ft °F		

The inner diameter of the pipe forming the annular region is 8 in. and the outer surface of that pipe is well insulated.

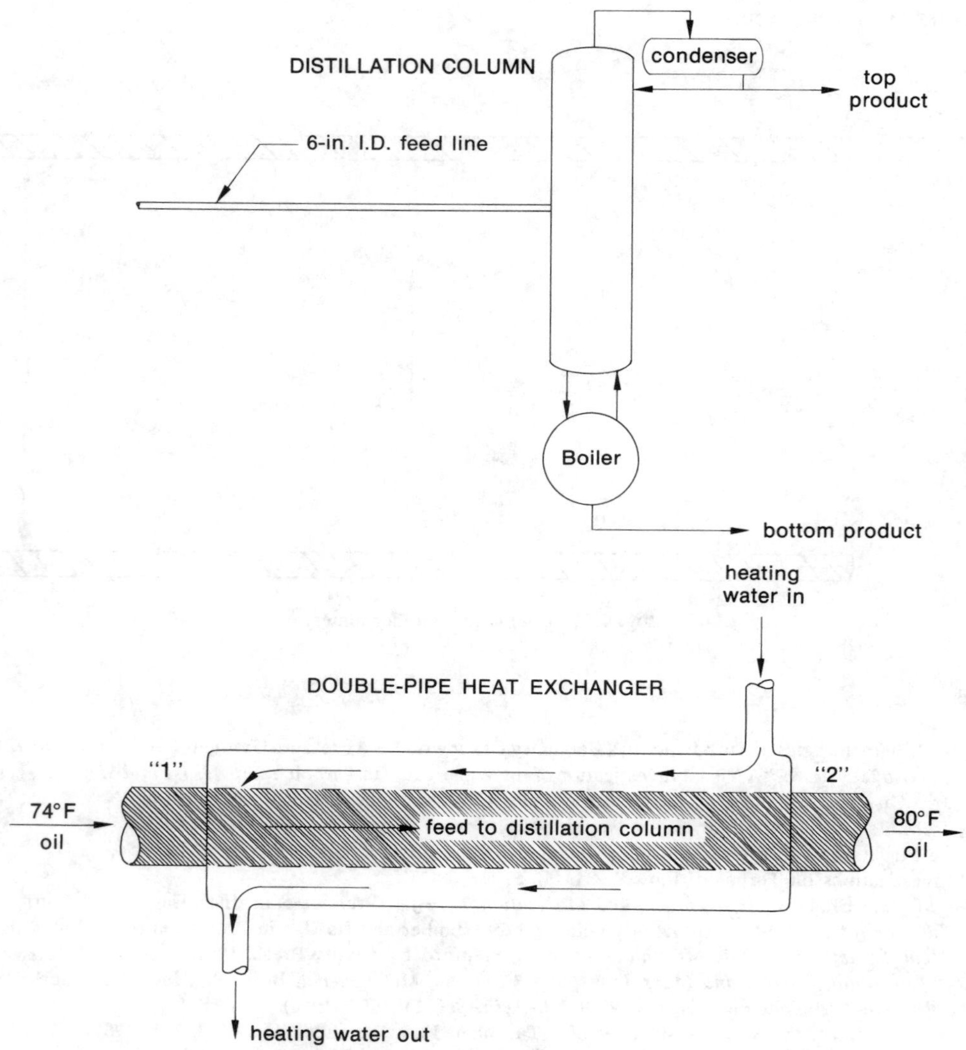

Fig. VII.1 Design of a feed stream heater.

7

Macroscopic Balances

PART I THEORY

In Chapters 2, 3, and 4 we studied steady and transient heat conduction and found that we could solve quite a number of practical heat transfer problems. Those students who explored the sections on numerical methods should have come away with the idea that practically any steady or transient heat conduction problem could be solved by the use of finite-difference methods and digital computers.

In Chapter 5 we considered heat transfer in the presence of fluid motion, and found that solutions of the transport equations could be obtained for laminar boundary layer flows. The results that we obtained in Secs. 5.9 and 5.11 were in remarkably good agreement with experimental data; however, it should have been clear that the theoretical results were only valid under certain restrictive conditions.

In Chapter 6 the problem of turbulent flow was discussed, and it became apparent that a theoretical analysis of turbulent momentum and energy transport was beyond our reach. Clearly we need experimental data if we are going to solve such problems, and unless we plan on doing an experiment for every problem for which we desire a solution, we had better learn to organize and apply experimental results in an efficient manner. The objective of this chapter will be to present guidelines for accomplishing this, and our first order of business will be to derive the governing macroscopic balances. These balances will give us a proper statement of the fundamental postulates for control volumes. With the macroscopic balances and appropriate experimental data we can determine flow rates and pressure differences, but not velocity fields and pressure fields; we can determine interphase heat transfer rates and average temperatures of process streams entering and leaving control volumes, but we cannot determine the details of the temperature field; we can determine mass flow rates, but not the density field. Perhaps at this point the student has realized that most of the time it is the pressure drop, flow rate, and interphase heat transfer rate that we really need, and the pressure field, velocity field, and temperature field is often something we can do without. Thus the material to be presented in this chapter is essential for the analysis of most practical heat transfer problems. Our starting point will be the governing differential equations for mass, momentum, and thermal energy.

$$\frac{\partial \rho}{\partial t} + \nabla \cdot (\rho \mathbf{v}) = 0, \quad \text{mass} \tag{7-1}$$

$$\rho\left(\frac{\partial \mathbf{v}}{\partial t} + \mathbf{v} \cdot \nabla \mathbf{v}\right) = \rho \mathbf{g} + \nabla \cdot \mathbf{T}, \quad \text{momentum} \tag{7-2}$$

$$\rho c_p\left(\frac{\partial T}{\partial t} + \mathbf{v} \cdot \nabla T\right) = -\nabla \cdot \mathbf{q} + T\beta \frac{Dp}{Dt} + \nabla \mathbf{v} : \boldsymbol{\tau} + \Phi, \quad \text{thermal energy} \tag{7-3}$$

Here we have taken the thermal energy equation for a general flow process given by Eq. 5.5-10, expanded the material derivative, and replaced $\nabla \cdot (k\nabla T)$ with $-\nabla \cdot \mathbf{q}$.

*7.1 The Macroscopic Mass Balance

In this section we wish to develop the macroscopic form of Eq. 7-1, and to do this in a general manner we consider the *arbitrary* moving volume $\mathscr{V}_a(t)$ shown in Fig. 7.1.1, and form the integral of Eq. 7-1 over $\mathscr{V}_a(t)$

$$\int_{\mathscr{V}_a(t)} \left[\left(\frac{\partial \rho}{\partial t}\right) + \nabla \cdot (\rho \mathbf{v})\right] dV = 0 \tag{7.1-1}$$

Remember from our discussion in Sec. 5.1 that points on the surface of $\mathscr{V}_a(t)$ move with a velocity designated by $\mathbf{w}$. If $\mathbf{w} = 0$ our control volume is fixed in space, and under these special circumstances we will designate the volume by $\mathscr{V}$. If $\mathbf{w}$ is a constant vector the volume is translating uniformly through space; if $\mathbf{w}$ is only a function of time the volume maintains its shape while accelerating through space; and if $\mathbf{w}$ depends on the spatial coordinates and time, the volume is deforming and accelerating. Most often we will be concerned with control volumes which are fixed in space, but if we wish to apply the macroscopic balances to a growing bubble in a boiling liquid we will need the generality presented here.

Eq. 7.1-1 is the macroscopic mass balance, but in its present form it is of little use to us. For example, evaluation of the term

$$\int_{\mathscr{V}_a(t)} \nabla \cdot (\rho \mathbf{v})\, dV$$

requires that we know the density and velocity fields, and that is just what we *don't* know for the complex problems we would now like to analyze. However, if we apply the divergence theorem to this term we obtain

$$\int_{\mathscr{V}_a(t)} \nabla \cdot (\rho \mathbf{v})\, dV = \int_{\mathscr{A}_a(t)} \rho \mathbf{v} \cdot \mathbf{n}\, dA \tag{7.1-2}$$

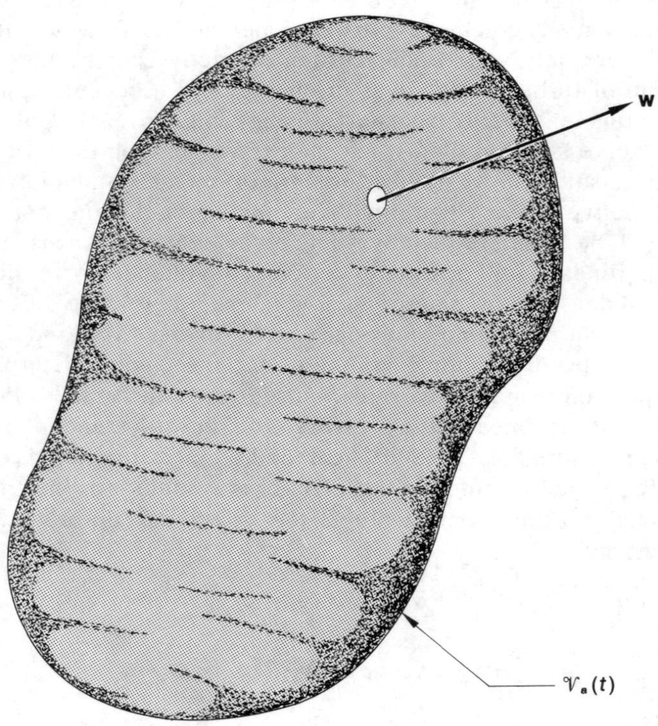

Fig. 7.1.1 Arbitrary moving control volume.

where $\mathcal{A}_a(t)$ represents the surface area of $\mathcal{V}_a(t)$. Here the divergence theorem has taken us one step away from the problem of having to know the density and velocity fields, and brought us one step closer to having to know only the mass flow rate into or out of the control volume.

Returning to the general transport theorem (Eq. 5.1-21) in Chapter 5 we let S be the density and write†

$$\frac{d}{dt}\int_{\mathcal{V}_a(t)} \rho\, dV = \int_{\mathcal{V}_a(t)} \left(\frac{\partial \rho}{\partial t}\right) dV + \int_{\mathcal{A}_a(t)} \rho \mathbf{w}\cdot\mathbf{n}\, dA \tag{7.1-3}$$

Substitution of Eqs. 7.1-2 and 7.1-3 into Eq. 7.1-1 and rearranging yields

$$\frac{d}{dt}\int_{\mathcal{V}_a(t)} \rho\, dV + \int_{\mathcal{A}_a(t)} \rho(\mathbf{v}-\mathbf{w})\cdot\mathbf{n}\, dA = 0 \tag{7.1-4}$$

time rate of change of mass in the control volume — net rate of mass leaving the control volume

Here we have been able to go from an equation (7-1) which concerns the *point* variations in ρ and $\mathbf{v}$ to an equation (or *balance*) which relates the net mass flux out of the control volume to the time rate of change of the mass contained in the control volume.

We can take advantage of the fact that the surface area of most control volumes can be expressed in terms of three distinct areas:

1. $A_e(t)$, the area of entrances and exits through which fluid may enter and leave the control volume.
2. $A_s(t)$, the area of impenetrable, moving surfaces.
3. A_s, the area of impenetrable fixed surfaces.

By *impenetrable*‡ we mean that no fluid crosses the surface, thus

$$\mathbf{v}\cdot\mathbf{n} = \mathbf{w}\cdot\mathbf{n}, \quad \text{impenetrable surfaces} \tag{7.1-5}$$

and an impenetrable *fixed* surface is defined by the condition

$$\mathbf{v} = \mathbf{w} = 0, \quad \text{impenetrable fixed surface} \tag{7.1-6}$$

Making use of these definitions of $A_e(t)$, $A_s(t)$, and A_s, Eq. 7.1-4 reduces to

$$\frac{d}{dt}\int_{\mathcal{V}_a(t)} \rho\, dV + \int_{A_e(t)} \rho(\mathbf{v}-\mathbf{w})\cdot\mathbf{n}\, dA = 0 \tag{7.1-7}$$

time rate of change of mass in the control volume — flux of mass entering and leaving the control volume through the the entrances and exits

Very often we will be concerned with control volumes which are fixed in space and Eq. 7.1-7 reduces to

$$\frac{d}{dt}\int_{\mathcal{V}} \rho\, dV + \int_{A_e} \rho\mathbf{v}\cdot\mathbf{n}\, dA = 0, \quad \text{control volume fixed in space} \tag{7.1-8}$$

Here $\mathcal{V}_a(t)$ and $A_e(t)$ have been replaced by $\mathcal{V}$ and A_e to indicate that the limits of integration are independent of time. If the process is steady or the flow is incompressible Eq. 7.1-8 simplifies to

$$\int_{A_e} \rho\mathbf{v}\cdot\mathbf{n}\, dA = 0, \quad \text{steady or incompressible flow in a fixed control volume} \tag{7.1-9}$$

We would express Eq. 7.1-9 in words as: *the mass flow rate into the control volume is equal to the mass flow rate out of the control volume.*

†Note that this is a mathematical relation having nothing to do with the principle of conservation of mass.
‡Such surfaces may be either solid–fluid or fluid–fluid interfaces.

*7.2 The Macroscopic Momentum Balance

The analysis presented here is in essence identical to that given in the previous section, except that here we must work with the more complex stress equations of motion. Beginning with Eq. 7-2,

$$\rho\left(\frac{\partial \mathbf{v}}{\partial t}+\mathbf{v}\cdot\nabla\mathbf{v}\right)=\rho\mathbf{g}+\nabla\cdot\mathbf{T} \tag{7.2-1}$$

we notice immediately that the terms on the left-hand-side are going to cause difficulties when we form the integral over $\mathscr{V}_a(t)$. Our problems will be eliminated if we add zero, i.e.,

$$0=\mathbf{v}\left[\frac{\partial\rho}{\partial t}+\nabla\cdot(\rho\mathbf{v})\right] \tag{7.2-2}$$

to the left-hand-side. A little algebraic effort will show that

$$\rho\left(\frac{\partial \mathbf{v}}{\partial t}+\mathbf{v}\cdot\nabla\mathbf{v}\right)+\mathbf{v}\left(\frac{\partial\rho}{\partial t}\right)+\mathbf{v}\nabla\cdot(\rho\mathbf{v})=\frac{\partial}{\partial t}(\rho\mathbf{v})+\nabla\cdot(\rho\mathbf{v}\,\mathbf{v}) \tag{7.2-3}$$

and Eq. 7.2-1 becomes

$$\frac{\partial(\rho\mathbf{v})}{\partial t}+\nabla\cdot(\rho\mathbf{v}\,\mathbf{v})=\rho\mathbf{g}+\nabla\cdot\mathbf{T} \tag{7.2-4}$$

Forming the integral over $\mathscr{V}_a(t)$ gives the macroscopic momentum balance

$$\int_{\mathscr{V}_a(t)}\frac{\partial}{\partial t}(\rho\mathbf{v})\,dV+\int_{\mathscr{V}_a(t)}\nabla\cdot(\rho\mathbf{v}\,\mathbf{v})\,dV=\int_{\mathscr{V}_a(t)}\rho\mathbf{g}\,dV+\int_{\mathscr{V}_a(t)}\nabla\cdot\mathbf{T}\,dV \tag{7.2-5}$$

None of the terms in Eq. 7.2-5, with the exception of the body force, is susceptible to interpretation from a macroscopic point of view. Application of the divergence theorem to the second and fourth terms is a step in the right direction and yields

$$\int_{\mathscr{V}_a(t)}\frac{\partial(\rho\mathbf{v})}{\partial t}\,dV+\int_{\mathscr{A}_a(t)}\rho\mathbf{v}\,\mathbf{v}\cdot\mathbf{n}\,dA=\int_{\mathscr{V}_a(t)}\rho\mathbf{g}\,dV+\int_{\mathscr{A}_a(t)}\mathbf{T}\cdot\mathbf{n}\,dA \tag{7.2-6}$$

Letting $\rho\mathbf{v}$ be equal to S in the general transport theorem (Eq. 5.1-21) allows us to write down the mathematical expression

$$\int_{\mathscr{V}_a(t)}\frac{\partial}{\partial t}(\rho\mathbf{v})\,dV=\frac{d}{dt}\int_{\mathscr{V}_a(t)}\rho\mathbf{v}\,dV-\int_{\mathscr{A}_a(t)}\rho\mathbf{v}\,\mathbf{w}\cdot\mathbf{n}\,dA \tag{7.2-7}$$

Substitution of this expression into Eq. 7.2-6 gives us

$$\frac{d}{dt}\int_{\mathscr{V}_a(t)}\rho\mathbf{v}\,dV+\int_{\mathscr{A}_a(t)}\rho\mathbf{v}(\mathbf{v}-\mathbf{w})\cdot\mathbf{n}\,dA=\int_{\mathscr{V}_a(t)}\rho\mathbf{g}\,dV+\int_{\mathscr{A}_a(t)}\mathbf{t}_{(\mathbf{n})}\,dA \tag{7.2-8}$$

Here we have substituted the stress vector $\mathbf{t}_{(\mathbf{n})}$ for $\mathbf{T}\cdot\mathbf{n}$, so the last term on the right-hand-side can be clearly interpreted as the total surface force acting *on*† the material within the arbitrary control volume.

Following the development in Sec. 7.1 we split the area $\mathscr{A}_a(t)$ into the three areas $A_e(t)$, $A_s(t)$, and A_s, and noting that $(\mathbf{v}-\mathbf{w})\cdot\mathbf{n}=0$ over the latter two areas gives us

$$\frac{d}{dt}\int_{\mathscr{V}_a(t)}\rho\mathbf{v}\,dV+\int_{A_e(t)}\rho\mathbf{v}(\mathbf{v}-\mathbf{w})\cdot\mathbf{n}\,dA=\int_{\mathscr{V}_a(t)}\rho\mathbf{g}\,dV+\int_{\mathscr{A}_a(t)}\mathbf{t}_{(\mathbf{n})}\,dA \tag{7.2-9}$$

time rate of change of the momentum of the material within the control volume	flux of momentum entering and leaving the control volume through the entrances and exits	body force acting on the material in the control volume	surface force acting on the surface of the control volume

†Remember that $\mathbf{t}_{(\mathbf{n})}$ represents the force exerted *by* the phase into which $\mathbf{n}$ points *on* the phase for which $\mathbf{n}$ is the outwardly directed unit normal.

If we compare this result with the macroscopic mass balance (Eq. 7.1-4) we see that on the left-hand-side we have replaced the *mass per unit volume*, ρ, with the *momentum per unit volume*, $\rho\mathbf{v}$. The two terms on the right-hand-side of Eq. 7.2-9 can be thought of as a *volume source of momentum* and a *surface source of momentum*; the analogous volume and surface mass source terms are zero in Eq. 7.1-4.

*7.3 The Macroscopic Thermal Energy Balance

We begin this development with the thermal energy equation as given by Eq. 7-3.

$$\rho c_p\left(\frac{\partial T}{\partial t}+\mathbf{v}\cdot\nabla T\right)=-\nabla\cdot\mathbf{q}+T\beta\frac{Dp}{Dt}+\nabla\mathbf{v}:\boldsymbol{\tau}+\Phi \tag{7.3-1}$$

If we choose T_0 as some constant, reference temperature, and note that

$$\frac{\partial}{\partial t}(T-T_0)=\frac{\partial T}{\partial t},\qquad \nabla(T-T_0)=\nabla T$$

we can express Eq. 7.3-1 as

$$\rho c_p\left[\frac{\partial}{\partial t}(T-T_0)+\mathbf{v}\cdot\nabla(T-T_0)\right]=-\nabla\cdot\mathbf{q}+T\beta\frac{Dp}{Dt}+\nabla\mathbf{v}:\boldsymbol{\tau}+\Phi \tag{7.3-2}$$

Later we will find that use of a reference temperature in this manner will be convenient, but certainly not a necessity. We can add zero, $c_p(T-T_0)[\partial\rho/\partial t+\nabla\cdot(\rho\mathbf{v})]$, to the left-hand-side of Eq. 7.3-2 yielding

$$c_p\left\{\frac{\partial}{\partial t}[\rho(T-T_0)]+\nabla\cdot[\rho\mathbf{v}(T-T_0)]\right\}=-\nabla\cdot\mathbf{q}+T\beta\frac{Dp}{Dt}+\nabla\mathbf{v}:\boldsymbol{\tau}+\Phi \tag{7.3-3}$$

however, this is not a suitable form for integration and we are forced to assume that the heat capacity, c_p, is constant so that we may express Eq. 7.3-3 as

$$\frac{\partial}{\partial t}[\rho c_p(T-T_0)]+\nabla\cdot[\rho c_p(T-T_0)\mathbf{v}]=-\nabla\cdot\mathbf{q}+T\beta\frac{Dp}{Dt}+\nabla\mathbf{v}:\boldsymbol{\tau}+\Phi \tag{7.3-4}$$

The assumption of constant heat capacity is quite reasonable as c_p changes only slowly with temperature for most materials. Gases near the critical point are an exception, but the heat capacity of water, for example, changes about 1 per cent for temperatures in the range 32°F–212°F.

We now form the macroscopic thermal energy balance by integrating Eq. 7.3-4 over the volume $\mathcal{V}_a(t)$ to obtain

$$\int_{\mathcal{V}_a(t)}\frac{\partial}{\partial t}[\rho c_p(T-T_0)]\,dV+\int_{\mathcal{A}_a(t)}\rho c_p(T-T_0)\mathbf{v}\cdot\mathbf{n}\,dA=-\int_{\mathcal{A}_a(t)}\mathbf{q}\cdot\mathbf{n}\,dA$$
$$+\int_{\mathcal{V}_a(t)}\left[T\beta\left(\frac{Dp}{Dt}\right)+\nabla\mathbf{v}:\boldsymbol{\tau}+\Phi\right]dV \tag{7.3-5}$$

Here we have used the divergence theorem to convert the second and third terms to area integrals. Once again we use the transport theorem, Eq. 5.1-21, to write

$$\frac{d}{dt}\int_{\mathcal{V}_a(t)}\rho c_p(T-T_0)\,dV=\int_{\mathcal{V}_a(t)}\frac{\partial}{\partial t}[\rho c_p(T-T_0)]\,dV+\int_{\mathcal{A}_a(t)}\rho c_p(T-T_0)\mathbf{w}\cdot\mathbf{n}\,dA \tag{7.3-6}$$

Substitution of this expression into Eq. 7.3-5 and rearranging leads to

$$\frac{d}{dt}\int_{\mathcal{V}_a(t)}\rho c_p(T-T_0)\,dV+\int_{\mathcal{A}_a(t)}\rho c_p(T-T_0)(\mathbf{v}-\mathbf{w})\cdot\mathbf{n}\,dA$$
$$=-\int_{\mathcal{A}_a(t)}\mathbf{q}\cdot\mathbf{n}\,dA+\int_{\mathcal{V}_a(t)}\left[T\beta\left(\frac{Dp}{Dt}\right)+\nabla\mathbf{v}:\boldsymbol{\tau}+\Phi\right]dV \tag{7.3-7}$$

Separating the area, $\mathscr{A}_a(t)$, into the three areas $A_e(t)$, $A_s(t)$, and A_s as described in Sec. 7.1, and noting that $(\mathbf{v}-\mathbf{w})\cdot\mathbf{n}=0$ over the latter two areas allows us to write Eq. 7.3-7 as

$$\frac{d}{dt}\int_{\mathscr{V}_a(t)} \rho c_p (T-T_0)\, dV + \int_{A_e(t)} \rho c_p (T-T_0)(\mathbf{v}-\mathbf{w})\cdot\mathbf{n}\, dA$$

$$= -\int_{\mathscr{A}_a(t)} \mathbf{q}\cdot\mathbf{n}\, dA + \int_{\mathscr{V}_a(t)} \left[T\beta\left(\frac{Dp}{Dt}\right) + \nabla\mathbf{v}:\boldsymbol{\tau} + \Phi\right] dV \tag{7.3-8}$$

Although this form of the *macroscopic thermal energy balance* appears to be quite complex, there are many steady flow processes for which the source terms, $T\beta(Dp/Dt)$, $\nabla\mathbf{v}:\boldsymbol{\tau}$, and Φ are negligible and Eq. 7.3-8 reduces to

$$\int_{A_e} \rho c_p (T-T_0)\mathbf{v}\cdot\mathbf{n}\, dA = -\int_{\mathscr{A}} \mathbf{q}\cdot\mathbf{n}\, dA, \quad \text{macroscopic thermal energy balance for a steady flow process and negligible source terms} \tag{7.3-9}$$

This form is quite easy to work with, and we will find it to be a powerful tool in the analysis of many practical heat transfer problems.

Macroscopic balances for turbulent flow

Our main purpose in formulating the macroscopic balances was to provide a means of analyzing turbulent flows, and we should remember that the terms in Eqs. 7-1, 7-2, and 7-3 must be interpreted as indicated in Table 6.2-1 when the flow is turbulent and incompressible.

Table 6.2-1

Laminar flow	*Turbulent flow*
$\mathbf{v}$	$\bar{\mathbf{v}}$
T	$\bar{T}$
p	$\bar{p}$
$\boldsymbol{\tau}$	$\boldsymbol{\tau}^{(T)} = \bar{\boldsymbol{\tau}} - \rho\overline{\mathbf{v}'\mathbf{v}'}$
$\mathbf{q}$	$\mathbf{q}^{(T)} = \bar{\mathbf{q}} + \rho c_p \overline{T'\mathbf{v}'}$
Φ	$\bar{\Phi}$

In Eq. 7.2-9 we must replace the stress vector, $\mathbf{t}_{(\mathbf{n})}$, with the time-averaged stress vector which is given by

$$\bar{\mathbf{t}}_{(\mathbf{n})} = -\bar{p}\mathbf{n} + (\bar{\boldsymbol{\tau}} - \rho\overline{\mathbf{v}'\mathbf{v}'})\cdot\mathbf{n} \tag{7.3-10}$$

In Chapter 6 we used Φ to represent the *entire* source term $T\beta(Dp/Dt) + \nabla\mathbf{v}:\boldsymbol{\tau} + \Phi$, and the time average, $\bar{\Phi}$, in Table 6.2-1 must be interpreted as

$$\left\{\begin{matrix}\text{time-averaged source}\\ \text{term to be used}\\ \text{in Eq. 6.3-8}\end{matrix}\right\} = \overline{T\beta\left(\frac{Dp}{Dt}\right)} + \overline{\nabla\mathbf{v}:\boldsymbol{\tau}} + \bar{\Phi} \tag{7.3-11}$$

Since the reversible work and viscous dissipation terms are the time average of products, some care must be given to their interpretation. This has been left as an exercise for the student.

PART II APPLICATIONS

With the macroscopic balances for mass, momentum, and thermal energy at our disposal we are in a position to analyze a wide variety of heat transfer problems. Although the physical phenomena associated with heat transfer problems may range from boiling on a horizontal tube to free convection on a vertical plate, each process has one characteristic in common. This characteristic is that the determination of the area integral of $\mathbf{q} \cdot \mathbf{n}$

$$\int_{\mathscr{A}_a(t)} \mathbf{q} \cdot \mathbf{n} \, dA$$

is the crux of most heat transfer problems.† The source term in the energy balance is generally a specified parameter or can be calculated with reasonable accuracy, and the convective flux terms are easily determined in terms of mass flow rates, heat capacities and temperatures. On the other hand, the area integral of $\mathbf{q} \cdot \mathbf{n}$ is given in terms of a film heat transfer coefficient and a characteristic temperature difference, thus we must make use of experimental values for h. Since process streams are very often heated and cooled while flowing in pipes, we will first consider the problem of heat transfer in pipe flow.

*7.4 Film Heat Transfer Coefficients for Pipe Flow: Analysis

If the unit normal, $\mathbf{n}$, for a solid–fluid interface is directed *from* the solid *into* the fluid, we define the local film heat transfer coefficient by

$$\mathbf{q} \cdot \mathbf{n} \equiv h_{\text{loc}}(T_i - T^*) \tag{7.4-1}$$

Here T_i represents the temperature at the *interface* and T^* represents some characteristic temperature for the fluid. Remember that in our analysis of boundary layer flows, T^* was taken to be T_∞; however, other choices could have been made. Note that if the characteristic temperature of the fluid is less than the interface temperature $T^* < T_i$, heat is being conducted from the solid to the fluid and Eq. 7.4-1 indicates that h_{loc} is a positive quantity.

Experimental values of the film heat transfer coefficient are generally correlated in terms of the dimensionless form of Eq. 7.4-1 which is written as

$$N_{\text{Nu,loc}} = \frac{h_{\text{loc}} L}{k} = \frac{(\mathbf{q} \cdot \mathbf{n}) L}{k(T_i - T^*)} \tag{7.4-2}$$

where k is the thermal conductivity of the fluid and L is some appropriate characteristic length. The correlation of heat transfer data in terms of a dimensionless heat transfer coefficient, N_{Nu}, is precisely analogous to the situation encountered in the analysis of turbulent flow in a course of fluid mechanics. There the *dimensionless momentum transfer coefficient*, i.e., the friction factor, f, or the drag coefficient, C_D, was used in the correlation of *momentum transfer* data, i.e., pressure drops and drag forces. Once the friction factor or drag coefficient was known the macroscopic momentum balance could be used to compute flow rates, or given the flow rates we could use friction factor and drag coefficient correlations to compute either pressure drops or drag forces.

The importance of establishing reliable Nusselt number correlations becomes clear when we examine the macroscopic thermal energy balance‡ previously given as Eq. 7.3-8

$$\frac{d}{dt}\int_{\mathscr{V}_a(t)} \rho c_p (T - T_0) \, dV + \int_{A_e(t)} \rho c_p (T - T_0)(\mathbf{v} - \mathbf{w}) \cdot \mathbf{n} \, dA$$
$$= -\int_{A_e(t)} \mathbf{q} \cdot \mathbf{n} \, dA - \int_{A_s(t)+A_s} \mathbf{q} \cdot \mathbf{n} \, dA + \int_{\mathscr{V}_a(t)} \left[T\beta \left(\frac{Dp}{Dt}\right) + \nabla \mathbf{v} : \boldsymbol{\tau} + \Phi \right] dV \tag{7.4-3}$$

Since the conductive heat flux at entrances and exits is generally small compared to the convective heat flux, only the area integral of $\mathbf{q} \cdot \mathbf{n}$ over the impenetrable surfaces needs to be specified in order to obtain a reasonably satisfactory solution of the macroscopic balance.

To begin our investigation of film heat transfer coefficients we examine the case of a fluid being heated in a pipe; the pipe having a *constant* wall temperature. This process is illustrated in Fig. 7.4.1. There we

†Remember that $\mathbf{q}$ is to be replaced with $\bar{\mathbf{q}}^{(T)}$ if the flow is turbulent.
‡Remember that we had to assume a constant value of c_p in order to derive Eq. 7.4-3.

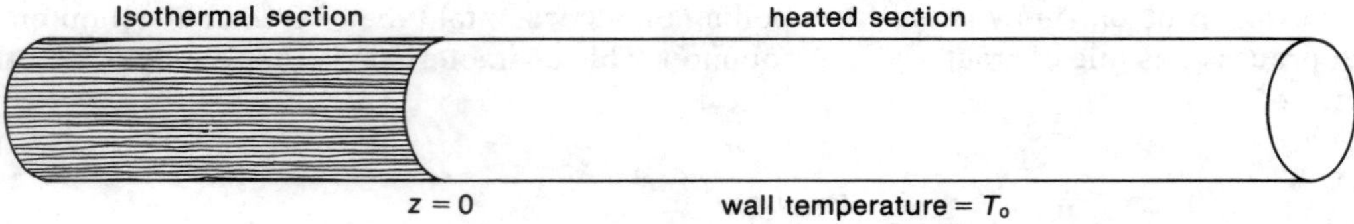

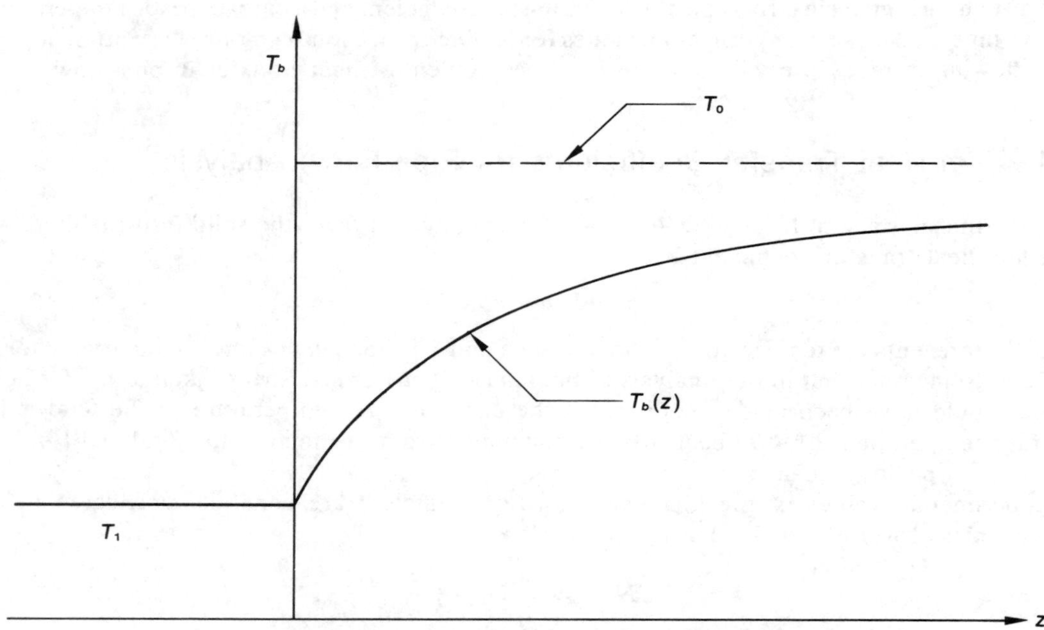

Fig. 7.4.1 Heat transfer in a tube having a constant wall temperature.

have shown the *bulk temperature* T_b as a function of z. The bulk temperature is generally used in heat transfer calculations because of its direct application in calculations and because of its ease of measurement. The *average temperature* $\langle T \rangle$ in a tube would be defined as

$$\langle T \rangle = \frac{\int_0^{2\pi} \int_0^{r_0} Tr \, dr \, d\theta}{\int_0^{2\pi} \int_0^{r_0} r \, dr \, d\theta} \tag{7.4-4}$$

while the *bulk temperature* is given by†

$$T_b = \frac{\langle v_z T \rangle}{\langle v_z \rangle} = \frac{\int_0^{2\pi} \int_0^{r_0} v_z Tr \, dr \, d\theta}{\int_0^{2\pi} \int_0^{r_0} v_z r \, dr \, d\theta} \tag{7.4-5}$$

The latter temperature is often called the "cup-mixing temperature" for it is the temperature one would measure if the fluid flowing past some section of the pipe were collected in a container and thoroughly mixed.

In this process the temperature varies in the z-direction and we would like to determine this variation.

†Once again it should be clear that the appropriate time-averaged quantities are to be used when the flow is turbulent.

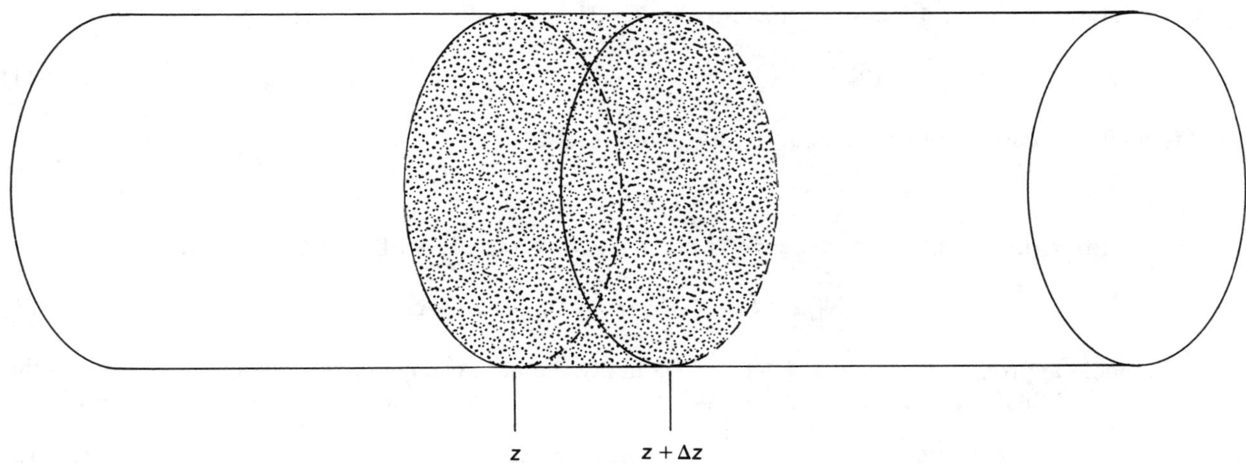

Fig. 7.4.2 Control volume for analysis of heat transfer in a tube.

To do so we need a macroscopic balance which is differential in the z-direction, i.e., we need a differential-macroscopic balance [1]. We make use of the control volume illustrated in Fig. 7.4.2 and consider the steady flow, fixed control volume form of Eq. 7.4-3 incorporating the appropriate time-averaged quantities listed in Table 6.2-1.

$$\int_{A_e} \rho c_p(\bar{T} - T_0)\bar{\mathbf{v}} \cdot \mathbf{n}\, dA = -\int_{A_e} \bar{\mathbf{q}}^{(T)} \cdot \mathbf{n}\, dA - \int_{A_s} \bar{\mathbf{q}}^{(T)} \cdot \mathbf{n}\, dA \tag{7.4-6}$$

Here we have assumed that the source terms are negligible; later we will investigate the validity of this assumption. Application of Eq. 7.4-6 to the control volume illustrated in Fig. 7.4.2 yields

$$-\int_{A_e} \rho c_p(\bar{T} - T_0)\bar{v}_z\, dA\big|_z + \int_{A_e} \rho c_p(\bar{T} - T_0)\bar{v}_z\, dA\big|_{z+\Delta z} = \int_{A_e} \bar{q}_z^{(T)}\, dA\big|_z - \int_{A_e} \bar{q}_z^{(T)}\, dA\big|_{z+\Delta z}$$
$$-\Delta z \int_0^{2\pi} \bar{q}_r r\, d\theta\big|_{r=r_0} \tag{7.4-7}$$

Here we have used the fact that

$$\bar{\mathbf{q}}^{(T)} = \bar{\mathbf{q}}, \quad \text{at } r = r_0$$

Dividing by Δz and taking the limit $\Delta z \to 0$ leads to

$$\frac{d}{dz}\int_{A_e} \rho c_p(\bar{T} - T_0)\bar{v}_z\, dA = -\frac{d}{dz}\int_{A_e} \bar{q}_z^{(T)}\, dA - \bar{q}_r\big|_{r_0} 2\pi r_0 \tag{7.4-8}$$

where $\bar{q}_r$ represents the average radial heat flux around the circumference of the pipe. We can use the definition of the bulk temperature given by Eq. 7.4-5 to express the convective transport term as

$$\int_{A_e} \rho c_p(\bar{T} - T_0)\bar{v}_z\, dA = \rho c_p(\bar{T}_b - T_0)\langle \bar{v}_z\rangle \pi r_0^2 \tag{7.4-9}$$

provided the density is constant across the pipe. The area integral of $\bar{q}_z^{(T)}$ can be written in terms of averages to yield

$$\int_{A_e} \bar{q}_z^{(T)}\, dA = \langle \bar{q}_z\rangle \pi r_0^2 + \rho c_p \langle \overline{v_z' T'}\rangle \pi r_0^2 \tag{7.4-10}$$

where the total heat flux has been expressed as

$$\bar{q}_z^{(T)} = \bar{q}_z + \rho c_p (\overline{v_z' T'})$$

according to Table 6.2-1.

Substitution of Eqs. 7.4-9 and 7.4-10 into Eq. 7.4-8 and dividing by πr_0 leads to

$$r_0 \frac{d}{dz}[\rho c_p(\bar{T}_b - T_0)\langle\bar{v}_z\rangle] = -\frac{d}{dz}\langle\bar{q}_z\rangle r_0 - r_0\frac{d}{dz}[\rho c_p \langle\overline{v_z' T'}\rangle] - 2\bar{q}_r|_{r_0} \tag{7.4-11}$$

At this point we can simplify our analysis by noting that

$$(\bar{T}_b - T_0)\langle\bar{v}_z\rangle \gg \langle\overline{v_z' T'}\rangle$$

and unless the structure of the turbulence is changing very rapidly with z, it follows that

$$r_0 \frac{d}{dz}[\rho c_p(\bar{T}_b - T_0)\langle\bar{v}_z\rangle] = -r_0\frac{d}{dz}\langle\bar{q}_z\rangle - 2\bar{q}_r|_{r_0} \tag{7.4-12}$$

is a reasonable approximation of Eq. 7.4-11. If we apply the macroscopic mass balance, Eq. 7.1-4, to the control volume illustrated in Fig. 7.4.2 and assume that ρ is constant across the tube, we obtain

$$\frac{d}{dz}(\rho\langle\bar{v}_z\rangle) = 0 \tag{7.4-13}$$

We can use this result, in addition to the expression for $\bar{q}_z$,

$$\bar{q}_z = -k\left(\frac{\partial \bar{T}}{\partial z}\right) = -k\frac{\partial}{\partial z}(\bar{T} - T_0) \tag{7.4-14}$$

to rewrite Eq. 7.4-12 in the form

$$\rho c_p\langle\bar{v}_z\rangle r_0 \frac{d}{dz}(\bar{T}_b - T_0) = k r_0 \frac{d^2}{dz^2}(\langle\bar{T}\rangle - T_0) - 2\bar{q}_r|_{r_0} \tag{7.4-15}$$

We should note at this point that there are two different temperatures in Eq. 7.4-15. One is a time-averaged *bulk* temperature, $\bar{T}_b$, while the other is a time-averaged *area-averaged* temperature, $\langle\bar{T}\rangle$. If the flow in the pipe is turbulent the velocity profile is nearly flat and Eq. 7.4-5 would indicate

$$\bar{T}_b = \langle\bar{T}\rangle, \quad \text{for a flat velocity profile} \tag{7.4-16}$$

however, if the flow is laminar these two temperatures are not equal to each other.

We can express the heat flux at $r = r_0$ in terms of a local film heat transfer coefficient and a characteristic temperature difference to obtain

$$\bar{q}_r|_{r_0} = h_{\text{loc}}(T^* - T_0) \tag{7.4-17}$$

Here T_0 is the wall temperature, which is in this case our reference temperature, and T^* is some characteristic temperature of the fluid flowing in the pipe. We can choose either $\bar{T}_b$ or $\langle\bar{T}\rangle$ as our reference temperature; however, the *bulk* temperature is most convenient. Setting $T^* = \bar{T}_b$ and substituting Eq. 7.4-17 into Eq. 7.4-15 leads to

$$\rho c_p\langle\bar{v}_z\rangle D\frac{d}{dz}(\bar{T}_b - T_0) = kD\frac{d^2}{dz^2}(\langle\bar{T}\rangle - T_0) - 4h_{\text{loc}}(\bar{T}_b - T_0) \tag{7.4-18}$$

If we multiply this result by the diameter, D, and divide by $k(T_1 - T_0)$, where T_1 is the temperature of the fluid at the entrance to the heated section (see Fig. 7.4.1), we obtain the dimensionless form

$$N_{\text{Pr}}N_{\text{Re}}\frac{d\Theta_b}{dZ} = \frac{d^2\langle\Theta\rangle}{dZ^2} - 4N_{\text{Nu,loc}}\Theta_b \tag{7.4-19}$$

where

$$\begin{aligned} N_{\text{Pr}} &= \mu c_p/k \\ N_{\text{Re}} &= \rho\langle\bar{v}_z\rangle D/\mu \\ \Theta_b &= (\bar{T}_b - T_0)/(T_1 - T_0) \\ \langle\Theta\rangle &= (\langle\bar{T}\rangle - T_0)/(T_1 - T_0) \\ Z &= z/D \\ N_{\text{Nu,loc}} &= h_{\text{loc}}D/k \end{aligned}$$

We should remember at this point that we made two major simplifications in our analysis of heat transfer to a fluid flowing in a pipe. The first simplification was the use of the macroscopic balance rather than the point equation, for this led to a differential equation containing the *average* temperatures $\bar{T}_b$ and $\langle \bar{T} \rangle$ which are only functions of z. The second simplification resulted from noting that the turbulent convective transport was small compared to the time-averaged convective transport so that Eq. 7.4-11 simplified to Eq. 7.4-12. We can further simplify Eq. 7.4-19 by using the material on *order-of-magnitude estimates* given in Sec. 2.9. If we let L be the length of pipe required to accomplish a significant change in the temperature difference $\bar{T}_b - \bar{T}_0$, then we can say that Θ_b and $\langle \Theta \rangle$ lie between 0 and 1 in the region $0 \leq z \leq L$. In terms of the dimensionless distance, $Z = z/D$, a significant change in Θ_b and $\langle \Theta \rangle$ takes place in the region $0 \leq Z \leq L/D$, and we can express the order-of-magnitude of the derivatives in Eq. 7.4-19 as

$$\frac{d\Theta_b}{dZ} = \mathbf{0}\left(\frac{1}{L/D}\right)$$

$$\frac{d^2\langle \Theta \rangle}{dZ^2} = \mathbf{0}\left[\frac{1}{(L/D)^2}\right]$$

Rewriting Eq. 7.4-19 and indicating the order-of-magnitude of each term leads to

$$\begin{array}{ccc} & \left(\frac{D}{L}\right) & \left(\frac{D}{L}\right)^2 \\ N_{\mathrm{Pr}}N_{\mathrm{Re}} & \dfrac{d\Theta_b}{dZ} = & \dfrac{d^2\langle \Theta \rangle}{dZ^2} - 4N_{\mathrm{Nu,loc}}\Theta_b \end{array}$$

Clearly the axial conduction will be negligible compared to convection when $N_{\mathrm{Pr}}N_{\mathrm{Re}}\,(D/L) \gg (D/L)^2$, and we can express this restriction as†

$$N_{\mathrm{Pr}}N_{\mathrm{Re}}(L/D) \gg 1, \quad \text{axial conduction negligible compared to convection} \tag{7.4-20}$$

Most practical heat transfer processes, with the exception of those involving liquid metals, satisfy this condition and Eq. 7.4-19 is simplified to

$$\left(\frac{d\Theta_b}{dZ}\right) = -4\left(\frac{N_{\mathrm{Nu,loc}}}{N_{\mathrm{Re}}N_{\mathrm{Pr}}}\right)\Theta_b \tag{7.4-21}$$

In order to integrate Eq. 7.4-21 and determine the temperature field we are forced to make a crucial assumption, namely that *all physical properties* are constant, and that the local film heat transfer coefficient is constant. This means that $(N_{\mathrm{Nu,loc}}/N_{\mathrm{Re}}N_{\mathrm{Pr}})$ is a constant and Eq. 7.4-21 may be integrated subject to the single boundary condition

B.C.1
$$\Theta_b = 1, \qquad Z = 0 \tag{7.4-22}$$

to obtain

$$\ln \Theta_b = -4(N_{\mathrm{Nu,loc}}/N_{\mathrm{Re}}N_{\mathrm{Pr}})Z \tag{7.4-23}$$

or

$$\frac{\bar{T}_b - T_0}{T_1 - T_0} = e^{-4(N_{\mathrm{Nu,loc}}/N_{\mathrm{Re}}N_{\mathrm{Pr}})Z} \tag{7.4-24}$$

This expression is useful if we wish to calculate the bulk temperature as a function of position; however, there is a more convenient method of using this result which we will discuss in the following paragraphs.

If we let $\dot{Q}$ be the total rate at which heat is transferred to the fluid in a pipe of length L, we can write

$$\dot{Q} = -\int_0^L \int_0^{2\pi} r\bar{q}_r\big|_{r_0}\, d\theta\, dz \tag{7.4-25}$$

†This constraint is reminiscent of that given by Eq. 5.9-45 for laminar boundary layer flows.

and quickly deduce from the macroscopic thermal energy balance that

$$\dot{Q} = \rho c_p \langle \bar{v}_z \rangle \frac{\pi D^2}{4} (\bar{T}_{b2} - \bar{T}_{b1}) \tag{7.4-26}$$

Here $\bar{T}_{b1}$ is the bulk temperature at $z = 0$ and $\bar{T}_{b2}$ is the bulk temperature at $z = L$. We can arrange this result in the form

$$\dot{Q} = \left(\frac{\mu c_p}{k}\right)\left(\frac{\rho \langle \bar{v}_z \rangle D}{\mu}\right)\left(\frac{\pi D k}{4}\right)(\bar{T}_{b2} - \bar{T}_{b1}) = N_{\text{Pr}} N_{\text{Re}} \left(\frac{\pi D k}{4}\right)(\bar{T}_{b2} - \bar{T}_{b1}) \tag{7.4-27}$$

If we now set $Z = L/D$ in Eq. 7.4-23 and note that $\Theta_b = \Theta_{b2}$ at $Z = L/D$, we can use Eq. 7.4-23 to write

$$N_{\text{Pr}} N_{\text{Re}} = -\frac{4\left(\frac{L}{D}\right) N_{\text{Nu,loc}}}{\ln \Theta_{b2}} \tag{7.4-28}$$

and substitute into Eq. 7.4-27 to obtain

$$\dot{Q} = -\frac{\pi L k N_{\text{Nu,loc}} (\bar{T}_{b2} - \bar{T}_{b1})}{\ln\left(\frac{\bar{T}_{b2} - T_0}{\bar{T}_{b1} - T_0}\right)} \tag{7.4-29}$$

Here we have used the fact that $T_1 = \bar{T}_{b1}$. A little more rearranging leads to

$$\dot{Q} = h_{\text{loc}}(\pi D L)\left\{\frac{[(T_0 - \bar{T}_{b2}) - (T_0 - \bar{T}_{b1})]}{\ln\left(\frac{T_0 - \bar{T}_{b2}}{T_0 - \bar{T}_{b1}}\right)}\right\} \tag{7.4-30}$$

Remember that this result is valid only for constant physical properties, a constant value of h_{loc}, and a constant wall temperature. It is usually written in the abbreviated form

$$\dot{Q} = h_{\text{loc}} A \Delta T_{\text{ln}} \tag{7.4-31}$$

where A is the area over which the heat transfer takes place and ΔT_{ln} is referred to as the *log-mean temperature difference* defined for a constant wall temperature as

$$\Delta T_{\text{ln}} = \frac{(T_0 - \bar{T}_{b2}) - (T_0 - \bar{T}_{b1})}{\ln\left(\frac{T_0 - \bar{T}_{b2}}{T_0 - \bar{T}_{b1}}\right)} \tag{7.4-32}$$

When an experimental determination of h is to be made in a system such as that shown in Fig. 7.4.1, the bulk temperatures and the flow rate are measured so that $\dot{Q}$ can be determined, and then Eq. 7.4-31 is used to compute h

$$h_{\text{ln}} \equiv \dot{Q}/A \Delta T_{\text{ln}} \tag{7.4-33}$$

Film heat transfer coefficients determined in this manner are referred to as *log-mean* film heat transfer coefficients and designated by h_{ln}. If the local film heat transfer coefficient is constant then $h_{\text{ln}} = h_{\text{loc}}$; however, if h_{loc} is not constant then h_{ln} will depend on the length of the pipe used in the experiment. This point will be explored in Sec. 7.6, but before going on to an examination of experimental data it will be helpful to perform a dimensional analysis of the heat transfer process just considered.

Example 7.4-1 Analysis of heat transfer data for turbulent flow in pipes

In 1928 F. H. Morris and W. G. Whitman published† the first experimental data for the cooling and heating of petroleum oils in pipes. Their apparatus was similar to the double-pipe heat exchanger shown in Fig. VII.1; however, in their heating experiments steam was condensed in the annular region so that the wall temperature

†See Reference 18.

was very nearly constant over the entire length of the pipe. Under these conditions their experimental configuration was identical to that shown in Fig. 7.4.1. Their run number C6 was for heating "straw oil" and yielded the following data:

$$D = 0.62 \text{ in., inner diameter}$$
$$L = 121.5 \text{ in., tube length}$$
$$T_0 = 207.2°\text{F, wall temperature}$$
$$T_{b1} = 78.1°\text{F, entrance bulk temperature}$$
$$T_{b2} = 88.8°\text{F, exit bulk temperature}$$
$$\rho\langle v_z\rangle = 316 \text{ lb}_m/\text{ft}^2\text{sec, mass velocity}$$
$$c_p = 0.453 \text{ Btu/lb}_m°\text{F}$$

We can use these data and Eq. 7.4-26 to calculate the total rate of heat transfer, $\dot{Q}$.

$$\dot{Q} = \rho c_p \langle v_z\rangle \left(\frac{\pi D^2}{4}\right)(\bar{T}_{b2} - \bar{T}_{b1})$$
$$= \left(\frac{0.453 \text{ Btu}}{\text{lb}_m °\text{F}}\right)\left(\frac{316 \text{ lb}_m}{\text{ft}^2\text{sec}}\right)\left[\frac{3.14}{4}\left(\frac{0.62}{12}\right)^2 \text{ft}^2\right](10.7°\text{F})\left(\frac{3600 \text{ sec}}{\text{hr}}\right)$$
$$= 11\,560 \text{ Btu/hr}$$

The log-mean temperature difference is given by Eq. 7.4-32, and for this case we have

$$\Delta T_{\text{ln}} = \frac{118.4°\text{F} - 129.1°\text{F}}{\ln\left(\frac{118.4}{129.1}\right)} = 123.7°\text{F}$$

Referring now to Eq. 7.4-33 we express the log-mean film heat transfer coefficient as

$$h_{\text{ln}} = \dot{Q}/A\,\Delta T_{\text{ln}}$$
$$= \frac{11\,560 \text{ Btu/hr}}{(3.14)(0.62 \text{ in.})(121.5 \text{ in.})(123.7°\text{F})}\left(\frac{144 \text{ in}^2}{\text{ft}^2}\right)$$
$$= 56.9 \text{ Btu/hr ft}^2 °\text{F}$$

For the purposes of correlating experimental data of this type, one expresses the result in terms of a Nusselt number. This has been done, and one of the points shown in Fig. 7.6.2 was obtained from the above calculation.

Summary of Section 7.5

In this section we perform the dimensional analysis of heat transfer to a fluid flowing in a tube. The approach is identical to that given in Sec. 5.6, but here we include the temperature dependence of the viscosity in our analysis. The result indicates that the functional dependence of the local Nusselt number is given by

$$N_{\text{Nu,loc}} = \mathcal{F}(Z, N_{\text{Re}}, N_{\text{Pr}}, \Lambda, \epsilon/D) \tag{7.5-25}$$

for a steady flow. Here Λ is given by

$$\Lambda = \frac{1}{\mu}\left(\frac{\partial \mu}{\partial \Theta}\right)$$

and is a parameter appearing in a differential equation which accounts for the temperature dependence of the viscosity. The parameter ϵ/D represents the effect of wall roughness where ϵ represents an average value of the roughness of the wall. The functional dependence of the log-mean Nusselt number is shown to be

$$N_{\text{Nu,ln}} = \mathcal{G}(L/D, N_{\text{Re}}, N_{\text{Pr}}, \Lambda, \epsilon/D) \tag{7.5-29}$$

*7.5 Dimensional Analysis for Heat Transfer to a Fluid Flowing in a Tube†

In this analysis we will assume that the density, heat capacity, and thermal conductivity are constant; however, we will allow the viscosity to be a function of temperature. From experimental observations we

†Our main purpose here is to extend previous studies of dimensional analysis to include the case of variable viscosity.

know that the variation of viscosity with temperature is of importance, thus inclusion of this effect in our analysis has practical implications in addition to illustrating the procedure one follows for analyzing systems with *nonuniform physical properties.*

We begin by specifying the differential equations which govern the process under consideration. These are the stress equations of motion

$$\rho\left(\frac{\partial \mathbf{v}}{\partial t}+\mathbf{v}\cdot\nabla\mathbf{v}\right)=-\nabla p+\rho\mathbf{g}+\nabla\cdot\boldsymbol{\tau} \tag{7.5-1}$$

the continuity equation

$$\nabla\cdot\mathbf{v}=0 \tag{7.5-2}$$

and the thermal energy equation for negligible viscous dissipation and reversible work, and no heat generation owing to electromagnetic effects.

$$\rho c_p\left(\frac{\partial T}{\partial t}+\mathbf{v}\cdot\nabla T\right)=-\nabla\cdot\mathbf{q} \tag{7.5-3}$$

If the flow is turbulent we interpret the dependent variables as

$$\begin{aligned}\mathbf{v}&=\bar{\mathbf{v}}\\ p&=\bar{p}\\ T&=\bar{T}\\ \boldsymbol{\tau}&=\bar{\boldsymbol{\tau}}-(\rho\overline{\mathbf{v}'\mathbf{v}'})\\ \mathbf{q}&=\bar{\mathbf{q}}-(\rho c_p\overline{\mathbf{v}'T'})\end{aligned}$$

and the governing equations take the form

$$\rho\left(\frac{\partial \bar{\mathbf{v}}}{\partial t}+\bar{\mathbf{v}}\cdot\nabla\bar{\mathbf{v}}\right)=-\nabla\bar{p}+\rho\mathbf{g}+\nabla\cdot[\bar{\boldsymbol{\tau}}-(\rho\overline{\mathbf{v}'\mathbf{v}'})] \tag{7.5-4}$$

$$\nabla\cdot\bar{\mathbf{v}}=0 \tag{7.5-5}$$

$$\rho c_p\left(\frac{\partial \bar{T}}{\partial t}+\bar{\mathbf{v}}\cdot\nabla\bar{T}\right)=-\nabla\cdot[\bar{\mathbf{q}}-(\rho c_p\overline{\mathbf{v}'T'})] \tag{7.5-6}$$

For fluids which obey Newton's law of viscosity and Fourier's law of heat conduction, we may write†

$$\bar{\boldsymbol{\tau}}=\mu(\nabla\bar{\mathbf{v}}+\nabla\bar{\mathbf{v}}^{\mathrm{T}})$$

$$\bar{\mathbf{q}}=-k\nabla\bar{T}$$

Assuming that the thermal conductivity is essentially constant, but allowing the viscosity to vary, the above relations may be substituted into the governing equations to obtain

$$\rho\left(\frac{\partial \bar{\mathbf{v}}}{\partial t}+\bar{\mathbf{v}}\cdot\nabla\bar{\mathbf{v}}\right)=-\nabla\bar{p}+\rho\mathbf{g}+\mu\nabla^2\bar{\mathbf{v}}+(\nabla\mu)\cdot(\nabla\bar{\mathbf{v}}+\nabla\bar{\mathbf{v}}^{\mathrm{T}})-\rho\nabla\cdot(\overline{\mathbf{v}'\mathbf{v}'}) \tag{7.5-7}$$

$$\nabla\cdot\bar{\mathbf{v}}=0 \tag{7.5-7a}$$

$$c_p\left(\frac{\partial \bar{T}}{\partial t}+\bar{\mathbf{v}}\cdot\nabla\bar{T}\right)=k\nabla^2\bar{T}-\rho c_p\nabla\cdot(\overline{\mathbf{v}'T'}) \tag{7.5-8}$$

Before obtaining the dimensionless form of these equations we should write out the applicable boundary conditions. At the entrance to the heated section we will assume that a well-established velocity profile

†The transpose of $\nabla\mathbf{v}$ is denoted by $\nabla\mathbf{v}^{\mathrm{T}}$.

exists, thus

B.C.1 $$v_z = f(r), \qquad v_r = v_\theta = 0, \qquad z = 0 \tag{7.5-9}$$

If the flow is laminar $f(r)$ would be parabolic function, and if the flow is turbulent $f(r)$ would represent the nearly flat profile characteristic of turbulent flows. Applying the "no slip" condition at the pipe wall gives

B.C.2 $$\mathbf{v} = 0, \qquad r = r_0 + e(\theta, z) \tag{7.5-10}$$

where $e(\theta, z)$ is the roughness function. At $z = 0$ we will assume that the fluid is at some uniform temperature designated as T_1 and write†

B.C.3 $$T = T_1, \qquad z = 0 \tag{7.5-11}$$

At $r = r_0 + e(\theta, z)$ the fluid temperature will be equal to the constant wall temperature T_0, thus

B.C.4 $$T = T_0, \qquad r = r_0 + e(\theta, z) \tag{7.5-12}$$

In this treatment we wish to include the effect of temperature on the viscosity, and our analysis of this effect will parallel the development given in Sec. 5.6 where we included the effect of temperature on the fluid density. We can expand μ in a Taylor series about the wall temperature to obtain

$$\mu(T) = \mu(T_0) + \left(\frac{\partial \mu}{\partial T}\right)_{T=T_0}(T - T_0) + \cdots \tag{7.5-13}$$

If we restrict the analysis to small variations in the viscosity, we can drop the higher order terms and express μ as

$$\mu = \mu_0\left[1 + \frac{1}{\mu_0}\left(\frac{\partial \mu}{\partial T}\right)_0(T - T_0)\right] \tag{7.5-14}$$

where the subscript zero indicates that the function is evaluated at the wall temperature. Substituting this result into the equations of motion yields

$$\rho\left(\frac{\partial \bar{\mathbf{v}}}{\partial t} + \bar{\mathbf{v}}\cdot\nabla\bar{\mathbf{v}}\right) = -\nabla\bar{p} + \rho\mathbf{g} + \mu_0\left[1 + \frac{1}{\mu_0}\left(\frac{\partial \mu}{\partial T}\right)_0(T - T_0)\right]\nabla^2\bar{\mathbf{v}} + \left(\frac{\partial \mu}{\partial T}\right)(\nabla T)\cdot[\nabla\bar{\mathbf{v}} + \nabla\bar{\mathbf{v}}^{\mathrm{T}}] - \rho\nabla\cdot(\overline{\mathbf{v}'\mathbf{v}'}) \tag{7.5-15}$$

Here we have used the chain rule to write

$$\nabla\mu = \left(\frac{\partial \mu}{\partial T}\right)\nabla\bar{T} \tag{7.5-16}$$

We can now make the governing equations dimensionless by multiplying the equations of motion by $D/\rho\langle\bar{v}_z\rangle^2$, the continuity equation by $L/\langle\bar{v}_z\rangle$, and the thermal energy equation by $L/\rho c_v\langle\bar{v}_z\rangle(T_1 - T_0)$ to obtain

$$\frac{\partial \bar{\mathbf{U}}}{\partial t^*} + \bar{\mathbf{U}}\cdot\nabla\bar{\mathbf{U}} = -\nabla\bar{\mathcal{P}} + \frac{1}{N_{\mathrm{Re}}}(1 + \Lambda\Theta)\nabla^2\bar{\mathbf{U}} + \frac{1}{N_{\mathrm{Re}}}[\Lambda(\nabla\Theta)\cdot(\nabla\bar{\mathbf{U}} + \nabla\bar{\mathbf{U}}^{\mathrm{T}})] - \nabla\cdot(\overline{\mathbf{U}'\mathbf{U}'}) \tag{7.5-17}$$

$$\nabla\cdot\bar{\mathbf{U}} = 0 \tag{7.5-18}$$

$$\frac{\partial \bar{\Theta}}{\partial t^*} + \bar{\mathbf{U}}\cdot\nabla\bar{\Theta} = \frac{1}{N_{\mathrm{Re}}N_{\mathrm{Pr}}}\nabla^2\bar{\Theta} - \nabla\cdot(\overline{\mathbf{U}'\Theta'}) \tag{7.5-19}$$

The dimensionless variables and parameters are as follows:

$$\bar{\mathbf{U}} = \bar{\mathbf{v}}/\langle\bar{v}_z\rangle$$

†This implies that the sudden jump in the wall temperature at $z = 0$ is not propagated upstream in the fluid. This is a reasonable assumption provided $N_{\mathrm{Re}}N_{\mathrm{Pr}} \gg 1$.

$$\bar{\mathcal{P}} = \frac{\bar{p} - p_0}{\rho\langle\bar{v}_z\rangle^2} + \frac{\phi}{\langle\bar{v}_z\rangle^2}$$
$$t^* = t\langle\bar{v}_z\rangle/D$$
$$\boldsymbol{\nabla} = D\nabla$$
$$\Theta = (T - T_0)/(T_1 - T_0)$$
$$\mathbf{U}' = \mathbf{v}'/\langle\bar{v}_z\rangle$$
$$\Theta' = (T' - T_0)/(T_1 - T_0)$$
$$\Lambda = \frac{1}{\mu}\left(\frac{\partial\mu}{\partial\Theta}\right)$$
$$N_{\text{Re}} = \rho\langle v_z\rangle D/\mu$$
$$N_{\text{Pr}} = c_p\mu_0/k$$

It is important to note here that the inclusion of the turbulent transport terms gives rise to no new dimensionless groups. Putting the boundary conditions in dimensionless form we find

B.C.1′ $$U_z = \mathcal{F}(R), \qquad U_r = U_\theta = 0, \qquad Z = 0 \tag{7.5-20}$$

B.C.2′ $$\mathbf{U} = 0, \qquad R = 1/2 + (\epsilon/D)\mathcal{G}(\theta, Z) \tag{7.5-21}$$

B.C.3′ $$\Theta = 1, \qquad Z = 0 \tag{7.5-22}$$

B.C.4′ $$\Theta = 0, \qquad R = 1/2 + (\epsilon/D)\mathcal{G}(\theta, Z)$$

Here the *function* $e(\theta, Z)/D$ has been replaced by the relative roughness *parameter* and the dimensionless function $\mathcal{G}(\theta, Z)$, the latter being on the order-of-magnitude of unity. From studies of flow in tubes we know that the effect of roughness can be correlated reasonably well by the *single* parameter ϵ/D, thus the function $\mathcal{G}(\theta, Z)$ will be dropped from the analysis.

On the basis of the differential equations and the boundary conditions we can express the functional dependence of the dimensionless temperature as

$$\Theta = \Theta(\underbrace{\{R, \theta, Z, t^*\}}_{\text{independent variables}}, \underbrace{\{N_{\text{Re}}, N_{\text{Pr}}, \Lambda\}}_{\text{parameters in the differential equations}}, \underbrace{\{\epsilon/D\}}_{\text{parameters in the boundary conditions}})$$

If the wall temperature is not constant, but varies with z, the additional dimensionless parameters necessary to represent the wall temperature should appear in the functional dependence of Θ. Sleicher and Tribus [2] have studied this problem in some detail for turbulent flows and find that when $N_{\text{Pr}} \geq 1$ the influence of a nonuniform wall temperature is relatively unimportant. For liquid metals, which have Prandtl numbers in the range of 10^{-3} to 10^{-2}, the effect is more important and can change the heat transfer coefficient or Nusselt number by as much as 30 per cent.

The local film heat transfer coefficient is defined by

$$h_{\text{loc}} = \frac{\int_0^{2\pi} q_r\, d\theta}{2\pi(\bar{T}_b - T_0)} = \frac{\int_0^{2\pi} k\left(\frac{\partial T}{\partial r}\right)_{r=r_0} d\theta}{2\pi(\bar{T}_b - T_0)} \tag{7.5-23}$$

In dimensionless form this becomes

$$N_{\text{Nu,loc}} = -\frac{\int_0^{2\pi}\left(\frac{\partial\bar{\Theta}}{\partial R}\right)_{R=1/2} d\theta}{2\pi\langle\bar{U}_z\bar{\Theta}\rangle} \tag{7.5-24}$$

Here we have used the fact that the time-averaged bulk temperature is given by

$$\bar{T}_b = \frac{\langle\bar{v}_z\bar{T}\rangle}{\langle\bar{v}_z\rangle}$$

or in dimensionless form

$$\frac{\bar{T}_b - T_0}{T_1 - T_0} = \frac{\langle \bar{v}_z \Theta \rangle}{\langle \bar{v}_z \rangle} = \langle \bar{U}_z \bar{\Theta} \rangle$$

From Eq. 7.5-24 and the functional dependence of Θ we see that the functional dependence of the local Nusselt number is given by

$$N_{\text{Nu,loc}} = \mathscr{F}(Z, t^*, N_{\text{Re}}, N_{\text{Pr}}, \Lambda, \epsilon/D)$$

For the practical case of steady flow this reduces to

$$N_{\text{Nu,loc}} = \mathscr{F}(Z, N_{\text{Re}}, N_{\text{Pr}}, \Lambda, \epsilon/D) \tag{7.5-25}$$

To determine the functional dependence of the log-mean Nusselt number we refer to Eq. 7.4-33 and express the log-mean film heat transfer as

$$h_{\ln} = \dot{Q}/A\,\Delta T_{\ln} \tag{7.5-26}$$

Inserting the expressions for $\dot{Q}$, A, and $\Delta T_{\ln}$ leads to

$$h_{\ln} = \frac{\displaystyle\int_0^L \int_0^{2\pi} k\left(\frac{\partial T}{\partial r}\right)_{r=r_0} d\theta\, dz}{2\pi L\left[\dfrac{(T_{w2} - \bar{T}_{b2}) - (T_{w1} - \bar{T}_{b1})}{\ln\left(\dfrac{T_{w2} - \bar{T}_{b2}}{T_{w1} - \bar{T}_{b1}}\right)}\right]} \tag{7.5-27}$$

Here T_{w1} and T_{w2} represent the wall temperatures at $z = 0$ and $z = L$ respectively. This *definition* of $\Delta T_{\ln}$ is a logical extension of the definition given by Eq. 7.4-32 for the case of constant wall temperature. In dimensionless form Eq. 7.5-27 can be expressed as

$$N_{\text{Nu,ln}} = \frac{\ln\langle \bar{U}_z \Theta_2 \rangle \displaystyle\int_0^{L/D} \int_0^{2\pi} \left(\frac{\partial \Theta}{\partial R}\right)_{R=1/2} d\theta\, dZ}{\pi(1 - \langle \bar{U}_z \Theta_2 \rangle)} \tag{7.5-28}$$

and we conclude that the functional dependence of the log-mean Nusselt number is

$$N_{\text{Nu,ln}} = \mathscr{G}(L/D, N_{\text{Re}}, N_{\text{Pr}}, \Lambda, \epsilon/D) \tag{7.5-29}$$

provided Λ is constant.

Example 7.5-1 Dimensional analysis for steady, one-dimensional, compressible flow in closed conduits

In this example we intend to examine the dimensionless form of the thermal energy equation for steady, one-dimensional flow taking into account the compressional work and viscous dissipation. In Sec. 5.5 we estimated the order-of-magnitude of these terms and found that very often they could be neglected; however, there are cases of high-speed gas flow and low-speed flow of polymers in which the compressional work and viscous dissipation must be taken into account. For such cases one would want to know the appropriate dimensionless parameters which characterize the phenomena.

We begin with Eq. 5.5-10.

$$\rho c_p\left(\frac{\partial T}{\partial t} + \mathbf{v}\cdot\nabla T\right) = \nabla\cdot(k\nabla T) + T\beta\frac{Dp}{Dt} + \nabla\mathbf{v}:\boldsymbol{\tau} + \Phi \tag{1}$$

and assume that the thermal conductivity is constant and electromagnetic effects are negligible to obtain

$$\rho c_p\left(\frac{\partial T}{\partial t} + \mathbf{v}\cdot\nabla T\right) = k\nabla^2 T + T\beta\frac{Dp}{Dt} + \nabla\mathbf{v}:\boldsymbol{\tau} \tag{2}$$

For steady flow we have

$$\frac{\partial T}{\partial t} = 0, \qquad \frac{Dp}{Dt} = \mathbf{v}\cdot\nabla p$$

and Eq. 2 simplifies to

$$\rho c_p \mathbf{v} \cdot \nabla T = k\nabla^2 T + T\beta \mathbf{v} \cdot \nabla p + \nabla \mathbf{v} : \boldsymbol{\tau} \tag{3}$$

For closed conduits the hydraulic diameter

$$D_h = \frac{4\,(\text{cross-sectional area})}{(\text{wetted perimeter})}$$

is the appropriate characteristic length, thus we make Eq. 3 dimensionless by multiplying by $D_h/\rho c_p \langle v_z \rangle \Delta T$ to obtain†

$$\mathbf{U} \cdot \nabla \Theta = \frac{1}{N_{\text{Re}} N_{\text{Pr}}} \nabla^2 \Theta + \frac{T\beta \mathbf{U} \cdot \nabla p}{\rho c_p \Delta T} + \frac{\nabla \mathbf{U} : \mathbf{T}}{\rho c_p \Delta T} \tag{4}$$

Here ΔT is some characteristic temperature difference, usually chosen to be the largest temperature difference in the system.

For one-dimensional flow in closed conduits the wall shear stress, τ_0, can be expressed in terms of the Fanning friction factor as

$$\tau_0 = f\left(\frac{1}{2} \rho \langle v_z \rangle^2\right) \tag{5}$$

and the pressure gradient (neglecting hydrostatic effects) can be expressed as

$$\nabla p = -4f\left(\frac{1}{2} \rho \langle v_z \rangle^2\right) \mathbf{k} \tag{6}$$

Remember once again that the "del" operator in Eq. 6 has been made dimensionless by multiplication by D_h. Since we want our analysis to include the case of polymer solutions it is best to make the viscous stress tensor dimensionless by dividing by the wall shear stress. We define the dimensionless viscous stress tensor as

$$\mathbf{T} = \boldsymbol{\tau}/\tau_0$$

and use Eqs. 5 and 6 to rearrange Eq. 4 in the form

$$\mathbf{U} \cdot \nabla \Theta = \frac{1}{N_{\text{Re}} N_{\text{Pr}}} \nabla^2 \Theta - 4U_z (T\beta) f \left[\frac{\frac{1}{2}\rho \langle v_z \rangle^2}{\rho c_p \Delta T}\right] + f(\nabla \mathbf{U} : \mathbf{T}) \left[\frac{\frac{1}{2}\rho \langle v_z \rangle^2}{\rho c_p \Delta T}\right] \tag{7}$$

The term in brackets is often referred to as the Eckert number‡

$$N_{\text{Ec}} = \frac{1}{2} \rho \langle v_z \rangle^2 / \rho c_p \Delta T$$

thus our final dimensionless form of the thermal energy equation is

$$\underset{(1)\,\downarrow}{\overset{(D_h/L)}{\mathbf{U} \cdot \nabla \Theta}} = \frac{1}{N_{\text{Re}} N_{\text{Pr}}} \underset{\downarrow}{\overset{[1,\, 1/4\pi^2,\, (D_h/L)^2]}{\nabla^2 \Theta}} \quad - 4\overbrace{U_z (T\beta)}^{(1)} f N_{\text{Ec}} + \overbrace{(\nabla \mathbf{U} : \mathbf{T})}^{(1)} f N_{\text{Ec}} \tag{8}$$

Here we have used the material presented in Sec. 2.9 to estimate the order-of-magnitude of several of the terms. For example, the term $\mathbf{U} \cdot \nabla \Theta$ can be expressed as

$$\mathbf{U} \cdot \nabla \Theta = U_z \frac{\partial \Theta}{\partial Z} = [\mathbf{0}\,(1)] \left[\frac{\mathbf{0}\,(1)}{L/D_h}\right] \tag{9}$$

Here we have used the fact that U_z and Θ are on the order of 1 and the range of Z is given by $0 \leq Z \leq L/D_h$. For flow in pipe, $\nabla^2 \Theta$ is given by

$$\nabla^2 \Theta = \frac{1}{R} \left[\frac{\partial}{\partial R} \left(R \frac{\partial \Theta}{\partial R}\right)\right] + \frac{1}{R^2} \left(\frac{\partial \Theta}{\partial \Theta^2}\right) + \frac{\partial^2 \Theta}{\partial Z^2} \tag{10}$$

and the order-of-magnitude estimates are given as

$$\frac{1}{R} \left[\frac{\partial}{\partial R} \left(R \frac{\partial \Theta}{\partial R}\right)\right] = \mathbf{0}\,(1)$$

†Note that in Eq. 4 we have used ∇ to represent the dimensionless vector operator.

‡Sometimes the Eckert number is given by $\rho \langle v_z \rangle^2 / \rho c_p \Delta T$ and occasionally it is referred to as the *recovery number.*

$$\frac{1}{R^2}\left(\frac{\partial^2\Theta}{\partial\theta^2}\right) = \mathbf{0}\left(\frac{1}{4\pi^2}\right)$$

$$\frac{\partial^2\Theta}{\partial Z^2} = \mathbf{0}\left[\frac{1}{(L/D)^2}\right]$$

Here we have noted that $0 \leqslant R \leqslant 1/2$ so that $R = \mathbf{0}(1)$.

From Eq. 8 we can predict that compressional work will be negligible provided

$$\frac{1}{N_{\text{Re}}N_{\text{Pr}}} \gg (T\beta)fN_{\text{Ec}}$$

and viscous dissipation will be unimportant when

$$\frac{1}{N_{\text{Re}}N_{\text{Pr}}} \gg fN_{\text{Ec}}$$

We can summarize our results in the form

$$(T\beta)fN_{\text{Ec}}N_{\text{Re}}N_{\text{Pr}} \ll 1, \quad \text{negligible compressional work}$$

$$fN_{\text{Ec}}N_{\text{Re}}N_{\text{Pr}} \ll 1, \quad \text{negligible viscous dissipation}$$

For gases near standard conditions $T\beta \sim 1$, and the two constraints are identical. For laminar flow in tubes $f = 16/N_{\text{Re}}$ and we have

$$16(T\beta)N_{\text{Ec}}N_{\text{Pr}} \ll 1, \quad \text{negligible compressional work in laminar flow}$$

$$16N_{\text{Ec}}N_{\text{Pr}} \ll 1, \quad \text{negligible viscous dissipation in laminar flow}$$

Clearly, the Eckert number must be small compared to 1 in order for compressional work and viscous dissipation to be neglected.

*7.6 Experimental Data and Empirical Correlations for Heat Transfer for Flow in Pipes

From our dimensional analysis for heat transfer in a pipe with a constant wall temperature, we concluded that the local Nusselt number has the functional dependence given by

$$N_{\text{Nu,loc}} = \mathcal{F}(Z, N_{\text{Re}}, N_{\text{Pr}}, \Lambda, \epsilon/D) \tag{7.6-1}$$

The Nusselt number does depend on the roughness factor, ϵ/D, increasing with increasing values of ϵ/D; however, the effect of roughness on heat transfer is much less pronounced than it is for momentum transfer. From an economic point of view, it is usually more important to minimize the friction loss by using a smooth tube than it is to rely on the wall roughness to increase the heat transfer rate.[3] In most practical calculations the effect of ϵ/D is neglected and the functional dependence of $N_{\text{Nu,loc}}$ is given by

$$N_{\text{Nu,loc}} = \mathcal{F}(Z, N_{\text{Re}}, N_{\text{Pr}}, \Lambda) \tag{7.6-2}$$

On the basis of Eq. 7.5-29 we can express the functional dependence of the log-mean Nusselt number as

$$N_{\text{Nu,ln}} = \mathcal{G}(L/D, N_{\text{Re}}, N_{\text{Pr}}, \Lambda) \tag{7.6-3}$$

Here we see that $N_{\text{Nu,ln}}$ depends on *four* parameters for the case of a constant tube wall temperature, and we can expect that obtaining satisfactory correlations for $N_{\text{Nu,ln}}$ and $N_{\text{Nu,loc}}$ will not be an easy task.

Laminar flow

If the fluid properties are taken to be constant the Navier–Stokes equations are easily solved for one-dimensional laminar flow to yield

$$v_z = 2\langle v_z \rangle \left[1 - \left(\frac{r}{r_0}\right)^2\right] \tag{7.6-4}$$

For steady, one-dimensional flow and constant physical properties the thermal energy equation takes the form

$$v_z\left(\frac{\partial T}{\partial z}\right) = \alpha\left(\frac{\partial^2 T}{\partial r^2} + \frac{1}{r}\frac{\partial T}{\partial r} + \frac{\partial^2 T}{\partial z^2}\right) \tag{7.6-5}$$

provided the temperature is independent of θ and the source terms are negligible. Assuming the conductive transport in the z-direction to be small compared to the convective transport we can drop the term $\partial^2 T/\partial z^2$ and substitute Eq. 7.6-4 to obtain

$$2\langle v_z \rangle \left[1 - \left(\frac{r}{r_0}\right)^2\right]\left(\frac{\partial T}{\partial z}\right) = \alpha\left(\frac{\partial^2 T}{\partial r^2} + \frac{1}{r}\frac{\partial T}{\partial r}\right) \tag{7.6-6}$$

This type of simplification was discussed in Sec. 7.4 where it was found that axial conduction is negligible compared to convection provided that $N_{Pr}N_{Re}(L/D) \gg 1$. The calculations of Schneider [4] for infinitely long tubes confirm the order-of-magnitude analysis given in Sec. 7.4, and suggest that axial conduction can be neglected when $N_{Pr}N_{Re}(L/D) \geq 100$. For a constant wall temperature T_0 and a uniform temperature T_1 at the entrance to a heat transfer section, Eq. 7.6-6 must be solved subject to the boundary conditions†

B.C.1 $\quad T = T_1, \quad z = 0, \quad 0 \leq r \leq r_0 \quad$ (7.6-7)

B.C.2 $\quad T = T_0, \quad r = r_0, \quad z > 0 \quad$ (7.6-8)

B.C.3 $\quad T$ is finite in the region $0 \leq r \leq r_0 \quad$ (7.6-9)

The problem posed by Eqs. 7.6-6 through 7.6-9 is often known as the *Graetz problem* [5, 6]. The solution for the temperature field is given in terms of an infinite series of exponential and Bessel functions (see Sec. 3.2 for solutions of this type); the solution for the heat flux being a considerably simpler series of exponential terms. For very long tubes the solution indicates that

$$N_{Nu,loc} = 3.66, \qquad L/D \to \infty \tag{7.6-10}$$

It must be kept in mind that this result is subject to the limitation of constant physical properties, and this may not be a satisfactory restriction for the case of viscous oils which have highly temperature-dependent viscosities.

A satisfactory expression for heat transfer rates in laminar flow is given by an empirical modification of the Graetz solution developed by Sieder and Tate [7]

$$N_{Nu,ln} = 1.86 N_{Re}^{1/3} N_{Pr}^{1/3} (L/D)^{-1/3} (\mu_b/\mu_0)^{0.14} \tag{7.6-11}$$

In this expression the physical properties of the fluid (ρ, μ, c_p, and k) are evaluated at the mean bulk fluid temperature, i.e., $(T_{b1} + T_{b2})/2$. This viscosity ratio (μ_b/μ_0) is the ratio of the viscosity evaluated at the mean bulk fluid temperature, μ_b, to the viscosity evaluated at the mean wall temperature, μ_0.

A comparison between experimental values [7, 8, 9] of the Nusselt number and values calculated using Eq. 7.6-11 is shown in Fig. 7.6.1. The range of variables represented in Fig. 7.6.1 and the definitions of N_{Re} and N_{Nu} are listed in Table 7.6-1. The agreement is reasonably good for $(N_{Re}N_{Pr})^{1/3}(L/D)^{-1/3}(\mu_b/\mu_0)^{0.14} > 2$ while at lower values of this parameter Eq. 7.6-11 will underestimate the value of the Nusselt number. If a single analytic expression for the Nusselt is desired we can draw upon the work of Hausen [10] and express $N_{Nu,ln}$ as

$$N_{Nu,ln} = 3.66 + \frac{0.0745\Psi^3}{1 + 0.04\Psi^2} \tag{7.6-12}$$

†If Eq. 7.6-6 is solved numerically B.C.3 is replaced with $\partial T/\partial r = 0$, $r = 0$. See Secs. 3.4 and 4.8 for a discussion of this point.

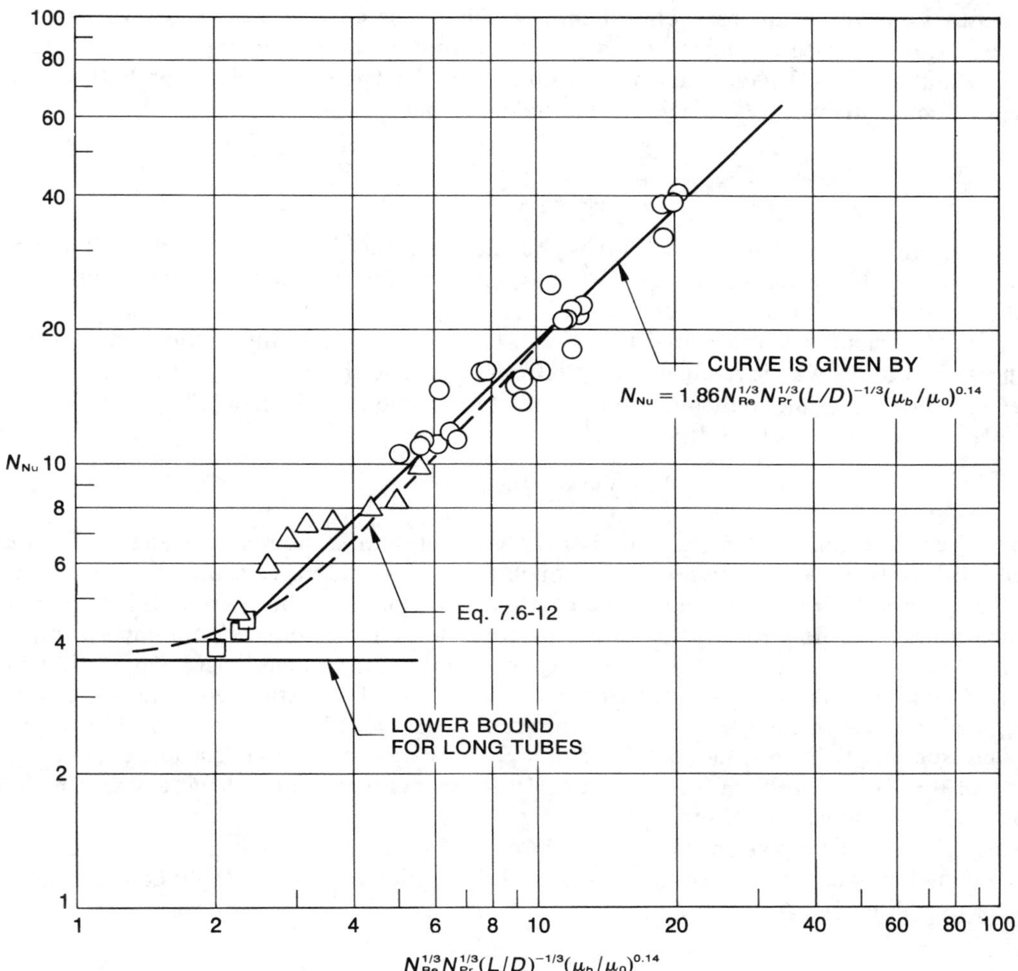

Fig. 7.6.1 Experimental heat transfer data for laminar flow in a tube.
○ Sieder and Tate, heating and cooling oil, $L/D = 82$. △ Drew, heating glycerol, $L/D = 220$. □ Colburn and Coghlan, heating hydrogen–nitrogen mixtures, $L/D = 97$.

where $\Psi = (N_{Re} N_{Pr})^{1/3} (L/D)^{-1/3} (\mu_b/\mu_0)^{0.14}$. This result provides a reasonably satisfactory expression for the Nusselt number as is indicated in Fig. 7.6.1.

Up to this point we have considered results for a constant or nearly constant wall temperature. While experimental studies can be carried out with a constant wall temperature, in practice one is likely to be

Table 7.6-1 Range and Definition of Variables for Heat Transfer in Laminar Pipe Flow†

Definition of the Reynolds number	$\rho_b \langle \bar{v}_z \rangle D/\mu_b$
Definition of the Nusselt number	$h_{\ln} D/k_b$
Definition of $h_{\ln}$	$\dot{Q}/\pi D L \Delta T_{\ln}$
Range of N_{Re}	13–2030
Range of N_{Pr}	0.48–16 700
Range of (μ_b/μ_0)	0.0044–9.75

†ρ_b, μ_b, and k_b are evaluated at the mean bulk temperature, $\frac{1}{2}(T_{b1} + T_{b2})$.

dealing with situations where this restriction is not satisfied. The case of a constant wall heat flux is an example of heat transfer with a nonisothermal wall, and thus is an interesting case for us to examine. Sellars, Tribus, and Klein[11] have presented solutions to the Graetz problem for both constant wall temperature and constant wall flux. Their results indicate that

$$\frac{N_{\mathrm{Nu}}\big|_{\text{constant wall flux}}}{N_{\mathrm{Nu}}\big|_{\text{constant wall temperature}}} \sim 1.20$$

thus the Nusselt number for a constant wall flux is about 20 per cent higher than the Nusselt number for an isothermal wall. Since the Sieder–Tate correlation is only accurate to about ±10 per cent, the effect of variable wall temperature is usually ignored.

Under certain circumstances free-convection effects can become important in laminar flow heat transfer. The effect in vertical tubes was investigated by Pigford[12], while the more important case of horizontal tubes has been studied experimentally and theoretically by Shannon and Depew[13]. They found that free-convection effects could be neglected provided

$$N_{\mathrm{Gr}} < 200 N_{\mathrm{Re}}^{4/3} N_{\mathrm{Pr}}^{1/3} (L/D)^{-4/3}$$

however, for larger values of the Grashof number the Nusselt number increased steadily with increasing Grashof number. It must be kept in mind that although there is considerable scatter in the data presented in Fig. 7.6.1, those points were obtained by careful experimentalists who were making every effort to measure temperatures and flow rates as carefully as possible in addition to eliminating or correcting for extraneous heat losses. In the design of heat exchange equipment the student must keep in mind the scatter of this data, and view the solid line passing through the data as the best estimate of the real process. For a more thorough discussion of heat transfer for laminar flow in closed conduits the interested student is referred to Knudsen and Katz[14], Jacob[6], and the recent work of Christiansen, Jensen, and Tao[15]. A detailed study of the Graetz problem for an arbitrary wall temperature and an arbitrary wall flux has been presented by Sellers, Tribus, and Klein[11].

When using an empirical equation such as Eq. 7.6-11 one must always be careful to note how the film heat transfer coefficient was defined. In Eq. 7.6-11 we have indicated that the log-mean film heat transfer coefficient was used, i.e.,

$$N_{\mathrm{Nu,ln}} = \frac{h_{\mathrm{ln}} D}{k} \tag{7.6-13}$$

This means that the heat transferred to the fluid is given by

$$\dot{Q} = h_{\mathrm{ln}}(\pi D L) \left\{ \frac{(T_{w1} - \bar{T}_{b1}) - (T_{w2} - \bar{T}_{b2})}{\ln\left(\dfrac{T_{w1} - \bar{T}_{b1}}{T_{w2} - \bar{T}_{b2}}\right)} \right\} \tag{7.6-14}$$

where h_{ln} can be calculated by Eq. 7.6-11.

Effect of variable viscosity

In Sec. 7.5 we found that the dimensionless parameter

$$\Lambda = \frac{1}{\mu_0}\left(\frac{\partial \mu}{\partial \Theta}\right)$$

should be used to correlate the effect of a temperature dependent viscosity on the film heat transfer coefficient or the Nusselt number. Noting that $\Theta = 0$ at the wall of the pipe and $\Theta \sim 1$ at the center of the pipe we could approximate the derivative $\partial\mu/\partial\Theta$ by

$$\frac{\partial \mu}{\partial \Theta} \sim \frac{\mu_b - \mu_0}{1 - 0}$$

thus Λ takes the form

$$\Lambda = \frac{\mu_b}{\mu_0} - 1$$

It is entirely satisfactory to use μ_b/μ_0 rather than $\mu_b/\mu_0 - 1$ as the correlating parameter, and this is what Sieder and Tate have done in their correlation of heat transfer rates for laminar flow.

Turbulent flow

For the correlation of turbulent flow heat transfer data we draw upon the early work of Sieder and Tate[7] and the more recent work of Friend and Metzner[16]. The results of these investigators indicate that the Nusselt number may be adequately predicted by the following equation

$$N_{\mathrm{Nu,ln}} = 0.015 N_{\mathrm{Re}}^{0.83} N_{\mathrm{Pr}}^{0.42} (\mu_b/\mu_0)^{0.14} \tag{7.6-15}$$

This expression has been rearranged in the form

$$N_{\mathrm{Nu,ln}}/N_{\mathrm{Pr}}^{0.42} (\mu_b/\mu_0)^{0.14} = 0.015 N_{\mathrm{Re}}^{0.83}$$

and compared with experimental data[9, 16–20] in Fig. 7.6.2. Reasonably good agreement is obtained with the results from several investigators using fluids having Prandtl numbers ranging from 0.46 to 592 provided the Reynolds number is greater than 4×10^3. The lines for laminar flow were calculated using Eq. 7.6-11 and a Prandtl number of 1. Since the Prandtl number dependence for the turbulent case differs from the laminar case by only $N_{\mathrm{Pr}}^{0.09}$ the lines for $L/D = 60$, 120, and 240 will be essentially independent of N_{Pr} for Prandtl numbers in the range 0.5 to 2.0. For larger values of the Prandtl number, one must use Eq. 7.6-11 or the curve in Fig. 7.6.1 to obtain laminar flow Nusselt numbers. Between Reynolds numbers of 2100 and 4000 smooth curves can be drawn connecting the lines for laminar flow with the single line for turbulent flow. From the comparison shown in Fig. 7.6.2 we conclude that Eq. 7.6-15 provides a reasonably satisfactory estimate of the Nusselt number for the turbulent flow of gases and liquids provided the Prandtl number is greater than 0.46. We should point out once again that all the physical properties contained in the dimensionless groups in Eqs. 7.6-11 and 7.6-15 are to be evaluated at the mean bulk temperature while μ_0 is the viscosity evaluated at the mean wall temperature. The range of variables represented in Fig. 7.6.2 and the definitions of N_{Re} and N_{Nu} are listed in Table 7.6-2.

The effect of length, or more appropriately L/D, does not show up in the data presented in Fig. 7.6.2; however, the local film heat transfer coefficient, and therefore the local Nusselt number, very definitely depends on position as can be seen from the data of Hartnett[21] plotted in Fig. 7.6.3. For values of $x/D \leq 50$ the local heat transfer coefficient changes considerably with length; however, for longer tubes the variation becomes negligible. Furthermore for Reynolds numbers greater than 10^4 the entrance region is only about 10 tube diameters long. When considering the results shown in Fig. 7.6.3 we must remember that those data are for *local* heat transfer coefficients, and the log-mean coefficient is related to h_{loc} through Eqs. 7.5-23 and 7.5-27 to give

$$h_{\mathrm{ln}} = \frac{1}{L} \int_0^L \left[\frac{(\bar{T}_b - T_0)}{\Delta T_{\mathrm{ln}}} \right] h_{\mathrm{loc}}\, dz \tag{7.6-16}$$

We can think of the term in brackets as a weighting factor and Eq. 7.6-16 as defining an average.

$$h_{\mathrm{ln}} = \frac{1}{L} \int_0^L w(z) h_{\mathrm{loc}}\, dz \tag{7.6-17}$$

Here we can see that the variations in the log-mean film heat transfer coefficient will be less than those for h_{loc}, and for most practical cases we can neglect the variation of $N_{\mathrm{Nu,ln}}$ with L/D for turbulent flows.

Before going on to the study of liquid metals we must again raise the question about the effect of a nonisothermal wall on the Sieder–Tate–Friend–Metzner correlation. To ascertain the effect of a variable wall temperature we can refer to the calculations of Sleicher and Tribus[2] for a constant wall temperature

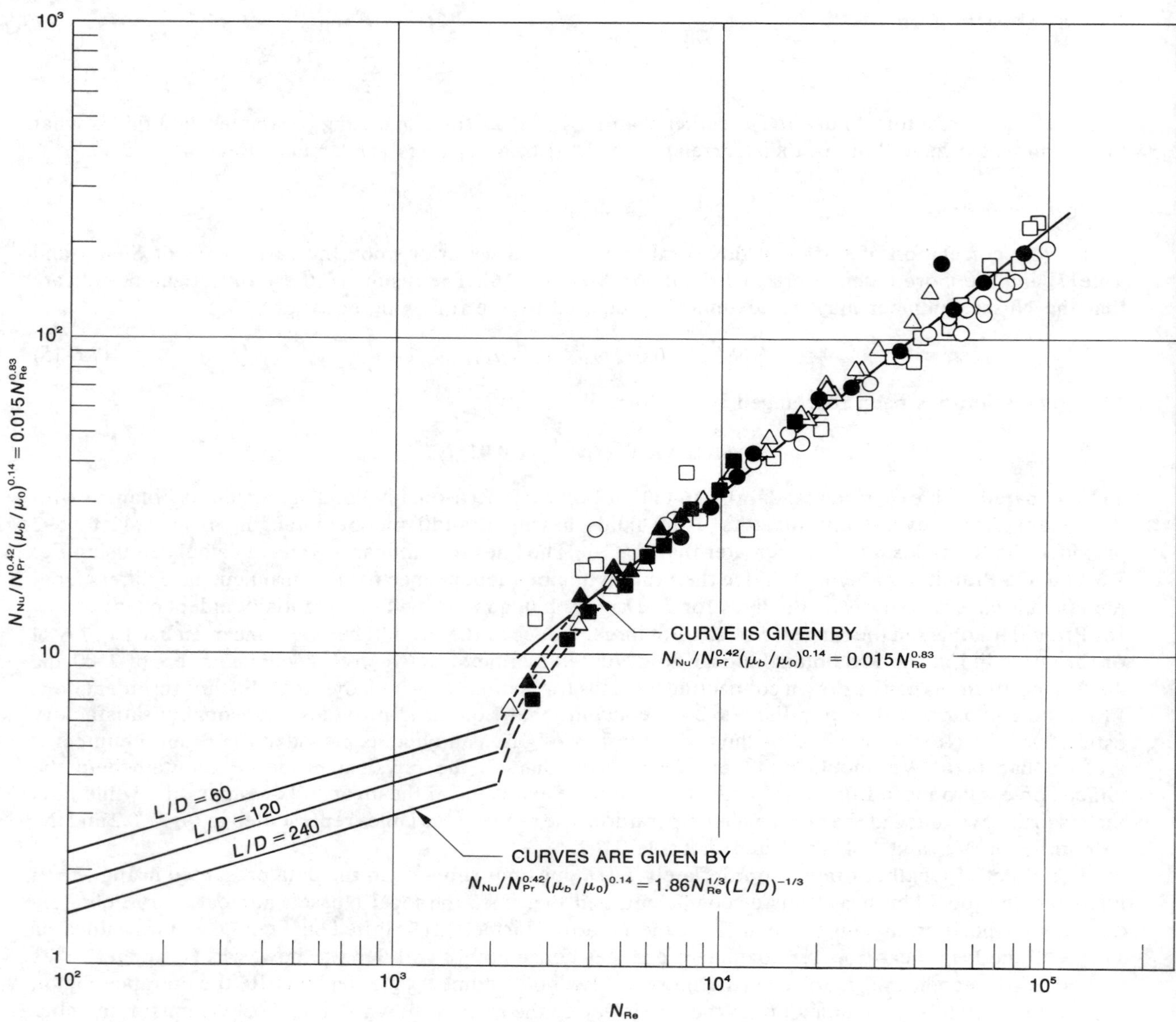

Fig. 7.6.2 Heat transfer to fluids in turbulent flow in tubes.
○ Lawrence and Sherwood, heating water, $L/D = 59$. △ Morris and Whitman, heating and cooling oil, $L/D = 196$. □ Sherwood and Petrie, heating acetone, $L/D = 96$. ● Deissler and Eian, heating air, $L/D = 100$. ▲ Colburn and Coghlan, heating hydrogen–nitrogen mixtures, $L/D = 97$. ■ Friend and Metzner, heating corn syrup, $L/D = 161$.

and a constant wall heat flux for turbulent flow in a tube. Their results for the ratio of the Nusselt number at a constant wall heat flux† to the Nusselt number at a constant wall temperature are given in Fig. 7.6.4 for various Prandtl numbers. From those results it is clear that variations in the wall temperature are unimportant provided $N_{Pr} > 0.7$; however, for liquid metal Prandtl numbers the Nusselt number very definitely is influenced by variations in the wall temperature.

†The effect of variations in the wall temperature is usually investigated by studying the constant flux condition as it is amenable to mathematical and experimental analysis.

Table 7.6-2 Range and Definition of Variables for Heat Transfer in Turbulent Pipe Flow†

Definition of the Reynolds number	$\rho_b \langle \bar{v}_z \rangle D / \mu_b$
Definition of the Nusselt number	$h_{\ln} D / k_b$
Definition of $h_{\ln}$	$\dot{Q} / \pi D L \Delta T_{\ln}$
Range of N_{Re}	(2.3×10^3)–(1×10^5)
Range of N_{Pr}	0.48–592
Range of (μ_b / μ_0)	0.44–2.5

†ρ_b, μ_b, and k_b are evaluated at the mean bulk temperature, $\frac{1}{2}(T_{b1} + T_{b2})$.

Liquid metals—the low Prandtl number case

The Prandtl numbers for liquid metals are on the order of 10^{-2}–10^{-3}, and remembering that $N_{Pr} = \nu / \alpha$ this means that the *thermal* diffusivity is much larger than the *momentum* diffusivity. This represents quite a different situation than we encountered for most fluids where $\alpha < \nu$ and we should expect that empirical correlations for turbulent heat transfer in liquid metals would take a different form than the correlation given by Eq. 7.6-15. For normal gases and liquids the main resistance to heat transfer is in the viscous sublayer, while for liquid metals this is not at all true as we saw in Sec. 6.4.

The interest in liquid metals as heat transfer fluids stems from their high thermal conductivity and high boiling points. This allows liquid metals to be used at high temperatures and relatively low pressures. The obvious disadvantage to the use of liquid metals is their toxic nature (mercury for example is quite poisonous) and difficult handling characteristics (sodium reacts violently with water and will react with air at elevated temperatures). However, the advantages of liquid metals for heat transfer, particularly for use in atomic reactors, has led to significant advances in the technology of their handling.

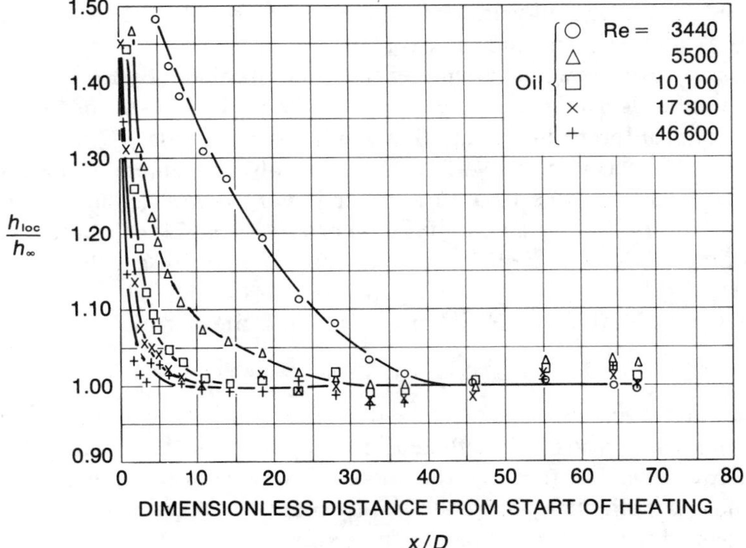

Fig. 7.6.3 Film heat transfer coefficients in the entrance region. (Adapted from Hartnett, J. P., "Experimental Determination of the Thermal Entrance Length for the Flow of Water and Oil in Circular Pipes," *Trans. ASME* **77**, 1211 (1955).)

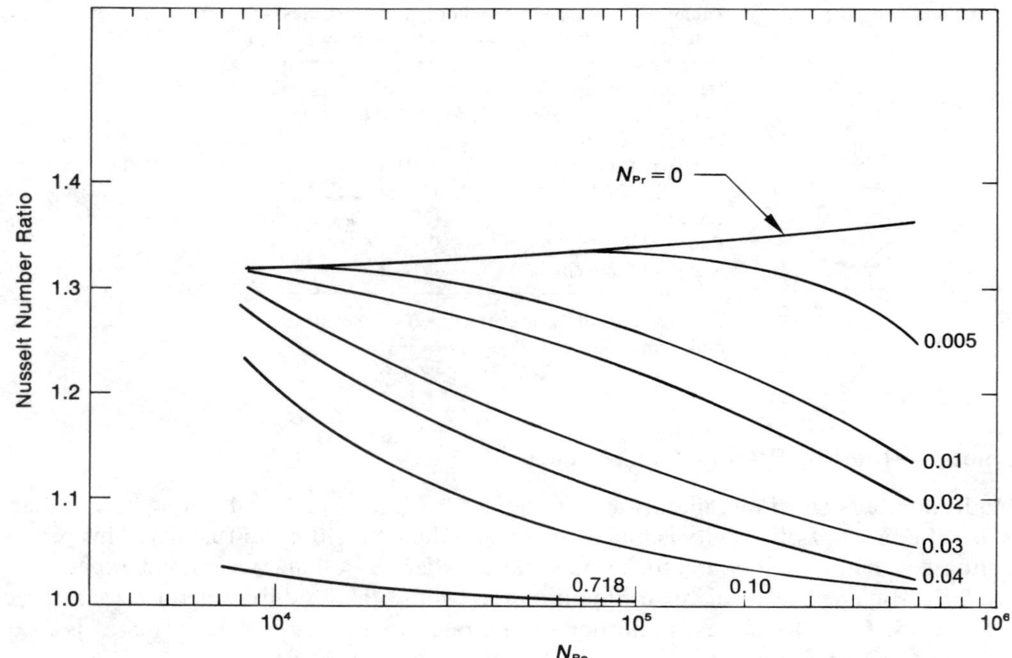

Fig. 7.6.4 Ratio of the Nusselt number at a constant wall heat flux to the Nusselt number at a constant wall temperature as a function of the Reynolds and Prandtl numbers. (Adapted from Sleicher, C. A., and Myron Tribus, "Heat Transfer in a Pipe with Turbulent Flow and Arbitrary Wall-Temperature Distribution," *Trans. ASME* **79**, 789 (1957).)

For a uniform wall temperature Notter and Sleicher [22] proposed the expression

$$N_{\mathrm{Nu,ln}} = 4.8 + 0.0156 N_{\mathrm{Re}}^{0.85} N_{\mathrm{Pr}}^{0.93}, \quad \text{uniform wall temperature} \tag{7.6-18}$$

for liquid metal Nusselt numbers. The physical properties used in calculating N_{Re} and N_{Pr} should be evaluated at the average bulk temperature, and the expression is restricted to lengths such that $L/D > 60$. For shorter lengths the Nusselt number would be higher than that predicted by Eq. 7.6-18. The dependence of $N_{\mathrm{Nu,ln}}$ on the Reynolds number is nearly the same as that given by Eq. 7.6-15; however, the dependence on the Prandtl number is quite different indicating that the dominant mode of energy transfer is not the same for low Prandtl number fluids as it is for $N_{\mathrm{Pr}} \geq 1$. One must always remember that the true functional dependence of the Nusselt number on the Prandtl number is very complex and the use of a fractional power dependence such as $N_{\mathrm{Pr}}^{0.42}$ or $N_{\mathrm{Pr}}^{0.93}$ is a simplifying approximation. Needless to say, if the scatter of the experimental data is comparable to that shown in Fig. 7.6.2, then there is little reason to seek a more sophisticated functional dependence.

For a uniform wall heat flux Notter and Sleicher recommend the correlation

$$N_{\mathrm{Nu,ln}} = 6.3 + 0.0167 N_{\mathrm{Re}}^{0.85} N_{\mathrm{Pr}}^{0.93}, \quad \text{uniform wall heat flux} \tag{7.6-19}$$

Here we see a considerable difference between the case for a uniform wall temperature and a uniform wall heat flux indicating that the heat transfer coefficient for liquid metals is definitely sensitive to the temperature gradient along the wall. The fact that the Nusselt number for liquid metals is sensitive to wall temperature gradients makes it difficult to correlate data except for the uniform wall temperature and uniform wall heat flux cases; however, in processes involving liquid metal heat transfer the dominant resistance to heat transfer very often is in the tube walls of the heat exchanger or in the fuel element of a nuclear reactor. Because of this, satisfactory design calculations can often be made using only crude estimates of the liquid metal heat transfer coefficient.

Noncircular conduits

Although heat transfer to fluids flowing in pipes is of predominant interest, there are many important processes for which noncircular conduits are used. The double-pipe heat exchanger illustrated in Design Problem VII is an example, for the hot water used to heat the oil flows in an annular region. For conduits which are not drastically different from circular tubes it is satisfactory to use Eqs. 7.6-11 and 7.6-15 with the diameter, D, replaced by the *hydraulic diameter*, D_h. The latter is defined as

$$D_h = \begin{Bmatrix} \text{hydraulic} \\ \text{diameter} \end{Bmatrix} = 4\left(\frac{\text{cross-sectional area}}{\text{wetted perimeter}}\right) \tag{7.6-20}$$

Thus we can rewrite Eqs. 6.6-11 and 6.6-15 as

$$N_{\text{Nu,ln}} = 1.86\left(\frac{\langle \bar{v}_z \rangle D_h}{\nu}\right)^{1/3} N_{\text{Pr}}^{1/3}(L/D_h)^{1/3}(\mu_b/\mu_0)^{0.14} \tag{7.6-21}$$

for laminar flow in noncircular conduits, and

$$N_{\text{Nu,ln}} = 0.015\left(\frac{\langle \bar{v}_z \rangle D_h}{\nu}\right)^{0.83} N_{\text{Pr}}^{0.42}(\mu_b/\mu_0)^{0.14} \tag{7.6-22}$$

for turbulent flow in noncircular ducts. We can expect the variation of h_{loc} in the entrance region of a noncircular conduit to be comparable to that found in tubes.

Example 7.6-1 Heat exchanger design

A heat exchanger is to be designed to cool a lubricating oil from 140°F to 110°F. The oil will flow through tubes at an average velocity of 3 ft/sec and the inside tube surface temperature will be 90°F. We wish to calculate the required tube length for an inside tube diameter of $\frac{1}{4}$ in.

The properties of the oil are given as

Physical Properties of Lubricating Oil

T,°F	ρ, lb$_m$/ft^3	k, Btu/hrft°F	μ, centipoise	c_p, Btu/lb$_m$°F
100	54.2	0.082	20.3	0.40
120	54.2	0.081	12.0	0.42
140	54.2	0.080	5.7	0.44

We begin our analysis by noting that the total rate of heat transfer to the oil is given by Eq. 7.6-14, or

$$\dot{Q} = h_{\text{ln}}(\pi DL)\Delta T_{\text{ln}} \tag{1}$$

Since the wall temperature is constant at 90°F, Eq. 1 takes the form

$$\dot{Q} = h_{\text{ln}}(\pi DL)\left[\frac{T_{b2} - T_{b1}}{\ln\left(\frac{T_0 - T_{b1}}{T_0 - T_{b2}}\right)}\right] \tag{2}$$

where $T_0 = 90$°F. A macroscopic thermal energy balance also yields (see Eq. 7.4-26)

$$\dot{Q} = \rho c_p \langle \bar{v}_z \rangle\left(\frac{\pi D^2}{4}\right)(T_{b2} - T_{b1}) \tag{3}$$

provided the axial molecular and turbulent transport is small compared to the time-averaged convective transport. Substitution of $\dot{Q}$ as given by Eq. 3 into Eq. 2 leads to an equation for the length

$$L = \left(\frac{\rho c_p \langle \bar{v}_z \rangle D}{4h_{\text{ln}}}\right)\ln\left(\frac{T_0 - T_{b1}}{T_0 - T_{b2}}\right) \tag{4}$$

Every term in Eq. 4 is known except for $h_{\ln}$, and we will require the use of a correlation to determine the log-mean film heat transfer coefficient. This means that N_{Re} and N_{Pr} must be calculated and because of this it will be convenient to arrange our expression for L in the form

$$L = \left(\frac{N_{Re}N_{Pr}}{N_{Nu}}\right)\left(\frac{D}{4}\right)\ln\left(\frac{T_0 - T_{b1}}{T_0 - T_{b2}}\right) \tag{5}$$

where N_{Nu} represents the *log-mean* Nusselt number.

In calculating the Reynolds number, we must remember that the viscosity and density are to be evaluated at the mean bulk temperature, $(T_{b1} + T_{b2})/2 = 125°\text{F}$. From a graphical interpolation of the viscosity data we find

$$\mu = 10.2 \text{ centipoise at } 125°\text{F}$$

and the Reynolds number is calculated to be

$$N_{Re} = \frac{(54.2 \text{ lb}_m/\text{ft}^3)(3 \text{ ft/sec})(\frac{1}{4} \text{ in.})}{(10.2 \text{ centipoise})}\left\{\frac{1}{(12 \text{ in./ft})(6.72 \times 10^{-4} \text{ lb}_m/\text{ft sec centipoise})}\right\}$$

$$= 494$$

Since the flow is laminar we express the log-mean Nusselt number by Eq. 7.6-11.

$$N_{Nu} = 1.86 N_{Re}^{1/3} N_{Pr}^{1/3} (L/D)^{-1/3} (\mu_b/\mu_0)^{0.14} \tag{6}$$

This expression for the Nusselt number may be substituted into Eq. 5 and the result rearranged to obtain

$$L/D = N_{Re}N_{Pr}\left[\frac{(\mu_0/\mu_b)^{0.14}}{(4)(1.86)}\ln\left(\frac{T_0 - T_{b1}}{T_0 - T_{b2}}\right)\right]^{3/2} \tag{7}$$

The fluid properties are all to be evaluated at the mean bulk temperature, 125 °F, and by interpolation we find

$$\rho_b = 54.2 \text{ lb}_m/\text{ft}^3$$

$$k_b = 0.081 \text{ Btu/hr ft °F}$$

$$\mu_b = 10.2 \text{ centipoise}$$

$$(c_p)_b = 0.42 \text{ Btu/lb}_m\text{°F}$$

In addition, the viscosity at the wall temperature, 90°F, is found by extrapolation to be 23.9 centipoise, and we can calculate the following quantities

$$N_{Re} = 494, \qquad N_{Pr} = 128, \qquad (\mu_b/\mu_0)^{0.14} = 1.13$$

$$\ln\left(\frac{90 - 140}{90 - 110}\right) = \ln\left(\frac{50}{20}\right) = 0.916$$

Substitution of these values into Eq. 7 yields

$$L/D = (494)(128)\left[\frac{(1.13)(0.916)}{(4)(1.86)}\right]^{3/2}$$

$$= 3.27 \times 10^3$$

Since $D = \frac{1}{48}$ ft we find the tube length to be

$$L = 68 \text{ ft}$$

We should remember at this point that our expression for the Nusselt number (or the film heat transfer coefficient) is accurate to within ± 10 per cent at best, thus we might choose the tube length to be 75 ft or perhaps 80 ft depending on how conservative we wish to be in our design.

Our final result for the tube length indicates a rather long and quite impractical heat exchanger. Clearly the process parameters need to be changed in order to obtain a practical design, and the exploration of this problem will be left as an exercise for the student.

*7.7 Heat Transfer to Fluids Flowing Past Flat Plates, Cylinders, and Spheres

In the previous section we examined the problem of heat transfer inside tubes for both laminar and turbulent flow; however, the heat transfer that takes place on the outside of tubes is a subject of equal importance. In studying heat transfer for flow past immersed bodies we will find that the correlations for the Nusselt number become more complex simply because the flow itself is more complex. Flow past a thin, flat plate represents the simplest case and we will consider it first.

Flow past a thin, flat plate

In Chapter 5 we studied the problem of heat transfer for laminar flow past a flat plate and found excellent agreement between theory and experiment provided the length Reynolds number was less than 2×10^5, i.e.,

$$N_{\mathrm{Re},L} = \rho u_\infty L/\mu < 2 \times 10^5, \quad \text{for laminar flow}$$

For larger Reynolds numbers a transition to turbulent flow takes place as illustrated in Fig. 7.7.1. The transition point depends on the intensity of the free-stream turbulence [23] and we should therefore expect the heat transfer coefficient or Nusselt number to be influenced by the free-stream turbulence.

On the basis of the experimental work of Zhukauskas and Ambrazyavichyus [24] we can modify Colburn's [25] empirical expression for the local Nusselt number to obtain

$$N_{\mathrm{Nu},x} = 0.029 N_{\mathrm{Re},x}^{0.8} N_{\mathrm{Pr}}^{0.43}, \quad \text{turbulent boundary layer} \tag{7.7-1}$$

Here $N_{\mathrm{Nu},x}$ is defined as

$$N_{\mathrm{Nu},x} = h_{\mathrm{loc}} x/k \tag{7.7-2}$$

As was the case for heat transfer in a laminar boundary layer, the characteristic temperature difference used to define the heat transfer coefficient is the plate temperature minus the free-stream temperature. The fluid properties used in Eq. 7.7-1 should be evaluated at the *free-stream temperature*, T_∞. This temperature

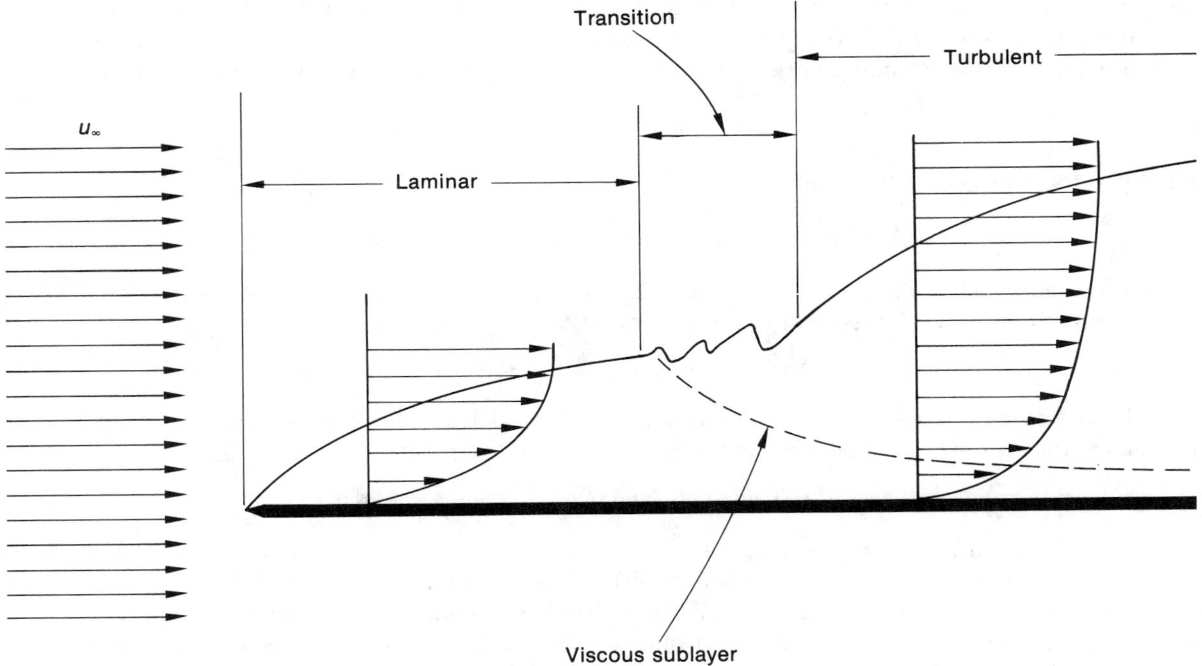

Fig. 7.7.1 Laminar and turbulent boundary layer flows.

is equivalent to the *average bulk temperature*, T_b, which would be defined as

$$T_b = \frac{\int_0^\infty T v_x \, dy}{\int_0^\infty v_x \, dy} \tag{7.7-3}$$

In order to determine the average Nusselt number for a plate of length L, we must make use of the local Nusselt number for laminar flow given in Sec. 5.9 as (see Eq. 5.9-52)

$$N_{\mathrm{Nu},x} = 0.323 N_{\mathrm{Re},x}^{1/2} N_{\mathrm{Pr}}^{1/3}, \quad \text{laminar boundary layer}$$

Using this expression in conjunction with Eq. 7.7-1 we can express the local film heat transfer coefficient for a flat plate as

$$h_{\mathrm{loc}} = 0.323 \left(\frac{k}{x}\right)\left(\frac{u_\infty x}{\nu}\right)^{1/2} N_{\mathrm{Pr}}^{1/3}, \qquad 0 \leq x \leq \ell \tag{7.7-4}$$

$$h_{\mathrm{loc}} = 0.029 \left(\frac{k}{x}\right)\left(\frac{u_\infty x}{\nu}\right)^{0.8} N_{\mathrm{Pr}}^{0.43}, \qquad \ell < x \leq L$$

The average heat transfer coefficient is given by

$$h_{\mathrm{av}} = \frac{1}{L}\left\{\int_0^\ell 0.323 \left(\frac{k}{x}\right)\left(\frac{u_\infty x}{\nu}\right)^{1/2} N_{\mathrm{Pr}}^{1/3}\, dx + \int_\ell^L 0.029 \left(\frac{k}{x}\right)\left(\frac{u_\infty x}{\nu}\right)^{0.8} N_{\mathrm{Pr}}^{0.43}\, dx\right\} \tag{7.7-6}$$

Defining the average Nusselt number as

$$N_{\mathrm{Nu}} = h_{\mathrm{av}} L/k \tag{7.7-7}$$

and carrying out the integration for $\ell = 2 \times 10^5(\mu/\rho u_\infty)$ yields

$$N_{\mathrm{Nu}} = 0.036 N_{\mathrm{Pr}}^{0.43}(N_{\mathrm{Re},L}^{0.8} - 17400) + 289 N_{\mathrm{Pr}}^{1/3} \tag{7.7-8}$$

We should remember at this point that the $\frac{1}{3}$ power on the Prandtl number was determined theoretically for laminar flow, while the 0.43 power is the experimentally determined functional dependence of the Nusselt number on the Prandtl number for a turbulent boundary layer flow. For Prandtl numbers near 1 we can write

$$289 N_{\mathrm{Pr}}^{1/3} \sim 289 N_{\mathrm{Pr}}^{0.43}, \quad \text{for Prandtl numbers near 1}$$

and Eq. 7.7-8 can be simplified to

$$N_{\mathrm{Nu}} = 0.036 N_{\mathrm{Pr}}^{0.43}(N_{\mathrm{Re},L}^{0.8} - 9400), \quad \text{laminar and turbulent boundary layer} \tag{7.7-9}$$

The data of Zhukauskas and Ambrazyavichyus [24] indicate that the dependence of the Nusselt number on the viscosity should be of the form $(\mu_\infty/\mu_0)^{1/4}$ thus Eq. 7.7-9 can be expressed as

$$N_{\mathrm{Nu}} = 0.036 N_{\mathrm{Pr}}^{0.43}(N_{\mathrm{Re},L}^{0.8} - 9400)(\mu_\infty/\mu_0)^{1/4} \tag{7.7-10}$$

If the Reynolds number is very large relative to the critical Reynolds number, the heat transfer in the laminar region becomes unimportant and Eq. 7.7-10 takes the form

$$N_{\mathrm{Nu}} = 0.036 N_{\mathrm{Pr}}^{0.43} N_{\mathrm{Re},L}^{0.8}(\mu_\infty/\mu_0)^{1/4}, \quad \text{large Reynolds numbers} \tag{7.7-11}$$

Both Eqs. 7.7-10 and 7.7-11 are compared with the experimental data of several investigators [24, 25, 26] in Fig. 7.7.2. For values of $N_{\mathrm{Re},L} > 2 \times 10^5$ the data of Parmalee and Huebscher [27] show a sudden increase in N_{Nu} with the data being well represented by Eq. 7.7-10. When great care is taken to eliminate free-stream turbulence the transition from laminar to turbulent flow is delayed and the Nusselt number is lower than that predicted by Eq. 7.7-10. This is the case for the negligible free-stream turbulence data of Edwards and Furber. When high intensity turbulence is generated in the free stream the transition to turbulent flow

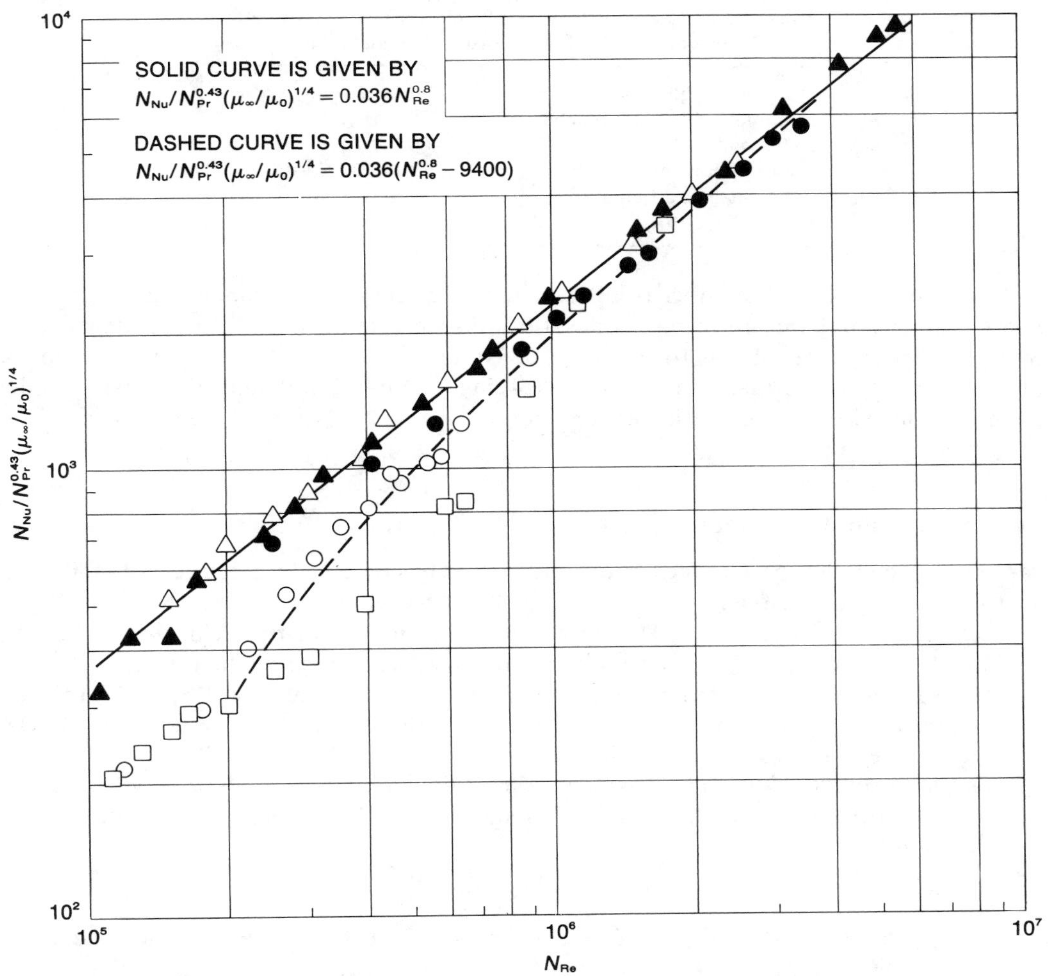

Fig. 7.7.2 Heat transfer to fluids flowing past a thin, flat plate.
○ Parmalee and Huebscher, heating air, unspecified free-stream turbulence. □ Edwards and Furber, heating air, negligible free-stream turbulence. △ Edwards and Furber, heating air, 5 per cent free-stream turbulence. ● Reynolds, Kays, and Kline, heating air, unspecified free-stream turbulence. ▲ Zhukauskas and Ambrazyavichyus, heating and cooling air, water, and oil, unspecified free-stream turbulence.

takes place at a lower Reynolds number and the experimentally determined Nusselt number is larger than that predicted by Eq. 7.7-10. This is the case for the 5 per cent free-stream turbulence data of Edwards and Furber which lie very close to the line given by Eq. 7.7-11. Although the level of turbulence was not specified by Zhukauskas and Ambrazyavichyus, it is clear from their results that a high level of turbulence was present in the free stream. The effect of free-stream turbulence illustrated in these heat transfer data is in good agreement with experimental studies of laminar boundary layer stability.†

The functional dependence of the Nusselt number on the Prandtl number is essentially identical to that found for turbulent pipe flow; however, the dependence on the viscosity ratio (μ_b/μ_0) or (μ_∞/μ_0) is quite different. In considering this point, one must remember that pinning down the best exponent for the viscosity ratio is a very difficult experimental task, and one could easily look upon the difference between 0.14 and 0.25 as being due to experimental uncertainty. In addition we must keep in mind that the film heat

†See G. B. Schubauer and H. K. Skramstad, "Laminar Boundary Layer Oscillations and Transition on a Flat Plate," *NACA Rept. 909*, 1949.

Table 7.7-1 Range and Definition of Variables for Heat Transfer to Fluids Flowing Past a Thin, Flat Plate

Definition of Reynolds number	$u_\infty L/\nu_\infty$
Definition of Nusselt number	hL/k_∞
Definition of h	$\dot{Q}/2wL(T_0 - T_\infty)$
Range of Reynolds number	(1×10^5)–(5.5×10^6)
Range of Prandtl number	0.70–380
Range of (μ_∞/μ_0)	0.26–3.5

transfer coefficient or the Nusselt number is influenced by the temperature dependence of the viscosity in some *complex* manner, and we are trying to describe this complex functional dependence with a very *simple* functional dependence of the form $(\mu_\infty/\mu_0)^n$. Under these conditions, what may appear to be experimental uncertainty could result in part from forcing a simple functional relationship to describe a complex phenomenon. The range of variables represented in Fig. 7.7.2 and the definitions of N_{Re} and N_{Nu} are listed in Table 7.7-1.

Flow normal to a single cylinder

Flow past a single cylinder is a complex phenomenon and has received a great deal of study concerning the flow field and the heat transfer rates. The type of flow that may occur is illustrated in Fig. 7.7.3 for various ranges of the Reynolds number. The flow over the front half of the cylinder will be a boundary layer type of flow, and is susceptible to the standard boundary layer analysis when the Reynolds number is large. The flow over the rear half of the cylinder is more complex. The low Reynolds number region, $N_{\text{Re}} < 4$, can be analyzed by direct numerical integration of the equations of motion[28]; however, for higher Reynolds numbers analysis becomes increasingly difficult[29].

In developing a correlation for heat transfer to a fluid flowing past a single tube we assume that the density is constant and make use of the fact that no steady-state heat conduction solution exists.† This leads to the requirement

$$N_{\text{Nu}} \to 0 \quad \text{as} \quad N_{\text{Re}} \to 0$$

Here we are ignoring the fact that as $N_{\text{Re}} \to 0$, free-convection effects become important since the density is always a function of the temperature. The matter of free convection will be explored in Sec. 7.9, and there we will find that as $N_{\text{Re}} \to 0$ we have $N_{\text{Nu}} = \mathcal{F}(N_{\text{Gr}})$. Here N_{Gr} represents the Grashof number which is the free-convection equivalent of the Reynolds number.

In choosing the functional dependence of the Nusselt number on the Reynolds number we draw upon the work of Richardson[30] who recommended that the heat transfer from a sphere be considered as two parallel processes. In the laminar boundary layer region the contribution to the Nusselt number should be of the form $N_{\text{Re}}^{1/2} N_{\text{Pr}}^{1/3}$, while in the wake region Richardson argues that the contribution should be of the form $N_{\text{Re}}^{2/3} N_{\text{Pr}}^{1/3}$. Under these circumstances we would attempt to correlate the experimentally determined Nusselt numbers by an equation of the form

$$N_{\text{Nu}} = (aN_{\text{Re}}^{1/2} + bN_{\text{Re}}^{2/3}) N_{\text{Pr}}^{1/3} (\mu_\infty/\mu_0)^n \tag{7.7-12}$$

The experimental data from a number of investigators[31–37] indicates that the Prandtl number dependence is more accurately represented by $N_{\text{Pr}}^{0.4}$ and the power on the viscosity ratio should be 0.25. Thus the correlation takes the form

$$N_{\text{Nu}} = (0.4N_{\text{Re}}^{1/2} + 0.06N_{\text{Re}}^{2/3}) N_{\text{Pr}}^{0.4} (\mu_\infty/\mu_0)^{1/4} \tag{7.7-13}$$

where the coefficients have been chosen to provide a satisfactory fit with the experimental data shown in Fig. 7.7.4. The agreement is generally better than ±25 per cent except in the region of low Reynolds

†It will be left as an exercise for the student to prove that only the trivial solution, $T = \text{constant}$, exists for this case.

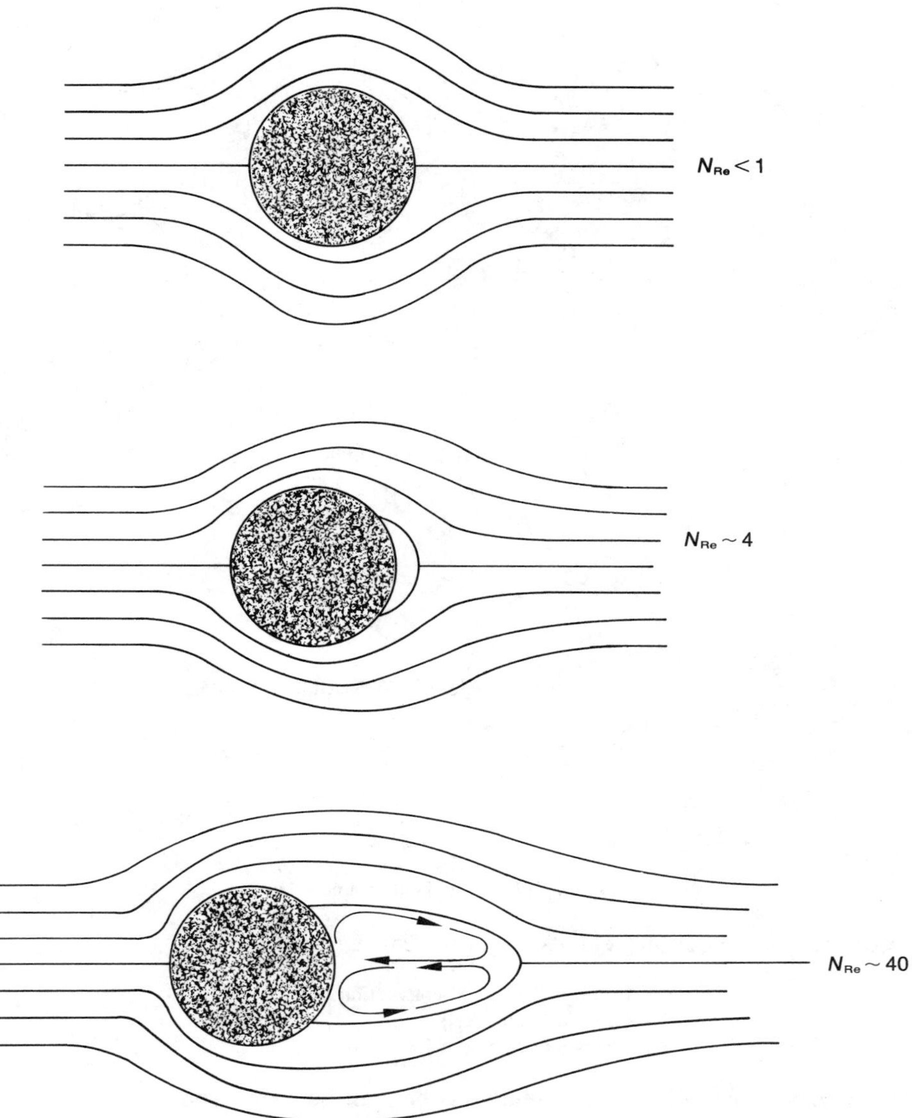

Fig. 7.7.3a Flow field around a cylinder.

numbers where the data of Hilpert and King are considerably higher than the values predicted by Eq. 7.7-13. Recent data obtained by Collis and Williams [38] follow the trend of the data of Hilpert and King and suggest that the problem of low Reynolds number heat transfer to single cylinders deserves further study.

In using Eq. 7.7-13 for the condition where the Reynolds number is low and the temperature difference between the cylinder and the fluid is large, there is always a possibility that free-convection effects may become important. From the development given in Sec. 5.10 or from the solution to Design Problem V we know that the characteristic velocity for a free-convection process can be expressed as

$$\{\text{characteristic free-convection velocity}\} = \beta g \Delta T L^2/\nu \tag{7.7-14}$$

where L is the characteristic length. In this case it could be either the diameter or the length of the cylinder depending on whether the cylinder was oriented horizontally or vertically. If we designate the

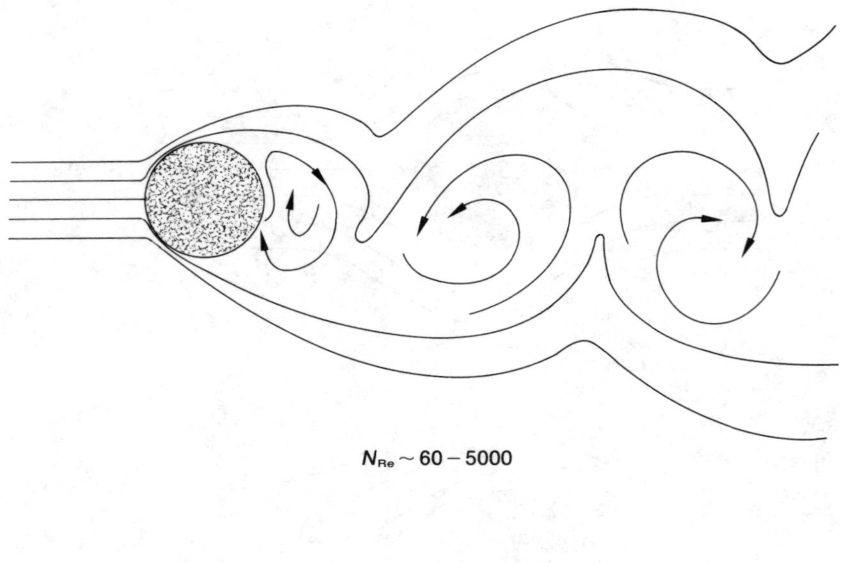

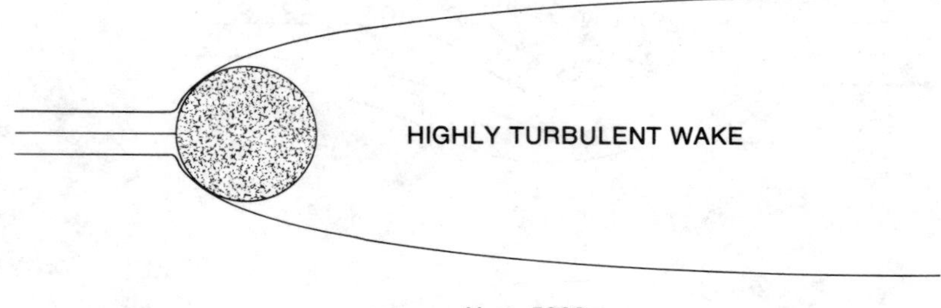

Fig. 7.7.3b Flow field around a cylinder.

characteristic forced-convection velocity as u we can write

$$\left\{\begin{matrix}\text{ratio of the forced-convection}\\ \text{velocity to the free-}\\ \text{convection velocity}\end{matrix}\right\} = \frac{u\nu}{\beta g \Delta T L^2} \tag{7.7-15}$$

In terms of the Reynolds and Grashof numbers this can be expressed as

$$\left\{\begin{matrix}\text{ratio of the forced-convection}\\ \text{velocity to the free-}\\ \text{convection velocity}\end{matrix}\right\} = \frac{N_{Re}}{N_{Gr}} \tag{7.7-16}$$

Here we see that the Grashof number could be thought of as a free-convection Reynolds number, and when it is small compared to the Reynolds number the effect of free-convection on the heat transfer rate should be negligible†

$$N_{Gr} \ll N_{Re}, \quad \text{negligible effect of free-convection on the heat transfer rate} \tag{7.7-17}$$

Although our argument presented here is plausible, it is not based on a rigorous application of the principles of dimensional analysis which would lead us to the result

$$N_{Gr} \ll N_{Re}^2, \quad \text{negligible effect of free-convection on the heat transfer rate} \tag{7.7-18}$$

Proof of Eq. 7.7-18 will be left as an exercise for the student; however, those with good intuition might be

†This assumes that "small causes lead to small effects."

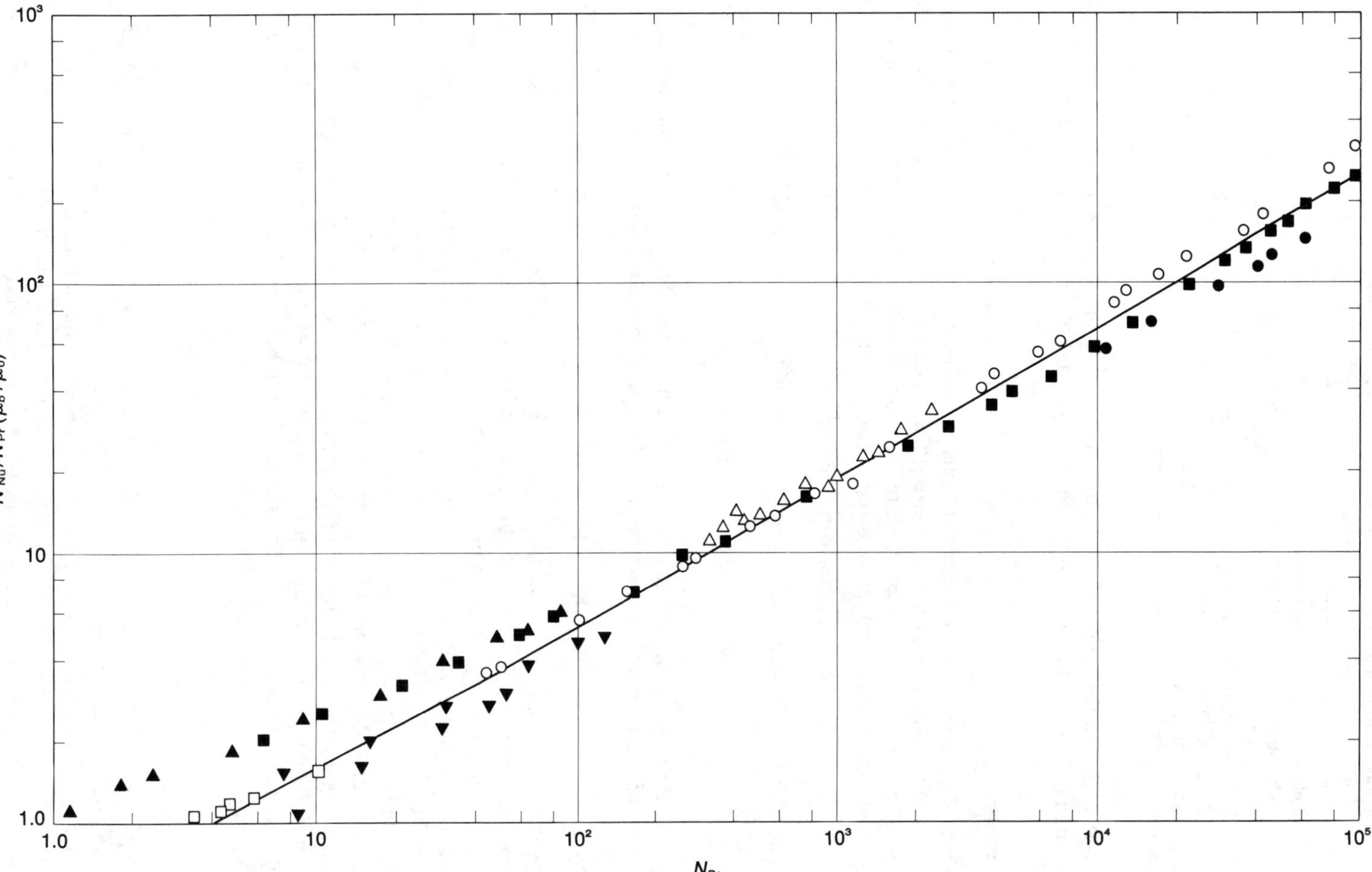

Fig. 7.7.4 Heat transfer to fluids flowing normal to a single cylinder.
○ Perkins and Leppert, water and ethylene glycol. △ Brier and Churchill, nitrogen. □ Piret, James, and Stacy, water. ● Fand, water. ▲ King, air. ■ Hilpert, air. ▼ Davis, water, paraffin, and transformer oil.

Curve is given by

$$N_{Nu}/N_{Pr}^{0.4}(\mu_b/\mu_0)^{1/4} = 0.40N_{Re}^{1/2} + 0.06N_{Re}^{2/3}$$

Table 7.7-2 Definition and Range of Variables for Heat Transfer to Fluids Flowing Normal to a Single Circular Cylinder

Definition of Reynolds number	$u_\infty D/\nu_\infty$
Definition of Nusselt number	hD/k_∞
Definition of h	$\dot{Q}/\pi DL(T_0 - T_\infty)$
Range of Reynolds number	1.0–(1.0×10^5)
Range of Prandtl number	0.67–300
Range of (μ_∞/μ_0)	0.25–5.2

able to guess why Eq. 7.7-18 is the correct type of restriction to place on the application of Eq. 7.7-13. The range of variables represented in Fig. 7.7.4 and the definitions of N_{Re} and N_{Nu} are listed in Table 7.7-2.

Flow past a single sphere

The flow past a sphere is somewhat similar to the flow past a cylinder and we can expect the two heat transfer processes to have similar characteristics. The two differ in one respect, and that is that a steady heat conduction solution exists for a sphere in an infinite medium. It will be left as an exercise for the student to prove that the steady-state heat conduction process for a sphere in an infinite medium leads to

$$N_{\mathrm{Nu}} = 2, \quad \text{steady-state conduction} \tag{7.7-19}$$

Under these circumstances the function dependence for the Nusselt number should be

$$N_{\mathrm{Nu}} = 2 + \mathscr{F}(N_{\mathrm{Re}}, N_{\mathrm{Pr}}, \mu_b/\mu_0) \tag{7.7-20}$$

where $\mathscr{F}(N_{\mathrm{Re}}) \to 0$ as $N_{\mathrm{Re}} \to 0$. Following our success in correlating heat transfer data for cylinders with the functional form suggested by Richardson we choose the same form and represent the Nusselt number as

$$N_{\mathrm{Nu}} = 2 + (0.4N_{\mathrm{Re}}^{1/2} + 0.06N_{\mathrm{Re}}^{2/3})N_{\mathrm{Pr}}^{0.4}(\mu_\infty/\mu_0)^{1/4} \tag{7.7-21}$$

A rearranged form of Eq. 7.7-21 is compared with the experimental data of three investigators [39–41] in Fig. 7.7.5. The agreement between Eq. 7.7-21 and the experimentally determined Nusselt numbers is reasonably good, although one must always keep in mind that the logarithmic scale tends to hide the error in the experimental data. It is convenient that we can represent heat transfer data for both spheres and cylinders with essentially the same equation; however, one must keep in mind that the coefficients and powers on the Reynolds numbers are not sacrosanct. In the study of both cylinders and spheres we are attempting to model the functional dependence of N_{Nu} on N_{Re} with a function of the form: $aN_{\mathrm{Re}}^b + cN_{\mathrm{Re}}^d$, and with four adjustable constants one could find other choices which might fit the data better than either Eq. 7.7-13 or Eq. 7.7-21. In any event there is some theoretical justification for the form of both Eqs. 7.7-13 and 7.7-21 and they do fit the data reasonably well. The range of variables for the data shown in Fig. 7.7.5 and the definition of N_{Re} and N_{Nu} are listed in Table 7.7-3.

Other bodies

In the preceding paragraphs we have discussed forced-convection heat transfer for a thin, flat plate, a circular cylinder, and a sphere. We chose to discuss these three cases because they have been studied extensively, both theoretically and experimentally; however, there are numerous other systems that one might encounter in practice. For example, one might want to know the heat transfer coefficient for flow past a *rough*, flat plate, or for a flat plate inclined at some angle to the direction of flow. We may wish to know the Nusselt number for *noncircular* cylinders, or *nonspherical* particles. During the evaporation of liquid droplets, circulation within the drop can alter the external flow field and Eq. 7.7-21 may not provide a very accurate estimate of the heat transfer coefficient. Heat transfer to a *liquid metal* flowing

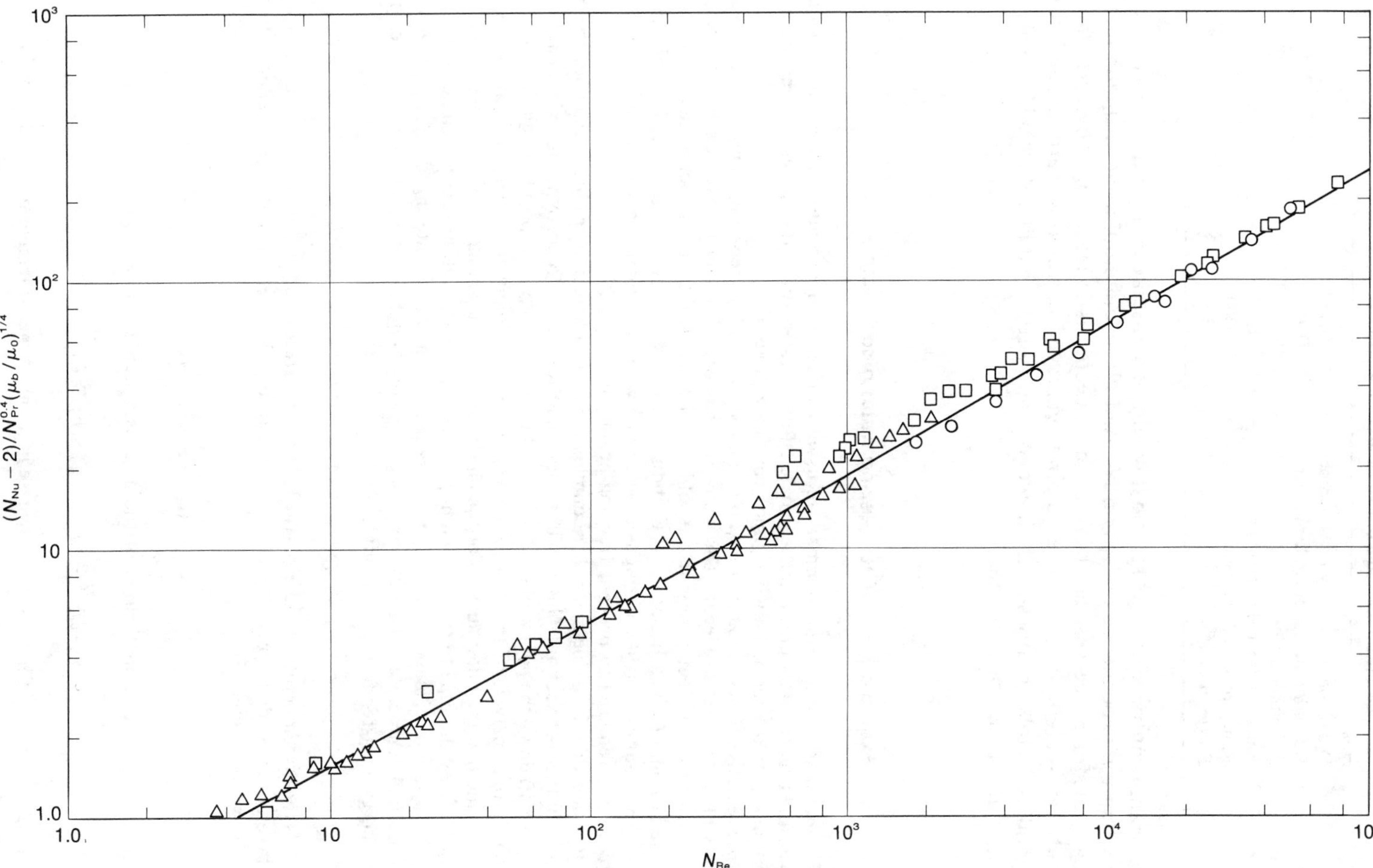

Fig. 7.7.5 Heat transfer to fluids flowing past a single sphere.
○ Vliet and Leppert, water. △ Kramers, air, water, and oil. □ Yuge, air.

Curve is given by

$$(N_{Nu}-2)/N_{Pr}^{0.4}(\mu_b/\mu_0)^{1/4} = 0.4N_{Re}^{1/2} + 0.06N_{Re}^{2/3}$$

Table 7.7-3 Definition and Range of Variables for Heat Transfer to a Fluid Flowing Past a Single Sphere

Definition of the Reynolds number	$u_\infty D/\nu_\infty$
Definition of the Nusselt number	hD/k_∞
Definition of h	$\dot{Q}/\pi D^2(T_0 - T_\infty)$
Range of Reynolds number	3.5–(7.6×10^4)
Range of Prandtl number	0.71–380
Range of (μ_∞/μ_0)	1.0–3.2

past a tube is an important heat transfer process, and it would be a mistake to use Eq. 7.7-13 to analyze the process for we know that the dependence of N_{Nu} on N_{Re} and N_{Pr} is quite different for liquid metals. The list of important heat transfer processes that have been neglected is indeed long; however, the student should now be ready to search the literature to find whatever correlations are needed. Certainly McAdams [42] is a good place to start any search; however, the more recent literature will usually provide improved experimental and theoretical studies.

Example 7.7-1 The freezing water pipe dilemma

The joys of a mountain cabin in the summer are usually offset by the anguish of the winter maintenance problems. Frozen and broken water pipes can be avoided if the lines are drained between the weekend visits, but when an exceptionally cold wind is blowing, pipes can freeze overnight.

In devising preventative measures attention should be focused on the incoming main line which is shown in Fig. 7.7.6, for it will be the first to freeze. The water line has been brought into the cabin in an unfortunate manner which exposes five full feet of pipe to the cold winter blasts which pass underneath the cabin. Water is obtained from the bottom of a nearby lake at 4°C and is transported below the frost line from the lake to the cabin. One way to prevent overnight freezing is to allow the water to run all night long, and we would like to know what flow rate is required to prevent freezing in the pipe.

The complete attack on this problem is rather complex for we would like to be able to calculate the minimum water temperature in the 5-ft section. This would require that we take into account the axial heat conduction from the cabin (at 68°F) down the pipe wall in addition to the radial energy transport through the water film, pipe wall, and air film. In our analysis of the process we will develop a simplified model in which we neglect axial conduction and assume that the outer surface of the pipe is at 4°C. This should provide an upper bound for the amount of energy lost by the pipe to the surrounding air. Assuming that all this energy comes from the water flowing in the pipe, we can calculate the bulk temperature of the water entering the cabin. It would seem plausible that if this bulk temperature were 3°C or greater we would not have to worry about the pipes freezing.

The rate of energy transfer to the air is given by

$$\dot{Q} = h\pi D_0 L(T_{b1} - T_\infty) \tag{1}$$

Here T_∞ represents the air temperature and T_{b1} is the bulk temperature of the water as it enters the 5-ft section. In Eq. 1 we have taken the outside temperature of the pipe to be equal to T_{b1} which in turn is taken to be 4°C. The energy lost by the water is given by

$$\dot{Q} = \rho c_p \langle v_z \rangle \frac{\pi D_i^2}{4}(T_{b1} - T_{b2}) \tag{2}$$

and substitution into Eq. 1 (i.e., application of the macroscopic thermal energy balance) leads to

$$\rho c_p \langle v_z \rangle \frac{\pi D_i^2}{4}(T_{b1} - T_{b2}) = h\pi D_0 L(T_{b1} - T_\infty) \tag{3}$$

We wish to derive an expression for the water flow rate in terms of the air temperature and air velocity, thus we rearrange Eq. 3 to obtain

$$Q = \langle v_z \rangle \frac{\pi D_i^2}{4} = \frac{h\pi D_0 L(T_{b1} - T_\infty)}{\rho c_p (T_{b1} - T_{b2})} \tag{4}$$

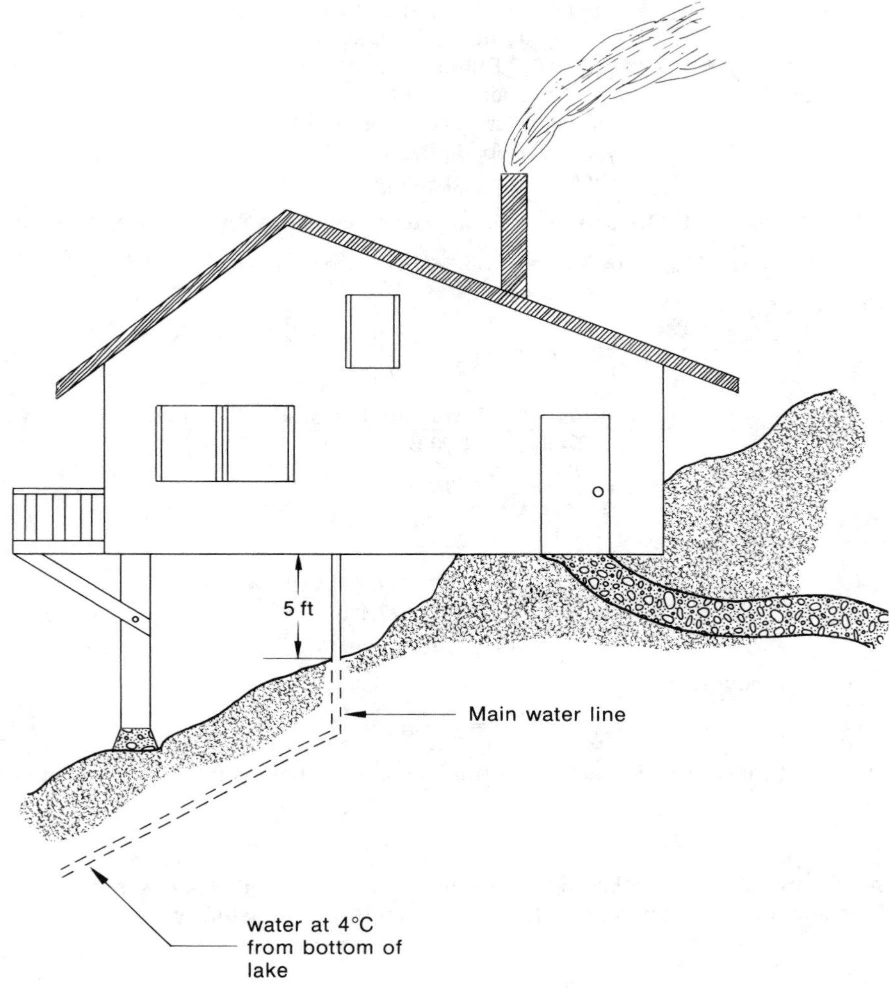

Fig. 7.7.6 Mountain cabin with exposed water pipe.

We should remember at this point that the Nusselt number is given by

$$N_{\mathrm{Nu}} = hD_0/k_{\mathrm{air}}$$

so that Eq. 4 can be expressed as

$$Q = \frac{N_{\mathrm{Nu}}\pi L k_{\mathrm{air}}}{\rho c_p}\left(\frac{T_{b1} - T_\infty}{T_{b1} - T_{b2}}\right) \tag{5}$$

Our Nusselt number correlation, shown in Fig. 7.7.4, is given by Eq. 7.7-13 and it allows us to express the water flow rate as

$$Q = \left(\frac{\pi L k_{\mathrm{air}}}{\rho c_p}\right)[0.4N_{\mathrm{Re}}^{1/2} + 0.06N_{\mathrm{Re}}^{2/3})N_{\mathrm{Pr}}^{0.4}(\mu_\infty/\mu_0)^{1/4}]\left(\frac{T_{b1} - T_\infty}{T_{b1} - T_{b2}}\right) \tag{6}$$

We have at this point derived a general expression for the volumetric flow rate in terms of the air temperature, T_∞, and air velocity, $u_\infty = N_{\mathrm{Re}}\nu/D_0$. In the Sierra Nevada winter, temperatures rarely get below $-10°\mathrm{F}$ and the wind velocity in the region between the cabin flow and the ground should not exceed 30 mph. Taking the outer pipe diameter to be 2 in. we have the following list of parameters and physical properties

$$D_0 = 2\ \mathrm{in.}$$
$$L = 5\ \mathrm{ft}$$

$$\begin{aligned}
\rho &= 62.4\ \mathrm{lb_m/ft^3}, \text{ water at } 4°\mathrm{C}\\
c_p &= 1.00\ \mathrm{Btu/lb_m\,°F}, \text{ water at } 4°\mathrm{C}\\
k_{\mathrm{air}} &= 0.013\ \mathrm{Btu/hr\,ft\,°F}, \text{ air at } -10°\mathrm{F}\\
N_{\mathrm{Pr}} &= 0.72, \text{ air at } -10°\mathrm{F}\\
\mu_\infty &= 0.039\ \mathrm{lb_m/hr\,ft}, \text{ air at } -10°\mathrm{F}\\
\mu_0 &= 0.042\ \mathrm{lb_m/hr\,ft}, \text{ air at } 4°\mathrm{C}\\
\nu &= 1.2\times 10^{-4}\ \mathrm{ft^2/sec}, \text{ air at } -10°\mathrm{F}
\end{aligned}$$

These values lead to $N_{\mathrm{Re}} = 6.1\times 10^4$ and the intermediate calculations for the Nusselt number are

$$(0.4N_{\mathrm{Re}}^{1/2} + 0.06N_{\mathrm{Re}}^{2/3}) = 191.8, \quad N_{\mathrm{Pr}}^{0.4} = 0.88, \quad (\mu_\infty/\mu_0)^{1/4} = 0.98$$

Substitution into Eq. 6 yields

$$\begin{aligned}
Q &= \left(\frac{\pi L k_{\mathrm{air}}}{\rho c_p}\right)(165.4)\left(\frac{T_{b1}-T_\infty}{T_{b1}-T_{b2}}\right)\\
&= \frac{(3.14)(5\ \mathrm{ft})(0.013\ \mathrm{Btu/hr\,ft\,°F})(165.4)}{(62.4\ \mathrm{lb_m/ft^3})(1.00\ \mathrm{Btu/lb_m\,°F})}\left(\frac{T_{b1}-T_\infty}{T_{b1}-T_{b2}}\right)\\
&= 0.54\left(\frac{T_{b1}-T_\infty}{T_{b1}-T_{b2}}\right)\mathrm{ft^3/hr}
\end{aligned}$$

The temperatures are taken to be

$$\begin{aligned}
T_{b1} &= 4°\mathrm{C} = 39.2°\mathrm{F}\\
T_{b2} &= 3°\mathrm{C} = 37.4°\mathrm{F}\\
T_\infty &= -10°\mathrm{F}
\end{aligned}$$

so that the volumetric flow rate is

$$Q = 14.8\ \mathrm{ft^3/hr}$$

If the flow rate must be measured in the kitchen sink, it would be best to give this result in quarts per minute which leads to

$$Q = 7.4\ \mathrm{qts/min}$$

This represents 1 qt every 8 sec; a rather high flow rate to maintain all night long. A more careful analysis might indicate a lower flow rate, and this will be left as an exercise for the student.

*7.8 Heat Transfer for Flow in Packed Beds and Tube Bundles

In the previous section we discussed forced-convection heat transfer for flat plates, single circular cylinders, and single spheres. These represent examples of heat transfer to *unconfined* or *external* flows, whereas the subject of heat transfer to fluids flowing in pipes, discussed in Sec. 7.6 represents an example of heat transfer to *confined* or *internal* flows. In studying heat transfer to fluids flowing in packed beds and tube bundles we will be dealing with an enormously practical aspect of heat transfer, for a major portion of all heat transfer processes occurs in systems of this type. The automobile radiator is a classic example of heat transfer to a fluid flowing in a tube bundle, and there are numerous chemical engineering processes which utilize the high heat and mass transfer rates that occur in packed beds.

Packed beds

In Fig. 7.8.1 we have illustrated a packed bed and indicated the control volume used in the analysis of the heat transfer process. If the packed bed represented a drier we would be using a hot gas stream to heat the solid material and vaporize a liquid, while if we think of it as a catalytic reactor the process stream would carry the reactants into the bed and the products out of the bed while also serving as a coolant if the reaction is exothermic or as a source of thermal energy if the reaction is endothermic.

Following our definition of a local heat transfer coefficient given by Eq. 7.4-1, we define h_{loc} for a

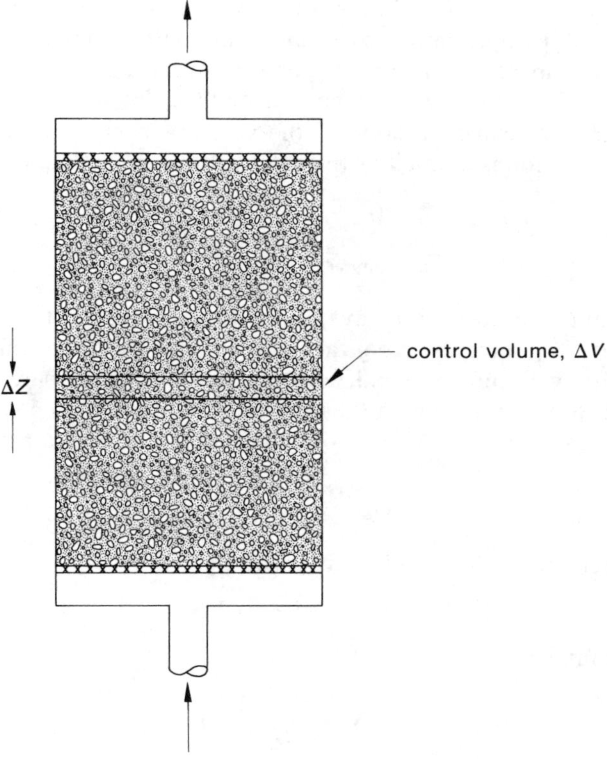

Fig. 7.8.1 Heat transfer in a packed bed.

packed bed as

$$\Delta \dot{Q} = \int_{\Delta\mathscr{A}} \mathbf{q} \cdot \mathbf{n} \, dA \equiv h_{\text{loc}} \, \Delta\mathscr{A} \, \Delta T^* \tag{7.8-1}$$

where $\Delta\mathscr{A}$ is the surface area contained in the volume, ΔV. The characteristic temperature difference, ΔT^*, is generally taken to be the difference between the surface temperature of the packing material, T_0, and the bulk temperature of the fluid, T_b.

$$\Delta T^* = T_0 - T_b \tag{7.8-2}$$

Here we either assume that the surface temperature of the solid is uniform across the bed or that T_0 represents an average surface temperature. In the design and analysis of packed bed chemical reactors there are often significant radial temperature gradients which must be considered;† however, in the experimental determination of heat transfer coefficients every effort is made to eliminate radial gradients. In most of the experimental studies of heat transfer in packed beds no effort is made to determine h_{loc}. Instead the macroscopic thermal energy balance is applied to the entire bed and the term involving the heat flux at the solid–fluid interface is expressed as

$$\dot{Q} = \int_{z=0}^{z=L} \int_{\Delta\mathscr{A}} \mathbf{q} \cdot \mathbf{n} \, dA \equiv h_{\text{ln}} \, \mathscr{A} \, \Delta T_{\text{ln}} \tag{7.8-3}$$

We can express $\mathscr{A}$ in terms of V, the volume of the bed and a_v, the area per unit volume‡ to obtain

$$\dot{Q} \equiv h_{\text{ln}} a_v V \Delta T_{\text{ln}} \tag{7.8-4}$$

†See W. B. Argo and J. M. Smith, "Heat Transfer in Packed Beds," *Chem. Engr. Prog.* **49**, 443 (1953).

‡The use of a_v to represent the surface area of the packing per unit volume of the packed bed is fairly universal. Note that the subscript v is used as a reminder that this is an area *per unit volume* and therefore has units of reciprocal length.

Note that $\dot{Q}$, the total rate of heat transfer, V, the total volume of the packed bed, and $\Delta T_{\ln}$, the log-mean temperature difference, can all be determined experimentally without much difficulty. This leaves us with *two* unknowns; the film heat transfer coefficient, $h_{\ln}$, and the surface area per unit volume of the bed, a_v. In order to determine $h_{\ln}$ from Eq. 7.8-4 we must have a method for determining a_v.

The area per unit volume, a_v, can be related to the void fraction, ϵ, if we know the geometry of the packing material. The void fraction is defined as the void volume in the bed divided by the total volume of the bed.

$$\epsilon = \frac{\{\text{void volume in the bed}\}}{\{\text{total volume in the bed}\}} = \frac{V_{\text{void}}}{V} \tag{7.8-5}$$

Correctly speaking we should refer to ϵ as the average void fraction, for it represents the void fraction of the entire bed. This may differ significantly from the local void fraction especially near the walls where the packing is influenced by the wall and the local void fraction is higher than the average value.

To see how ϵ is related to a_v, let us imagine that a bed of volume V is packed with N particles which have a volume V_p and a surface area A_p. If the void fraction in our bed is ϵ, the volume occupied by the particles is $V(1-\epsilon)$, thus

$$V_p N = V(1-\epsilon) \tag{7.8-6}$$

The number of particles per unit volume, N/V, is given by

$$N/V = (1-\epsilon)/V_p \tag{7.8-7}$$

and the surface area per unit volume is

$$a_v = A_p(N/V) = \left(\frac{A_p}{V_p}\right)(1-\epsilon) \tag{7.8-8}$$

In writing Eq. 7.8-8 we are assuming that all of the surface of a particle is exposed to the fluid. This requires that the area involved in particle–particle contact is negligible. If we know the surface area and volume of the particles in the bed, and if we measure the void fraction we can quickly compute a_v from Eq. 7.8-8 and therefore specify one of the unknowns in Eq. 7.8-4. If the geometry of the particles is unknown then one can only measure the product $h_{\ln}a_v$. This quantity can then be used only for the analysis and design of a packed bed containing precisely the same type of packing used in the experimental study.

In order to correlate heat transfer data for packed beds we must decide on a characteristic length and a characteristic velocity. These quantities should be chosen with the thought that there should be a strong correlation between the heat transfer rate and the characteristic length and velocity. In considering the characteristic length, it would seem unreasonable to choose the height of the bed for variations in this dimension would have little or no effect on the structure of the velocity and temperature fields within the bed.† Similarly, the diameter of the bed would be unsuitable as a characteristic length. A little thought should convince one that the characteristic length should be a measure of either the *size of the packing* or the *size of the void spaces* through which the fluid flows. We shall see shortly that the *hydraulic diameter*, D_h, is a measure of both the packing size and the void size and is therefore an especially suitable choice for a characteristic length. The hydraulic diameter is traditionally used to characterize turbulent flow in noncircular ducts and is defined by

$$D_h = 4\left(\frac{\text{cross section available for flow}}{\text{wetted perimeter of the cross section}}\right) \tag{7.8-9}$$

For straight channels the hydraulic diameter is easily computed; however, for a packed bed this definition must be extended as follows:

$$D_h = 4\left(\frac{\text{cross section available for flow}}{\text{wetted perimeter of the cross section}}\right)$$

†This would not be true for very shallow beds where the entrance and end effects may dominate the heat transfer process.

$$= 4\left(\frac{\text{volume of the bed available for flow}}{\text{wetted surface of the bed}}\right)$$

$$= 4\left(\frac{\text{void volume/total volume}}{\text{wetted surface/total volume}}\right)$$

$$= 4\epsilon / a_v \tag{7.8-10}$$

In the last step in Eq. 7.8-10 we are neglecting the walls of the packed bed as being a negligible portion of the wetted surface. Using our previously derived expression for a_v we can write Eq. 7.8-10 as

$$D_h = 4\left(\frac{V_p}{A_p}\right)\frac{\epsilon}{1-\epsilon} \tag{7.8-11}$$

Rather than use D_h as the characteristic length we will use $\frac{3}{2}$ times the hydraulic diameter, thus

$$L^* = \left(\frac{3}{2}\right) D_h = \left(\frac{6V_p}{A_p}\right)\frac{\epsilon}{1-\epsilon} \tag{7.8-12}$$

We now *define* the "particle diameter" D_p as

$$D_p \equiv 6V_p / A_p \tag{7.8-13}$$

so that our expression for the characteristic length becomes

$$L^* = \left(\frac{3}{2}\right) D_h = D_p\left(\frac{\epsilon}{1-\epsilon}\right) \tag{7.8-14}$$

The definition for D_p given by Eq. 7.8-13 was chosen so that the particle diameter for a sphere is the actual diameter of the sphere.

In choosing a characteristic velocity it seems logical that the average velocity of the fluid flowing in the void space, $\langle v_z \rangle$, would be suitable. This velocity is defined by

$$\langle v_z \rangle = \frac{1}{A_{\text{void}}}\int_{A_{\text{void}}} v_z \, dA \tag{7.8-15}$$

The volumetric flow rate, Q, is given by

$$Q = \int_{A_{\text{void}}} v_z \, dA \tag{7.8-16}$$

and the void area is related to the cross-sectional area of the bed, A, by the expression[43]

$$A_{\text{void}} = \epsilon A \tag{7.8-17}$$

We can now express our characteristic velocity as

$$u^* = \langle v_z \rangle = Q/\epsilon A \tag{7.8-18}$$

The volumetric flow rate divided by the cross-sectional area is referred to as the *superficial velocity*

$$\{\text{superficial velocity}\} = Q/A \tag{7.8-19}$$

and is often used as a characteristic velocity for packed bed catalytic chemical reactors. The superficial velocity is of course completely insensitive to variations in the void fraction and is therefore judged to be a less suitable characteristic velocity.

At this point we have chosen our characteristic length and velocity

$$L^* = D_p\left(\frac{\epsilon}{1-\epsilon}\right), \quad \text{where } D_p = 6V_p/A_p$$

$$u^* = Q/\epsilon A$$

and we can now express the Reynolds number and Nusselt number as

$$N_{\mathrm{Re}} = \rho u^* L^*/\mu = \rho Q D_p/\mu A(1-\epsilon) \tag{7.8-20}$$

$$N_{\mathrm{Nu}} = hL^*/k = \left(\frac{hD_p}{k}\right)\left(\frac{\epsilon}{1-\epsilon}\right) \tag{7.8-21}$$

The quantity $\rho Q/A$ is usually referred to as the *mass velocity* and denoted by G so that our expression for the Reynolds number becomes

$$N_{\mathrm{Re}} = D_p G/\mu(1-\epsilon) \tag{7.8-22}$$

From dimensional analysis we know that the functional dependence of the Nusselt number can be expressed as

$$N_{\mathrm{Nu}} = \mathcal{F}(N_{\mathrm{Re}}, N_{\mathrm{Pr}}, \mu_b/\mu_0, N_{\mathrm{BC}}) \tag{7.8-23}$$

where N_{BC} refers to the dimensionless parameters appearing in the boundary conditions. The types of packing that are used in commercial mass and heat transfer operations are shown in Fig. 7.8.2. Packed bed chemical reactors usually consist of cylindrical catalyst pellets with the length approximately equal to the diameter. Heat transfer data [44–48, 55, 56] have been obtained for beds packed with a variety of packings and these data are shown in Fig. 7.8.3. The Nusselt numbers can be adequately represented by the expression

$$N_{\mathrm{Nu}} = (0.4N_{\mathrm{Re}}^{1/2} + 0.2N_{\mathrm{Re}}^{2/3})N_{\mathrm{Pr}}^{0.4} \tag{7.8-24}$$

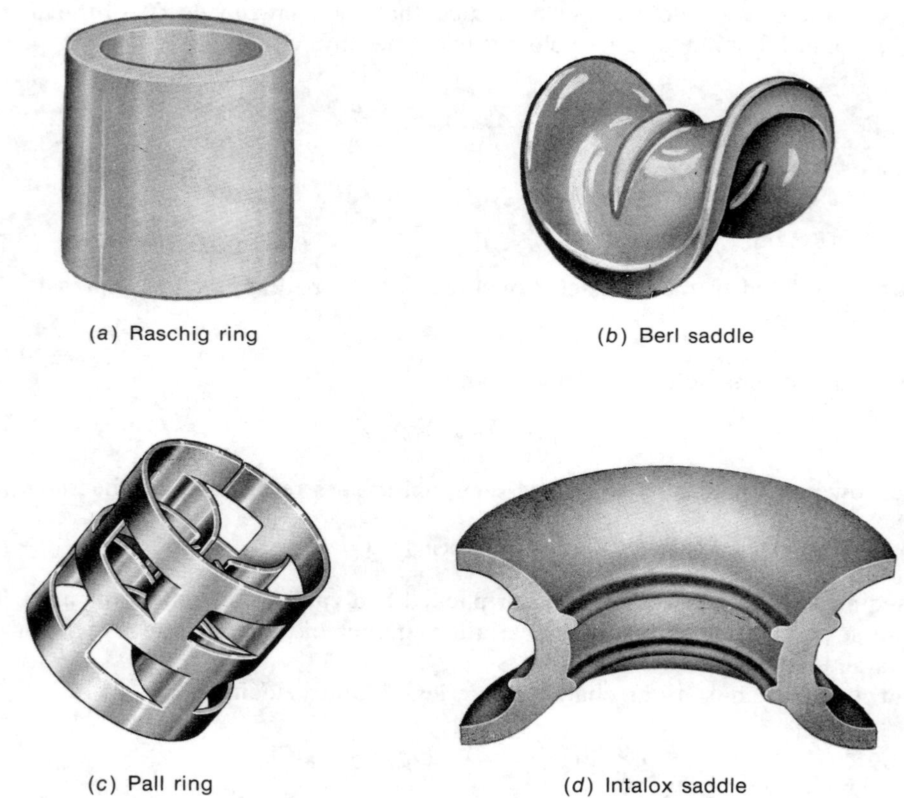

(*a*) Raschig ring

(*b*) Berl saddle

(*c*) Pall ring

(*d*) Intalox saddle

Fig. 7.8.2 Commercial packing materials for heat and mass transfer processes.

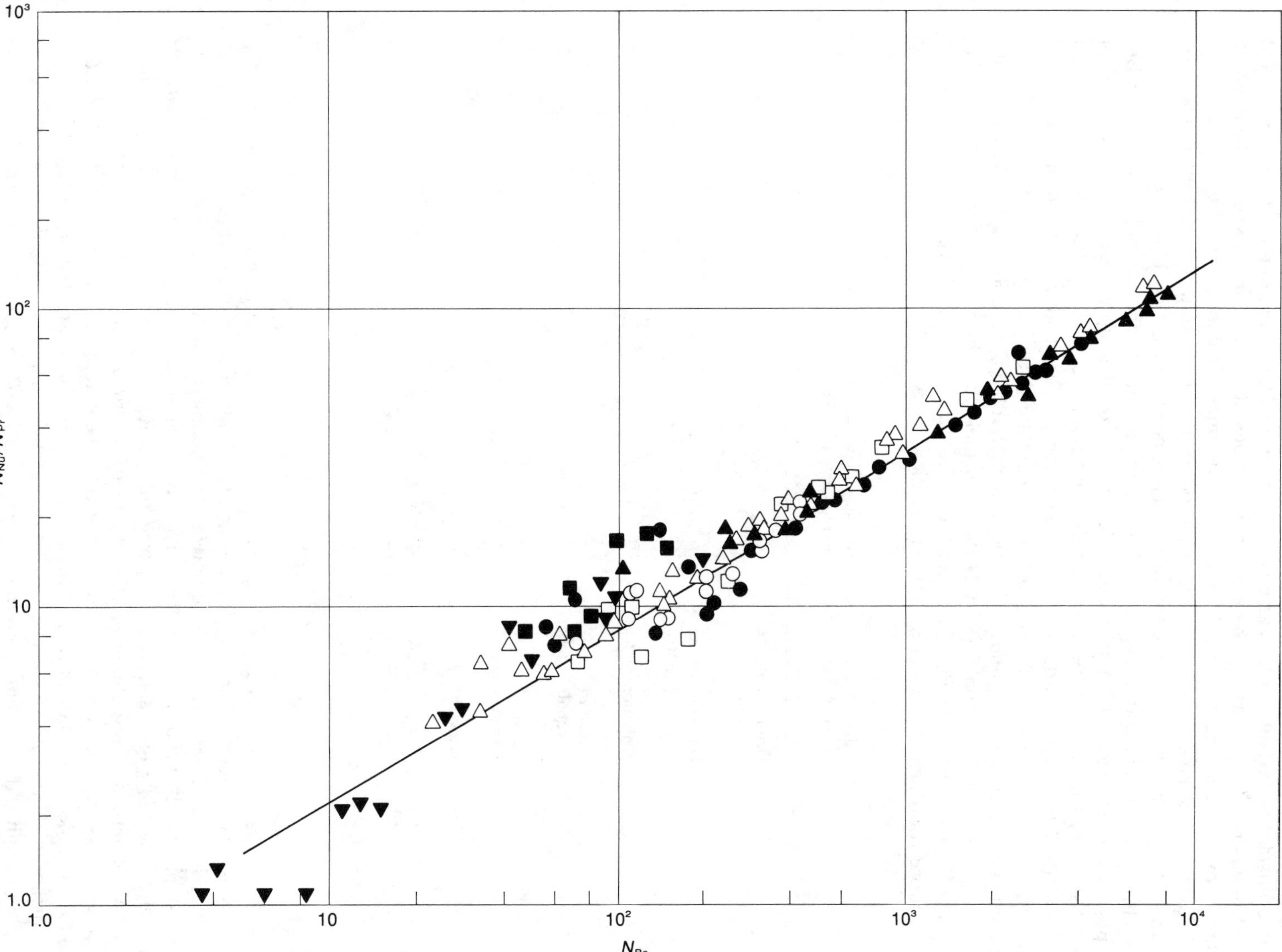

Fig. 7.8.3 Heat transfer to gases flowing in packed beds.
○ Wilke and Hougen, $\epsilon = 0.34$–0.44, cylinders with $L/D \sim 1$. △ Taecker and Hougen, $\epsilon = 0.60$–0.74, commercial packings. □ McConnachie and Thodos, $\epsilon = 0.42$, spheres. ● Glaser and Thodos, $\epsilon = 0.44$–0.48, spheres and cylinders with $L/D \sim 1$. ▲ Gamson, Thodos, and Hougen, $\epsilon = 0.36$–0.43, spheres and cylinders with $L/D \sim 1$. ■ Gliddon and Cranfield, $\epsilon = 0.43$. ▲ Littman, Barile, and Pulsifer, $\epsilon \sim 0.4$, spheres.
Curve is given by

$$N_{Nu}/N_{Pr}^{0.4} = 0.4N_{Re}^{1/2} + 0.2N_{Re}^{2/3}$$

One should keep in mind that the Reynolds number dependence in Eq. 7.8-24 is of the form $aN_{Re}^b + cN_{Re}^d$, thus there are four adjustable constants which can be chosen to provide a correlation between the Nusselt number and the Reynolds number. Certainly there are other values of these four constants which would also yield acceptable correlations. The powers of $\frac{1}{2}$ and $\frac{2}{3}$ on the Reynolds number were chosen because an expression of this form provided a satisfactory correlation for single spheres and single circular cylinders. The flow field in a packed bed can bear only the faintest resemblance to the flow field around a sphere or a cylinder, thus we should not attach undue importance to the exponents on the Reynolds number in Eq. 7.8-24. The 0.4 power for the Prandtl number dependence was used simply because this functional dependence was satisfactory for heat transfer from spheres and cylinders. Since all the experimental data shown in Fig. 7.8.3 were obtained with either air or nitrogen there is negligible variation in the Prandtl number, thus the functional dependence of N_{Nu} on N_{Pr} cannot be determined from these results. In addition, the experiments were performed under conditions such that large variations in the fluid viscosity were not encountered, and for this reason Eq. 7.8-24 does not include a term of the form $(\mu_b/\mu_0)^n$. The range of variables for the data shown in Fig. 7.8.2 and the definitions of N_{Nu} and N_{Re} are listed in Table 7.8-1. A somewhat more thorough discussion of this correlation is given elsewhere [49].

Table 7.8-1 Definition and Range of Variables for Heat Transfer to a Gas Flowing a Packed Bed

Definition of the Reynolds number	$D_pG/\mu(1-\epsilon)$
Definition of the Nusselt number	$\left(\frac{hD_p}{k}\right)\left(\frac{\epsilon}{1-\epsilon}\right)$
Definition of h	$\dot{Q}/a_v V \Delta T_{ln}$
Range of Reynolds number	3.7–8000
Range of Prandtl number	~0.7
Range of (μ_b/μ_0)	~1
Range of ϵ	0.34–0.74

Tube bundles

The use of tube bundles in heat exchange equipment is a common industrial practice, and the knowledge of heat transfer coefficients for tube bundles and for fluids flowing inside tubes is required for the accurate design of industrial heat transfer equipment. The geometry of tube bundles could be quite varied, but for most practical purposes there are only two geometrical arrangements; *staggered* and *in-line.* These are illustrated in Fig. 7.8.4. The staggered tube bundle generally provides a higher heat transfer rate for the same mass flow rate; however, the in-line arrangement provides less resistance to flow and is preferable when pressure drop across the tube bundle must be minimized. As illustrated in Fig. 7.8.4 the geometry of a tube bundle is specified in terms of the transverse *pitch*, s_t, and the longitudinal *pitch*, s_ℓ, and a statement indicating whether it is a staggered or an in-line tube bundle. We will treat only staggered tube bundles here, and require the student to go to the literature [50–54] for heat transfer coefficients for in-line tube bundles.

If there are at least 10 rows of tubes in a tube bundle, if the length of the tubes is large compared to the diameter, and if there are approximately 10 or more tubes in each row, we can neglect entrance, exit, and

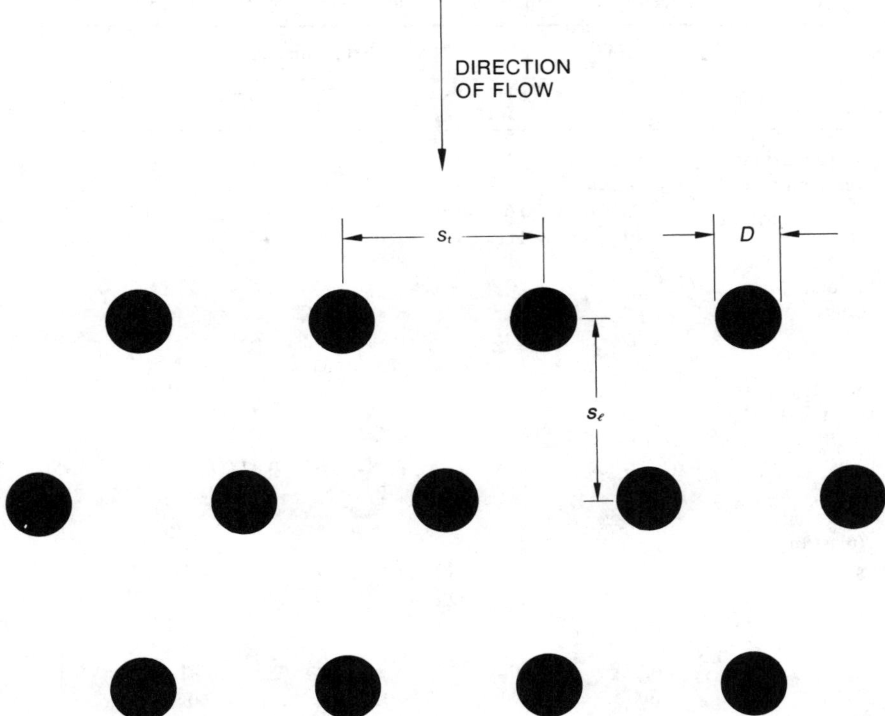

Fig. 7.8.4a Geometry for a staggered tube bundle.

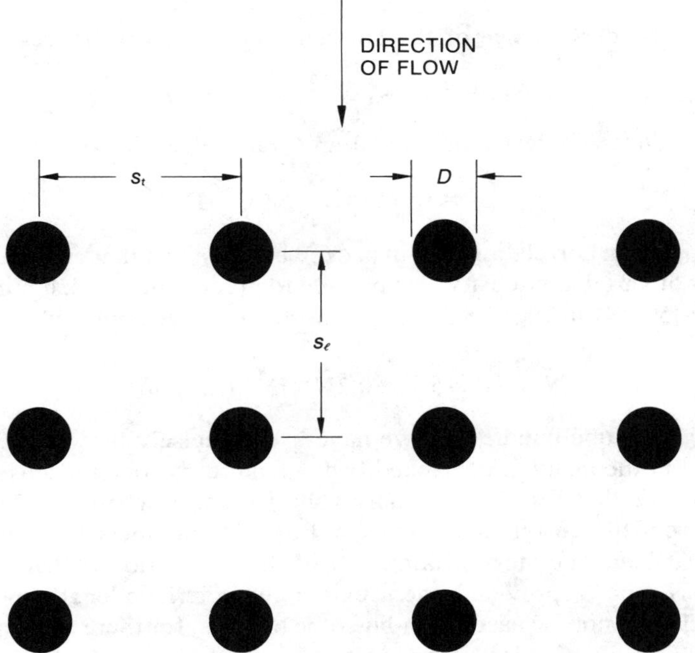

Fig. 7.8.4b Geometry for an in-line tube bundle.

Table 7.8-2 Properties of Randomly Packed Beds†

Packing	Nominal size, inches									
	$\frac{1}{4}$	$\frac{3}{8}$	$\frac{1}{2}$	$\frac{5}{8}$	$\frac{3}{4}$	1	$1\frac{1}{4}$	$1\frac{1}{2}$	2	3
Raschig rings (ceramic)										
ϵ	0.73	0.68	0.63	0.68	0.73	0.73	0.74	0.71	0.74	0.78
a_v	240	155	111	100	80	58	45	38	28	19
Raschig rings (metal, $\frac{1}{32}$-in. wall)										
ϵ	0.69		0.84		0.88	0.92				
a_v	236		128		83	63				
Raschig rings (metal, $\frac{1}{16}$-in. wall)										
ϵ			0.73		0.78	0.85	0.87	0.90	0.92	0.95
a_v			118		72	57	49	41	31	21
Pall rings (plastic)										
ϵ				0.88		0.90		0.90	0.91	
a_v				110		63		39	31	
Intalox saddles (ceramic)										
ϵ	0.75		0.78		0.77	0.78		0.81	0.79	
a_v	300		190		102	78		60	36	
Berl saddles (ceramic)										
ϵ	0.60		0.63		0.66	0.69		0.75	0.72	
a_v	274		142		82	76		44	32	

†From the Norton Company, Akron, Ohio. Values of a_v are given in ft^{-1}.

edge effects and functional dependence of the Nusselt number can be expressed as

$$N_{\text{Nu}} = \mathscr{F}(N_{\text{Re}}, N_{\text{Pr}}, \mu_b/\mu_0, S_\ell, S_t) \tag{7.8-25}$$

Here S_ℓ and S_t are the dimensionless longitudinal and transverse pitches given by

$$S_\ell = s_\ell/D, \qquad S_t = s_t/D \tag{7.8-26}$$

Based on our experience in correlating data in packed beds we find that *essentially the same correlation*, corrected for the effect of variable viscosity, can be used to predict the Nusselt numbers for staggered tube bundles. Thus the data[50–54] in Fig. 7.8.5 are in reasonable agreement with a rearranged form of Eq. 7.8-27

$$N_{\text{Nu}} = (0.4N_{\text{Re}}^{1/2} + 0.2N_{\text{Re}}^{2/3})N_{\text{Pr}}^{0.4}(\mu_b/\mu_0)^{0.14} \tag{7.8-27}$$

In correlating the staggered tube bundle data we have used precisely the same characteristic length and velocity that were used in the analysis of packed beds. A more thorough discussion[49] of the available experimental data indicates that Eq. 7.8-27 is only valid for cases where $\epsilon \leq 0.65$, and we can see that significant deviations from the correlation occur for Reynolds numbers less than 20 and for Reynolds numbers in the range 80–200. The most striking fact of the correlation is that the Nusselt numbers are *nearly* independent of S_ℓ and S_t provided one uses the characteristic length and velocity as defined by Eqs. 7.8-12 and 7.8-18. This is not the case for in-line tube handles, for there the Nusselt number is strongly influenced by S_ℓ and S_t. This situation is illustrated elsewhere[49]. The range of variables for the data shown in Fig. 7.8.5 and the definitions of N_{Nu} and N_{Re} are listed in Table 7.8-3.

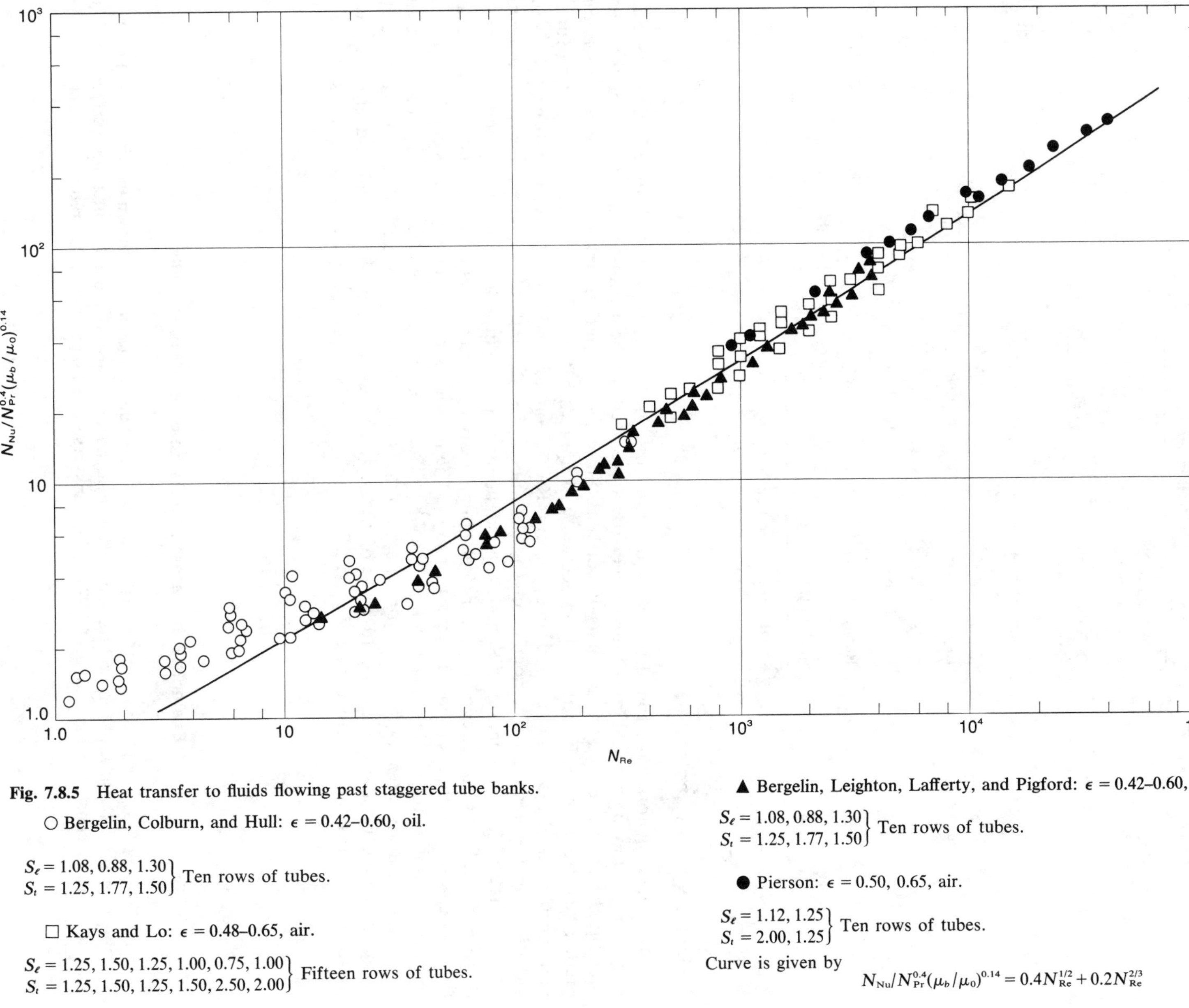

Fig. 7.8.5 Heat transfer to fluids flowing past staggered tube banks.

○ Bergelin, Colburn, and Hull: $\epsilon = 0.42\text{–}0.60$, oil.

$S_\ell = 1.08, 0.88, 1.30$; $S_t = 1.25, 1.77, 1.50$ } Ten rows of tubes.

□ Kays and Lo: $\epsilon = 0.48\text{–}0.65$, air.

$S_\ell = 1.25, 1.50, 1.25, 1.00, 0.75, 1.00$; $S_t = 1.25, 1.50, 1.25, 1.50, 2.50, 2.00$ } Fifteen rows of tubes.

▲ Bergelin, Leighton, Lafferty, and Pigford: $\epsilon = 0.42\text{–}0.60$, oil.

$S_\ell = 1.08, 0.88, 1.30$; $S_t = 1.25, 1.77, 1.50$ } Ten rows of tubes.

● Pierson: $\epsilon = 0.50, 0.65$, air.

$S_\ell = 1.12, 1.25$; $S_t = 2.00, 1.25$ } Ten rows of tubes.

Curve is given by

$$N_{Nu}/N_{Pr}^{0.4}(\mu_b/\mu_0)^{0.14} = 0.4N_{Re}^{1/2} + 0.2N_{Re}^{2/3}$$

Table 7.8-3 Definition and Range of Variables for Heat Transfer to Fluids Flowing in Staggered Tube Bundles

Definition of the Reynolds number*	$D_pG/\mu_b(1-\epsilon)$
Definition of the Nusselt number*	$\left(\frac{hD_p}{k_b}\right)\left(\frac{\epsilon}{1-\epsilon}\right)$
Definition of h	$\dot{Q}/a_v V\Delta T_{\ln}$
Range of Reynolds number	1–40000
Range of Prandtl number	0.7–763
Range of (μ_b/μ_0)	0.18–4.3
Range of ϵ	0.42–0.65

*D_p for a tube bundle is $\frac{3}{2}D$.

Shallow tube bundles

Most investigators have found that if 10 or more rows of tubes are used in a tube bundle there is a negligible entrance or end effect. When fewer rows are used the heat transfer coefficient for the whole tube bundle can be reduced as much as 40 per cent. Since the correlation presented in Fig. 7.8.5 can only predict heat transfer coefficients with an accuracy of approximately ± 20 per cent the correction for the number of rows of tubes is not a pressing problem. Kays, London, and Lo[54] have measured row-to-row variations in the heat transfer coefficient for a number of staggered tube arrangements. Their results indicate that h_N/h_∞ is a function of S_ℓ and S_t, but depended only slightly on the Reynolds number. Here h_N represents the heat transfer coefficient for a tube bundle having N rows of tubes, while h_∞ is the coefficient for a tube bundle with a very large number of rows. The individual experimental results can be expressed reasonably well by the single curve given in Fig. 7.8.6. There we see that even for a tube bundle containing 10 rows the heat transfer coefficient is still 7 per cent lower than h_∞. From a practical point of view we can consider a tube bundle containing 10 rows of tubes to be devoid of entrance and end effects, and a reasonable expression for correcting Eq. 7.8-27 for tube bundles having less than 10 rows is

$$\frac{h_N}{h_\infty} = \left(\frac{N}{10}\right)^{0.18}, \qquad 1 \leq N \leq 10$$

Example 7.8-1 Heat transfer to oil in a tube bundle

Oil at 60°F is to be heated to 150°F in a staggered tube bundle such as that shown in Fig. 7.8.4a. The tubes have an outer diameter of 1 in. and are to be heated by condensing steam so that the outer tube surface should be at a nearly constant temperature of 200°F. The transverse and longitudinal pitch ratios are given by

$$s_t = 1.75 \text{ in.}$$

$$s_\ell = 1.27 \text{ in.}$$

and the physical properties of the oil are given in the following table:

Physical Properties of Oil

T °F	k Btu/hr ft °F	ρ lb$_m$/ft^3	c_p Btu/lb$_m$ °F	μ lb$_m$/ft sec
70	0.0767	54.3	0.41	4.17×10^{-2}
140	0.0758	54.3	0.43	6.38×10^{-3}
212	0.0748	54.3	0.46	2.15×10^{-3}

For a superficial velocity, Q/A, of 0.8 ft/sec we wish to know how many rows of tubes are required to accomplish the desired heating.

We begin our analysis by using Eq. 7.8-4 to express the total rate of heat transfer in the tube bundle as

$$\dot{Q} = h_{\ln} a_v V \Delta T_{\ln} \tag{1}$$

Here V is the total volume of the tube bundle and a_v is the surface area for heat transfer *per unit volume.* Making the usual assumptions, the total rate of heat transfer is also given by

$$\dot{Q} = \rho c_p Q (T_{b2} - T_{b1}) \tag{2}$$

where Q is the volumetric flow rate of the oil, and T_{b1} and T_{b2} are the bulk oil temperatures at the entrance and exit. Substitution of Eq. 1 into Eq. 2 leads to

$$h_{\ln} a_v V \Delta T_{\ln} = \rho c_p Q (T_{b2} - T_{b1}) \tag{3}$$

If we express the volume of the tube bundle as $V = AL$ we can rearrange Eq. 3 to obtain an equation for the length of the tube bundle in the direction of flow.

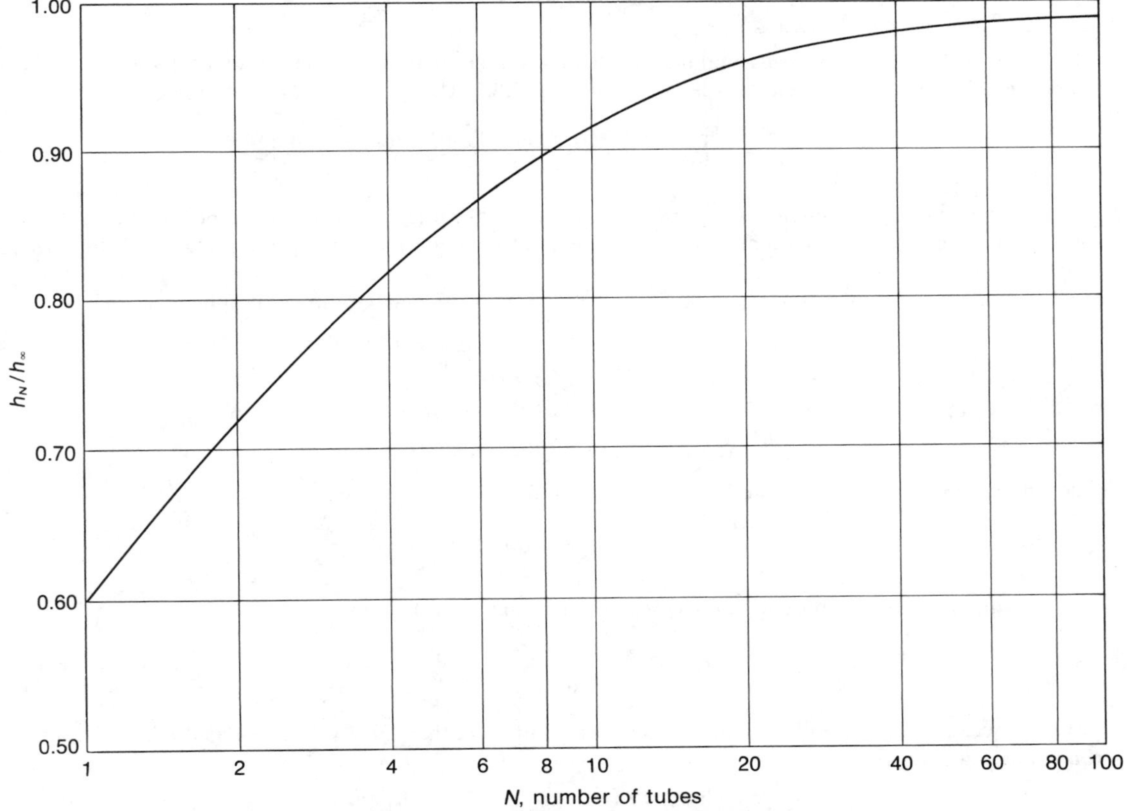

Fig. 7.8.6 Effect of the number of rows of tubes on the overall heat transfer coefficient for staggered tube bundles.

$$L = \frac{\rho c_p (Q/A)}{h_{\ln} a_v} \ln\left(\frac{T_0 - T_{b1}}{T_0 - T_{b2}}\right) \tag{4}$$

Here we have made use of the relation

$$\frac{T_{b2} - T_{b1}}{\Delta T_{\ln}} = \frac{T_{b2} - T_{b1}}{\dfrac{(T_0 - T_{b1}) - (T_0 - T_{b2})}{\ln\left(\dfrac{T_0 - T_{b1}}{T_0 - T_{b2}}\right)}} = \ln\left(\frac{T_0 - T_{b1}}{T_0 - T_{b2}}\right) \tag{5}$$

where T_0 is the outer tube surface temperature of 200°F.

Referring to Eq. 7.8-8 we find that the surface area per unit volume, a_v, can be expressed as

$$a_v = \left(\frac{A_p}{V_p}\right)(1 - \epsilon) = \frac{4}{D}(1 - \epsilon) \tag{6}$$

so that Eq. 4 can be written in the form

$$\frac{L}{D} = \frac{\rho c_p (Q/A)}{4 h_{\ln}(1 - \epsilon)} \ln\left(\frac{T_0 - T_{b1}}{T_0 - T_{b2}}\right) \tag{7}$$

We now make use of the definitions given by Eqs. 7.8-20 and 7.8-21 which are

$$N_{\mathrm{Re}} = \rho (Q/A) D_p / \mu (1 - \epsilon)$$
$$N_{\mathrm{Nu}} = h D_p \epsilon / k (1 - \epsilon)$$
$$N_{\mathrm{Pr}} = \mu c_p / k$$

Use of these definitions in Eq. 7 allows us to express that result as

$$\frac{L}{D} = \left(\frac{\epsilon}{1 - \epsilon}\right)\left(\frac{N_{\mathrm{Re}} N_{\mathrm{Pr}}}{4 N_{\mathrm{Nu}}}\right) \ln\left(\frac{T_0 - T_{b1}}{T_0 - T_{b2}}\right) \tag{8}$$

The expression for the Nusselt number for heat transfer in tube bundles is given by Eq. 7.8-27, and the comparison with experimental data is shown in Fig. 7.8.5. Using Eq. 7.8-27 leads to

$$\frac{L}{D} = \left(\frac{\epsilon}{1 - \epsilon}\right)\left\{\frac{N_{\mathrm{Re}} N_{\mathrm{Pr}} \ln\left[(T_0 - T_{b1})/(T_0 - T_{b2})\right]}{4(0.4 N_{\mathrm{Re}}^{1/2} + 0.2 N_{\mathrm{Re}}^{2/3}) N_{\mathrm{Pr}}^{0.4} (\mu_b / \mu_0)^{0.14}}\right\} \tag{9}$$

At this point we have developed a general expression for the length of the tube bundle in terms of the appropriate dimensionless parameters, and we need only evaluate these parameters in order to determine the length.

The mean bulk temperature is given by $(T_{b1} + T_{b2})/2 = 105$°F, and we can use graphical interpolation to find

$$k_b = 0.0757 \text{ Btu/hr ft°F}$$
$$\rho_b = 54.3 \text{ lb}_m/\text{ft}^3$$
$$(c_p)_b = 0.43 \text{ Btu/lb}_m\text{°F}$$
$$\mu_b = 5.1 \times 10^{-3} \text{ lb}_m/\text{ft sec}$$

The "particle diameter" is defined by Eq. 7.8-13 and yields

$$D_p = 6 V_p / A_p = \left(\frac{3}{2}\right) D = 1.5 \text{ in.}$$

For a staggered tube bundle we can express the average void fraction as

$$\epsilon = 1 - (\pi D^2 / 4 s_\ell s_t)$$
$$= 0.64$$

provided we can neglect end and edge effects. Remembering that Q/A was given as 0.8 ft/sec allows us to do the following calculations:

$$N_{\mathrm{Re}} = \left(\frac{54.3 \text{ lb}_m}{\text{ft}^3}\right)\left(\frac{0.8 \text{ ft}}{\text{sec}}\right)(1.5 \text{ in.}) \Big/ \left(\frac{5.1 \times 10^{-3} \text{ lb}_m}{\text{ft sec}}\right)(0.36)\left(\frac{12 \text{ in.}}{\text{ft}}\right)$$
$$= 2958$$

$$N_{Pr} = \left(\frac{5.1\times 10^{-3}\ \text{lb}_m}{\text{ft sec}}\right)\left(\frac{0.43\ \text{Btu}}{\text{lb}_m\,°\text{F}}\right)\bigg/\left(\frac{0.0757\ \text{Btu}}{\text{hr ft}\,°\text{F}}\right)\left(\frac{\text{hr}}{3600\ \text{sec}}\right)$$
$$= 104$$

$$(\mu_b/\mu_0)^{0.14} = \left(\frac{5.1\times 10^{-3}}{2.4\times 10^{-3}}\right)^{0.14} = 1.11$$

We can make some intermediate calculations leading to

$$\frac{\epsilon}{1-\epsilon} = 1.78$$

$$N_{Re}N_{Pr} = 3.08\times 10^5$$

$$\ln[(T_0 - T_{b1})/(T_0 - T_{b2})] = 1.03$$

$$(0.4N_{Re}^{1/2} + 0.2N_{Re}^{2/3})N_{Pr}^{0.4}(\mu_b/\mu_0)^{0.14} = 448$$

Substitution of these values into Eq. 9 gives

$$\frac{L}{D} = \frac{(1.78)(3.08\times 10^5)(1.03)}{(4)(448)}$$
$$= 315$$

Since D was given as 1 in. we find the length of the tube bundle to be

$$L = (315)(1\ \text{in.})/(12\ \text{in./ft})$$
$$= 26.3\ \text{ft}$$

Each row of tubes will occupy a distance equal to s_ℓ (refer to Fig. 7.8.4a), thus the number of rows of tubes required is 252. Under these circumstances a designer would be wise to consider the use of baffled shell and tube heat exchangers described in Chapter 11.

*7.9 Free Convection

In Sec. 5.10 we demonstrated that the Nusselt number for free convection should depend on the Grashof and Prandtl numbers

$$N_{Nu} = N_{Nu}(N_{Gr}, N_{Pr}) \tag{7.9-1}$$

in addition to $\boldsymbol{\lambda}$, the direction of the gravity vector, and the dimensionless parameters appearing in the boundary conditions for the temperature and velocity fields (see Eqs. 5.10-32 and 5.10-33). The Grashof number is defined as

$$N_{Gr} = \frac{\beta\Delta T g L^3}{\nu^2} \tag{7.9-2}$$

where β is the coefficient of thermal expansion

$$\beta = -\frac{1}{\rho}\left(\frac{\partial\rho}{\partial T}\right)_p \tag{7.9-3}$$

and L is a characteristic length. The Grashof number can be thought of as being analogous to the Reynolds number. This becomes clear if we note that the characteristic velocity, u^*, for free-convection flows is given by

$$u^* = \beta\Delta T g L^2/\nu$$

so that the Grashof number can be expressed as

$$N_{Gr} = u^* L/\nu$$

In Sec. 5.11 we were able to develop a reasonably satisfactory solution for the Nusselt number when the free convection gave rise to a boundary layer type of flow. For other types of flows we must resort to experimental data and empirical expressions for the Nusselt number. In the following paragraphs we will list several of the more useful of these expressions. In free-convection correlations it is customary to evaluate the physical properties at the *film temperature*, T_f, where

$$T_f = \tfrac{1}{2}(T_0 + T_\infty) \tag{7.9-4}$$

The characteristic temperature difference used in defining the free-convection film heat transfer coefficient is generally taken to be the difference between the average surface temperature $\langle T_0 \rangle$ and T_∞. This film heat transfer coefficient will be designated by h_m, thus

$$\int_A \mathbf{q} \cdot \mathbf{n}\, dA = h_m A (\langle T_0 \rangle - T_\infty) \tag{7.9-5}$$

and the Nusselt number is given by

$$N_{\mathrm{Nu},m} = h_m L / k_f \tag{7.9-6}$$

Here the subscript on the thermal conductivity indicates that it is evaluated at the film temperature, and it is understood that this is an *average* film temperature given by $(\langle T_0 \rangle + T_\infty)/2$.

Horizontal cylinders

One of the most important free-convection heat transfer processes is in the transfer taking place at a heated or cooled horizontal pipe. This situation quite naturally arises when hot or cold process streams are transported in horizontal pipes. The correlation for this situation is shown in Fig. 7.9.1 where the logarithm of N_{Nu}, where

$$N_{\mathrm{Nu}} = \frac{h_m D}{k_f} \tag{7.9-7}$$

is plotted as a function of the product $N_{\mathrm{Gr}} N_{\mathrm{Pr}}$ in which all the physical properties are evaluated at the average film temperature. For $10^3 < N_{\mathrm{Gr}} N_{\mathrm{Pr}} < 10^9$ the curve in Fig. 7.9.1 is adequately represented by

$$N_{\mathrm{Nu}} = 0.52(N_{\mathrm{Gr}} N_{\mathrm{Pr}})^{1/4}, \quad \text{for } 10^3 < N_{\mathrm{Gr}} N_{\mathrm{Pr}} < 10^9 \tag{7.9-8}$$

The characteristic length for a horizontal cylinder is the diameter, thus the Grashof number to be used in Eq. 7.9-8 is defined as

$$N_{\mathrm{Gr}} = \beta \Delta T g D^3 / \nu^2 \tag{7.9-9}$$

Vertical plates

Experimental data for experiments on heated, vertical plates in air are represented in Fig. 7.9.2. Although the experimental data are for air, the curve should be reasonably satisfactory for other fluids, since dimensional analysis tells us that the same Nusselt number should result from a given set of values of the Grashof and Prandtl numbers. This, of course, is based on the assumption that the physical properties are independent of temperature, which is not strictly true. For $N_{\mathrm{Gr}} N_{\mathrm{Pr}} > 10^9$ the flow is no longer laminar; however, the onset of turbulence in free-convection flows is obviously a relatively gentle process compared to the transition that takes place in forced-convection flows. The curve given in Fig. 7.9.2 can also be used to calculate film heat transfer coefficients for vertical cylinders provided the boundary layer thicknesses, δ_T and δ_H, are small compared to the diameter of the cylinder, D. Under these circumstances the curvature of the surface will have little effect on the velocity or temperature fields. The recommended analytical expressions for the curve shown in Fig. 7.9.2 are†

$$N_{\mathrm{Nu}} = 0.58(N_{\mathrm{Gr}} N_{\mathrm{Pr}})^{1/4}, \qquad N_{\mathrm{Gr}} N_{\mathrm{Pr}} < 10^9, \quad \text{laminar flow} \tag{7.9-10}$$

$$N_{\mathrm{Nu}} = 0.021(N_{\mathrm{Gr}} N_{\mathrm{Pr}})^{2/5}, \qquad N_{\mathrm{Gr}} N_{\mathrm{Pr}} > 10^9, \quad \text{turbulent flow} \tag{7.9-11}$$

†E. R. G. Eckert and T. W. Jackson, "Analysis of Turbulent Free Convection Boundary Layer on a Flat Plate," NACA Rept. 1015 (1951).

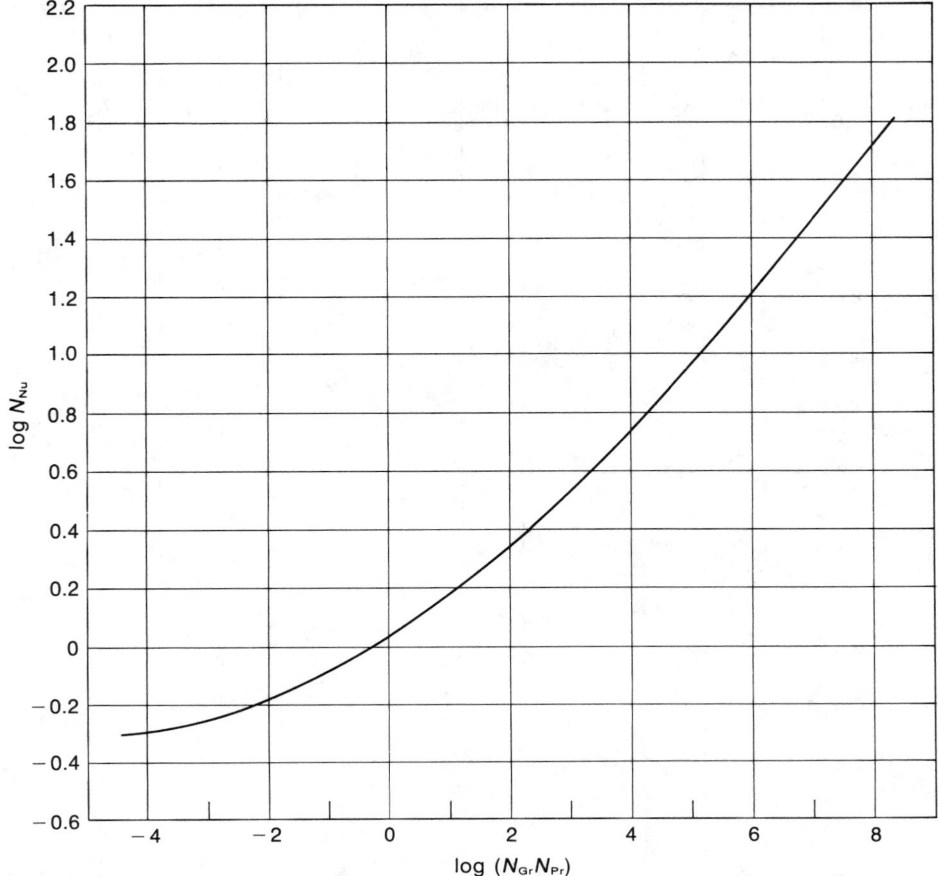

Fig. 7.9.1 Free convection for long horizontal cylinders. (Curve is recommended by W. H. McAdams, *Heat Transmission*, McGraw-Hill Book Co., Inc., New York, 1954.)

For vertical plates the characteristic length to be used in the definition of the Grashof number is the height of the plate.

Single sphere

Free convection from a single sphere has not been studied as extensively as have horizontal cylinders and vertical plates and cylinders; however, the measurements which have been made indicate that the Nusselt number is satisfactorily represented by the expression

$$N_{Nu} = 2 + 0.60 N_{Gr}^{1/4} N_{Pr}^{1/3} \tag{7.9-12}$$

provided $N_{Gr}^{1/4} N_{Pr}^{1/3} < 200$.

Because natural convection heat transfer rates are generally quite low, radiant heat transfer can become significant even at relatively low temperatures. We must keep in mind that radiant energy heat transfer has been completely neglected up to this point. In Chapters 8 and 9 we will learn how to include the effect of radiation on heat transfer rates.

Example 7.9-1 Energy losses during the morning shower

Each morning millions of Americans rely on a hot shower to ease the transition from sleep to work. The average shower lasts for 8 min and consumes hot water at the rate of 1.5 gals/min. Hot water

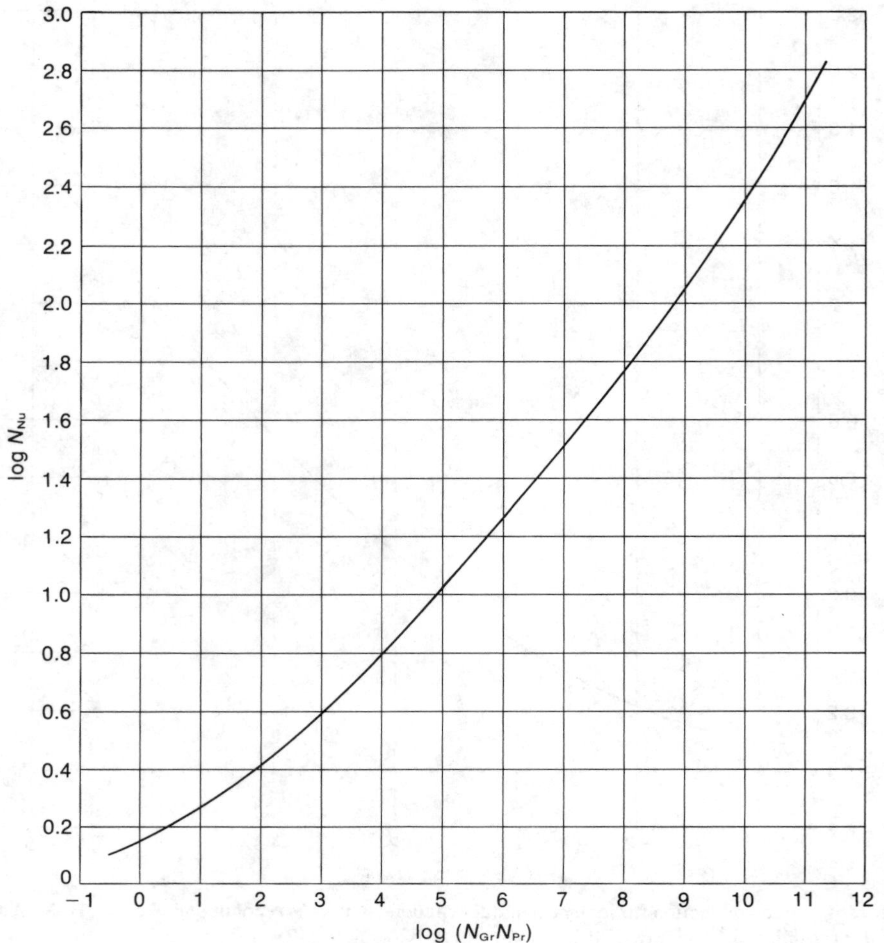

Fig. 7.9.2 Free convection for vertical plates. (Curve is recommended by W. H. McAdams, *Heat Transmission*, McGraw-Hill Book Co., Inc., New York, 1954.)

is supplied by a heater which provides water at about 60°C *at the heater*, and the energy demand on the heater per pound of water is $c_p(T_1 - T_0)$. Here c_p is the heat capacity of water, T_0 is the temperature of the water entering the heater, and T_1 is the output temperature of about 60°C.

In most homes hot water is distributed underneath the floor in copper pipes (O.D. = 0.75 in., I.D. = 0.65 in.) which are uninsulated. In this example we would like to determine the fraction of energy lost per shower, and the cost of this energy loss per year. The problem under consideration is a complex transient heat transfer process. At short times energy is lost in heating the pipes, while at long times we have a problem of steady heat flow through the pipe walls and the surrounding air film.

In our simplified analysis of this problem we will neglect the transient period and assume that all the resistance to heat transfer is in the surrounding air film. We will further assume that only a small fraction of the energy supplied at the hot water heater is lost so that we can assume that the outer temperature of the copper pipe is constant at T_1. Under these circumstances the rate at which energy is supplied at the heater can be expressed as

$$\dot{Q}_1 = \rho c_p \langle v_z \rangle \frac{\pi D_i^2}{4} (T_1 - T_0) \tag{1}$$

while the loss owing to free convection is given by

$$\dot{Q}_2 = h\pi D_0 L (T_1 - T_\infty) \tag{2}$$

Here L is the length of pipe between the heater and the shower, and T_∞ is the ambient air temperature. A reasonable correction for the radiation losses would be†

$$\dot{Q}_2 = h\pi D_0 L(T_1 - T_\infty) + \epsilon\sigma(T_1^4 - T_\infty^4)\pi D_0 L \quad (3)$$

This subject will be taken up in Chapters 8 and 9, and for the present we will neglect radiant energy exchange and use Eqs. 1 and 2 to express the fractional energy loss as

$$\eta = \frac{\dot{Q}_2}{\dot{Q}_1} = \frac{h\pi D_0 L(T_1 - T_\infty)}{\rho Q c_p (T_1 - T_0)} \quad (4)$$

Here we have represented the volumetric flow rate as $Q = \langle v_z \rangle \pi D_i^2/4$.

In the winter the ambient water temperature, T_0, is greater than the ambient air temperature, T_∞, while in the summer the situation is reversed; however, we will assume that $T_0 \sim T_\infty$ so that Eq. 4 simplifies to

$$\eta = \frac{h\pi D_0 L}{\rho Q c_p} \quad (5)$$

By making use of the appropriate dimensionless groups we can express the fraction of energy lost as

$$\eta = \frac{4N_{\mathrm{Nu}}(L/D_i)(k_{\mathrm{air}}/k_{\mathrm{water}})}{N_{\mathrm{Re}} N_{\mathrm{Pr}}} \quad (6)$$

Here N_{Nu} is given by the curve in Fig. 7.9.1 and the Reynolds number and Prandtl number are for the water. At 60°C (or 140°F) and a volumetric flow rate of 1.5 gals/min we have‡

$$N_{\mathrm{Re}} = 4Q/\nu\pi D_i = 1.52 \times 10^4$$

$$N_{\mathrm{Pr}} = 3.01$$

The ratio $(k_{\mathrm{air}}/k_{\mathrm{water}})$ is only a weak function of temperature and can be taken as

$$(k_{\mathrm{air}}/k_{\mathrm{water}}) = 0.0425$$

If we take the distance between the water heater and the shower to be 50 ft we have

$$L/D_i = 923$$

and η can be expressed as

$$\eta = 3.43 \times 10^{-3}\, N_{\mathrm{Nu}} \quad (7)$$

At this point we are left with only the task of computing $N_{\mathrm{Gr}}N_{\mathrm{Pr}}$ in order to determine N_{Nu}. Referring to Eq. 7.9-9 we write

$$N_{\mathrm{Gr}}N_{\mathrm{Pr}} = \left(\frac{\beta \Delta T g D_0^3}{\nu^2}\right)\left(\frac{\nu}{\alpha}\right) = \Delta T D_0^3 \left(\frac{\beta g \rho^2 c_p}{\mu k}\right) \quad (8)$$

The term $(\beta g \rho^2 c_p/\mu k)$ varies with temperature as follows:

$(\beta g \rho^2 c_p/\mu k)$	T
1122/in^3°F	50°F
729/in^3°F	100°F
498/in^3°F	150°F

Since our film temperature, $(T_1 + T_\infty)/2$, is about 100°F and $D_0 = 0.75$ in., we can write Eq. 8 as

$$N_{\mathrm{Gr}}N_{\mathrm{Pr}} = 308(T_1 - T_\infty)/°\mathrm{F} \quad (9)$$

We have previously indicated that T_1 is fixed at 140°F; however, T_∞ varies during the year. In the wintertime it might be reasonable to set $T_\infty = 40°$F while in the summertime an ambient air temperature of 65°F would be

†This expression for the radiant energy exchange will be derived in Ex. 9.5-1, and was given earlier in Sec. 1.3.
‡See Appendix A for physical property data.

appropriate. This leads to the following results:

Winter

$$N_{\mathrm{Gr}}N_{\mathrm{Pr}} = 3.08 \times 10^4 \quad \text{(from Eq. 9)}$$
$$N_{\mathrm{Nu}} = 6.89 \quad \text{(from Eq. 7.9-8)}$$
$$\eta = 2.4 \times 10^{-2} \quad \text{(from Eq. 7)}$$

Summer

$$N_{\mathrm{Gr}}N_{\mathrm{Pr}} = 2.31 \times 10^4$$
$$N_{\mathrm{Nu}} = 6.41$$
$$\eta = 2.2 \times 10^{-2}$$

Here we see that about 2 per cent of the energy is lost and our assumption that the surface temperature of the pipe is constant at 140°F is perhaps not unreasonable.

The energy loss per shower is given by

$$\{\text{energy loss per shower}\} = \eta \dot{Q}_1 \quad (8\text{ min})$$

and from Eq. 1 we have

$$\{\text{energy loss per shower}\} = \eta \rho c_p Q(T_1 - T_0) \quad (8\text{ min})$$

In the wintertime this loss amounts to 240 Btu while the summertime loss is 165 Btu. In order to determine the total loss of energy during one year, we assume one shower per day per person and consider a household of four which leads to

$$\{\text{total energy loss per year}\} = \left(\frac{240\text{ Btu} + 165\text{ Btu}}{2}\right)(4)(365)$$
$$= 2.96 \times 10^5\text{ Btu}$$

In order to see what effect this has on one's utility bill we convert to kilowatt hours to find

$$\{\text{total energy loss per year}\} = 86.7\text{ kw hr}$$

In Northern California the energy cost for natural gas is 0.46¢ per kilowatt hour,† thus the cost of the energy loss is a mere 40¢ per year.

Solution to design problem VII

As the first step toward designing an auxiliary heater for the feed stream to the distillation column we need to determine whether there is sufficient energy available from the water to raise the oil temperature from 74°F to 80°F. The energy which must be supplied to the oil is denoted by $\dot{Q}$ and expressed as

$$\dot{Q} = \dot{m}_{\mathrm{I}} c_p^{\mathrm{I}} (T_2^{\mathrm{I}} - T_1^{\mathrm{I}}) \tag{VII-1}$$

Here we use the subscript or superscript I to denote the oil stream, and T_1^{I} and T_2^{I} represents the bulk or cup-mixing temperatures at the entrance and exit of the heater. The energy required is calculated to be

$$\dot{Q} = 3.91 \times 10^5\text{ Btu/day} \tag{VII-2}$$

The maximum amount of energy which could be extracted from the water in this case is given by

$$\{\text{maximum energy available from the water per day}\} = \dot{m}_{\mathrm{II}} c_p^{\mathrm{II}} (200°\mathrm{F} - 74°\mathrm{F}) \tag{VII-3}$$
$$= 7.2 \times 10^6\text{ Btu/day}$$

We should note at this point that the heat exchanger must be infinitely long in order to lower the water temperature to 74°F; nevertheless, there appears to be sufficient water available for our purposes and we can proceed with the analysis. Before going on to the final design it would be wise to calculate the *minimum*

†The cost for electrical heating is about four times this value, and represents one of those rare examples where the second law of thermodynamics has been used to enhance an industry's profit.

length of the double-pipe heat exchanger, for if this length turns out to be excessively long we would not want to proceed with this particular design. The maximum rate at which energy could be transferred from the water to the oil would occur if the outside of the feed line were maintained at 200°F and the inside at 74°F. The rate of heat transfer under these circumstances is given by

$$\dot{Q} = \pi D_o L \langle q_r \rangle|_{r=D_o/2} \tag{VII-4a}$$

$$= \pi D_i L \langle q_r \rangle|_{r=D_i/2} \tag{VII-4b}$$

$$= \frac{2\pi k L_{\min}(T_0 - T_i)}{\ln\left(\dfrac{D_o}{D_i}\right)} \tag{VII-4c}$$

Here D_i and D_0 are the inner and outer diameters of the feed line, and T_i and T_0 represent the inner and outer surface temperatures which are set equal to 74°F and 200°F respectively. Solving for the minimum length gives

$$L_{\min} = \frac{\dot{Q}\ln(D_o/D_i)}{2\pi k(126°\text{F})} \tag{VII-5}$$

$$= 0.32\text{ ft}$$

We should be aware that this calculation is based on the assumption that the entire resistance to heat transfer is in the pipe wall, and no change in temperature takes place in either fluid. These are unlikely conditions; however, they allow us to quickly calculate a minimum length. If this minimum length were 100 ft we would immediately seek an alternate plan for heating the oil, and waste no time in the design of a double-pipe heat exchanger.

In Sec. 7.4 we analyzed the process of heat transfer to a fluid flowing in a tube having a constant wall temperature, T_0. The process that occurs in a double-pipe heat exchanger is somewhat more complicated; however, the approach used in Sec. 7.4 is easily extended to this case. We begin with the macroscopic thermal energy balance for steady flow and a fixed control volume

$$\int_{A_e} \rho c_p(\bar{T} - T_0)\bar{\mathbf{v}}\cdot\mathbf{n}\,dA = -\int_{A_e} \bar{\mathbf{q}}^{(T)}\cdot\mathbf{n}\,dA - \int_{A_s} \bar{\mathbf{q}}^{(T)}\cdot\mathbf{n}\,dA \tag{VII-6}$$

and apply it to the two control volumes shown in Fig. VII.2. Following the development given by Eqs. 7.4-6 through 7.4-21 we obtain†

$$\dot{m}_{\text{I}} c_p^{\text{I}}\left(\frac{dT^{\text{I}}}{dz}\right) = -\langle \bar{q}_r \rangle|_{r=D_i/2}\pi D_i \tag{VII-7}$$

$$-\dot{m}_{\text{II}} c_p^{\text{II}}\left(\frac{dT^{\text{II}}}{dz}\right) = \langle \bar{q}_r \rangle|_{D_o/2}\pi D_o \tag{VII-8}$$

Here $\dot{m}_{\text{I}}$ and $\dot{m}_{\text{II}}$ represent the mass flow rates (lb_m/hr) of the feed stream (I) and the heating water (II) respectively. The *bulk* or *cup-mixing* temperatures of these two streams are designated by T^{I} and T^{II}, and the inner and outer diameters of the feed pipeline are given by D_i and D_o. From Eq. 2.4-13 we know that the right-hand-side of Eqs. VII-7 and VII-8 can be expressed as‡

$$\langle \bar{q}_r \rangle|_{r=D_o/2}\pi D_o = \langle \bar{q}_r \rangle|_{r=D_i/2}\pi D_i = \frac{\pi D_o(T^{\text{I}} - T^{\text{II}})}{\dfrac{1}{h^{\text{I}}}\left(\dfrac{D_o}{D_i}\right) + \dfrac{D_o}{2k}\ln\left(\dfrac{D_o}{D_i}\right) + \dfrac{1}{h^{\text{II}}}} \tag{VII-9}$$

In terms of the *overall* heat transfer coefficient U_o, based on the outer area of the pipe we can express Eq. VII-9 as

$$\langle \bar{q}_r \rangle \pi D_o = \langle \bar{q}_r \rangle \pi D_i = U_o \pi D_o (T^{\text{I}} - T^{\text{II}}) \tag{VII-10}$$

Making use of Eq. VII-10 we can rewrite Eqs. VII-7 and VII-8 as

$$\frac{dT^{\text{I}}}{dz} = -\left(\frac{U_o \pi D_o}{\dot{m}_{\text{I}} c_p^{\text{I}}}\right)(T^{\text{I}} - T^{\text{II}}) \tag{VII-11}$$

$$\frac{dT^{\text{II}}}{dz} = -\left(\frac{U_o \pi D_o}{\dot{m}_{\text{II}} c_p^{\text{II}}}\right)(T^{\text{I}} - T^{\text{II}}) \tag{VII-12}$$

†For a more detailed discussion see Sec. 11.1.

‡Note that this result is correct only if q_z in the pipe wall is negligible compared to q_r.

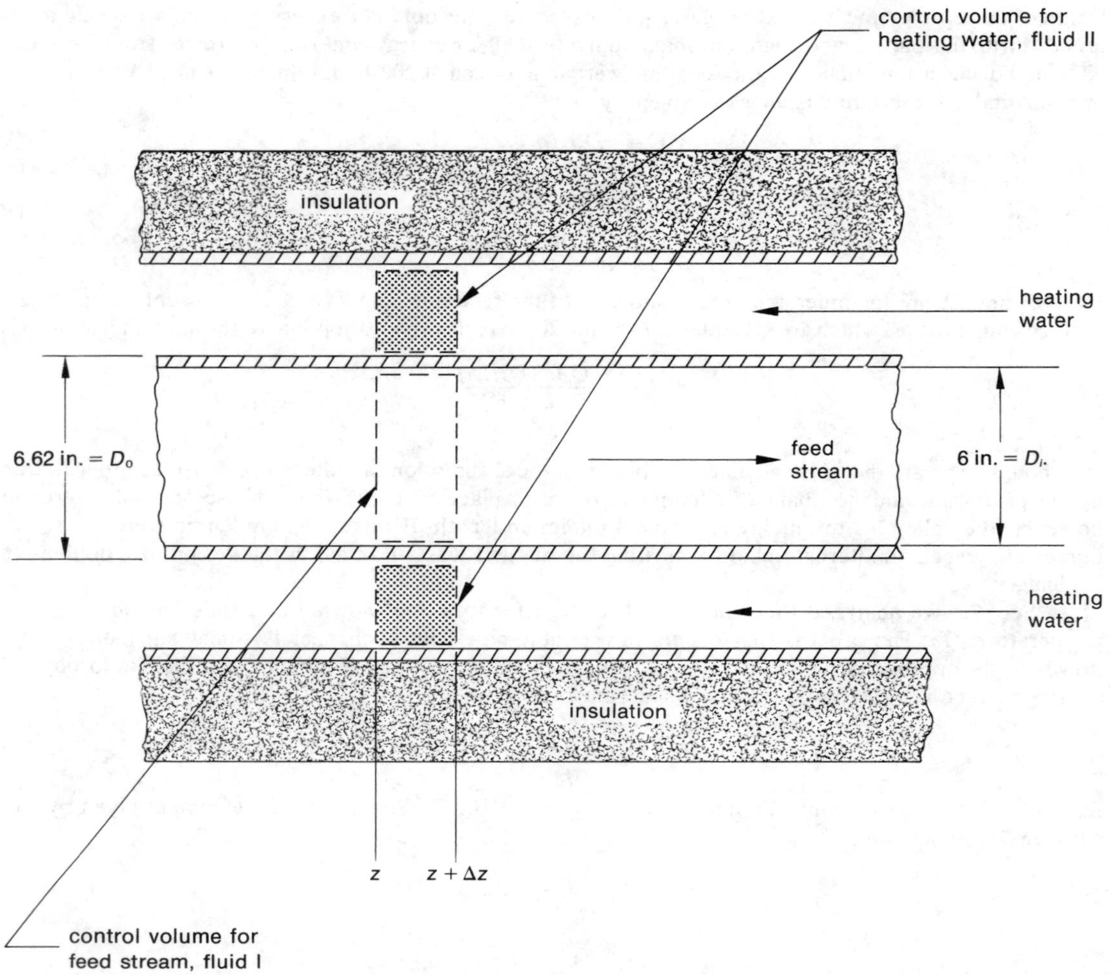

Fig. VII.2 Control volumes for double-pipe heat exchanger.

Subtracting Eq. VII-12 from Eq. VII-11 leads to a differential equation for the difference between the temperatures of the two streams.

$$\frac{d}{dz}(T^{\mathrm{I}} - T^{\mathrm{II}}) = U_o \pi D_o \left[\frac{1}{\dot{m}_{\mathrm{II}} c_p^{\mathrm{II}}} - \frac{1}{\dot{m}_{\mathrm{I}} c_p^{\mathrm{I}}}\right)(T^{\mathrm{I}} - T^{\mathrm{II}}) \tag{VII-13}$$

Referring to Fig. VII.1 we see that the point at which the oil stream enters the exchanger is denoted by "1" and the exit is denoted by "2". This leads to boundary conditions for Eq. VII-13 of the form

B.C.1 $$T^{\mathrm{I}} - T^{\mathrm{II}} = T_1^{\mathrm{I}} - T_1^{\mathrm{II}}, \qquad z = 0 \tag{VII-14}$$

B.C.2 $$T^{\mathrm{I}} - T^{\mathrm{II}} = T_2^{\mathrm{I}} - T_2^{\mathrm{II}}, \qquad z = L \tag{VII-15}$$

however, only one of the boundary conditions is independent since the second can always be obtained from the first by the overall energy balance

$$\dot{Q} = \dot{m}_{\mathrm{I}} c_p^{\mathrm{I}}(T_2^{\mathrm{I}} - T_1^{\mathrm{I}}) = \dot{m}_{\mathrm{II}} c_p^{\mathrm{II}}(T_2^{\mathrm{II}} - T_1^{\mathrm{II}}) \tag{VII-16}$$

Separating variables and integrating Eq. VII-13 from $z = 0$ to $z = L$ gives

$$\ln\left(\frac{T_2^{\mathrm{I}} - T_2^{\mathrm{II}}}{T_1^{\mathrm{I}} - T_1^{\mathrm{II}}}\right) = U_o \pi D_o \left(\frac{1}{\dot{m}_{\mathrm{II}} c_p^{\mathrm{II}}} - \frac{1}{\dot{m}_{\mathrm{I}} c_p^{\mathrm{I}}}\right) L \tag{VII-17}$$

We can now use Eq. VII-16 to eliminate $\dot{m}_I c_p^{\mathrm{I}}$ and $\dot{m} c_p^{\mathrm{II}}$ from Eq. VII-17 and obtain an expression for $\dot{Q}$

$$\dot{Q} = U_o A_o \left[\frac{(T_2^{\mathrm{II}} - T_2^{\mathrm{I}}) - (T_1^{\mathrm{II}} - T_1^{\mathrm{I}})}{\ln\left(\dfrac{T_2^{\mathrm{II}} - T_2^{\mathrm{I}}}{T_1^{\mathrm{II}} - T_1^{\mathrm{I}}}\right)} \right] \tag{VII-18}$$

Here A_o represents the *outer* area, $\pi D_o L$, of the feed pipeline, and U_o is referred to as the overall heat transfer coefficient *based on the outer area.* One can easily show that

$$U_o A_o = U_i A_i \tag{VII-19}$$

so that Eq. VII-18 can be expressed as

$$\dot{Q} = U_o A_o \Delta T_{\ln} = U_i A_i \Delta T_{\ln} \tag{VII-20}$$

where $\Delta T_{\ln}$ is the log-mean temperature difference given by

$$\Delta T_{\ln} = \frac{(T_2^{\mathrm{II}} - T_2^{\mathrm{I}}) - (T_1^{\mathrm{II}} - T_1^{\mathrm{I}})}{\ln\left\{\dfrac{T_2^{\mathrm{II}} - T_2^{\mathrm{I}}}{T_1^{\mathrm{II}} - T_1^{\mathrm{I}}}\right\}} \tag{VII-21}$$

In the problem we are attacking here $\dot{Q}$ is given by Eqs. VII-1 and VII-2 and we seek an expression for L which can be written as

$$L = \dot{Q} / U_o \pi D_o \Delta T_{\ln} \tag{VII-22}$$

The log-mean temperature can be determined by noting that

$$T_2^{\mathrm{II}} = 200°\mathrm{F}, \qquad T_1^{\mathrm{I}} = 74°\mathrm{F}, \qquad T_2^{\mathrm{I}} = 80°\mathrm{F}$$

and that the single unspecified temperature can be determined by Eq. VII-16 which can be rearranged to yield

$$T_1^{\mathrm{II}} = T_2^{\mathrm{II}} - \left(\frac{\dot{Q}}{\dot{m}_{\mathrm{II}} c_p^{\mathrm{II}}}\right) \tag{VII-23}$$

Carrying out the calculation we find that $T_1^{\mathrm{II}} = 193°\mathrm{F}$ and the log-mean temperature is given by

$$\Delta T_{\ln} = 119.5°\mathrm{F} \tag{VII-24}$$

Note that the log-mean temperature difference lies between the temperature difference at the inlet (119°F) and the temperature difference at the exit (120°F).

We now know each term on the right-hand-side of Eq. VII-22 except for U_o. This means we must determine the film heat transfer coefficients for the oil and water before we can specify the length of the exchanger. We begin with the oil stream and calculate the Reynolds number and Prandtl number

$$N_{\mathrm{Re}}^{\mathrm{I}} = 41.5$$
$$N_{\mathrm{Pr}}^{\mathrm{I}} = 1520$$

Since the flow of the oil is laminar we need to use the Sieder–Tate correlation given by

$$N_{\mathrm{Nu}} = 1.86 N_{\mathrm{Re}}^{1/3} N_{\mathrm{Pr}}^{1/3} (L/D)^{-1/3} (\mu_b/\mu_0)^{0.14} \tag{VII-25}$$

and compared with experimental data in Fig. 7.6.1. Here we see that we should know (μ_b/μ_0) and L/D in order to determine the Nusselt number and therefore the heat transfer coefficient; however, we are given no information on the temperature dependence of the viscosity of the oil, therefore, we are forced to take $(\mu_b/\mu_0) = 1$. Since $\mu_b > \mu_0$ this will tend to underestimate the magnitude of the heat transfer coefficient. Determination of L/D will require a trial-and-error calculation, and on the basis of the minimum length given by Eq. VII-5 as 0.32 ft we will take L to be 5 ft for the first trial. This gives

$$L/D = (5\ \mathrm{ft}/0.5\ \mathrm{ft}) = 10, \qquad \text{for the first trial} \tag{VII-26}$$

The Nusselt number for the oil is now given by

$$\begin{aligned} N_{\mathrm{Nu}} &= (1.86)(41.5)^{1/3}(1520)^{1/3}/(10)^{1/3} \\ &= 34.4 \end{aligned} \tag{VII-27}$$

and the film heat transfer coefficient is

$$h^{\mathrm{I}} = 34.4k/D = 7.6\ \text{Btu/hr ft}^2\,°\text{F} \tag{VII-28}$$

We must now consider the film heat transfer coefficient for the water flowing in the annular region. The correlations that we presented in Sec. 7.6 were for pipes; however, they give reasonably good results for noncircular conduits provided the Reynolds number and Nusselt number are defined in terms of the hydraulic diameter, D_h,

$$N_{\text{Re}} = \frac{\rho \langle v_z \rangle D_h}{\mu}$$

$$N_{\text{Nu}} = \frac{hD_h}{k} \tag{VII-29}$$

The hydraulic diameter is defined as

$$D_h = 4\,\frac{\text{cross-sectional area for flow}}{\text{wetted perimeter}} \tag{VII-30}$$

and in our case D_h is given by

$$D_h = 1.38\ \text{in.} \tag{VII-31}$$

The Reynolds and Prandtl numbers for the water stream are given by

$$N_{\text{Re}}^{\text{II}} = 3550$$

$$N_{\text{Pr}}^{\text{II}} = 2.98$$

Since the flow is turbulent we can use Eq. 7.6-15, which is compared with experimental data in Fig. 7.6.2, to calculate the Nusselt number.

$$N_{\text{Nu}} = \frac{hD_h}{k} = 22.6 \tag{VII-32}$$

The value of the film heat transfer coefficient can now be determined as

$$h^{\text{II}} = 119\ \text{Btu/hr ft}^2\,°\text{F} \tag{VII-33}$$

Returning to Eqs. VII-9 and VII-10 we see that U_0 can be expressed as

$$U_o = \frac{1}{\dfrac{1}{h^{\text{I}}}\left(\dfrac{D_o}{D_i}\right) + \dfrac{D_o}{2k}\ln\left(\dfrac{D_o}{D_i}\right) + \dfrac{1}{h^{\text{II}}}} \tag{VII-34}$$

Substituting in the appropriate numerical values we find

$$U_o = \frac{\text{Btu/hr ft}^2\,°\text{F}}{\underset{\substack{\uparrow \\ \text{resistance in} \\ \text{the oil}}}{0.145} + \underset{\substack{\uparrow \\ \text{resistance in} \\ \text{the pipe}}}{0.00098} + \underset{\substack{\uparrow \\ \text{resistance in} \\ \text{the pipe}}}{0.0084}} \tag{VII-35}$$

Here we see that the resistance to heat transfer is almost all in the oil stream, and the resistance of the pipe wall is negligible. Completing the calculation yields

$$U_o = 6.32\ \text{Btu/hr ft}^2\,°\text{F} \tag{VII-36}$$

We are now in a position to carry out the calculation indicated by Eq. VII-22 to obtain

$$L = \left\{\frac{3.91 \times 10^5\ \text{Btu/day}}{(6.32\ \text{Btu/hr ft}^2\,°\text{F})(3.14)(6.62\ \text{in.})(119.5°\text{F})}\right\}\left\{\left(\frac{\text{day}}{24\ \text{hr}}\right)\left(\frac{12\ \text{in.}}{\text{ft}}\right)\right\} = 12.5\ \text{ft} \tag{VII-37}$$

We must remember at this point that we used a length of 5 ft in calculating the log-mean Nusselt number for the oil stream. Using the value of 12.5 ft, Eq. VII-25 gives

$$N_{\text{Nu}} = 25.3, \qquad \text{for the oil stream}$$

and we recalculate to overall heat transfer coefficient to be

$$U_o = 4.72\ \text{Btu/hr ft}^2\,°\text{F}, \qquad \text{based on } L = 12.5\ \text{ft}$$

Using this result in Eq. VII-37 leads to

$$L = 16.7\ \text{ft}, \qquad \text{second trial}$$

A third trial leads to

$$L = 18.2\ \text{ft}, \qquad \text{third trial}$$

and we estimate that a 19 ft long double-pipe heat exchanger will be sufficient.

PROBLEMS†

VII-1. Insulation having a thermal conductivity of 0.08 Btu/hrft°F is available for insulating the double-pipe heat exchanger. Specify the thickness of insulation required in order that Eq. VII-8, which neglects energy losses to the surroundings, be a satisfactory approximation for the temperature of the water stream.

VII-2. Derive an expression for $\langle q_r \rangle$ so that Eq. VII-4c can be obtained from either Eq. VII-4a or Eq. VII-4b.

VII-3. Derive Eq. VII-7 beginning with Eq. 7.3-8. Carefully list your assumptions.

VII-4. Derive Eq. VII-18 from Eqs. VII-16 and VII-17.

VII-5. Prove that $U_oA_o = U_iA_i$.

VII-6. Prove that Eq. VII-21 yields

$$\Delta T_{\ln} = (T_2^{\text{II}} - T_2^{\text{I}}) \quad \text{or} \quad \Delta T_{\ln} = (T_1^{\text{II}} - T_1^{\text{I}})$$

when

$$(T_2^{\text{II}} - T_2^{\text{I}}) = (T_1^{\text{II}} - T_1^{\text{I}})$$

VII-7. Given two values of the viscosity of the oil

$$\mu = 200\ \text{centipoise}, \qquad T = 70°\text{F}$$

$$\mu = 80\ \text{centipoise}, \qquad T = 100°\text{F}$$

rework Design Problem VII so as to include the effect of (μ_b/μ_0) in calculating the heat transfer coefficient for the oil.

VII-8. Calculate the length of the double-pipe heat exchanger if the oil and the heating water are flowing in the same direction.

VII-9. Estimate the effect of reversible work and viscous dissipation on the temperature of the oil stream. Use the order-of-magnitude analysis described in Sec. 2.9, and follow the development presented in Sec. 5.5 or in Ex. 7.5-1.

VII-10. Perform an order-of-magnitude analysis to justify the assumption $q_z \ll q_r$ that led to Eq. VII-9.

7-1. (7.1) Derive Eq. 7.1-8 by integrating Eq. 7-1 over a volume, $\mathscr{V}$, fixed in space.

7-2. (7.2) Prove Eq. 7.2-3 by expanding the right-hand-side and making use of the continuity equation. Use of index notation might be helpful.

7-3. (7.3) Sometimes compressible flows (Mach number near 1) are more easily analyzed in terms of the macroscopic total energy balance rather than the thermal energy balance. Derive the macroscopic total energy balance starting with Eq. 5.3-6 and indicate why the terms in your result might be more susceptible to macroscopic interpretation than some of the terms in Eq. 7.3-8.

7-4. (7.3) In going from Eq. 7.3-3 to Eq. 7.3-4 we assumed that c_p was constant. Use order-of-magnitude analysis (see Sec. 2.9) to determine how small $(\partial c_p/\partial T)$ must be in order that Eq. 7.3-4 be valid. Use a dimensionless temperature defined by $\Theta = (T - T_0)/(T_1 - T_0)$ where T_0 is the lowest temperature and T_1 is the highest.

7-5. (7.3) Show that $\overline{\nabla \mathbf{v} : \boldsymbol{\tau}}$ is satisfactorily approximated by $\nabla \bar{\mathbf{v}} : \bar{\boldsymbol{\tau}}$, and develop a similar form for $\overline{T\beta(Dp/Dt)}$.

†Problems numbered VII-1, VII-2, etc. deal directly with Design Problem VII, and problems marked with an asterisk (*) are concerned with the solved example problems.

7-6. (7.4) Derive Eq. 7.4-13 starting with the general macroscopic mass balance given by Eq. 7.1-4.

7-7. (7.4) Prove that $\bar{T}_b = \langle \bar{T} \rangle$ for a flat velocity profile.

7-8. (7.4) Show how Eq. 7.4-19 is obtained from Eq. 7.4-18.

7-9. (7.4) Show how Eq. 7.4-20 results from Eq. 7.4-19 and the order-of-magnitude estimates given in the text.

7-10. (7.4) What is the difference between the Nusselt number and the Biot number encountered in Chapter 2? Are they related through another dimensionless number?

***7-11.** (7.4) In Ex. 7.4-1 we used Eq. 7.4-26 to calculate the overall rate of heat transfer. Use of Eq. 7.4-26 requires that the restriction indicated by Eq. 7.4-20 be valid. Determine if this is true for the system considered in Ex. 7.4-1. Take the thermal conductivity of straw oil to be 0.078 Btu/hr ft °F.

***7-12.** (7.4) If the average temperature difference, $T_0 - (T_{b1} + T_{b2})/2$, is used to calculate the film heat transfer coefficient in Ex. 7.4-1, what value of h is obtained? In this case the film heat transfer coefficient would be defined by $h_{av} = \dot{Q}/A\,\Delta T_{av}$.

7-13. (7.5) Repeat the dimensional analysis given in Sec. 7.5 for the case where the wall temperature is not constant, but is a linear function of the distance along the pipe, i.e.,

$$T = T_0 + \beta z, \qquad r = r_0 + e(\theta z)$$

where β has units of degrees per unit length.

***7-14.** (7.5) Use the results given in Ex. 7.5-1 to see whether it was satisfactory to neglect compressible work and viscous dissipation in the analysis given in Ex. 7.4-1. The friction factor can be determined by the Blasins equation $f = 0.079/N_{Re}^{1/4}$ if the flow is turbulent and $f = 16/N_{Re}$ if the flow is laminar. The additional physical property data are given as

$$\rho = 54.8\ \text{lb}_m/\text{ft}^3$$
$$k = 0.078\ \text{Btu/hr ft °F}$$
$$\beta = 9.1 \times 10^{-4}\,°\text{C}^{-1}$$
$$\mu = 15.8\ \text{centipoise}$$

7-15. (7.6) Sketch the laminar velocity profiles for heating and cooling a liquid in a tube under conditions such that significant variations in viscosity occur. Indicate which process would yield the larger film heat transfer coefficient.

***7-16.** (7.6) In the correlation for variable viscosity fluids we used the approximation

$$\frac{1}{\mu_0}\left(\frac{\partial \mu}{\partial \Theta}\right) \sim \left(\frac{\mu_b}{\mu_0} - 1\right)$$

Use the data given in Ex. 7.6-1 to evaluate $(\partial\mu/\partial\Theta)$ at the wall and compare the two terms listed above.

***7-17.** (7.6) If the surface temperature is lowered from 90°F to 60°F in Ex. 7.6-1, what is the required tube length?

***7-18.** (7.6) How many 5 ft long tubes would be required to accomplish the same amount of cooling as the single tube discussed in Ex. 7.6-1. Remember that the velocity in the 5-ft tubes would be (3 ft/sec)/N where N is the number of tubes.

7-19. (7.6) In Sec. 7.6 an empirical expression was presented for laminar flow heat transfer in a tube. This expression is given by Eq. 7.6-11 and is restricted by the conditions $N_{Re}N_{Pr}(L/D) > 100$ and $N_{Nu,ln} > 3.66$. For short tubes the temperature disturbance caused by the heating or cooling does not propagate far into the fluid stream, i.e., $\delta_T \ll r_0$. If the product, $N_{Re}N_{Pr}$, is large enough or the ratio, L/D, is small enough, the thermal boundary layer is confined to a region very near the wall. Under these circumstances a boundary layer analysis can be performed and the effect of curvature neglected. Perform such an analysis, following the approach used in Chapter 5, and develop an expression for the Nusselt number. Compare this expression with Eq. 7.6-11. Remember that the log-mean film heat transfer coefficient is related to the local film heat transfer coefficient by Eq. 7.6-16.

7-20. (7.6) Nitrogen at atmospheric pressure is to be heated from 60°F to 120°F in smooth-walled tubes whose inside walls are maintained at 140°F. If the inner diameter is $\frac{3}{4}$ in. and the average velocity of the nitrogen is 28 ft/sec, what is the required tube length? If a shorter tube is required to accomplish the same degree of heating for the same volumetric flow rate, should the tube diameter be smaller or larger than $\frac{3}{4}$ in.?

7-21. (7.6) Liquid sodium is to be circulated through $\frac{1}{2}$-in. diameter tubes for cooling a nuclear reactor. The liquid metal inlet temperature and velocity are to be 600°F and 30 ft/sec. If the tubes are 3 ft long and have an inside surface temperature of 700°F, determine the temperature rise of the sodium and the energy gained per unit mass of the liquid metal.

7-22. (7.7) Consider an infinitely long cylinder of radius r_0 with a surface temperature fixed at T_0. If the temperature at $r \to \infty$ in the media surrounding the cylinder is designated at T_∞, prove that at steady state $T_\infty = T_0$ for the case where $\mathbf{v} = 0$.

7-23. (7.7) Use dimensional analysis to show that Eq. 7.7-18 represents a reasonable criterion for neglecting the effect of free convection.

7-24. (7.7) Repeat Prob. 7-22 for a sphere in an infinite, stagnant media to prove Eq. 7.7-19.

7-25. (7.7) Explain why the bulk temperature defined by Eq. 7.7-3 is equal to T_∞.

7-26. (7.7) Air at atmospheric pressure and 90°F flows past a flat plate maintained at 600°F. The plate is 3 ft long and the air velocity is 105 ft/sec. Find the heat transferred from the plate, per foot of width.

7-27. (7.7) Water at 100°F flows at a velocity of 14 ft/sec past a steam-heated tube 1 in. in diameter. If the outside surface of the tube is 187°F, find the heat transfer per unit length of tube.

7-28. (7.7) Metal spheres $\frac{1}{2}$ in. in diameter at a temperature of 225°F are dropped into a pool of water at 78°F for cooling after a machining process. If the spheres settle at a velocity of 4 ft/sec, calculate the film heat transfer coefficient and the initial rate of heat transfer.

***7-29.** (7.7) In Ex. 7.7-1 a crude analysis indicated that a flow rate of over 7 qts/min must be maintained in order to prevent freezing overnight. This flow rate could certainly be reduced if the water pipe was insulated. Estimate a new flow rate for the case where the water pipe is insulated with newspaper. The daily edition of the *Mountain Gazette*, when wrapped around the pipe, will provide a $\frac{1}{4}$ in. thick insulating layer with a thermal conductivity on the order of 0.04 Btu/hr ft °F. Neglect any resistance to heat transfer in the water and pipe wall.

***7-30.** (7.7) In Ex. 7.7-1 we assumed that the outer surface of the pipe was at 4°C in order to calculate the heat lost to the surrounding air. A more accurate analysis would take into account the resistance to heat transfer of the water film, and the pipe wall. The inner diameter of the pipe is 1.73 in. and the thermal conductivity is 23 Btu/hr ft °F. In a more exact analysis one would want to know the temperature at the water–pipe interface at the point where it enters the cabin. The minimum flow rate could then be specified by setting this temperature equal to 0°C. The attack on this problem should follow the procedure given in Sec. 7.4, i.e., a differential balance is required. Keep in mind that the bulk water temperature is not the temperature at the interface, and that a trial-and-error solution is required since the inside film heat transfer coefficient depends on the flow rate. Neglect axial conduction in the pipe and determine the minimum flow rate required to keep the water from freezing.

7-31. A wire is to be heated from 70°F to 200°F by blowing hot air past it as shown in Fig. 7.31. If the length of the

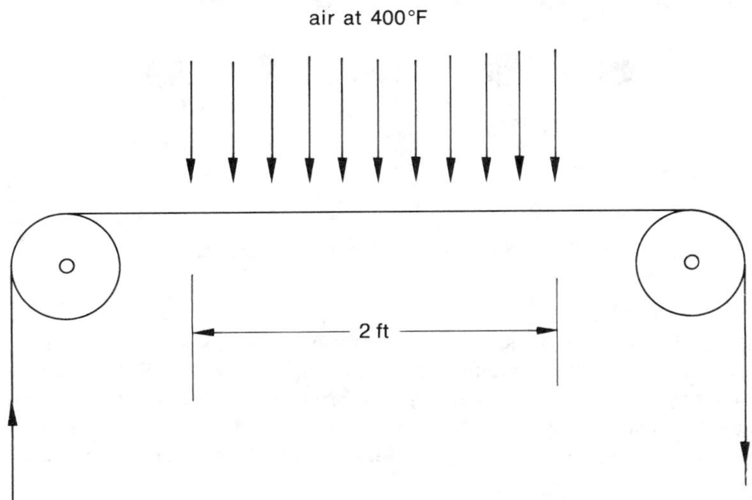

Fig. 7.31 Wire heating device.

(7.7) heating section is 2 ft, determine the wire velocity required in order to accomplish the desired heating. Assume that the air temperature is constant at 400°F and the temperature of the wire is uniform at any cross section ($N_{Bi} \ll 1$). Neglect axial conduction, and take the air velocity to be 100 ft/sec. The properties of the wire are

$$D = 0.0875 \text{ in.}$$
$$\rho = 488 \text{ lb}_m/\text{ft}^3$$
$$c_p = 0.11 \text{ Btu/lb}_m\,°\text{F}$$
$$k = 9.4 \text{ Btu/hr ft °F}$$

***7-32.** (7.8) In Ex. 7.8-1 the macroscopic thermal energy balance is applied to the tube bundle in order to obtain Eq. 3. List the assumptions that are made in order to simplify the macroscopic thermal energy balance.

7-33. (7.8) Express a_v in terms of ϵ for a packed bed of spheres.

***7-34.** (7.8) If the oil under consideration in Ex. 7.8-1 is to be heated to 110°F, how many rows of tubes are required?

7-35. (7.8) A heat exchanger is to consist of 300 tubes 5 ft long and 1 in. in outer diameter. The tubes are to be arranged in 15 staggered rows with transverse and longitudinal pitch of 2 in. For a tube surface temperature of 210°F and air at atmospheric pressure and 95°F flowing normal to the tube bank at a superficial velocity of 20 ft/sec, determine the total rate of heat transfer.

7-36. (7.8) An automobile radiator is constructed of six rows of staggered tubes as illustrated in Fig. 7.36. There are twenty tubes in each row. Water at about 200°F is pumped through each tube at a high enough rate so that the resistance to heat transfer inside the tubes is negligible and the water temperature is nearly constant at 200°F. The resistance to heat transfer in the tube walls can also be neglected so that the outside surface of the tubes are maintained at 200°F. If the average air velocity in the tube bundle is 60 ft/sec, what is the total rate of heat transfer from the radiator to the air if the ambient air temperature is 76°F and the tubes are 18 in. long? If it is necessary to *increase* the total rate of heat transfer, while maintaining the longitudinal and transverse pitch constant and keeping the mass velocity constant, should the tube diameter be increased or decreased?

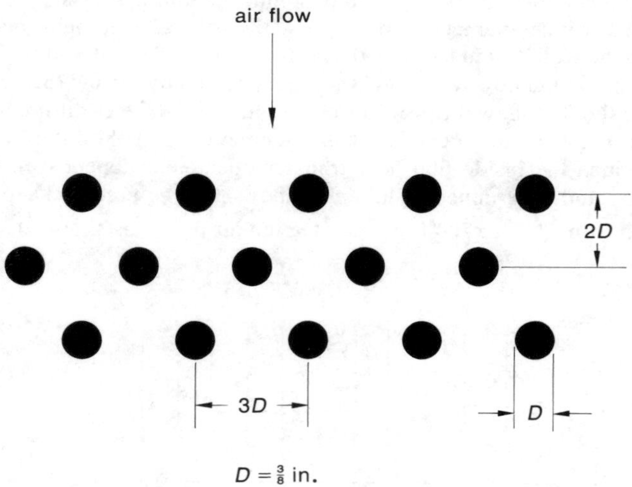

Fig. 7.36 Automobile radiator tube configuration.

7-37. (7.9) In the central valley of California the summer temperatures can reach 110°F and air conditioners are in steady use trying to maintain home and office temperatures at a comfortable 72°F. Much of the heat transfer in homes takes place at the large glass doors which are used to bring the outdoors indoors on more pleasant days. If the doors are 7 ft high, with glass ($k = 0.4$ Btu/hr ft^2°F) $\frac{1}{4}$ in. thick, and the inner surface of the glass is maintained at 80°F, what is the rate of heat transfer per square foot of glass door when the outside temperature is 110°F and the air is still?

7-38. (7.9) A horizontal steam pipe passes through a room in which the ambient air temperature is 80°F. If the outer diameter of the pipe is 4 in. and the surface temperature is 800°F, what is the heat loss *owing to natural convection* per foot of pipe?

7-39. (7.9) Repeat Prob. 7-28 for the case where the velocity of the sphere is zero.

***7-40.** (7.9) Estimate the transient time for the process described in Ex. 7.9-1.

***7-41.** (7.9) In Ex. 7.9-1 the energy loss owing to radiation was neglected. Use Eq. 3 to include the effect of radiant energy exchange and recalculate the fractional energy loss, η.

***7-42.** (7.9) In Ex. 7.9-1 the outer surface of the pipe was assumed to be 140°F. Take into account the resistance to heat transfer in the water film and the pipe wall in order to calculate the outer surface temperature.

***7-43.** (7.9) Use the calculated value of the Nusselt number in Ex. 7.9-1 in order to obtain a value of h. Compare this value with those listed in Table 1.3-1.

REFERENCES

1. Whitaker, S., *Introduction to Fluid Mechanics*, Prentice-Hall, Inc., Englewood Cliffs, N.J., 1968.
2. Sleicher, C. A., and Tribus, M., "Heat Transfer in a Pipe with Turbulent Flow and Arbitrary Wall-Temperature Distribution," *Trans. ASME* **79**, 789 (1957).
3. Webb, R. L., Eckert, E. R. G., and Goldstein, R. J., "Heat Transfer and Friction in Tubes with Repeated-Rib Roughness," *Int. J. Heat Mass Transfer* **14**, 601 (1971).
4. Schneider, P. J., "Effect of Axial Fluid on Heat Transfer in the Entrance Regions of Parallel Plates and Tubes," *Trans. ASME* **79**, 765 (1957).
5. Graetz, L., *Ann. d. Physik* **25**, 337–357 (1885).
6. Jakob, M., *Heat Transfer*, Vol. I, John Wiley & Sons, Inc., New York, 1949.
7. Sieder, E. N., and Tate, G. E., "Heat Transfer and Pressure Drop of Liquids in Tubes," *Ind. Eng. Chem.* **28**, 1429–1435 (1936).
8. Drew, T. B., "Heat Transfer in Streamline Flow," *Ind. Eng. Chem.* **24**, 152 (1932).
9. Colburn, A. P., and Coghlan, C. A., "Heat Transfer to Hydrogen–Nitrogen Mixtures Inside Tubes," *Trans. ASME* **63**, 561 (1941).
10. Hausen, H., "Darstellung des Warmenberganges in Rohren durch verallgemeinerte Potenzbeziehungen," *Zeit. V.D.I. Beihefte Verfahrenstechnik* **4**, 91 (1943).
11. Sellars, J. R., Tribus, M., and Klein, J. S., "Heat Transfer to Laminar Flow in a Round Tube or a Flat Conduit—The Graetz Problem Extended," *Trans. ASME* **78**, 441 (1956).
12. Pigford, R. L., "Nonisothermal Flow and Heat Transfer Inside Vertical Tubes," *Chem. Engr. Prog. Symposium Series* **51**, 79 (1955).
13. Shannon, R. L., and Depew, C. A., "Forced Laminar Flow Convection in a Horizontal Tube with Variable Viscosity and Free Convection Effects," *Trans. ASME* **91C**, 251 (1969).
14. Knudsen, J. G., and Katz, D. L., *Fluid Dynamics and Heat Transfer*, McGraw-Hill Book Co., Inc., New York, 1958.
15. Christiansen, E. B., Jensen, G. E., and Tao, F. S., "Laminar Flow Heat Transfer," *AIChE Journal* **12**, 1196 (1966).
16. Friend, W. L., and Metzner, A. B., "Turbulent Heat Transfer Inside Tubes and the Analogy Among Heat, Mass, and Momentum Transfer," *AIChE Journal* **4**, 393 (1958).
17. Lawrence, A. E., and Sherwood, T. K., "Heat Transmission to Water Flowing in Pipes," *Ind. Eng. Chem.* **23**, 301 (1931).
18. Morris, F. H., and Whitman, W. G., "Heat Transfer for Oils and Water in Pipes," *Ind. Eng. Chem.* **20**, 234 (1928).
19. Sherwood, T. K., and Petrie, J. M., "Heat Transmission to Liquids Flowing in Pipes," *Ind. Eng. Chem.* **24**, 736 (1932).
20. Deissler, R. G., and Eian, C. S., "Analytical and Experimental Investigation of Fully Developed Turbulent Flow of Air in a Smooth Tube with Variable Fluid Properties," *NACA Tech. Note. 2629*, 1952.
21. Hartnett, J. P., "Experimental Determination of the Thermal Entrance Length for the Flow of Water and Oil in Circular Pipes," *Trans. ASME* **77**, 1211 (1955).
22. Notter, R. H., and Sleicher, C. A., "A Solution to the Turbulent Graetz Problem—III. Fully Developed and Entry Region Heat Transfer Rates," *Chem. Eng. Sci.*
23. Schubauer, G. B., and Skramstad, H. K., "Laminar Boundary Layer Oscillations and Transition on a Flat Plate," *NACA Rept. 909*, 1949.
24. Zhukauskas, A. A., and Ambrazyavichyus, A. B., "Heat Transfer of a Plate in a Liquid Flow," *Int. J. Heat and Mass Transfer* **3**, 305 (1961).
25. Colburn, A. P., "A Method of Correlating Forced Convection Heat Transfer Data and a Comparison with Fluid Friction," *Trans. AIChE* **29**, 174 (1933).
26. Edwards, A., and Furber, B. N., "The Influence of Free-Stream Turbulence on Heat Transfer by Convection from an Isolated Region of a Plane Surface in Parallel Air Flow," *Proc. Inst. Mech. Engrs. (London)* **170**, 941 (1956).
27. Parmalee, G. V., and Huebscher, R. G., "Heat Transfer by Forced Convection Along a Smooth Flat Surface," *Heating, Piping, and Air Conditioning* **19**, No. 8, 115, Aug. 1947.
28. Thom, A., "The Flow Past Circular Cylinders at Low Speeds," *Proc. Roy. Soc.* **A141**, 651 (1933).
29. Acrivos, A., Snowden, D. D., Grove, A. S., and Petersen, E. E., "The Steady Separated Flow Past a Circular Cylinder at Large Reynolds Numbers," *J. Fluid Mech.* **21**, 737 (1965).
30. Richardson, P. D., "Estimation of the Heat Transfer from the Rear of an Immersed Body to the Region of Separated Flow," *WADD, TN-59-1*, 1968.
31. Churchill, S. W., and Brier, J. C., "Convective Heat Transfer from a Gas Stream at High Temperature to a Circular Cylinder Normal to the Flow," *Chem. Engr. Prog. Sym. Ser.* **51**, 57 (1955).
32. Davis, A. H., "Convective Cooling of Wires in Streams of Viscous Liquids," *Phil. Mag.* **47**, 1057 (1924).
33. Perkins, H. C., and Leppert, G., "Forced Convection Heat Transfer from Uniformly Heated Cylinder," *Journal of Heat Transfer, Trans. ASME, Series C* **84**, 257 (1962).
34. Piret, E. L., James, W., and Stacy, M., "Heat Transmission from Fine Wires to Water," *I & EC* **39**, 1098 (1947).
35. Fand, R. M., "Heat Transfer by Forced Convection from a Cylinder to Water in Crossflow," *Int. J. Heat Mass Transfer* **8**, 995 (1965).
36. King, L. V., "On the Convection of Heat from Small Cylinders in a Stream of Fluid," *Phil. Trans. Roy. Soc. (London)* **214**, 373 (1914).
37. Hilpert, Von R., "Warmeabgabe von Geheizten Drahten und Rohren im Luftstrom," *Forsch. Gebiete Ingenieurw.* **4**, 215 (1933).
38. Collis, D. C., and Williams, M. J., "Two-Dimensional Convection from Heated Wires at Low Reynolds Numbers," *J. Fluid Mech.* **6**, 357 (1959).

39. Kramers, H., "Heat Transfer from Spheres to a Flowing Media," *Physica* **12**, 61 (1946).
40. Vliet, G. C., and Leppert, G., "Forced Convection Heat Transfer from an Isothermal Sphere to Water," *Trans. ASME* **83C**, 163 (1961).
41. Yuge, T., "Experiments on Heat Transfer from Spheres Including Combined Natural and Forced Convection," *Trans. ASME* **82C**, 214 (1960).
42. McAdams, W. H., *Heat Transmission*, Third Edition, McGraw-Hill Book Co., Inc., New York, 1954.
43. Whitaker, S., "Advances in the Theory of Fluid Motion in Porous Media," *I & EC* **61**, 14 (1969).
44. Gamson, B. W., Thodos, G., and Hougen, O. A., "Heat, Mass, and Momentum Transfer in the Flow of Gases Through Granular Solids," *Trans. AIChE* **39**, 1 (1943).
45. Glaser, M. B., and Thodos, G., "Heat and Momentum Transfer in the Flow of Gases Through Packed Beds," *AIChE J.* **4**, 63 (1958).
46. McConnachie, J. T. L., and Thodos, G., "Transfer Processes in the Flow of Gases Through Packed and Distended Beds of Spheres," *AIChE J.* **9**, 60 (1963).
47. Taecker, R. G., and Hougen, O. A., "Heat, Mass Transfer of Gas Film in Flow of Gases Through Commercial Tower Packings," *Chem. Engr. Prog.* **45**, 188 (1949).
48. Wilke, C. R., and Hougen, O. A., "Mass Transfer in the Flow of Gases through Granular Solids Extended to Low Modified Reynolds," *Trans. AIChE* **41**, 445 (1945).
49. Whitaker, S., "Forced Convection Heat Transfer Correlations for Flow in Pipes, Past Flat Plates, Single Cylinders, Single Spheres, and for Flow in Packed Beds and Tube Bundles," *AIChE Journal* **18**, 361 (1972).
50. Bergelin, O. P., Colburn, A. P., and Hull, H. L., "Heat Transfer and Pressure Drop During Viscous Flow Across Unbaffled Tube Banks," *Bulletin No. 2*, University of Delaware Engineering Experiment Station, June 1950.
51. Bergelin, O. P., Leighton, M. D., Lafferty, W. L., and Pigford, R. L., "Heat Transfer and Pressure Drop During Viscous and Turbulent Flow Across Baffled and Unbaffled Tube Banks," *Bulletin No. 4*, University of Delaware Engineering Experiment Station, April 1958.
52. Fairchild, H. N., and Welch, C. P., "Convection Heat Transfer and Pressure Drop of Air Flowing Across In-Line Tube Banks at Close Back Spacings," Paper No. 61-WA-250, presented at ASME Annual Winter Meeting, 1961.
53. Pierson, O. L., "Experimental Investigation of the Influence of Tube Arrangement on Convection Heat Transfer and Flow Resistance in Cross Flow of Gases Over Tube Banks," *Trans. ASME* **59**, 563 (1931).
54. Kays, W. M., London, A. L., and Lo, R. K., "Heat Transfer and Friction Characteristics for Gas Flow Normal to Tube Banks—Use of a Transient Test Technique," *Trans. ASME* **76**, 387 (1954).
55. Glidden, B. J., and Cranfield, R. R., "Gas Particle Heat Transfer Coefficients in Packed Beds at Reynolds Numbers Between 2 and 100," *British Chem. Engr.* **15**, 481 (1970).
56. Littman, H., Barile, R. G., and Pulsifer, A. H., "Gas-Particle Heat Transfer Coefficients in Packed Beds at Low Reynolds Numbers," *I & EC Fund. Quart.* **7**, 554 (1968).

Design Problem VIII

Water skiers at Lake Tahoe claim the lake is getting warmer every summer, and the hardiest of this group claims the water is colder every winter. Ecologists theorize that the "warmer in the summer, colder in the winter" trend is due to the increased algae concentration which is caused by the nutrients being dumped into the lake from sewage treatment plants and other sources. If the trend continues the lake will freeze in the winter, and the oxygen supplied to the lake will be reduced leading to irreversible changes in the ecology of the lake.

Explain why an increase in the algae concentration would lead to warmer surface water in the summer and colder surface water in the winter.

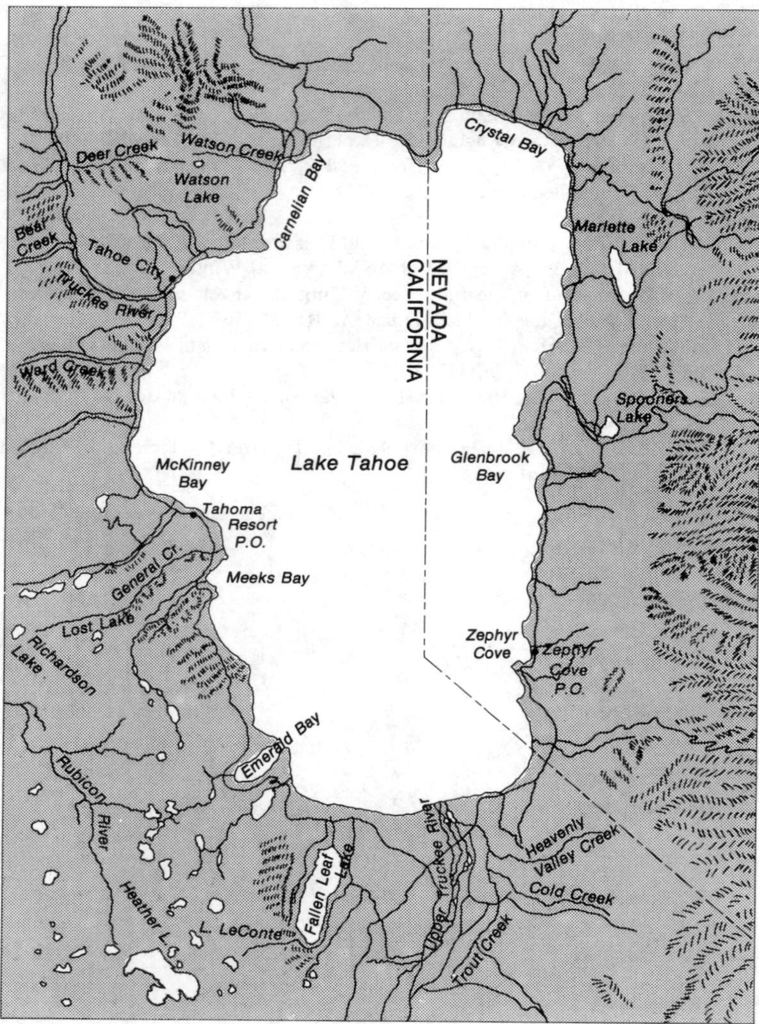

Fig. VIII Lake Tahoe: Elevation 6225 ft.

"It was a vast oval, and one would have to use up eighty or a hundred miles in traveling around it. As it lay there with the shadows of the mountains brilliantly photographed upon its still surface I thought it must surely be the fairest picture the whole earth affords."

Mark Twain's comments in 1861 upon seeing Lake Tahoe for the first time.

8
Thermal Radiation

Up to this point we have covered two modes of energy transfer: (1) energy transported by macroscopic motion, i.e., *convection*, and (2) energy transported by molecular motion, i.e., *conduction*. Both of these transport mechanisms require the presence of *matter*. We now turn our attention to energy transported by *radiation*, a mechanism which may take place in the absence of matter.† Although the subject of radiation has been delayed while we studied the more easily understood mechanisms of conduction and convection, we must not think of radiation as being any less important than these two mechanisms. The simple fact that all the earth's energy comes from the sun by radiation should stir our interest in this subject. Furthermore, our interest is demanded by the fact that subtle changes in the radiation balance between the earth, the sun, and the surrounding universe can lead to catastrophic events such as the ice ages[1], while the daily bombardment of the noxious gases over the Los Angeles basin by photons from the sun leads to a more immediate disaster[2]. For an engineer there is often an incentive to operate processes at high temperatures where the thermodynamic efficiency is improved or a chemical reaction is carried more closely to completion. At high temperatures radiation is often the dominant mechanism of heat transfer, thus it is important that we are able to accurately calculate radiant energy transport rates if we are to design high-temperature processes with confidence. While radiation and high temperatures usually go hand-in-hand we must not dismiss this mechanism at low temperatures, for any competent mountaineer negotiating the higher altitudes will always sleep under the "shade" of a tree or rock rather than participate in the esthetically pleasing but often bone-chilling experience of a night out under the stars.

*8.1 Electromagnetic Radiation

All bodies are capable of emitting electromagnetic radiation. At room temperature most bodies emit radiation in the infrared region at such low rates that the radiant energy emitted can often be neglected in heat transfer calculations. As the temperature of a body increases, the wavelength of the predominant radiation decreases and we pass from the infrared region to the red, white (all visible colors), and on to the violet and ultraviolet regions. As the wavelength decreases with increasing temperature, the rate of emission of electromagnetic energy increases and radiant energy transport becomes more important. The full spectrum of electromagnetic radiation is shown in Fig. 8.1.1. The radiation with wavelengths in the

†A more general point of view considers the photon gas to be a form of matter in the traditional sense.

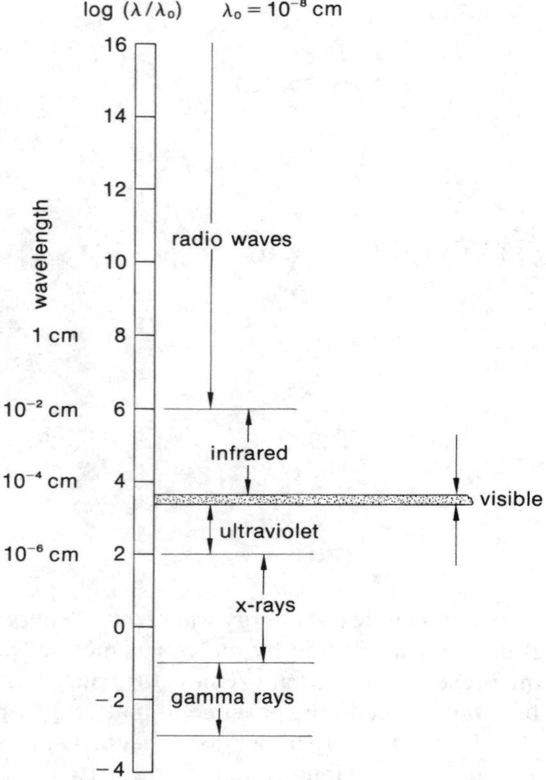

Fig. 8.1.1 Spectrum of electromagnetic radiation.

range of 10^{-2} cm to 5×10^{-5} cm is of the greatest concern to us for it is in this region that significant energy transfer usually takes place. Because of this, radiation ranging from the infrared to the ultraviolet is often referred to as *thermal radiation* in heat transfer texts. Thermal radiation in the visible spectrum has been studied by the students in physics courses, and there it is referred to simply as *light*.

We denote the velocity of propagation of electromagnetic waves in any medium by c. In a vacuum the value of c is given by

$$c = 3 \times 10^{10} \text{ cm/sec} = 186\,000 \text{ miles/sec}$$

The wavelength of electromagnetic radiation will be denoted by λ and the frequency is related to c and λ by the equation

$$\nu = c/\lambda \tag{8.1-1}$$

Throughout this chapter the symbol ν will be used to denote the frequency; there should be no confusion with the prior use of ν to indicate the kinematic viscosity, μ/ρ.

A complete understanding of the physics of electromagnetic radiation is rather difficult to obtain; the subject currently being the domain of the quantum-electrodynamacist. The engineer is in no position to delve into the physics of electromagnetic radiation to an extent which would do the subject justice, and in fact we need not, for a reasonable *picture* of radiation can be obtained without doing so. However, it is still wise to know upon what ice one is skating, and before going on to the development of a simplified theory of thermal radiation we had best try to set down what we do, and do not, understand about radiation.

From a previous course in physics the student has confronted the dual nature of light, i.e., it has both wave and particulate characteristics. We wish to briefly review these characteristics to clarify why the particular point of view taken in Sec. 8.2 can be followed in our analysis of thermal radiation. The wave nature of light was apparently confirmed in 1801 by Thomas Young by observing the interference pattern produced when light passed through two closely spaced, narrow slits. A schematic illustration of this experiment is shown in Fig. 8.1.2 which illustrates a beam of light striking two closely spaced slits and then impinging on a screen a large distance away from the slits. The maximum and minimum intensities observed on the screen can be explained by the wave nature of light, the maxima occurring where the waves emitted from the slits reinforce each other, and the minima occurring where the waves cancel. Such interference patterns are relatively easy to observe provided the beam is monochromatic, and they can be used to measure the wavelength of the light. The pattern that is observed results from relatively large amounts of light striking the screen, and an interesting question to ask is what happens when the intensity of the light source is reduced to a very low level. The result is shown in Fig. 8.1.3 for the case where a photographic plate is placed in the position of the screen for various times. At short times we see a pattern that surely results from *individual particles* of light striking the photographic plate. In fact, this experiment can be performed with such low light intensities that only one particle of light is striking the photographic plate at any given time. Clearly this experiment illustrates the particulate nature of the light, yet if a large enough number of these particles, called *photons*, strike the photographic plate an interference pattern is obtained and it is readily explainable only if we consider light to behave as a wave. Thus, in this single experiment we have seen both the particulate nature of light and the wave nature of light, and we have established that the wave properties of light are associated with each photon rather than with the entire beam. This same type of phenomenon can be visualized very nicely in a ripply tank in which water waves impinge upon a narrow slit. In Fig. 8.1.4 we have shown the diffraction pattern caused by a slit having a width slightly smaller than the wavelength of the water waves. A circular wave pattern emerges from the slit in the same way that circular light waves emerge from the two slits illustrated in Fig. 8.1.2. The diffraction pattern on the screen is interpreted in terms of the amplitudes of the waves adding so that when waves arrive in phase the amplitude is doubled and when they arrive 180° out of phase the amplitudes

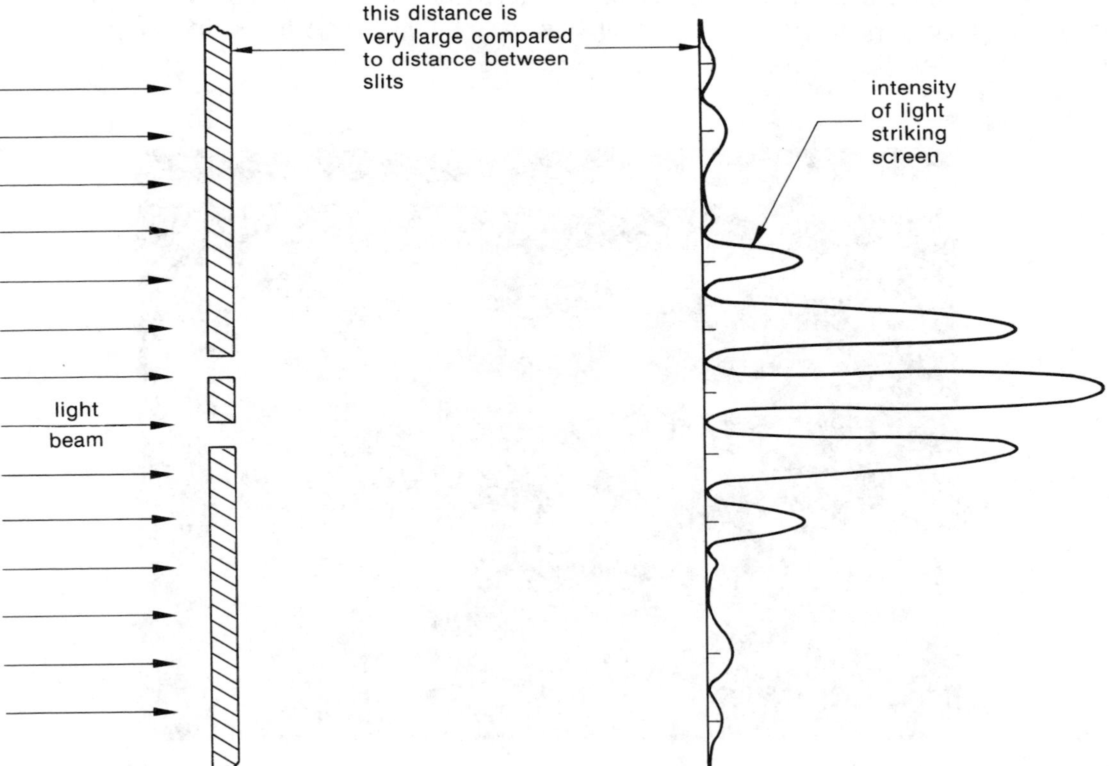

Fig. 8.1.2 The two-slit experiment.

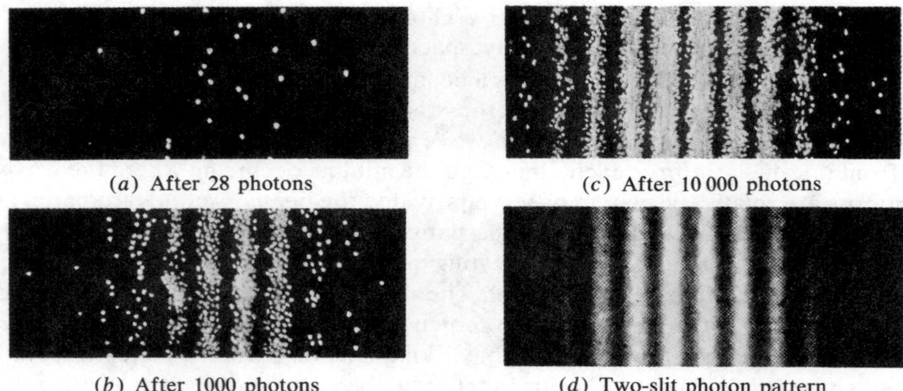

Fig. 8.1.3 Results for the two-slit experiment at very low light intensities. (Adapted from E. R. Huggins, *Physics I*, W. A. Benjamin, Inc., Menlo Park, California, 1968.)

cancel and the intensity is zero. In Fig. 8.1.5 we show what happens when the width of the slit is large compared to the wavelength of the water waves. Here we see that the waves pass through the slit with very little diffraction and travel in a straight line. Light waves behave in essentially the same manner as the water waves shown in Figs. 8.1.4 and 8.1.5. If the width of the slit is comparable to or smaller than the wavelength of the light, the *wave nature* of light is important and diffraction occurs. If the width of the slit is large compared to the wavelength of the light, the *particulate nature* of light prevails and the beam of light travels in a straight line.

Referring to Fig. 8.1.1 we see that we are primarily interested in electromagnetic radiation with wavelengths in the range of 10^{-2} cm to 5×10^{-5} cm. In the analysis of most engineering heat transfer processes, we are concerned with systems having characteristic dimensions much larger than 10^{-2} cm, thus we can disregard the wave nature of thermal radiation and treat the energy transport simply in terms of the transport of photons.

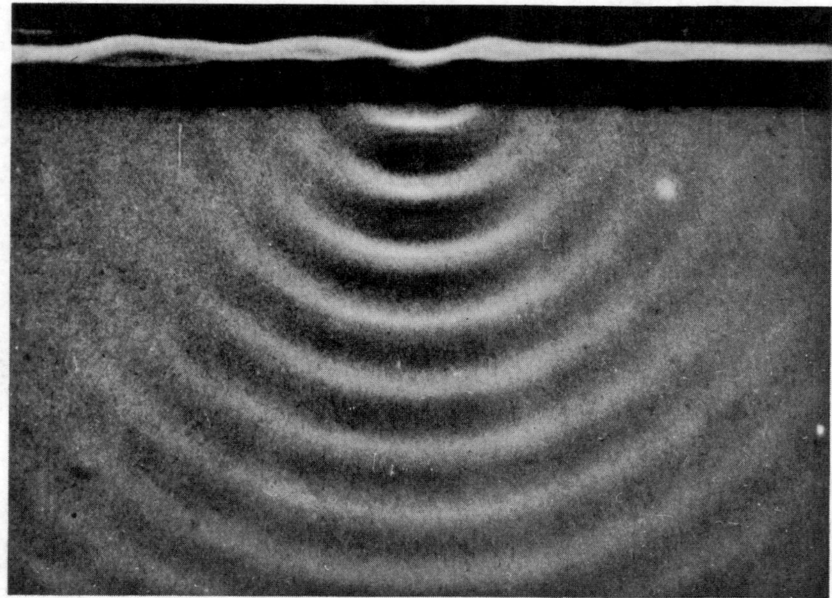

Fig. 8.1.4 Diffraction of water waves by a narrow slit. (From *PSSC Physics*, D. C. Heath and Company, Lexington, Mass., 1965.)

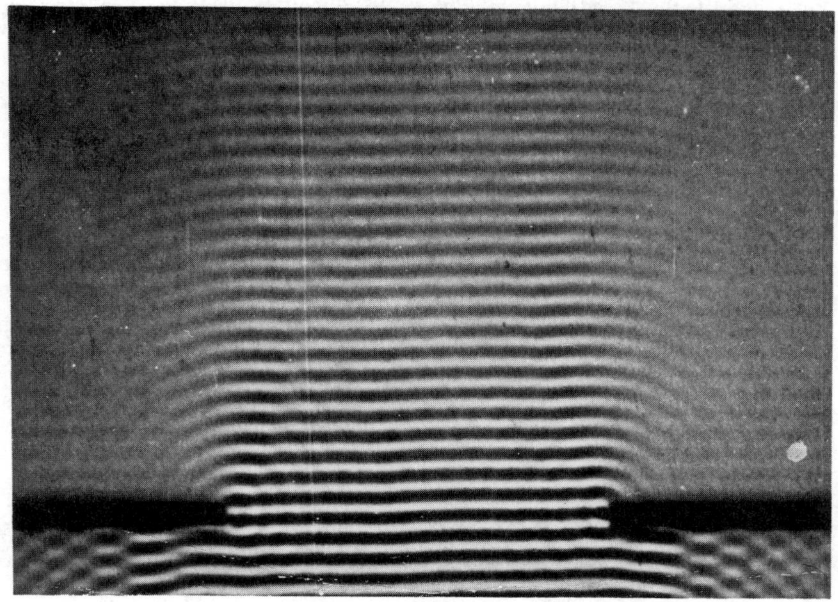

Fig. 8.1.5 Diffraction of water waves by a wide slit. (From *PSSC Physics*, D. C. Heath and Company, Lexington, Mass., 1965.)

Summary of Section 8.2

In this section we derive the photon transport equation. In terms of the photon density function, $n_{\lambda\omega}$, it takes the form

$$\frac{\partial n_{\lambda\omega}}{\partial t} + \nabla \cdot (n_{\lambda\omega} c \mathbf{\Omega}) = e_{\lambda\omega} - a_{\lambda\omega} \tag{8.2-4}$$

Here $n_{\lambda\omega}$ represents the number of photons per unit volume having wavelengths in the range λ to $\lambda + d\lambda$, and having flight paths within a solid angle $d\omega$ about the direction $\mathbf{\Omega}$. The terms $e_{\lambda\omega}$ and $a_{\lambda\omega}$ represent the rate of emission and absorption of these photons.

The energy of a photon having a wavelength λ or a frequency $\nu = c/\lambda$ is

$$\{\text{energy of a } \lambda\omega\text{-photon}\} = h\nu$$

where h is Planck's constant. Multiplication of Eq. 8.2-4 by $h\nu$ leads to an energy equation,

$$\frac{\partial u_{\lambda\omega}}{\partial t} + \nabla \cdot (u_{\lambda\omega} c \mathbf{\Omega}) = \mathscr{E}_{\lambda\omega} - \mathscr{A}_{\lambda\omega} \tag{8.2-5}$$

and integration of this equation over all wavelengths and over the solid angle 4π yields the radiant energy transport equation,

$$\frac{\partial u^R}{\partial t} + \nabla \cdot \mathbf{q}^R = -\Phi \tag{8.2-15}$$

Here the electromagnetic energy source term is defined by

$$\Phi = -\int_{4\pi} \int_0^\infty (\mathscr{E}_{\lambda\omega} - \mathscr{A}_{\lambda\omega})\, d\lambda\, d\omega \tag{8.2-18}$$

and the radiant energy flux vector is given by

$$\mathbf{q}^R = \int_{4\pi} \int_0^\infty u_{\lambda\omega} c \mathbf{\Omega}\, d\lambda\, d\omega \tag{8.2-17}$$

The difficulty in solving Eq. 8.2-15 is that $\mathbf{q}^R$ cannot be specified in terms of *local conditions*. It should be clear, for example, that the net flux of photons at the earth's surface is greatly influenced by the cloud cover and events at the surface of the sun several minutes earlier. It is this character of the radiant energy transport equation that requires an entirely new approach to solving radiant energy transfer problems. We begin to construct a framework for solving these problems in Sec. 8.3.

*8.2 The Photon Transport Equation

In the previous section we have set forth the arguments that justify treating thermal radiation in terms of photons, and we would now like to develop the photon balance equation, or in keeping with previous terminology, the *photon transport equation*. We begin by defining a photon density function $n_{\lambda\omega}$ as

$$n_{\lambda\omega}\, d\lambda\, d\omega\, dV = \left\{ \begin{array}{l} \text{the number of photons in a volume} \\ dV\text{, having wavelengths in the range} \\ \text{of } \lambda \text{ to } \lambda + d\lambda\text{, and whose flight} \\ \text{paths lie within a solid angle } d\omega \\ \text{about the direction } \mathbf{\Omega} \end{array} \right\} \tag{8.2-1}$$

The nomenclature used here is to be noted for throughout Chapters 8 and 9 we will use a subscript λ to indicate *per unit wavelength* and a subscript ω to indicate *per unit solid angle.*

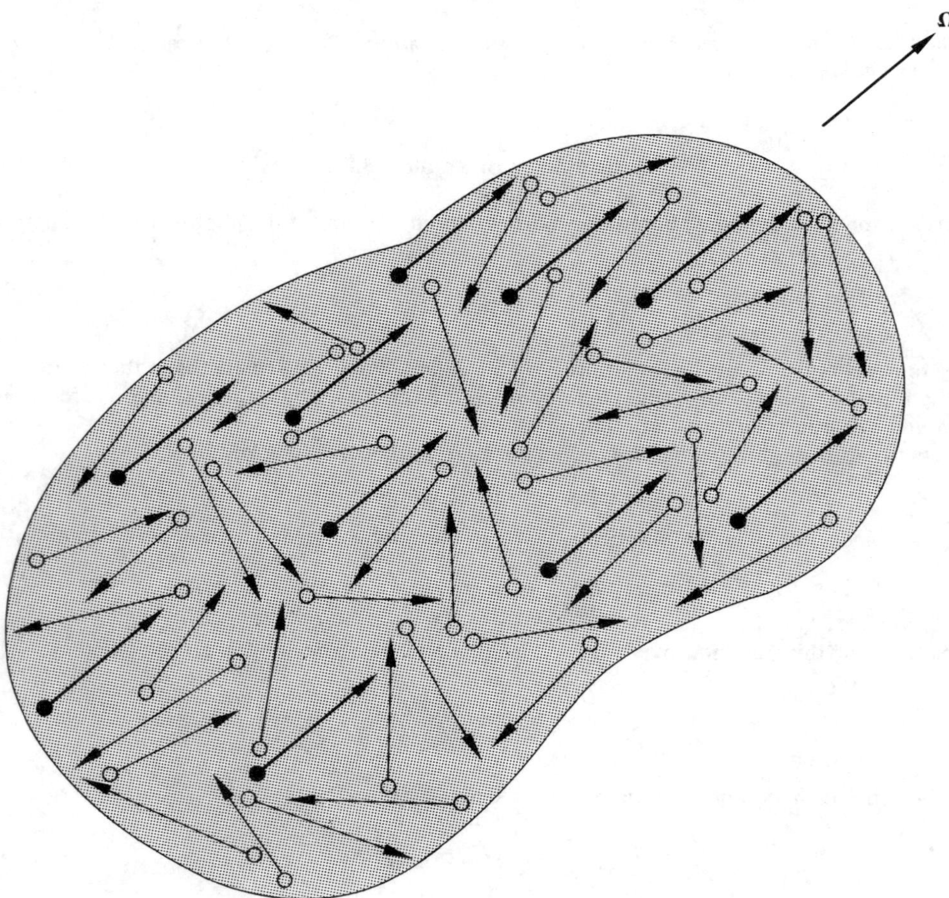

Fig. 8.2.1 Photon balance.

We now wish to write a photon balance for the volume, fixed in space, shown in Fig. 8.2.1. The arrows indicate photons traveling in all directions and having all wavelengths. The photons in which we are interested are indicated by the solid dots and boldfaced arrows, for these photons have flight paths lying within $d\omega$ of $\mathbf{\Omega}$. In addition we require that these particular photons have wavelengths in the range of λ to $\lambda + d\lambda$, and they will be referred to as the $\lambda\omega$-photons. In words we express the $\lambda\omega$-photon balance for the volume $\mathcal{V}$, having a surface area $\mathcal{A}$, as

$$\begin{Bmatrix} \text{time rate of change of} \\ \text{the number of } \lambda\omega\text{-photons} \\ \text{in the volume } \mathcal{V} \end{Bmatrix} + \begin{Bmatrix} \text{net flux of } \lambda\omega\text{-photons} \\ \text{leaving } \mathcal{V} \text{ across the} \\ \text{surface } \mathcal{A} \end{Bmatrix} = \begin{Bmatrix} \text{net gain of } \lambda\omega\text{-photons} \\ \text{owing to emission, absorption,} \\ \text{and scattering in the volume } \mathcal{V} \end{Bmatrix} \tag{8.2-2}$$

The symbolic representation of this balance expression takes the form

$$\frac{\partial}{\partial t}\int_{\mathcal{V}} n_{\lambda\omega}\, dV + \int_{\mathcal{A}} n_{\lambda\omega}(c\mathbf{\Omega})\cdot\mathbf{n}\, dA = \int_{\mathcal{V}} (e_{\lambda\omega} - a_{\lambda\omega})\, dV + \int_{\mathcal{V}} J_{\lambda\omega,\text{net}}\, dV \tag{8.2-3}$$

Here $e_{\lambda\omega}$ and $a_{\lambda\omega}$ represent the rate of $\lambda\omega$-photon emission and absorption per unit time per unit volume.† Everyone is familiar with emission phenomenon in the sun of course, but somewhat closer to home this phenomenon has been observed while warming oneself in front of a cozy fire. The "light" from the fire results from photons being emitted when the excited electronic states of the various molecules and free radicals in the flame undergo quantum changes to lower energy electronic states. Absorption phenomenon is illustrated by the orange color of the harvest moon, and is caused by the preferential absorption of the high-energy photons in the atmospheric murk. Contrary to the romantic ramblings of poets, the phenomenon is best observed from a sooty perch in a polluted metropolitan region, rather than across the endless reaches of the prairie.

The term $J_{\lambda\omega,\text{net}}$ represents the net increase in the $\lambda\omega$-photons per unit time per unit volume owing to scattering phenomenon. This occurs when a photon undergoes a collision which alters its energy and direction, but does not lead to absorption or capture of the photon by the scattering site. This phenomenon is responsible for the blue color of the sky[3]. Scattering is of little importance in thermal radiation, and we will drop this term from our $\lambda\omega$-photon balance.

Interchanging differentiation and integration in the first integral in Eq. 8.2-3, and applying the divergence theorem to the area integral allows us to put all the terms under the same integral sign and thus derive the differential photon balance, or the photon transport equation.

$$\frac{\partial n_{\lambda\omega}}{\partial t} + \nabla\cdot(n_{\lambda\omega}c\mathbf{\Omega}) = e_{\lambda\omega} - a_{\lambda\omega} \tag{8.2-4}$$

Here we have obtained the governing transport equation for the photon density function. If we knew $e_{\lambda\omega}$ and $a_{\lambda\omega}$ in terms of the thermodynamic state of the system and could specify appropriate boundary conditions for $n_{\lambda\omega}$ we could solve this differential equation and completely determine the photon density and transport rates. There are some difficulties in doing this, but before going on to a discussion of these difficulties we wish to explore some other forms of the photon transport equation.

The energy of a photon having a frequency ν is given by $h\nu = hc/\lambda$ where h is Planck's constant, thus we can multiply Eq. 8.2-4 by $h\nu$ to obtain

$$\frac{\partial u_{\lambda\omega}}{\partial t} + \nabla\cdot(u_{\lambda\omega}c\mathbf{\Omega}) = \mathcal{E}_{\lambda\omega} - \mathcal{A}_{\lambda\omega} \tag{8.2-5}$$

Here $u_{\lambda\omega}$ represents the $\lambda\omega$-radiant energy density and $\mathcal{E}_{\lambda\omega}$ and $\mathcal{A}_{\lambda\omega}$ represents the rates at which radiant energy from $\lambda\omega$-photons is being emitted and absorbed respectively. Later we will see that it is somewhat

†Note that in accordance with our subscript nomenclature, $e_{\lambda\omega}$ has units of photons/time–volume–wavelength–solid angle or photons/sec-cm^3-cm-radian.

more convenient to work with a radiant energy *intensity*, and to this end we define the *specific intensity* by

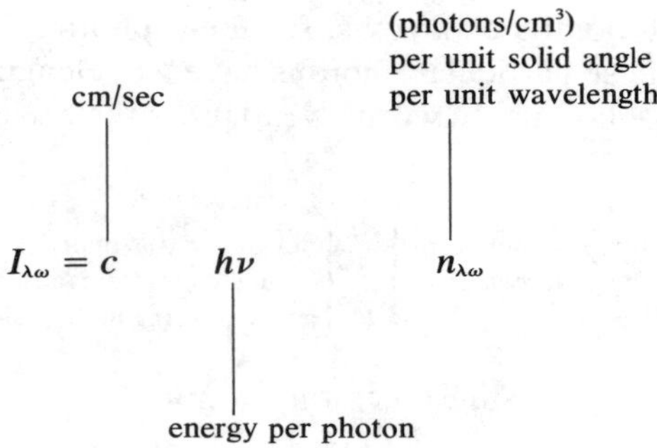

= (energy/cm²-sec) per unit solid angle per unit wavelength

Here we see that $I_{\lambda\omega}$ represents the magnitude of an energy flux; the direction being given by $\mathbf{\Omega}$. In terms of the specific intensity, Eq. 8.2-5 takes the form

$$\frac{1}{c}\left(\frac{\partial I_{\lambda\omega}}{\partial t}\right) + \nabla \cdot (I_{\lambda\omega}\mathbf{\Omega}) = \mathscr{E}_{\lambda\omega} - \mathscr{A}_{\lambda\omega} \tag{8.2-7}$$

Eq. 8.2-7 represents a *single* scalar equation containing *three* unknowns, $I_{\lambda\omega}$, $\mathscr{E}_{\lambda\omega}$, and $\mathscr{A}_{\lambda\omega}$. We regard $\mathbf{\Omega}$ as a specified parameter, and if $\mathscr{E}_{\lambda\omega}$ and $\mathscr{A}_{\lambda\omega}$ can be specified we could solve Eq. 8.2-7, subject to appropriate boundary conditions, to determine $I_{\lambda\omega}$ along a path designated by $\mathbf{\Omega}$. The rate of emission $\mathscr{E}_{\lambda\omega}$ certainly must depend on the *state* of the system, i.e., the temperature, pressure, and composition. The rate of absorption $\mathscr{A}_{\lambda\omega}$ must also depend on these same variables, but in addition it must be strongly dependent on the photon density, $n_{\lambda\omega}$. Although we are going to restrict most of our analysis of thermal radiation to conditions such that absorption and emission are generally unimportant, it will be helpful to consider these phenomena briefly.

Lambert–Beer law: the smog effect

If we have a parallel light beam passing through a non-emitting medium ($\mathscr{E}_{\lambda\omega} = 0$) under steady-state conditions, Eq. 8.2-7 reduces to

$$\frac{dI_{\lambda\omega}}{dx} = -\mathscr{A}_{\lambda\omega} \tag{8.2-8}$$

Here we have chosen $\mathbf{\Omega} = \mathbf{i}$ to represent the direction of the parallel light beam. If we assume that $\mathscr{A}_{\lambda\omega}$ is a *linear* function of $I_{\lambda\omega}$ and the concentration C of some absorbing species, we write the *linear constitutive equation* for $\mathscr{A}_{\lambda\omega}$ as:†

$$\mathscr{A}_{\lambda\omega} = \beta(\lambda) C I_{\lambda\omega} \tag{8.2-9}$$

where β is a proportionality constant usually referred to as the extinction coefficient. Note that in Eq. 8.2-9 we have indicated that the extinction coefficient is a function of the wavelength but is independent of direction, thus Eq. 8.2-9 represents a linear constitutive equation for an *isotropic* media.

Substitution of Eq. 8.2-9 into Eq. 8.2-8 yields

$$\frac{dI_{\lambda\omega}}{dx} = -\beta(\lambda) C I_{\lambda\omega} \tag{8.2-10}$$

This may be integrated subject to a boundary condition of the type

B.C. $$I_{\lambda\omega} = I_0, \qquad x = 0 \tag{8.2-11}$$

†This is comparable to assuming that $\mathscr{A}_{\lambda\omega}$ is a linear function of $n_{\lambda\omega}$, since $n_{\lambda\omega}$ and $I_{\lambda\omega}$ are linearly related.

to yield

$$I_{\lambda\omega}(x) = I_0 e^{-\beta(\lambda)Cx} \tag{8.2-12}$$

This is known as the Lambert–Beer law which is used extensively in chemical analysis [4]. It indicates that the intensity falls off exponentially with distance which accounts for the drastic effect that smog can have on the visibility. On a moderate day in the Los Angeles basin the intensity of radiation leaving the nearby San Gabriel mountains is reduced by a factor of ten as it travels to a mountain-watcher in the center of the city, thus

$$I_1 = I_0 e^{-\beta C_1 L} \tag{8.2-13}$$

where $I_1/I_0 = 10^{-1}$. If the concentration of the absorbing species is doubled we find

$$I_2 = I_0 e^{-2\beta C_1 L} = I_0(I_1/I_0)^2 \tag{8.2-14}$$

and the intensity is reduced by a factor of one hundred, $I_2/I_0 = 10^{-2}$. Under these circumstances the mountains are obliterated and what was once a fine view becomes a dreary scene that is repeated all too often in our metropolitan areas.

The greenhouse effect

Absorption and emission phenomena play an important role in the flow of energy in the biosphere. The oxygen in the earth's atmosphere absorbs ultraviolet radiation decomposing to atomic oxygen and forming ozone, while carbon dioxide and water vapor absorb and emit radiation in the infrared region. The atmosphere is essentially transparent to the sun's radiation in the visible range; however, radiation leaving the earth is entirely in the infrared region, and a portion of this radiation is absorbed by the carbon dioxide and water vapor. The absorbed energy is then reradiated in two directions: back toward the earth and into outer space. In this way the earth's atmosphere acts in precisely the same manner as the glass roof on a greenhouse; visible radiation is freely admitted while infrared radiation from the green plants is absorbed by the glass and a cozy garden results.

Coupled thermal and radiant energy transport

The previous paragraphs have provided some insight into the phenomena of absorption and emission, and should help the student to understand the discussion of Design Problem VIII given at the end of the chapter. In general, problems involving absorption and emission are exceedingly complex for they usually involve coupled thermal and radiant energy transport. To illustrate, let us return to the $\lambda\omega$-radiant energy density equation, Eq. 8.2-5, and integrate over all wavelengths and all directions to obtain

$$\frac{\partial u^R}{\partial t} + \nabla \cdot \mathbf{q}^R = -\Phi \tag{8.2-15}$$

Here the *radiant energy density*, u^R, is given by

$$u^R = \int_{4\pi} \int_0^\infty u_{\lambda\omega}\, d\lambda\, d\omega \tag{8.2-16}$$

the *radiant energy heat flux vector*, $\mathbf{q}^R$, takes the form

$$\mathbf{q}^R = \int_{4\pi} \int_0^\infty u_{\lambda\omega} c\, \mathbf{\Omega}\, d\lambda\, d\omega \tag{8.2-17}$$

and the all important source term, Φ, is expressed as

$$\Phi = -\int_{4\pi} \int_0^\infty (\mathscr{E}_{\lambda\omega} - \mathscr{A}_{\lambda\omega})\, d\lambda\, d\omega \tag{8.2-18}$$

Notice that Φ is defined so that it is *positive* when radiant energy is being absorbed. Remembering that the thermal energy equation can be expressed as

$$\rho c_p \frac{DT}{Dt} = -\nabla \cdot \mathbf{q} + T\beta \frac{Dp}{Dt} + \nabla \mathbf{v} : \boldsymbol{\tau} + \Phi \tag{8.2-19}$$

we see that the thermal energy equation and the radiant energy transport equation are coupled through the source term, Φ, where Φ is generally a function of both the temperature and the radiant energy density

$$\Phi = \Phi(T, u^R) \tag{8.2-20}$$

in addition to the concentration of the absorbing or emitting species.

At this point the task of obtaining solutions of the radiant energy transport equation appears to be quite difficult primarily because it is coupled to the thermal energy equation. However, there is a more important reason why solutions to Eq. 8.2-15 are difficult to obtain and that is that the radiant energy *flux vector* $\mathbf{q}^R$ *cannot be specified in terms of local conditions.* Remember that the thermal energy flux vector is specified in terms of the *local* temperature gradient by the expression

$$\mathbf{q} = -k\nabla T \tag{8.2-21}$$

This, along with an expression for the thermal energy in terms of the temperature and pressure, gave us a single scalar equation which could be solved to determine the temperature field. Consider for a moment the net flux of photons at the earth's surface. Certainly the rate leaving the surface will depend on local conditions, but how about the rate of arrival of photons? That rate will depend on what has been going on at the surface of the sun and what kind of cloud cover there may be. Clearly then the *net* flux of photons cannot be expressed in terms of local conditions, and it is this fact that makes radiant energy transport problems different and more difficult from the type of problems we have encountered up to this point.

*8.3 Radiant Energy Transfer at Surfaces

In the previous section we derived the photon transport equation, and illustrated how it could be used to obtain equations for the specific intensity $I_{\lambda\omega}$, and the radiant energy densities, $u_{\lambda\omega}$, and u^R. It was illustrated how these equations could be coupled with the thermal energy equation, and why the flux could not be specified in terms of local conditions. Because of the complexities of the general radiation transport problem we will confine our attention for the present to the problem of steady-state radiation in the absence of absorption or emission in the bulk phase.†

Under these circumstances the photon transport equation takes the form,

$$\nabla \cdot (n_{\lambda\omega} c \,\boldsymbol{\Omega}) = 0 \tag{8.3-1}$$

and the specific intensity is governed by

$$\nabla \cdot (I_{\lambda\omega} \boldsymbol{\Omega}) = 0 \tag{8.3-2}$$

where $I_{\lambda\omega}$ is given by

$$I_{\lambda\omega} = \underbrace{c}_{\text{cm/sec}} \quad \underbrace{h\nu}_{\text{energy per photon}} \quad \underbrace{n_{\lambda\omega}}_{(\text{photons/cm}^3)\text{ per unit solid angle per unit wavelength}} \tag{8.2-6}$$

$= (\text{energy/cm}^2\text{ sec})$ per unit solid angle per unit wavelength

Under these conditions nothing of interest is occurring within the volume $\mathscr{V}$, and we are only concerned

†Remember that scattering has already been neglected.

with what happens at the surface $\mathscr{A}$. Integrating Eq. 8.3-2 over the volume $\mathscr{V}$ and applying the divergence theorem we obtain

$$\int_{\mathscr{A}} I_{\lambda\omega} \mathbf{\Omega} \cdot \mathbf{n} \, dA = 0 \tag{8.3-3}$$

Clearly what we need at this point is a satisfactory method of determining the quantity $I_{\lambda\omega} \mathbf{\Omega} \cdot \mathbf{n}$ at the surface $\mathscr{A}$. More explicitly our objective is to be able to determine the rate at which photons are emitted by a solid surface and the rate at which photons, emitted elsewhere, strike the surface and are absorbed by it.

Example 8.3-1 Derivation of the steady-state intensity equation in the absence of absorption and emission

Since Eq. 8.3-2 represents the starting point for all of the analysis in Chapters 8 and 9, it may be helpful to derive this equation from a somewhat different point of view. We will restrict our development to steady conditions with no absorption or emission of photons. Under these circumstances photons are conserved and we state this idea as

$$\begin{Bmatrix} \text{the rate at which} \\ \lambda\omega\text{-photons enter} \\ \text{a region in space} \end{Bmatrix} = \begin{Bmatrix} \text{the rate at which} \\ \lambda\omega\text{-photons leave the} \\ \text{same region in space} \end{Bmatrix} \tag{1}$$

We wish to apply this conservation principle to the differential cube shown in Fig. 8.3-1. The number of photons crossing any one of the surfaces of the cube is represented as

$$\begin{Bmatrix} \text{number of} \\ \lambda\omega\text{-photons crossing} \\ \text{the surface} \end{Bmatrix} = \begin{Bmatrix} \text{area} \\ \text{of} \\ \text{surface} \end{Bmatrix} \begin{Bmatrix} \text{density} \\ \text{of} \\ \lambda\omega\text{-photons} \end{Bmatrix} \begin{Bmatrix} \text{velocity of the} \\ \lambda\omega\text{-photons normal to} \\ \text{the surface} \end{Bmatrix} \tag{2}$$

Since the velocity of a $\lambda\omega$-photon is $c\mathbf{\Omega}$, the velocities normal to the surfaces of the cube are $c\Omega_x$, $c\Omega_y$, and $c\Omega_z$. Applying Eqs. 1 and 2 to the differential cube yields

$$\begin{aligned} &\Delta y \Delta z (n_{\lambda\omega} c\Omega_x)_x + \Delta x \Delta z (n_{\lambda\omega} c\Omega_y)_y + \Delta x \Delta y (n_{\lambda\omega} c\Omega_z)_z \\ &\qquad = \Delta y \Delta z (n_{\lambda\omega} c\Omega_x)_{x+\Delta x} + \Delta x \Delta z (n_{\lambda\omega} c\Omega_y)_{y+\Delta y} + \Delta x \Delta y (n_{\lambda\omega} c\Omega_z)_{z+\Delta z} \end{aligned} \tag{3}$$

Dividing by $\Delta x \Delta y \Delta z$ and rearranging this result leads to

$$\left[\frac{(n_{\lambda\omega} c\Omega_x)_{x+\Delta x} - (n_{\lambda\omega} c\Omega_x)_x}{\Delta x}\right] + \left[\frac{(n_{\lambda\omega} c\Omega_y)_{y+\Delta y} - (n_{\lambda\omega} c\Omega_y)_y}{\Delta y}\right] + \left[\frac{(n_{\lambda\omega} c\Omega_z)_{z+\Delta z} - (n_{\lambda\omega} c\Omega_z)_z}{\Delta z}\right] = 0 \tag{4}$$

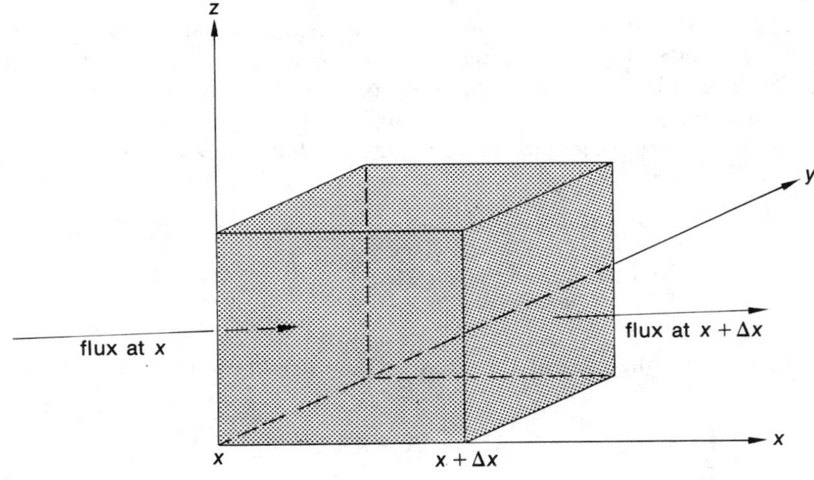

Fig. 8.3.1 Photon balance for a differential cube.

Taking the limit $\Delta x \to 0$, $\Delta y \to 0$, and $\Delta z \to 0$ gives us

$$\frac{\partial}{\partial x}(n_{\lambda\omega} c\,\Omega_x) + \frac{\partial}{\partial y}(n_{\lambda\omega} c\,\Omega_y) + \frac{\partial}{\partial z}(n_{\lambda\omega} c\,\Omega_z) = 0 \tag{5}$$

and if we remember that $\mathbf{\Omega} = \mathbf{i}\Omega_x + \mathbf{j}\Omega_y + \mathbf{k}\Omega_z$ we can express Eq. 5 in more compact vector notation

$$\nabla \cdot (n_{\lambda\omega} c\,\mathbf{\Omega}) = 0 \tag{6}$$

This represents the $\lambda\omega$-photon density equation, and when multiplied by the energy per photon, $h\nu$, we obtain

$$\nabla \cdot (n_{\lambda\omega} ch\nu\,\mathbf{\Omega}) = 0 \tag{7}$$

Referring now to the definition of the specific intensity given by Eq. 8.2-6,

$$I_{\lambda\omega} = ch\nu n_{\lambda\omega} \tag{8}$$

we can express Eq. 7 as

$$\nabla \cdot (I_{\lambda\omega}\,\mathbf{\Omega}) = 0 \tag{9}$$

Integration over an arbitrary region in space yields,

$$\int_{\mathscr{V}} \nabla \cdot (I_{\lambda\omega}\,\mathbf{\Omega})\,dV = 0 \tag{10}$$

and application of the divergence theorem provides us with the final desired result

$$\int_{\mathscr{A}} I_{\lambda\omega}\,\mathbf{\Omega} \cdot \mathbf{n}\,dA = 0 \tag{11}$$

In Fig. 8.3.2 we have illustrated a beam of $\lambda\omega$-photons striking a solid surface; the fraction absorbed being designated by $\alpha_{\lambda\omega}$. It should be clearly understood that the fraction of incident photons absorbed by the solid depends on the wavelength λ, and therefore on the energy $h\nu = hc/\lambda$, and on the incident angle, i.e., it depends on $\mathbf{\Omega}$. This dependence on wavelength and direction (or angle of incidence) of the fraction absorbed is indicated by the subscripts on $\alpha_{\lambda\omega}$. An important question to be asked is what happens to the photons which are reflected from the solid surface? In Fig. 8.3.2 we have depicted a situation in which the photons which are not absorbed are reflected *diffusely*.† Another possibility is illustrated in Fig. 8.3.3. There the angle of incidence is equal to the angle of reflection and the reflection is often referred to as *specular.* Such a situation occurs when visible light is incident upon a highly polished surface or mirror. Diffuse reflection is more likely to occur on rough surfaces such as one is likely to encounter in most heat transfer processes.

Since solid surfaces can emit, absorb, and reflect photons, we need to set down some expressions for the incident, reflected, absorbed, and emitted radiant energy. It will turn out that these quantities are expressible in terms of $I_{\lambda\omega}$, and will fit naturally into our overall photon balance as given by Eq. 8.3-3.

Consider the surface shown in Fig. 8.3.4. The angle of incidence θ is measured as illustrated, and the unit normal for the surface is the outwardly directed unit normal for the photon gas phase. Consider a stream of photons approaching the solid surface along the path indicated by $\mathbf{\Omega}$ and passing through a differential area dA_ω which is perpendicular to $\mathbf{\Omega}$. The rate at which radiant energy crosses the area of dA_ω is given by

$$\left\{\begin{array}{l}\text{radiant energy crossing } dA_\omega \\ \text{in the direction } \mathbf{\Omega} \text{ per unit} \\ \text{time per unit solid angle} \\ \text{per unit wavelength}\end{array}\right\} = ch\nu n_{\lambda\omega}\,dA_\omega \tag{8.3-4}$$

$$= I_{\lambda\omega}\,dA_\omega$$

The relations between dA_ω and the area of the solid surface dA upon which the photons impinge is given by [5]

$$\mathbf{\Omega} \cdot \mathbf{n}\,dA = dA_\omega \tag{8.3-5}$$

†We will give a precise definition of diffuse reflection in subsequent paragraphs.

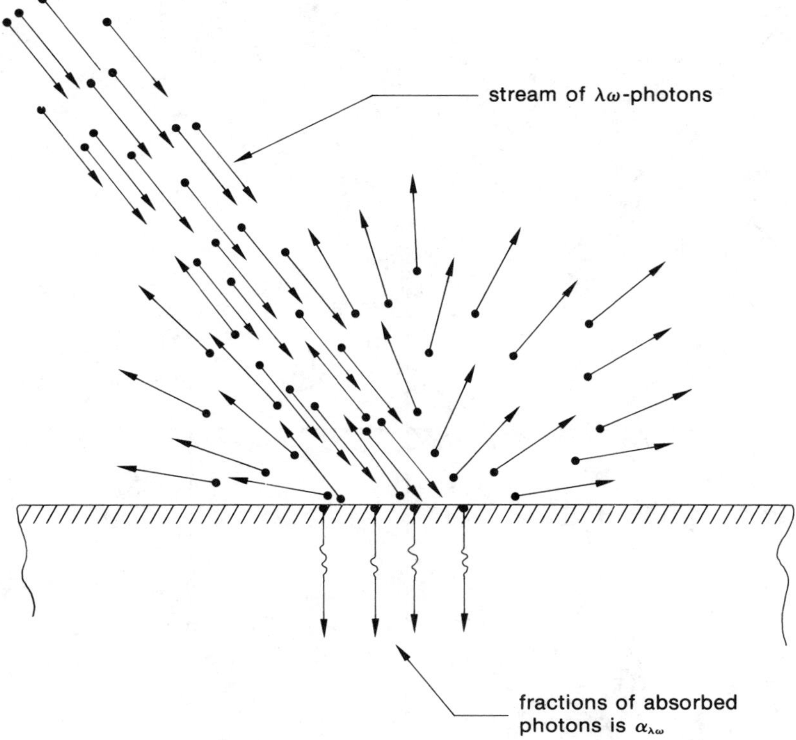

Fig. 8.3.2 Stream of photons striking a solid surface.

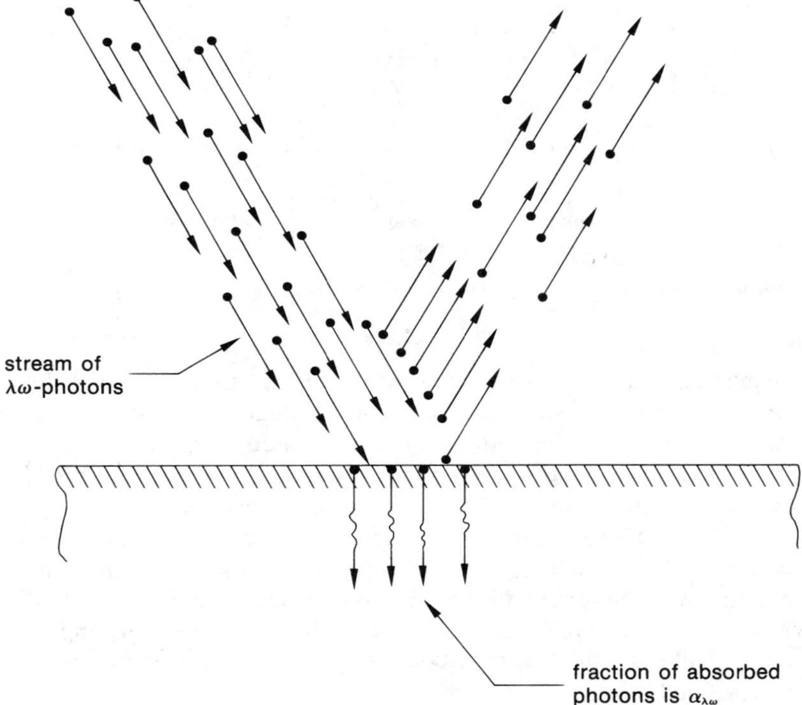

Fig. 8.3.3 Stream of photons striking a highly polished surface.

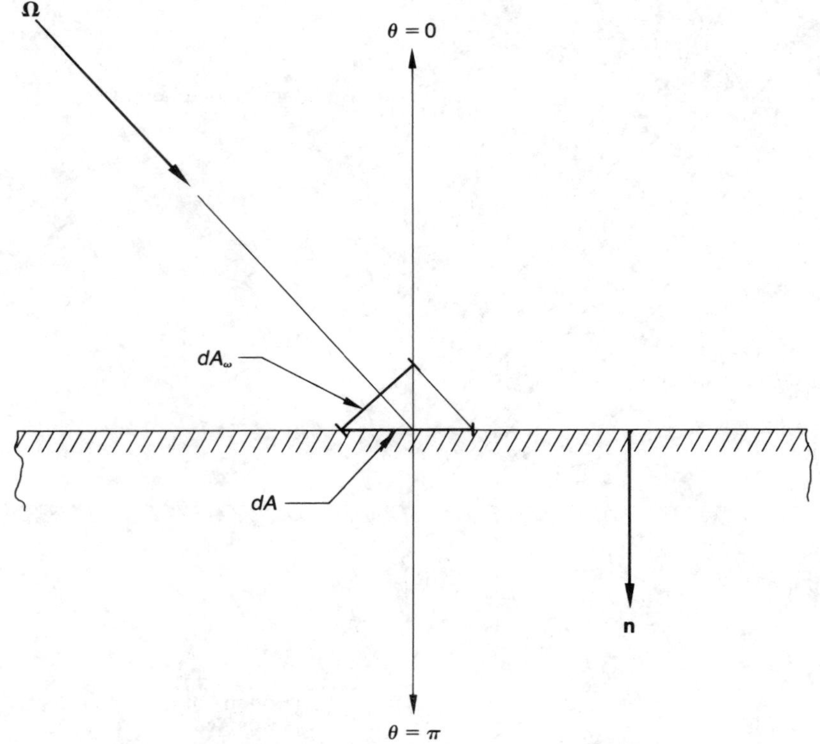

Fig. 8.3.4 Geometrical considerations for incident photons.

and Eq. 8.3-4 can be written as

$$\left\{\begin{array}{l}\text{radiant energy incident upon the}\\ \text{area } dA \text{ from the direction } \mathbf{\Omega} \text{ per}\\ \text{unit time per unit solid angle}\\ \text{per unit wavelength}\end{array}\right\} = I_{\lambda\omega}\,\mathbf{\Omega}\cdot\mathbf{n}\,dA \tag{8.3-6}$$

If we now divide Eq. 8.3-6 by the area dA we get an expression for the flux of energy,

$$\left\{\begin{array}{l}\text{radiant energy per unit } \textit{surface area}\\ \text{per unit time per unit solid}\\ \text{angle per unit wavelength}\end{array}\right\} = I_{\lambda\omega}\,\mathbf{\Omega}\cdot\mathbf{n} \tag{8.3-7}$$

We now define the *incident surface flux* $q^{(i)}_{\lambda\omega}$ by the expression

$$q^{(i)}_{\lambda\omega} = I^{(i)}_{\lambda\omega}\mathbf{\Omega}\cdot\mathbf{n} \tag{8.3-8}$$

Here we have made use of the superscript (i) on both $q_{\lambda\omega}$ and $I_{\lambda\omega}$ to indicate the *direction* of the flow of energy. This is, of course, superfluous since the direction of the flow of energy is specified in terms of $\mathbf{\Omega}$ and $\mathbf{n}$; however, we will soon see that the bookkeeping associated with radiant energy fluxes is best done with superscripts rather than with vectors. When considering Eq. 8.3-8 we should remember that the symbol, I, will always be used to denote a flux of photons across an area orthogonal to $\mathbf{\Omega}$, while the symbol, q, will always be used to denote a flux of photons across an area orthogonal to $\mathbf{n}$. In keeping with the use of *specific intensity* to describe $I_{\lambda\omega}$ we will refer to $q^{(i)}_{\lambda\omega}$ as the *specific incident flux.*

Very often we wish to know the incident radiation upon a surface coming from all possible directions. This is known as the *hemispherical incident flux* and it is obtained by integrating $I_{\lambda\omega}\mathbf{\Omega}\cdot\mathbf{n}$ over the solid angle 2π, i.e., we must sum all the radiant energy coming from a hemisphere bounded by the solid surface. This integral can be expressed as

$$q_\lambda^{(i)} = \int_{2\pi} I^{(i)}_{\lambda\omega}\mathbf{\Omega}\cdot\mathbf{n}\,d\omega \tag{8.3-9}$$

We can express this integral more explicitly by referring to Fig. 8.3.5 and noting that the differential solid angle $d\omega$ is given in terms of θ and ϕ by

$$d\omega = \sin\theta\, d\theta\, d\phi \tag{8.3-10}$$

We may substitute this expression for $d\omega$ into Eq. 8.3-9 and represent $q_\lambda^{(i)}$ as

$$q_\lambda^{(i)} = \int_{\phi=0}^{\phi=2\pi} \int_{\theta=\pi/2}^{\theta=\pi} I_{\lambda\omega}^{(i)} \mathbf{\Omega} \cdot \mathbf{n} \sin\theta\, d\theta\, d\phi \tag{8.3-11}$$

Notice that the values of θ for *incident* radiation vary from $\pi/2$ to π indicating that the unit vector $\mathbf{\Omega}$ is pointing *into* the surface. Note also that $\mathbf{\Omega} \cdot \mathbf{n}$ is positive, thus $q_\lambda^{(i)}$ as defined by Eq. 8.3-9 or 8.3-11 is a positive flux.

The total radiant energy incident upon a surface can be obtained by summing the energy over all wavelengths. We refer to this quantity as the *total hemispherical incident flux* and express it as

$$q^{(i)} = \int_0^\infty \int_{2\pi} I_{\lambda\omega}^{(i)} \mathbf{\Omega} \cdot \mathbf{n}\, d\omega\, d\lambda \tag{8.3-12}$$

In talking about the incident flux we have been very careful about the use of the subscripts λ and ω and about the use of the words *total* and *hemispherical.* It is important to understand the precise meaning of these symbols and words for this nomenclature will be used throughout Chapters 8 and 9. To be sure that these ideas are clear we will list the various fluxes and their definitions:

$$\text{specific incident flux} \quad q_{\lambda\omega}^{(i)} = I_{\lambda\omega}^{(i)} \mathbf{\Omega} \cdot \mathbf{n} \tag{8.3-13a}$$

$$\text{hemispherical incident flux} \quad q_\lambda^{(i)} = \int_{2\pi} I_{\lambda\omega}^{(i)} \mathbf{\Omega} \cdot \mathbf{n}\, d\omega \tag{8.3-13b}$$

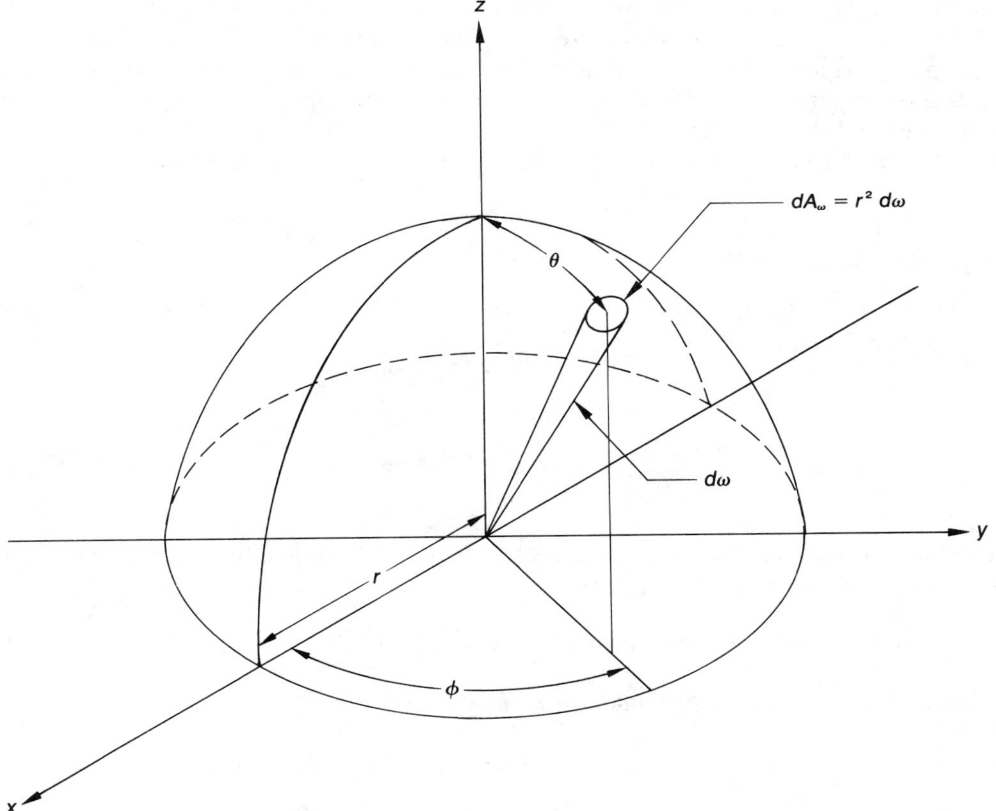

Fig. 8.3.5 Differential solid angle.

$$\text{total hemispherical incident flux} \quad q^{(i)} = \int_0^\infty \int_{2\pi} I_{\lambda\omega}^{(i)} \mathbf{\Omega} \cdot \mathbf{n} \, d\omega \, d\lambda \tag{8.3-13c}$$

From these definitions it should be clear that the *total incident flux* is given by

$$\text{total incident flux} \quad q_\omega^{(i)} = \int_0^\infty I_{\lambda\omega}^{(i)} \mathbf{\Omega} \cdot \mathbf{n} \, d\lambda \tag{8.3-13d}$$

When a photon strikes a surface two processes can occur: (1) it can be absorbed and (2) it can be reflected. In Figs. 8.3.2 and 8.3.3 we have indicated that some fraction, $\alpha_{\lambda\omega}$, of the incident $\lambda\omega$-photons are absorbed. We refer to the quantity $\alpha_{\lambda\omega}$ as the *specific absorptivity* and define it in the following:

$$q_{\lambda\omega}^{(a)} = \alpha_{\lambda\omega} I_{\lambda\omega}^{(i)} \mathbf{\Omega} \cdot \mathbf{n} \tag{8.3-14}$$

Here $q_{\lambda\omega}^{(a)}$ represents the flux of absorbed $\lambda\omega$-photons and we refer to it as the *specific absorbed flux.* A set of definitions comparable to those given by Eqs. 8.3-13 can also be written. If the fraction of *absorbed* $\lambda\omega$-photons is $\alpha_{\lambda\omega}$, then the fraction of *reflected* photons must be $1 - \alpha_{\lambda\omega}$ and we naturally define the *specific* reflectivity as

$$\rho_{\lambda\omega} = 1 - \alpha_{\lambda\omega} \tag{8.3-15}$$

Dealing with the reflected photons presents something of a problem, for even if we know the number that are reflected we do not necessarily know the distribution of directions for these photons. In Figs. 8.3.2 and 8.3.3 we illustrated two possible types of reflection; however, for the present we will ignore this problem and simply assume that given $I_{\lambda\omega}^{(i)}$ and $\rho_{\lambda\omega}$ we can determine the specific intensity of the reflected radiation $I_{\lambda\omega}^{(r)}$. This allows us to express the *specific reflected flux* $q_{\lambda\omega}^{(r)}$ as

$$q_{\lambda\omega}^{(r)} = I_{\lambda\omega}^{(r)} \mathbf{\Omega} \cdot \mathbf{n} \tag{8.3-16}$$

Note that for reflected radiation $\mathbf{\Omega}$ points *away* from the surface and $\mathbf{n}$ points *into* the surface so that $\mathbf{\Omega} \cdot \mathbf{n}$ is a *negative* quantity. As we mentioned earlier the use of vectors as a bookkeeping method for radiant energy fluxes is not particularly desirable, for it is much more convenient to keep track of the direction of the flow of energy in terms of the specific incident flux, $q_{\lambda\omega}^{(i)}$; the specific absorbed flux, $q_{\lambda\omega}^{(a)}$; the specific reflect flux, $q_{\lambda\omega}^{(r)}$; and the specific emitted flux, $q_{\lambda\omega}^{(e)}$. The use of the superscripts (i), (a), (r), and (e) supplies all the information we need since the direction in which the *emitted* radiant energy (for example) is flowing is quite clear from the description of the system. Because of this we will now change our sign convention.

Change of sign convention

We now consider the fluxes $q_{\lambda\omega}^{(i)}$, $q_{\lambda\omega}^{(a)}$, $q_{\lambda\omega}^{(r)}$, and $q_{\lambda\omega}^{(e)}$ to be always positive and defined in terms of the specific intensity as follows:

$$q_{\lambda\omega}^{(i)} = I_{\lambda\omega}^{(i)} |\mathbf{\Omega} \cdot \mathbf{n}| \tag{8.3-17a}$$

$$q_{\lambda\omega}^{(a)} = \alpha_{\lambda\omega} I_{\lambda\omega}^{(i)} |\mathbf{\Omega} \cdot \mathbf{n}| \tag{8.3-17b}$$

$$q_{\lambda\omega}^{(r)} = I_{\lambda\omega}^{(r)} |\mathbf{\Omega} \cdot \mathbf{n}| \tag{8.3-17c}$$

$$q_{\lambda\omega}^{(e)} = I_{\lambda\omega}^{(e)} |\mathbf{\Omega} \cdot \mathbf{n}| \tag{8.3-17d}$$

A set of definitions comparable to those given by Eqs. 8.3-13 exists for each of these four fluxes. For example, the *total emitted flux* is given by

$$\text{total emitted flux} \quad q_\omega^{(e)} = \int_0^\infty I_{\lambda\omega}^{(e)} |\mathbf{\Omega} \cdot \mathbf{n}| \, d\lambda \tag{8.3-18}$$

and the *hemispherical reflected flux* may be expressed as

$$\text{hemispherical reflected flux} \quad q_\lambda^{(r)} = \int_{2\pi} I_{\lambda\omega}^{(r)} |\mathbf{\Omega} \cdot \mathbf{n}| \, d\omega \tag{8.3-19}$$

The quantity that we seek in most radiant energy transfer problems is the *net* radiant energy transfer at a solid surface and this is given by

$$\{\text{net rate of radiant energy absorbed at a solid surface}\} = \int_0^\infty \int_{2\pi} [q_{\lambda\omega}^{(a)} - q_{\lambda\omega}^{(e)}]\, d\omega\, d\lambda \tag{8.3-20}$$

In order to compute this quantity we must know $\alpha_{\lambda\omega}$ and $I_{\lambda\omega}^{(i)}$ so that $q_{\lambda\omega}^{(a)}$ can be calculated and we must know $I_{\lambda\omega}^{(e)}$ so that $q_{\lambda\omega}^{(e)}$ can be determined. Since the incident radiation can come from both emitted and reflected radiation we must also know how to calculate $I_{\lambda\omega}^{(r)}$ given $I_{\lambda\omega}^{(i)}$. Thus we require an experimental determination of $\alpha_{\lambda\omega}$ and $I_{\lambda\omega}^{(e)}$ in addition to some kind of a constitutive relation which allows us to derive $I_{\lambda\omega}^{(r)}$ from $I_{\lambda\omega}^{(i)}$ if we are to have a *complete* description of the radiation process. In the next section we will examine black body radiation as a first step toward obtaining this complete description.

*8.4 Black Body Radiation

We have seen in the previous section that the interaction of a stream of photons with a solid surface can be quite complex. A fraction of the photons can be absorbed, and this fraction may depend on the energy and the angle of incidence of the photons. This functional dependence is indicated by the subscripts on $\alpha_{\lambda\omega}$ as defined by Eq. 8.3-14. Those incident photons which are not absorbed are reflected, and the reflection process can also be quite complex. Two simple types of reflection are *specular reflection* (angle of reflectance equal to angle of incidence) and *diffuse reflection*. In the latter case the direction in which a photon leaves a surface is independent of the incoming flight direction. This means that $I_{\lambda\omega}^{(r)}$ is independent of $\mathbf{\Omega}$, i.e.,

$$I_{\lambda\omega}^{(r)} = \text{function of } \lambda \text{ alone for diffuse reflection}$$

Other more complex types of reflection can occur; however, we will not cover them in this text. A qualitative description of diffuse reflection can be given as follows: Imagine that we could place an observer anywhere on the hemisphere shown in Fig. 8.3.5. This observer is capable of detecting photons in the frequency range λ to $\lambda + d\lambda$ that are reflected from the surface at the origin of the hemisphere which pass through an area element of fixed magnitude, dA_ω. If the reflection is diffuse our observer detects the same flux of reflected photons anywhere on the hemisphere. If the reflection is specular the flux of photons that our observer would detect would depend entirely on the angular distribution of the incident radiation. Such a situation leads to extremely complex calculations and surfaces are often assumed to be diffuse in order to simplify the analysis of radiant energy transfer. Even the analysis of *diffuse surfaces*† is difficult, and rather than tackle this problem we will back off a bit and study surfaces which absorb *all* incident radiation. Certainly this is a highly simplified situation, still there is much to be learned from the study of such surfaces which are termed *black surfaces*, or more generally *black bodies*. We *define* a black body in the following way:

A black body absorbs all incident radiant energy

The radiant energy which such a body emits is referred to as *black body radiation*; however, we must be careful to remember that a black body is *defined* in terms of its absorption characteristics (i.e., $\alpha_{\lambda\omega} = 1$ for all λ and ω) rather than its emission characteristics.

Not only does a black body give us a surface that is quite susceptible to analysis, but it is an experimentally realizable body. Consider the cavity shown in Fig. 8.4.1. If the hole in the cavity is very small and the cavity is very large, any radiation entering the hole is quite unlikely to ever escape being absorbed in the cavity and then returning out of the hole. If the cavity were made of a *perfectly* reflecting material then *all* the incident radiation would eventually escape through the hole; however, for any real cavity constructed in the laboratory this is not possible. We will assume then that a cavity, with a hole in it, can be constructed such that all radiation incident upon the hole is absorbed in the cavity. Under these circumstances we can say

A hole in a cavity acts as a black body

†The term *diffuse surface* generally refers to a surface which both reflects *and* emits diffusely.

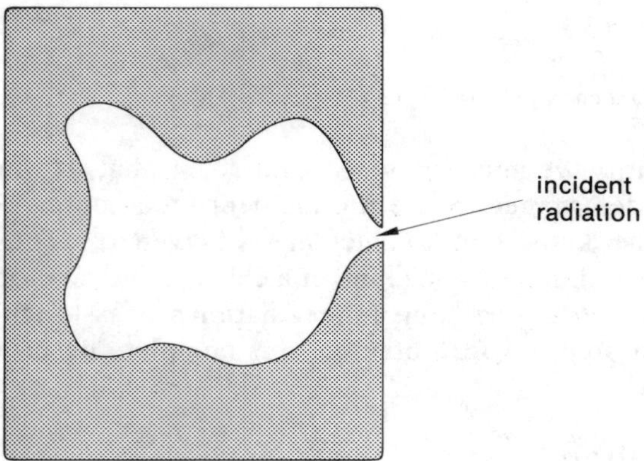

Fig. 8.4.1 Cavity radiation.

It is understood here that by "hole" we mean "small hole" and by "cavity" we mean "large cavity." It is clear that all holes in cavities absorb like black bodies, but is the emitted radiation from each cavity the same at the same temperature? If it is not, then the idea of black body radiation is of little use to us.

We can determine something about cavity radiation if we consider two cavities made of different materials but at the same temperature and joined together at a small hole as shown in Fig. 8.4.2. All the radiation emitted by cavity I and striking the hole is absorbed by II and vice versa. If both cavities are at the same temperature the system will be at steady state, thus the energy transported from I to II must be equal to that transported from II to I. We express the equivalence of the radiant energy transfer at the hole as

$$\int_{A_{hole}} \int_0^\infty \int_{2\pi} q^{(e)}_{\lambda\omega,\mathrm{I}}\, d\lambda\, d\omega\, dA = \int_{A_{hole}} \int_0^\infty \int_{2\pi} q^{(e)}_{\lambda\omega,\mathrm{II}}\, d\lambda\, d\omega\, dA \tag{8.4-1}$$

Carrying out the integration over all solid angles and wavelengths allows us to express this result in terms of the total hemispherical emitted fluxes.

$$\int_{A_{hole}} [q_{\mathrm{I}}^{(e)} - q_{\mathrm{II}}^{(e)}]\, dA = 0 \tag{8.4-2}$$

Since the area of the hole is arbitrary, subject only to the restriction that it be small compared to the cavity, the integrand must be zero, and we have

$$q_{\mathrm{I}}^{(e)} = q_{\mathrm{II}}^{(e)} \tag{8.4-3}$$

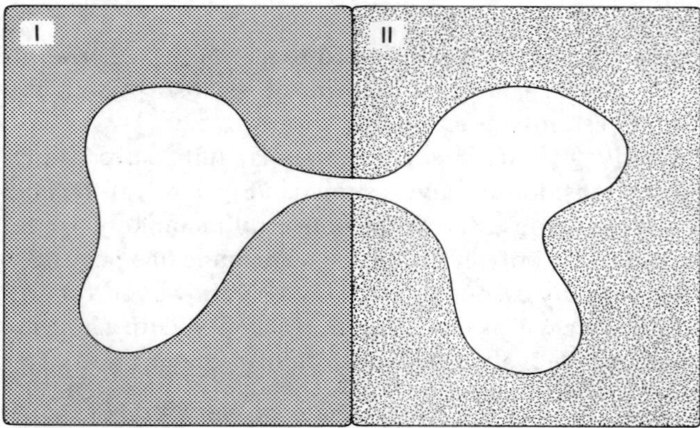

Fig. 8.4.2 Radiant energy exchange between two cavities.

Thus the *total* radiant energy per unit time per unit area emitted by a cavity is independent of the material of the cavity and depends only on the temperature. But what of the distribution of the emitted radiant energy? Is $q_\lambda^{(e)}$ independent of the cavity material?

To examine this question we imagine that we have at our disposal a series of filters which allow only the passage of a narrow range of wavelengths, i.e., we have filters which pass wavelengths in the range λ to $\lambda + \Delta\lambda$. We insert such filters between the two cavities I and II as illustrated in Fig. 8.4.3. Since there can be no net exchange of energy between cavities we have

$$\int_{A_{\text{hole}}} q_{\lambda,\text{I}}^{(e)} \Delta\lambda \, dA = \int_{A_{\text{hole}}} q_{\lambda,\text{II}}^{(e)} \Delta\lambda \, dA \tag{8.4-4}$$

Here the integral over all frequencies used in Eq. 8.4-1 has been dropped owing to the existence of the band pass filter placed between the two cavities. Since the area of the hole is arbitrary subject only to the restriction that it be small compared to the cavity we obtain

$$q_{\lambda,\text{I}}^{(e)} = q_{\lambda,\text{II}}^{(e)} \tag{8.4-5}$$

In summary, these two thought experiments, which are based on the appealing intuitive assumption that *a hole in a cavity absorbs all incident radiation,* have demonstrated that:

> The *total hemispherical flux*, $q^{(e)}$, and the *hemispherical flux*, $q_\lambda^{(e)}$, emitted by a hole in a cavity depends only on the temperature of the cavity and is independent of the material of which the cavity is made†

Now we can begin to see that the radiation in a cavity has some rather universal characteristics which will allow us to use this type of radiation as a suitable standard for comparing radiation from other bodies. For example, let us assume that we have a *body*, not a hole in a cavity, which absorbs all incident radiation. It is thus a black body in the sense that a hole in a cavity is a black body, but does it *emit* the same type of radiation that a hole in a cavity emits? Let us perform a thought experiment in order to explore this question. Take any black body, place it in a cavity at some uniform temperature, and let it come to equilibrium. Because the body can be neither losing nor accumulating energy we have

$$\int_{\mathscr{A}_{\text{body}}} \int_0^\infty (q_{\lambda,\text{cavity}}^{(i)} - q_{\lambda,\text{body}}^{(e)}) \, d\lambda \, dA = 0 \tag{8.4-6}$$

Since the limits of integration for the wavelength are *not* arbitrary we can say nothing definite about the

†A question can be raised here about the existence of sufficiently narrow band pass filters so that our thought experiments could in actual fact be carried out in the laboratory. If such filters *don't* exist can we use them in thought experiments? The answer is yes provided their existence would not violate some experimentally observed law of physics.

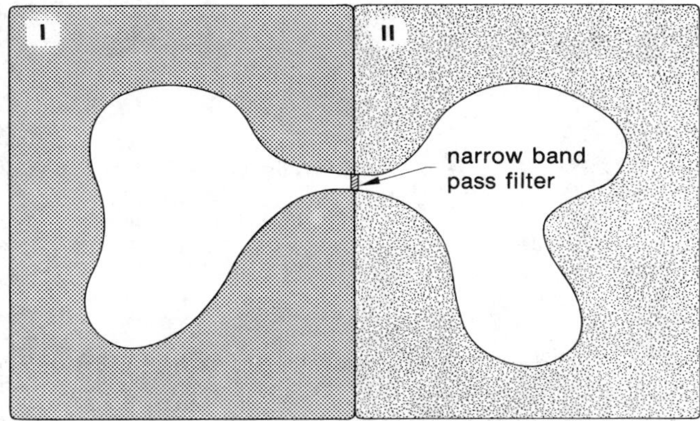

Fig. 8.4.3 Narrow band radiant energy exchange between two cavities.

integrand, it must either be identically zero or take on both positive and negative values. Let us extend our thought experiment to surround our body with a perfectly reflecting shield everywhere except for a small hole which we cover with one of the filters we used in the previous thought experiment. This situation is illustrated in Fig. 8.4.4. When the body comes to equilibrium with the cavity we obtain

$$\int_{A_{\text{hole}}} (q^{(i)}_{\lambda,\text{cavity}} - q^{(e)}_{\lambda,\text{body}})\Delta\lambda \, dA = 0 \tag{8.4-7}$$

Since the area of the hole is arbitrary we can now say

$$q^{(i)}_{\lambda,\text{cavity}} = q^{(e)}_{\lambda,\text{body}} \tag{8.4-8}$$

in the limit as $\Delta\lambda \to 0$. We now *define* cavity radiation as black body radiation and write

$$q^{(i)}_{\lambda,\text{cavity}} = q^{(e)}_{b,\lambda} \tag{8.4-9}$$

thus Eq. 8.4-8 indicates that a body which absorbs all incident radiation emits radiation in a very definite manner, i.e., it emits the same type of radiation that is observed coming from a hole in a cavity which is at the same temperature as the body. We must ask one more question before our discussion of black body radiation is complete, that is: Are the emission characteristics which we have found for our body shown in Fig. 8.4.4 dependent on the incident radiation? Put another way: If we remove our body from the cavity, maintaining the temperature of the body constant, will it continue to emit radiation that is characteristic of cavity radiation? It seems plausible and throughout our studies of thermal radiation we will assume that:

> The nature of the radiation emitted from a surface depends only on the thermodynamic and mechanical state of the surface

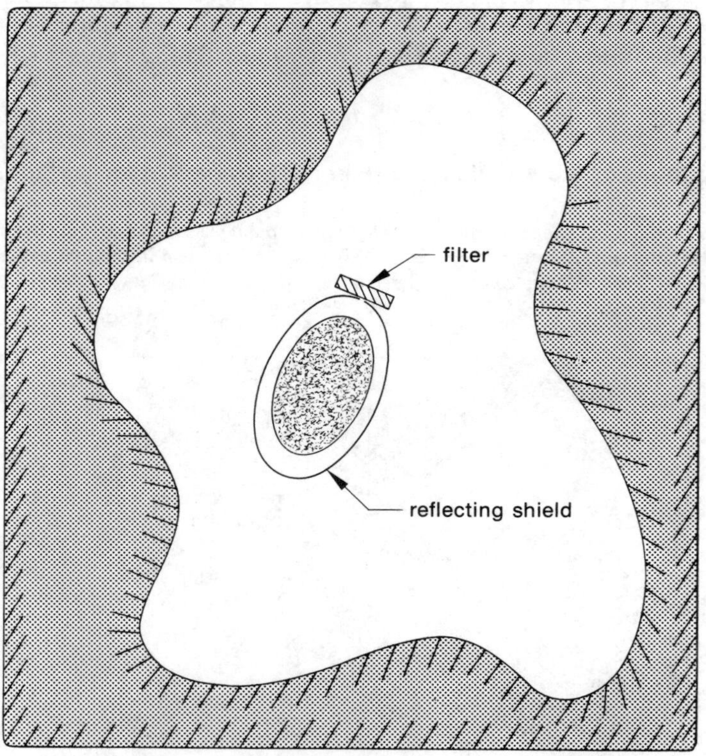

Fig. 8.4.4 Narrow band radiant energy exchange in a cavity.

This is essentially an extension of what Planck [6] refers to as *Prevost's Principle*, and acceptance of this assumption rules out the possible study of fluorescence for there the emitted radiation clearly depends on the incident radiation.

The results deduced here by a series of thought experiments have also been obtained by Planck† who applied the ideas of quantum mechanics to thermal radiation. Planck was able to show that the specific intensity for a cavity at thermal equilibrium is‡

$$I_{b,\lambda\omega} = \frac{2hc^2}{\lambda^5} \frac{1}{e^{hc/\lambda kT} - 1}, \quad \text{Planck's law} \tag{8.4-10}$$

where h is Planck's constant and k is Boltzmann's constant. Eq. 8.4-10 is known as *Planck's radiation law* and it is in excellent agreement with experimental measurements of cavity radiation.

We can use Eq. 8.4-10 to determine the hemispherical emitted flux by integrating $q^{(e)}_{b,\lambda\omega} = I^{(e)}_{b,\lambda\omega}|\mathbf{\Omega} \cdot \mathbf{n}|$ over the solid angle 2π.

$$q^{(e)}_{b,\lambda} = \int_{2\pi} I^{(e)}_{b,\lambda\omega}|\mathbf{\Omega} \cdot \mathbf{n}|\, d\omega \tag{8.4-11}$$

From Fig. 8.4.5 we see that

$$|\mathbf{\Omega} \cdot \mathbf{n}| = \mathbf{\Omega} \cdot \mathbf{n}' = \cos\theta \tag{8.4-12}$$

†See Reference 6.

‡Note that $I_{b,\lambda\omega}$ is independent of direction implying that cavity radiation is isotropic. Proof of this will be left as an exercise for the student.

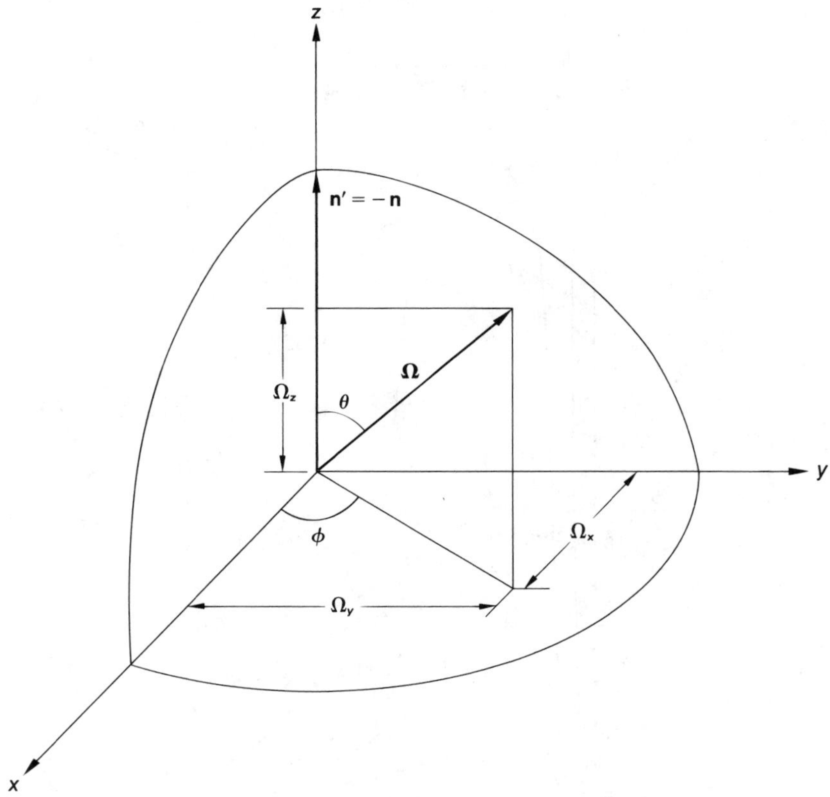

Fig. 8.4.5 Geometry for radiation into a hemisphere.

thus an explicit expression for $q^{(e)}_{b,\lambda}$ is

$$q^{(e)}_{b,\lambda} = \int_{\phi=0}^{\phi=2\pi} \int_{\theta=0}^{\theta=\pi/2} \left(\frac{2hc^2}{\lambda^5}\right)\left(\frac{1}{e^{hc/\lambda kT}-1}\right) \cos\theta \sin\theta \, d\theta \, d\phi \tag{8.4-13}$$

Carrying out the integration yields

$$q^{(e)}_{b,\lambda} = \left(\frac{2\pi hc^2}{\lambda^5}\right)\left(\frac{1}{e^{hc/\lambda kT}-1}\right) \tag{8.4-14}$$

This result is plotted in Fig. 8.4.6. There we see that the temperature must be larger than 2000°K in order for a significant portion of the emitted radiation to be in the visible region, and for temperatures less than 1000°K virtually all the energy is emitted in the infrared region. It is important to keep in mind that many thermal radiation processes occur under conditions such that infrared radiation dominates the transport process. For these conditions the idea that "black absorbs and white reflects" may not be nearly as applicable as it is with solar radiation which lies predominately in the visible region. We can determine the wavelength, λ_{max}, for which $q^{(e)}_{b,\lambda}$ is a maximum by differentiating Eq. 8.4-14 with respect to λ and setting the result equal to zero.

$$0 = \frac{\partial q^{(e)}_{b,\lambda}}{\partial \lambda} = \frac{2\pi hc^2}{(e^{hc/\lambda kT}-1)^2}\left\{\frac{\lambda^{-7}hc}{kT} e^{hc/\lambda kT} - 5\lambda^{-6}(e^{hc/\lambda kT}-1)\right\} \tag{8.4-15}$$

This leads to

$$5\lambda = \frac{\left(\frac{hc}{kT}\right) e^{(1/\lambda)(hc/kT)}}{e^{(1/\lambda)(hc/kT)}-1} \tag{8.4-16}$$

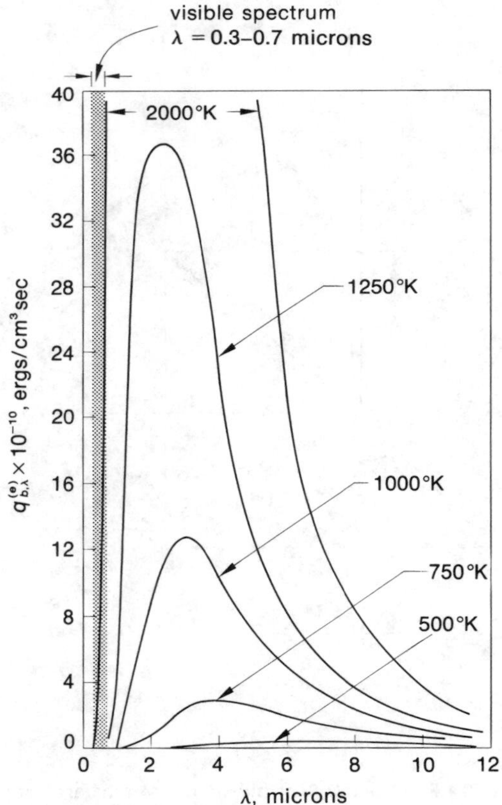

Fig. 8.4.6 Hemispherical flux for a black body.

which can be solved for λ_{max} as a function of (hc/kT). If we substitute the values,

$$h = 6.624 \times 10^{-27} \text{ erg sec}$$
$$c = 3.0 \times 10^{10} \text{ cm/sec}$$
$$k = 1.38 \times 10^{-16} \text{ erg/°K}$$

we obtain

$$\lambda_{max} T = 0.29 \text{ cm °K} \tag{8.4-17}$$

This result is known as Wien's displacement law[6], and it simply indicates that as the temperature increases, the dominant wavelength of the radiation will decrease.

The total hemispherical emitted flux for a black body can be obtained by integrating Eq. 8.4-14 over all wavelengths to obtain

$$q_b^{(e)} = \int_0^\infty q_{b,\lambda}^{(e)}\, d\lambda = \int_0^\infty \left(\frac{2\pi hc^2}{\lambda^5}\right)\left(\frac{1}{e^{hc/\lambda kT} - 1}\right) d\lambda \tag{8.4-18}$$

If we use a change of variable defined by

$$\eta = hc/\lambda kT, \qquad d\eta = -(hc/\lambda^2 kT)\, d\lambda$$

we can express $q_b^{(e)}$ as

$$q_b^{(e)} = -\int_{\eta=\infty}^{\eta=0} \left[\frac{2\pi k^4 T^4}{h^3 c^2}\right]\left[\frac{\eta^3}{e^\eta - 1}\right] d\eta \tag{8.4-19}$$

Changing the limits of integration and rearranging yields

$$q_b^{(e)} = \frac{2\pi k^4 T^4}{h^3 c^2} \int_0^\infty \frac{\eta^3}{e^\eta - 1}\, d\eta \tag{8.4-20}$$

The value of the definite integral is given by

$$\int_0^\infty \frac{\eta^3}{e^\eta - 1}\, d\eta = \frac{\pi^4}{15}$$

and Eq. 8.4-20 takes the form

$$q_b^{(e)} = \left(\frac{2\pi^5 k^4}{15 h^3 c^2}\right) T^4 \tag{8.4-21}$$

This result is generally written as

$$q_b^{(e)} = \sigma T^4 \tag{8.4-22}$$

where σ is the Stefan–Boltzmann constant having a value of 1.356×10^{-12} cal/cm^2 sec °K^4. This is a very important result since it illustrates the fourth power temperature dependence for black body radiation, and establishes the fact that radiant energy transfer becomes increasingly important as the temperature increases.

So far we have shown in this section that cavity radiation or black body radiation is a suitable standard with which to compare all other radiation. One point that we have not demonstrated is that a black body has the highest possible emission rate at any given temperature. This is easily proved by a thought experiment similar to those that we have already used and the proof will be left as an exercise for the student.

Example 8.4-1 Radiation losses and the basal metabolic rate

In this example we want to begin to think more quantitatively about a problem that was raised in Chapter 1, i.e., Prob. 1-15 which dealt with radiant energy exchange in a classroom. We consider a well-clothed student in a classroom at 70°F and assume that any clothing or skin exposed to the air is also at 70°F. In actual fact we know† that the average skin temperature will be about 93°F, and from our knowledge of conduction we know that the temperature of the outer surface of the clothing would be greater than 70°F in the absence of radiation. Nevertheless we will assume a surface temperature of 70°F and treat our student as a black body so that the energy *loss* owing to radiation is

$$\dot{Q}_{\text{loss}} = \sigma T^4 A$$

Here A is the surface area which is about 2 m². Substitution of the appropriate numbers leads to

$$\dot{Q}_{\text{loss}} = \left\{\left(\frac{1.356\times 10^{-12}\ \text{cal}}{\text{cm}^2\,\text{sec}\,°\text{K}^4}\right)(294\,°\text{K})^4(2\ \text{m}^2)\right\}\left\{\frac{10^4\ \text{cm}^2}{\text{m}^2}\right\}$$
$$= 203\ \text{cal/sec}$$

The basal metabolic rate‡ represents the rate at which the body dissipates energy and for the average adult is about 20–25 cal/sec. Here we have seen that radiant energy loss is about *ten times greater* than the basal metabolic rate and a student would quickly freeze if it were not for the radiant energy gained from the walls of the room. In Chapter 9 we will consider the complete radiant energy exchange process and see why small changes in the room temperature can cause significant changes in one's comfort. The details for this specific problem will be worked out in Ex. 9.1-1.

Summary of Section 8.5

In this section we extend the discussion of Sec. 8.4 to radiation in an enclosure which is not at equilibrium, and our thought experiments are extended to include the use of a $\lambda\omega$-photon filter which allows us to derive Kirchhoff's law,

$$\epsilon_{\lambda\omega} = \alpha_{\lambda\omega} \tag{8.5-9}$$

This result is of considerable help in calculating the specific absorbed flux,

$$q_{\lambda\omega}^{(a)} = \alpha_{\lambda\omega} I_{\lambda\omega}^{(i)} |\mathbf{\Omega}\cdot\mathbf{n}| \tag{8.5-2}$$

and the specific emitted flux,

$$q_{\lambda\omega}^{(e)} = \epsilon_{\lambda\omega} I_{b,\lambda\omega}^{(e)} |\mathbf{\Omega}\cdot\mathbf{n}| \tag{8.5-3}$$

One must always be careful to remember that Eq. 8.5-9 *cannot* be used to conclude that the total emissivity, ϵ, given by

$$q^{(e)} = \epsilon q_b^{(e)} \tag{8.5-23}$$

and the total absorptivity, α, given by

$$q^{(a)} = \alpha q^{(i)} \tag{8.5-24}$$

are equal, i.e., $\alpha \neq \epsilon$, for most processes.

The reason for this is that ϵ is a *material coefficient* depending only on the state of the surface, while α is a *process variable* depending both on the state of the surface and the nature of the incident radiation.

*8.5 Non-Black Bodies

We can learn something about the surfaces of non-black bodies by performing a more sophisticated version of the thought experiment illustrated in Fig. 8.4.4. From that experiment we learned something about the spectral distribution of cavity radiation by using a narrow band pass filter so that energy exchange between the body and the cavity could take place only in the range of wavelengths from λ to $\lambda + \Delta\lambda$ where $\Delta\lambda$ could be made arbitrarily small. Now we wish to use a device, illustrated in Fig. 8.5.1, which we will call a directional band pass filter. It will allow the passage of photons having wavelengths in

†See R. C. Seagrave, *Biomedical Applications of Heat and Mass Transfer*, Iowa State University Press, Ames, Iowa, 1971.
‡See W. F. Ganong, *Review of Medical Physiology*, Sixth Edition, Lange Medical Publications, Los Altos, Calif., 1973.

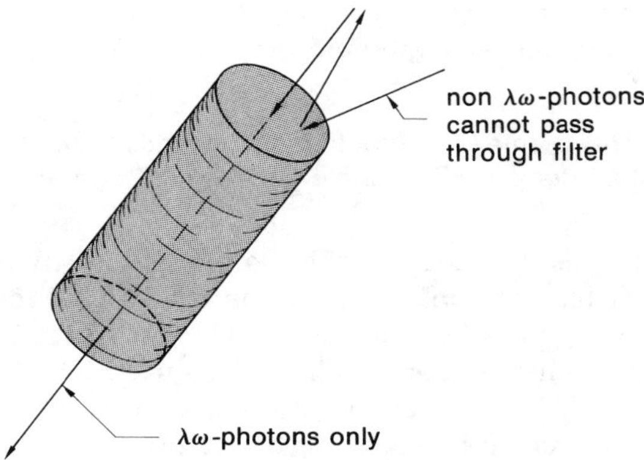

Fig. 8.5.1 Directional band pass filter.

the range λ to $\lambda + \Delta\lambda$, and having flight directions within a solid angle $\Delta\omega$ about the direction $\pm\mathbf{\Omega}$. Thus in terms of the terminology used in Secs. 8.2 and 8.3 we have a $\lambda\omega$-photon filter. The actual construction of such a filter presents something of a puzzle; however, as long as we cannot use such a filter to perform a thought experiment which violates the fundamental laws of physics we can assume that such a filter exists and can be used in our thought experiments.†

We now consider the thought experiment illustrated in Fig. 8.5.2. Our enclosure is made up of four different materials which are maintained at four different temperatures. In this enclosure we have placed a non-black body which has reached some steady-state temperature T_0. Note that the radiation in our enclosure is not *cavity* or *black body* radiation since the system is not at equilibrium. The four temperatures, T_1, T_2, T_3, and T_4, are controlled by the experimentalist while the temperature of the body, T_0, is not.

The body can exchange energy with its surroundings only through the $\lambda\omega$-photon filter, thus an energy balance on the body takes the form

$$q^{(e)}_{\lambda\omega} = q^{(a)}_{\lambda\omega} \tag{8.5-1}$$

Remember from Sec. 8.3 that the specific absorbed flux could be written in terms of the specific absorptivity as

$$q^{(a)}_{\lambda\omega} = \alpha_{\lambda\omega} q^{(i)}_{\lambda\omega} = \alpha_{\lambda\omega} I^{(i)}_{\lambda\omega} |\mathbf{\Omega} \cdot \mathbf{n}| \tag{8.5-2}$$

In Sec. 8.4 we found that black body radiation provided a suitable standard with which to compare all other radiation, thus we define the *specific emissivity* as

$$q^{(e)}_{\lambda\omega} = \epsilon_{\lambda\omega} q^{(e)}_{b,\lambda\omega} = \epsilon_{\lambda\omega} I^{(e)}_{b,\lambda\omega} |\mathbf{\Omega} \cdot \mathbf{n}| \tag{8.5-3}$$

Knowledge of $\alpha_{\lambda\omega}$ and $\epsilon_{\lambda\omega}$ would put us well on our way toward having a complete description of the radiation process, leaving only the problem of relating the reflected radiation to the incident radiation. In treating the specific emissivity and absorptivity we will make two assumptions which are essentially restatements of Prevost's Principle mentioned in Sec. 8.4. The first of these is:

> The specific emissivity $\epsilon_{\lambda\omega}$ may be a function of λ, $\mathbf{\Omega}$, and the *state of the surface*, but it is independent of the intensity of the incident and emitted radiation

As was mentioned earlier, the acceptance of this assumption excludes from our consideration such phenomena as fluorescence; however, it appears to be satisfactory for a wide range of heat transfer surfaces. By *state of the surface* we mean both the thermodynamic and the mechanical state, and for most

†For a discussion of this point see F. Reif, *Fundamentals of Statistical and Thermal Physics*, Sec. 9.15, McGraw-Hill Book Co., Inc., New York, 1965.

cases this means the temperature, the degree of roughness, and the chemical composition. A logical extension of the above assumption can be expressed as:

> The specific absorptivity $\alpha_{\lambda\omega}$ may be a function of λ, $\mathbf{\Omega}$, and the *state of the surface*, but it is independent of the intensity of the incident and emitted radiation

The physical content of these two assumptions is that photons essentially never undergo photon–photon collisions, and the photon fluxes that one encounters in practice are so low that the probability of two photons arriving at the same "absorption site" is negligible. Under these circumstances a photon striking a surface will not be influenced by other photons striking the surface, nor will it be influenced by other photons emitted from the surface. We might state our position more succinctly by saying that $\epsilon_{\lambda\omega}$ and $\alpha_{\lambda\omega}$ are *material properties* and are therefore independent of the process.

We can now return our attention to the energy balance on the body illustrated in Fig. 8.5.2. Substitution of Eqs. 8.5-2 and 8.5-3 into Eq. 8.5-1 yields

$$\epsilon_{\lambda\omega} I^{(e)}_{b,\lambda\omega} = \alpha_{\lambda\omega} I^{(i)}_{\lambda\omega} \tag{8.5-4}$$

which may be rearranged in the form

$$\frac{\epsilon_{\lambda\omega}}{\alpha_{\lambda\omega}} = \frac{I^{(i)}_{\lambda\omega}}{I^{(e)}_{b,\lambda\omega}} \tag{8.5-5}$$

We must be careful at this point to remember that the *enclosure* shown in Fig. 8.5.2 is not a *cavity*, thus we

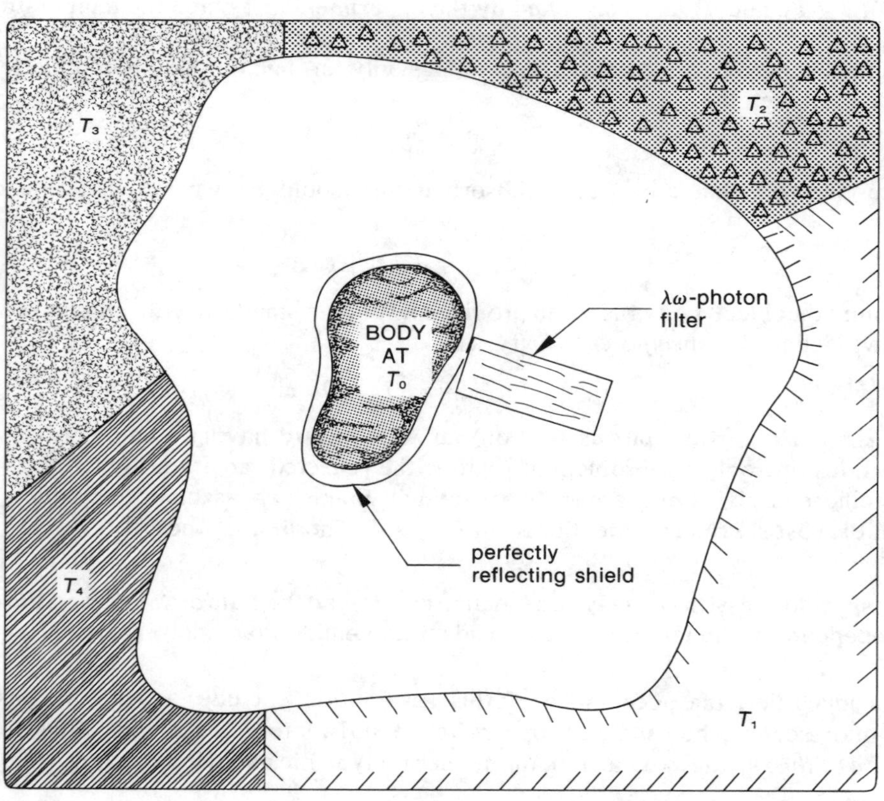

Fig. 8.5.2 Steady-state $\lambda\omega$-radiant energy exchange.

cannot say at this point that $I^{(i)}_{\lambda\omega}$ is cavity radiation. On the basis of our statements about $\epsilon_{\lambda\omega}$ and $\alpha_{\lambda\omega}$ we can write

$$\frac{\epsilon_{\lambda\omega}}{\alpha_{\lambda\omega}} = \frac{I^{(i)}_{\lambda\omega}}{I^{(e)}_{b,\lambda\omega}} = \mathscr{F}(\lambda, \mathbf{\Omega}, \text{ state of the surface}) \tag{8.5-6}$$

Now imagine that the following changes are made in our thought experiment pictured in Fig. 8.5.2. We hold our $\lambda\omega$-photon filter in place thus *fixing* the variables λ and $\mathbf{\Omega}$, and adjust the temperatures T_1, T_2, T_3, and T_4 so that

$$T_1 = T_2 = T_3 = T_4 = T_0 \tag{8.5-7}$$

In making this change we have kept λ, $\mathbf{\Omega}$, and the state of the surface *constant*, thus the value of the function $\mathscr{F}$ has not changed. However, the incident radiation is now cavity radiation, i.e., $I^{(i)}_{\lambda\omega} = I^{(e)}_{b,\lambda\omega}$, and Eq. 8.5-6 in conjunction with Eq. 8.5-5 takes the form

$$\frac{\epsilon_{\lambda\omega}}{\alpha_{\lambda\omega}} = 1 = \mathscr{F}(\lambda, \mathbf{\Omega}, \text{ state of the surface}) \tag{8.5-8}$$

Since this thought experiment can be performed for any values of λ and $\mathbf{\Omega}$, and for any state of the surface, we conclude that

$$\epsilon_{\lambda\omega} = \alpha_{\lambda\omega} \tag{8.5-9}$$

This is often referred to as Kirchhoff's law.

Very often in heat transfer problems we wish only to know the *hemispherical* radiant energy fluxes. These are given by

$$q_\lambda^{(a)} = \int_{2\pi} \alpha_{\lambda\omega} I^{(i)}_{\lambda\omega} |\mathbf{\Omega} \cdot \mathbf{n}| \, d\omega \tag{8.5-10}$$

$$q_\lambda^{(e)} = \int_{2\pi} \epsilon_{\lambda\omega} I^{(e)}_{b,\lambda\omega} |\mathbf{\Omega} \cdot \mathbf{n}| \, d\omega \tag{8.5-11}$$

In order to determine these quantities we need to know $\alpha_{\lambda\omega}$ and $\epsilon_{\lambda\omega}$ in addition to the incident intensity. In general $\alpha_{\lambda\omega}$ and $\epsilon_{\lambda\omega}$ are not available and one must make use of the *hemispherical* absorptivity and emissivity which are defined by

$$q_\lambda^{(a)} = \int_{2\pi} \alpha_{\lambda\omega} I^{(i)}_{\lambda\omega} |\mathbf{\Omega} \cdot \mathbf{n}| \, d\omega = \alpha_\lambda \int_{2\pi} I^{(i)}_{\lambda\omega} |\mathbf{\Omega} \cdot \mathbf{n}| \, d\omega \tag{8.5-12}$$

$$q_\lambda^{(e)} = \int_{2\pi} \epsilon_{\lambda\omega} I^{(e)}_{b,\lambda\omega} |\mathbf{\Omega} \cdot \mathbf{n}| \, d\omega = \epsilon_\lambda \int_{2\pi} I^{(e)}_{b,\lambda\omega} |\mathbf{\Omega} \cdot \mathbf{n}| \, d\omega \tag{8.5-13}$$

Because $I^{(e)}_{b,\lambda\omega}$ is independent of $\mathbf{\Omega}$ this last equation can be written as

$$\begin{aligned} q_\lambda^{(e)} &= \epsilon_\lambda I^{(e)}_{b,\lambda\omega} \int_{2\pi} |\mathbf{\Omega} \cdot \mathbf{n}| \, d\omega \\ &= \epsilon_\lambda \pi I^{(e)}_{b,\lambda\omega} \end{aligned} \tag{8.5-14}$$

In terms of the hemispherical black body emitted flux this result takes the form

$$q_\lambda^{(e)} = \epsilon_\lambda q^{(e)}_{b,\lambda} \tag{8.5-15}$$

where $q^{(e)}_{b,\lambda}$ is given by Eq. 8.4-14. The hemispherical emissivity is a very useful quantity for it depends *only* on the wavelength and the *state of the surface.* In conjunction with Eqs. 8.5-15 one can use ϵ_λ to calculate the hemispherical emission rate for any surface. The situation is not so simple with the hemispherical absorption rate. Let us rearrange the *definition* of α_λ so that we can see where the difficulty lies.

$$\alpha_\lambda = \frac{\int_{2\pi} \alpha_{\lambda\omega} I^{(i)}_{\lambda\omega} |\mathbf{\Omega} \cdot \mathbf{n}| \, d\omega}{\int_{2\pi} I^{(i)}_{\lambda\omega} |\mathbf{\Omega} \cdot \mathbf{n}| \, d\omega} \tag{8.5-16}$$

Here we see that α_λ depends not only on the *state of the surface* through $\alpha_{\lambda\omega}$, but it also depends on the *process* through $I^{(i)}_{\lambda\omega}$. If the incident radiation is black body radiation Eq. 8.5-16 reduces to

$$\alpha_\lambda = \frac{1}{\pi} \int_{2\pi} \alpha_{\lambda\omega} |\mathbf{\Omega} \cdot \mathbf{n}| \, d\omega, \quad \text{black body radiation} \tag{8.5-17}$$

and α_λ depends only on the state of the surface. If the surface is diffuse $\alpha_{\lambda\omega}$ is independent of $\mathbf{\Omega}$ and Eq. 8.5-16 leads to

$$\alpha_\lambda = \alpha_{\lambda\omega}, \quad \text{diffuse surfaces} \tag{8.5-18}$$

In terms of the hemispherical incident energy flux, Eq. 8.5-12 can be written as

$$q_\lambda^{(a)} = \alpha_\lambda q_\lambda^{(i)} \tag{8.5-19}$$

which can be used along with Eq. 8.5-15 to compute net rates of energy exchange provided we know ϵ_λ and α_λ for the *particular process in question.*

Often experimental values for ϵ_λ and α_λ are unavailable and we must be content to work with the *total, hemispherical* absorptivity and emissivity. These are defined as

$$\alpha = \frac{\int_0^\infty \int_{2\pi} \alpha_{\lambda\omega} I^{(i)}_{\lambda\omega} |\mathbf{\Omega} \cdot \mathbf{n}| \, d\omega \, d\lambda}{\int_0^\infty \int_{2\pi} I^{(i)}_{\lambda\omega} |\mathbf{\Omega} \cdot \mathbf{n}| \, d\omega \, d\lambda} \tag{8.5-20}$$

$$\epsilon = \frac{\int_0^\infty \int_{2\pi} \epsilon_{\lambda\omega} I^{(e)}_{b,\lambda\omega} |\mathbf{\Omega} \cdot \mathbf{n}| \, d\omega \, d\lambda}{\int_0^\infty \int_{2\pi} I^{(e)}_{b,\lambda\omega} |\mathbf{\Omega} \cdot \mathbf{n}| \, d\omega \, d\lambda} \tag{8.5-21}$$

Because $I^{(e)}_{b,\lambda\omega}$ is independent of $\mathbf{\Omega}$ the definition of ϵ reduces to

$$\epsilon = \frac{\int_0^\infty \epsilon_\lambda I^{(e)}_{b,\lambda\omega} \, d\lambda}{\int_0^\infty I^{(e)}_{b,\lambda\omega} \, d\lambda} \tag{8.5-22}$$

In terms of the total fluxes we can express this result as

$$q^{(e)} = \epsilon q_b^{(e)} = \epsilon \sigma T^4 \tag{8.5-23}$$

where the total emissivity depends only on the *state of the surface.* The total rate of absorption can be expressed in a similar manner as;

$$q^{(a)} = \alpha q^{(i)} \tag{8.5-24}$$

however, we must remember that the total absorptivity depends on the *process* as well as the *state of the surface.*

Now that we have properly defined the absorptivities $\alpha_{\lambda\omega}$, α_λ, and α, and the emissivities $\epsilon_{\lambda\omega}$, ϵ_λ, and ϵ, we should explore the experimental methods used to determine these quantities and present some experimental results for some typical surfaces. However, we cannot appreciate the experimental methods until we have learned something about the solution of radiant energy transfer problems, and this will be done in the first four sections of the next chapter.

Solution to Design Problem VIII

To develop a qualitative explanation of the phenomena occurring in Lake Tahoe we need only consider the simple process of a stream of photons passing through an absorbing medium. From the photon transport equation and the Lambert–Beer law discussed in Sec. 8.2 we conclude that the intensity of a stream of photons is given by

$$I = I_0 \, e^{-\beta C x} \tag{VIII-1}$$

Here I_0 is the intensity at the surface of the lake; I is the intensity at a depth, x; the algae concentration is denoted by C, and β is the so-called *extinction coefficient*. Regardless of the algae concentration, all of the radiant energy which penetrates the surface is absorbed in the lake. If the lake is very clear some of this energy is absorbed very deep in the lake; if the lake is very "murky" most of the energy is absorbed near the surface. We can use Eq. VIII-1 to show that 90 per cent of the penetrating radiation is absorbed in a depth L given by

$$L = 2.3/\beta C \tag{VIII-2}$$

Here we see that as the concentration of the algae increases the region in which most of the radiation is absorbed is more closely confined to the surface. This would explain why the surface water is getting warmer in the summer, but why would it get colder in the winter? The answer is simply this: the radiant energy absorbed by the lake is essentially constant from year to year, but as the surface water becomes warmer the *energy lost* at the surface owing to radiation, conduction, and convection (evaporation) *increases* and the total energy content of the lake *decreases*. As a result the average water temperature (not just the surface water) is slowly decreasing and the future may indeed bring a frozen Lake Tahoe some winter and the accompanying ecological changes.

PROBLEMS†

VIII-1. If the intensity is given by Eq. VIII-1, derive an expression for the temperature distribution in the lake. Because of the great depth of the lake, the temperature at the bottom can be taken to be constant at $T_0 = 4°C$. Assume that the conductive heat flux at the surface of the lake can be represented by $h(T_i - T_a)$ where T_i is the surface temperature and T_a is the ambient temperature.

8-1. (8.2) About 70 per cent of the radiation emitted by the earth is absorbed by the water vapor and carbon dioxide in the earth's atmosphere. This energy is then re-emitted toward the earth and outer space. Above 10000 ft with a clear sky radiation emitted by the earth escapes to outer space with negligible absorption in the earth's atmosphere. Under these circumstances what is the effective value of βC in Eq. 8.2-12.

8-2. (8.2) Show that $\mathbf{q}^R = 0$ if $n_{\lambda\omega}$ is independent of $\mathbf{\Omega}$.

8-3. (8.2) Use order-of-magnitude analysis to show that the characteristic time for radiation transport is on the order of L/c, and is thus negligible for the typical heat transfer problem.

8-4. (8.3) When radiation emitted from a surface is independent of direction, i.e., $I_{\lambda\omega}^{(e)}$ is independent of $\mathbf{\Omega}$, the radiation is termed *diffuse*. Show that for such radiation $q_\lambda^{(e)}$ is equal to $\pi I_{\lambda\omega}^{(e)}$.

8-5. (8.3) For diffuse radiation from a surface show that the energy emitted within the cone bounded by $0 \leq \theta \leq \eta$ is given by $q_\lambda^{(e)}(1 - \cos^2 \eta)$.

***8-6.** (8.3) Extend the development given in Ex. 8.3-1 to include transient effects, emission and absorption, thus leading to the complete photon transport equation.

8-7. (8.5) Prove that ϵ_λ for any body is always less than or equal to 1. Do this by assuming that the body in the cavity shown in Fig. 8.4.4 has an emissivity greater than 1, and then noting the obvious contradiction.

8-8. (8.4) Prove that cavity radiation is isotropic, i.e., $I_{\lambda\omega}$ is independent of $\mathbf{\Omega}$. Hint: Make use of the $\lambda\omega$-photon filter described in Sec. 8.5 and consider a two-cavity thought experiment such as that shown in Fig. 8.4.3.

8-9. (8.4) Use Wien's displacement law to estimate the temperature of the sun.

†Problem numbered VIII-1 deals directly with Design Problem VIII, and problems marked with an asterisk (*) are concerned with the solved example problems.

***8-10.** (8.4) In Ex. 8.4-1 we found that the rate of radiant energy emitted (*not the net rate of radiant energy exchange*) by a person was large compared to the basal metabolic rate. It would be interesting to compare the rate of radiant energy emitted to the rate of energy loss owing to convection. To do this assume a surface temperature of 90°F and estimate a free-convection film heat transfer coefficient from the material given in Sec. 7.9.

8-11. (8.5) Prove that $\alpha_\lambda = \epsilon_\lambda$ when the incident radiation is black body radiation under equilibrium conditions.

8-12. (8.5) If $\epsilon_{\lambda\omega}$ and $\alpha_{\lambda\omega}$ are independent of $\mathbf{\Omega}$, i.e., the surface is diffuse, prove that $\alpha_\lambda = \epsilon_\lambda$.

8-13. (8.5) Show how Eq. 8.5-22 is obtained from Eq. 8.5-21.

8-14. (8.5) Prove that $\alpha = \epsilon$ when the incident radiation is black body radiation under equilibrium conditions.

8-15. (8.5) A *gray* surface is one for which $\alpha_{\lambda\omega}$ and $\epsilon_{\lambda\omega}$ are independent of both $\mathbf{\Omega}$ and λ. Prove that $\alpha = \epsilon$ for such surfaces.

REFERENCES

1. Fletcher, J. O., "Polar Ice and the Global Climate Machine," *Bulletin of Atomic Scientists*, Dec. 1970.
2. Oster, G., "The Chemical Effects of Light," *Scientific American* **219**, 158, Sept. 1968.
3. Weiskopf, V. F., "How Light Interacts with Matter," *Scientific American* **219**, 174, Sept. 1968.
4. Calder, A. B., *Photometric Methods of Analysis*, Amer. Elsevier Pub. Co., Inc., New York, 1969.
5. Whitaker, S., *Introduction to Fluid Mechanics*, Prentice-Hall, Inc., Englewood Cliffs, N.J., 1968.
6. Planck, M., *The Theory of Heat Radiation*, Dover Publications, Inc., New York, 1959.

Design Problem IX

In order not to miss a fantastic sunrise a hardy climber has bivouacked on the summit block of Mt. Whitney as illustrated in Fig. IX.1. If the summit was reached at midnight and the sun rises at 5:00 A.M., how many chocolate bars, at 3×10^5 calories† per bar, must the climber consume in order to just balance his loss of energy owing to radiation? It might be reasonable to assume that the air temperature is 20°F and that the climber is well clothed in wool pants and down jacket. If our sun watcher snuggles up against a nearby vertical wall, how much is his candy consumption reduced? Assume a clear sky so that there is no radiation from clouds to the climber.

Fig. IX.1 Bivouac on Mt. Whitney summit.

†These are scientific calories, i.e., the energy required to raise the temperature of 1 gram of water 1°C. For a detailed discussion of food requirements and energy losses see *Freedom of the Hills*, The Mountaineers, P.O. Box 122, Seattle, Wash., 1967.

9

Radiant Energy Exchange

In the previous chapter the phenomenon of thermal radiation was explored and the $\lambda\omega$-photon transport equation was derived.

$$\frac{\partial n_{\lambda\omega}}{\partial t} + \nabla \cdot (n_{\lambda\omega} c \mathbf{\Omega}) = e_{\lambda\omega} - a_{\lambda\omega} \tag{1}$$

From this fundamental equation we could obtain the specific intensity transport equation

$$\frac{1}{c}\left(\frac{\partial I_{\lambda\omega}}{\partial t}\right) + \nabla \cdot (I_{\lambda\omega}\mathbf{\Omega}) = \mathscr{E}_{\lambda\omega} - \mathscr{A}_{\lambda\omega} \tag{2}$$

There are many important processes for which absorption and emission are negligible except at phase interfaces, and since terrestrial radiant energy exchange is always quasi-steady the specific intensity equation can be simplified to

$$\nabla \cdot (I_{\lambda\omega}\mathbf{\Omega}) = 0 \tag{3}$$

Integration of Eq. 3 over all wavelengths and over the solid angle 4π yields the radiant energy flux equation

$$\nabla \cdot \mathbf{q}^R = 0 \tag{4}$$

where

$$\mathbf{q}^R = \int_0^\infty \int_{4\pi} I_{\lambda\omega}\mathbf{\Omega}\, d\omega\, d\lambda \tag{5}$$

If we are interested in the radiant energy transport process in a region $\mathscr{V}$ bounded by the surface area $\mathscr{A}$ we can integrate Eq. 4 over the volume $\mathscr{V}$ and use the divergence theorem to obtain

$$\int_{\mathscr{A}} \mathbf{q}^R \cdot \mathbf{n}\, dA = 0 \tag{6}$$

The quantity $\mathbf{q}^R \cdot \mathbf{n}$ represents the *net* radiant energy flux at the surface $\mathscr{A}$, and can be expressed as†

$$\mathbf{q}^R \cdot \mathbf{n} = \int_0^\infty \int_{2\pi} \alpha_{\lambda\omega} I_{\lambda\omega}^{(i)} |\mathbf{\Omega} \cdot \mathbf{n}|\, d\omega\, d\lambda - \int_0^\infty \int_{2\pi} I_{\lambda\omega}^{(r)} |\mathbf{\Omega} \cdot \mathbf{n}|\, d\omega\, d\lambda - \int_0^\infty \int_{2\pi} \epsilon_{\lambda\omega} I_{b,\lambda\omega}^{(e)} |\mathbf{\Omega} \cdot \mathbf{n}|\, d\omega\, d\lambda \tag{7}$$

Here we are reminded that in order to solve this simple (steady-state, no absorption or emission, and negligible scattering) class of radiant energy exchange problems we must know $\alpha_{\lambda\omega} = \epsilon_{\lambda\omega}$ and be able to compute $I_{\lambda\omega}^{(r)}$ given $I_{\lambda\omega}^{(i)}$. At this point we do not even know how to measure $\epsilon_{\lambda\omega}$ or $\alpha_{\lambda\omega}$, thus we will back up a bit to the very simplest of all radiant exchange problems, i.e., black body radiation where $\epsilon_{\lambda\omega} = \alpha_{\lambda\omega} = 1$ and $I_{\lambda\omega}^{(r)} = 0$. Solution of the black body radiation problem will provide us with some experience with a new type of analysis. We can then proceed with some degree of confidence to more complex problems.

†Remember that it is our inability to express $\mathbf{q}^R$ in terms of *local conditions* that forces us into the type of analysis to be discussed in this chapter.

*9.1 Black Body Radiant Energy Exchange

In treating the problem of radiant energy exchange between black bodies it is convenient to define a *view factor* F_{ij} as follows:

$$F_{ij} = \begin{Bmatrix} \text{the fraction of radiant} \\ \text{energy leaving the} \\ i\text{th surface which is} \\ \text{incident upon the } j\text{th} \\ \text{surface} \end{Bmatrix} \tag{9.1-1}$$

Often the view factor is denoted by $F_{i\to j}$ or $F_{A_i \to A_j}$ in order to clearly indicate that the radiant energy is *emitted* by the ith surface and is *incident* upon the jth surface; however, we will work with the simpler notation given by Eq. 9.1-1. For the case of an enclosure containing N surfaces we note that the view factors must satisfy the constraint

$$\sum_{j=1}^{j=N} F_{ij} = 1 \tag{9.1-2}$$

where i is any integer between 1 and N. This expression simply means that all the radiant energy emitted by the ith surface is incident upon the surfaces $j = 1, 2, \ldots, N$. It should be clear that F_{ii} need not be zero, for it is quite possible for a surface to "see itself" as is illustrated in Fig. 9.1.1. From that figure it also becomes clear that F_{ij} need not be equal to F_{ji}, although this situation can occur and does in this example when $\theta = \pi$.

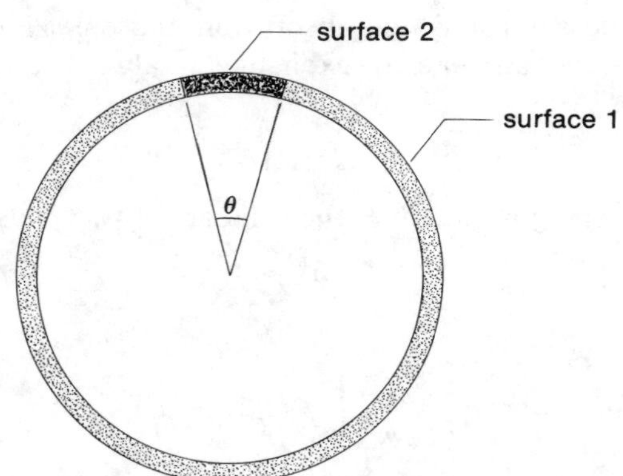

Fig. 9.1.1 View factors. ($F_{11} \sim 1, F_{12} \ll 1, F_{21} \sim 1, F_{22} \sim 0.$)

If the view factor F_{12} is known and the rate of emission of radiant energy is uniform over surface 1, then the rate of incident radiation upon surface 2 from surface 1 is given by

$$\dot{Q}_{12}^{(i)} = \underbrace{F_{12}}_{\substack{\text{fraction of radiation}\\ \text{leaving surface 1}\\ \text{incident upon}\\ \text{surface 2}}} \underbrace{(q_1^{(e)} A_1)}_{\substack{\text{total rate of}\\ \text{emission from}\\ \text{surface 1}}} \tag{9.1-3}$$

As usual we use $\dot{Q}$ to represent energy/time, and the superscript (i) indicates that this is incident radiation while the subscript 12 follows the view factor convention, i.e., $\dot{Q}_{12}^{(i)}$ represents energy/time *emitted* from surface 1 and *incident* upon surface 2. In this section we will be treating only black body surfaces so that the incident radiation is the absorbed radiation; however, this will not be true for the more general case and we wish to keep this in mind.

As an example of the determination of a view factor we will analyze the radiant energy transfer from surface 1 to surface 2 illustrated in Fig. 9.1.2. From Sec. 8.3 we know

$$\left\{\begin{array}{l}\text{radiant energy emitted in the } \mathbf{\Omega} \text{ direction per} \\ \text{unit time, per unit surface area, per unit} \\ \text{wavelength, per unit solid angle}\end{array}\right\} = I_{\lambda\omega}^{(e)}\mathbf{\Omega}\cdot\mathbf{n}. \tag{9.1-4}$$

Here $\mathbf{n}$ is taken to be the outwardly directed unit normal pointing *into* the photon gas phase. If we multiply Eq. 9.1-4 by dA_1 we have an expression for the energy leaving dA_1,

$$\left\{\begin{array}{l}\text{radiant energy emitted from } dA_1 \text{ in the } \mathbf{\Omega} \\ \text{direction per unit time, per unit wavelength,} \\ \text{per unit solid angle}\end{array}\right\} = I_{\lambda\omega}^{(e)}\mathbf{\Omega}\cdot\mathbf{n}_1\, dA_1 \tag{9.1-5}$$

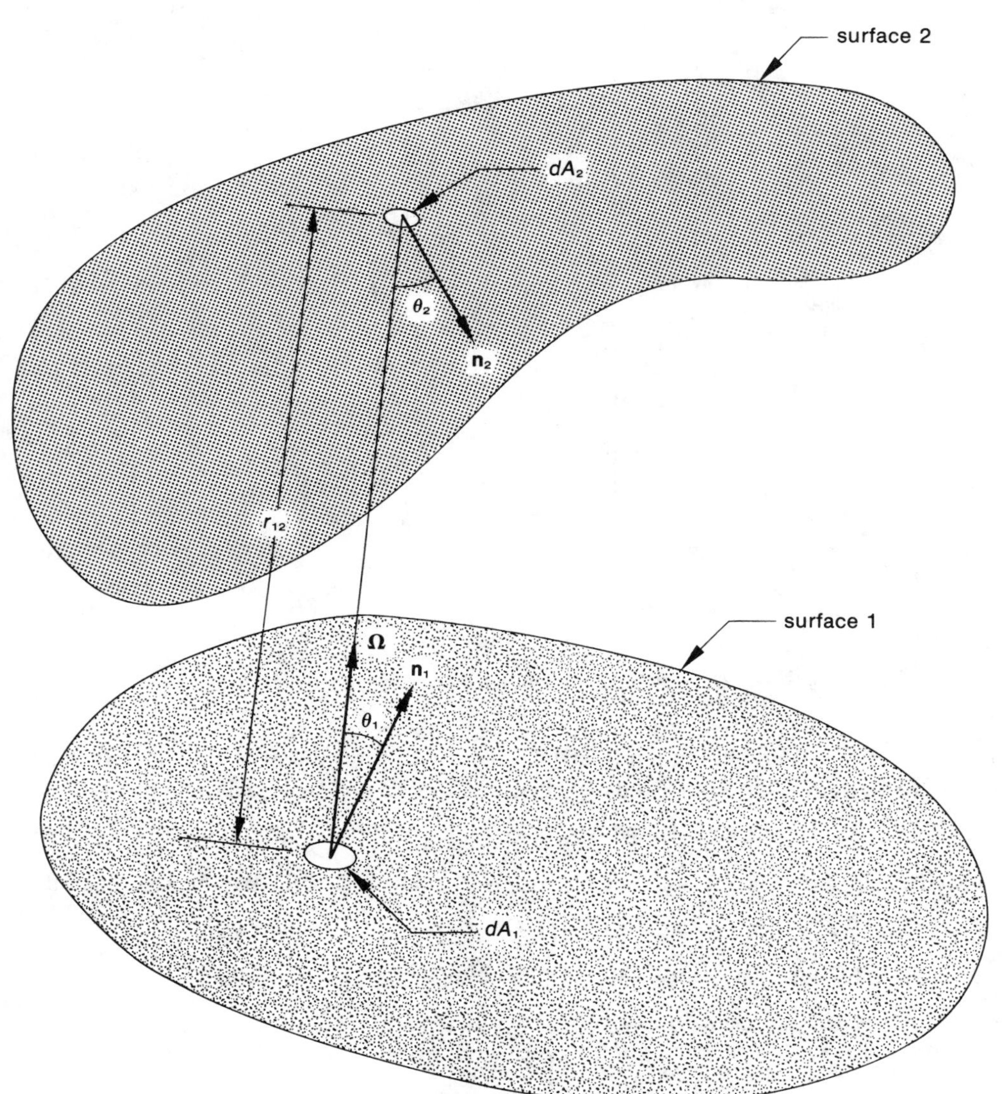

Fig. 9.1.2 Radiant energy exchange between two surfaces.

Here we have denoted the unit normal by $\mathbf{n}_1$ in accordance with Fig. 9.1.2. The question that we need to answer now is: How much of the energy which leaves dA_1 on surface 1 is incident upon the element of area dA_2 on surface 2? From Fig. 9.1.3 we can see that all the energy emitted which lies within the solid angle $d\omega$ is incident upon dA_2, the relation between dA_2 and dA_ω being the same as that illustrated in Fig. 8.3.3. We can now multiply Eq. 9.1-5 by $d\omega$ and write

$$\left\{\begin{array}{l}\text{radiant energy emitted from } dA_1 \\ \text{and incident upon } dA_2 \text{ per unit time,} \\ \text{per unit wavelength}\end{array}\right\} = I_{\lambda\omega}^{(e)}\boldsymbol{\Omega}\cdot\mathbf{n}_1\, dA_1\, d\omega \tag{9.1-6}$$

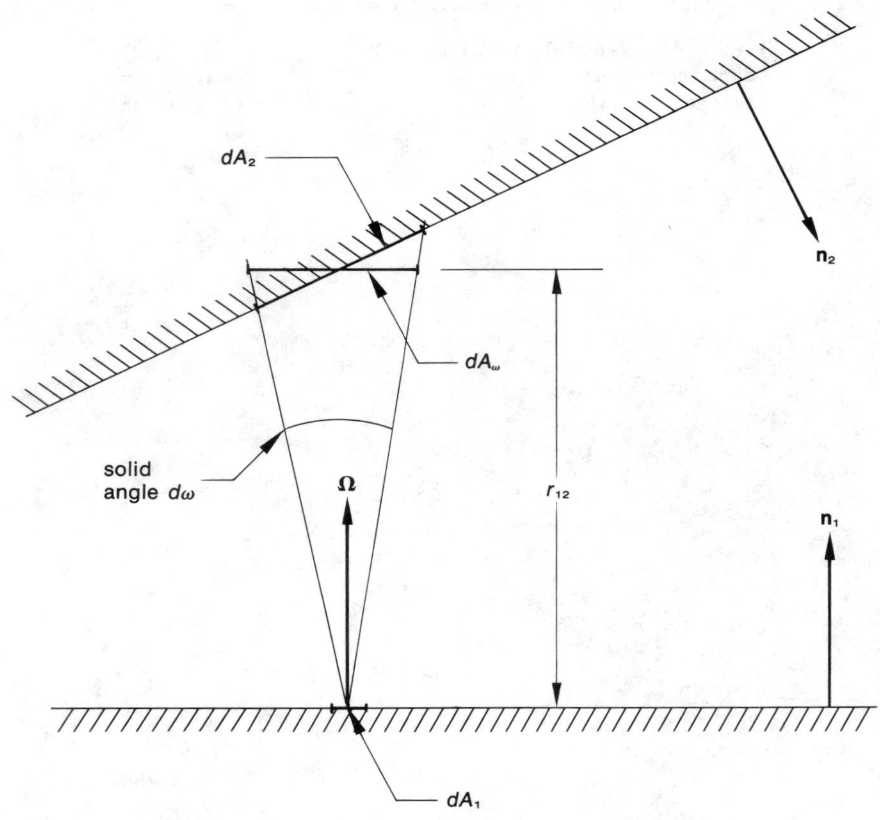

Fig. 9.1.3 Geometrical considerations for radiant energy exchange.

If we think of $d\omega$ in Fig. 9.1.3 as being made arbitrarily small, then the area dA_ω is just the surface area element of a sphere of radius r_{12} contained within the solid angle $d\omega$ and is given by†

$$dA_\omega = r_{12}^2\, d\omega \tag{9.1-7}$$

As we have noted previously in Sec. 8.3 the area dA_2 is related to dA_ω by the expression

$$dA_\omega = (-\boldsymbol{\Omega}\cdot\mathbf{n}_2)\, dA_2 \tag{9.1-8}$$

Substitution of Eqs. 9.1-7 and 9.1-8 into Eq. 9.1-6 yields

$$\left\{\begin{array}{l}\text{radiant energy emitted from } dA_1 \\ \text{and incident upon } dA_2 \text{ per unit time,} \\ \text{per unit wavelength}\end{array}\right\} = \left(\frac{I_{\lambda\omega}^{(e)}}{r_{12}^2}\right)(\boldsymbol{\Omega}\cdot\mathbf{n}_1)(-\boldsymbol{\Omega}\cdot\mathbf{n}_2)\, dA_1\, dA_2 \tag{9.1-9}$$

†See Fig. 8.3.5.

From Fig. 9.1.2 we can see that

$$\mathbf{\Omega} \cdot \mathbf{n}_1 = \cos \theta_1$$

$$-\mathbf{\Omega} \cdot \mathbf{n}_2 = \cos \theta_2$$

so we can express Eq. 9.1-9 as

$$\left\{\begin{array}{l}\text{radiant energy emitted from } dA_1 \\ \text{and incident upon } dA_2 \text{ per unit time,} \\ \text{per unit wavelength}\end{array}\right\} = \left(\frac{I_{\lambda\omega}^{(e)}}{r_{12}^2}\right) \cos \theta_1 \cos \theta_2 \, dA_1 \, dA_2 \tag{9.1-10}$$

To get $\dot{Q}_{12}^{(i)}$ from Eq. 9.1-10 we need to integrate over A_1, A_2, and all possible wavelengths to obtain

$$\dot{Q}_{12}^{(i)} = \int_{A_2} \int_{A_1} \int_0^\infty \left(\frac{I_{\lambda\omega}^{(e)}}{r_{12}^2}\right) \cos \theta_1 \cos \theta_2 \, d\lambda \, dA_1 \, dA_2 \tag{9.1-11}$$

Evaluation of these integrals in the general case is extremely difficult; however, if the specific intensity $I_{\lambda\omega}^{(e)}$ is independent of $\mathbf{\Omega}$, i.e., the surface is *diffuse*, we can write†

$$\int_0^\infty I_{\lambda\omega}^{(e)} \, d\lambda = \frac{q^{(e)}}{\pi} \tag{9.1-12}$$

so that Eq. 9.1-11 takes the form

$$\dot{Q}_{12}^{(i)} = \int_{A_1} \int_{A_2} \left(\frac{q_1^{(e)}}{\pi r_{12}^2}\right) \cos \theta_1 \cos \theta_2 \, dA_1 \, dA_2, \quad \text{for diffuse surfaces} \tag{9.1-13}$$

Up to this point we have avoided using a subscript on $I_{\lambda\omega}^{(e)}$ to indicate that this was the specific intensity emitted from surface 1 because we were rather overburdened with subscripts. Now, however, the nomenclature is simplified somewhat and we denote the total hemispherical emitted flux from surface 1 by $q_1^{(e)}$. If $q_1^{(e)}$ is constant over surface 1 we can simplify Eq. 9.1-13 to obtain

$$\dot{Q}_{12}^{(i)} = \left\{\frac{1}{\pi A_1} \int_{A_2} \int_{A_1} \left(\frac{1}{r_{12}^2}\right) \cos \theta_1 \cos \theta_2 \, dA_1 \, dA_2\right\} q_1^{(e)} A_1 \tag{9.1-14}$$

Comparing this result with Eq. 9.1-3 we see that the view factor F_{12} is given by

$$F_{12} = \frac{1}{\pi A_1} \int_{A_2} \int_{A_1} \left(\frac{1}{r_{12}^2}\right) \cos \theta_1 \cos \theta_2 \, dA_1 \, dA_2 \tag{9.1-15}$$

The general expression for the view factor F_{ij} can now be written as

$$F_{ij} = \frac{1}{\pi A_i} \int_{A_j} \int_{A_i} \left(\frac{1}{r_{ij}^2}\right) \cos \theta_i \cos \theta_j \, dA_i \, dA_j \tag{9.1-16}$$

By interchanging i and j we obtain an expression for F_{ji},

$$F_{ji} = \frac{1}{\pi A_j} \int_{A_i} \int_{A_j} \left(\frac{1}{r_{ji}^2}\right) \cos \theta_j \cos \theta_i \, dA_j \, dA_i \tag{9.1-17}$$

Since $r_{ij} = r_{ji}$, and since the value of the integral is independent of the order of integration we can see from Eqs. 9.1-16 and 9.1-17 that

$$A_i F_{ij} = A_j F_{ji} \tag{9.1-18}$$

which we will refer to as the *reciprocity condition.* This result is completely general, for the special case illustrated in Fig. 9.1.1 this gives us

$$A_1 F_{12} = A_2 F_{21} \tag{9.1-19}$$

Calculation of the view factors can be quite a tedious task; however, once they have been calculated

†Here we are making use of a result from Prob. 8-4.

the energy transfer problem becomes quite simple provided we restrict our system to black bodies. For example, if surfaces 1 and 2 in Fig. 9.1.1 are black bodies at uniform temperatures T_1 and T_2 we can express $q_1^{(e)}$ and $q_2^{(e)}$ as†

$$q_1^{(e)} = \sigma T_1^4 \quad \text{and} \quad q_2^{(e)} = \sigma T_2^4$$

and the *net* radiant energy transfer from surface 1 to surface 2 is

$$\begin{aligned} \dot{Q}_{12} &= \dot{Q}_{12}^{(i)} - \dot{Q}_{21}^{(i)} \\ &= \sigma T_1^4 F_{12} A_1 - \sigma T_2^4 F_{21} A_2 \end{aligned} \tag{9.1-20}$$

Here we have used the fact that the incident radiation is the absorbed radiation when the surfaces are black. Making use of Eq. 9.1-19 we can express $\dot{Q}_{12}$ as

$$\dot{Q}_{12} = A_1 F_{12} \sigma (T_1^4 - T_2^4), \quad \text{for black body radiation} \tag{9.1-21}$$

If we know the uniform temperatures of two black surfaces and the view factor for these two surfaces, the radiant energy exchange between the two surfaces is easily computed by Eq. 9.1-21. At this point we have done nothing more than rederive Eq. 1.3-20 in a more rigorous manner than was given in Chapter 1. However, we have laid the groundwork for the solution of more complex black body radiation problems (Sec. 9.3), and gray body radiation problems (Sec. 9.7).

Example 9.1-1 Radiant energy exchange in the classroom

We are now ready to enhance our understanding of the radiant energy exchange process first mentioned in Prob. 1-15, and considered briefly in Ex. 8.4-1. Remember that our problem dealt with the radiant energy exchange for a student in a classroom during the summer and the winter. We will assume that the air temperature in the room is constant at 70°F, and that the wall temperature varies from 65°F in the winter to 75°F in the summer.

In this example we wish to calculate the rate of energy loss from a body and compare it to the basal metabolic rate which is about 20 cal/sec for the average individual in a relaxed state. The energy loss will occur by radiation, evaporation, free convection, and respiration cooling. The rate of energy loss can be expressed as

$$\begin{Bmatrix} \text{total rate} \\ \text{of energy} \\ \text{loss} \end{Bmatrix} = \begin{Bmatrix} \text{rate of} \\ \text{radiant} \\ \text{energy loss} \end{Bmatrix} + \begin{Bmatrix} \text{rate of energy} \\ \text{loss owing to} \\ \text{evaporation} \end{Bmatrix} + \begin{Bmatrix} \text{rate of energy} \\ \text{loss owing to} \\ \text{free convection} \end{Bmatrix} + \begin{Bmatrix} \text{rate of energy} \\ \text{loss owing} \\ \text{to respiration} \end{Bmatrix} \tag{1}$$

In order to calculate these energy losses, we will approximate our student in the following manner:

(a) The total surface area will be 2 m^2 and 90 per cent of this area will be covered with clothes or hair.

(b) The covered area, designated as A_1, will be at room temperature and will exchange energy by radiation alone. This means that our student is well clothed with long pants, long-sleeved shirt, sweater, etc.

(c) The exposed surface area, designated as A_2, will be at 93°F and will exchange energy by free convection and radiation.

We can write Eq. 1 more explicitly as

$$\begin{Bmatrix} \text{total rate} \\ \text{of energy} \\ \text{loss} \end{Bmatrix} = A_1 F_{13} \sigma (T_1^4 - T_3^4) + A_2 F_{23} \sigma (T_2^4 - T_3^4) + \dot{Q}_{\text{evap}} + h A_2 (T_2 - T_1) + \dot{Q}_{\text{resp}} \tag{2}$$

indicating that we intend to treat the student and the surrounding walls as black surfaces. The wall temperature is designated by T_3, the room temperature (70°F) by T_1, and the skin temperature (93°F) by T_2. Seagrave‡ indicates that the respiratory losses amount to approximately 2.7 cal/sec and the evaporation losses at the skin and surface of the lungs contribute about 2.0 cal/sec, thus

$$\dot{Q}_{\text{evap}} = 2.7 \text{ cal/sec} \tag{3}$$

†See Eq. 8.4-18.

‡R. C. Seagrave, *Biomedical Applications of Heat and Mass Transfer*, The Iowa State University Press, Ames, Iowa, 1971.

$$\dot{Q}_{resp} = 2.0 \text{ cal/sec} \tag{4}$$

and we are left with the problem of estimating the free-convection losses and the radiant energy exchange.

In order to estimate a film heat transfer coefficient we will assume a characteristic length of 6 in. and refer to the material in Sec. 7.9 to write

$$N_{Gr}N_{Pr} = \left(\frac{\beta \Delta T g L^3}{\nu^2}\right)\left(\frac{\nu}{\alpha}\right) = \Delta T L^3 \left(\frac{\beta g \rho^2 c_p}{\mu k}\right)$$

where

$$(\beta g \rho^2 c_p / \mu k) = 1.53 \times 10^6/\text{ft}^3\,°\text{F}$$
$$L = 6 \text{ in.}$$
$$\Delta T = 23°\text{F}$$

Under these circumstances the product of the Grashof number times the Prandtl number is given by $N_{Gr}N_{Pr} = 4.40 \times 10^6$. Referring to Figs. 7.9.1 and 7.9.2, we can determine the Nusselt number for horizontal cylinders and vertical plates:

$$N_{Nu} = 23.4, \quad \text{horizontal cylinder}$$
$$N_{Nu} = 26.6, \quad \text{vertical plate}$$

We choose the average value as an estimate of the free-convection Nusselt number for the exposed surface of the body and determine the film heat transfer coefficient to be

$$\begin{aligned} h &= N_{Nu}k/L \\ &= (25.0)(0.0154 \text{ Btu/hr ft °F})/(0.5 \text{ ft}) \\ &= 0.77 \text{ Btu/hr ft}^2 °\text{F} \end{aligned}$$

Taking the area of the exposed surface to be $A_2 = (0.1)(2 \text{ m}^2) = 0.2 \text{ m}^2$ we find the free-convection loss to be

$$\begin{aligned} hA_2(T_2 - T_1) &= \left\{\left(\frac{0.77 \text{ Btu}}{\text{hr ft}^2 °\text{F}}\right)(0.2 \text{ m}^2)(23°\text{F})\left(\frac{1 \text{ ft}^2}{0.093 \text{ m}^2}\right)\left(\frac{252 \text{ cal}}{\text{Btu}}\right)\left(\frac{\text{hr}}{3600 \text{ sec}}\right)\right\} \\ &= 2.7 \text{ cal/sec} \end{aligned} \tag{5}$$

In order to determine the radiant energy loss we need to know the view factors F_{13} and F_{23}. We will guess that $F_{23} = 1.0$, i.e., all the radiation from the exposed surface is incident upon the walls of the room, and $F_{13} = 0.85$, i.e., 15 per cent of the radiation *emitted* from the covered surface is *incident* upon the covered surface while the remaining 85 per cent strikes the walls. This estimate of F_{13} attempts to take care of the radiation from the inside surface of the arms and legs. For wintertime conditions (wall temperature = 65°F) we find the radiant energy loss from the covered surface to be

$$A_1F_{13}\sigma(T_1^4 - T_3^4) = \left[\frac{(0.9)(2 \text{ m}^2)(0.85)(1.356 \times 10^{-12} \text{ cal})}{\text{cm}^2 \text{ sec °K}^4}\right][(294.27°\text{K})^4 - (291.49°\text{K})^4]\left[\frac{10^4 \text{ cm}^2}{\text{m}^2}\right] = 5.8 \text{ cal/sec} \tag{6}$$

while the loss from the exposed surface is given as

$$\begin{aligned} A_2F_{23}\sigma(T_2^4 - T_3^4) &= \left[\frac{(0.1)(2 \text{ m}^2)(1.0)(1.356 \times 10^{-12} \text{ cal})}{\text{cm}^2 \text{ sec °K}^4}\right][(307.05°\text{K})^4 - (291.49°\text{K})^4]\left[\frac{10^4 \text{ cm}^2}{\text{m}^2}\right] \\ &= 4.5 \text{ cal/sec} \end{aligned} \tag{7}$$

Substituting Eqs. 3 through 7 into Eq. 2 yields the total rate of energy loss

$$\begin{aligned} \left\{\begin{matrix}\text{total rate} \\ \text{of energy} \\ \text{loss}\end{matrix}\right\} &= 5.8 \text{ cal/sec} + 4.5 \text{ cal/sec} + 2.7 \text{ cal/sec} + 2.7 \text{ cal/sec} + 2.0 \text{ cal/sec} \\ &= 17.7 \text{ cal/sec}, \quad \text{wintertime} \end{aligned}$$

Since the basal metabolic rate is about 20 cal/sec our student probably feels a bit warm under the conditions we have provided, for he or she is losing less energy than is being dissipated by the body. Probably rolling up the sleeves would suffice to bring the rate of energy loss up to the standard basal metabolic rate.

In the summertime we take the wall temperature to be 75°F, and the calculations given by Eqs. 6 and 7 lead to

$$A_1F_{13}\sigma(T_1^4 - T_3^4) = -6.0 \text{ cal/sec} \tag{8}$$

$$A_2F_{23}\sigma(T_2^4 - T_3^4) = 3.0 \text{ cal/sec} \tag{9}$$

Here we see that there is a net gain in energy owing to the radiant energy exchange, and substitution of Eqs. 3, 4, 5, 8, and 9 into Eq. 2 gives

$$\begin{Bmatrix}\text{total rate}\\ \text{of energy}\\ \text{loss}\end{Bmatrix} = -6.0 \text{ cal/sec} + 3.0 \text{ cal/sec} + 2.7 \text{ cal/sec} + 2.7 \text{ cal/sec} + 2.0 \text{ cal/sec}$$

$$= 4.4 \text{ cal/sec}, \quad \text{summertime}$$

Under these circumstances our student would be sweating profusely in order to increase the evaporative losses, or peeling off clothes to increase the convective and radiative losses. Just how much clothing must be removed will be left as an exercise for the student.

The crux of black body radiation calculations is surely the determination of the view factors, for once they are known simple algebra leads to the desired rate of radiant energy exchange. Before going on to a discussion of the determination of view factors, it would be best to review the nomenclature used in this and subsequent sections. For the view factors F_{jk} we intend the meaning

$$F_{jk} = \begin{Bmatrix}\text{the fraction of radiant energy}\\ \textit{leaving} \text{ the } j\text{th surface which}\\ \text{is } \textit{incident} \text{ upon the } k\text{th surface}\end{Bmatrix} \tag{9.1-22}$$

For all practical purposes the view factor is restricted in its use to diffuse, uniform surfaces. This definition was given earlier as Eq. 9.1-1. By $\dot{Q}_{jk}^{(i)}$ we mean

$$\dot{Q}_{jk}^{(i)} = \begin{Bmatrix}\text{rate of energy } \textit{emitted} \text{ from the}\\ j\text{th surface which is } \textit{incident}\\ \text{upon the } k\text{th surface}\end{Bmatrix} \tag{9.1-23}$$

The energy which is emitted by the jth surface and absorbed by the kth surface is naturally denoted by

$$\dot{Q}_{jk}^{(a)} = \begin{Bmatrix}\text{rate of energy } \textit{emitted} \text{ from}\\ \text{the } j\text{th surface which is}\\ \textit{absorbed} \text{ by the } k\text{th surface}\end{Bmatrix} \tag{9.1-24}$$

By $\dot{Q}_{jk}$ we mean the net rate of exchange between the jth and kth surfaces, thus

$$\dot{Q}_{jk} = \dot{Q}_{jk}^{(a)} - \dot{Q}_{kj}^{(a)} \tag{9.1-25}$$

and it follows that

$$\dot{Q}_{jk} = -\dot{Q}_{kj} \tag{9.1-26}$$

Finally we note that $\dot{Q}_j$ means the net rate of exchange between the jth surface and all other surfaces. For an enclosure containing N surfaces $\dot{Q}_j$ is defined as

$$\dot{Q}_j = \sum_{k=1}^{k=N} \dot{Q}_{jk} \tag{9.1-27}$$

*9.2 Evaluation of View Factors

In order to illustrate the procedure that one can use to calculate a view factor, we consider the two surfaces shown in Fig. 9.2.1. In order to evaluate the integral in Eq. 9.1-13 we need to express r_{12}, $\cos\theta_1$, $\cos\theta_2$, dA_1, and dA_2 in terms of x, y, and z. To express r_{12}^2 in terms of x, y, and z, we first construct the vectors locating dA_1 and dA_2,

$$\mathbf{r}_1 = \mathbf{i}x_1 + \mathbf{j}y_1 \tag{9.2-1}$$

$$\mathbf{r}_2 = \mathbf{j}y_2 + \mathbf{k}z_2 \tag{9.2-2}$$

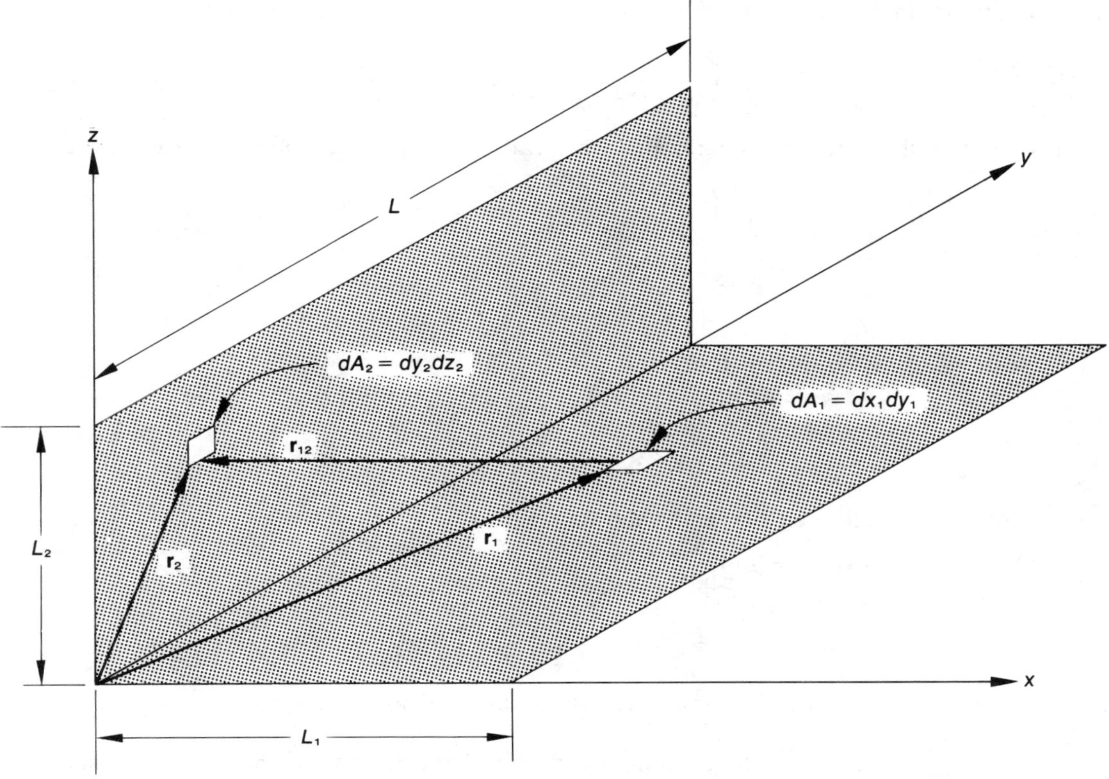

Fig. 9.2.1 Radiant energy exchange between orthogonal rectangular plates.

Note that the use of subscripts on x and z is superfluous since there can be no confusion that x locates dA_1 and z locates dA_2; however, we will carry the subscripts in order to keep the nomenclature consistent. The vector from dA_1 pointing to dA_2 is given by

$$\mathbf{r}_{12} = \mathbf{r}_2 - \mathbf{r}_1 = -\mathbf{i}x_1 + \mathbf{j}(y_2 - y_1) + \mathbf{k}z_2 \tag{9.2-3}$$

and the magnitude squared, r_{12}^2, becomes

$$r_{12}^2 = \mathbf{r}_{12} \cdot \mathbf{r}_{12} = x_1^2 + (y_2 - y_1)^2 + z_2^2 \tag{9.2-4}$$

The cosines of θ_1 and θ_2 can be easily computed by use of the vector equations,

$$\cos\theta_1 = \mathbf{k} \cdot \left(\frac{\mathbf{r}_{12}}{r_{12}}\right) \tag{9.2-5a}$$

$$\cos\theta_2 = \mathbf{i} \cdot \left(\frac{-\mathbf{r}_{12}}{r_{12}}\right) \tag{9.2-5b}$$

which lead to

$$\cos\theta_1 = z_2/\sqrt{x_1^2 + (y_2 - y_1)^2 + z_2^2} \tag{9.2-6a}$$

$$\cos\theta_2 = x_1/\sqrt{x_1^2 + (y_2 - y_1)^2 + z_2^2} \tag{9.2-6b}$$

We have already indicated in Fig. 9.1.4 that the differential areas are given by

$$dA_1 = dx_1\, dy_1$$

$$dA_2 = dy_2\, dz_2$$

thus all the quantities in the integrand in Eq. 9.1-13 are expressed in terms of x, y, and z and we can write

$$F_{12} = \frac{1}{\pi L_1 L} \int_{z_2=0}^{z_2=L_2} \int_{y_2=0}^{y_2=L} \int_{y_1=0}^{y_1=L} \int_{x_1=0}^{x_1=L_1} \left(\frac{1}{x_1^2 + (y_2 - y_1)^2 + z_2^2}\right) \left(\frac{x_1 z_2}{x_1^2 + (y_2 - y_1)^2 + z_2^2}\right) dx_1\, dy_1\, dy_2\, dz_2 \quad (9.2\text{-}7)$$

If we use L as the characteristic length, Eq. 9.2-7 can be put in dimensionless form to yield

$$F_{12} = \frac{1}{\pi \mathscr{L}_1} \int_0^{\mathscr{L}_2} \int_0^1 \int_0^1 \int_0^{\mathscr{L}_1} \frac{X_1 Z_2}{[X_1^2 + (Y_2 - Y_1)^2 + Z_2^2]^2} dX_1\, dY_1\, dY_2\, dZ_2 \quad (9.2\text{-}8)$$

where

$$\mathscr{L}_1 = L_1/L$$
$$\mathscr{L}_2 = L_2/L$$
$$X_1 = x_1/L$$
$$Y_1 = y_1/L$$
$$Y_2 = y_2/L$$
$$Z_2 = z_2/L$$

The integration in Eq. 9.2-8 can be performed to yield

$$F_{12} = \frac{1}{\pi \mathscr{L}_1} \left\{ \frac{1}{4} \ln \left[\frac{(1 + \mathscr{L}_1^2 + \mathscr{L}_2^2)^{\mathscr{L}_1^2 + \mathscr{L}_2^2 - 1} (\mathscr{L}_1^2)^{\mathscr{L}_1^2} (\mathscr{L}_2^2)^{\mathscr{L}_2^2}}{(1 + \mathscr{L}_1^2)^{\mathscr{L}_1^2 - 1} (1 + \mathscr{L}_2^2)^{\mathscr{L}_2^2 - 1} (\mathscr{L}_1^2 + \mathscr{L}_2^2)^{\mathscr{L}_1^2 + \mathscr{L}_2^2}} \right] + \mathscr{L}_1 \tan^{-1}\left(\frac{1}{\mathscr{L}_1}\right) + \mathscr{L}_2 \tan^{-1}\left(\frac{1}{\mathscr{L}_2}\right) - (\mathscr{L}_1^2 + \mathscr{L}_2^2)^{1/2} \tan^{-1} \frac{1}{(\mathscr{L}_1^2 + \mathscr{L}_2^2)^{1/2}} \right\} \quad (9.2\text{-}9)$$

Values of F_{12} have been obtained [1] for a range of values of $\mathscr{L}_1$ and $\mathscr{L}_2$, and the results are shown in Fig. 9.2.2.

There are many configurations for which view factors have already been calculated, and one should always attempt to find and use published results before plunging into the tedious task of either analytical or numerical evaluation of the integrals defining the view factor. In addition to the view factor for two orthogonal plates having a common edge, Hamilton and Morgan [1] have calculated F_{12} for parallel rectangular plates of the same size. These results are shown in Fig. 9.2.3, and can be used with the values given in Fig. 9.2.2 to determine all the view factors for radiation within a rectangular parallelepiped. In Fig. 9.2.4 we have shown values of F_{12} (curves 1, 2, 3, and 4) for parallel disks, squares, and rectangles. The values for squares and rectangles are already given in Fig. 9.2.3, and the view factors, F_{12} and F_{21}, for parallel disks of unequal diameter are the object of an exercise for the student. The view factors $\bar{F}_{12}$ shown in Fig. 9.2.4 are for parallel surfaces which are bounded by orthogonal *reradiating surfaces*. Systems of this type are discussed in Sec. 9.4.

In Fig. 9.2.5 we have shown view factors for concentric, coaxial cylinders of equal length; the case of cylinders of infinite length is given as an exercise for the student to prove using only intuition. Fig. 9.2.6 gives the view factor F_{12} for two configurations involving infinite cylinders, and one should always remember that the view factor F_{21} can be obtained by means of the reciprocity condition given by Eq. 9.1-18. In Fig. 9.2.7 we have shown the view factor F_{PT} (plate to tube) which represents the fraction of radiant energy leaving the infinite flat plate and incident upon the row of infinite tubes. In heat exchangers the ratio C/D rarely exceeds 3.0, thus we can see that only a small fraction of the radiant energy leaving the flat plate would travel directly to the third and more distance rows. It will be left as an exercise for the student to find the upperbound for F_{P3} from the data given in Fig. 9.2.7.

Alternate view factors

It is important to realize that a variety of other view factors can be calculated or estimated using the information given in Figs. 9.2.2 through 9.2.7. In order to do so we should remember the definition† of the

†See Eq. 9.1-16 for the mathematical definition.

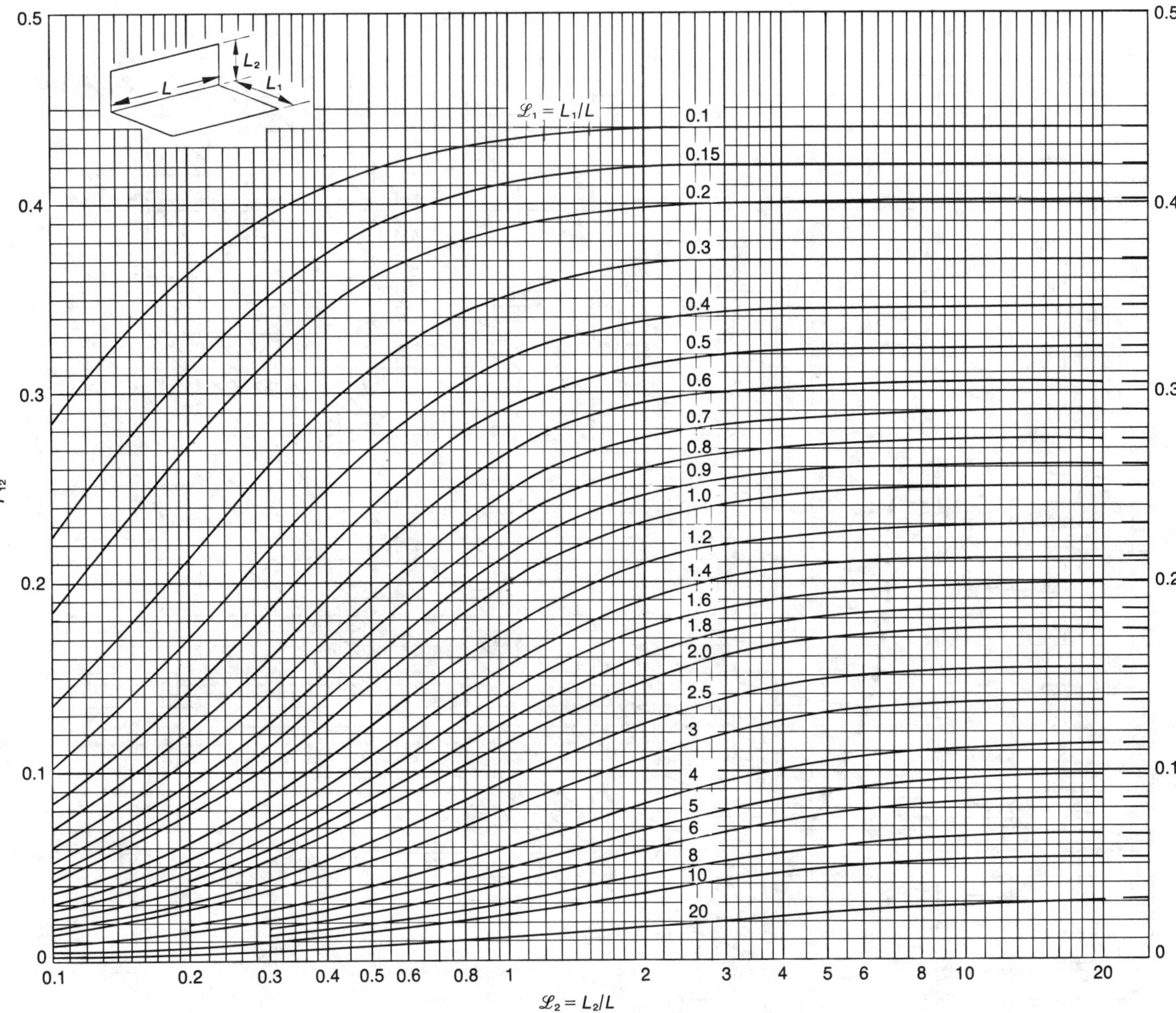

Fig. 9.2.2 View factors for two orthogonal rectangles having a common edge.

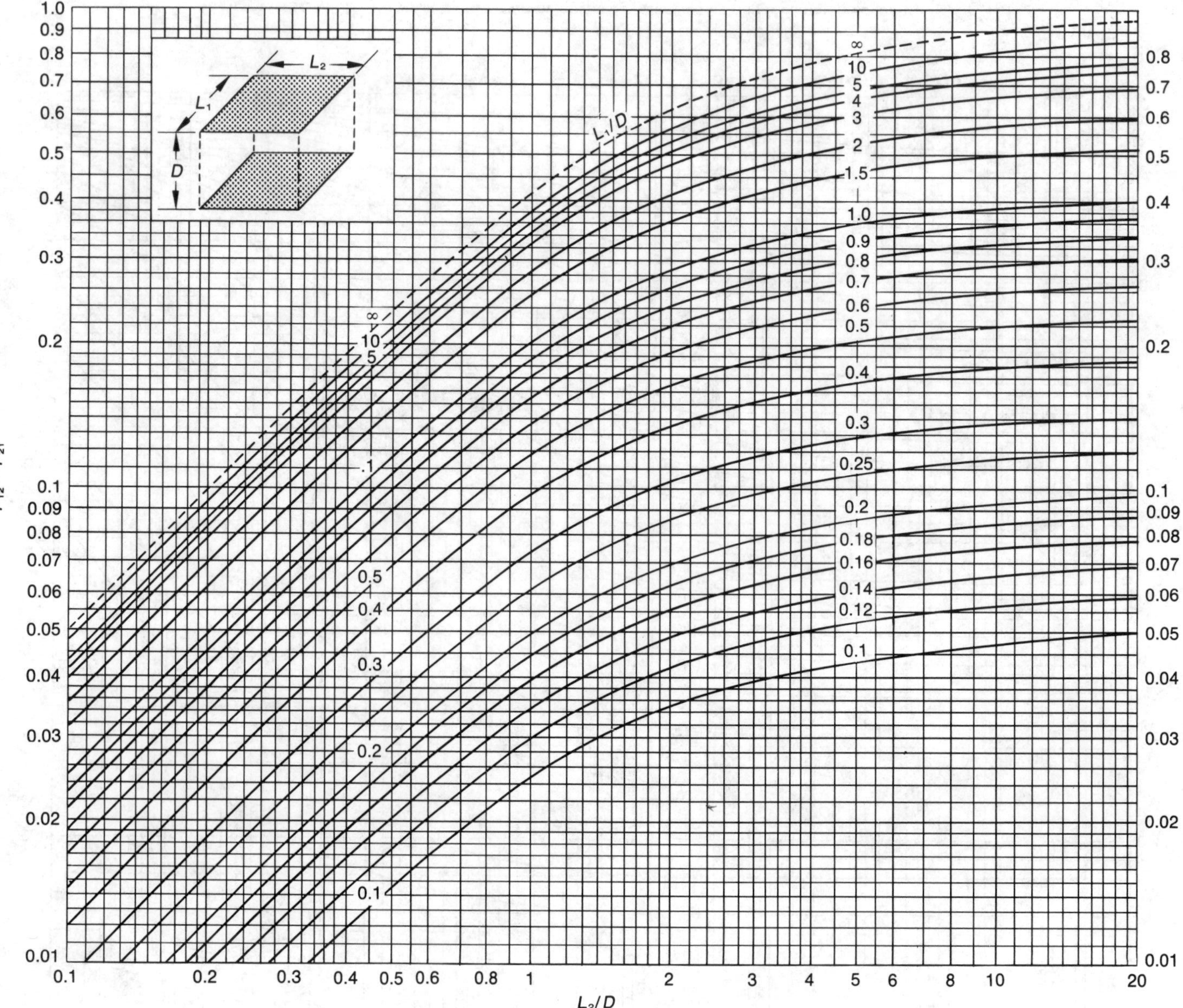

Fig. 9.2.3 View factors for parallel rectangular plates of the same size.

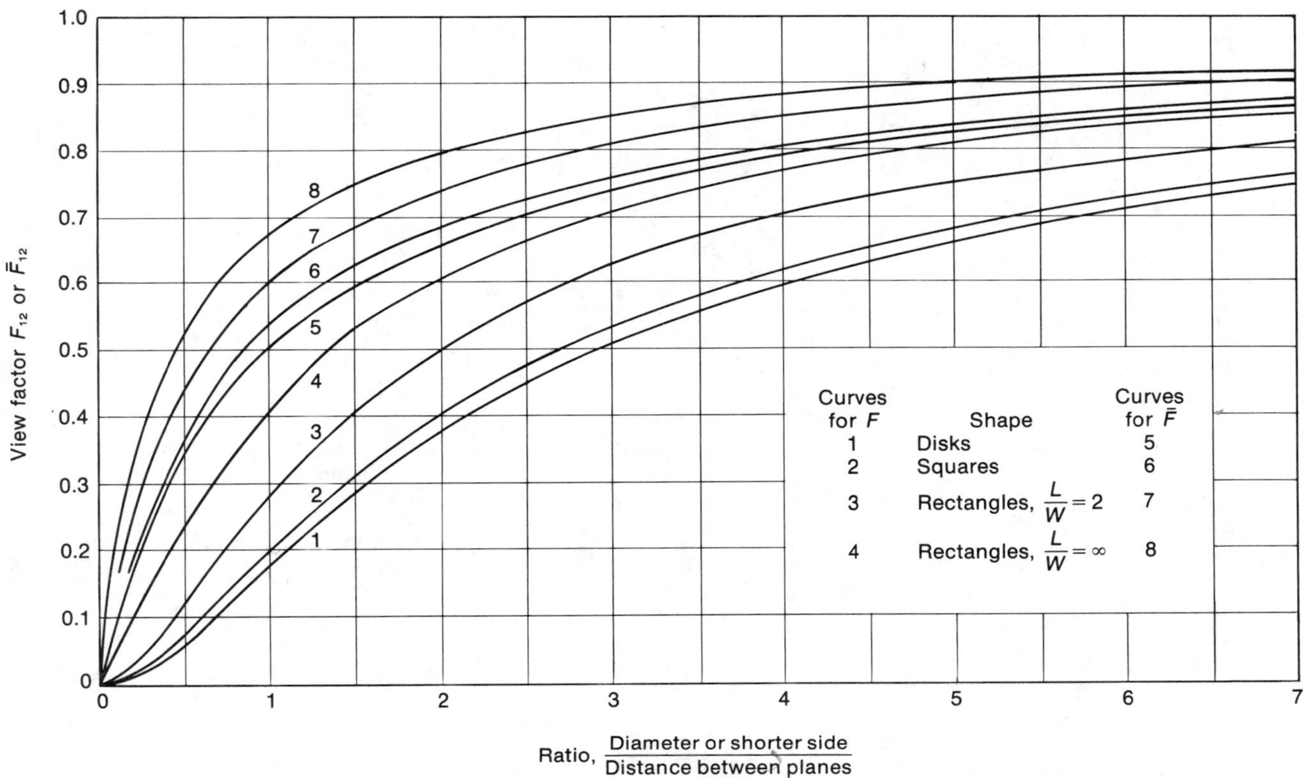

Fig. 9.2.4 View factors for parallel surfaces of identical shape. (From W. H. McAdams, *Heat Transmission*, Third Edition, McGraw-Hill Book Co., Inc., New York, 1954.)

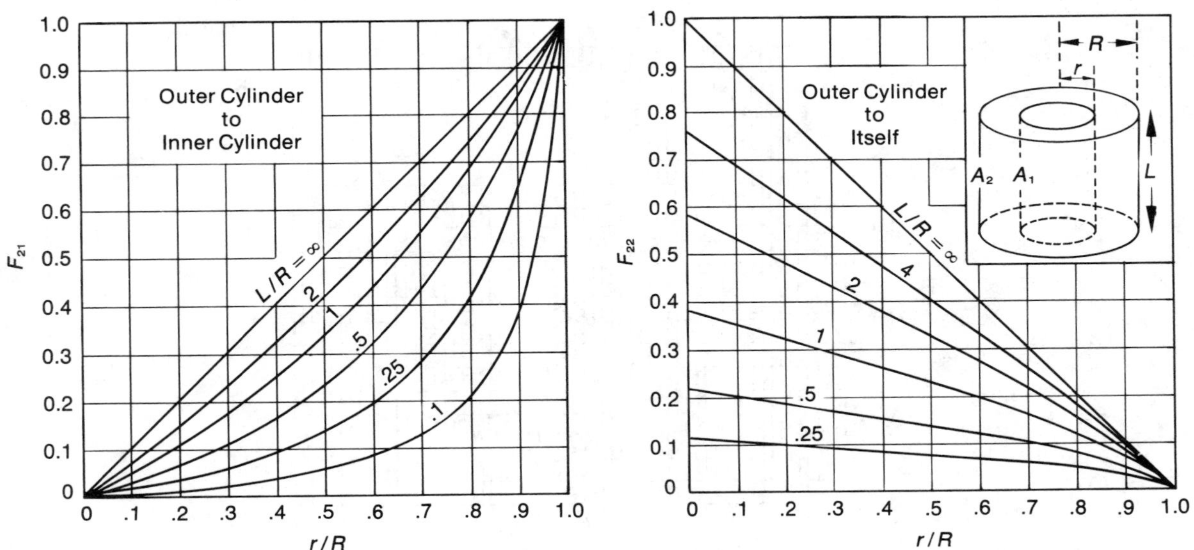

Fig. 9.2.5 View factors for concentric, coaxial cylinders of equal length. (Adapted from H. C. Hottel and A. F. Sarofin, *Radiative Transfer*, McGraw-Hill Book Co., Inc., New York, 1967.)

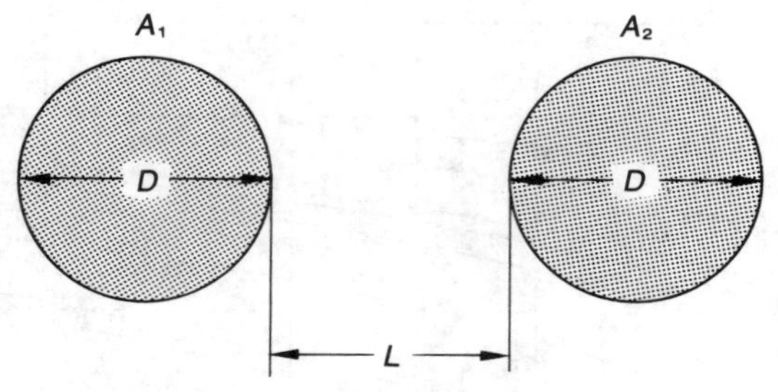

A_1 = portion of the infinite cylinder seen by the parallel infinite cylinder

$A_2 = A_1$

$$F_{12} = F_{21} = \frac{2}{\pi}\left[(\xi^2 - 1)^{1/2} - \xi + \sin^{-1}\left(\frac{1}{\xi}\right)\right], \quad \xi = 1 + \left(\frac{L}{D}\right)$$

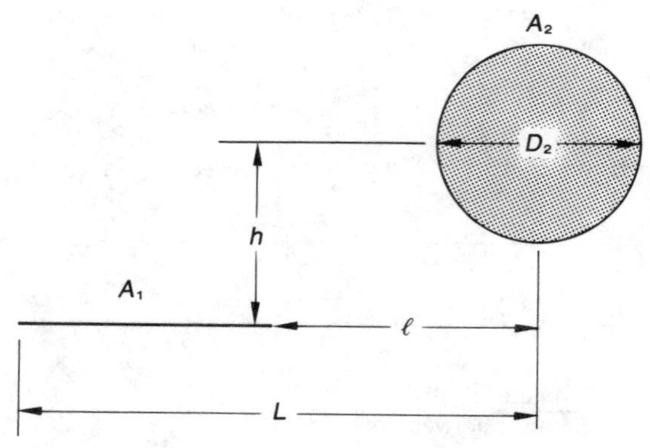

A_1 = horizontal plane of finite width and infinite extent

A_2 = portion of infinite parallel cylinder seen by A_1

$$F_{12} = \frac{1}{\zeta - \eta}\tan^{-1}\left(\frac{\zeta}{\xi}\right) - \tan^{-1}\left(\frac{\eta}{\xi}\right) \quad \text{where} \quad \zeta = L/D_2, \quad \eta = \ell/D_2, \ \xi = h/D_2$$

Fig. 9.2.6 View factors for infinite cylinders.

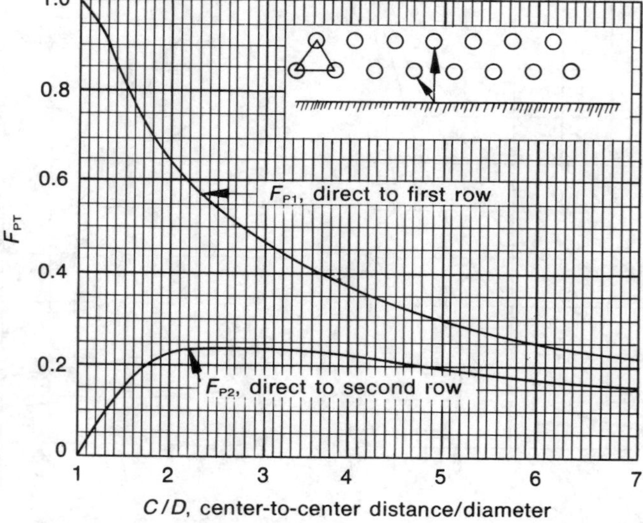

C/D, center-to-center distance/diameter

Fig. 9.2.7 View factors for rows of staggered tubes irradiated from one side. (Adapted from H. C. Hottel and A. F. Sarofin, *Radiative Transfer*, McGraw-Hill Book Co., Inc., New York, 1967.)

view factor,

$$F_{ij} = \begin{Bmatrix} \text{fraction of radiant energy } \textit{emitted} \\ \text{from the } i\text{th surface which is} \\ \textit{incident} \text{ upon the } j\text{th surface} \end{Bmatrix}$$

the reciprocity condition given by Eq. 9.1-18,

$$A_i F_{ij} = A_j F_{ji} \tag{9.1-18}$$

and the summation constraint given by Eq. 9.1-2,

$$\sum_{j=1}^{j=N} F_{ij} = 1 \tag{9.1-2}$$

Referring to Fig. 9.2.8 we note that the view factor F_{23} could be computed directly by means of the

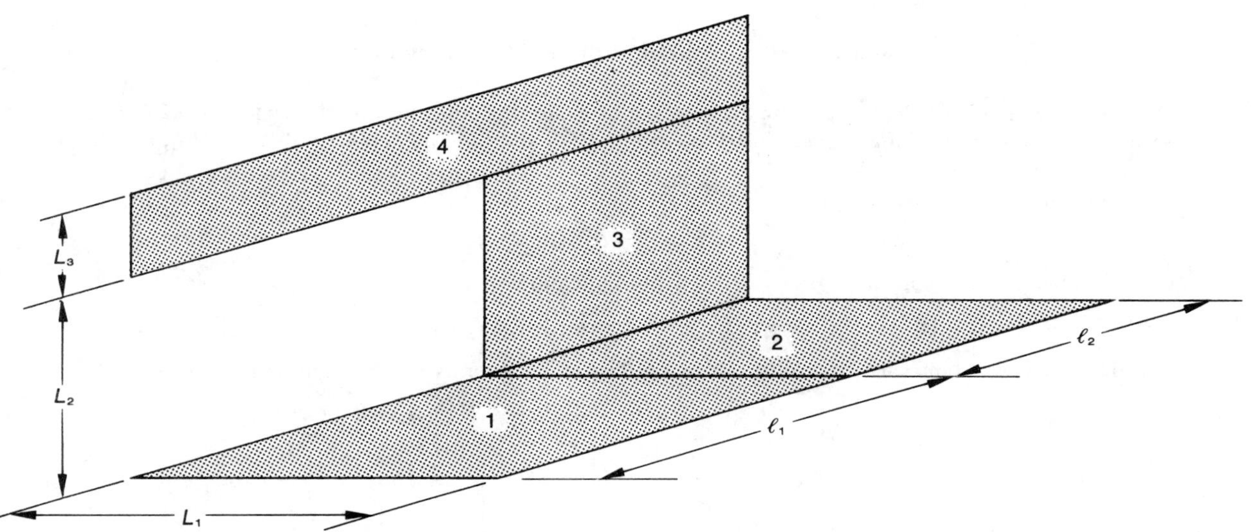

Fig. 9.2.8 Alternate view factors.

values given in Fig. 9.2.2; however, the other view factors present something of a problem. If we focus our attention on the area A_4 and the combined area $A_{⑫} = A_1 + A_2$ we note that the view factor for radiant energy exchange between A_4 and $A_{⑫}$ can be written as,

$$F_{4⑫} = F_{41} + F_{42} \tag{9.2-10}$$

i.e., the total view factor is the sum of its parts. Eq. 9.2-10 can be derived formally by application of Eq. 9.1-16, and we should be careful to point out that the inverse of Eq. 9.2-10 is *not true*, i.e.,

$$F_{⑫4} \neq F_{14} + F_{24}$$

as can be seen by further application of Eq. 9.1-16. We can use Eq. 9.2-10 to derive an auxiliary reciprocity condition by multiplying by A_4 to obtain

$$A_4 F_{4⑫} = A_4 F_{41} + A_4 F_{42} \tag{9.2-11}$$

and applying Eq. 9.1-18 to give

$$A_{⑫} F_{⑫4} = A_1 F_{14} + A_2 F_{24} \tag{9.2-12}$$

We summarize our results for radiant energy exchange between A_4 and $A_1 + A_2$ as;

$$A_{⑫} = A_1 + A_2$$
$$F_{4⑫} = F_{41} + F_{42}$$
$$A_{⑫} F_{⑫4} = A_1 F_{14} + A_2 F_{24}.$$

and note that the following generalizations can be easily proved:

$$A_{(ijk)} = A_i + A_j + A_k, \quad \text{area summation convention} \tag{9.2-13}$$

$$F_{i(jk\ell)} = F_{ij} + F_{ik} + F_{i\ell}, \quad \text{view factor summation convention} \tag{9.2-14}$$

$$A_{(jk\ell)} F_{(jk\ell)i} = A_j F_{ji} + A_k F_{ki} + A_\ell F_{\ell i}, \quad \text{auxiliary reciprocity condition} \tag{9.2-15}$$

These results,† along with Eq. 9.1-2, will prove to be most helpful in extracting a variety of view factors from published charts and previously derived results. In Ex. 9.2-1 we will show how F_{13} can be calculated using only information available from Fig. 9.2.2. The determination of $F_{⑫4}$ will be left as an exercise for the student.

Example 9.2-1 Calculation of alternate view factors

In this example we wish to calculate the view factor F_{13} for the configuration shown in Fig. 9.2.8. To do so we examine the alternate configuration illustrated in Fig. 9.2.9 and note immediately that F_{15}, F_{23}, and $F_{⑫㉟}$ are available from Fig. 9.2.2.

We begin by expressing $F_{⑫㉟}$ as

$$F_{⑫㉟} = F_{⑫3} + F_{⑫5} \tag{1}$$

which represents an application of Eq. 9.2-14. Multiplication by $A_{⑫}$ gives,

$$A_{⑫} F_{⑫㉟} = A_{⑫} F_{⑫3} + A_{⑫} F_{⑫5} \tag{2}$$

and the auxiliary reciprocity condition can be applied to both terms on the right-hand-side to yield

$$A_{⑫} F_{⑫㉟} = A_1 F_{13} + A_2 F_{23} + A_1 F_{15} + A_2 F_{25} \tag{3}$$

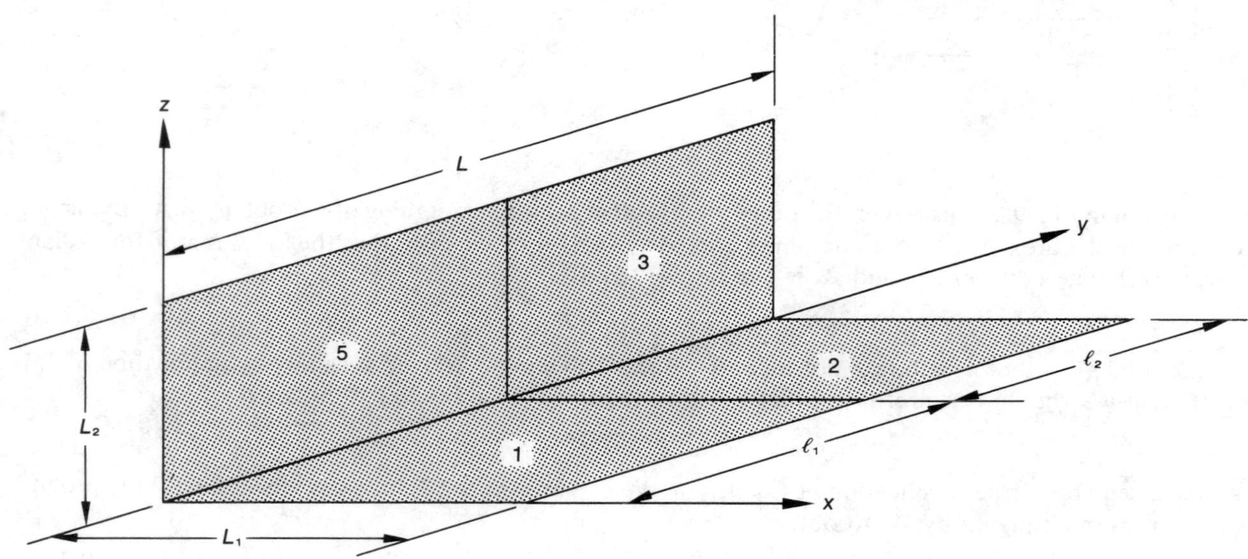

Fig. 9.2.9 Calculation of alternate view factors.

†Eqs. 9.2-14 and 9.2-15 can be proved directly using the definition of F_{ij} given by Eq. 9.1-16 and the reciprocity condition given by Eq. 9.1-18.

Grouping the known view factors together gives us a single equation with two unknowns, F_{13} and F_{25}.

$$A_1F_{13}+A_2F_{25}=A_{⑫}F_{⑫\,㉟}-A_2F_{23}-A_1F_{15} \tag{4}$$

For the case where $\ell_1=\ell_2$ we can make use of symmetry arguments to conclude that

$$F_{13}=F_{25}, \qquad \text{for} \quad \ell_1=\ell_2 \tag{5}$$

and Eq. 4 can be solved for F_{13}.

$$F_{13}=\frac{1}{2A_1}[A_{⑫}F_{⑫\,㉟}-A_2F_{23}-A_1F_{15}], \qquad \text{for} \quad \ell_1=\ell_2 \tag{6}$$

When $\ell_1\neq\ell_2$ we can only solve for F_{13} when $L_1=L_2$, for this allows us to write

$$F_{13}=F_{52}, \qquad \text{for} \quad L_1=L_2$$

Imposing the reciprocity condition yields

$$F_{25}=\left(\frac{A_5}{A_2}\right)F_{52}=\left(\frac{A_5}{A_2}\right)F_{13} \tag{7}$$

Substitution of Eq. 7 into Eq. 4 and noting that $A_5=A_1$ leads to

$$F_{13}=\frac{1}{2A_1}[A_{⑫}F_{⑫\,㉟}-A_2F_{23}-A_1F_{15}], \qquad \text{for} \quad L_1=L_2 \tag{8}$$

The fact that Eq. 8 is identical to Eq. 6 suggests that it may be valid for arbitrary values of L_1, L_2, ℓ_1, and ℓ_2. This would require that $A_2F_{25}=A_1F_{13}$, and while this relation has some intuitive appeal (particularly in the form $A_2F_{25}=A_3F_{31}$) it does not appear to be provable with the information currently at our disposal. However, a proof can be established by making use of the mathematical expressions for F_{25} and F_{13}. Referring to Eq. 9.2-7, we can express A_2F_{25} as

$$A_2F_{25}=\frac{1}{\pi}\int_{z=0}^{z=L_2}\int_{y_5=0}^{y_5=\ell_1}\int_{y_2=\ell_1}^{y_2=L}\int_{x=0}^{x=L_1}\mathscr{G}_{25}(x,y_2,y_5,z)\,dx\,dy_2\,dy_5\,dz \tag{9}$$

where y_5 represent the y-coordinate associated with A_5, and y_2 represent the y-coordinate associated with A_2. The integrand in Eq. 9 is given by

$$\mathscr{G}_{25}(x,y_2,y_5,z)=\frac{xz}{[x^2+(y_5-y_2)^2+z^2]^2} \tag{10}$$

In the same manner we can express A_3F_{31} as

$$A_1F_{13}=\frac{1}{\pi}\int_{z=0}^{z=L_2}\int_{y_3=\ell_1}^{y_3=L}\int_{y_1=0}^{y_1=\ell_1}\int_{x=0}^{x=L_1}\mathscr{G}_{13}(x,y_1,y_3,z)\,dx\,dy_1\,dy_3\,dz_1 \tag{11}$$

where

$$\mathscr{G}_{13}(x,y_1,y_3,z)=\frac{xz}{[x^2+(y_3-y_1)^2+z^2]^2} \tag{12}$$

Since the limits of integration for y_1 and y_5 are the same, as are the limits for y_3 and y_2, we can make the following change of variables [2]

$$y_1=y_5 \quad \text{and} \quad y_3=y_2$$

leading to the following expression for $\mathscr{G}_{13}$

$$\mathscr{G}_{13}=\frac{xz}{[x^2+(y_5-y_2)^2+z^2]^2}=\mathscr{G}_{25} \tag{13}$$

Here we have noted that $(y_5-y_2)^2=(y_2-y_5)^2$. Changing these same variables in Eq. 11 leads to

$$A_1F_{13}=\frac{1}{\pi}\int_{z=0}^{z=L_2}\int_{y_5=0}^{y_5=\ell_1}\int_{y_2=\ell_1}^{y_2=L}\int_{x=0}^{x=L_1}\mathscr{G}_{25}\,dx\,dy_2\,dy_5\,dz \tag{14}$$

Comparing Eqs. 9 and 14 we find the desired reciprocal relation

$$A_2 F_{25} = A_1 F_{13} \tag{15}$$

Substitution of this result into Eq. 4 provides a completely general expression for F_{13},

$$F_{13} = \frac{1}{2A_1}[A_{\textcircled{12}} F_{\textcircled{12}\textcircled{35}} - A_2 F_{23} - A_1 F_{15}] \tag{16}$$

which can be computed directly in terms of view factors available from Fig. 9.2.2.

In the previous example we have shown how one can extract a variety of view factors from previously derived results. There are other methods for determining view factors which are described by Hottel and Sarofin [3] and by Sparrow and Cess [4] and the interested student should study their discussion of this problem before plunging into a complicated numerical or analytical evaluation of view factors.

*9.3 Radiant Energy Exchange in an Enclosure

In this section we consider the system shown in Fig. 9.3.1 which is essentially the same system we considered in Sec. 8.5; however, in our analysis we will consider the case of an arbitrary number of surfaces. We assume that the various surfaces are isothermal as indicated in the figure, and that either the temperature of the body is specified as T_0 or the net energy flux for the body is specified. In the former case we can compute the energy flux while in the latter case the temperature of the body, T_0, can be calculated.

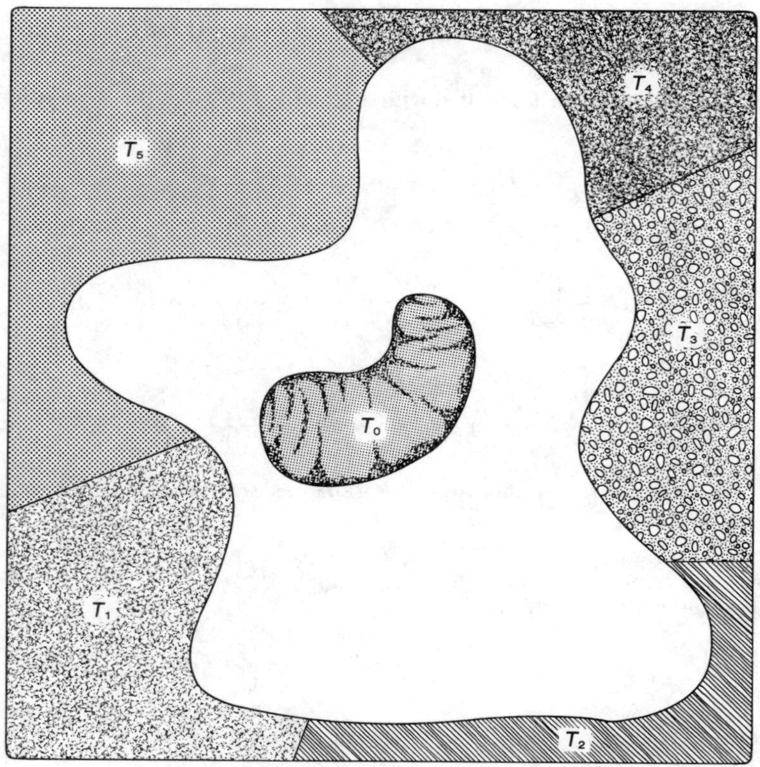

Fig. 9.3.1 Black body radiant energy exchange in an enclosure.

The rate of emission of radiant energy is given by

$$\begin{Bmatrix}\text{rate of emission of} \\ \text{radiant energy} \\ \text{from the body}\end{Bmatrix} = A_0\sigma T_0^4 \tag{9.3-1}$$

and the rate at which radiant energy is absorbed by the body can be expressed as

$$\begin{Bmatrix}\text{rate of absorption of} \\ \text{radiant energy by} \\ \text{the body}\end{Bmatrix} = \sum_{j=0}^{j=N} A_j F_{j0} \sigma T_j^4 \tag{9.3-2}$$

Here we have assumed that there are $N+1$ surfaces in our enclosure. Note that a term of the form $A_0F_{00}\sigma T_0^4$ is included in Eq. 9.3-2 in order to account for the energy radiated by the body which is directly absorbed by the body. The net rate at which energy is transferred from the body to the surroundings is given by

$$\dot{Q}_0 = A_0\sigma T_0^4 - \sum_{j=0}^{j=N} A_j F_{j0}\sigma T_j^4 \tag{9.3-3}$$

Remember from our discussion in Sec. 9.1 that the view factors satisfied the constraint,†

$$\sum_{j=0}^{j=N} F_{0j} = 1 \tag{9.3-4}$$

thus we can multiply $A_0\sigma T_0^4$ in Eq. 9.3-3 by 1 obtain

$$\dot{Q}_0 = A_0\sigma T_0^4 \sum_{j=0}^{j=N} F_{0j} - \sum_{j=0}^{j=N} A_j F_{j0}\sigma T_j^4$$

$$= \sum_{j=0}^{j=N} A_0 F_{0j}\sigma T_0^4 - \sum_{j=0}^{j=N} A_j F_{j0}\sigma T_j^4 \tag{9.3-5}$$

Making use of the reciprocity condition given by Eq. 9.1-18

$$A_j F_{j0} = A_0 F_{0j} \tag{9.3-6}$$

allows us to write Eq. 9.3-5 as

$$\dot{Q}_0 = \sum_{j=0}^{j=N} A_0 F_{0j}\sigma (T_0^4 - T_j^4) \tag{9.3-7}$$

Knowing the view factors and all the temperatures, we can use Eq. 9.3-7 to calculate the net rate at which radiant energy is transferred from a body or a surface to the surroundings. For the ith surface in an enclosure, Eq. 9.3-7 takes the form

$$\dot{Q}_i = \sum_{j=0}^{j=N} A_i F_{ij}\sigma (T_i^4 - T_j^4) \tag{9.3-8}$$

Note that if the ith surface is that of a high-altitude hiker sleeping comfortably under the shade of a rock, one of the surfaces in the enclosure is outer space to which we would assign the temperature of absolute zero.

It is possible to derive Eq. 9.3-8 in another manner by simply generalizing the result obtained in Secs. 1.3 and 9.1,

$$\dot{Q}_{12} = A_1 F_{12}\sigma (T_1^4 - T_2^4)$$

to the case of radiant energy exchange between the ith and jth surfaces

$$\dot{Q}_{ij} = A_i F_{ij}\sigma (T_i^4 - T_j^4) \tag{9.3-9}$$

†See Eq. 9.1-2.

Remember that our definition of $\dot{Q}_1$ was given by Eq. 9.1-27 as

$$\dot{Q}_i = \sum_{j=1}^{j=N} \dot{Q}_{ij} \tag{9.1-27}$$

for an enclosure with N surfaces, thus if we sum Eq. 9.3-9 over all $N+1$ surfaces we obtain

$$\dot{Q}_i = \sum_{j=0}^{j=N} \dot{Q}_{ij} = \sum_{j=0}^{j=N} A_i F_{ij} \sigma (T_i^4 - T_j^4)$$

Example 9.3-1 A black surface as a reflector

In this example we wish to analyze a black body radiant energy exchange process in which one surface acts like a reflector. The system consists of a hemisphere exchanging radiant energy with the two half-circles located at the base of the hemisphere. This configuration is illustrated in Fig. 9.3.2.

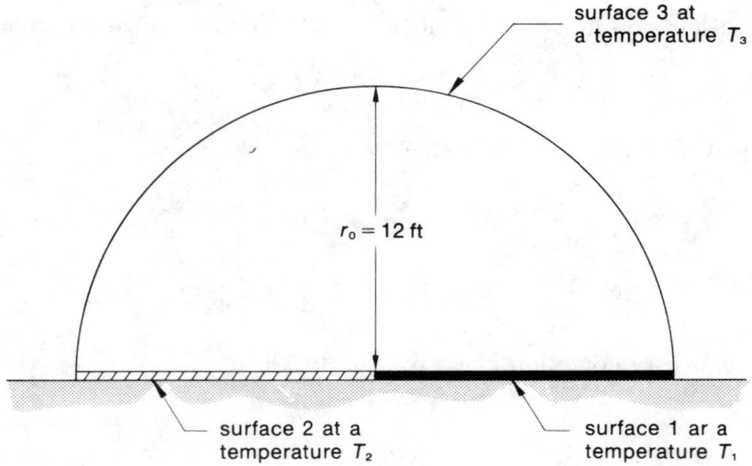

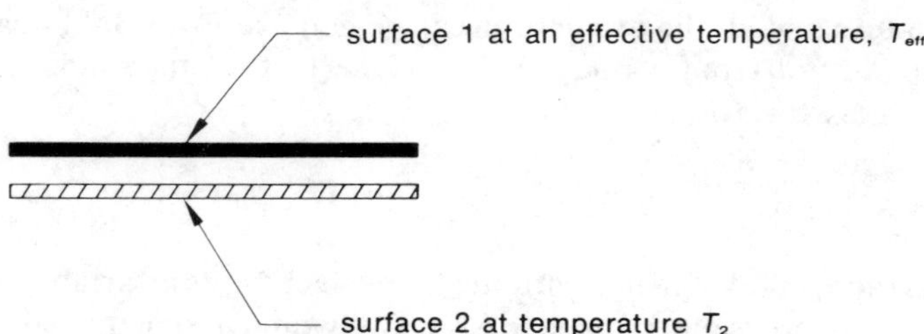

Fig. 9.3.2 A black hemisphere as a "reflector."

The temperature of surface 1 is fixed at 320°F and the temperature of surface 2 is maintained at 68°F. The temperature of the hemisphere is unknown; however, it is an adiabatic surface, i.e., $\dot{Q}_3 = 0$. We would like to know the heat transfer rate between surface 1 and surface 2, and we would like to know the *effective temperature* of surface 1. This is determined by specifying the rate of exchange between surface 2 and a parallel plate at T_{eff} to be the same as in the hemispherical configuration.

The net heat exchange between surfaces 1 and 2 and the surroundings is

$$\dot{Q}_1 = \sum_{j=1}^{j=3} A_1 F_{1j} \sigma (T_1^4 - T_j^4) \tag{1}$$

$$\dot{Q}_2 = \sum_{j=1}^{j=3} A_2 F_{2j} \sigma (T_2^4 - F_j^4) \tag{2}$$

and for surface 3 we impose the adiabatic restriction and write

$$\dot{Q}_3 = \sum_{j=1}^{j=3} A_3 F_{3j} \sigma (T_3^4 - T_j^4) = 0 \tag{3}$$

In order to determine the view factors we note that surfaces 1 and 2 see only surface 3 so that

$$F_{11} = F_{12} = F_{21} = F_{22} = 0 \tag{4}$$

$$F_{13} = F_{23} = 1 \tag{5}$$

The reciprocity condition allows us to write

$$A_1 F_{13} = A_3 F_{31} \quad \text{and} \quad A_2 F_{23} = A_3 F_{32} \tag{6}$$

and it follows that

$$F_{31} = F_{32} = \tfrac{1}{4} \tag{7}$$

The summation condition requires that $F_{31} + F_{32} + F_{33} = 1$, and we have the final view factor

$$F_{33} = \tfrac{1}{2} \tag{8}$$

Writing out Eq. 3 gives us

$$A_3 F_{31}(T_3^4 - T_1^4) + A_3 F_{32}(T_3^4 - T_2^4) = 0 \tag{9}$$

from which we can compute T_3

$$T_3^4 = (A_1 T_1^4 + A_2 T_2^4)/(A_1 + A_2) \tag{10}$$

Our absolute temperatures, T_1 and T_2, are given by

$$T_1 = (320 + 459.67)°\text{R} = 780°\text{R}$$

$$T_2 = (68 + 459.67)°\text{R} = 528°\text{R}$$

so that T_3 is calculated to be 688°R or 228°F. Since surface 3 is adiabatic we require that $\dot{Q}_2 = -\dot{Q}_1$ and we can use either Eq. 1 or 2 to calculate that

$$\left\{\begin{array}{l}\text{the rate of heat} \\ \text{transfer from surface 1} \\ \text{to surface 2}\end{array}\right\} = A_1 F_{13} \sigma (T_1^4 - T_3^4) \tag{11}$$

Denoting this by $\dot{Q}_{12}$ we write

$$\begin{aligned}\dot{Q}_{12} &= A_1 F_{13} \sigma (T_1^4 - T_3^4) \\ &= (226\ \text{ft}^2)(1)\left(\frac{1.71 \times 10^{-9}\ \text{Btu}}{\text{hr ft}^2\,°\text{R}^4}\right)[(780°\text{R})^4 - (688°\text{R})^4] \\ &= 5.65 \times 10^4\ \text{Btu/hr}\end{aligned} \tag{12}$$

In order to find the effective temperature we write

$$\dot{Q}_{12} = A_2 \sigma (T_{\text{eff}}^4 - T_2^4)$$

and solve for T_{eff} to find $T_{\text{eff}} = 688°\text{R}$ or 228°F.

At this point we can see the calculation of radiant energy exchange rates between black bodies is relatively straightforward, but may require some tedious labor if complicated geometries are encountered. If the temperatures of the various surfaces are not uniform one can segment the surfaces into smaller regions over which the temperature is essentially uniform, or one can return to Eq. 9.1-11 and evaluate the integrals taking into account the variation of the specific intensity $I_{\lambda\omega}^{(e)}$ with position. Once again the calculation is conceptually straightforward, but may become quite tedious. In the next section we will examine a minor variation of the problem we have considered here and allow our enclosure to contain *diffuse, adiabatic* surfaces which are often referred to as reradiating surfaces. This will provide us with an opportunity to examine a problem of some practical importance, and to consider the problem of calculating $I_{\lambda\omega}^{(r)}$ given $I_{\lambda\omega}^{(i)}$. In addition, we will have a chance to examine the assumption of *uniform irradiation* which is used so extensively in the analysis of gray body radiation problems, and was tacitly assumed in Ex. 9.3-1.

9.4 Reradiating Surfaces

An interesting and practical variation of the problem of black body radiation in an enclosure is the problem of an enclosure consisting of two black surfaces and N-2 diffuse, adiabatic surfaces. Such surfaces are often referred to as *reradiating* surfaces (see Fig. 9.4.1).

We wish to consider problems of the type that occur in industrial furnace design where the furnace consists of a heat source (a fuel bed or a bank of electrical heaters), a heat sink (the tube bank of a boiler or heat exchanger), and the connecting refractory walls. The conduction through the refractory walls is usually small (by design) compared to the radiant energy transfer, thus the walls can be considered adiabatic. In addition the refractory walls, being rough and composed of nonmetallic oxides, can be considered as diffuse surfaces. There are two ways of thinking about these surfaces and we will consider both of them in the following paragraphs.

Remember that the specific incident flux is given by

$$q_{\lambda\omega}^{(i)} = I_{\lambda\omega}^{(i)}|\mathbf{\Omega} \cdot \mathbf{n}| \tag{9.4-1}$$

The hemispherical incident flux is obtained by integrating over the solid angle 2π to obtain

$$q_\lambda^{(i)} = \int_{2\pi} I_{\lambda\omega}^{(i)}|\mathbf{\Omega} \cdot \mathbf{n}|\, d\omega \tag{9.4-2}$$

and the hemispherical reflected flux is given by

$$q_\lambda^{(r)} = \int_{2\pi} \rho_\lambda \omega I_{\lambda\omega}^{(i)}|\mathbf{\Omega} \cdot \mathbf{n}|\, d\omega \tag{9.4-3}$$

One *possible model* of an adiabatic surface would be that all the incident radiation is reflected, i.e., $\rho_{\lambda\omega} = 1$ and

$$q_\lambda^{(r)} = q_\lambda^{(i)}, \quad \text{for a perfect reflector} \tag{9.4-4}$$

If the surface is *diffuse* we know that $I_{\lambda\omega}^{(r)}$ is *isotropic* or independent of $\mathbf{\Omega}$ and the results of Prob. 8-4 can be used to write

$$I_{\lambda\omega}^{(r)} = \frac{q_\lambda^{(r)}}{\pi} = \frac{q_\lambda^{(i)}}{\pi} = \frac{1}{\pi}\int_{2\pi} I_{\lambda\omega}^{(i)}|\mathbf{\Omega} \cdot \mathbf{n}|\, d\omega, \quad \text{for a diffuse perfect reflector} \tag{9.4-5}$$

Here we have shown how to calculate $I_{\lambda\omega}^{(r)}$ given $I_{\lambda\omega}^{(i)}$ for one possible model of a diffuse adiabatic surface. We could use this result to construct a solution for the radiant energy transfer in our enclosure containing two black surfaces and N-2 diffuse, adiabatic surfaces; however, there is another model of a diffuse, adiabatic surface which is perhaps more realistic for refractory surfaces.

Let us now think of a diffuse, adiabatic surface as one which absorbs all incident radiation and in turn emits precisely the same amount of radiation *as a black body*. We call this type of surface a *reradiating* surface, and the total, hemispherical emitted flux is given by

$$q^{(e)} = \sigma T_R^4 = q^{(i)} = \int_0^\infty \int_{2\pi} I_{\lambda\omega}^{(i)}|\mathbf{\Omega} \cdot \mathbf{n}|\, d\omega\, d\lambda, \quad \text{for a reradiating surface} \tag{9.4-6}$$

From this we see that the total hemispherical emitted flux for a reradiating surface is equal to the total hemispherical reflected flux for a diffuse, perfect reflector,

$$q^{(e)}\big|_{\text{reradiating}} = q^{(r)}\big|_{\text{diffuse, perfect reflector}} \tag{9.4-7}$$

provided of course we choose T_R by means of Eq. 9.4-6. The specific intensity of the emitted flux for the reradiating surface is naturally given by

$$I_{b,\lambda\omega} = \frac{2hc^2}{\lambda^5} \frac{1}{e^{hc/\lambda k T_R} - 1} \tag{9.4-8}$$

Since the reradiating surface is diffuse it follows that the total fluxes for radiation leaving the surface are equal:

$$q_\omega^{(e)}\big|_{\text{reradiating}} = q_\omega^{(r)}\big|_{\text{diffuse, perfect reflector}} \tag{9.4-9}$$

however, the specific fluxes are not

$$q_{\lambda\omega}^{(e)}\big|_{\text{reradiating}} \neq q_{\lambda\omega}^{(r)}\big|_{\text{diffuse, perfect reflector}} \tag{9.4-10}$$

unless the incident radiation comes from a black body at a temperature T_R. The reason for this is that the distribution of radiant energy with respect to wavelength is governed by Eq. 9.4-8 for the reradiating surface and Eq. 9.4-5 for the diffuse, perfect reflector. However, the distribution of radiant energy with respect to wavelength is of no concern to us since the absorptivities of the two black surfaces are equal to one, i.e., $\alpha_{\lambda\omega} = 1$, and either model for the diffuse, adiabatic surface will yield the same result for the rate of energy transfer between the two black surfaces. We choose the reradiating surface as our model of a diffuse, adiabatic surface both because it is physically more reasonable, i.e., $\alpha_{\lambda\omega} = 1$ is a more reasonable approximation than $\rho_{\lambda\omega} = 1$, and because it allows us to treat this type of problem with the same methods used in Sec. 9.3.

We consider now the case where surface 1 is a heat source having a temperature T_1, surface 2 is a heat sink having a temperature T_2, and the N-2 refractory surfaces are reradiating surfaces having unknown temperatures. Following Eq. 9.3-8 we can express the net rate at which energy is transferred from surface 1 to the surroundings as†

$$\dot{Q}_1 = \sum_{j=1}^{j=N} A_1 F_{1j} \sigma (T_1^4 - T_j^4) \tag{9.4-11}$$

provided the total hemispherical emitted flux $q^{(e)}$ is uniform over each refractory surface. This is known as the assumption of *uniform irradiation* and we will explore the nature of this assumption after we have completed the analysis of this problem. For the N-2 refractory surfaces, Eq. 9.3-8 takes the form

$$\dot{Q}_r = 0 = \sum_{j=1}^{j=N} A_r F_{rj} \sigma (T_r^4 - T_j^4), \qquad r = 3, 4, \ldots, N \tag{9.4-12}$$

In Eqs. 9.4-12 we have N-2 unknown temperatures and N-2 independent equations, thus the temperatures of the refractory surfaces can be determined and used in Eq. 9.4-11 to specify the net rate of heat transfer from surface 1 to surface 2. What we would like to prove at this point is that the general solution of this problem takes the simple form

$$\dot{Q}_{12} = A_1 \bar{F}_{12} (T_1^4 - T_2^4) \tag{9.4-13}$$

where $\bar{F}_{12}$ is a modified view factor. The proof will be straightforward for those students who are familiar with matrix algebra. Those who are not may wish to accept this result and skip directly to Eq. 9.4-34. We begin by adding and subtracting $\Sigma_{j=1}^{j=N} A_r F_{rj} T_1^4$ to Eq. 9.4-12 to obtain‡

$$0 = \sum_{j=1}^{j=N} A_r F_{rj} T_r^4 - \sum_{j=1}^{j=N} A_r F_{rj} T_1^4 - \sum_{j=1}^{j=N} A_r F_{rj} T_j^4 + \sum_{j=1}^{j=N} A_r F_{rj} T_1^4, \qquad r = 3, 4, \ldots, N \tag{9.4-14}$$

This can be put in the form

$$0 = \sum_{j=1}^{j=N} A_r F_{rj} (T_r^4 - T_1^4) - \sum_{j=1}^{j=N} A_r F_{rj} (T_j^4 - T_1^4), \qquad r = 3, 4, \ldots, N \tag{9.4-15}$$

†Since all the surfaces except 1 and 2 are adiabatic it follows that $\dot{Q}_1 = \dot{Q}_{12}$ where $\dot{Q}_{12}$ represents the total rate of exchange from 1 to 2 both directly and via the reradiating surfaces.

‡Here the coefficient σ has been canceled from Eq. 9.4-12.

Writing out the first two terms of the second sum and rearranging the result leads to

$$(T_r^4 - T_1^4)\left\{\sum_{j=1}^{j=N} A_r F_{rj}\right\} - \sum_{j=3}^{j=N} A_r F_{rj}(T_j^4 - T_1^4) = A_r F_{r2}(T_2^4 - T_1^4), \qquad r = 3, 4, \ldots, N \tag{9.4-16}$$

If we define a dimensionless temperature difference as

$$\Theta_j = \frac{T_j^4 - T_1^4}{T_2^4 - T_1^4} \tag{9.4-17}$$

and divide Eq. 9.4-16 by $T_1^4 - T_2^4$ we obtain

$$\Theta_r\left\{\sum_{j=1}^{j=N} A_r F_{rj}\right\} - \sum_{j=3}^{j=N} A_r F_{rj}\Theta_j = A_r F_{r2}, \qquad r = 3, 4, \ldots, N \tag{9.4-18}$$

In matrix form we could express this result as

$$\begin{bmatrix} M_{33} & M_{34} & M_{35} & \cdot & \cdot & M_{3N} \\ M_{43} & M_{44} & & & & M_{4N} \\ M_{53} & & & & & \cdot \\ \cdot & & & & & \cdot \\ \cdot & & & & & \cdot \\ \cdot & & & & & \cdot \\ M_{N3} & & & & & M_{NN} \end{bmatrix} \begin{bmatrix} \Theta_3 \\ \Theta_4 \\ \cdot \\ \cdot \\ \cdot \\ \cdot \\ \Theta_N \end{bmatrix} = \begin{bmatrix} A_3 & F_{32} \\ A_4 & F_{42} \\ \cdot & \\ \cdot & \\ \cdot & \\ \cdot & \\ A_N & F_{N2} \end{bmatrix} \tag{9.4-19}$$

Here the coefficient M_{33} is given by

$$M_{33} = \left\{\sum_{j=1}^{N} A_3 F_{3j}\right\} - A_3 F_{33} \tag{9.4-20}$$

and the coefficient M_{54} is given by

$$M_{54} = -A_5 F_{54} \tag{9.4-21}$$

In more compact form we could express Eqs. 9.4-18 and Eq. 9.4-19 as

$$\mathbf{M} \cdot \mathbf{\Theta} = \mathbf{C} \tag{9.4-22}$$

Where **M** represents the N-2 by N-2 matrix of known coefficients, **Θ** represents the unknown column vector of temperature differences, and **C** is a column vector of known coefficients. Being more explicit we note that the elements of the matrix **M** are given by

$$M_{rk} = \delta_{rk}\left\{\sum_{j=1}^{j=N} A_r F_{rj}\right\} - A_r F_{rk} \tag{9.4-23}$$

where δ_{rk} represents the elements of the unit matrix and are given by

$$\delta_{rk} = \begin{cases} 1, & r = k \\ 0, & r \neq k \end{cases} \tag{9.4-24}$$

The elements of the column vector **Θ** are given by

$$\Theta_k = \frac{T_k^4 - T_1^4}{T_2^4 - T_1^4} \tag{9.4-25}$$

and the elements of the column vector **C** can be expressed as

$$C_r = A_r F_{r2} \tag{9.4-26}$$

In terms of Eqs. 9.4-23 through 9.4-26 we can express Eq. 9.4-18 as

$$\sum_{k=3}^{k=N} M_{rk}\Theta_k = C_r, \qquad r = 3, 4, \ldots, N \tag{9.4-27}$$

Returning now to Eq. 9.4-22 we multiply by the inverse of **M** to obtain

$$\mathbf{M}^{-1} \cdot \mathbf{M} \cdot \boldsymbol{\Theta} = \mathbf{M}^{-1} \cdot \mathbf{C} \tag{9.4-28}$$

and remember that the inverse of a matrix is defined by

$$\mathbf{M}^{-1} \cdot \mathbf{M} = \mathbf{U} \tag{9.4-29}$$

where **U** is the unit matrix having the elements δ_{rk}. Eq. 9.4-28 is now reduced to

$$\mathbf{U} \cdot \boldsymbol{\Theta} = \mathbf{M}^{-1} \cdot \mathbf{C} \tag{9.4-30}$$

but the product of a unit matrix and a column vector is just the column vector, thus our solution for $\boldsymbol{\Theta}$ takes the form

$$\boldsymbol{\Theta} = \mathbf{M}^{-1} \cdot \mathbf{C} \tag{9.4-31}$$

Once again we can be more explicit and express this result as

$$\Theta_j = \sum_{r=3}^{r=N} M_{jr}^{-1} A_r F_{r2} \tag{9.4-32}$$

Here M_{jr}^{-1} represents the elements of the inverse matrix $\mathbf{M}^{-1}$ which are only functions of areas and view factors. Returning to our definition of Θ_j given by Eq. 9.4-17 we express the temperature difference as

$$(T_j^4 - T_1^4) = (T_2^4 - T_1^4)\left\{\sum_{r=3}^{r=N} M_{jr}^{-1} A_r F_{r2}\right\} \tag{9.4-33}$$

Substitution of this result into Eq. 9.4-11 yields

$$\dot{Q}_1 = \left\{A_1 F_{12} + \sum_{j=3}^{j=N} \sum_{r=3}^{r=N} A_1 F_{1j} M_{jr}^{-1} A_r F_{r2}\right\} \sigma (T_1^4 - T_2^4) \tag{9.4-34}$$

We now *define* $A_1 \bar{F}_{12}$ by the relation

$$A_1 \bar{F}_{12} = A_1 F_{12} + \sum_{j=3}^{j=N} \sum_{r=3}^{r=N} A_1 F_{1j} M_{jr}^{-1} A_r F_{r2} \tag{9.4-35}$$

and note that $\dot{Q}_1 = \dot{Q}_{12}$ in order to recover Eq. 9.4-13. Since energy is transferred only between surfaces 1 and 2, it should be clear that

$$\dot{Q}_{21} = A_2 \bar{F}_{21} \sigma (T_2^4 - T_1^4) \tag{9.4-36}$$

where the modified view factor satisfies the reciprocity condition

$$A_2 \bar{F}_{21} = A_1 \bar{F}_{12} \tag{9.4-37}$$

Eq. 9.4-34 is an important result for it indicates that the rate of heat transfer between surfaces 1 and 2 is independent of the temperatures of the refractory surfaces. Values of $\bar{F}_{12}$ for several configurations are given in Fig. 9.2.4.

Uniform irradiation

In the previous development we made use of the expression

$$q^{(e)} = \sigma T_R^4 = \int_0^\infty \int_{2\pi} I_{\lambda\omega}^{(i)} |\boldsymbol{\Omega} \cdot \mathbf{n}| \, d\omega \, d\lambda \tag{9.4-6}$$

for the *local* flux, and then went to assume in the writing of Eqs. 9.4-11 and 9.4-12 that $q^{(e)}$ was *uniform* over each of the N surfaces in our enclosure. In order for this to be true the thermal conductivity of the walls of the enclosure must be very large, or the specific intensity $I_{\lambda\omega}^{(i)}$ must be uniform over each surface. This latter condition is termed *uniform irradiation.* In Fig. 9.4.1 we have shown a system consisting of two black surfaces and a refractory surface. We consider surface 1 to be a black surface at a very high temperature and surface 2 to be a black surface at a relatively low temperature. Under these conditions the

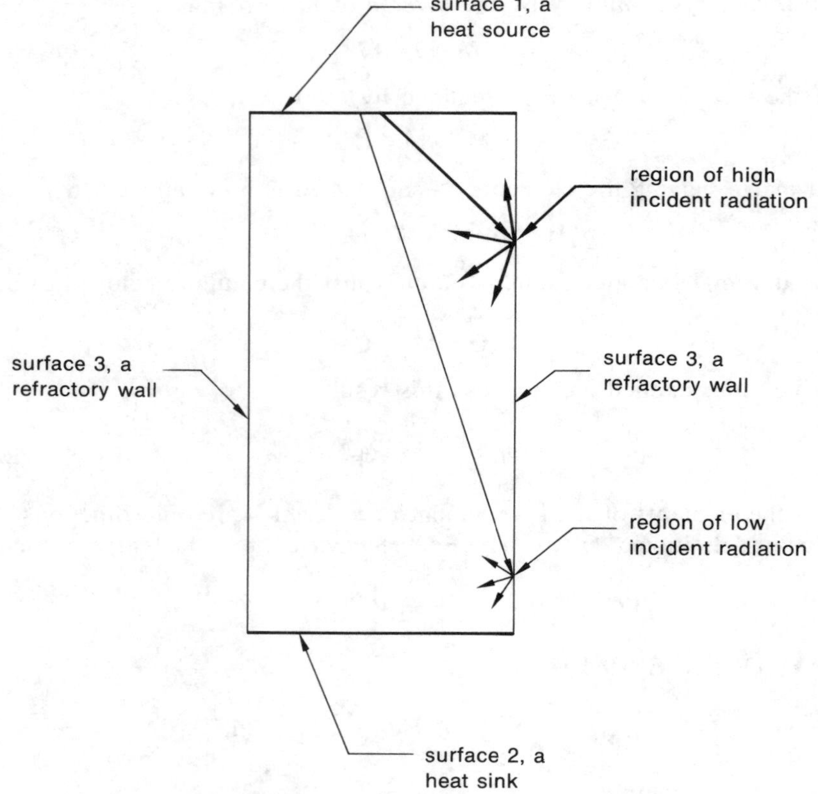

Fig. 9.4.1 Radiation in an enclosure with refractory surfaces.

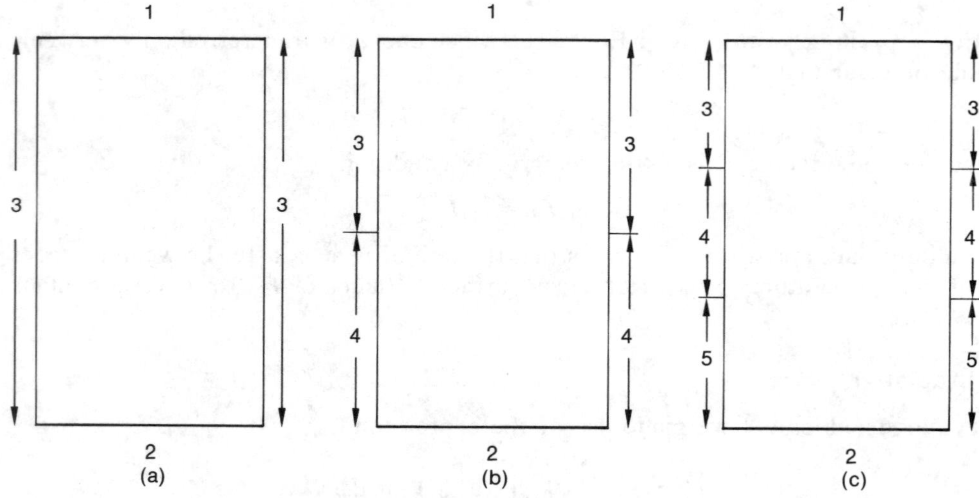

Fig. 9.4.2 Testing the assumption of uniform irradiation.

incident radiation is due essentially to the radiation coming from surface 1, and clearly the assumption of uniform irradiation is a poor one. The effect of the assumption of uniform irradiation on the value of $\dot{Q}_{12}$ can always be determined by breaking up the refractory surface into smaller and smaller segments until the calculated value of $\dot{Q}_{12}$ is independent of the number of refractory surfaces. In Fig. 9.4.2 we have illustrated how this can be done. The configuration in Fig. 9.4.2a would provide a poor value of $\dot{Q}_{12}$ because the assumption of uniform irradiation clearly does not hold. The arrangement shown in Fig. 9.4.2b would certainly yield a better value of $\dot{Q}_{12}$, and the system of surfaces illustrated in Fig. 9.4.2c would provide a still better value of $\dot{Q}_{12}$. If $(\dot{Q}_{12})_b$ is about the same as $(\dot{Q}_{12})_c$ we would assume that a satisfactory answer has been obtained; however, if $(\dot{Q}_{12})_c$ is quite different from $(\dot{Q}_{12})_b$ we know that the assumption of uniform irradiation has not been satisfied, and the refractory surface must be broken up into still smaller segments. In principle this approach is straightforward; however, in practice it requires an increasing number of view factors. If these are available the calculation is easily completed; if not the calculation may become long and tedious.

9.5 Experimental Determination of Emissivities and Absorptivities

In the previous section we learned how to analyze radiant energy exchange in a black body enclosure, and it was shown how these same methods could be used to analyze enclosures containing *reradiating* (or diffuse and adiabatic) surfaces. We must now confront the problem of dealing with non-black surfaces, i.e., surfaces for which $\epsilon_{\lambda\omega}$ and $\alpha_{\lambda\omega}$ are less than one and may be complex functions of $\mathbf{\Omega}$.

In a series of fascinating memoirs Tyndall[5] has pointed out that the application of the thermoelectric effect in the form of a thermopile provided the necessary tool for sensing radiant heat fluxes. In Fig. 9.5.1a we have illustrated two thermocouples which can be used to measure the temperature T relative to some reference temperature T_0. In many laboratory applications the reference temperature is taken to be 0°C since this temperature is easily obtained with a mixture of ice and water. In Fig. 9.5.1b we have illustrated a thermopile which can be constructed so as to give a much larger emf for any given temperature difference, $T - T_0$. The thermopile represents a sensitive temperature measuring device; however, it can be used to measure the heat flux if one uses an energy balance around the thermopile to relate the temperature at the measuring junctions to the heat flux at the measuring junctions. We will leave this aspect of the

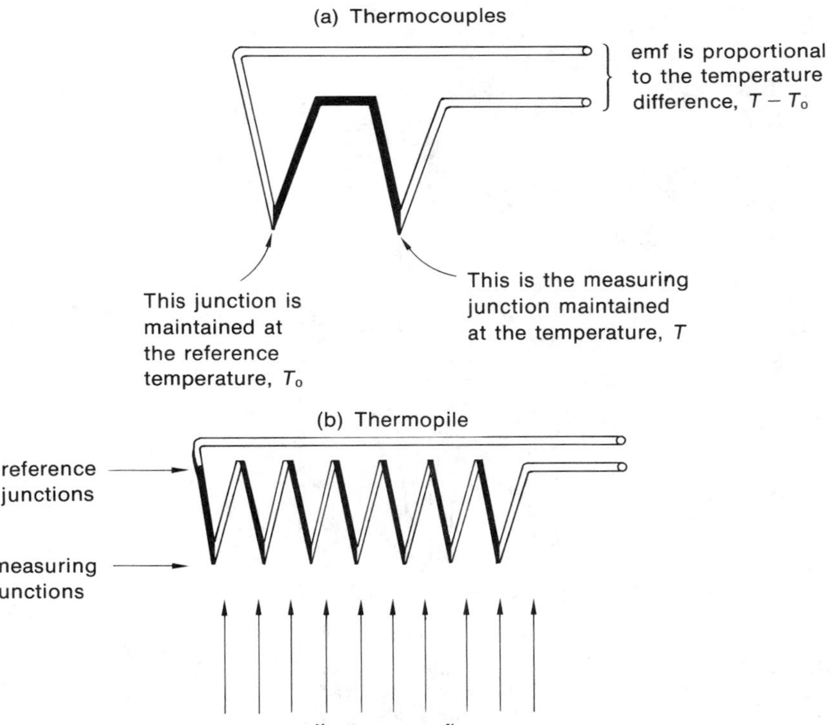

Fig. 9.5.1 Use of thermocouples to construct a thermopile.

experimental determination of emissivities as a problem for the student and continue our discussion assuming that a thermopile can be used to measure a heat flux.

In Fig. 9.5.2 we have shown an optical device called a radiometer. Its function is to select a narrow beam of radiant energy emitted from a sample or reference surface and direct it to a thermopile which measures the energy flux. In Fig. 9.5.3 we have shown the arrangement of the surface to be studied and the radiometer. The test surface is maintained at a temperature T_2 by a heater, and contained in an enclosure having walls maintained at a temperature T_1 by circulating water. The sample can be arranged so that the angle between the surface normal and the line-of-sight to the radiometer is θ and a narrow band pass filter can be used to permit only a narrow range of wavelengths to reach the radiometer. The apparatus includes two cavities which provide black body radiation at the temperatures T_1 and T_3 where the latter temperature is usually set to be close to the sample temperature T_2. This apparatus is essentially identical to that described by Eckert, Hartnett, and Irvine [6].

The radiation which reaches the thermopile from the sample comes from two sources: the emitted radiation from the sample and the reflected radiation from the enclosure. We can express the flux at the thermopile coming from the sample as†

$$Q_{2T}^{(i)} = CF_{2T}[\epsilon_{\lambda\omega}(I_{b,\lambda\omega}^{(e)})_2 \cos\theta + (I_{\lambda\omega}^{(r)})_2 \cos\theta]\pi\,\Delta A\,\Delta\lambda \tag{9.5-1}$$

Here $\Delta\lambda$ is the effective "width" of the band pass filter and ΔA is the area of the sample that is seen by the radiometer. The coefficient C is used to take into account the losses due to absorption in the gas phase, at the filter, and at the mirror. In Eq. 9.5-1 we have used the subscript T to designate the thermopile.

†See Eqs. 9.1-11 and 9.1-15.

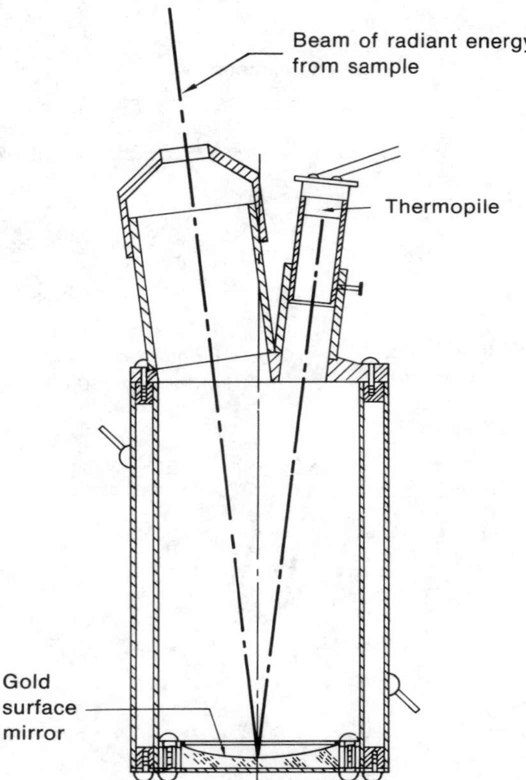

Fig. 9.5.2 Radiometer.

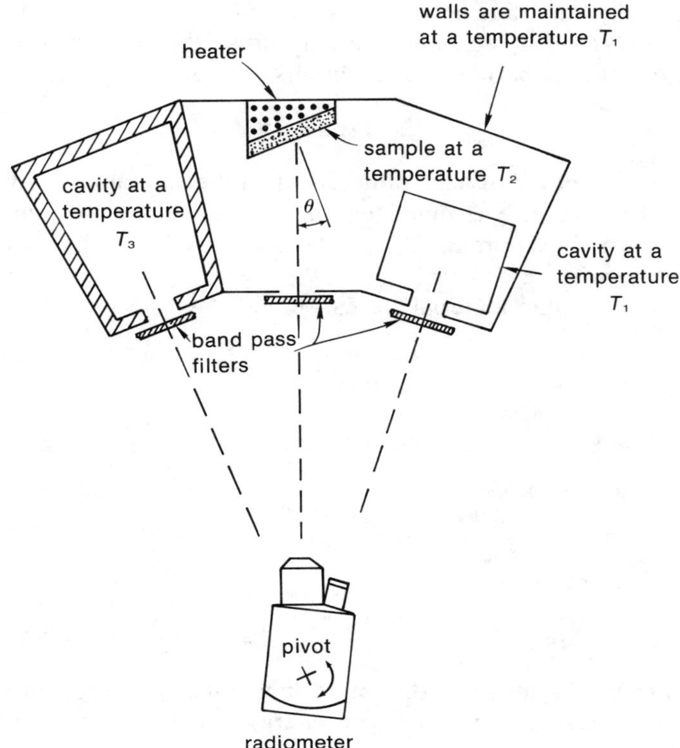

Fig. 9.5.3 Experimental equipment for emissivity measurement.

Determination of $(I^{(r)}_{\lambda\omega})_2$ represents something of a problem. The hemispherical reflected flux is given by†

$$q_\lambda{}^{(r)} = \int_{2\pi} \rho_{\lambda\omega} I^{(i)}_{\lambda\omega} |\mathbf{\Omega} \cdot \mathbf{n}|\, d\omega \tag{9.5-2}$$

but the incident radiation can be taken as black body radiation at a temperature T_1, thus

$$q_\lambda{}^{(r)} = \int_{2\pi} \rho_{\lambda\omega} (I^{(e)}_{b,\lambda\omega})_1 |\mathbf{\Omega} \cdot \mathbf{n}|\, d\omega \tag{9.5-3}$$

At this point we are simply forced to assume that the reflected radiation is diffuse so that $(I^{(r)}_{\lambda\omega})_2$ is given by‡

$$(I^{(r)}_{\lambda\omega})_2 = \frac{1}{\pi} \int_{2\pi} \rho_{\lambda\omega} (I^{(e)}_{b,\lambda\omega})_1 |\mathbf{\Omega} \cdot \mathbf{n}|\, d\omega \tag{9.5-4}$$

If we define some mean reflectivity $\bar{\rho}_\lambda$ by

$$\bar{\rho}_\lambda = \frac{1}{\pi} \int_{2\pi} \rho_{\lambda\omega} |\mathbf{\Omega} \cdot \mathbf{n}|\, d\omega \tag{9.5-5}$$

and remember that $(I^{(e)}_{b,\lambda\omega})$ is independent of $\mathbf{\Omega}$ we can write $(I^{(r)}_{\lambda\omega})_2$ as

$$(I^{(r)}_{\lambda\omega})_2 = \bar{\rho}_\lambda (I^{(e)}_{b,\lambda\omega})_1 \tag{9.5-6}$$

We can now express $\dot{Q}^{(i)}_{2T}$ as

$$\dot{Q}^{(i)}_{2T} = CF_{2T}[\epsilon_{\lambda\omega} (I^{(e)}_{b,\lambda\omega 2} \cos\theta + \bar{\rho}_\lambda (I^{(e)}_{b,\lambda\omega})_1 \cos\theta]\pi\, \Delta A\, \Delta\lambda \tag{9.5-7}$$

†See Eq. 9.4-3.
‡See Eq. 9.4-5.

If the surface of the sample is truly diffuse then $\epsilon_{\lambda\omega} = \epsilon_\lambda$ and $\bar{\rho}_\lambda = \rho_\lambda = \rho_{\lambda\omega}$ and Eq. 9.5-7 is likely to be reasonably accurate. If the surface of the sample is not diffuse then one must properly account for the reflected radiation or arrange the experimental conditions so that

$$(I_{\lambda\omega}^{(r)})_1 \ll \epsilon_{\lambda\omega}(I_{b,\lambda\omega}^{(e)})_2 \tag{9.5-8}$$

In addition to our approximate method of accounting for the reflected radiation we must also note that in going from Eq. 9.5-2 to Eq. 9.5-3 we have assumed that the radiation in the *enclosure* is *cavity radiation* at a temperature T_1. This is, of course, an approximation and is another reason why we would like the inequality indicated by Eq. 9.5-8 to be satisfied.

Provided our sample is an opaque material we can write

$$\rho_{\lambda\omega} + \alpha_{\lambda\omega} = 1 \tag{9.5-9}$$

or since $\alpha_{\lambda\omega} = \epsilon_{\lambda\omega}$ we express $\rho_{\lambda\omega}$ as

$$\rho_{\lambda\omega} = 1 - \epsilon_{\lambda\omega} \tag{9.5-10}$$

Following our previous line of attack we write

$$\bar{\rho}_\lambda = 1 - \epsilon_{\lambda\omega} \tag{9.5-11}$$

so that Eq. 9.5-7 can be put in the form

$$\dot{Q}_{2T}^{(i)} = CF_{2T}\{\epsilon_{\lambda\omega}[(I_{b,\lambda\omega}^{(e)})_2 - (I_{b,\lambda\omega}^{(e)})_1] + (I_{b,\lambda\omega}^{(e)})_1\} \cos\theta\, \pi\, \Delta A\, \Delta\lambda \tag{9.5-12}$$

The radiometer shown in Fig. 9.5.3 is mounted on a pivot so that it can be directed at the two cavities which are maintained at the temperatures T_1 and T_3. The energy leaving these cavities and arriving at the thermopile can be expressed as

$$\dot{Q}_{1T}^{(i)} = CF_{2T}\{(I_{b,\lambda\omega}^{(e)})_1\}\pi\, \Delta A\, \Delta\lambda \tag{9.5-13}$$

$$\dot{Q}_{3T}^{(i)} = CF_{2T}\{(I_{b,\lambda\omega}^{(e)})_3\}\pi\, \Delta A\, \Delta\lambda \tag{9.5-14}$$

Here we have assumed that the geometry of the experimental apparatus is such that $F_{1T} = F_{2T} = F_{3T}$. This will be the case provided the area ΔA seen by the radiometer is small compared to the surface areas of the sample and the cavities. Subtracting Eq. 9.5-13 from Eqs. 9.5-12 and 9.5-14 and then dividing one equation into the other to eliminate $CF_{2T}\pi\, \Delta A\, \Delta\lambda$ yields

$$\epsilon_{\lambda\omega} = \frac{1}{\cos\theta}\left\{\left[\frac{\dot{Q}_{2T}^{(i)} - \dot{Q}_{1T}^{(i)}}{\dot{Q}_{3T}^{(i)} - \dot{Q}_{1T}^{(i)}}\right]\left[\frac{(I_{b,\lambda\omega}^{(e)})_3 - (I_{b,\lambda\omega}^{(e)})_1}{(I_{b,\lambda\omega}^{(e)})_2 - (I_{b,\lambda\omega}^{(e)})_1}\right] + \frac{(I_{b,\lambda\omega}^{(e)})_1(1-\cos\theta)}{(I_{b,\lambda\omega}^{(e)})_2 - (I_{b,\lambda\omega}^{(e)})_1}\right\} \tag{9.5-15}$$

From Eq. 9.4-8 we know that

$$(I_{b,\lambda\omega}^{(e)})_k = \frac{2hc^2}{\lambda^5}\frac{1}{e^{hc/\lambda kT_k} - 1} \tag{9.5-16}$$

thus all the terms on the right-hand-side of Eq. 9.5-15 can be measured or calculated and $\epsilon_{\lambda\omega}$ is determined. This also provides us with the absorptivity

$$\alpha_{\lambda\omega} = \epsilon_{\lambda\omega}$$

and the reflectivity

$$\rho_{\lambda\omega} = 1 - \epsilon_{\lambda\omega}$$

Hopefully $\rho_{\lambda\omega}$ is small compared to one, or nearly independent of $\mathbf{\Omega}$, i.e., $\rho_{\lambda\omega} \sim \rho_\lambda$. If it is neither we require that the inequality indicated by Eq. 9.5-8 to be satisfied in order that Eq. 9.5-15 be a good approximation for $\epsilon_{\lambda\omega}$.

A complete experimental survey of a particular surface might require perhaps ten different values of θ

and ten different band pass filters leading to a possible one hundred experimental runs. In general, statistical methods [7] can be used to reduce the number of potential runs, but in any event a complete map of $\epsilon_{\lambda\omega}$ entails an enormous amount of experimental work. In practice, one often finds that band pass filters are not used and θ is set equal to zero so that the so-called *total, normal* emissivity is measured according to a special form of Eq. 9.5-15

$$\{\text{total, normal emissivity}\} = \epsilon_\omega|_{\theta=0} = \left(\frac{Q_{2T}^{(i)} - Q_{1T}^{(i)}}{Q_{3T}^{(i)} - Q_{1T}^{(i)}}\right)\left(\frac{T_3^4 - T_1^4}{T_2^4 - T_1^4}\right) \tag{9.5-17}$$

If the surface of the sample is truly diffuse ϵ_ω is independent of $\boldsymbol{\Omega}$ and the total, normal emissivity is equal to the total, hemispherical emissivity which is in turn equal to the total emissivity

$$\epsilon_\omega|_{\theta=0} = \epsilon_\omega = \epsilon, \quad \text{for diffuse surfaces} \tag{9.5-18}$$

When the emissivity and absorptivity are small the experimental method described in this section is not satisfactory and other methods [8–10] must be used. These are based on measuring the amount of radiant energy *reflected* from a test surface rather than measuring the amount of energy *emitted.*

9.6 Properties of Real Surfaces

In the previous section a method of measuring the specific emissivity $\epsilon_{\lambda\omega}$ was described, and now we would like to examine a few experimental results for some surfaces of engineering importance. When considering experimental values of $\epsilon_{\lambda\omega}$ or ϵ_λ or ϵ we must always remember that the quantities may be strong functions of the mechanical and thermodynamic state of the surface, and that accurately *characterizing* this state is not easily accomplished. The influence of the state of the surface may be illustrated by the results of Gier *et al.*† who measured the normal emissivity for three different aluminum surfaces. Their results are reproduced in Fig. 9.6.1. As we might expect the anodized surface tends to have a higher emissivity; however, it is a strong function of the wavelength and is actually lower than that for the commercial finish in the wavelength range of 1–2 microns. Both the commercial and polished surfaces exhibit emissivities which

†J. T. Gier and R. V. Dunkle, Progress Report, June 27, 1953, Contract No. DA-11-190-ENG-3, University of California, Institute of Engineering Research, Berkeley, California.

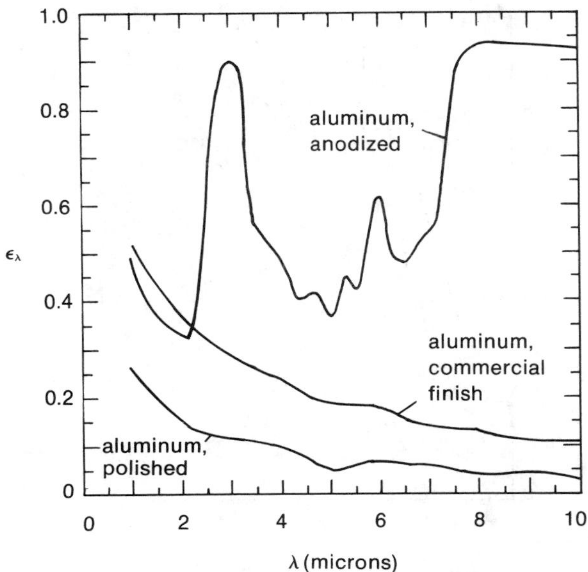

Fig. 9.6.1 Normal emissivities for three surface conditions.

are less dependent on the wavelength, but the difference between these two finishes is considerable. One should always remember that terms such as "anodized," "commercial finish," and "polished" are *qualitative* descriptions of the surface, and one man's commercial finish may be another man's polished surface. What is needed to characterize the metal surface is a quantitative measure of the roughness, and an accurate description of the anodized surface should specify the thickness and porosity of the oxide film. However, such quantitative descriptions of the state of the surface are usually unavailable,† and we must learn to make cautious use of whatever descriptions are available.

The decrease in ϵ_λ with increasing wavelength for the polished aluminum is characteristic of electrical conductors. Nonconductors generally exhibit the opposite trend with ϵ_λ increasing with increasing wavelength. This effect is illustrated by the data of Siebel[11] shown in Fig. 9.6.2. The rather irregular variation of ϵ_λ for nonconductors is typical as they tend to emit and absorb predominantly over certain bands. Note that the three surfaces illustrated in Fig. 9.6.2 are "white" in the visible region of the spectrum, but are very nearly black bodies in the infrared region. Our thoughts about radiant energy transfer are often based on the behavior of surfaces relative to solar energy, a large part of which is in the visible region. Thus white is a "cool" color and is preferred during the hot summer months while black is a "warm" color and is acceptable during the colder winter months. When dealing with radiant energy exchange problems we must remember that the range of wavelengths for significant radiant energy transfer is considerably greater than the range of wavelengths in the visible region, and the absorptivity and emissivity outside the visible region may be quite different than that in the visible region. In Fig. 9.6.3 we have illustrated the distribution of solar energy incident upon the surface of the earth and there we see that the peak in the distribution corresponds to the visible region.‡ If we compare this with the distribution of radiant energy from a black body at 1000°F shown in Fig. 9.6.4 we see that the energy emitted in the visible region is negligible and essentially all the energy is emitted in the infrared region. To such a source of radiant energy the white enamel surface illustrated in Fig. 9.6.2 would appear as a rather effective black body absorber rather than the "cool" surface that we would think of it as in the presence of solar radiation.

†The effect of oxide film thickness, and surface roughness on the emissivity are discussed by R. Siegel and J. R. Howell, *Thermal Radiation Heat Transfer*, Chap. 5, *NASA SP-164*, U.S. Government Printing Office, Wash., D.C., 1968.

‡The theory of evolution would probably have it no other way, although one should note that certain insects and animals see primarily in the infrared region. No doubt they evolved in that way in order to avoid the hazards of daytime living.

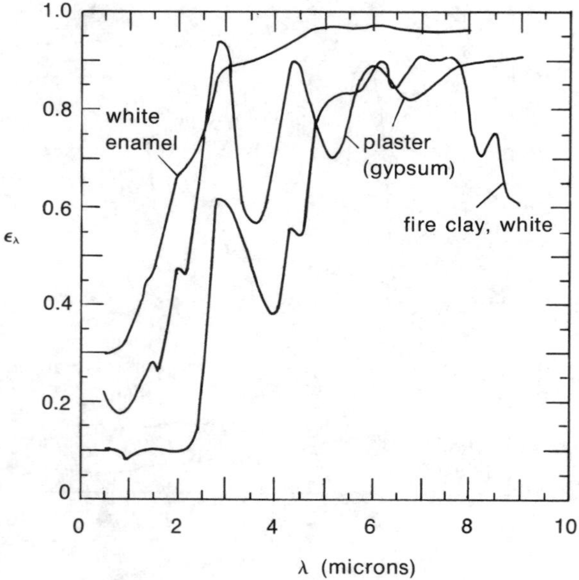

Fig. 9.6.2 Hemispherical emissivities for several "white" nonconductors.

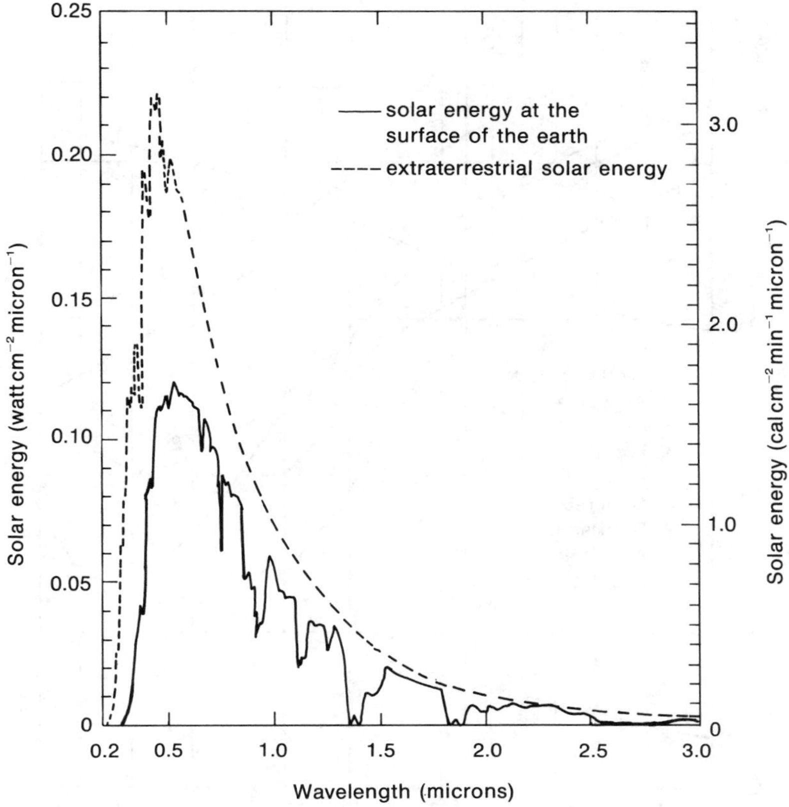

Fig. 9.6.3 Distribution of solar radiation at the surface of the earth.

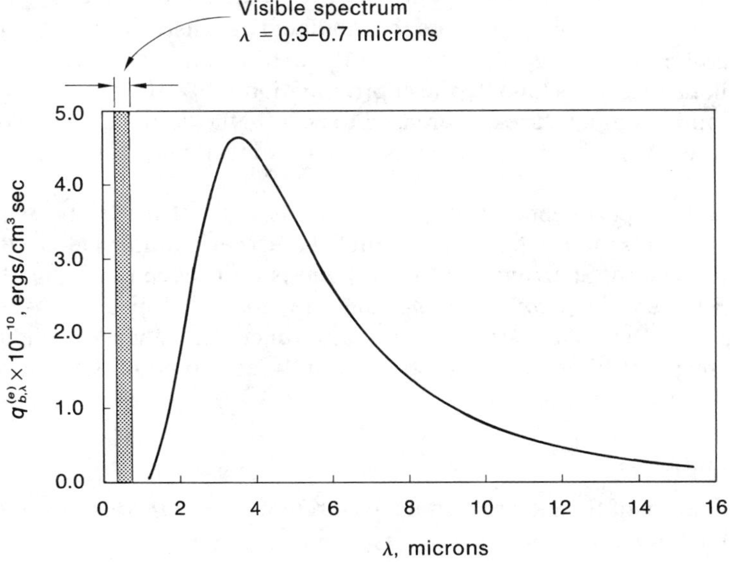

Fig. 9.6.4 Distribution of energy emitted from a black body at 1000°F.

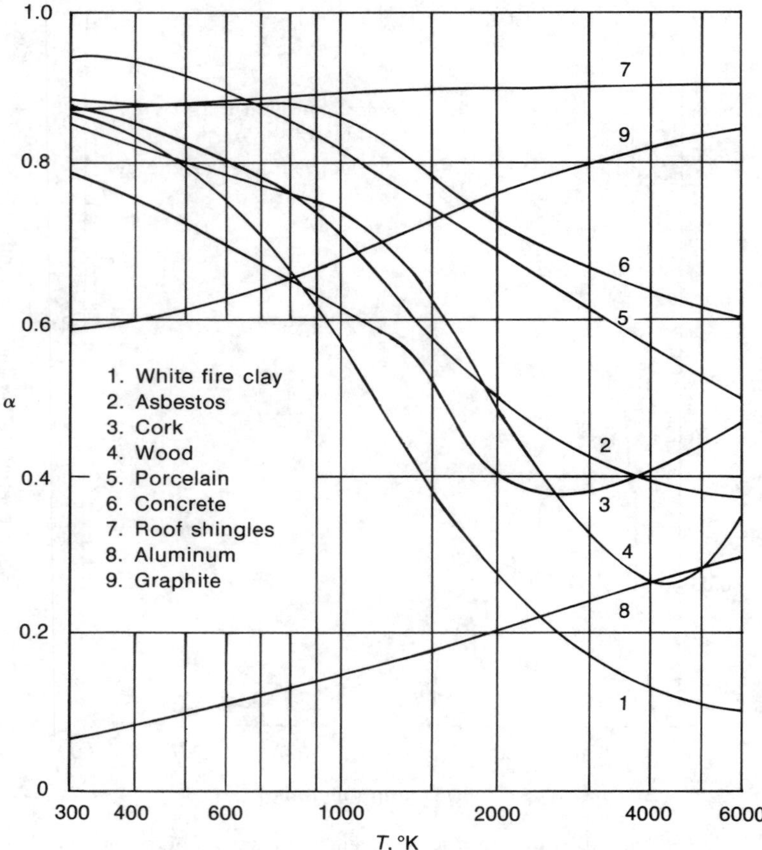

Fig. 9.6.5 Total hemispherical absorptivities for surfaces at room temperature receiving radiation from a black body as a function of temperature. (From W. Sieber, "Zusammensensetzung der von Werk und Baustoffen zurückgeworfenen Wärmestrahlung," *Z. Tech. Physik* **22**, 130 (1941).)

The general trends shown in Figs. 9.6.1 and 9.6.2 are further illustrated by the total hemispherical absorptivity data of Sieber shown in Fig. 9.6.5 and the tabulated data listed in Table 9.6-1. When the radiation source is at a low temperature the energy is predominantly in the infrared and such surfaces as white fire clay and porcelain are excellent absorbers (and by the approximation $\alpha \sim \epsilon$ they are also excellent emitters). On the other hand, as the source temperature is increased to 6000°K the dominate wavelength becomes shorter and the absorptivity of the "white" surfaces decreases as we know it must if it is to appear to be white in the visible range.

There have been many experimental studies of the emissivity of a variety of materials, and several thorough reviews [12–14] of this material. A convenient list of experimental values, which is neither too long nor too short, has been given by Sparrow and Cess [4] and is reproduced in Table 9.6-2. No distinction is made in this listing between the *hemispherical* and the *normal* emissivities because it is felt that experimental error and uncertainties arising from differences in surface condition overshadow the distinction between hemispherical and normal. Sparrow and Cess do point out that most of the data in the table are total normal emissivities.

Directional characteristics

Because of the complexity of the experimental measurements very few values of $\epsilon_{\lambda\omega}$ are available in the literature. Values of the *total emissivity* defined by

$$\epsilon_\omega = \int_0^\infty \epsilon_{\lambda\omega}\, d\lambda \tag{9.6-1}$$

Table 9.6-1 Total Emissivities, ϵ_λ

Surface	Wavelength (microns)									
	0.50	0.60	0.95	1.8	2.1	3.6	4.4	5.4	8.8	9.3
Aluminum										
polished			0.26		0.17	0.08		0.05		0.04
oxidized						0.18		0.12		0.11
Duralumin		0.53								
Chromium		0.49	0.43		0.36	0.26		0.17		0.08
Copper										
polished			0.26		0.17	0.18		0.05		0.04
oxidized						0.77		0.83		0.87
Gold										
polished					0.03	0.03		0.02		0.02
Steel										
polished		0.45	0.37		0.23	0.14		0.10		0.07
Iron										
polished		0.45	0.35		0.22	0.13		0.08		0.06
cast, oxidized						0.76		0.66		0.63
galvanized, new	0.66	0.66	0.67	0.42						0.23
galvanized, dirty	0.89	0.89	0.89	0.90						0.28
galvanized whitewashed	0.24	0.21	0.22	0.37						
Magnesium		0.30	0.26		0.23	0.18		0.13		0.07
Monel		0.43	0.29		0.16	0.10				
Molybdenum	0.55		0.43		0.18	0.11		0.08		0.06
Brass										
polished										0.05
oxidized										0.61
Paint										
lampblack		0.97	0.97				0.97		0.96	
red		0.74	0.59				0.70		0.96	
yellow	0.39	0.30					0.59		0.95	
white	0.18	0.14	0.16				0.77		0.95	
aluminum		0.45								
Silver										
polished	0.11		0.04		0.03	0.03		0.02		0.01
Platinum black	0.97		0.97		0.97	0.97	0.96	0.96	0.93	0.93
White paper		0.28	0.25			0.82				0.95
White marble		0.47				0.93				0.95
Graphite	0.78		0.73		0.64	0.54		0.49		0.41

have been obtained by Schmidt and Eckert [15] and these are reproduced in Figs. 9.6.6 and 9.6.7. In Fig. 9.6.6 we have shown ϵ_ω as a function of θ for a number of nonconductors. Presumably these surfaces are isotropic and ϵ_ω is therefore independent of ϕ. All of the surfaces appear to have nearly constant values of ϵ_ω in the range $0 \leq 0 \leq 60°$ while for values of θ greater than 60° the emissivity decreases rapidly tending toward zero as $\theta \rightarrow \pi/2$. It is particularly important to note that aluminum oxide and copper oxide are among the electrical nonconductors which exhibit a nearly constant value of ϵ_ω for it is the *oxide* of a metal which most often participates in a radiant heat transfer process. This is not the case for satellites where the lack of oxygen prohibits the build-up of an oxide film, or for low temperature heat transfer processes where the rate of chemical reaction is very slow and the oxide film requires a great deal of time to form; however, the majority of important radiant heat transfer processes occurs under conditions where an oxide film is readily formed. This fact is quite helpful for if we examine Fig. 9.6.7 we see that ϵ_ω varies drastically with θ for several of the metals studied by Schmidt and Eckert. For $0 \leq \theta \leq 30°$ the emissivity is nearly constant, but for larger values of θ the value of ϵ_ω increases rapidly. Incorporation of this kind of behavior for the emissivity is quite tedious and will not be done in this text; however, we can analyze radiant energy exchange between electrical nonconductors with some degree of accuracy and we will treat this problem in the next section.

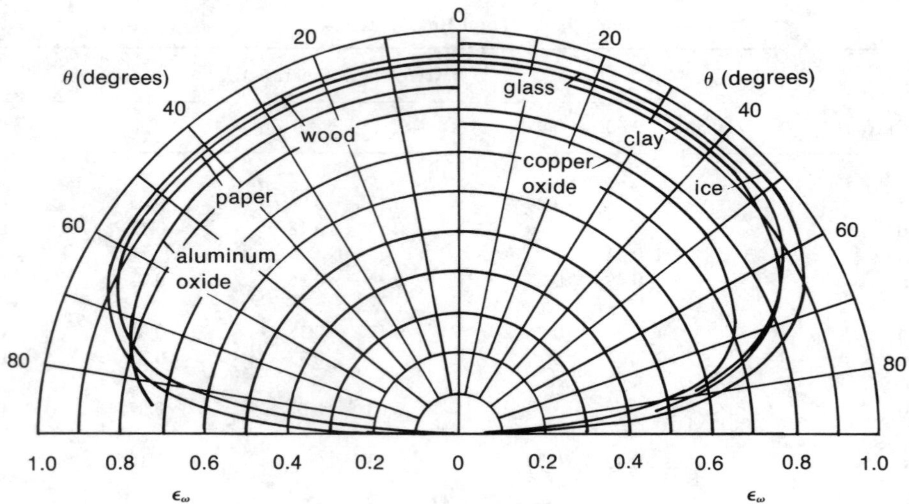

Fig. 9.6.6 Total directional emissivity for several nonconductors. (From E. Schmidt and E. R. G. Eckert, "Über die Richtungsverteilung der Wärmestrahlung," *Forsch. Gebiete Ingenieurw.* **6**, 175 (1935).)

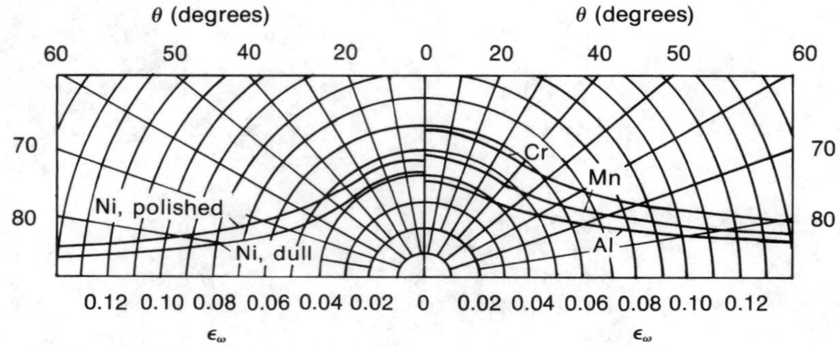

Fig. 9.6.7 Total directional emissivity for several metals. (From E. Schmidt and E. R. G. Eckert, "Uber die Richtungsverteilung der Wärmestrahlung," *Forsch. Gebiete Ingenieurw.* **6**, 175 (1935).)

Table 9.6-2 Total Hemispherical and Total Normal Emissivities†

I. METALS

Surface	Temperature, °F	ϵ
Aluminum		
polished, 98 per cent pure	400–1100	0.04–0.06
commercial sheet	200	0.09
rough plate	100	0.07
heavily oxidized	200–1000	0.20–0.33
Antimony		
polished	100–500	0.28–0.31
Bismuth		
bright	200	0.34
Brass		
highly polished	500	0.03
polished	100	0.07
dull plate	100–500	0.22
oxidized	100–500	0.46–0.56

Table 9.6-2 (*Contd.*)

Surface	Temperature, °F	ϵ
Chromium		
polished sheet	100–1000	0.08–0.27
Cobalt		
unoxidized	500–1000	0.13–0.23
Copper		
highly polished electrolytic	200	0.02
polished	100	0.04
slightly polished	100	0.12
polished, lightly tarnished	100	0.05
dull	100	0.15
black oxidized	100	0.76
Gold		
pure, highly polished	200–1100	0.02–0.035
Inconel		
X, stably oxidized	450–1600	0.55–0.78
B, stably oxidized	450–1750	0.32–0.55
X and B, polished	300–600	0.20
Iron and Steel		
mild steel, polished	300–900	0.14–0.32
steel, polished	100–500	0.07–0.10
sheet steel, ground	1700	0.55
sheet steel, rolled	100	0.66
sheet steel, strong rough oxide	100	0.80
steel, oxidized at 1100°F	500	0.79
cast iron, with skin	100	0.70–0.80
cast iron, newly turned	100	0.44
cast iron, polished	400	0.21
cast iron, oxidized	100–500	0.57–0.66
iron, red rusted	100	0.61
iron, heavily rusted	100	0.85
wrought iron, smooth	100	0.35
wrought iron, dull oxidized	70–680	0.94
stainless, polished	100	0.07–0.17
stainless, after repeated heating and cooling	450–1650	0.50–0.70
Lead		
polished	100–500	0.05–0.08
gray, oxidized	100	0.28
oxidized at 390°F	400	0.63
oxidized at 1100°F	100	0.63
Magnesium		
polished	100–500	0.07–0.13
Manganin		
bright rolled	200	0.05
Mercury		
pure, clean	100–200	0.10–0.12
Molybdenum		
polished	100–500	0.06–0.08
polished	1000–2000	0.11–0.18
filament	1000–5000	0.08–0.29
Monel		
after repeated heating and cooling	450–1650	0.45–0.70
oxidized at 1100°F	400–1100	0.41–0.46
polished	100	0.17
Nickel		
polished	100–500	0.05–0.07
oxidized	100–500	0.35–0.49
wire	500–2000	0.10–0.19

Table 9.6-2 (*Contd.*)

Surface	Temperature, °F	ϵ
Platinum		
pure, polished plate	400–1100	0.05–0.10
oxidized at 1100°F	500–1000	0.07–0.11
electrolytic	500–1000	0.06–0.10
strip	1000–2000	0.12–0.14
filament	100–2000	0.04–0.19
wire	400–2500	0.07–0.18
Silver		
polished or deposited	100–1000	0.01–0.03
oxidized	100–1000	0.02–0.04
German silver,‡ polished	500–1000	0.07–0.09
Tin		
bright tinned iron	100	0.04–0.06
bright	100	0.06
polished sheet	200	0.05
Tungsten		
filament	1000–2000	0.11–0.16
filament	5000	0.39
filament, aged	100–6000	0.03–0.35
polished	100–1000	0.04–0.08
Zinc		
pure polished	100–500	0.02–0.03
oxidized at 750°F	750	0.11
galvanized, gray	100	0.28
galvanized, fairly bright	100	0.23
dull	100–500	0.21
II. NONMETALS		
Asbestos		
board	100	0.96
cement	100	0.96
paper	100	0.93–0.95
slate	100	0.97
Brick		
red, rough	100	0.93
silica	1800	0.80–0.85
fire clay	1800	0.75
ordinary refractory	2000	0.59
magnesite refractory	1800	0.38
white refractory	2000	0.29
gray, glazed	2000	0.75
Carbon		
filament	1900–2600	0.53
lampsoot	100	0.95
Clay		
fired	200	0.91
Concrete		
rough	100	0.94
Corundum		
emery rough	200	0.86
Glass		
smooth	100	0.94
quartz glass (2 mm)	500–1000	0.96–0.66
pyrex	500–1000	0.94–0.75
Gypsum	100	0.80–0.90
Ice		
smooth	32	0.97
rough crystals	32	0.99
hoarfrost	0	0.99

‡German silver is actually an alloy of copper, nickel, and zinc.

Table 9.6-2 (*Contd.*)

Surface	Temperature, °F	ϵ
Limestone	100–500	0.95–0.83
Marble		
light gray, polished	100	0.93
white	100	0.95
Mica	100	0.75
Paints		
aluminum, various ages and compositions	200	0.27–0.62
black gloss	100	0.90
black lacquer	100	0.80–0.93
white paint	100	0.89–0.97
white lacquer	100	0.80–0.95
various oil paints	100	0.92–0.96
red lead	200	0.93
Paper		
white	100	0.95
writing paper	100	0.98
any color	100	0.92–0.94
roofing	100	0.91
Plaster		
lime, rough	100–500	0.92
Porcelain		
glazed	100	0.93
Quartz	100–1000	0.89–0.58
Rubber		
hard	100	0.94
soft, gray rough	100	0.86
Sandstone	100–500	0.83–0.90
Snow	10–20	0.82
Water		
0.1 mm or more thick	100	0.96
Wood		
oak, planed	100	0.90
walnut, sanded	100	0.83
spruce, sanded	100	0.82
beech	100	0.94
planed	100	0.78
various	100	0.80–0.90
sawdust	100	0.75

†Adapted from E. M. Sparrow and R. D. Cess, *Radiation Heat Transfer*, Brooks/Cole Publishing Co., Belmont, California, 1966.

9.7 Radiant Energy Exchange Between Gray Surfaces

In this section we wish to consider a system such as the one illustrated in Fig. 9.3.1; however, at this time we wish to relax the restriction of black body radiation and go on to a more satisfactory model of real surfaces. The model that we have in mind is the *gray surface* or the *Lambert gray surface* for which

$$\epsilon = \epsilon_\lambda = \epsilon_{\lambda\omega} = \alpha_{\lambda\omega} = \alpha_\lambda = \alpha, \quad \text{for a gray surface} \tag{9.7-1}$$

but rather than accept Eq. 9.7-1 as a definition and plunge into an extension of the analysis presented in Sec. 9.3, it may be helpful to give some thought to the conditions under which the gray surface model may be a realistic one.

If the materials making up the enclosure illustrated in Fig. 9.7.1 are electrical nonconductors or the oxides

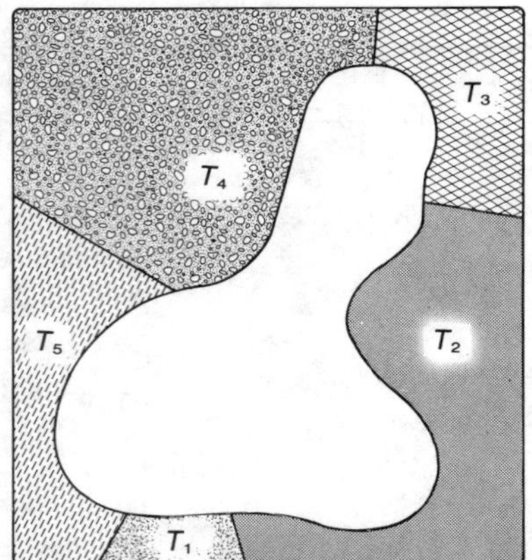

Fig. 9.7.1 Gray body enclosure.

of electrical conductors we can assume that the directional nature of the emissivities is represented by the behavior illustrated in Fig. 9.6.6, i.e., the emissivity is independent of the direction for θ between 0° and about 60°. Now, from the results of Prob. 8-5 we know that the radiant energy emitted by a black body within the cone bounded by $0 \leq \theta \leq \eta$ is given by

$$\{\text{radiant energy emitted by a black body within a cone bounded by } 0 \leq \theta \leq \eta\} = q_{b,\lambda}^{(e)}(1 - \cos^2 \eta) \tag{9.7-2}$$

Using Eq. 9.7-2 we find that three-quarters of the energy is emitted within the cone $0 \leq \theta \leq 60°$, and that 97 per cent of the energy is emitted within the cone defined by $0 \leq \theta \leq 80°$. From these results we can see that it would not cause serious error if we assume that ϵ_ω for electrical nonconductors is a constant. This assumption will cause us to slightly overestimate the total energy emitted by a surface, and in particular it will cause us to overestimate the amount of energy emitted at values of θ approaching $\pi/2$. Neither of these errors is judged to be serious in comparison to the error involved in measuring the emissivity and the uncertainty involved in characterizing the state of the surface. On the basis of these arguments we will make our first engineering assumption

A1

$$\epsilon_{\lambda\omega} = \epsilon_\lambda \tag{9.7-3}$$

Keep in mind that this should be quite satisfactory for electrical nonconductors among which we include the metal oxides, but would be a very poor assumption for a clean, smooth metal surface.

We must now come to grips with the wavelength dependence of ϵ_λ. From Figs. 9.6.1 and 9.6.2 we know that ϵ_λ for electrical nonconductors is an irregular function of λ in the infrared region and can undergo large variations as the wavelength moves from the infrared to the visible or solar region. One can always correctly compute the total, hemispherical emitted flux by the expression

$$q^{(e)} = \epsilon\sigma T^4 \tag{9.7-4}$$

where ϵ is defined by

$$\epsilon = \frac{\int_0^\infty \epsilon_\lambda I_{b,\lambda\omega}^{(e)}\, d\lambda}{\int_0^\infty I_{b,\lambda\omega}^{(e)}\, d\lambda} \tag{9.7-5}$$

Remember now that $I_{b,\lambda\omega}^{(e)}$ is a relatively "flat" function of λ at low temperatures where radiant energy exchange is often less important, and is a rather "peaked" function of λ at high temperatures where radiation usually dominates the heat transfer process. As an extreme case we could represent $I_{b,\lambda\omega}^{(e)}$ as

$$I_{b,\lambda\omega}^{(e)} = \left(\frac{q_b^{(e)}}{\pi}\right)\delta(\lambda_{\max} - \lambda), \quad \text{for very high temperatures} \tag{9.7-6}$$

where λ_{max} is the wavelength given by Wein's displacement law

$$\lambda_{max} T = 0.29\ \text{cm}^\circ\text{K} \tag{9.7-7}$$

and $\delta(\lambda_{max} - \lambda)$ is the Dirac delta function which has the property

$$f(\lambda_{max}) = \int_0^\infty f(\lambda)\delta(\lambda_{max} - \lambda)\, d\lambda \tag{9.7-8}$$

Substitution of Eq. 9.7-6 into Eq. 9.7-5 and carrying out the integration yields

$$\epsilon = \epsilon_\lambda|_{\lambda=\lambda_{max}}, \quad \text{for very high temperatures} \tag{9.7-9}$$

Eq. 9.7-9 represents, of course, an extreme case; however, the fact that $I^{(e)}_{b,\lambda\omega}$ is peaked around λ_{max} means that the value ϵ calculated from Eq. 9.7-5 is determined primarily by the values of ϵ_λ in the region near $\lambda = \lambda_{max}$. Thus if the variations of ϵ_λ are not severe in the region of λ_{max} it may be reasonable to make a second engineering approximation

A2
$$\epsilon_\lambda = \epsilon, \quad \text{for values of } \lambda \text{ near } \lambda_{max} \tag{9.7-10}$$

Having made assumptions A1 and A2 we are left with

$$\epsilon = \epsilon_\lambda = \epsilon_{\lambda\omega} = \alpha_{\lambda\omega} = \alpha_\lambda = \alpha, \quad \text{for values of } \lambda \text{ near } \lambda_{max} \tag{9.7-11}$$

The value of ϵ in this expression can be used to correctly compute $q^{(e)}$ by means of Eq. 9.7-4, but what about computing the rate at which energy is absorbed by the formula

$$q^{(a)} = \alpha q^{(i)} \tag{9.7-12}$$

Here we must remember that the *correct* value of α to be used in Eq. 9.7-12 is *defined* by

$$\alpha \equiv \frac{\int_0^\infty \int_{2\pi} \alpha_{\lambda\omega} I^{(i)}_{\lambda\omega} |\mathbf{\Omega} \cdot \mathbf{n}|\, d\omega\, d\lambda}{\int_0^\infty \int_{2\pi} I^{(i)}_{\lambda\omega} |\mathbf{\Omega} \cdot \mathbf{n}|\, d\omega\, d\lambda} \tag{9.7-13}$$

and that $\alpha = \epsilon$ is strictly correct only for the two cases:

(I) $\alpha_{\lambda\omega} = \epsilon_{\lambda\omega} = \text{constant}$

(II) the incident radiation is black body radiation at the same temperature as the surface, i.e., $I^{(i)}_{\lambda\omega} = I^{(e)}_{b,\lambda\omega}$

In general neither of these conditions will be met for most practical applications, and the expression for the rate at which energy is absorbed given by Eq. 9.7-12 will be in error. This is an error which we must be content to accept or else be prepared to engage in a much more difficult and thorough analysis of the problem. This is a somewhat discouraging note with which to begin our analysis of gray body radiant energy exchange; however, we must keep in mind that we are making progress and the restriction of black body radiation will soon be behind us.

At this point we have accepted assumption A1 as quite reasonable, and A2 as quite necessary if we are to proceed without undue difficulty. Since the surfaces we are considering emit radiation diffusely (assumption A1) it would seem reasonable to assume that these surfaces also reflect diffusely, thus we state our third engineering assumption as

A3
$$I^{(r)}_{\lambda\omega} \quad \text{is isotropic}$$

We now define a gray surface as one which satisfies assumptions A1, A2, and A3:

> A gray surface is one for which the specific emissivity, $\epsilon_{\lambda\omega}$, is a constant, and which reflects radiation diffusely

We begin our analysis by assuming that the surfaces illustrated in Fig. 9.7.1 are gray surfaces and express the emitted and reflected radiation as

$$\{\text{total, hemispherical emitted flux for a gray surface}\} = \epsilon q_b^{(e)} \tag{9.7-14}$$

$$\{\text{total, hemispherical reflected flux for a gray surface}\} = \rho q^{(i)} \tag{9.7-15}$$

where the total, hemispherical reflectivity, ρ, is given by

$$\rho = 1 - \epsilon \tag{9.7-16}$$

The rate at which radiant energy *leaves* a surface both by emission and reflection is called the *radiosity* and is often denoted by J, thus we write

$$\{\text{total, hemispherical flux leaving a gray surface}\} = J = \epsilon q_b^{(e)} + \rho q^{(i)} \tag{9.7-17}$$

We now assume that the surfaces are isothermal and uniformly irradiated so that $q_b^{(e)}$ and $q^{(i)}$ are constant over any given surface. For the jth surface we can write

$$A_j J_j = \epsilon_j A_j \sigma T_j^4 + \rho_j A_j q_j^{(i)} \tag{9.7-18}$$

where the total incident radiation from the N surfaces in the enclosure is given by

$$A_j q_j^{(i)} = \sum_{k=1}^{k=N} A_k F_{kj} J_k \tag{9.7-19}$$

We should remark once again that J represents *diffuse* radiation leaving a surface, thus all the geometrical arguments developed in Secs. 9.1, 9.2, and 9.3 are applicable and Eq. 9.7-19 follows from Eq. 9.3-2, for example. We must also remember that isothermal assumption and the assumption of uniform irradiation discussed in Sec. 9.4 can always be satisfied by subdividing any surface into sufficiently small segments.

A radiant energy balance for the jth surface will give us $\dot{Q}_j$, the net rate of transfer of radiant energy from the jth surface to the enclosure

$$\dot{Q}_j = \epsilon_j A_j \sigma T_j^4 - \alpha_j A_j q_j^{(i)} \tag{9.7-20}$$

(The first term: emitted energy from the jth gray surface; the second term: absorbed energy from the N gray surfaces.)

We can use Eq. 9.7-19 and the fact that $\alpha_j = \epsilon_j$, and $\rho_j = 1 - \epsilon_j$ to rearrange Eq. 9.7-20 in the form

$$\dot{Q}_j = \left(\frac{\epsilon_j}{1-\epsilon_j}\right) A_j [\sigma T_j^4 - J_j] \tag{9.7-21}$$

In order to solve for J_j we must eliminate $q_i^{(i)}$ between Eqs. 9.7-18 and 9.7-19 to obtain

$$A_j J_j = \epsilon_j A_j \sigma T_j^4 + \rho_j \sum_{k=1}^{k=N} A_k F_{kj} J_k \tag{9.7-22}$$

We can now use the reciprocity condition

$$A_k F_{kj} = A_j F_{jk} \tag{9.7-23}$$

to write

$$\sum_{k=1}^{k=N} A_k F_{kj} J_k = A_j \sum_{k=1}^{k=1} F_{jk} J_k \tag{9.7-24}$$

Use of Eq. 9.7-24 allows us to express Eq. 9.7-22 in the form

$$\sum_{k=1}^{k=N} F_{jk} J_k - J_j (1-\epsilon_j)^{-1} = \left(\frac{\epsilon_j}{\epsilon_j - 1}\right) \sigma T_j^4, \qquad j = 1, 2, \ldots, N \tag{9.7-25}$$

where $1 - \epsilon_j$ has been substituted for ρ_j.

The solution of the N equations represented by Eq. 9.7-25 for the N radiosities is straightforward and follows precisely the approach presented in Sec. 9.4. Once again we will present the analysis in detail, and the student who is unfamiliar with matrix algebra may wish to skip directly to the final result given by Eq. 9.7-32. We can write the N equations represented by Eq. 9.7-25 in matrix form as

$$\begin{bmatrix} F_{11}-(1-\epsilon_1)^{-1} & F_{12} & F_{13} & \cdots & F_{1N} \\ F_{21} & F_{22}-(1-\epsilon_2)^{-1} & F_{23} & \cdots & F_{2N} \\ F_{31} & F_{32} & & \cdots & F_{3N} \\ \cdot & \cdot & & & \cdot \\ \cdot & \cdot & & & \cdot \\ \cdot & \cdot & & & \cdot \\ F_{N1} & F_{N2} & & F_{NN}-(1-\epsilon_N)^{-1} & \end{bmatrix} \begin{bmatrix} J_1 \\ J_2 \\ J_3 \\ \cdot \\ \cdot \\ \cdot \\ J_N \end{bmatrix} = \begin{bmatrix} \left(\frac{\epsilon_1}{\epsilon_1-1}\right)\sigma T_1^4 \\ \left(\frac{\epsilon_2}{\epsilon_2-1}\right)\sigma T_2^4 \\ \left(\frac{\epsilon_3}{\epsilon_3-1}\right)\sigma T_3^4 \\ \cdot \\ \cdot \\ \cdot \\ \left(\frac{\epsilon_N}{\epsilon_N-1}\right)\sigma T_N^4 \end{bmatrix} \tag{9.7-26}$$

Symbolically we can express this result as

$$\mathbf{M}\cdot\mathbf{B}=\mathbf{C} \tag{9.7-27}$$

where **M** represents the known matrix of coefficients, **B** represents the column vector of unknown radiosities, and **C** represents the column vector of known values of $\epsilon\sigma T^4/(\epsilon-1)$. The elements of the matrix **M** can be expressed as

$$M_{jk} = F_{jk} - \delta_{jk}(1-\epsilon_k)^{-1} \tag{9.7-28}$$

where δ_{jk} represents the elements of the unit matrix which are given by

$$\delta_{jk} = \begin{cases} 1, & j=k \\ 0, & j\neq k \end{cases} \tag{9.7-29}$$

The elements of the two column vectors, **B** and **C**, are given by

$$B_j = J_j \tag{9.7-30}$$

$$C_j = \epsilon_j\sigma T_j^4/(\epsilon_j-1) \tag{9.7-31}$$

In terms of Eqs. 9.7-28 through 9.7-31 we could write Eq. 9.7-25 as

$$\sum_{k=1}^{k=N} M_{jk}B_j = C_j, \qquad j=1,2,\ldots,N \tag{9.7-32}$$

The solution for the column vector **B** is obtained by multiplying Eq. 9.7-27 by the inverse of **M** giving

$$\mathbf{M}^{-1}\cdot\mathbf{M}\cdot\mathbf{B}=\mathbf{M}^{-1}\cdot\mathbf{C} \tag{9.7-33}$$

Remember that a matrix times its inverse is the unit matrix, **U**, so that Eq. 9.7-33 reduces to

$$\mathbf{U}\cdot\mathbf{B}=\mathbf{M}^{-1}\cdot\mathbf{C} \tag{9.7-34}$$

Since the product of the unit matrix with a column vector is simply the column vector, our solution for the column vector of unknown radiosities is

$$\mathbf{B}=\mathbf{M}^{-1}\cdot\mathbf{C} \tag{9.7-35}$$

If we designate the elements of the inverse matrix as M_{jk}^{-1} we can express the elements of **B** as

$$J_j = \sum_{k=1}^{k=N} M_{jk}^{-1}[\epsilon_k\sigma T_k^4/(\epsilon_k-1)] \tag{9.7-36}$$

Here we have used Eqs. 9.7-30 and 9.7-31 to substitute for B_j and C_k. We have now solved for the previously unknown radiosities, and we can return to Eq. 9.7-21 to express the rate of radiant heat transfer from the jth surface to the surroundings as

$$\dot{Q}_j = \left(\frac{\epsilon_j}{1-\epsilon_j}\right)A_j\left\{\sigma T_j^4 + \sum_{k=1}^{k=N} M_{jk}^{-1}\left(\frac{\epsilon_k}{1-\epsilon_k}\right)\sigma T_k^4\right\} \tag{9.7-37}$$

This type of analysis can be extended to the case where N_1 surface temperatures are specified, and N_2 heat fluxes are specified in order to calculate N_1 heat fluxes and N_2 surface temperatures. This case will be left as an exercise for the student.

Infinite, parallel, gray surfaces

As an example of an application of Eq. 9.7-37 we will analyze the radiant energy exchange between the infinite, parallel, gray surfaces shown in Fig. 9.7.2. Since there are only two surfaces, Eq. 9.7-37 takes the form†

$$\frac{Q_1}{A_1} = \left(\frac{\epsilon_1}{1-\epsilon_1}\right)\left\{\sigma T_1^4 + M_{11}^{-1}\left(\frac{\epsilon_1}{1-\epsilon_1}\right)\sigma T_1^4 + M_{12}^{-1}\left(\frac{\epsilon_2}{1-\epsilon_2}\right)\sigma T_2^4\right\} \tag{9.7-38}$$

and all we need to do is to find the elements of the inverse, M_{11}^{-1} and M_{12}^{-1}. Returning to Eq. 9.7-26 we write

$$\begin{bmatrix} F_{11}-(1-\epsilon_1)^{-1} & F_{12} \\ F_{21} & F_{22}-(1-\epsilon_2)^{-1} \end{bmatrix}\begin{bmatrix} J_1 \\ J_2 \end{bmatrix} = \begin{bmatrix} \left(\frac{\epsilon_1}{\epsilon_1-1}\right)\sigma T_1^4 \\ \left(\frac{\epsilon_2}{\epsilon_2-1}\right)\sigma T_2^4 \end{bmatrix} \tag{9.7-39}$$

Since $F_{11}=F_{22}=0$ and $F_{12}=F_{21}=1$, the matrix $\mathbf{M}$ is given by

$$\mathbf{M} = \begin{bmatrix} -(1-\epsilon_1)^{-1} & 1 \\ 1 & -(1-\epsilon_2)^{-1} \end{bmatrix} \tag{9.7-40}$$

The inverse is defined by

$$\mathbf{M}^{-1}\cdot\mathbf{M} = \begin{bmatrix} 1 & 0 \\ 0 & 1 \end{bmatrix} \tag{9.7-41}$$

thus $\mathbf{M}^{-1}$ can be found and the result is

$$\mathbf{M}^{-1} = \begin{bmatrix} \frac{(1-\epsilon_1)}{(1-\epsilon_1)(1-\epsilon_2)-1} & \frac{(1-\epsilon_1)(1-\epsilon_2)}{(1-\epsilon_1)(1-\epsilon_2)-1} \\ \frac{(1-\epsilon_1)(1-\epsilon_2)}{(1-\epsilon_1)(1-\epsilon_2)-1} & \frac{(1-\epsilon_2)}{(1-\epsilon_1)(1-\epsilon_2)-1} \end{bmatrix} \tag{9.7-42}$$

†Note that the assumption of uniform irradiation is satisfied.

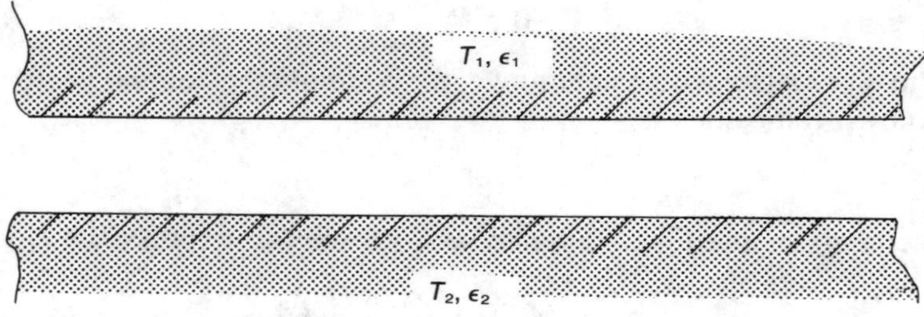

Fig. 9.7.2 Infinite, parallel, gray surfaces.

Substitution of M_{11}^{-1} and M_{12}^{-1} into Eq. 9.7-38 and rearranging the results eventually leads to

$$\frac{\dot{Q}_1}{A_1} = \frac{\epsilon_1\epsilon_2\sigma}{1-(1-\epsilon_1)(1-\epsilon_2)}[T_1^4 - T_2^4] \tag{9.7-43}$$

Note that if both surfaces are black bodies this result reduces to

$$\frac{\dot{Q}_1}{A_1} = \sigma(T_1^4 - T_2^4), \quad \text{for black body surfaces} \tag{9.7-44}$$

and if surface 2 is a perfect reflector $\rho_2 = 1$ and $\epsilon_2 = 0$ so that

$$\frac{\dot{Q}_1}{A_1} = 0, \quad \text{for surface 2 a perfect reflector} \tag{9.7-45}$$

The problem that we have chosen to illustrate the use of Eq. 9.7-37 is an especially simple one; however, the general problem of computing $\dot{Q}_j$ in a gray body enclosure is still relatively straightforward provided that the view factors are available and one has access to a high-speed digital computer for evaluating the elements of the inverse, M_{jk}^{-1}.

Method of successive reflections

There is another approach to solving gray body radiation problems which is suitable for simple geometries such as the infinite, parallel plate problem analyzed above. Even though the method has limited application it does provide a very nice picture of the radiant energy exchange process, and as such it can serve to strengthen our understanding of this process.

In Fig. 9.7.3 we have again shown our two infinite, parallel, gray surfaces, but here we have also shown the history of the energy associated with a stream of photons that was originally emitted from surface 1.

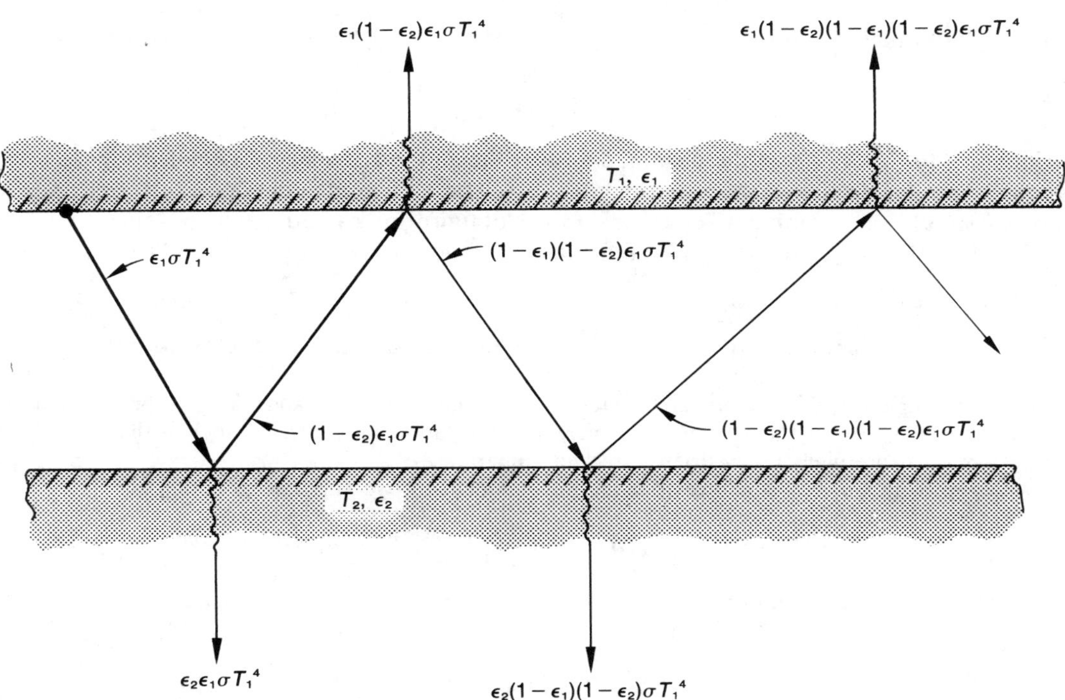

Fig. 9.7.3 Successive reflections between parallel, infinite, gray surfaces.

From that picture we can deduce that the rate of energy emitted from surface 1 which is absorbed by surface 2 is given by

$$\left\{\begin{array}{l}\text{rate at which energy emitted by}\\ \text{surface 1 is absorbed by surface 2}\end{array}\right\} = \underset{\text{1st reflection}}{\epsilon_2[\epsilon_1\sigma T_1^4]} + \underset{\text{2nd reflection}}{\epsilon_2(1-\epsilon_1)(1-\epsilon_2)[\epsilon_1\sigma T_1^4]} + \underset{\text{3rd reflection}}{\epsilon_2(1-\epsilon_1)(1-\epsilon_2)(1-\epsilon_1)(1-\epsilon_2)[\epsilon_1\sigma T_1^4]} + \cdots + \underset{n\text{th reflection}}{\epsilon_2[(1-\epsilon_1)(1-\epsilon_2)]^{n-1}[\epsilon_1\sigma T_1^4]} \tag{9.7-46}$$

We can express this result in more compact form as

$$\left\{\begin{array}{l}\text{rate at which energy emitted by}\\ \text{surface 1 is absorbed by surface 2}\end{array}\right\} = \epsilon_2[\epsilon_1\sigma T_1^4] \sum_{n=0}^{\infty} [(1-\epsilon_1)(1-\epsilon_2)]^n \tag{9.7-47}$$

It should be obvious that we can also write

$$\left\{\begin{array}{l}\text{rate at which energy emitted by}\\ \text{surface 2 is absorbed by surface 1}\end{array}\right\} = \epsilon_1[\epsilon_2\sigma T_2^4] \sum_{n=0}^{\infty} [(1-\epsilon_2)(1-\epsilon_1)]^n \tag{9.7-48}$$

so that our expression for $\dot{Q}_1/A_1$ becomes

$$\frac{\dot{Q}_1}{A_1} = \epsilon_1\epsilon_2\sigma(T_1^4 - T_2^4) \sum_{n=0}^{\infty} [(1-\epsilon_1)(1-\epsilon_2)]^n \tag{9.7-49}$$

However, it can be shown that the summation reduces to†

$$\sum_{n=0}^{\infty} [(1-\epsilon_1)(1-\epsilon_2)]^n = \frac{1}{1-(1-\epsilon_1)(1-\epsilon_2)} \tag{9.7-50}$$

so that Eq. 9.7-49 takes the form

$$\frac{\dot{Q}_1}{A_1} = \frac{\epsilon_1\epsilon_2\sigma}{1-(1-\epsilon_1)(1-\epsilon_2)}[T_1^4 - T_2^4] \tag{9.7-51}$$

which is identical to Eq. 9.7-43. Note the application of the method of successive reflections to this problem was especially simple because all the radiation that left surface 1 was incident upon surface 2 and vice versa. In addition we should keep in mind that the *assumption* of uniform irradiation which went into the derivation of Eq. 9.7-37 and was therefore incorporated into the solution given by Eq. 9.7-43 is satisfied.

Example 9.7-1 Gray body radiation in a two surface enclosure

In this example we wish to examine the gray body radiant energy exchange process for a system such as that shown in Fig. 9.3.1 where the enclosure walls are at a constant temperature, or such as that shown in Fig. 9.7.1 where the enclosure walls are restricted to two temperatures.

We begin with Eq. 9.7-37 and restrict the development to two surfaces to obtain

$$\dot{Q}_{12} = \left(\frac{\epsilon_1}{1-\epsilon_1}\right)A_1\left[\sigma T_1^4 + M_{11}^{-1}\left(\frac{\epsilon_1}{1-\epsilon_1}\right)\sigma T_1^4 + M_{12}^{-1}\left(\frac{\epsilon_2}{1-\epsilon_2}\right)\sigma T_2^4\right] \tag{1}$$

In order to obtain the elements of the inverse $\mathbf{M}^{-1}$ we return to Eq. 9.7-28 to note that the elements of $\mathbf{M}$ are given by

$$M_{11} = F_{11} - \frac{1}{1-\epsilon_1}$$

†This will be left as an exercise for the student.

$$M_{12} = F_{12}$$

$$M_{21} = F_{21}$$

$$M_{22} = F_{22} - \frac{1}{1-\epsilon_2}$$

and that the elements of the inverse are defined by

$$\begin{pmatrix} M_{11} & M_{12} \\ M_{21} & M_{22} \end{pmatrix} \begin{pmatrix} M_{11}^{-1} & M_{12}^{-1} \\ M_{21}^{-1} & M_{22}^{-1} \end{pmatrix} = \begin{pmatrix} 1 & 0 \\ 0 & 1 \end{pmatrix} \tag{2}$$

Carrying out the matrix multiplication leads to

$$\begin{pmatrix} M_{11}M_{11}^{-1} + M_{12}M_{21}^{-1} & M_{11}M_{12}^{-1} + M_{12}M_{22}^{-1} \\ M_{21}M_{11}^{-1} + M_{22}M_{21}^{-1} & M_{21}M_{12}^{-1} + M_{22}M_{22}^{-1} \end{pmatrix} = \begin{pmatrix} 1 & 0 \\ 0 & 1 \end{pmatrix} \tag{3}$$

and the required elements of $\mathbf{M}^{-1}$ are given by

$$M_{11}^{-1} = \frac{1}{M_{11}\left[1 - \left(\frac{M_{12}}{M_{11}}\right)\left(\frac{M_{21}}{M_{22}}\right)\right]} \tag{4}$$

$$M_{12}^{-1} = \frac{-(M_{12}/M_{22})}{M_{11}\left[1 - \left(\frac{M_{12}}{M_{11}}\right)\left(\frac{M_{21}}{M_{22}}\right)\right]} \tag{5}$$

Substitution of the expressions for M_{11}, M_{12}, M_{21}, and M_{22} into Eqs. 4 and 5 and substitution of Eqs. 4 and 5 into Eq. 1 provides our result for $\dot{Q}_1$. After an enormous amount of algebraic manipulation we can put this result in the form

$$\dot{Q}_{12} = A_1 \mathscr{F}_{12} \sigma (T_1^4 - T_2^4) \tag{6}$$

where the gray body view factor $\mathscr{F}_{12}$ is given by

$$\mathscr{F}_{12} = \frac{\epsilon_1 \epsilon_2 F_{12}}{[F_{11}(1-\epsilon_1) - 1][F_{22}(1-\epsilon_2) - 1] - F_{12}F_{21}(1-\epsilon_1)(1-\epsilon_2)} \tag{7}$$

Often it is convenient to express Eq. 7 as

$$\frac{1}{\epsilon_1 A_1 \mathscr{F}_{12}} = \frac{1}{A_1 F_{12}} + \frac{1}{A_1}\left(\frac{1-\epsilon_1}{\epsilon_1}\right) + \frac{1}{A_2}\left(\frac{1-\epsilon_2}{\epsilon_2}\right) \tag{8}$$

There are three special cases for $\mathscr{F}_{12}$ which we should examine.

(I) *Infinite Parallel Plates*

In this case $F_{11} = F_{22} = 0$ and $F_{12} = F_{21} = 1$, and Eq. 7 reduces to

$$\mathscr{F}_{12} = \frac{\epsilon_1 \epsilon_2}{1 - (1-\epsilon_1)(1-\epsilon_2)} \tag{9}$$

Substitution of Eq. 9 into Eq. 6 leads, of course, to Eq. 9.7-43 or Eq. 9.7-51 which was obtained by the method of successive reflections.

(II) *Gray Body in a Black Enclosure*

This case was first discussed in Chapter 1 and it requires that $\epsilon_2 = 1$ and Eq. 7 reduces to

$$\mathscr{F}_{12} = \frac{\epsilon_1 F_{12}}{[1 - F_{11}(1-\epsilon_1)]} \tag{10}$$

Substitution of Eq. 10 into Eq. 6 gives us

$$\dot{Q}_{12} = \frac{\epsilon_1 A_1 F_{12} \sigma}{[1 - F_{12}(1-\epsilon_1)]} (T_1^4 - T_2^4) \tag{11}$$

which is the previously given Eq. 1.3-21. When surface 1 cannot see itself $F_{11} = 0$ and $F_{12} = 1$ so that Eq. 11 reduces to

$$\dot{Q}_{12} = \epsilon_1 A_1 \sigma (T_1^4 - T_2^4) \tag{12}$$

which was previously given as Eq. 1.3-16.

(III) *Gray Body in a Very Large Enclosure*

For a very large enclosure we can make the approximation $F_{22} \sim 1$ and $F_{21} \sim 0$ so that Eq. 7 reduces to

$$\mathscr{F}_{12} = \frac{\epsilon_1 F_{12}}{[1 - F_{11}(1 - \epsilon_1)]} \tag{13}$$

In arriving at Eq. 13 we have imposed the approximation

$$F_{12}F_{21}(1 - \epsilon_1)(1 - \epsilon_2) \ll 1 - F_{11}(1 - \epsilon_1)$$

because F_{21} is much, much less than one. Here we have seen that the large enclosure is equivalent to a black enclosure as per the discussion in Sec. 8.4.

9.8 The Monte Carlo Method

Up to this point we have examined the two simplest versions of the general radiant energy exchange problem, and we are now in a position to solve gray body radiation problems with confidence. We will proceed no further into the increasingly complex array of radiation problems, for if the student has grasped the physics of thermal radiation presented in Chapter 8, and has understood the analysis of gray body radiation given in Sec. 9.7, then much has been accomplished and the more complex problems can be dealt with as they arise in the future. However, it does seem worthwhile to present a brief description of a convenient method for solving arbitrarily complex radiation problems, so that we are not left with the idea that gray body radiation is the end of the line. The method we propose to outline here is called the Monte Carlo method after games of chance that are played in the casinos at Monte Carlo. What one does in the Monte Carlo method is to set up a "game" that has the same expected outcome as the real physical process, and then "play" the game many times in order to find the average outcome. The attractiveness of this method is twofold: first it is a powerful computing technique in its own right, and second, everyone loves to play a game of chance where winning is essentially assured. Thus what may appear to be an impossibly tedious radiation problem, takes on some aspects of a not unpleasant game when the Monte Carlo method is used. While this method has only recently been used in the solution of complex radiation problems, it does have wide application and Howell [16] points out that a determination of π was made several thousand years ago by this method [17].

In order to present a qualitative description of how Monte Carlo can be used to solve complex radiant energy exchange problems we consider the enclosure illustrated in Fig. 9.8.1. For simplicity we assume that the several surfaces are isothermal and we neglect the possibility that absorption and emission can occur in the region enclosed by the solid surfaces. In thinking about the radiation process occurring in this enclosure it is natural to visualize photons being emitted from all the surfaces and traveling in straight lines until they intercept a solid surface. The probability of the photon being absorbed depends on its energy (wavelength) and the direction of its flight path; the probability being $\alpha_{\lambda\omega}$. If we followed the history of a sufficiently large number of photons we should be able to learn what the rate of radiant energy exchange was between the various surfaces. However, following the progress of photons emitted from the various surfaces is really not very convenient, for it is the rate at which energy leaves a surface that is of interest to us and is easily characterized. For example, the rate at which energy leaves a surface is given by

$$q^{(e)} = \epsilon \sigma T^4 \tag{9.8-1}$$

and the rate at which energy leaves in a certain direction with a certain wavelength is given by

$$q_{\lambda\omega}^{(e)} = \epsilon_{\lambda\omega} I_{b,\lambda\omega}^{(e)} |\mathbf{\Omega} \cdot \mathbf{n}| \tag{9.8-2}$$

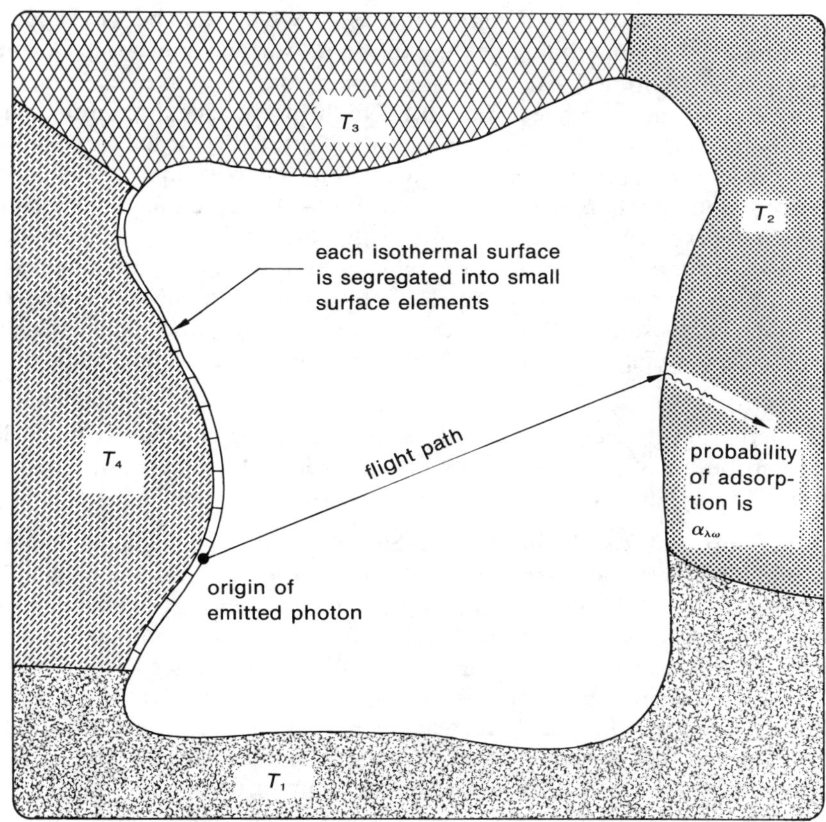

Fig. 9.8.1 Non-black body radiant energy exchange.

where

$$I^{(e)}_{b,\lambda\omega} = \left(\frac{2hc^2}{\lambda^5}\right)\left(\frac{1}{e^{hc/\lambda kT} - 1}\right) \tag{9.8-3}$$

Obviously it is the energy flux rather than the photon flux that will be convenient to follow. In a sense we have already seen this in our analysis of gray body radiation by the method of successive reflections. We now wish to think about following "bundles of photons" which are moving in a certain direction $\mathbf{\Omega}$ with a certain wavelength λ, and having a constant amount of energy. We will call these bundles of constant energy *ergons*, or perhaps being more specific we should refer to them as $\lambda\omega$-ergons. This should be set down as a definition and we write

> A $\lambda\omega$-ergon is a group of $\lambda\omega$-photons having a total energy which is constant for all values of $\mathbf{\Omega}$ and λ

Clearly the number of photons in an ergon depends on the wavelength of the ergon.

In the game we wish to play on the computer we are going to follow the history of a large number of ergons emitted by the several surfaces shown in Fig. 9.8.1. After we have examined the histories of perhaps 100 000 or a million ergons we need to have played our game so that the total energy emitted from any surface, or a segment of a surface, is proportional to $A\epsilon\sigma T^4$. This can be accomplished in the following way: let N represent the total number of ergons emitted during the course of the game, and N_j the number of ergons emitted from the jth surface. We then require that the ratio N_j/N be given by

$$\frac{N_j}{N} \Rightarrow \left\{\begin{array}{l}\text{fraction of ergons emitted}\\ \text{from the } j\text{th surface}\end{array}\right\} = \frac{A_j\epsilon_j\sigma T_j^4}{A_1\epsilon_1\sigma T_1^4 A_1 + A_2\epsilon_2\sigma T_2^4 + \cdots + A_N\epsilon_N\sigma T_N^4} \tag{9.8-4}$$

Here we use the symbol $\Rightarrow$ to mean *expected value* for reasons which shall become apparent. The rule for this part of the game usually goes something like this: to the jth surface one assigns a fractional number f_j determined by Eq. 9.8-4. The fraction f_j can then be assigned some region in the range from 0 to 1. For example, if $f_j = 0.137$ we can assign the range $0.400 \rightarrow 0.537$ to the jth surface. For an enclosure of N surfaces the range assigned to these N surface will vary from 0 to 1, and for the jth surface we will designate this range as $f_j^0 \rightarrow f_j^0 + f_j$. One then asks a computer to produce a random number from a routine which provides a uniform distribution of random numbers between 0 and 1. We will denote this random number by ξ_1 and if $f_j^0 \leq \xi_1 < f_j^0 + f_j$ we allow an ergon to be emitted from the jth surface. Having decided on the origin of the emitted ergon we choose a second random number ξ_2 which is used to specify the direction or flight path of the ergon consistent with the distribution given by $\epsilon_{\lambda\omega}$. A third random number ξ_3 is chosen in order that a wavelength can be specified consistent with the distribution of energy with wavelength given by Eq. 9.8-2. Although we have avoided specifying the details of the rules of our game, the outcome after many plays must be such that:

1. The energy emitted from the several surfaces is distributed according to Eq. 9.8-4.
2. The directional distribution of emitted ergons must coincide with the directional distribution of $\epsilon_{\lambda\omega}$.
3. The distribution of wavelengths of emitted ergons must satisfy Eq. 9.8-2.

Once the origin, direction, and wavelength for an emitted ergon have been specified, the flight path is easily calculated and one can determine where it will intersect a solid surface. The probability of absorption is $\alpha_{\lambda\omega}$, thus we select a fourth random number ξ_4 and if $\xi_4 \leq \alpha_{\lambda\omega}$ we consider the ergon to be absorbed. If $\xi_4 > \alpha_{\lambda\omega}$ we consider the ergon to be reflected and we choose a fifth random number ξ_5 which is used to specify the new flight path and the calculation is continued. When an ergon is absorbed we simply note the transfer of one ergon from the original surface to the surface at which the absorption took place and begin the process again of selecting a location, direction, and wavelength for another emitted ergon. Depending on the complexity of the system we may have to repeat this process hundreds of thousands of times before acceptable values of the energy fluxes are obtained. The programming involved in this type of computation is not necessarily simple, but there is a definite advantage in this kind of simulation of a physical process over the numerical solution of integral or algebraic equations. This is because errors in the program are more easily spotted in a simulation and debugging is less of a problem.

Infinite, parallel, gray surfaces

As an illustration of the Monte Carlo method we will re-examine the radiant energy exchange between infinite, parallel, gray surfaces which are shown in Figs. 9.7.1 and 9.7.2. In this case the game we play will be terribly simple since we need not choose a direction or a wavelength for the emitted ergons since all flights lead to the opposite surface and the probability of absorption is independent of $\mathbf{\Omega}$ and λ.

From Eq. 9.8-4 we can develop our first rule for this game, i.e., the rule governing the process of specifying the location of the emitted ergon. We denote the fraction of ergons emitted from surface 1 as f_1 and write

$$f_1 = \frac{\epsilon_1 \sigma T_1^4}{\epsilon_1 \sigma T_1^4 + \epsilon_2 \sigma T_2^4} \tag{9.8-5}$$

It follows that $f_2 = 1 - f_1$ and our rule for specifying the origin of an emitted ergon becomes:

Rule 1: Generate a random number ξ_1. If $\xi_1 \leq f_1$ consider the ergon to be emitted from surface 1. If $\xi_1 > f_1$ take the ergon to be emitted from surface 2

The remaining rules for our game concern the absorption or reflection of ergons and are straightforward:

Rule 2: Generate a random number ξ_2. If the ergon is incident upon surface 1 consider it to be absorbed if $\xi_2 \leq \epsilon_1$ and reflected if $\xi_2 > \epsilon_1$. If the ergon is incident upon surface 2 consider it to be absorbed if $\xi_2 \leq \epsilon_2$ and reflected if $\xi_2 > \epsilon_2$

Let us now assume that we have specified f_1, ϵ_1, and ϵ_2 and we have played our game a total of N times. Of that total N_1 ergons were emitted from surface 1 and N_2 were emitted from surface 2 where

$$N_1 + N_2 = N \tag{9.8-6}$$

Of the N_1 ergons emitted from surface 1 a number $N_{1\to2}$ will be absorbed by surface 2, and of the N_2 ergons emitted from surface 2, a number $N_{2\to1}$ of them will be absorbed by surface 1. Having determined $N_{1\to2}$ and $N_{2\to1}$ we now need to derive an expression for the rate of energy transfer per unit area. We choose the energy of our ergons to be

$$\{\text{energy of an ergon}\} = (\epsilon_1\sigma T_1^4 + \epsilon_2\sigma T_2^4)At/N \tag{9.8-7}$$

Here A represents the area over which the process is taking place and t represents the process time for the emission of N ergons. Remember that $\epsilon\sigma T^4$ has the units of (energy)/(time)(area), thus Eq. 9.8-7 is a satisfactory definition of the energy of an ergon. The total energy emitted during the process is simply given by

$$\{\text{total energy emitted by } N \text{ ergons}\} = (\epsilon_1\sigma T_1^4 + \epsilon_2\sigma T_2^4)At \tag{9.8-8}$$

and the total energy flux is obtained by dividing by the area A and the process time t to obtain

$$\{\text{total energy flux}\} = \epsilon_1\sigma T_1^4 + \epsilon_2\sigma T_2^4 \tag{9.8-9}$$

We can express the total energy transferred from surface 1 to surface 2 as

$$\begin{Bmatrix}\text{total energy transferred from surface1} \\ \text{to surface 2 during } N \text{ plays of the game}\end{Bmatrix} = \underbrace{N_{1\to2}}_{\substack{\text{number of ergons}\\\text{emitted by 1 and}\\\text{absorbed by 2}}}\overbrace{[(\epsilon_1\sigma T_1^4 + \epsilon_2\sigma T_2^4)At/N]}^{\text{energy per ergon}} - \underbrace{N_{2\to1}}_{\substack{\text{number of ergons}\\\text{emitted by 2 and}\\\text{absorbed by 1}}}\overbrace{[(\epsilon_1\sigma T_1^4 + \epsilon_2\sigma T_2^4)At/N]}^{\text{energy per ergon}} \tag{9.8-10}$$

We are interested in computing the energy transferred per unit time and per unit area, thus we must divide Eq. 9.8-10 by the area associated with the process and the time during which the process took place. Thus we divide Eq. 9.8-10 by At to obtain

$$\left(\frac{\dot{Q}_1}{A}\right)_{\text{M.C.}} = \left(\frac{N_{1\to2} - N_{2\to1}}{N}\right)(\epsilon_1\sigma T_1^4 + \epsilon_2\sigma T_2^4) \tag{9.8-11}$$

Here the subscript M.C. is used to indicate that this is a Monte Carlo result and is not an exact calculation. Returning to Eq. 9.8-5 we note that $\epsilon_2\sigma T_2^4$ can be expressed as

$$\epsilon_2\sigma T_2^4 = \left(\frac{1-f_1}{f_1}\right)\epsilon\sigma T_1^4 \tag{9.8-12}$$

so that Eq. 9.8-11 can be expressed as

$$\left(\frac{\dot{Q}_1}{A}\right)_{\text{M.C.}} = \left(\frac{N_{1\to2} - N_{2\to1}}{f_1 N}\right)\epsilon_1\sigma T_1^4 \tag{9.8-13}$$

We will certainly want to compare this result with the exact value given by Eq. 9.7-43 or Eq. 9.7-51, which can be put in the form

$$\left(\frac{\dot{Q}_1}{A}\right)_{\text{exact}} = \left\{\frac{f_1(\epsilon_1 + \epsilon_2) - \epsilon_1}{f_1[1-(1-\epsilon_1)(1-\epsilon_2)]}\right\}\epsilon_1\sigma T_1^4 \tag{9.8-14}$$

In order to compare the Monte Carlo method with the exact solution we need only compare the coefficient of $\epsilon_1 \sigma T_1^4$ in Eqs. 9.8-13 and 9.8-14. We should note at this point that the game we are about to play is not an exact simulation of the photon transport process, for we are not following the progress of photons but the progress of "bundles of photons" called ergons. However, we have chosen the rates of emission so that the expected outcome of our game is the same as the real process, i.e.,

$$\left(\frac{\dot{Q}_1}{A}\right)_{\text{M.C.}} \Rightarrow \left(\frac{\dot{Q}_1}{A}\right)_{\text{exact}} \tag{9.8-15}$$

In Fig. 9.8.2 we have shown the flow diagram for the computer program. After the first decision made on the basis of comparing f_1 and ξ_1 we note that we have essentially two separate programs; one for following the history of ergons emitted from surface 1 and one for following the history of ergons emitted from surface 2. If there were more than two surfaces the program would be considerably more complex; however, the essential characteristic of following the history of an ergon in terms of a sequence of random numbers would remain. It should be clear from Fig. 9.8.2 that we will need many random numbers, perhaps on the order of a million or more. Furthermore, we need these numbers produced at a rather high rate, and it would be unacceptable to obtain them on a roulette wheel, for example. For high-speed digital computer usage we must rely on pseudo-random number generator routines [18, 19]; however, these routines must always be used with caution. Note in Fig. 9.8.2 that in addition to calculating the quantity of interest, $(N_{1\to2} - N_{2\to1})/f_1 N$, we also calculate N_1/N for we know the expected value of the latter to be

$$\frac{N_1}{N} \Rightarrow f_1 \tag{9.8-16}$$

and it will be helpful to see how closely N_1/N approaches f_1. The Fortran program that follows the flow diagram is illustrated in Fig. 9.8.3 and the results of our Monte Carlo calculation are shown in Tables 9.8-1 and 9.8-2. In Tables 9.8-1 we have shown results for three different sequences of pseudo-random numbers when $f_1 = 0.75$, $\epsilon_1 = 0.82$, and $\epsilon_2 = 0.47$. Although it is not indicated in either the flow diagram or the Fortran program, there are simple ways of generating different sequences of pseudo-random numbers. When debugging a program it is helpful to have precisely the same sequence of numbers; however, for computation it is often desirable to have different sequences available. An examination of N_1/N for various values of N indicates that after about ten thousand "plays" the value of N_1/N has settled down to a value very near the expected value of 0.750. The variance for N_1/N is given by [20]

$$\sigma_{N_1/N} = \sqrt{\frac{f_1(f_1 - 1)}{N}} \tag{9.8-17}$$

For $N = 10^4$ and $f_1 = 0.75$ the variance is

$$\sigma_{N_1/N} \sim 0.004 \tag{9.8-18}$$

which means that two-thirds of the time that we play this game with $N = 10^4$ we should expect to find N_1/N within 0.004 of 0.750. For the calculations shown in Table 9.8-1a we find that N_1/N appears to be well behaved; however, the values of $(N_{1\to2} - N_{2\to1})/f_1 N$ lies consistently above the expected value of 0.217. This is more clearly shown in Table 9.8-1b where the results of a million plays are shown. There it becomes clear that the calculated value of $(N_{1\to2} - N_{2\to1})/f_1 N$ lies consistently above the expected value of 0.217. This is highly improbable† and one is inclined to suspect the uniformity of the pseudo-random number generator. The calculations shown in Tables 9.8-1 were obtained on a B6500 using a Burrough's library pseudo-random number generator which had been modified by the UCD Computer Center. In order to explore the effect of the pseudo-random number generator, the calculations were repeated using a CDC 3400 through the courtesy of the Applied Science Department of UCD. The results are shown in Tables 9.8-2. The numbers

†This does *not* mean it is impossible, it simply means that it does not occur often. The author became painfully aware of the occasional occurrence of the improbable when, after an argument between his two sons was settled by the flip of a coin, a demonstration of probability was given in order to console the loser. To my horror, dismay, and anguish the coin came up "heads" fourteen times in a row, and such arguments are now settled by other means.

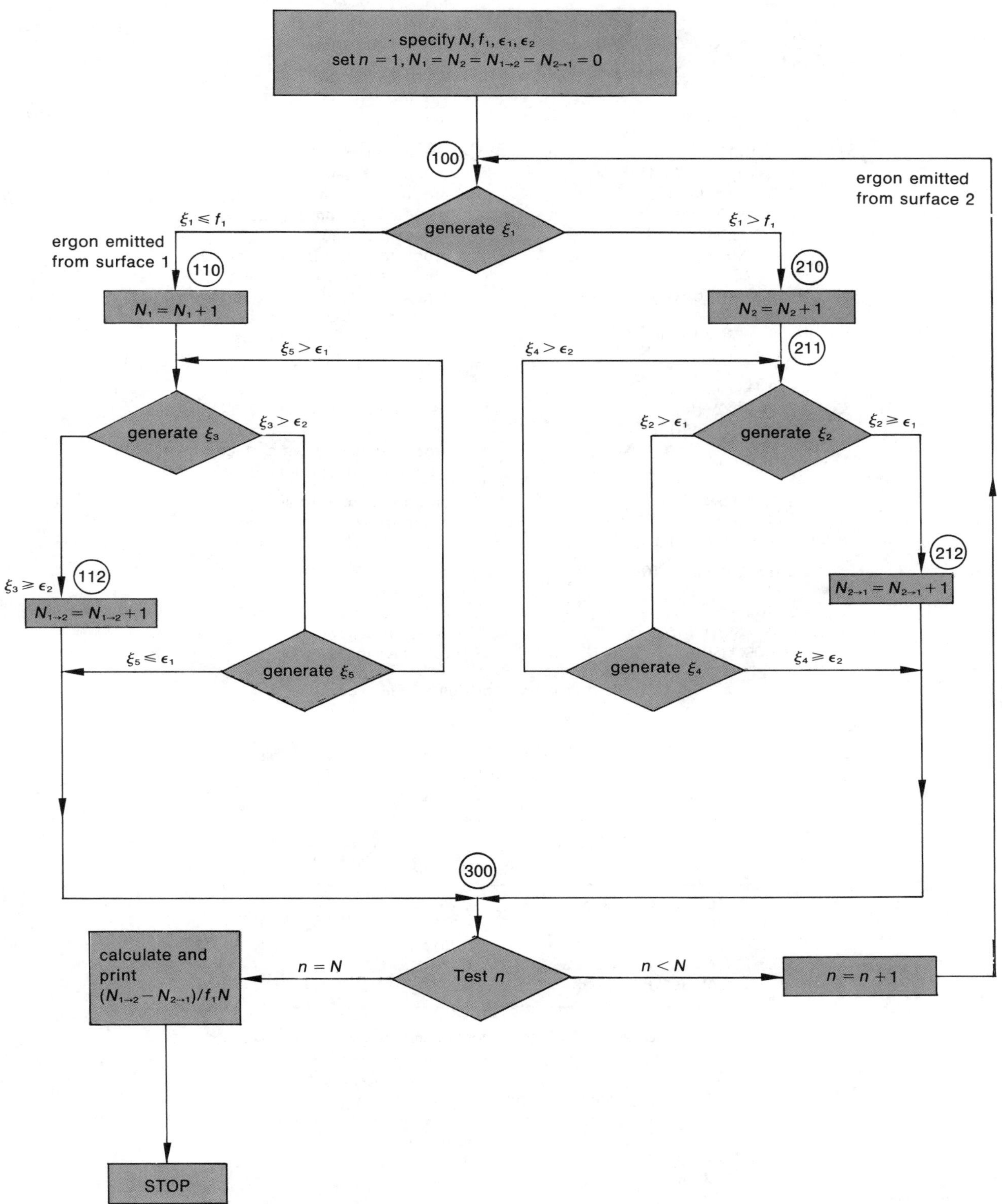

Fig. 9.8.2 Flow diagram for Monte Carlo calculation.

Fortran Statements	*Comments*
TOTAL = 100000.0	set $N = 10^5$
F1 = 0.75	set $f_1 = 0.75$ and $\epsilon_1\sigma T_1^4/\epsilon_2\sigma T_2^4 = 3$
E1 = 0.82	set $\epsilon_1 = 0.82$
E2 = 0.47	set $\epsilon_2 = 0.47$
A = 1.0	set $n = 1$
SUM 1 = 0.0	set $N_1 = 0$
SUM 2 = 0.0	set $N_2 = 0$
SUM 12 = 0.0	set $N_{1\to 2} = 0$
SUM 21 = 0.0	set $N_{2\to 1} = 0$
100 R1 = RANDOM (1)	generate random number ξ_1
1F (R1.GT.F1) GO TO 210	compare ξ_1 and f_1
110 SUM 1 = SUM 1 + 1.0	ergon emitted from surface 1
111 R3 = RANDOM (1)	generate random number ξ_3
1F(R3.LE.E2) GO TO 112	compare ξ_3 and ϵ_2
R5 = RANDOM (1)	ergon reflected from surface 2 generate random number ξ_5
1F(R5.LE.E1) GO TO 300	ergon absorbed at surface 1
GO TO 111	ergon reflected from surface 1
112 SUM 12 = SUM 12 + 1.0	ergon absorbed at surface 2
GO TO 300	
210 SUM 2 = SUM 2 + 1.0	ergon emitted from surface 2
211 R2 = RANDOM (1)	generate random number ξ_2
1F(R2.LE.E1) GO TO 212	compare ξ_2 and ϵ_1
R4 = RANDOM (1)	ergon reflected from surface 1 generate random number ξ_4
1F(R4.LE.E2) GO TO 300	ergon absorbed at surface 2
GO TO 211	ergon reflected at surface 2
212 SUM 21 = SUM 21 + 1.0	ergon absorbed at surface 1
300 1F (A.GE.TOTAL) GO TO 301	compare n and N
A = A + 1.0	$n = n + 1$
GO TO 100	begin new ergon history
301 RATIO = SUM 1/TOTAL	calculate N_1/N
ANSWER = (SUM 12 − SUM 21)/(F1*TOTAL)	calculate the answer

Fig. 9.8.3 Fortran program for Monte Carlo calculation.

Table 9.8-1a Tabulated Results for Monte Carlo Calculation†

First sequence of pseudo-random numbers

N	N_1/N	Expected value	$(N_{1\to 2} - N_{2\to 1})/f_1 N$	Expected value
10	0.600	0.750	−0.267	0.217
10^2	0.760		0.227	
10^3	0.735		0.205	
10^4	0.751		0.221	
10^5	0.751		0.221	

Second sequence of pseudo-random numbers

N	N_1/N	Expected value	$(N_{1\to 2} - N_{2\to 1})/f_1 N$	Expected value
10	0.800	0.750	0.267	0.217
10^2	0.750		0.280	
10^3	0.750		0.223	
10^4	0.752		0.228	
10^5	0.750		0.220	

Table 9.8-1a (*contd.*)

Third sequence of pseudo-random numbers

N	N_1/N	Expected value	$(N_{1\to2} - N_{2\to1})/f_1N$	Expected value
10	0.600	0.750	0.000	0.217
10^2	0.760		0.307	
10^3	0.737		0.169	
10^4	0.752		0.218	
10^5	0.751		0.223	

†Calculations were done on a B6500.

Table 9.8-1b Tabulated Results for Monte Carlo Calculation Using Ten Sequences of Pseudo-Random Numbers

N	N_1/N	Expected value	$(N_{1\to2} - N_{2\to1})/f_1N$	Expected value
10^5	0.751	0.750	0.221	0.217
	0.750		0.220	
	0.751		0.223	
	0.752		0.223	
	0.749		0.216	
	0.750		0.219	
	0.750		0.222	
	0.750		0.220	
	0.749		0.219	
	0.750		0.222	
10^6	0.750	0.750	0.220	0.217

shown in Table 9.8-2a are not particularly informative, but in Table 9.8-2b we see that the expected value is obtained to within three significant figures.

From these results we should learn to be cautious when using computer subroutines to generate random numbers, for we cannot rely on them as we do the sine, cosine, and other standard routines. In time the use of Monte Carlo methods will increase, and pseudo-random number generators will become more reliable.

Table 9.8-2a Tabulated Results for Monte Carlo Calculation†

First sequence of pseudo-random numbers

N	N_1/N	Expected value	$(N_{1\to2} - N_{2\to1})/f_1N$	Expected value
10	0.700	0.750	0.400	0.217
10^2	0.760		0.307	
10^3	0.771		0.269	
10^4	0.753		0.222	
10^5	0.750		0.216	

Table 9.8-2a (*contd.*)

Second sequence of pseudo-random numbers

N	N_1/N	Expected value	$(N_{1\to 2} - N_{2\to 1})/f_1N$	Expected value
10	0.900	0.750	0.400	0.217
10^2	0.670		−0.053	
10^3	0.745		0.193	
10^4	0.751		0.215	
10^5	0.749		0.212	

Third sequence of pseudo-random numbers

N	N_1/N	Expected value	$(N_{1\to 2} - N_{2\to 1})/f_1N$	Expected value
10	0.700	0.750	0.000	0.217
10^2	0.780		0.200	
10^3	0.729		0.156	
10^4	0.743		0.207	
10^5	0.749		0.218	

†Calculations were done on a CDC 3400.

Table 9.8-2b Tabulated Results for Monte Carlo Calculation Using Ten Sequences of Pseudo-Random Numbers

N	N_1/N	Expected value	$(N_{1\to 2} - N_{2\to 1})/f_1N$	Expected value
10^5	0.750	0.750	0.216	0.217
	0.749		0.212	
	0.749		0.218	
	0.750		0.219	
	0.749		0.212	
	0.752		0.218	
	0.749		0.221	
	0.750		0.216	
	0.752		0.224	
	0.750		0.218	
10^6	0.750	0.750	0.217	0.217

Solution to design problem IX

Since our climber is well clothed we will assume that the surface temperature of his clothing is 20°F. This is, of course, a lower limit; however, an error of 10°F is only an error of 2 per cent in the absolute temperature and our radiation calculation should not be greatly effected. We will assume that the climber is a black body, thus we can use the material presented in Secs. 9.1–9.3 to estimate the heat loss. The geometry of this radiation problem is very complex, and in order to obtain a solution we will approximate our climber by a 3-ft diameter hemisphere as illustrated in Fig. IX.2. This yields a surface area for radiation of 1.3 m^2, whereas the average body surface area is on the order of 2 m^2.

In our calculation we will assume that all of the surface area of the surroundings below the horizon is at 20°F and thus does not participate in the radiant energy exchange process. Under these circumstances the rate of radiant energy loss is given by Eq. 9.3-8 as

$$\dot{Q} = AF\sigma(T_0^4 - T_\infty^4) \tag{IX-1}$$

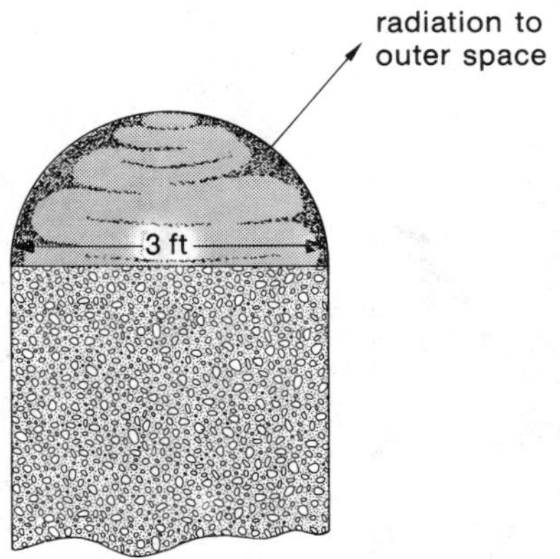

Fig. IX.2 Geometrical approximation of bivouacked climber.

Here T_0 is 480°R and T_∞ is the temperature of the clear night sky† at 14 000 ft above sea level, i.e., $T_\infty = 0$°R. Referring to the material presented in Secs. 8.3 and 9.1 we can deduce, without recourse to the calculation of view factors, that the fraction of radiant energy leaving the hemisphere which is directed below the horizon is $\frac{1}{3}$. Thus the view factor for radiation from the hemisphere to the sky is given by

$$F = 0.67 \tag{IX-2}$$

The rate of energy loss can now be computed as

$$\dot{Q} = (0.67)\left(\frac{\pi D^2}{2}\right)\sigma T_0^4 = 55.3 \text{ cal/sec} \tag{IX-3}$$

Note that this is nearly three times the basal metabolic rate of 20 cal/sec given in Ex. 9.1-1. This loss of energy *cannot* be reduced by adding more clothing unless the emissivity is decreased, thus the use of a metallic coated "space blanket" would be a great help in reducing the chill that our climber is sure to experience if he maintains the posture illustrated in Fig. IX.1. The energy loss during the five-hour period from midnight to 5:00 A.M. is obtained from Eq. IX-3 and is

$$\{\text{energy loss during five hours}\} = 1.00 \times 10^6 \text{ cal}$$

At 300 000 calories per bar our climber requires $3\frac{1}{3}$ chocolate bars just to sustain his energy losses owing to radiation.

In moving from Fig. IX.1 to Fig. IX.2 we accomplished a great simplification in the geometry without losing the essential features of the radiation problem. The loss determined by Eq. IX-1 will be somewhat higher than the actual loss since the emissivity of the climbers clothing must certainly be less than 1. Nevertheless, we can consider the calculated energy loss to be a reasonable estimate. If our climber seeks the protection of a vertical wall our calculation becomes more complicated, and in order to simplify our problem we will consider the radiation from two infinitely long bodies shown in Fig. IX.3. Referring to part (a) we note that half the emitted radiation leaving the vertical sides is incident upon the sky while half is incident upon some surface below the horizon. This means that the view factor is given by

$$F_1 = \tfrac{2}{3}, \tag{IX-4}$$

and the energy loss per unit length can be expressed as

$$q_1 = 3DF_1\sigma T_0^4 \tag{IX-5}$$

Once again we have assumed that the surroundings below the horizon are at 20°F so that the net exchange of radiation between the climber and these surroundings is zero. For the case shown in part (b) of Fig. IX.3 we write

$$q_2 = 2DF_2\sigma T_0^4 \tag{IX-6}$$

† We should point out that at sea level the effective radiation temperature of the sky is much greater than 0°R owing to the radiation from the carbon dioxide and water vapor. For a clear night sky at sea level this temperature is on the order of 250°K or 450°R and is quite sensitive to the partial pressure of the water vapor in the atmosphere.

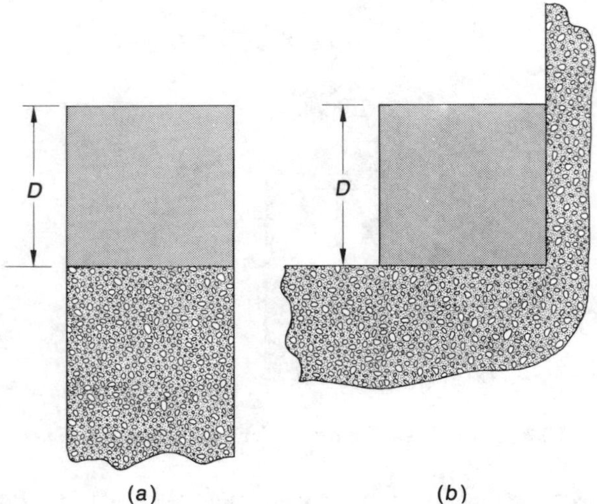

Fig. IX.3 Two-dimensional analog of the climber perched on the summit block and the climber protected by a wall.

for the rate of energy loss to the sky. We consider the surrounding rock to stretch to infinity, thus the view factor is given by Eq. 9.2-9 with the restriction that $\mathscr{L}_1 \to 0$ and $\mathscr{L}_2 \to 1$. This gives us

$$F_2 = \tfrac{1}{2} \tag{IX-7}$$

i.e., one-half the radiation leaving the surface of the "climber" is incident upon the night sky while one-half is incident upon the surrounding rock. The ratio of q_2 to q_1 is an *estimate* of the reduction in the radiant energy loss that occurs when our climber seeks the shelter of a vertical rock wall.

$$\{\text{reduction in radiation loss}\} = \frac{q_2}{q_1} = \frac{2DF_2}{3DF_1} = \frac{1}{2}$$

Thus we might expect, under these conditions, that the radiation loss during a five-hour period is reduced to 0.5×10^6 cal and the candy consumption is cut from $3\frac{1}{3}$ bars to less than 2. After an exhausting climb of the 2400-ft east face of Mt. Whitney, this reduction in energy loss is not to be scoffed at, for the rate of 28 cal/sec is comfortably close to the basal metabolic rate and the night can be passed in relative comfort.

PROBLEMS†

IX-1. How does one obtain Eq. IX-5 or IX-6 from Eq. 9.3-8?

IX-2. Recalculate the reduction in radiation loss for the model shown in Fig. IX.4. There are two view factors to be determined; use your intuition to obtain both of them. Assume that the rock slab stretches to infinity in both directions.

IX-3. Show that the view factor for radiant energy exchange between the hemisphere in Fig. IX.2 and the surface below the horizon is $\frac{1}{3}$ by finding the fraction of energy emitted in a direction below the horizontal plane.

9-1. (9.1) Find the view factors for an enclosure formed by a hemisphere of radius r_0 and its circular base.

9-2. (9.1) A black sphere 2 in. in diameter is placed in an oven as illustrated in Fig. 9.2. The walls of the oven are maintained at 800°F and we can assume that the air in the oven is also at 800°F. Estimate the percentage of the total heat flux to the sphere which results from radiation when the surface temperature of the sphere is 200°F, 400°F, and 600°F. Use the results of Sec. 7.9 to estimate the free-convection film heat transfer coefficient.

9-3. (9.1) Using only your intuition and Eqs. 9.1-2 and 9.1-18, obtain expressions for the view factors for the infinite, concentric cylinders shown in Fig. 9.3.

†Problems numbered IX-1, IX-2, etc. deal directly with Design Problem IX, and problems marked with an asterisk (*) are concerned with the solved example problems.

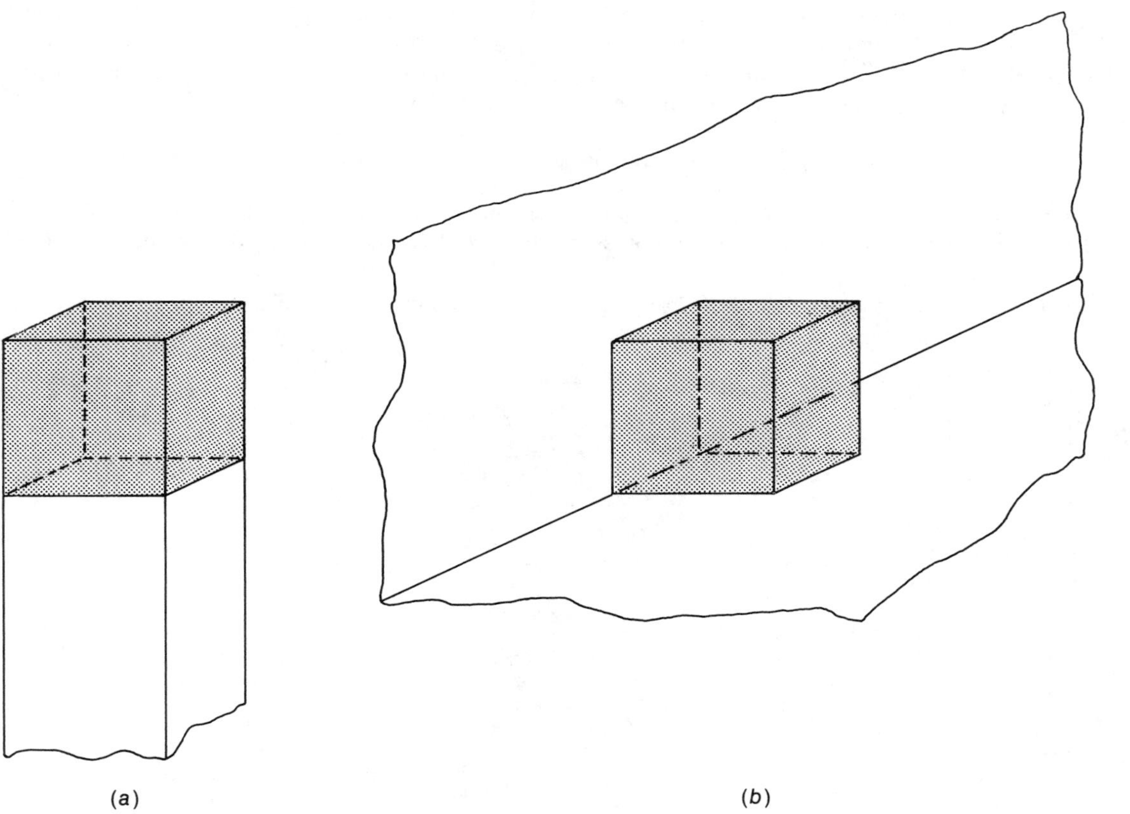

Fig. IX.4 Three-dimensional model for reduction in radiation losses.

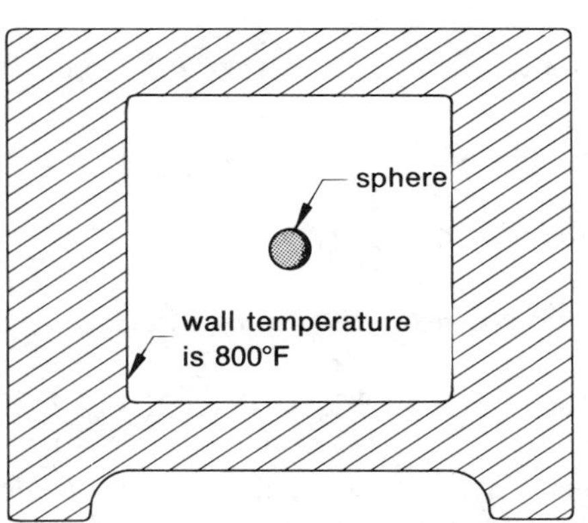

Fig. 9.2 Sphere in an oven.

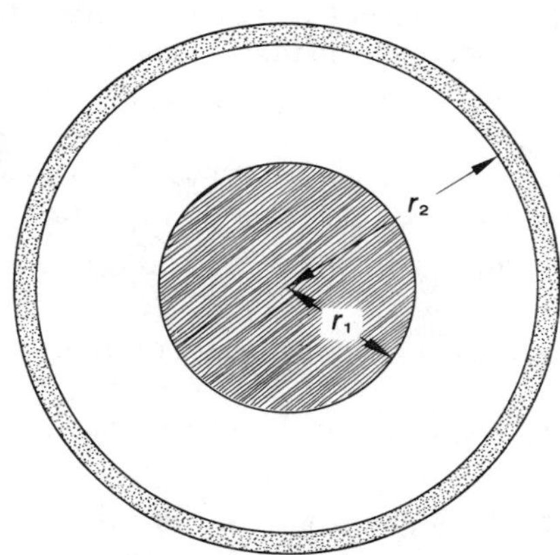

Fig. 9.3 Infinite, concentric cylinders.

***9-4.** In Ex. 9.1-1 we found the loss of energy from a body in the summertime was much less than the basal metabolic
(9.1) rate when 90 per cent of the surface area was well insulated. For summertime conditions what fraction of the skin must be exposed in order to increase the heat loss to 20 cal/sec?

9-5. Prove that the incident flux of solar energy on the earth's upper atmosphere is given by $q^{(i)} = I_0 \cos \theta$ where θ
(9.1) is the angle between the outwardly directed normal and the vector between the earth and the sun. Here I_0 represents the total intensity of radiant energy directed at the earth from the sun, and is referred to as the *solar*

constant. The value of I_0 is about 440 Btu/hr ft^2; however, the intensity at the earth's surface is considerably reduced owing to scattering and absorption in the carbon dioxide and water vapor (see Fig. 9.6.3).

9-6. (9.1) Prove that the radiant energy intensity at the surface of a hemisphere owing to diffuse emission from an area dA at the origin of the base of the hemisphere (see Fig. 8.3.5) is given by

$$\{\text{radiant energy intensity}\} = \left(\frac{q^{(e)}\,dA}{\pi r^2}\right)\cos\theta$$

where θ is the angle between the normal to the surface and the vector locating the position on the hemisphere. This result indicates that the intensity falls off as the square of the distance, and is distributed over the surface of the hemisphere as $\cos\theta$. This result is often referred to as *Lambert's cosine law*.

9-7. (9.2) Calculate the view factors F_{12} and F_{21} for the parallel disks illustrated in Fig. 9.7.

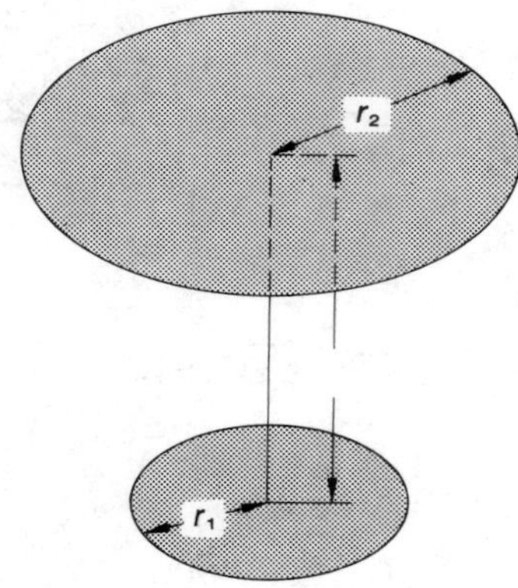

Fig. 9.7 Parallel disks.

9-8. (9.2) Given the diameter and temperature of the sun as 860 000 miles and 6000°K, calculate the temperature of the earth assuming that the earth and the sun are black bodies, and that the surrounding universe is at 0°K. Because of the large distance between the earth and the sun (93 million miles) there are some simplifying assumptions that can be made regarding the geometry.

9-9. (9.2) Determine the upperbound for F_{P3} from the information given in Fig. 9.2.7. Take the ratio C/D to be 2.0.

9-10. (9.2) Prove Eqs. 9.2-14 and 9.2-15 by direct application of the definition of the view factor given by Eq. 9.1-16 and the reciprocity condition given by Eq. 9.1-18.

***9.11.** (9.2) Use the results from Ex. 9.2-1 to derive an expression for $F_{⑫3}$ in Fig. 9.2.9.

***9-12.** (9.2) Follow the approach outlined in Ex. 9.2-1 to derive an expression for $F_{⑫4}$ in Fig. 9.2.8.

***9-13.** (9.2) Use the results from Ex. 9.2-1 to derive an expression for F_{14} in Fig. 9.2.8.

9-14. (9.3) A cubical enclosure has two opposing surfaces at a temperature T_1 while the four connecting sides are maintained at T_2. Derive an expression for the rate of heat transfer from one of the connecting sides assuming that all the surfaces are black. If $T_1 = 1800°\text{F}$, $T_2 = 370°\text{F}$, and the cube is 4 ft on a side, what is the rate of energy transfer from the two hot sides to the four cold sides?

***9-15.** (9.3) In Ex. 9.3-1 use Eqs. 1, 2, and 3 to prove that $\dot{Q}_1 = -\dot{Q}_2$.

***9-16.** (9.3) Determine an effective radiation film heat transfer coefficient for the process analyzed in Ex. 9.3-1. Define h_r by the expression

$$h_r = \frac{\dot{Q}_{12}/\sqrt{A_1A_2}}{(T_1 - T_2)}$$

9-17. (9.3) In Sec. 9.3 black body radiant energy exchange was analyzed for the case where all the surface temperatures we specified. Develop general solutions for an N-surface enclosure when: (1) All heat fluxes are specified and all surface temperatures are unknown, and (2) the heat fluxes are specific for the remaining N_2 surfaces where $N_1 + N_2 = N$.

9-18. (9.4) In Fig. 9.18 we have shown an enclosure consisting of a hot surface, a cold surface, and a refractory wall. Given the view factors F_{12}, F_{23}, and F_{31} and the three surface areas A_1, A_2, and A_3 derive an expression for $\dot{Q}_{12}$ by treating surfaces 1 and 2 as black bodies and the refractory wall as a reradiating surface.

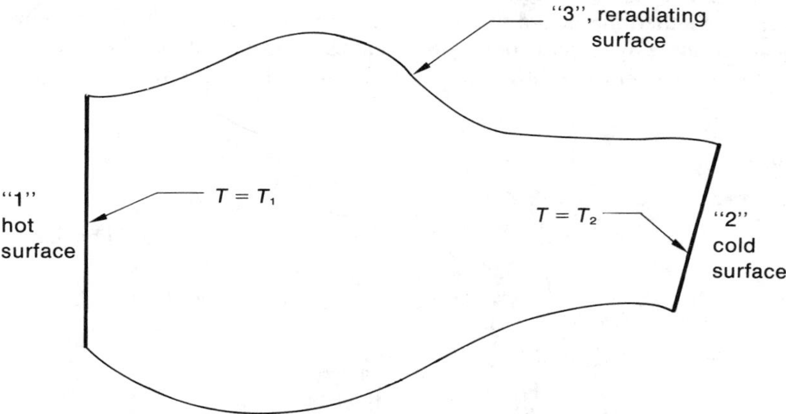

Fig. 9.18 Black body radiation with a reradiating surface.

9-19. (9.4) The 12 in. thick walls of a furnace are maintained at 2300°F on the inside. What is the energy loss from a square 6 in. by 6 in. duct cut in one of the walls? Assume that the sides of the duct are reradiating surfaces and use the uniform irradiation assumption. Take the room outside the furnace to be a black enclosure at 85°F.

9-20. (9.4) Show how Eq. 9.4-13, along with Eq. 9.4-35, can be used to obtain the result given in Ex. 9.3-1.

9-21. (9.4) Derive an expression for the rate of energy transfer between two black surfaces which are the ends of a cylinder as illustrated in Fig. 9.21. Base your derivation on Eqs. 9.4-13, 9.4-23, and 9.4-35, and note that the appropriate view factors, $F_{12} = F_{21}$ and $F_{13} = F_{23}$, are available from curve 1 in Fig. 9.2.4. For $D/L = 2$, compare your result with that obtained by using $\bar{F}_{12}$ from Fig. 9.2.4.

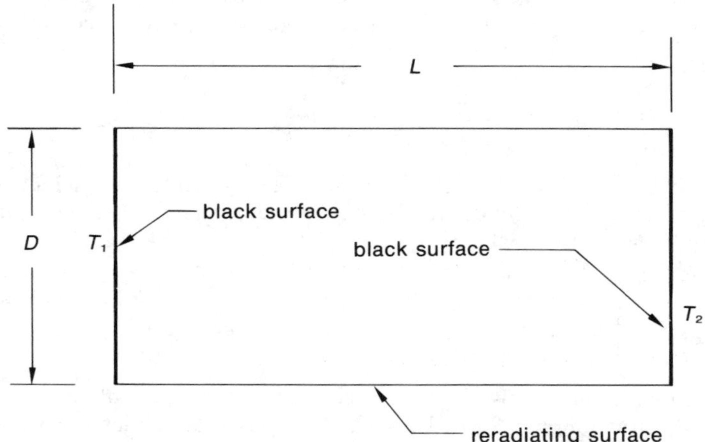

Fig. 9.21 Radiation between the ends of a cylinder.

9-22. (9.4) In order to examine the validity of the assumption of uniform irradiation used in the solution of Prob. 9-21, repeat that derivation, subdividing the reradiating surface into two equal parts. The required view factors can be obtained from Fig. 9.2.4 provided one makes use of the techniques discussed in Ex. 9.2-1. Compare your result with that obtained by direct determination of $\bar{F}_{12}$ from Fig. 9.2.4 for $D/L = 2$.

9-23. (9.5) In Fig. 9.23 we have shown a thermopile imbedded in some nonconducting material. One side of the thermopile is maintained at a reference temperature T_0 while the other side is subjected to radiation as illustrated in Fig. 9.5.2. This surface is coated with lampblack to provide an emissivity very close to unity. You are asked to analyze the energy transfer at the surface of the thermopile in order to develop an expression relating the ratio of fluxes in Eq. 9.5-15 to the galvanometer deflection. Keep in mind that radiant energy is absorbed and emitted at the surface of the thermopile and that energy can be lost through the thermopile by conduction and to the surrounding atmosphere by natural convection. Make use of the fact that the galvanometer deflection is directly proportional to the temperature difference $T_s - T_0$ where T_s is the surface temperature.

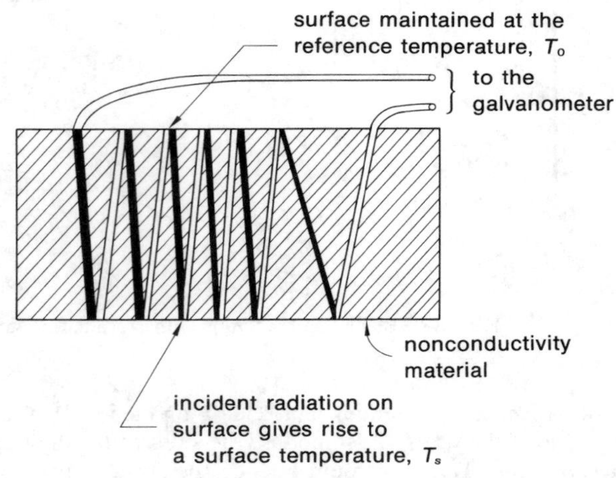

Fig. 9.23 Thermopile.

9-24. (9.5) Derive Eq. 9.5-17 from Eq. 9.5-15.

9-25. Explain how the apparatus described in Sec. 9.5 could be used to measure absorptivities by placing the sample on the surface of the thermopile and directing the radiometer at the two cavities illustrated in Fig. 9.5.4.

9-26. (9.6) To demonstrate the error in treating nonconductors, such as those illustrated in Fig. 9.6.6, as diffuse radiators, compare $q^{(e)}$ based on $\epsilon_\omega = \epsilon =$ constant with the value of $q^{(e)}$ calculated with ϵ_ω given by

$$\epsilon_\omega = \epsilon, \qquad 0 \leqslant \theta \leqslant 70°$$

$$\epsilon_\omega = \epsilon\left(\frac{90° - \theta}{20°}\right), \qquad 70° \leqslant \theta \leqslant 90°$$

9-27. (9.7) Consider two gray bodies whose dimensions are small compared to the distance between them. If these bodies are enclosed by a surface at absolute zero, i.e., outer space, and if neither body can see itself, show that the rate of radiant energy exchange is given by

$$\dot{Q}_{12} = \epsilon_1 \epsilon_2 A_1 F_{12} \sigma (T_1^4 - T_2^4)$$

Note that this result can be obtained without recourse to matrix methods provided one thinks about the problem carefully.

9-28. (9.7) The radiant energy exchange between two surfaces can often be greatly reduced by use of a radiation shield such as the one illustrated in Fig. 9.28. Use the results in Sec. 9.7 to derive an expression for $\dot{Q}_{12}$ assuming the surfaces to be gray. For the case $\epsilon_1 = \epsilon_2 = 1$ and $\epsilon_i = 0.06$ calculate the percentage reduction in $\dot{Q}_{12}$ owing to the presence of the radiation shield.

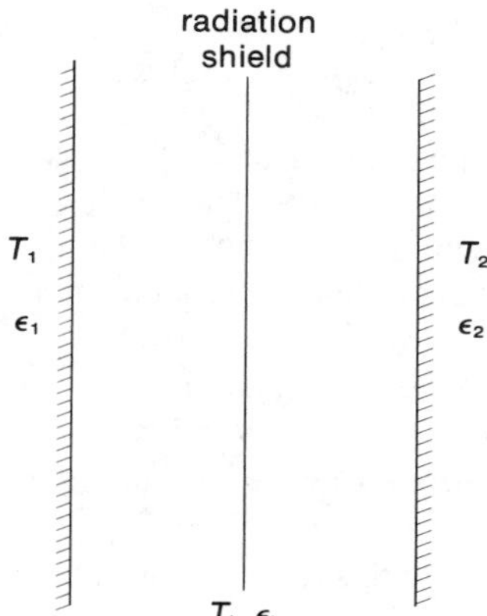

Fig. 9.28 Radiation shield for infinite, parallel plates.

9-29. (9.7) A thermocouple, illustrated in Fig. 9.29, is being used to measure the temperature of a non-radiating, non-absorbing gas stream. Ideally we would like the temperature of the junction to be T_g, the temperature of the gas; however, the temperature of the junction is controlled by the heat transfer between the gas and the junction, conduction in the lead wires and radiation from the junction to the surroundings. The heat transfer in the lead wires can be made small by reducing the size of the wires, and at high temperatures and heat transfer between the gas and the junction and radiation from the junction to the surroundings are the dominant mechanisms. If the film heat transfer coefficient is h and the total hemispherical emissivity of the junction is ϵ, develop an approximate expression for the temperature of the junction T_J in terms of the gas temperature T_g. If $T_g = 1800°F$, $h = 20$ Btu/hr ft^2°F and $\epsilon = 0.64$, calculate the temperature of the thermocouple junction T_J.

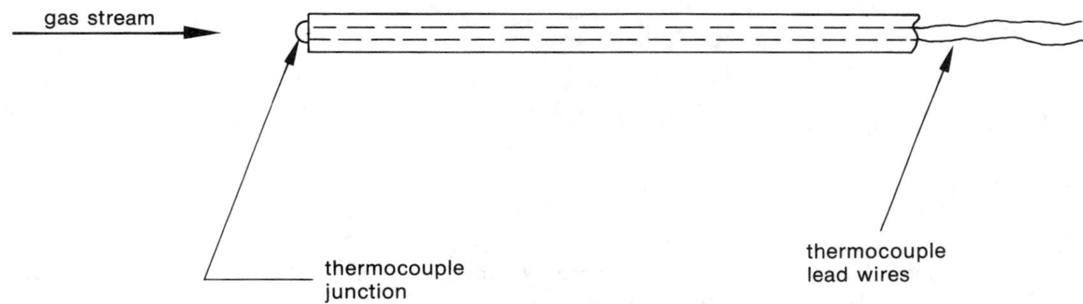

Fig. 9.29 Temperature measurement using a thermocouple.

***9-30.** (9.7) In Ex. 9.7-1, derive Eqs. 4 and 5 from Eq. 3.

9-31. (9.7) With a little thought one can conclude that Eq. 6 of Ex. 9.7-1 can be interpreted to mean that†

$$\dot{Q}_{12}^{(a)} = A_1 \mathscr{F}_{12} \sigma T_1^4$$

$$\dot{Q}_{21}^{(a)} = A_1 \mathscr{F}_{12} \sigma T_2^4$$

If surface 1 is a hole in a cavity ($F_{11} = 0$, $F_{12} = 1.0$) receiving radiation from a black body ($\epsilon_1 = 1.0$) at a temperature T_1, the amount of radiation entering the cavity from the hole is $\dot{Q}_1^{(e)} = A_1 \sigma T_1^4$ and the fraction of entering radiation absorbed is $\dot{Q}_{12}^{(a)}/\dot{Q}_1^{(e)}$. Use this definition and the results of Ex. 9.7-1 to show that the effective emissivity or absorptivity for a hole in a cavity is given by

†Consider, for example, the cases $T_2 \to 0$ and $T_1 \to 0$ and refer to Eq. 9.1-25.

$$\epsilon_{\text{eff}} = \frac{\epsilon_2}{\epsilon_2 + F_{21}(1 - \epsilon_2)}$$

Thus we see that $\epsilon_{\text{eff}} \to 1.0$ as $F_{21} \to 0$.

9-32. (9.7) Two concentric spheres, 10 and 12 in. of diameter, with the space between them evacuated, are to be used to store liquid nitrogen which boils at $-228°$F. The surfaces of the spheres have been plated with a smooth aluminum coating to provide an emissivity of 0.08. Although the gray body assumption is probably a poor one, use it to determine the rate of evaporation of nitrogen (latent heat of vaporization = 89 Btu/lb$_m$) assuming that the outer surface is at 72°F.

9-33. (9.7) Repeat the derivation given in Sec. 9.7 for the case where N_1 surface temperatures are specified and N_2 heat fluxes are specified for an enclosure having $N = N_1 + N_2$ surfaces.

9-34. (9.7) Prove that the inverse of **M** as defined by Eq. 9.7-40 is given by Eq. 9,7-42.

9-35. (9.7) Prove Eq. 9.7-50. You may wish to do this by expanding $(1 - x)^{-1}$ in a Taylor series around $x = 0$ and then letting $x = (1 - \epsilon_1)(1 - \epsilon_2)$.

9-36. (9.7) The surface of a gray body, emissivity = ϵ, has a hemispherical cavity of radius r_0 as illustrated in Fig. 9.36. Find the fraction of radiant energy emitted from the surface of the cavity which escapes from the cavity.

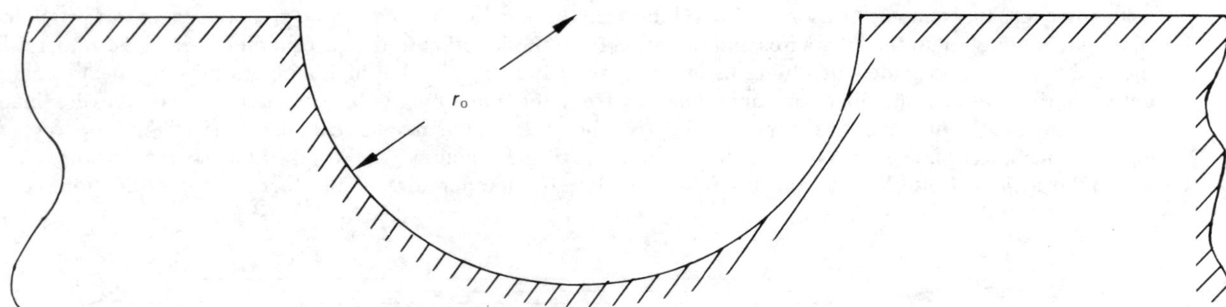

Fig. 9.36 Radiant energy escaping from a hemispherical cavity.

9-37. (9.7) Show how Eq. 9.7-43 is obtained from Eq. 9.7-38 and Eq. 9.7-42.

9-38. (9.7) Use the results of Prob. 9-3 to derive an expression for $\dot{Q}_{12}$ for the two concentric cylinders shown in Fig. 9.3. Assume that the two cylinders are gray surfaces, and use the matrix method discussed in Sec. 9.7. Take the temperature and emissivity of the inner surface to be T_1 and ϵ_1, and the temperature and emissivity of the outer surface to be T_2 and ϵ_2.

9-39. (9-7) Repeat Prob. 9-38 using the *method of successive reflections* and the results of Prob. 9-3.

9-40. (9.7) In Fig. 9.40 we have shown a flat slab which is a gray surface having an emissivity ϵ. The total energy per unit width emitted from the length L is $\epsilon q_b^{(e)} L$. If grooves are cut into this surface as illustrated in Fig. 9.40 derive an expression for an "effective emissivity" ϵ' such that the total energy per unit width emitted from the grooved surface is $\epsilon' q_b^{(e)} L$. Assume that there is no incident radiation, i.e., $q^{(i)} = 0$. Note: This is a long, hard problem; however, it provides experience in determining view factors and solving a fairly simple gray body radiation problem.

9-41. (9.8) Repeat Prob. 9-38 using the Monte Carlo method described in Sec. 9.8. Take $\epsilon_1 = 0.82$, $\epsilon_2 = 0.47$,

$$f_1 = 0.75 = \frac{\pi D_1 \epsilon_1 \sigma T_1^4}{\pi D_1 \epsilon_1 \sigma T_1^4 + \pi D_2 \epsilon_2 \sigma T_2^4}$$

and $F_{21} = 0.5$.

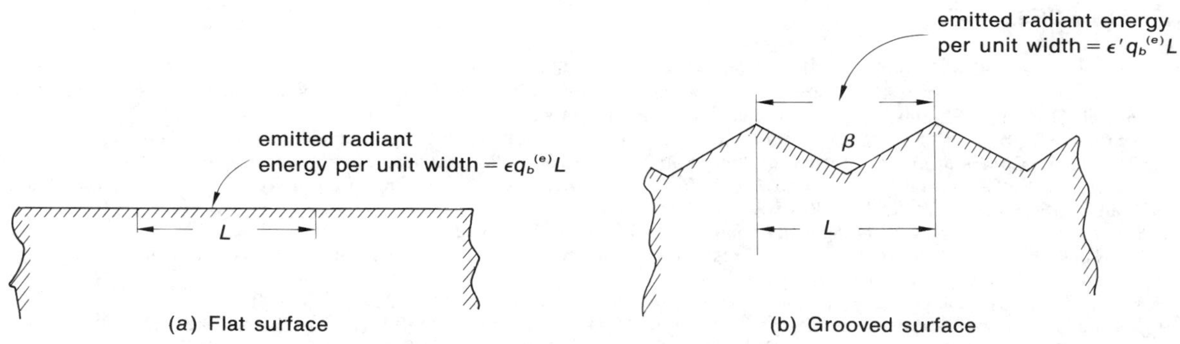

Fig. 9.40 Radiation from a grooved surface.

9-42. (9.8) Prob. 9-38 can be solved without the use of the view factors obtained in Prob. 9-3 provided we assign a direction to the ergons emitted from the outer surface and specify that $r_2 = 2r_1$. This will allow us to predict whether an ergon emitted from the outer surface will strike the inner or outer surface. Although the problem of specifying the angle θ in terms of random numbers which are uniformly distributed between 0 and 1 has not been discussed it is well known† that θ should be specified by

$$\cos\theta = \xi^{1/2}$$

For $r_2 = 2r_1$ we know that ergons emitted from the outer surface will strike the inner surface only if $\cos\theta \leq 2/\sqrt{5}$, thus the value of ξ provides all the information we need regarding the flight path of ergons emitted from surface 2.

†For example, see W. K. Talley and S. Whitaker, "Monte Carlo Analysis of Knudsen Flow," *J. Comp. Phys.* **4**, 389 (1969) for a convenient algorithm for generating flight paths.

REFERENCES

1. Hamilton, D. C., and Morgan, W. R., "View Factors for Radiant Energy Exchange," *NACA Tech. Note. No. 2836*, 1952.
2. Wylie, C. R., Jr., *Advanced Engineering Mathematics*, Third Edition, McGraw-Hill, Book Co., Inc., New York, 1966.
3. Hottel, H. C. and Sarofin, A. F., *Radiative Transfer*, McGraw-Hill Book Co., Inc., New York, 1967.
4. Sparrow, E. M., and Cess, R. D., *Radiation Heat Transfer*, Brooks/Cole Publishing Co., Belmont, California, 1966.
5. Tyndall, J., *Contributions to Molecular Physics in the Domain of Radiant Heat*, D. Appleton and Co., New York, 1882.
6. Eckert, E. R. G., Hartnett, J. P., and Irvine, T. F, Jr., "Measurement of Total Emissivity of Porous Materials in Use for Transpiration Cooling," *Jet Propulsion*, April 1956.
7. Mann, H. B., *Analysis and Design of Experiments*, Dover Publications, Inc., New York, 1949.
8. Birkebak, R. C., and Hartnett, J. P., "Measurements of the Total Absorptivity for Solar Radiation of Several Engineering Materials," *Trans. ASME* **80c**, 373 (1958).
9. Benford, F., "A Reflectometer for all Types of Surfaces," *J. Opt. Soc. Amer.* **24**, 165 (1934).
10. Jacquez, J. A., and Kuppenheim, H. F., "Theory of the Integrating Sphere," *J. Opt. Soc. Amer.* **45**, 460 (1955).
11. Sieber, W., "Zusammensetzung der von Werk und Baustoffen zurückgeworfenen Wärmestrahlung," *Z. Tech. Physik.* **22**, 130 (1941).
12. Gubareff, G. G., Janssen, J. E., and Torborg, R. H., *Thermal Radiation Properties Survey*, Honeywell Research Center, Minneapolis, Minn., 1960.
13. Siegel, R., and Howell, J. R., *Thermal Radiation Heat Transfer*, McGraw-Hill Book Co., Inc., New York, 1972.
14. Singham, J. R., "Tables of Emissivity of Surfaces," *Int. J. Heat Mass Trans.* **5**, 67 (1962).
15. Schmidt, E., and Eckert, E. R. G., "Über die Richtungsverteilung der Wärmestrahlung," *Forsch. Gebiete Ingenieurw.* **6**, 175 (1935).
16. Howell, J. R., "Applications of Monte Carlo to Heat Transfer Problems," in *Advances in Heat Transfer*, Vol. 5, edited by J. P. Hartnett and T. F. Irvine, Academic Press, New York, 1968.
17. The Holy Bible, 1 Kings 7:23 and 2 Chronicles 4:2.
18. *The Monte Carlo Method*, edited by Yu. A. Schreider, Pergamon Press, Inc., New York, 1966.
19. Taussky, O., and Todd, J., in *Generating and Testing of Pseudo-Random Numbers*, edited by H. A. Meyer, John Wiley & Sons, Inc., New York, 1956.
20. Hammersley, J. M., and Handscomb, D. C., *Monte Carlo Methods*, Methuen & Co., Ltd., London, 1964.

10

Heat Transfer with Boiling and Condensation

In this chapter we intend to study heat transfer during boiling and condensation. These two phenomena are rather different in nature, and are usually dealt with in separate chapters in textbooks; however, there are two reasons for bringing them together in a single chapter. The first is that boiling and condensation most often occur together in real processes. For example, in Fig. 10.1a we have shown a refrigeration cycle where boiling is caused by thermal energy supplied by air coming from the freezer compartment of a refrigerator. The vapor from the boiler is compressed and passed through a condenser. This is usually constructed from a bank of finned tubes placed at the back of the refrigerator where heat is transferred to the surrounding air by free convection. On some models the condenser is placed on the bottom of the refrigerator and a fan is necessary to provide a sufficient flow of cooling air. In Fig. 10.1b we have illustrated a simple distillation column which is used to separate a feed stream into a low boiling point top product and a high boiling point bottom product. The vapor leaving the top of the column is condensed and some of it is returned to flow down the column. At the bottom of the column a boiler provides a source of vapor which rises through the column contacting the liquid and thus enhancing the mass transfer which acts to separate the constituents in the feed. In Fig. 10.1c a typical steam power plant has been illustrated. An economical condenser is always desirable, and it is this aspect of the power plant operation which is usually responsible for the location of these plants along our coastlines where a large supply of cold ocean water is available at the expense of scenic blight and possible marine thermal pollution.

In each of these three examples the boiling and condensation processes are intimately related, for in general what is boiled in one part of the process is condensed in another. If one is concerned with boiling heat transfer in some process, it is likely that a condensation heat transfer process is also of importance.

There is a second reason for covering boiling and condensation in a single chapter, and that is that both are two-phase flow processes, thus the analysis presented in Sec. 10.3 of mass, momentum, and energy transfer at a vapor–liquid interface is applicable to both processes. Before going on to the study of boiling we need to briefly review some concepts previously encountered in thermodynamics and fluid mechanics courses.

Vapor pressure

If we enclose a liquid and its vapor in a system, such as that illustrated in Fig. 10.2, and allow equilibrium conditions to be reached we find that for each temperature, T_{sat}, at which we maintain the system there corresponds a pressure, p_{vap}, at which the two phases can co-exist. We will refer to this temperature as the *saturation temperature* and the pressure as the *vapor pressure.* Boiling, or formation of vapor bubbles within the liquid phase, usually occurs when the vapor pressure is greater than the surrounding ambient pressure. This can be caused by either raising the temperature of the liquid above the saturation temperature or lowering the ambient pressure below the vapor pressure. The former occurs when a coffee

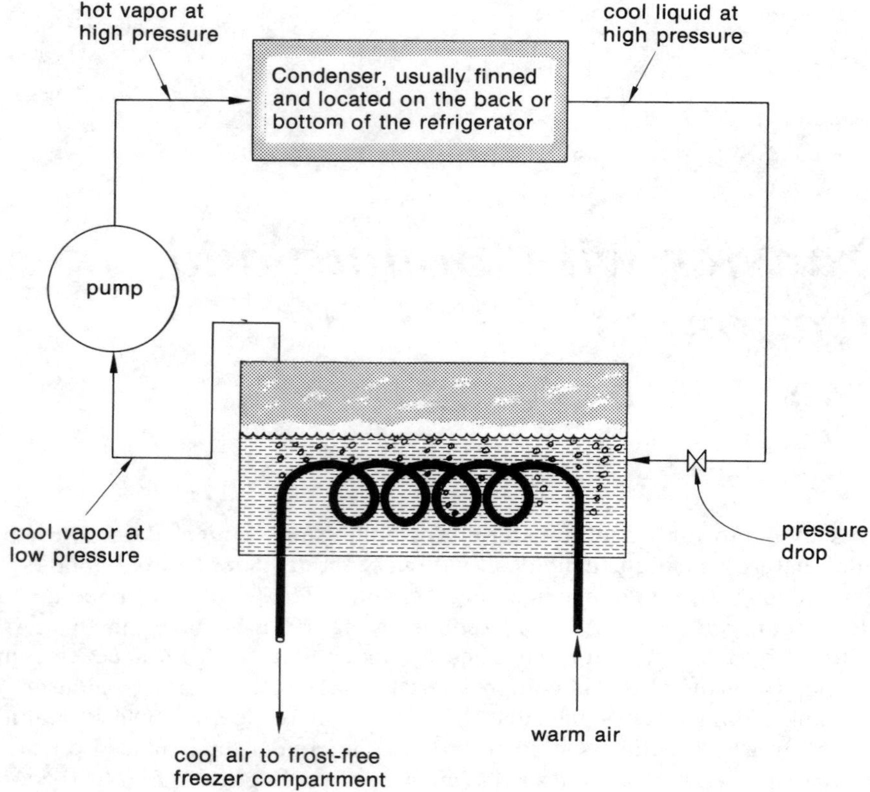

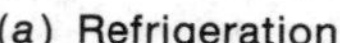

(a) Refrigeration

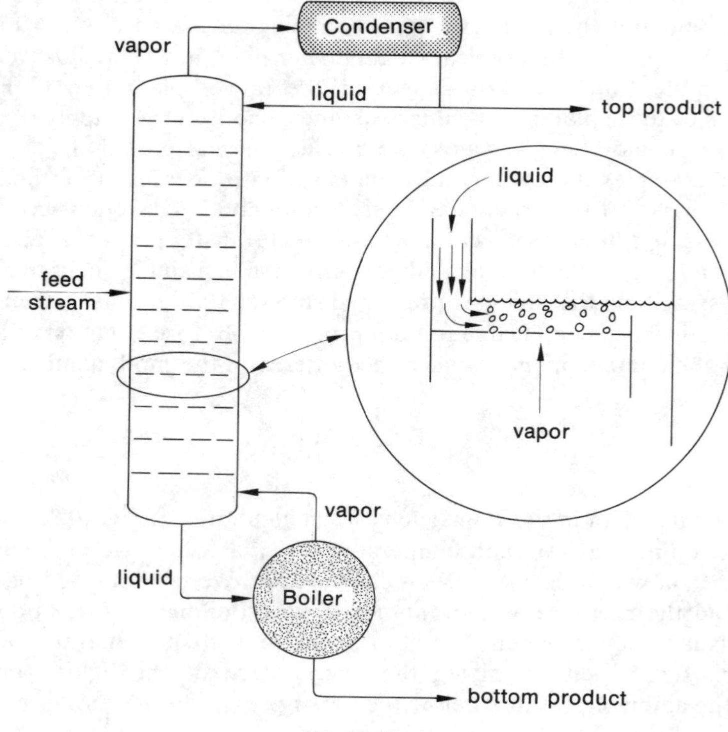

(b) Distillation

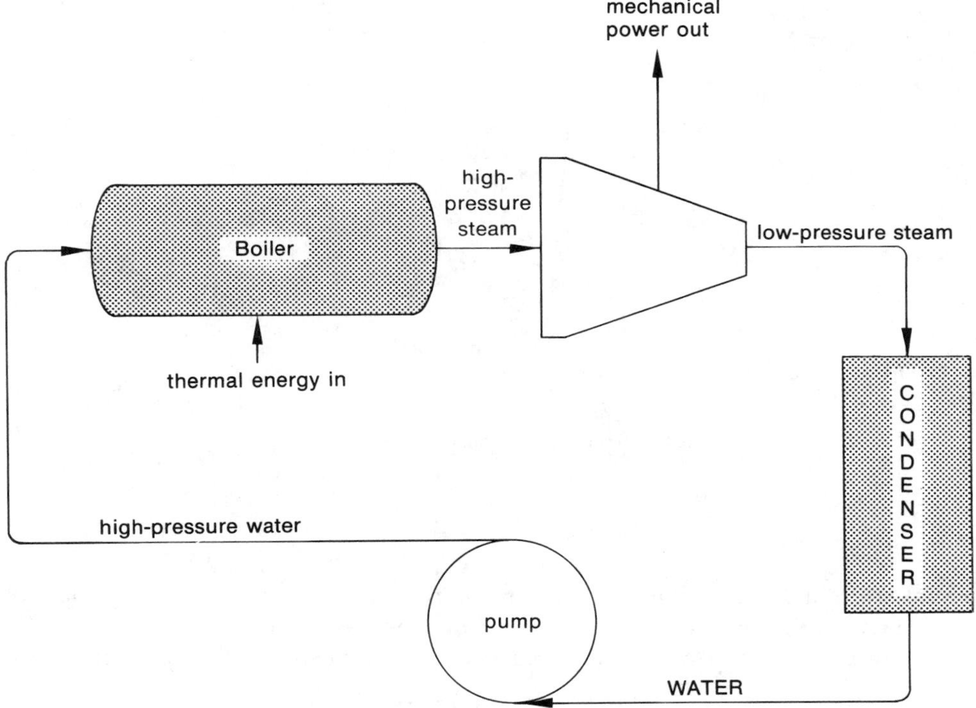

(c) Steam power plant

Fig. 10.1 Boiling and condensation processes.

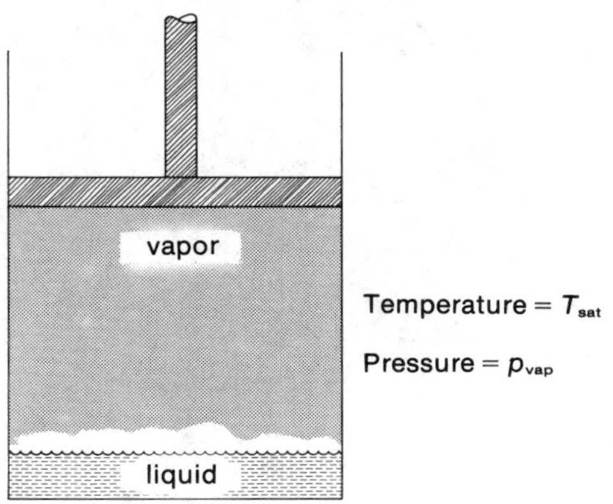

Fig. 10.2 Vapor pressure.

pot is placed on a hot stove, and the latter can occur if a deep-sea diver is forced to surface quickly, thus causing the nitrogen in his blood to "boil" giving rise to the bends. If we measure T_{sat} and p_{vap} we can construct a *vapor-pressure curve* such as the one shown in Fig. 10.3 for water. On the basis of simplifying assumptions which are generally valid away from the critical point one can derive the Clausius–Clapeyron equation which relates the vapor pressure to the temperature by the expression

$$\ln\left(\frac{p_{vap,2}}{p_{vap,1}}\right) = \frac{-\Delta H_{vap}}{R}\left(\frac{1}{T_{sat,2}} - \frac{1}{T_{sat,1}}\right) \qquad (10\text{-}1)$$

Eq. 10-1 illustrates the exponential dependence of vapor pressure on temperature.

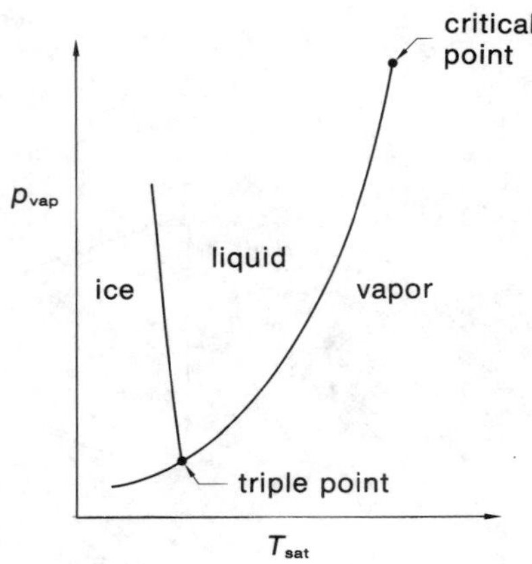

Fig. 10.3 Vapor-pressure curve for water.

Surface tension

The tangential stress associated with an interface is referred to as the *surface tension* or *interfacial tension.* It can give rise to enormously important forces in two-phase systems when the ratio of surface area to bulk volume becomes large. If we write a force balance on the hemisphere illustrated in Fig. 10.4 we obtain

$$p_i(\pi r^2) = p_o(\pi r^2) + \sigma(2\pi r) \tag{10-2}$$

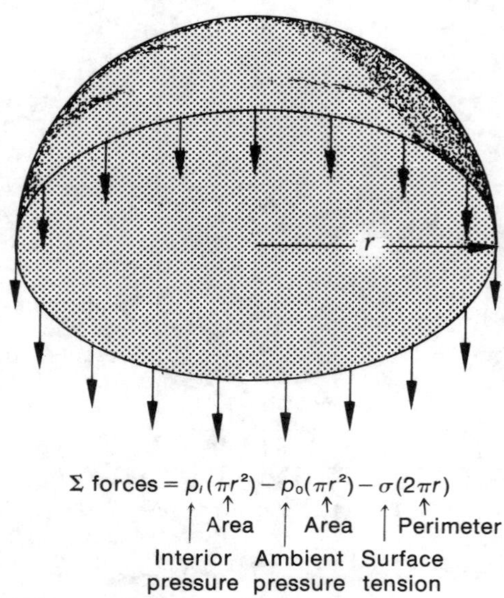

Fig. 10.4 Surface tension.

where p_i is the interior pressure and p_o is the pressure on the outside of the sphere. The pressure difference across the interface *under equilibrium conditions* is given by

$$\Delta p = \frac{2\sigma}{r}, \quad \text{pressure difference across a spherical interface} \tag{10-3}$$

For an arbitrary interface this relation takes the form

$$\Delta p = \sigma\left(\frac{1}{r_1} + \frac{1}{r_2}\right), \quad \text{pressure difference across an arbitrary interface} \tag{10-4}$$

where r_1 and r_2 are the two principal radii of curvature. From Eqs. 10-1 and 10-3 we can calculate the temperature $T_{\text{sat},2}$ at which a vapor bubble of radius r will be in equilibrium with the surrounding liquid.

$$T_{\text{sat},2} = \frac{T_{\text{sat},1}}{1 - \left(\frac{RT_{\text{sat},1}}{\Delta H_{\text{vap}}}\right) \ln\left(1 + \frac{2\sigma}{rp_{\text{vap},1}}\right)} \tag{10-5}$$

If the temperature is larger than $T_{\text{sat},2}$ the bubble will grow because of vaporization at the vapor–liquid interface, while condensation occurs and the bubble collapses if the temperature is less than $T_{\text{sat},2}$. If $T_{\text{sat},1}$ is the *boiling point*, i.e., $p_{\text{vap},1}$ is equal to the ambient pressure, then $T_{\text{sat},2} - T_{\text{sat},1}$ is referred to as the *superheat* and will often be denoted simply by ΔT. For small bubbles Eq. 10-5 indicates that the superheat can become quite large. When $2\sigma/rp_{\text{vap},1} \ll 1$ the superheat is approximated by

$$T_{\text{sat},2} - T_{\text{sat},1} = \left(\frac{RT_{\text{sat},2}T_{\text{sat},1}}{\Delta H_{\text{vap}}}\right)\left(\frac{2\sigma}{rp_{\text{vap},1}}\right), \tag{10-6}$$

indicating that large values of the superheat are to be expected for small values of the radius.

PART I BOILING

10.1 Pool Boiling

Pool boiling is a fairly descriptive term which refers to the type of boiling that occurs when a pool of liquid is brought into contact with a heated surface. A common example is a pan of water being heated on the kitchen stove, but a more practical example would be the situation illustrated in Fig. 10.1.1 where we have shown a heated tube immersed in a pool of liquid.

In order to explore the different regimes of pool boiling we wish to consider the case where the tube shown in Fig. 10.1.1 is being heated by condensing steam. The temperature of the tube can be controlled by fixing the pressure of the steam. Imagine now that we have a pool of water at some temperature T_{liq} which is less than T_{sat}, i.e., think of a pan of water at 72°F. Into this pool of water we immerse our tube heated by condensing steam and adjust the tube temperature T_0 so that it is greater than T_{liq} but less than T_{sat}. Under these conditions free convection occurs as illustrated in Fig. 10.1.1a and the temperature of the water begins to rise. If the vapor pressure at the surface of the pool is greater than the partial pressure of the water in the air above the pool, evaporation will take place at the surface. The heat transfer rate for this process can be treated by means of the theory presented in Secs. 5.11 and 7.9. As the temperature of the liquid increases we can raise the tube temperature by increasing the steam pressure until $T_0 = T_{\text{liq}} = T_{\text{sat}}$, i.e., for water at one atmosphere the temperature of the tube and the liquid is 212°F. Let us imagine now that we further increase the tube temperature and measure the heat flux $q = \mathbf{q} \cdot \mathbf{n}|_{r=r_0}$ by determining the rate at which condensate is formed. We can now plot q versus $T_0 - T_{\text{sat}} = \Delta T$ to obtain a curve similar to that shown in Fig. 10.1.2. For small values of ΔT no boiling takes place and the heat transfer mechanism is simply free convection. This condition occurs in Region I of Fig. 10.1.2. When ΔT becomes large enough (usually a few degrees Fahrenheit) vapor bubbles are formed at a few selected sites on the surface of the tube and a stream of bubbles will rise from these sites to the surface of the pool as illustrated in Fig. 10.1.1b.† The dependence of q on ΔT for this condition is shown as Region II in Fig. 10.1.2. As we continue to increase

†If the liquid temperature is lower than the saturation temperature, $T_{\text{liq}} < T_{\text{sat}}$, the bubbles formed will rise from the surface and collapse as heat is transferred from the bubble to the subcooled liquid and condensation takes place. This phenomenon is usually referred to as *subcooled boiling*.

Evaporation may take place if the vapor pressure is greater than the partial pressure.

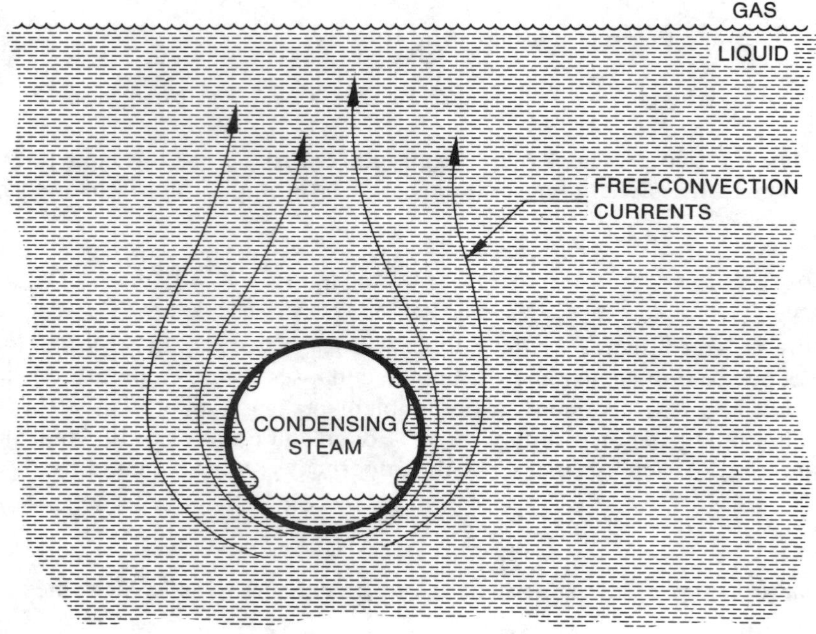

$T_0 < T_{sat}$, free convection

Fig. 10.1.1a Regimes of pool boiling.

Fig. 10.1.1b Regimes of pool boiling; $(T_0 - T_{sat}) \sim 4$–10°F, nucleate boiling. (Repetitive formation of bubbles at a nucleation site. A natural nucleation site exists at the left end of a heated $\frac{1}{4}$-in. diameter copper rod. The column of 8 bubbles on the left has formed from one site. The liquid is isopropyl alcohol. From K. W. Haley and J. W. Westwater, "Heat Transfer from a Fin to a Boiling Liquid," *Chem. Eng. Science* **20**, 711 (1964).)

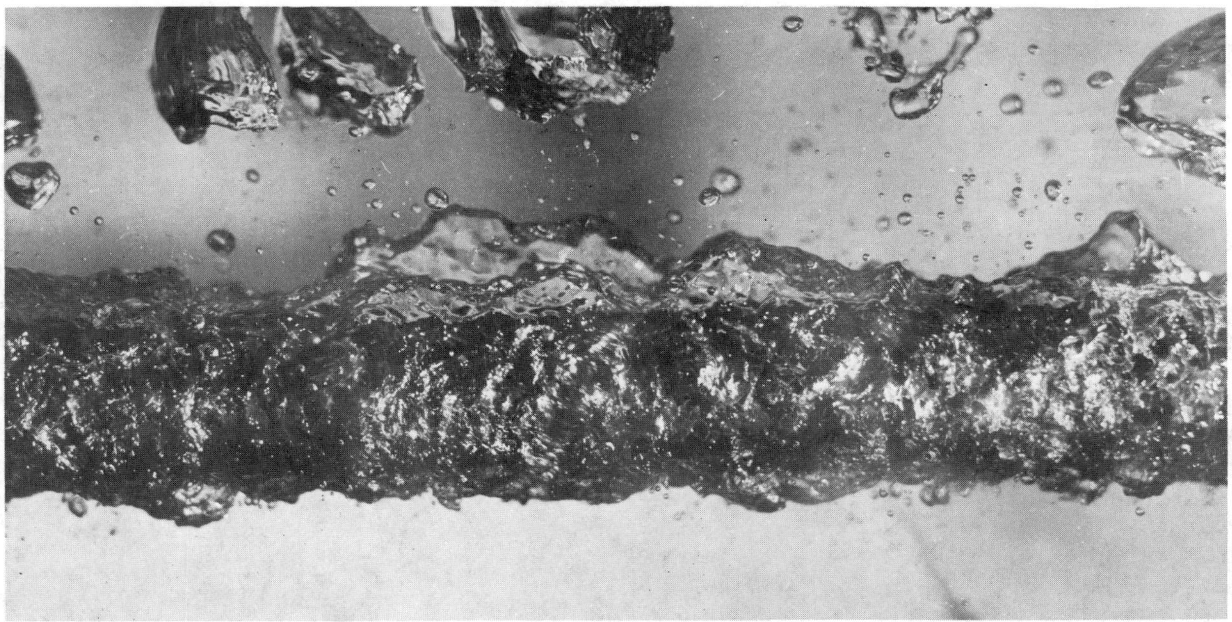

Fig. 10.1.1c Regimes of pool boiling; $(T_0 - T_{sat}) \sim 10$–$65°F$, nucleate boiling. (Nucleate boiling of methanol on a $\frac{3}{8}$-in. steam-heated copper tube. The overall ΔT is 67°F, and the heat flux is 76800 Btu/hr sq ft. Note that part of the tube is bare. This part will produce no bubbles until the temperature of the metal is increased. From J. W. Westwater, "The Boiling of Liquids," *Scientific American* **190**, No. 6, 64–67 (1954).)

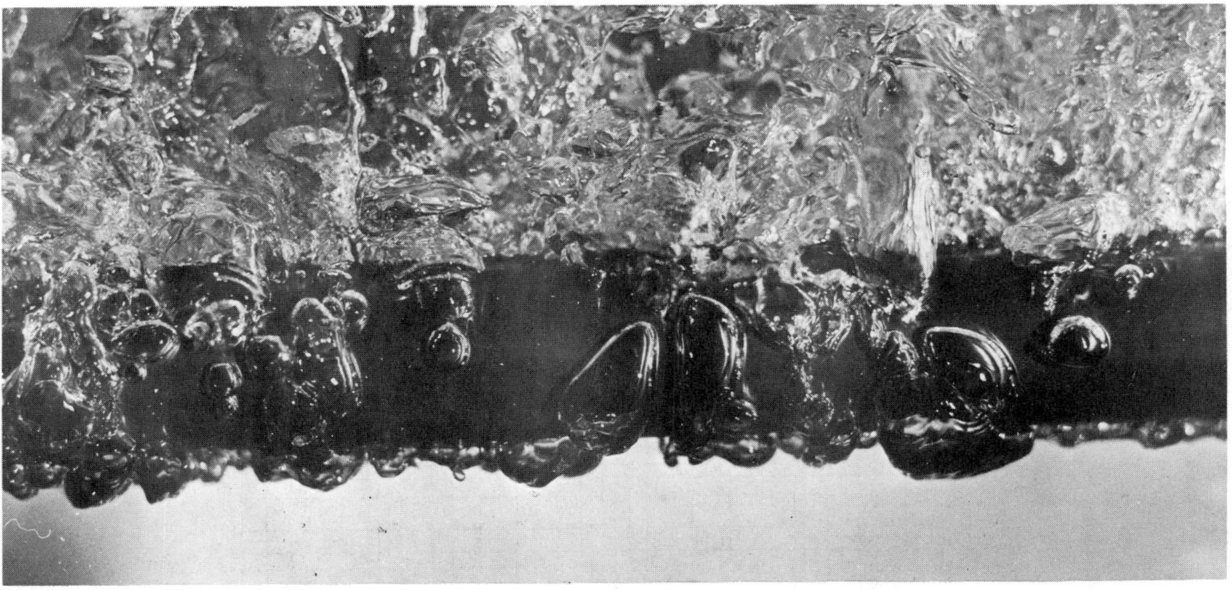

Fig. 10.1.1d Regimes of pool boiling; $(T_0 - T_{sat}) \sim 65$–$200°F$, partial nucleate boiling and unstable film boiling. (Transition boiling of methanol on a $\frac{3}{8}$-in. steam-heated copper tube. The overall ΔT is 124°F, and the heat flux is 27 200 Btu/hr sq ft. From J. W. Westwater and J. G. Santangelo, "Photographic Study of Boiling," *Ind. Eng. Chem.* **47**, 1605–1610 (1955).)

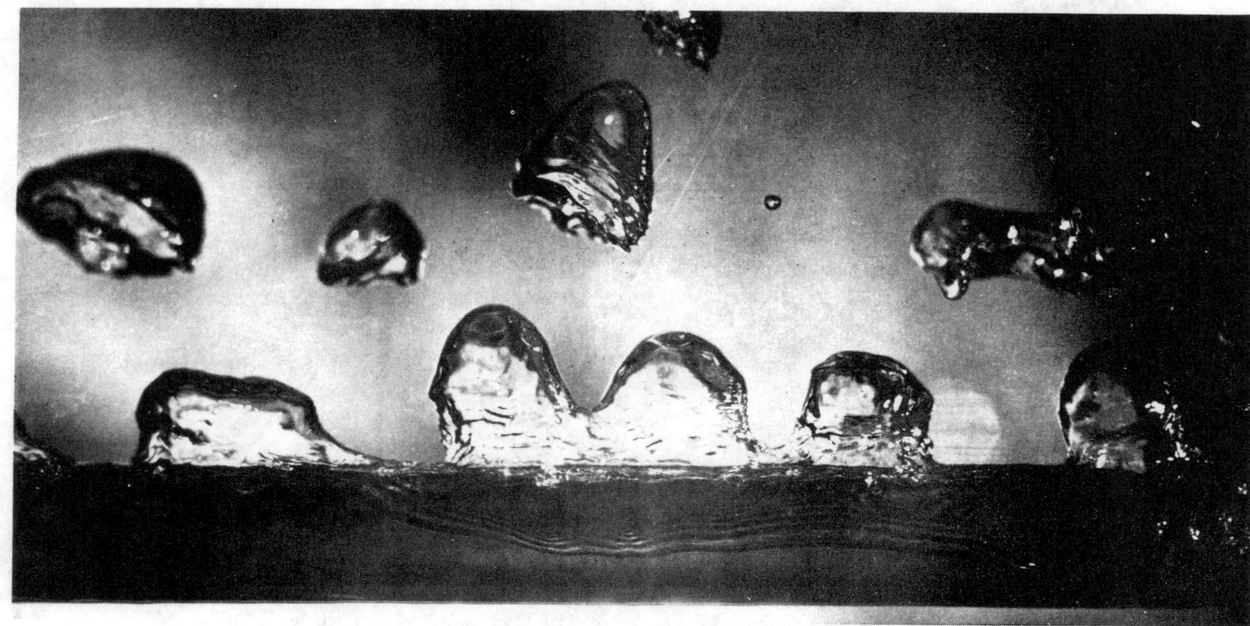

Fig. 10.1.1e Regimes of pool boiling; $(T_0 - T_{sat}) > 200°F$, stable film boiling, radiation becoming increasingly important. (Film boiling of methanol on a $\frac{3}{8}$-in. steam-heated copper tube. The overall ΔT is 148°F and the heat flux is 12970 Btu/hr sq ft or about 8 per cent of the peak flux. From J. W. Westwater and J. G. Santangelo, "Photographic Study of Boiling," *Ind. Eng. Chem.* **47**, 1605–1610 (1955).)

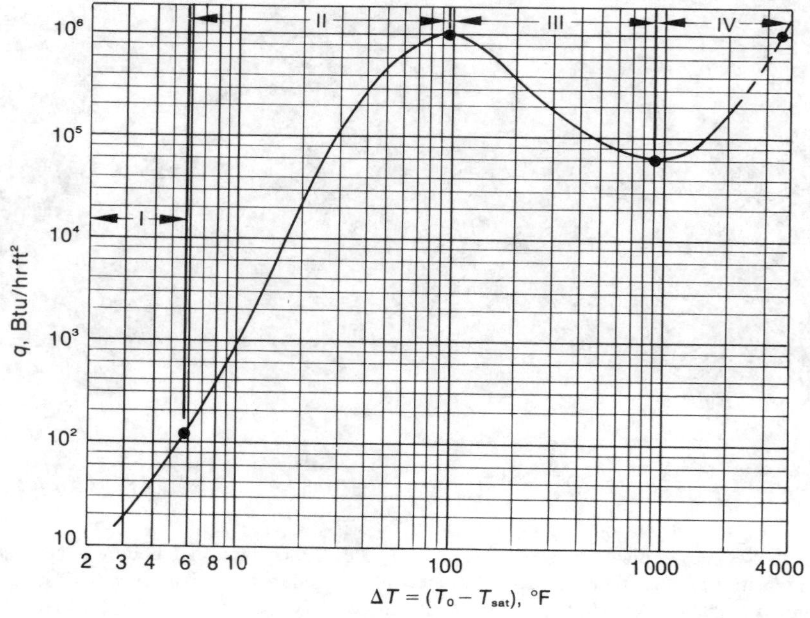

Fig. 10.1.2 Boiling curve.

the tube temperature more nucleation sites become active and the concentration of bubbles around the tube increases as shown in Fig. 10.1.1c. The bubbles grow and break away from the surface giving rise to considerable fluid motion which tends to bring the cooler liquid into contact with the hot surface. This is illustrated in Fig. 10.1.3. As more nucleating sites become active the overall fluid motion increases and the

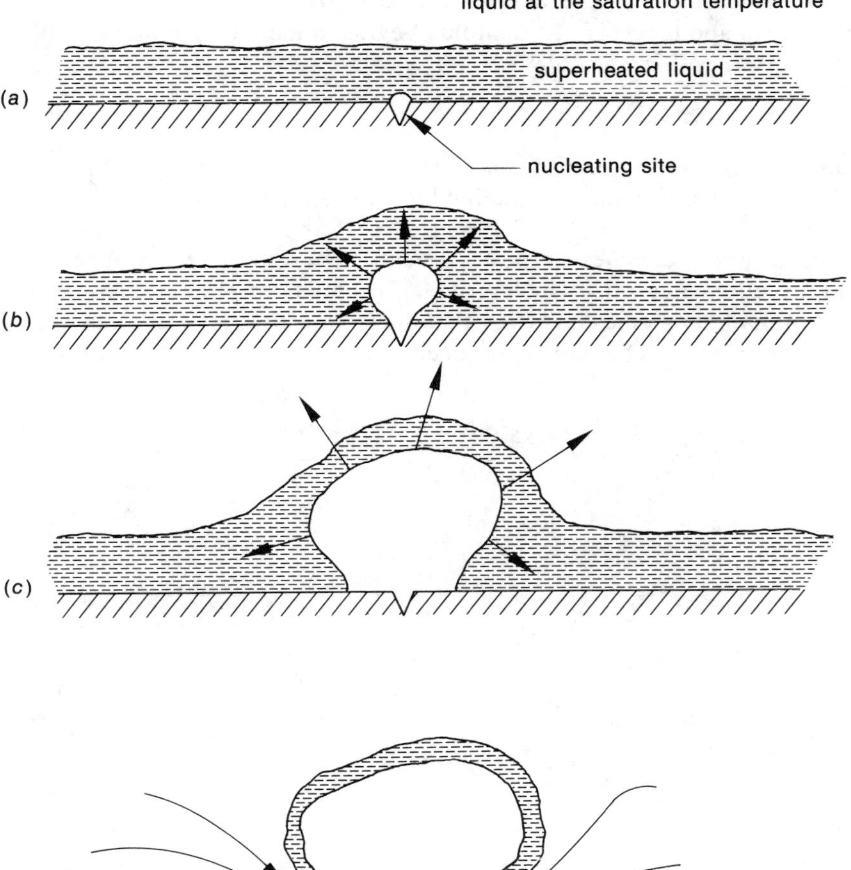

Fig. 10.1.3 Fluid motion during bubble growth and departure.

heat flux q increases rapidly with increasing ΔT. Eventually the high concentration of bubbles around the tube begins to hinder the fluid motion and the plot of q versus ΔT begins to level off and the *critical superheat*, ΔT_c, is reached. Further increases in ΔT lead to severe vapor blanketing of the tube and the heat flux begins to decrease in this region. This represents a curious phenomenon for which the rate of heat transfer *decreases* with *increasing* temperature difference. It is a region which one wishes to avoid in the design of boilers and knowledge of ΔT_c for a given process is crucial to the efficient operation of the process. If the tube at which the boiling takes place is electrically heated the transition region cannot be reached for a slight increase in the heat flux will cause the system to quickly pass the transition region and progress toward the new stable condition. For most metals this gives rise to temperatures greater than the melting point of the tube and the tube is destroyed. Because of this the critical superheat is often referred to as the *burnout point*.

In the transition region portions of the tube become completely surrounded by a vapor film as illustrated in Fig. 10.1.1d. For still larger values of ΔT the vapor-blanketing mechanism comes into full play and a stable film surrounds the tube. This is known as *stable film boiling* and is designated by Region IV in Fig. 10.1.2. Everyone has observed film boiling in the Leidenfrost phenomenon of water droplets dancing on a very hot surface. The vapor film formed between the droplet and the surface provides a nearly frictionless support and the drops move rapidly about the surface. During film boiling the vapor film undulates in a rather regular manner and comparatively large bubbles break off from the film as illustrated in Fig. 10.1.1e. For values of ΔT larger than about 1000°F the heat flux begins to increase as radiation becomes the dominant heat transfer mechanism.

Nucleation

From the discussion on vapor pressure and surface tension given in the previous section we know that the superheat ΔT tends toward infinity as the bubble size tends toward zero. This relation, which can be inferred from Eq. 10-5, does not actually hold true for $r \to 0$ for molecular effects come into play and vapor bubbles can be formed at finite values of the superheat. Nevertheless, for practical purposes, boiling will not occur unless nucleation sites exist which provide for bubble formation at low values of the superheat. From numerous experimental studies it is clear that nucleation sites consist of cavities in the solid surface such as the one shown in Fig. 10.1.3 and reproduced in greater detail in Fig. 10.1.4. For most liquid–solid

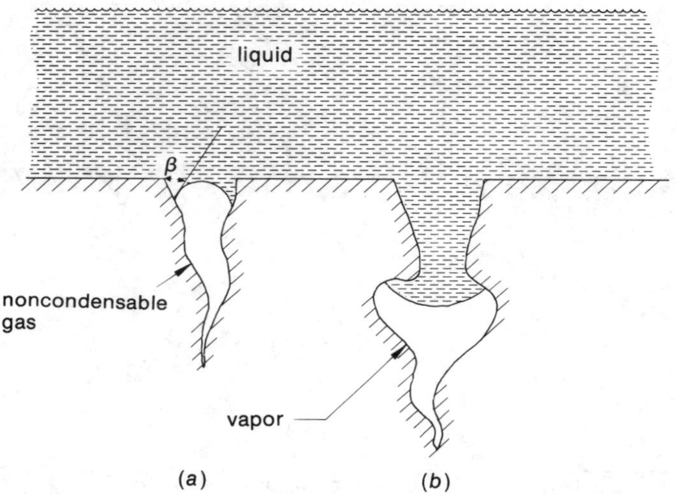

Fig. 10.1.4 Nucleation sites.

systems the *contact angle* β is less than $\pi/2$ and the surface curvature which occurs at a nucleating site such as the one shown in Fig. 10.1.4a is such that the pressure is increased because of surface tension. Under these circumstances the nucleating site is active as long as it contains some noncondensable gas such as air; however, as the cavity becomes filled with vapor it tends to condense and the site may become filled with liquid and therefore inactive. The demise of active nucleating sites does not seem to occur often presumably because the noncondensable gas is difficult to remove completely and because of the existence of re-entrant sections such as illustrated in Fig. 10.1.4b. There surface tension lowers the pressure in the cavity and a stable vapor filled cavity can exist.

In any natural surface there will be a spectrum of cavity sizes such as we have illustrated in Fig. 10.1.5. Under these conditions cavity I will begin boiling at relatively low values of ΔT while cavity II will be the last nucleating site as ΔT is increased. This distribution of cavity sizes is of course responsible for the nucleate boiling phenomena illustrated in Figs. 10.1.1b,c and for the shape of the curve in Region II of Fig. 10.1.2. If all the surface cavities were nearly the same size the plot of q versus ΔT would be very steep, whereas a broad distribution of cavity sizes would yield a slower increase of q with ΔT.

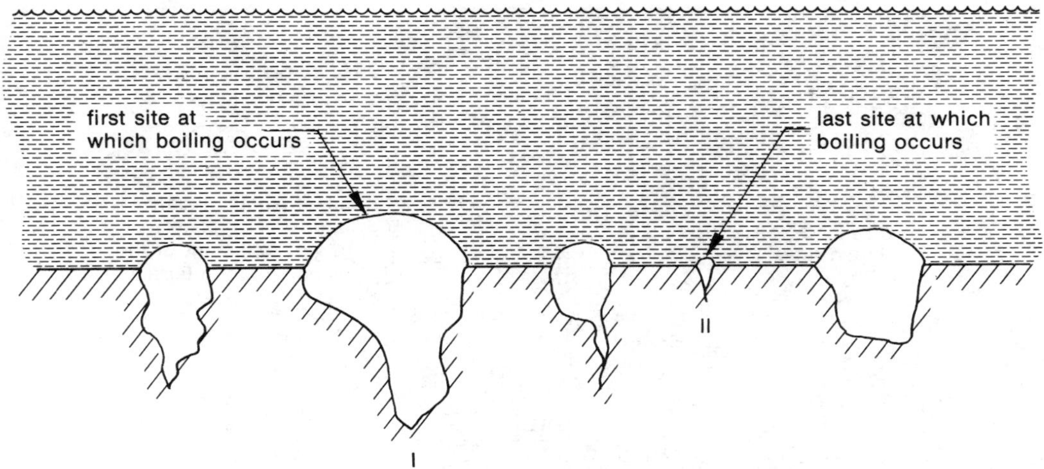

Fig. 10.1.5 Distribution of cavity sizes on a real surface.

When the heat flux at a surface is sufficiently high so that film boiling takes place the nucleating sites are of no importance; however, most boiling processes operate in the nucleate boiling regime and knowledge of the q versus ΔT curve and the critical superheat ΔT_c are of utmost importance to the designer. Clearly the boiling curve can differ considerably depending on the nature of the surface and the contact angle at the liquid–solid–vapor interface, and we can expect that correlating boiling heat transfer data will be a difficult task.

10.2 Dimensional Analysis for a Two-Phase System with Phase Changes

Having briefly explored the phenomena of pool boiling and nucleation, we now need to consider the dimensional analysis of a two-phase system so that we can understand the correlations for the nucleate boiling Nusselt number and the critical heat flux Nusselt number. We can neglect the temperature dependence of the physical properties in the governing equations and write them as:

$$\rho\left(\frac{\partial \mathbf{v}}{\partial t}+\mathbf{v}\cdot\nabla\mathbf{v}\right)=-\nabla p+\rho\mathbf{g}+\mu\nabla^2\mathbf{v},\quad \text{equations of motion for both the vapor and liquid phases} \tag{10.2-1}$$

$$\nabla\cdot\mathbf{v}=0,\quad \text{continuity equation for both the vapor and liquid phases} \tag{10.2-2}$$

$$\rho c_p\left(\frac{\partial T}{\partial t}+\mathbf{v}\cdot\nabla T\right)=k\nabla^2 T,\quad \text{thermal energy equation for both the vapor and liquid phases} \tag{10.2-3}$$

The governing differential equations are easily expressed and put into dimensionless form; however, as we shall see in subsequent paragraphs it is the boundary conditions that require considerable thought. Although the development of the boundary conditions is tedious, the effort is necessary if we are to understand the form of the correlations for boiling and the analysis of film condensation. In constructing these boundary conditions we will denote the solid surface as $\mathscr{S}$ and the vapor–liquid interface as $\mathscr{A}(t)$ as illustrated in Fig. 10.2.1.

At the solid–vapor and solid–liquid interface we express the velocity and temperature boundary conditions as

B.C.1
$$\mathbf{v}=0,\qquad T=T_0,\quad \text{at } \mathscr{S} \tag{10.2-4}$$

Here we have designated the temperature at $\mathscr{S}$ as T_0 and assumed that the thermal conductivity of the solid is sufficiently high so that the temperature in the solid is essentially uniform. Developing the boundary

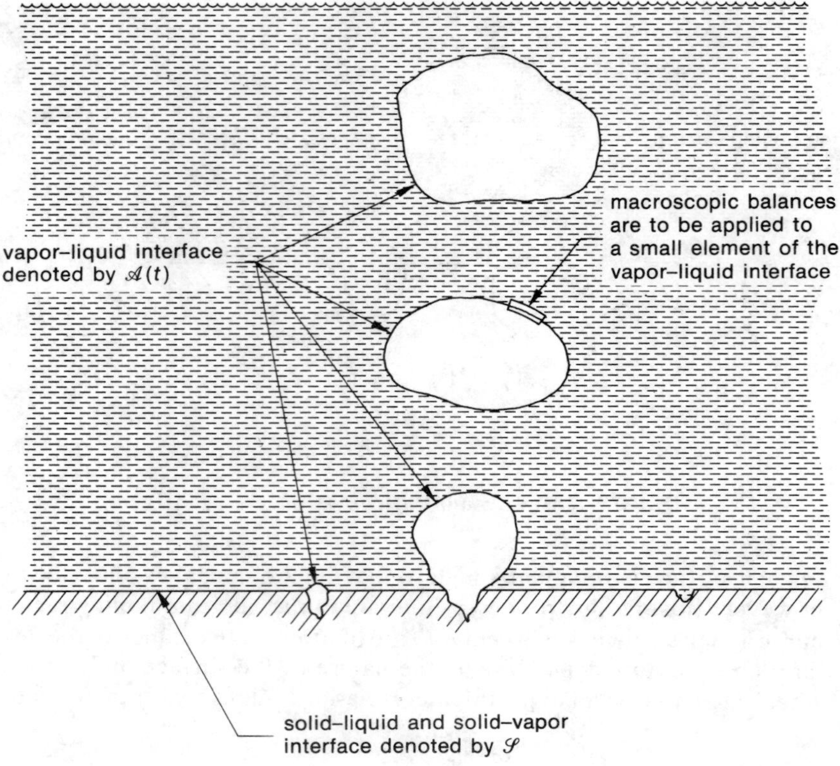

Fig. 10.2.1 Interfaces for a boiling process.

conditions at the vapor–liquid interface will require considerable analysis,† and we will accomplish this by applying the macroscopic mass, momentum, and total energy balances to the small section of interface illustrated in Fig. 10.2.1 and shown in more detail in Fig. 10.2.2:

$$\frac{d}{dt}\int_{\mathscr{V}_a(t)} \rho\, dV + \int_{\mathscr{A}_e(t)} \rho(\mathbf{v}-\mathbf{w})\cdot\mathbf{n}\, dA = 0, \quad \text{macroscopic mass balance} \tag{10.2-5}$$

$$\frac{d}{dt}\int_{\mathscr{V}_a(t)} \rho\mathbf{v}\, dV + \int_{A_e(t)} \rho\mathbf{v}(\mathbf{v}-\mathbf{w})\cdot\mathbf{n}\, dA = \int_{\mathscr{A}_a(t)} \mathbf{t}_{(\mathbf{n})}\, dA + \int_{\mathscr{V}_a(t)} \rho\mathbf{g}\, dV, \quad \text{macroscopic momentum balance} \tag{10.2-6}$$

$$\frac{d}{dt}\int_{\mathscr{V}_a(t)} \rho e\, dV + \int_{A_e(t)} \rho e(\mathbf{v}-\mathbf{w})\cdot\mathbf{n}\, dA = -\int_{\mathscr{A}_a(t)} \mathbf{q}\cdot\mathbf{n}\, dA + \int_{\mathscr{A}_a(t)} \mathbf{t}_{(\mathbf{n})}\cdot\mathbf{v}\, dA + \int_{\mathscr{V}_a(t)} \rho\mathbf{g}\cdot\mathbf{v}\, dV, \quad \text{macroscopic total energy balance} \tag{10.2-7}$$

In applying the macroscopic balances we plan to let the control volume shrink to an arbitrarily small volume containing the interface, thus all the volume integrals in Eqs. 10.2-5 through 10.2-7 will tend toward zero.

†The question might naturally arise as to why we do not simply impose the normal constraints of continuity of $\mathbf{v}$, T, $\mathbf{q}\cdot\mathbf{n}$, and $\mathbf{t}_{(\mathbf{n})}$ at the interface. The answer is that the vapor–liquid interface is treated as a *singular surface* which means that we will assign certain intrinsic properties to the surface itself, i.e., surface tension for example, and for singular surfaces the normal continuity requirements are no longer valid.

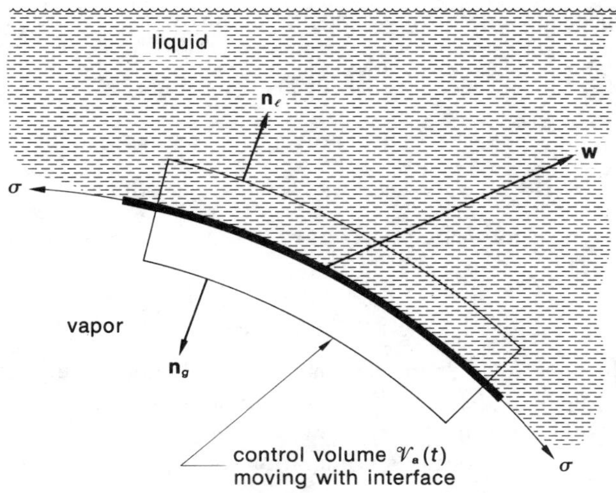

Fig. 10.2.2 Element of vapor–liquid interface.

Mass

The mass balance is particularly simple to apply and it yields

$$\rho_\ell(\mathbf{v}_\ell - \mathbf{w}) \cdot \mathbf{n}_\ell + \rho_g(\mathbf{v}_g - \mathbf{w}) \cdot \mathbf{n}_g = 0 \tag{10.2-8a}$$

Here the subscript ℓ is used to denote the liquid phase and the subscript g is used to denote the vapor or gas phase. Note that $\mathbf{n}_\ell$ and $\mathbf{n}_g$ are *not* the outwardly directed unit normal vectors for the liquid and vapor phases; rather they are the *inwardly* directed normal vectors. In addition to the relation given by Eq. 10.2-8a for the normal components of the velocity we will continue to impose the traditional constraint on the tangential components of the velocity at the interface, i.e.,

$$\mathbf{v}_\ell \cdot \boldsymbol{\lambda} = \mathbf{v}_g \cdot \boldsymbol{\lambda}, \quad \text{at the interface} \tag{10.2-8b}$$

where $\boldsymbol{\lambda}$ is any tangent vector to the surface.

Momentum

A rigorous application of the momentum equation to the control volume shown in Fig. 10.2.2 has been presented by Slattery [1]; and we will draw upon that result to provide us with the proper expression for the contribution of surface tension. Application of Eq. 10.2-6 leads to

$$\rho_\ell \mathbf{v}_\ell(\mathbf{v}_\ell - \mathbf{w}) \cdot \mathbf{n}_\ell + \rho_g \mathbf{v}_g(\mathbf{v}_g - \mathbf{w}) \cdot \mathbf{n}_g = \mathbf{t}^\ell_{(\mathbf{n}_\ell)} + \mathbf{t}^g_{(\mathbf{n}_g)} + \sigma\left(\frac{1}{r_1} + \frac{1}{r_2}\right)\mathbf{n}_g. \tag{10.2-9}$$

Here r_1 and r_2 represent the two principal radii of curvature and we have included the effect of surface tension on a purely intuitive basis. We will now neglect viscous effects so that the stress vectors are given by

$$\mathbf{t}^\ell_{(\mathbf{n}_\ell)} = -\mathbf{n}_\ell p_\ell \tag{10.2-10a}$$

$$\mathbf{t}^g_{(\mathbf{n}_g)} = -\mathbf{n}_g p_g. \tag{10.2-10b}$$

Substituting Eqs. 10.2-10 into Eq. 10.2-9 and forming the scalar product with $\mathbf{n}_\ell = -\mathbf{n}_g$ yields

$$\rho_\ell \mathbf{v}_\ell \cdot \mathbf{n}_\ell(\mathbf{v}_\ell - \mathbf{w}) \cdot \mathbf{n}_\ell + \rho_g \mathbf{v}_g \cdot \mathbf{n}_\ell(\mathbf{v}_g - \mathbf{w}) \cdot \mathbf{n}_g = p_g - p_\ell - \sigma\left(\frac{1}{r_1} + \frac{1}{r_2}\right). \tag{10.2-11}$$

We can make use of the mass balance to simplify this result to

$$(p_g - p_\ell) = \sigma\left(\frac{1}{r_1} + \frac{1}{r_2}\right) + \rho_\ell(\mathbf{v}_\ell - \mathbf{w}) \cdot \mathbf{n}_\ell(\mathbf{v}_\ell - \mathbf{v}_g) \cdot \mathbf{n}_\ell \tag{10.2-12}$$

Note that if there is no change of phase,

$$\mathbf{v}_\ell \cdot \mathbf{n} = \mathbf{v}_g \cdot \mathbf{n} = \mathbf{w} \cdot \mathbf{n}, \quad \text{for no change of phase} \tag{10.2-13}$$

and Eq. 10.2-12, which neglects viscous effects, reduces to the result given by Eq. 10-4 at the beginning of this chapter.

Energy

Application of the macroscopic total energy balance to the element of interface presents some difficult steps if we do a thorough analysis of the rate of work term, and in order to simplify our development we will neglect the work done by viscous stresses and include the work done by surface tension forces in an intuitive manner. Subject to these restrictions application of Eq. 10.2-7 leads to

$$\rho_\ell e_\ell(\mathbf{v}_\ell - \mathbf{w}) \cdot \mathbf{n}_\ell + \rho_g e_g(\mathbf{v}_g - \mathbf{w}) \cdot \mathbf{n}_g = \mathbf{v}_\ell \cdot (-\mathbf{n}_\ell p_\ell) + \mathbf{v}_g \cdot (-\mathbf{n}_g p_g) - \sigma\left(\frac{1}{r_1} + \frac{1}{r_2}\right) \mathbf{w} \cdot \mathbf{n}_\ell - (\mathbf{q}_\ell \cdot \mathbf{n}_\ell + \mathbf{q}_g \cdot \mathbf{n}_g) \tag{10.2-14}$$

Adding and subtracting $p_\ell \mathbf{w} \cdot \mathbf{n}_\ell$ and $p_g \mathbf{w} \cdot \mathbf{n}_g$ allows us to rearrange the energy equation to obtain

$$(\rho_\ell e_\ell + p_\ell)(\mathbf{v}_\ell - \mathbf{w}) \cdot \mathbf{n}_\ell + (\rho_g e_g + p_g)(\mathbf{v}_g - \mathbf{w}) \cdot \mathbf{n}_g = (p_g - p_\ell)\mathbf{w} \cdot \mathbf{n}_\ell - \sigma\left(\frac{1}{r_1} + \frac{1}{r_2}\right) \mathbf{w} \cdot \mathbf{n}_\ell - (\mathbf{q}_\ell - \mathbf{q}_g) \cdot \mathbf{n}_\ell \tag{10.2-15}$$

Here we have used $\mathbf{n}_\ell = -\mathbf{n}_g$ in some of the terms. Noting that the enthalpy of the gas and liquid phases can be expressed as

$$\rho_\ell h_\ell = \rho_\ell e_\ell + p_\ell$$

$$\rho_g h_g = \rho_g e_g + p_g$$

leads to

$$\rho_\ell h_\ell(\mathbf{v}_\ell - \mathbf{w}) \cdot \mathbf{n}_\ell + \rho_g h_g(\mathbf{v}_g - \mathbf{w}) \cdot \mathbf{n}_g = (p_g - p_\ell)\mathbf{w} \cdot \mathbf{n}_\ell - \sigma\left(\frac{1}{r_1} + \frac{1}{r_2}\right) \mathbf{w} \cdot \mathbf{n}_\ell - (\mathbf{q}_\ell - \mathbf{q}_g) \cdot \mathbf{n}_\ell \tag{10.2-16}$$

Expressing the latent heat of vaporization as $\Delta H_{\text{vap}} = h_g - h_\ell$ and using the mass balance allows us to simplify Eq. 10.2-16 to obtain

$$-\Delta H_{\text{vap}} \rho_\ell(\mathbf{v}_\ell - \mathbf{w}) \cdot \mathbf{n}_\ell + (\mathbf{q}_\ell - \mathbf{q}_g) \cdot \mathbf{n}_\ell = \left[(p_g - p_\ell) - \sigma\left(\frac{1}{r_1} + \frac{1}{r_2}\right)\right] \mathbf{w} \cdot \mathbf{n}_\ell \tag{10.2-17}$$

We can eliminate the pressure and surface tension terms by use of Eq. 10.2-12 so that Eq. 10.2-17 takes the form

$$(\mathbf{q}_\ell - \mathbf{q}_g) \cdot \mathbf{n}_\ell = [\Delta H_{\text{vap}} + (\mathbf{v}_\ell - \mathbf{v}_g) \cdot \mathbf{n}_\ell(\mathbf{w} \cdot \mathbf{n}_\ell)]\rho_\ell(\mathbf{v}_\ell - \mathbf{w}) \cdot \mathbf{n}_\ell \tag{10.2-18}$$

At this point it becomes apparent that $\sqrt{\Delta H_{\text{vap}}}$ has the units of velocity. Furthermore an order-of-magnitude estimate indicates that

$$\Delta H_{\text{vap}} \gg (\mathbf{v}_\ell - \mathbf{v}_g) \cdot \mathbf{n}_\ell(\mathbf{w} \cdot \mathbf{n}_\ell)$$

which allows us to further simplify Eq. 10.2-18. A summary of our boundary conditions at the vapor–liquid interface can now be expressed as

B.C.2
$$\rho_\ell(\mathbf{v}_\ell - \mathbf{w}) \cdot \mathbf{n}_\ell = \rho_g(\mathbf{v}_g - \mathbf{w}) \cdot \mathbf{n}_g \quad \text{mass} \tag{10.2-19}$$

B.C.3 $$(p_g - p_\ell) = \sigma\left(\frac{1}{r_1} + \frac{1}{r_2}\right), \quad \text{momentum} \tag{10.2-20}$$

B.C.4 $$(-k_\ell \nabla T_\ell + k_g \nabla T_g) \cdot \mathbf{n}_\ell = \Delta H_{\text{vap}} \rho_\ell (\mathbf{v}_\ell - \mathbf{w}) \cdot \mathbf{n}_\ell, \quad \text{energy} \tag{10.2-21}$$

In addition we will require that the temperature at the vapor–liquid interface is the saturation temperature

B.C.5 $$T = T_{\text{sat}}, \quad \text{at } \mathscr{A}(t) \tag{10.2-22}$$

and we will assume that the contact angle β is all that is needed to describe the state of the solid–liquid–vapor interface.

We now have available the governing differential equations, Eqs. 10.2-1 through 10.2-3, and the boundary conditions for the vapor–liquid interface, Eqs. 10.2-19 through 10.2-22. The "no slip" condition and the continuity of temperature condition at the solid–vapor and solid–liquid interface have previously been given as B.C.1. We are now confronted with the problem of choosing a characteristic length and velocity, L^* and u^*. Aside from perhaps some average cavity diameter the characteristic length and velocity for nucleate boiling are not obvious quantities. Many investigators like to think of the bubble diameter and velocity as it leaves the surface as being representative of L^* and u^*; however, these quantities are unknown except by experimental observation or by solution of the very complex governing equations and boundary conditions. Because of this the bubble diameter and velocity are not suitable characteristic quantities, and any dimensional analysis which begins with these quantities must always replace them with other parameters which are known *a priori.* An examination of the governing equations and boundary conditions indicates that a wide variety of characteristic values can be constructed in terms of known parameters. For example, we could use the following characteristic lengths

$$L_1^* = \frac{\nu}{\sqrt{\Delta H_{\text{vap}}}}, \qquad L_2^* = \frac{\alpha}{\sqrt{c_p(T_0 - T_{\text{sat}})}}, \qquad L_3^* = \frac{\Delta H_{\text{vap}}}{g}$$

In choosing the values of L^* and u^* one usually tries to pick quantities which *strongly influence* the process under consideration. Certainly the bubble diameter and velocity strongly influence the nucleate boiling heat transfer rate, but these are unknown except to the extent that their order-of-magnitude can be predicted by approximate theories.

With essentially no real justification other than the knowledge of the form of current correlations we will choose L^* and u^* as follows:

$$L^* = \rho_\ell \Delta H_{\text{vap}} / g(\rho_\ell - \rho_g) \tag{10.2-23}$$

$$u^* = \alpha_\ell g / \Delta H_{\text{vap}} \tag{10.2-24}$$

Our thought here is that the bubble diameter should become large as either $g \to 0$ or $(\rho_\ell - \rho_g) \to 0$, and that the bubble growth rate will increase with increasing thermal diffusivity, α, since large values of α mean that energy is rapidly supplied to the interface where vaporization occurs. Similarly, large values of ΔH_{vap} should mean a slow bubble growth rate since more energy must be supplied to the interface for each cubic centimeter of vapor formed.

Having chosen L^* and u^* we can put Eqs. 10.2-1 through 10.2-2 in dimensionless form to obtain

$$\frac{\partial \mathbf{U}_\ell}{\partial t^*} + \mathbf{U}_\ell \cdot \nabla \mathbf{U}_\ell = -\nabla \mathscr{P}_\ell + N_{\text{Pr}}(1 - N_\rho)\nabla^2 \mathbf{U}_\ell \tag{10.2-25a}$$

$$\frac{\partial \mathbf{U}_g}{\partial t^*} + \mathbf{U}_g \cdot \nabla \mathbf{U}_g = -\nabla \mathscr{P}_g + N_{\text{Pr}}(1 - N_\rho) N_\nu \nabla^2 \mathbf{U}_g \tag{10.2-25b}$$

Here N_{Pr} is the Prandtl number and N_ρ and N_ν represent density and kinematic viscosity ratios:

$$N_\rho = \rho_g / \rho_\ell \tag{10.2-26a}$$

$$N_\nu = \nu_g / \nu_\ell \tag{10.2-26b}$$

The two continuity equations take the form

$$\nabla \cdot \mathbf{U}_\ell = 0 \tag{10.2-27a}$$

$$\nabla \cdot \mathbf{U}_g = 0 \tag{10.2-27b}$$

and the two thermal energy equations become

$$\frac{\partial \Theta_\ell}{\partial t^*} + \mathbf{U}_\ell \cdot \nabla \Theta_\ell = (1 - N_\rho)\nabla^2 \Theta_\ell \tag{10.2-28a}$$

$$\frac{\partial \Theta_g}{\partial t^*} + \mathbf{U}_g \cdot \nabla \Theta_g = N_\alpha (1 - N_\rho)\nabla^2 \Theta_g \tag{10.2-28b}$$

where $\Theta = (T_0 - T)/(T_0 - T_{\text{sat}})$ and the dimensionless number N_α is given by

$$N_\alpha = \alpha_g / \alpha_\ell \tag{10.2-29}$$

Going on to the boundary conditions we obtain

B.C.1' $$U = \Theta = 0, \quad \text{on } \mathscr{S} \tag{10.2-30}$$

B.C.2' $$(\mathbf{U}_\ell - \mathbf{W}) \cdot \mathbf{n}_\ell = N_\rho (\mathbf{U}_g - \mathbf{W}) \cdot \mathbf{n}_g, \quad \text{mass at } \mathscr{A}(t) \tag{10.2-31}$$

B.C.3' $$N_\rho \mathscr{P}_g - \mathscr{P}_\ell + \frac{\phi}{u^{*2}}(1 - N_\rho) = \frac{1 - N_\rho}{N_{\text{We}}}\left(\frac{1}{R_1} + \frac{1}{R_2}\right), \quad \text{momentum at } \mathscr{A}(t) \tag{10.2-32}$$

Here N_{We} represents a nucleate boiling Weber number given by

$$N_{\text{We}} = \rho_\ell g \alpha_\ell^2 / \sigma \Delta H_{\text{vap}} \tag{10.2-33}$$

B.C.4' $$(\nabla \Theta_\ell - N_k \nabla \Theta_g) \cdot \mathbf{n}_\ell = N_{\text{Bo}}^{-1}(1 - N_\rho)^{-1}(\mathbf{U}_\ell - \mathbf{W}) \cdot \mathbf{n}_\ell, \quad \text{energy at } \mathscr{A}(t) \tag{10.2-34}$$

The dimensionless number N_k is just the ratio of thermal conductivities,

$$N_k = k_g / k_\ell \tag{10.2-35}$$

and N_{Bo} will be referred to as the boiling number and is defined by

$$N_{\text{Bo}} = \frac{k_\ell (T_0 - T_{\text{sat}})}{\rho_\ell \alpha_\ell \Delta H_{\text{vap}}} \tag{10.2-36}$$

B.C.5' $$\Theta = 1, \quad \text{at } \mathscr{A}(t) \tag{10.2-37}$$

The gravitational potential function can be expressed as

$$\phi = gz \tag{10.2-38}$$

for the case where the gravity vector g is pointing in the negative z-direction. If we designate the z-position of the interface as

$$z = \eta(x, y, t), \quad \text{locates the interface } \mathscr{A}(t)$$

the term $\phi/(u^*)^2$ can be expressed as

$$\frac{\phi}{(u^*)^2} = \frac{g\eta}{(u^*)^2} = \frac{gL^*}{(u^*)^2}\left(\frac{\eta}{L^*}\right) = \left(\frac{gL^*}{(u^*)^2}\right) Z$$

Here we have used Z to represent the dimensionless position of the interface. We can now rewrite B.C.3 as

B.C.3'' $$N_\rho \mathscr{P}_g - \mathscr{P}_\ell + ZN_{\text{Ve}}(1 - N_\rho) = N_{\text{We}}^{-1}(1 - N_\rho)\left(\frac{1}{R_1} + \frac{1}{R_2}\right), \quad \text{momentum at } \mathscr{A}(t) \tag{10.2-39}$$

The term $N_{Ve} = (\Delta H_{vap}^3/\alpha_\ell^2 g^2)$ takes the place of the Froude number in non-boiling, forced-convection, two-phase flow problems [2]; however, the physical significance of this dimensionless group is not at all clear. Since it is a ratio of velocities to the sixth power we will refer to it as the velocity number.

In Table 10.2-1 we have summarized the dimensionless parameters which can be used to characterize nucleate boiling heat transfer rates under pool boiling conditions. In addition to these parameters, we must keep in mind that there are unknown parameters describing the state of the surface which strongly influence the heat transfer rate. It seems likely that the distribution of cavity sizes and the number of cavities per unit area of heating surface will be the most important characteristic of the surface along with the contact angle, β. We should keep in mind that β probably varies over the surface and can change with time as surface contaminants are removed by the boiling action. These effects are nicely illustrated by boiling curves presented in Fig. 10.2.3 for a variety of surface conditions. It should be obvious from the

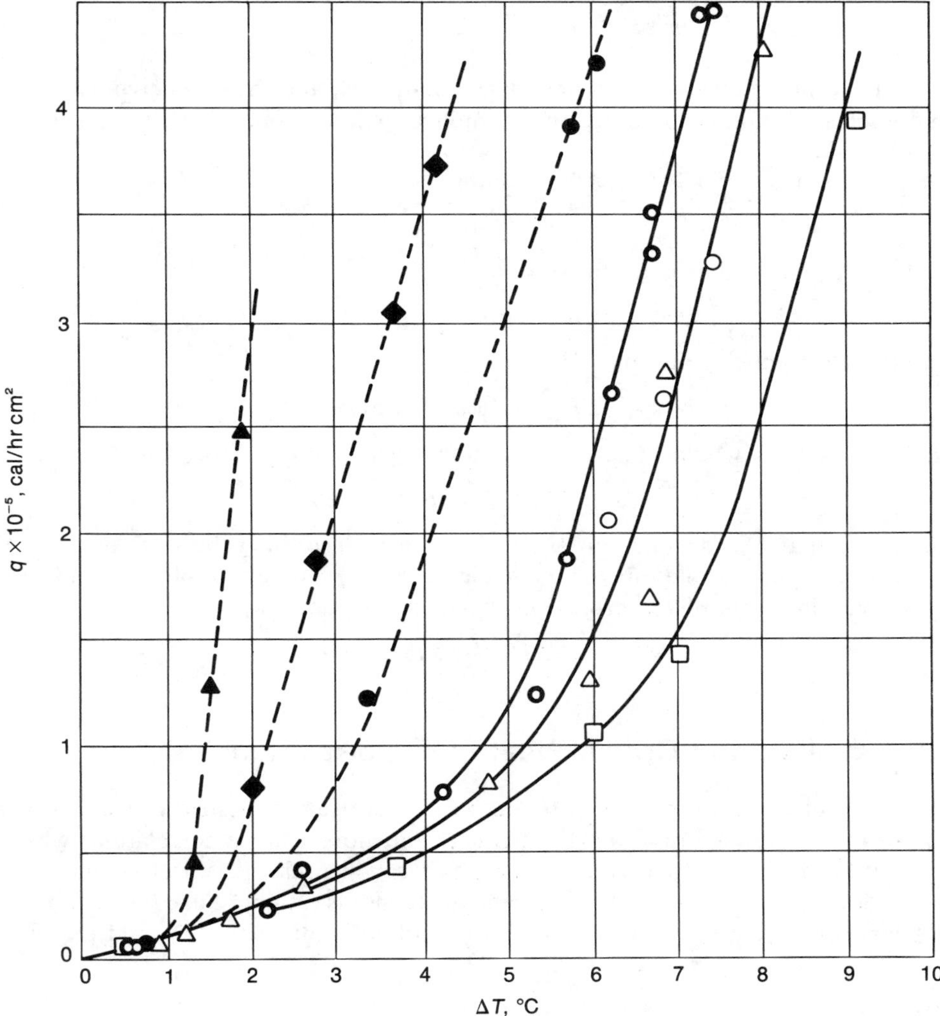

Fig. 10.2.3 Effect of surface conditions on the nucleate boiling heat flux for water. (Adapted from Jakob, M., *Heat Transfer*, Vol. I, John Wiley & Sons, Inc., New York, 1949.)

Surface Condition: **O** recently roughened by a sand blast; ○ same, oxidized by longer use; △ same, roughened once more by sand blast; □ same, after long use; ▲ recently fitted with a roughness screen and cleaned; ◆ same, after 4 hours of boiling, followed by 24 hours of lying in water; ● same, after 8 more hours of boiling, followed by another 24 hours of lying in water.

Table 10.2-1 Dimensionless Parameters Describing Nucleate Boiling

From the governing equations
1. $N_{Pr} = \nu_\ell/\alpha_\ell$, the Prandtl number
2. $N_\rho = \rho_g/\rho_\ell$, ratio of densities
3. $N_\nu = \nu_g/\nu_\ell$, ratio of kinematic viscosities
4. $N_\alpha = \alpha_g/\alpha_\ell$, ratio of thermal diffusivities
From the boundary conditions
5. β, the contact angle
6. $N_{We} = \rho_\ell g \alpha_\ell^2/\sigma \Delta H_{vap}$, a nucleate boiling Weber number
7. $N_{Ve} = (\Delta H_{vap}^3/\alpha_\ell^2 g^2)$, the velocity number
8. $N_{Bo} = k_\ell(T_0 - T_{sat})/\rho_\ell \alpha_\ell \Delta H_{vap}$, the boiling number $= (c_p)_\ell (T_0 - T_{sat})/\Delta H_{vap}$

complexity of the governing equations and boundary conditions, and the extensive list of dimensionless parameters, that nucleate boiling is an extremely complex phenomenon, and that correlating boiling data presents a difficult task.

We define the Nusselt number for nucleate boiling as

$$N_{Nu} = hL^*/k_\ell \tag{10.2-40}$$

where the heat transfer coefficient is given by

$$h = q/(T_0 - T_{sat}) \tag{10.2-41}$$

This leads to a Nusselt number given by

$$N_{Nu} = q\Delta H_{vap}/k_\ell(T_0 - T_{sat})g(1 - N_\rho) \tag{10.2-42}$$

and our dimensional analysis would indicate a functional dependence of the form

$$N_{Nu} = \mathcal{F}(N_{Pr}, N_\rho, N_\nu, N_\alpha, \beta, N_{We}, N_{Ve}, N_{Bo}) \tag{10.2-43}$$

where it is understood that N_{Nu} depends on other parameters describing the state of the surface. In the next section we will consider correlations for the nucleate boiling Nusselt number and the critical Nusselt number which is given in terms of the critical heat flux and critical superheat.

$$N_{Nu,c} = q_c \Delta H_{vap}/k_\ell \Delta T_c g(1 - N_\rho) \tag{10.2-44}$$

10.3 Nucleate Boiling and Critical Heat Flux Correlations

There are a number of correlations in the literature for nucleate boiling heat transfer, several of which are discussed by Rohsenow[3] in a review article. One of the more reliable correlations was presented by Rohsenow[4] in 1952, and in the following paragraphs we will present a brief outline of Rohsenow's approach. The development begins by defining a boiling Reynolds number based on the *mass velocity* of bubbles at their departure from the heating surface, G_b, a bubble diameter, D_b, and the viscosity of the liquid, μ_ℓ.

$$N_{Re,b} = \frac{G_b D_b}{\mu_\ell} \tag{10.3-1}$$

The mass velocity was used previously in Sec. 7.8 and we can express it explicitly for this case as

$$G_b = \rho_g Q_g/A \tag{10.3-2}$$

Here Q_g is the volumetric flow rate of vapor leaving the heating surface of area A. The boiling Reynolds number should indeed be a measure of the local agitation of the fluid at the heating surface; however, it does have the drawback that neither G_b nor D_b are known *a priori.*

A force balance on a bubble attached to the surface indicates that the diameter of the bubble as it leaves the surface should be given by

$$D_b = C_d\beta\sqrt{\frac{2\sigma}{g(\rho_\ell - \rho_g)}} \tag{10.3-3}$$

where C_d is a coefficient depending on the shape of the bubble and is typically on the order of 10^{-2}. Eq. 10.3-3 was derived for the static case and growing bubbles tend to have a somewhat larger diameter [5].

The heat flux at the heating surface can be expressed in terms of the heat of vaporization times the mass flux of vapor leaving the surface.

$$q = \Delta H_{\text{vap}} G_b \tag{10.3-4}$$

Substitution of Eqs. 10.3-3 and 10.3-4 into Eq. 10.3-1 provides the following expression for the boiling Reynolds number:

$$N_{\text{Re},b} = \left(\frac{\sqrt{2}C_d\beta q}{\mu_\ell \Delta H_{\text{vap}}}\right)\sqrt{\frac{\sigma}{g(\rho_\ell - \rho_g)}} \tag{10.3-5}$$

Rohsenow goes on to define the boiling Nusselt number as

$$N_{\text{Nu},b} = \frac{hD_b}{k_\ell} \tag{10.3-6}$$

$$= \sqrt{2}C_d\beta\left(\frac{h}{k_\ell}\right)\sqrt{\frac{\sigma}{g(\rho_\ell - \rho_g)}}$$

Since the heat transfer coefficient is defined as

$$h \equiv q/(T_0 - T_{\text{sat}}) \tag{10.3-7}$$

the Nusselt number can be expressed as

$$N_{\text{Nu},b} = \frac{\sqrt{2}C_d\beta q}{k_\ell(T_0 - T_{\text{sat}})}\sqrt{\frac{\sigma}{g(\rho_\ell - \rho_g)}} \tag{10.3-8}$$

The Prandtl number is defined as listed in Table 10.2-1, and Rohsenow suggests a correlation for the Nusselt number in terms of only the boiling Reynolds number and the Prandtl number which takes the form

$$\frac{N_{\text{Re},b}N_{\text{Pr}}}{N_{\text{Nu},b}} = N_{\text{Re},b}^{1/3}N_{\text{Pr}}^{1.7} \tag{10.3-9}$$

In the literature one usually finds this result listed as

$$\frac{(c_p)_\ell(T_0 - T_{\text{sat}})}{\Delta H_{\text{vap}}} = C_{\text{sf}}\left(\frac{q}{\mu_\ell \Delta H_{\text{vap}}}\sqrt{\frac{\sigma}{g(\rho_\ell - \rho_g)}}\right)^{1/3} N_{\text{Pr}}^{1.7} \tag{10.3-10}$$

where the coefficient $C_{\text{sf}} = (\sqrt{2}C_d\beta)^{1/3}$ is to be evaluated experimentally. This result has met with considerable success and is an excellent example of how a judicious choice of variables can lead to a fairly satisfactory correlation of a complex phenomenon. One should note carefully that only three dimensionless groups were used to correlate the data as compared to the formidable array of dimensionless groups listed in Table 10.2-1. Values of C_{sf} for several solid–liquid combinations have been presented by Rohsenow [3] and are listed in Table 10.3-1. The variations in C_{sf} are considerable especially if one notes that q is inversely proportional to the third power of C_{sf}. Clearly the contact angle and the mechanical state of the surface are extremely important factors in the boiling mechanism, and one should always keep the results of Fig. 10.2.3 in mind when considering the reliability of the values of C_{sf} presented in Table 10.3-1.

At this point one might well ask: "What became of all the parameters that came from our dimensional analysis in Sec. 10.3?" Surely a thorough analysis of the governing equations and boundary conditions

Table 10.3-1 Values of C_{sf} in Eq. 10.3-10

Solid–Liquid Combination	C_{sf}
water–nickel	0.006
water–platinum	0.013
water–copper	0.013
water–brass	0.006
CCl_4–copper	0.013
benzene–chromium	0.010
n-pentane–chromium	0.015
ethyl alcohol–chromium	0.0027
isopropyl alcohol–copper	0.0025
35% K_2CO_3–copper	0.0054
50% K_2CO_3–copper	0.0027
n-butyl alcohol–copper	0.0030

should yield an appropriate set of dimensionless groups with which we could correlate the Nusselt number, and indeed this is the case. In terms of the Nusselt number defined by Eq. 10.2-42 and the parameters listed in Table 10.2-1 we can express Eq. 10.3-10 as

$$N_{\mathrm{Nu}} = C N_{\mathrm{Bo}}^{2} N_{\mathrm{Pr}}^{-4.1} N_{\mathrm{We}}^{1/2} N_{\mathrm{Ve}}^{1/2} \tag{10.3-11}$$

where the appropriate values of C are listed in Table 10.3-2. Here we can see the value of having a

Table 10.3-2 Values of C in Eq. 10.3-11

Solid–Liquid Combination	C
water–nickel	4.6×10^6
water–platinum	0.46×10^6
water–copper	0.46×10^6
water–brass	4.6×10^6
CCl_4–copper	0.46×10^6
benzene–chromium	1.0×10^6
n-pentane–chromium	0.30×10^6
ethyl alcohol–chromium	51×10^6
isopropyl alcohol–copper	64×10^6
35% K_2CO_3–copper	6.4×10^6
50% K_2CO_3–copper	51×10^6
n-butyl alcohol–copper	37×10^6

reasonable "picture" of the physical process in mind before trying to correlate the experimental data. In Rohsenow's approach one has only to determine the functional dependence of $(c_p)_\ell (T_0 - T_{\mathrm{sat}})/\Delta H_{\mathrm{vap}}$ on the *two* parameters

$$\frac{q}{\mu_\ell \Delta H_{\mathrm{vap}}} \sqrt{\frac{\sigma}{g(\rho_\ell - \rho_g)}} \quad \text{and} \quad N_{\mathrm{Pr}}$$

while, at best, the straightforward dimensional analysis approach would require that the functional dependence of N_{Nu} on the *four* dimensionless parameters on the right-hand-side of Eq. 10.3-11 be determined experimentally. There are certain limitations to Eq. 10.3-10 or Eq. 10.3-11, and Rohsenow points out that they apply only to clean surfaces and the Prandtl number dependence can change significantly for contaminated surfaces. In addition it is an established fact [6] that $q \sim g^{1/4}$ whereas Eq. 10.3-10 indicates $q \sim g^{1/2}$, thus Rohsenow's correlation should not be used to estimate reduced gravity boiling heat transfer coefficients. It should be clear that Eqs. 10.3-10 and 10.3-11 can only provide an estimate of the heat flux for most real systems, and at least one experiment to determine C_{sf} or C is recommended for a reliable design.

Current research efforts are always improving our knowledge of boiling heat transfer rates and the literature should always be consulted prior to making any design decision. One of the more attractive new theories is that of Mikic and Rohsenow [7] for an attempt is made to take into account the distribution of cavity sizes which exists for any real surface. A recent review article by Westwater [8] considers a number of the more recent attempts to correlate nucleate boiling heat transfer data.

The critical heat flux

In the previous section we discussed the problem of correlating boiling heat transfer data for the case of nucleate pool boiling. In order to design a boiling system one must be able to predict the heat flux q, and in addition one must know the value of the critical heat flux for the particular system under consideration. If electrical heaters are used, exceeding the critical heat flux will usually lead to a "burnout," while if condensing vapor is used to supply the energy the heat flux will be reduced if the superheat exceeds the critical value. In either case we need a correlation for the critical heat flux.

We are already aware that nucleate pool boiling is a complex phenomenon that is difficult to correlate. As the critical heat flux is approached the process becomes even more complex owing to the interaction of the vapor bubbles. There are several correlations discussed by Rohsenow [3], and the most attractive of these is a correlation by Noyes [9]. In terms of the dimensionless groups listed in Table 10.2-1 and the Nusselt number defined by Eq. 10.2-43 this correlation takes the form

$$N_{\mathrm{Nu},c} = 0.14 N_\rho^{1/2} N_{\mathrm{Ve}}^{1/3} / N_{\mathrm{Pr}}^{0.24} N_{\mathrm{Bo}} N_{\mathrm{We}}^{1/4} (1 - N_\rho)^{3/4} \tag{10.3-12}$$

We should note that this, and other correlations indicate that the critical heat flux appears to be independent of the nature of the surface. This is perhaps not unreasonable when we remember that it is the interaction of the rising bubbles which leads to an insulating blanket of vapor as we progress from nucleate boiling to film boiling. Thus at the critical heat flux it is the bubble interaction which controls the heat transfer process.

10.4 Film Boiling

The nucleate boiling region ends when the critical heat flux is reached, and for larger values of the superheat transition boiling occurs. Correlations are not available for this type of boiling, both because of its complexity and because boiling processes usually do not operate in this region. At large enough values of ΔT the heating surface becomes completely covered by a vapor film, and the heat transfer takes place by conduction and radiation across the vapor film. Under these circumstances the complex fluid motion that occurs during nucleate boiling is replaced by a comparatively simple motion which is much more susceptible to theoretical analysis.

The first comprehensive investigation of stable film boiling was done by Bromley [10] in 1950 and discussed in more detail by Jordan [11] in a recent review article. The flow field that exists around a horizontal cylinder is illustrated in Fig. 10.4.1. Bromley developed an approximate analysis for this flow much along the lines of the free-convection analysis presented in Sec. 5.11, and found that in the *absence* of radiation the heat transfer coefficient was given by

$$h_{co} = C \left[\frac{k_g^3 g \Delta H_{\mathrm{vap}} (\rho_\ell - \rho_g)}{\nu_g D (T_0 - T_{\mathrm{sat}})} \right]^{1/4} \tag{10.4-1}$$

A number of simplifying assumptions were made by Bromley; however, there are two which are considerably more important than the rest. The first of these was that the flow field was steady and independent of position along the cylinder. From Fig. 10.1.1e we can see that this assumption cannot hold at the top of the vapor film where the vapor flow is clearly unsteady and has a nonzero component of velocity along the cylinder. Stated another way, we could say that Bromley assumed that the rate of removal of vapor was controlled by the flow in the lower portion of the vapor film. The second key assumption was

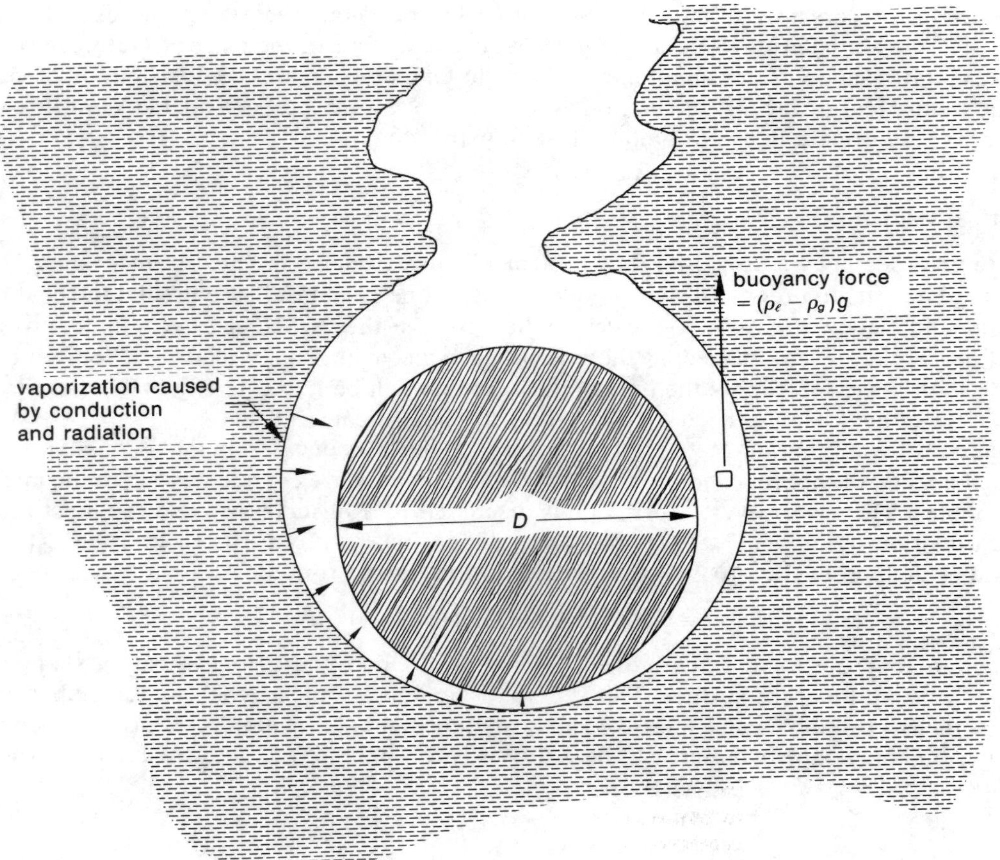

Fig. 10.4.1 Film boiling around a horizontal cylinder.

that the flow in the vapor film could be treated as rectilinear, i.e., neither the curvature of the cylinder nor the varying vapor film thickness was included in the determination of the flow field.

The approximate analysis for the velocity profile indicated that the coefficient C was bracketed by $0.51 \leq C \leq 0.72$ and experimental studies indicated that $C = 0.62$ gave good agreement between theory and experiment provided the diameter of the cylinder was neither too large nor too small. During film boiling, radiation is generally important and the derivation leading to Eq. 10.4-1 must be extended to include radiant energy exchange. The *total* heat transfer coefficient can be expressed as the sum of the conduction and radiation coefficients as

$$h = h_c + h_r \tag{10.4-2}$$

where h_c represents the conduction film heat transfer coefficient in the *presence* of radiant energy exchange. Again drawing upon an approximate analysis Bromley found that h_c, h_{co}, and h could be related to each other by the expression

$$h_c = h_{co}\left(\frac{h_{co}}{h}\right)^{1/3} \tag{10.4-3}$$

Under these circumstances the total heat transfer coefficient is given implicitly as

$$h = h_{co}\left(\frac{h_{co}}{h}\right)^{1/3} + h_r \tag{10.4-4}$$

One can estimate h_r by means of the methods covered in Chapter 9, use Eq. 10.4-1 to determine h_{co}, and then solve Eq. 10.4-4 by trial-and-error to determine the total heat transfer coefficient.

Since the vapor flow field was assumed to be rectilinear one might expect that the analysis would not hold for small cylinders which would give rise to a flow pattern having highly curved streamlines. Experiments confirm this point of view and Jordan indicates that the lower limit for the tube diameter is about 0.04 in. in order that Eq. 10.4-1 holds. In addition to the assumed rectilinear flow field, the theory does not take into account the method of vapor removal at the top of the tube, thus if conditions exist where the vapor film thickness is governed by the rate of removal at the top of the film we would expect the theory to break down. Again this is confirmed by experiments [12] which indicate that the main factor controlling the vapor film thickness for large diameter cylinders is the bubble growth at the top of the film. It is easy to understand that the top of the film should be unstable since gravity tends to "pull" the liquid down toward the cylinder and "push" the vapor upward through the liquid. While gravity is a destabilizing effect, surface tension is stabilizing and tends to inhibit the growth of waves which eventually form into bubbles and break away from the vapor film. Surface tension dominates for the short wavelength waves, and the critical wavelength, λ_c, which separates the smaller stable waves† from the larger unstable waves is given by

$$\lambda_c = 2\pi[\sigma/g(\rho_\ell - \rho_g)]^{1/2} \tag{10.4-5}$$

The work of Breen and Westwater [12] indicates that when the tube diameter is larger than the critical wavelength, i.e., $D > \lambda_c$, Bromley's theory begins to break down and bubble formation at the top of the vapor film plays an increasingly important role in the vapor removal process.

For the full range of tube diameters Jordan suggests the following equations:

$$h_{co} = 0.60 \left[\frac{k_g^3 g \Delta H_{vap}(\rho_\ell - \rho_g)}{\nu_g D(T_0 - T_{sat})}\right]^{1/4} \lambda_c^{-1/4}, \quad \text{for } \lambda_c < 0.8D \tag{10.4-6a}$$

$$h_{co} = 0.62 \left[\frac{k_g^3 g \Delta H_{vap}(\rho_\ell - \rho_g)}{\nu_g D(T_0 - T_{sat})}\right]^{1/4} D^{-1/4}, \quad \text{for } 0.8D \leq \lambda_c \leq 8D \tag{10.4-6b}$$

$$h_{co} = 0.16 \left(\frac{\lambda_c}{D}\right)^{0.83} \left[\frac{k_g^3 g \Delta H_{vap}(\rho_\ell - \rho_g)}{\nu_g D(T_0 - T_{sat})}\right]^{1/4} \lambda_c^{-1/4}, \quad \text{for } 8D < \lambda_c \tag{10.4-6c}$$

Bromley [13] also analyzed film boiling at vertical surfaces, the result being satisfactory provided the surface is sufficiently short. When longer surfaces are used the vapor film becomes unstable and can no longer be described by simple forms of the governing equations of motion. Recent work in this area is described in detail by Jordan.

10.5 Forced-Convection Boiling

Up to this point we have given a very brief discussion of nucleate and stable film boiling under pool boiling conditions. The fluid motion associated with both these conditions is complex, although film boiling is indeed susceptible to theoretical analysis because of the fairly well behaved types of flow that are encountered. Thinking back to Chapter 7 and remembering the variety of forced-convection flows that we studied, it is not hard to imagine that the problem of forced-convection boiling represents both a complex and far-ranging problem. In general it would seem safe to say that any forced convection would lead to a heat transfer rate which would be higher than the corresponding pool boiling rate; however, it is not clear what effect a downward convective flow would have on film boiling on a horizontal cylinder. Quite possibly it would hinder the departure of bubbles from the vapor film and thus reduce the heat transfer rate. Because of the complexity of this problem we will not discuss it here, but refer the interested student to the reviews by Rohsenow [3] and Jordan [11] and the general literature.

†By *stable waves* we mean those waves which tend to decrease in amplitude with time. Unstable waves are those which grow with time and can eventually form bubbles.

PART II CONDENSATION

10.6 Condensation

When a saturated vapor comes in contact with a surface having a temperature lower than the saturation temperature, $T_0 < T_{sat}$, condensation takes place and liquid or *condensate* appears on the cold surface. The role of condensation in refrigeration, distillation, and power generation has been illustrated in Fig. 10.1. If the condensate tends to wet the surface a film forms which is generally removed by gravitational forces. If the condensate does not tend to wet the surface the vapor will condense on the cooled surface as droplets which tend to be held in place by interfacial forces. This type of condensation is referred to as *dropwise* condensation. When a droplet becomes large enough gravity overcomes the interfacial forces and it flows down the surface sweeping off other droplets and leaving an essentially bare surface† in its wake. In Fig. 10.6.1 we have shown the visual difference between dropwise condensation (left side) and filmwise condensation (right side). The system is steam condensing on a vertical copper wall. The left-hand-side of the surface was treated with cupric oleate to promote dropwise condensation.

Since condensation is not accompanied by the violent fluid motion associated with nucleate boiling, the heat fluxes that occur with condensation are considerably lower than those for boiling. However, the

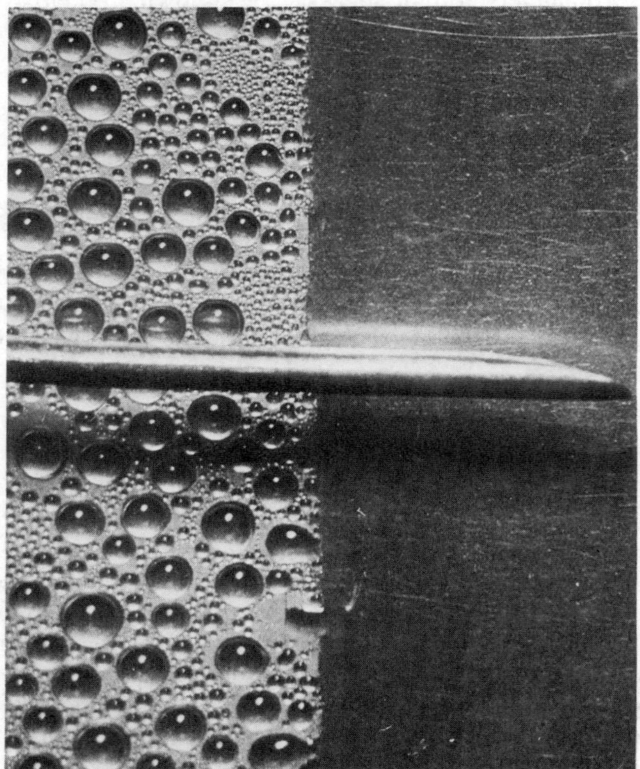

Fig. 10.6.1 Visual difference between film and dropwise condensation. (Photograph by J. F. Welch, from "Dropwise Condensation" by J. W. Westwater, in *Advanced Heat Transfer*, edited by B. T. Chao, University of Illinois Press, Urbana, Illinois, 1969.)

†The work of Umur and Griffith (*Tech. Rept. No. 9041-25*, Dept. of Mech. Engr., M.I.T., May 1963) indicates that between the drops no liquid film that has a thickness greater than one molecular layer can form or exist. This is also true of the region swept by a droplet flowing down the surface.

sweeping action that occurs with dropwise condensation does provide excellent contact between the vapor and the cool surface, and heat fluxes on the order of 10^5 Btu/hr ft^2 can be easily obtained with dropwise condensation. During film condensation the cool surface is effectively insulated by the condensate film and the heat flux is generally an order-of-magnitude less than that for dropwise condensation.

Because of the higher heat fluxes obtained with dropwise condensation there is a definite incentive to cause this type of condensation to occur in commercial operations and it has been found that fatty acids and waxes applied to surfaces can promote dropwise condensation. Unfortunately the condensate itself carries away the contaminant and effectively cleans the surface, thus giving rise to film condensation. Because of this, one is generally forced to design condensers for film condensation and thus forgo the obvious economic advantage of the higher heat fluxes obtained with dropwise condensation. Westwater[14] has recently surveyed the general problem of dropwise condensation in considerable detail.

10.7 Film Condensation

Film condensation on a flat surface is susceptible to theoretical analysis provided the flow is taken to be laminar. Under most practical circumstances the flow is either wavy or turbulent depending on the Reynolds number. Nevertheless, the laminar flow solution provides an excellent approximation to the wavy flow case and a lower bound on the heat flux for the turbulent flow case. In Fig. 10.7.1 we have shown a vertical surface upon which film condensation is taking place. The temperature at the vapor–liquid interface is assumed to be at the saturation temperature T_{sat} and the cooling surface is assumed to be at a constant temperature T_0. At the top of the surface the film is thin and the heat flux will be high, while

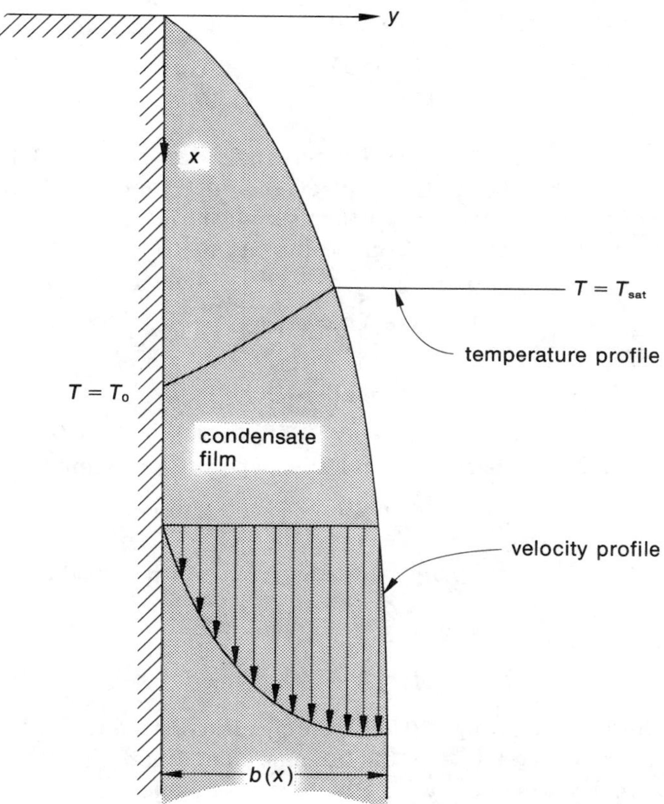

Fig. 10.7.1 Film condensation on a vertical surface.

further down the surface the heat flux steadily decreases as the condensate film becomes thicker. The governing differential equations for steady, two-dimensional laminar flow can be expressed as

$$\rho\left(v_x\frac{\partial v_x}{\partial x}+v_y\frac{\partial v_x}{\partial y}\right)=-\frac{\partial p}{\partial x}+\rho g_x+\mu\left(\frac{\partial^2 v_x}{\partial x^2}+\frac{\partial^2 v_x}{\partial y^2}\right) \tag{10.7-1}$$

$$\rho\left(v_x\frac{\partial v_y}{\partial x}+v_y\frac{\partial v_y}{\partial y}\right)=-\frac{\partial p}{\partial y}+\rho g_y+\mu\left(\frac{\partial^2 v_y}{\partial x^2}+\frac{\partial^2 v_y}{\partial y^2}\right) \tag{10.7-2}$$

$$\frac{\partial v_x}{\partial x}+\frac{\partial v_y}{\partial y}=0 \tag{10.7-3}$$

$$v_x\frac{\partial T}{\partial x}+v_y\frac{\partial T}{\partial y}=\alpha\left(\frac{\partial^2 T}{\partial x^2}+\frac{\partial^2 T}{\partial y^2}\right) \tag{10.7-4}$$

Following the boundary layer analyses presented in Chapter 5 we assume that the film thickness varies only slowly in the x-direction,† $db/dx \ll 1$, thus leading to

$$v_y \ll v_x, \quad \frac{\partial^2 v_x}{\partial x^2}\ll\frac{\partial^2 v_x}{\partial y^2}, \quad \frac{\partial^2 T}{\partial x^2}\ll\frac{\partial^2 T}{\partial y^2}$$

Under these circumstances we obtain the standard boundary layer equations for a zero pressure gradient along the film:

$$\rho\left(v_x\frac{\partial v_x}{\partial x}+v_y\frac{\partial v_x}{\partial y}\right)=\rho g\sin\theta+\mu\left(\frac{\partial^2 v_x}{\partial y^2}\right) \tag{10.7-5}$$

$$\frac{\partial v_x}{\partial x}+\frac{\partial v_y}{\partial y}=0 \tag{10.7-6}$$

$$v_x\frac{\partial T}{\partial x}+v_y\frac{\partial T}{\partial y}=\alpha\left(\frac{\partial^2 T}{\partial y^2}\right) \tag{10.7-7}$$

Here we have replaced ρg_x with $\rho g \sin\theta$ where θ is the angle between the plate and the gravity vector. These equations can be solved by the methods discussed in Chapter 5; however, for the thin films encountered in many condensation processes further simplications can be made since the convective terms in both Eqs. 10.7-5 and 10.7-7 can be dropped leading us to

$$0=\rho g\sin\theta+\mu\left(\frac{\partial^2 v_x}{\partial y^2}\right) \tag{10.7-8}$$

$$0=\alpha\left(\frac{\partial^2 T}{\partial y^2}\right) \tag{10.7-9}$$

The boundary conditions which are appropriate for this type of approximation are as follows:

B.C.1 $\quad v_x = 0, \quad y = 0,$ "no slip" at the wall (10.7-10)

B.C.2 $\quad \dfrac{\partial v_x}{\partial y} = 0, \quad y = b(x),$ zero shear stress at the vapor–liquid interface (10.7-11)

B.C.3 $\quad T = T_0, \quad y = 0$ (10.7-12)

B.C.4 $\quad T = T_{sat}, \quad y = b(x)$ (10.7-13)

The analysis as stated by Eqs. 10.7-8 through 10.7-13 represents a quasi one-dimensional analysis, since the governing equations are one-dimensional while the boundary conditions imposed at $y = b(x)$ require that we determine the variation in film thickness with x by means of some constraint other than the governing

†Clearly this is not true in the region near $x = 0$.

differential equations and boundary conditions. Solving Eqs. 10.7-8 and 10.7-9 and imposing the boundary conditions leads to

$$v_x = \frac{g \sin\theta}{\nu}\left(by - \frac{y^2}{2}\right) \tag{10.7-14}$$

$$T = T_0 + \frac{y}{b}(T_{\text{sat}} - T_0) \tag{10.7-15}$$

Here we have solved for the velocity and temperature fields, and now must contend with the unknown film thickness, $b(x)$. We can determine $b(x)$ by applying the macroscopic mass balance to the control volume shown in Fig. 10.7.2, and then making use of the energy boundary condition given by Eq. 10.2-21.

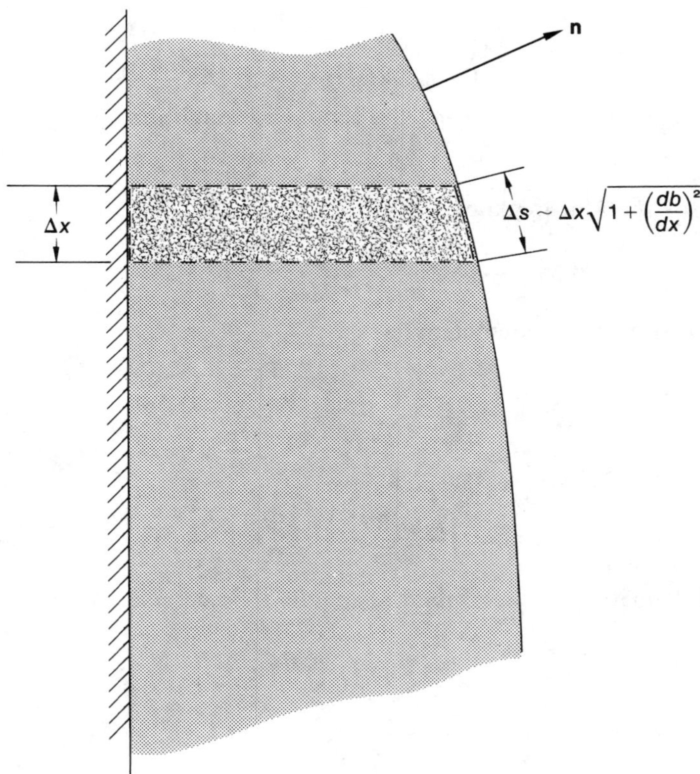

Fig. 10.7.2 Control volume for macroscopic mass balance.

Imposing the steady-state condition on Eq. 10.2-5 we obtain

$$\int_0^{b(x)} \rho_\ell \mathbf{v}_\ell \cdot (-\mathbf{i})\, dy \bigg|_x + \int_0^{b(x)} \rho_\ell \mathbf{v}_\ell \cdot (+\mathbf{i})\, dy \bigg|_{x+\Delta x} + \rho_\ell \mathbf{v}_\ell \cdot \mathbf{n}\Delta s = 0 \tag{10.7-16}$$

We can now make use of Eq. 10.2-21, noting that at the interface $\mathbf{n}_\ell = -\mathbf{n}$, to obtain

$$\int_0^{b(x)} \rho_\ell v_x\, dy \bigg|_{x+\Delta x} - \int_0^{b(x)} \rho_\ell v_x\, dy \bigg|_x - \left[\frac{k_\ell(\nabla T_\ell)\cdot \mathbf{n}}{\Delta H_{\text{vap}}}\right]\Delta s = 0 \tag{10.7-17}$$

We can now divide by Δx and make the approximations

$$\frac{\Delta s}{\Delta x} \sim 1, \qquad (\nabla T_\ell)\cdot \mathbf{n} \sim \left(\frac{\partial T_\ell}{\partial y}\right)$$

to obtain

$$\frac{\left.\int_0^{b(x)} \rho_\ell v_x \, dy\right|_{x+\Delta x} - \left.\int_0^{b(x)} \rho_\ell v_x \, dy\right|_x}{\Delta x} = \frac{k_\ell \left(\frac{\partial T}{\partial y}\right)_{y=b(x)}}{\Delta H_{\text{vap}}} \tag{10.7-18}$$

Taking the limit as $\Delta x \to 0$ yields

$$\frac{d}{dx} \int_0^{b(x)} \rho_\ell v_x \, dy = \frac{k_\ell \left(\frac{\partial T}{\partial y}\right)_{y=b(x)}}{\Delta H_{\text{vap}}} \tag{10.7-19}$$

Substituting Eqs. 10.7-14 and 10.7-15 for v_x and T and carrying out the integration and differentiation gives us a differential equation for $b(x)$.

$$b^3 \left(\frac{db}{dx}\right) = \left[\frac{k_\ell (T_{\text{sat}} - T_0)}{\rho_\ell \Delta H_{\text{vap}}}\right] \left(\frac{\nu_\ell}{g \sin \theta}\right) \tag{10.7-20}$$

Separating variables, integrating, and imposing the boundary condition

B.C.5 $\qquad b(x) = 0, \qquad x = 0$ (10.7-21)

leads to an expression for the film thickness,

$$b(x) = \left[\frac{4\nu_\ell k_\ell (T_{\text{sat}} - T_0)x}{\rho_\ell \Delta H_{\text{vap}} g \sin \theta}\right]^{1/4} \tag{10.7-22}$$

Defining the local film heat transfer coefficient as

$$h_x = \frac{q}{T_{\text{sat}} - T_0} = \frac{k_\ell \left(\frac{\partial T}{\partial y}\right)_{y=b(x)}}{T_{\text{sat}} - T_0} \tag{10.7-23}$$

leads to

$$h_x = \left[\frac{k_\ell^3 \rho_\ell \Delta H_{\text{vap}} g \sin \theta}{4\nu_\ell (T_{\text{sat}} - T_0)x}\right]^{1/4} \tag{10.7-24}$$

The average heat transfer coefficient for a plate of length L is defined by

$$h_{\text{av}} = \frac{1}{L} \int_0^L h_x \, dx \tag{10.7-25}$$

and leads to

$$h_{\text{av}} = \left(\frac{2}{3}\right) \sqrt{2} \left[\frac{k_\ell^3 \rho_\ell^2 \Delta H_{\text{vap}} g \sin \theta}{\mu_\ell (T_{\text{sat}} - T_0)L}\right]^{1/4} \tag{10.7-26}$$

In addition to calculating the heat transfer coefficient it will be helpful to derive an expression for the Reynolds number defined as

$$N_{\text{Re}} = \frac{\rho_\ell \langle v_x \rangle D_h}{\mu_\ell} \tag{10.7-27}$$

Here D_h is the hydraulic *diameter* given by

$$D_h = 4 \left(\frac{\text{cross-sectional area of flow}}{\text{wetted perimeter}}\right) \tag{10.7-28}$$

and Eq. 10.7-27 represents the standard definition of the Reynolds number for flow in non-circular conduits and open channel or free surface flows. Taking the plate to be infinitely wide in the z-direction leads to

$$D_h = 4b(x) \tag{10.7-29}$$

and one can show that the Reynolds number takes the form

$$N_{\mathrm{Re}} = \left(\frac{4}{3}\right)\left(\frac{g\sin\theta}{\nu_\ell^2}\right)\left[\frac{4\nu_\ell k_\ell(T_{\mathrm{sat}} - T_0)L}{\rho_\ell \Delta H_{\mathrm{vap}} g\sin\theta}\right]^{3/4}, \quad \text{at } x = L \tag{10.7-30}$$

In terms of the Reynolds number we can express the average heat transfer coefficient as

$$h_{\mathrm{av}} = k_\ell\left(\frac{4}{3}\right)^{4/3}\left(\frac{g\sin\theta}{\nu^2}\right)^{1/3} N_{\mathrm{Re}}^{-1/3} \tag{10.7-31}$$

$$= 1.47 k_\ell\left(\frac{g\sin\theta}{\nu^2}\right)^{1/3} N_{\mathrm{Re}}^{-1/3}$$

where it is understood that the Reynolds number is evaluated at $x = L$. We should note at this point that the heat transfer coefficient *decreases* with *increasing* Reynolds number; a situation contrary to the usual Reynolds number dependences. The reason is that the condensate film acts as an "insulating" layer and as it becomes thicker the heat transfer rate is reduced. Eq. 10.7-31 was derived for a steady, laminar flow whereas in fact most films flow with a rippling motion. The presence of waves tends to increase the surface area and gives rise to a velocity component normal to the direction of flow. Both these phenomena tend to increase the heat transfer rate by about 20 per cent. The recommended correlation for vertical surfaces when the Reynolds number is less than 1800 is

$$h_{\mathrm{av}} = 1.76 k_\ell\left(\frac{g}{\nu^2}\right)^{1/3} N_{\mathrm{Re}}^{-1/3}, \quad \text{recommended correlation for vertical surfaces when } N_{\mathrm{Re}} \leqslant 1800 \tag{10.7-32}$$

The wave motion for condensate films is strongly dependent on the angle of inclination, θ, and there is not sufficient experimental data for values of $\theta < \pi/2$ so that we can recommend a correlation for inclined surfaces. However, we do know that the wave motion diminishes as θ becomes smaller, thus Eq. 10.7-31 will be in better agreement with experiment the smaller the value of θ.

When the Reynolds number is increased beyond 1800 the wave motion of the film degenerates into a turbulent motion. Under these circumstances the heat transfer data for vertical films are adequately correlated by

$$h_{\mathrm{av}} = 0.0076 k_\ell\left(\frac{g}{\nu^2}\right)^{1/3} N_{\mathrm{Re}}^{0.4}, \quad \text{recommended correlation for vertical surfaces when } N_{\mathrm{Re}} \geqslant 1800 \tag{10.7-33}$$

Here we see that for turbulent flow the heat transfer coefficient *increases* with *increasing* Reynolds number. Both Eqs. 10.7-32 and 10.7-33 are also valid for the inside and outside of vertical tubes provided the tube diameter is large compared to the film thickness. We should be careful to note that N_{Re} must be determined by trial-and-error for turbulent flow since Eq. 10.7-30 is no longer valid.

Horizontal cylinders

Condensers always require some coolant to maintain a solid surface at a temperature below the saturation temperature, T_{sat}. In general the easiest way to construct a condenser is with a bundle of tubes through which the coolant is passed. If these tubes are placed in a vertical position the results given for film condensation on a vertical plate can be used provided $b(x) \ll D$; however, long vertical tubes can lead to low values of h_{av} if the flow is laminar. For this reason horizontal tubes are often used, for they give rise to relatively thin films and therefore high heat transfer rates. Laminar condensate flow around a horizontal cylinder is illustrated in Fig. 10.7.3 and it will be left as an exercise for the student to show that the average heat transfer coefficient is given by

$$h_{\mathrm{av}} = 0.72\left[\frac{k_\ell^3 \rho_\ell^2 g \Delta H_{\mathrm{vap}}}{D\mu_\ell(T_{\mathrm{sat}} - T_0)}\right]^{1/4} \tag{10.7-34}$$

provided $\rho_g \ll \rho_\ell$. In the construction of horizontal tube condensers we often encounter several tubes located in vertical tiers so that the condensate from one tube drains onto the tube below it, and so on until the condensate is finally collected in the bottom of the condenser. If one continues to apply all the stringent

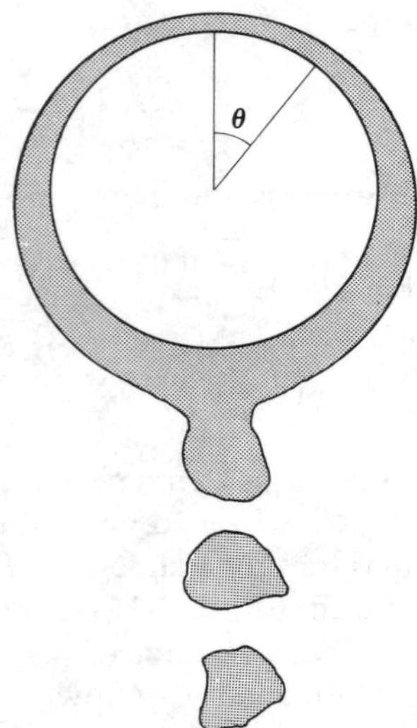

Fig. 10.7.3 Film condensation on a horizontal cylinder.

restrictions that went into the derivation of Eq. 10.7-34 it can be shown that the average heat transfer coefficient for each tube in a vertical tier of n tubes is

$$h_{av} = 0.72 \left[\frac{k_\ell^3 \rho_\ell^2 g \Delta H_{vap}}{nD\mu_\ell(T_{sat} - T_0)}\right]^{1/4} \tag{10.7-35}$$

One must keep in mind that like Eq. 10.7-31 this result and Eq. 10.7-34 give values of h_{av} that are low by 10 to 20 per cent.

Effect of vapor velocity

Up to this point we have considered condensate films which were acted upon only by gravity. If the magnitude of the vapor velocity is sufficient to exert a significant shear stress on the vapor–liquid interface the developments presented thus far must be altered to include this effect. If the shear stress is in the direction of the flow it will tend to *decrease* the film thickness and therefore *increase* the heat transfer coefficient. If the shear stress opposes the flow it will tend to *increase* the film thickness and therefore *decrease* the heat transfer rate *under most circumstances.* If the opposing shear stress is sufficiently large it will cause a normally laminar film to become unstable giving rise to a turbulent flow and under these circumstances an opposing shear stress could lead to increased heat transfer rates.

Effect of noncondensable gases

Throughout this chapter we have considered single-component, two-phase systems, and thus avoided the complication of boiling and condensation in multicomponent systems; however, we must not avoid discussing the problem that can arise in the operation of a condenser if appreciable amounts of noncondensable gases are present. Although a comprehensive study of condensation in the presence of noncondensable gases must be done in a text on mass transfer we can give a qualitative account of the process that occurs. As vapor moves toward a cool surface it will tend to "drag" or convect with it any noncondensable gases contained within the vapor. Since these gases do not condense at the vapor–liquid interface their concentration tends to build up at the interface until a balance is reached between the rate at which noncondensables are *convected* to the interface and the rate at which they *diffuse* away from the interface. This situation is illustrated in Fig. 10.7.4. The presence of noncondensables at the interface hinders the flow of the vapor to the interface and thus lowers the heat transfer rate. The extent of this phenomenon depends on the concentration of the noncondensables in the vapor, and for this reason

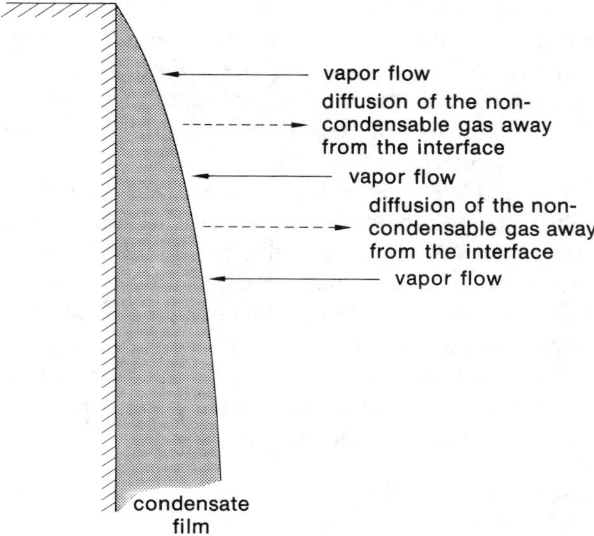

Fig. 10.7.4 Effect of noncondensable gases.

condensers should always be provided with a vent to bleed off the noncondensable gases. This arrangement is illustrated in Fig. 10.7.5 and from that sketch it should be clear that noncondensables can enter a condenser with the vapor and can be trapped in the condenser. If this occurs the concentration can build up and drastically alter the operating characteristics of the condenser [15].

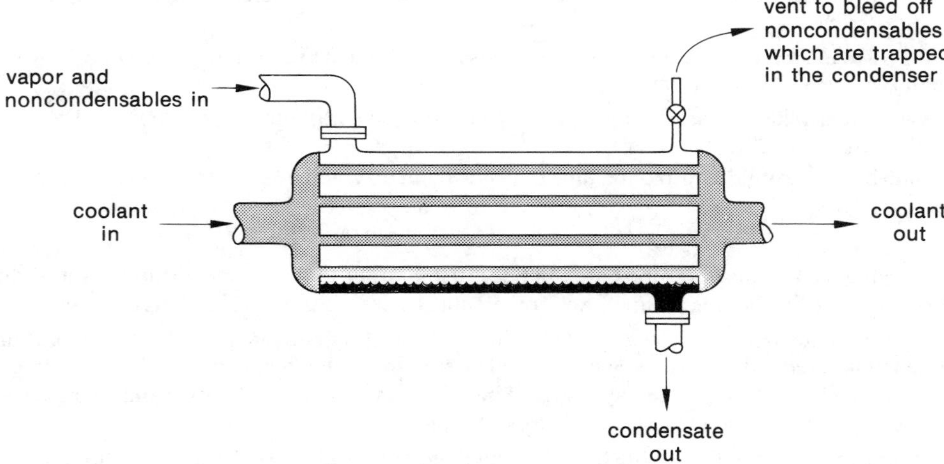

Fig. 10.7.5 Venting of noncondensable gases.

10.8 Dropwise Condensation

Condensation of a vapor on a solid surface is described by Westwater [14] as a nucleation phenomenon. The nucleation sites are apparently quite different from the nucleation sites for boiling for the concentration of these sites is on the order of a few million per square inch. If all the sites are active millions of small drops are formed on a surface and they soon coalesce to form a continuous film. Under these circumstances the condensate covers the solid surface and the condensation is no longer a nucleation phenomenon. The role of the fatty acids and waxes that are used to coat the surface and promote dropwise condensation is apparently to reduce the number of nucleation sites sufficiently to prevent the formation of a continuous film. As one might expect the heat transfer coefficients for dropwise condensation depend on the promoter used and the mechanical and thermodynamic state of the surface. For example, Tanner *et al.*[16] found that the heat flux for dropwise condensation promoted by mantanic acid was about five times larger for copper than it was for stainless steel.

From the work of McCormick and Westwater[17] it is clear that the rate of heat transfer for dropwise condensation is closely related to the concentration of active sites on the condensing surface; however, knowledge of the number of sites on a surface is not sufficient to allow a theoretical prediction of the heat flux since adsorption of vapor molecules on the solid surface followed by surface diffusion and capture by the drops is also an important mechanism. In addition one must be able to predict the size of a droplet that will break loose and flow down the surface in order to construct a satisfactory theory, for the process of "sweeping" the surface by the larger droplets must certainly play a key role in the heat transfer mechanism. At present these problems remain unsolved, and in general, designs of condensers are based on the heat transfer rates that occur with film condensation.

PROBLEMS

10-1. (10.1) Use Eq. 10-5 to calculate the degrees of superheat required in order that a vapor bubble of radius 10^{-2} cm grow. Consider the ambient pressure to be one atmosphere and take $\sigma = 60$ dyne/cm and $\Delta H_{\text{vap}} = 970$ Btu/lb$_m$.

10-2. (10.1) Show how Eq. 10-6 can be obtained from Eq. 10-5.

10-3. (10.2) Determine the order-of-magnitude of the velocity $\sqrt{\Delta H_{\text{vap}}}$ to see if it is large compared to the velocities one might expect to find in boiling systems.

10-4. (10.2) Indicate how viscous effects in the vapor and liquid phases can be included in Eq. 10.2-12.

10-5. (10.3) Use Eq. 10.3-10 to estimate the heat flux for the process illustrated in Fig. 10.1.1c and compare the result with the experimental value of 76800 Btu/hr ft^2.

10-6. (10.3) Estimate the critical heat flux for water pool boiling on a flat plate at 1 and 10 atmospheres. Use Eq. 10.3-12 and eliminate the unknown ΔT_c.

10-7. (10.4) (10.2) For stable film boiling around a horizontal tube the tube diameter could be used as a characteristic length. Let

$$L^* = D \qquad \text{and} \qquad u^* = \alpha_\ell g / \Delta H_{\text{vap}}$$

and redo the dimensional analysis presented in Sec. 10.2 in order to determine a suitable set of dimensionless parameters for stable film boiling around a horizontal tube. Express Eq. 10.4-1 in terms of these parameters.

10-8. (10.4) Derive an approximate expression for the film boiling heat transfer coefficient, h_{co}, for the stable film boiling at a vertical plate illustrated in Fig. 10.8. Neglect inertial effects and estimate the viscous forces acting on the vapor by assuming zero shear stress at the vapor–liquid interface and a linear velocity profile across the vapor film. Take the pressure in the liquid to be the hydrostatic pressure.

10-9. (10.7) Develop an approximate solution to the boundary layer equations given by Eqs. 10.7-5 through 10.7-7. Use the approximate or integral method discussed in Secs. 4.3 and 5.9.

10-10. (10.7) In the analysis of film condensation the pressure gradient in the vapor phase was set equal to zero. Repeat the analysis taking the pressure in the vapor phase to be hydrostatic, i.e.,

$$\frac{\partial p_g}{\partial x} = \rho_g g \sin \theta$$

10-11. (10.7) In Fig. 10.11 we have shown a tube bundle being used as a horizontal tube condenser. The total heat transfer rate is designated as Q_H. The outer diameter of the tubes is 1 in. and they are 4 ft long. If the condenser is set at a vertical position under the same operating conditions the total heat transfer rate is Q_V. Determine the ratio of Q_V to Q_H assuming that the flow is always laminar.

10-12. (10.7) Derive Eq. 10.7-34 following the method used to analyze film condensation on a flat plate.

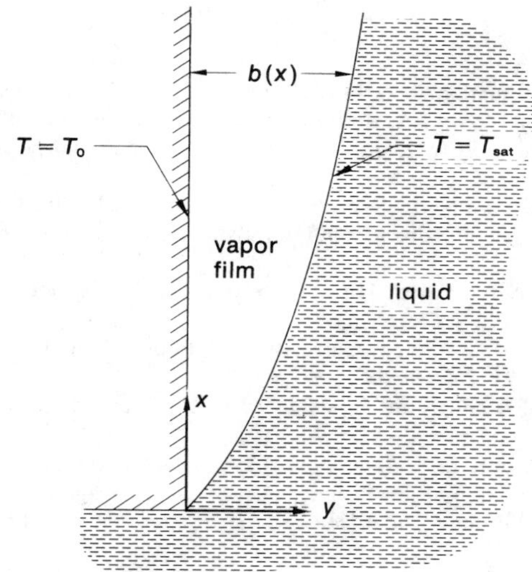

Fig. 10.8 Stable film boiling on a vertical plate.

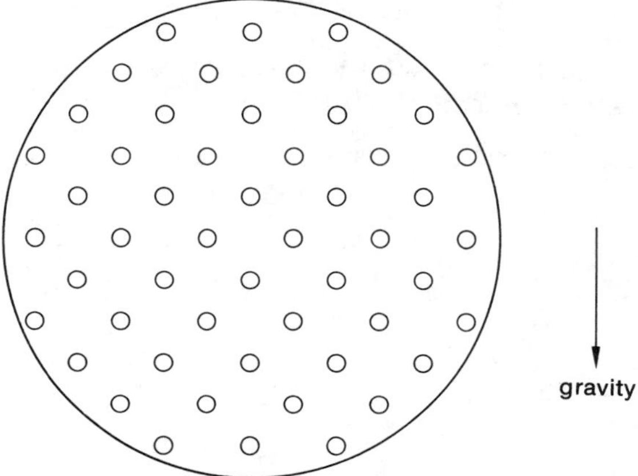

Fig. 10.11 Horizontal tube condenser.

10-13. (10.7) Derive Eq. 10.7-35 starting with Eq. 10.7-34. State your assumptions clearly.

10-14. (10.7) If the vapor velocity during condensation on a vertical plate is sufficiently large, the viscous shear exerted by the vapor on the liquid can change the film thickness and alter the heat transfer rate. Investigate this phenomenon by replacing Eq. 10.7-11 with the boundary condition

B.C.2 $$\mu_\ell \frac{\partial v_x}{\partial y} = \tau_0, \qquad y = b(x)$$

and derive a new expression for h_{av}. If the condensate film is formed on the inside of a vertical tube, what would the vapor phase Reynolds number have to be in order that this effect be significant. Take the vapor viscosity to be 2.2×10^{-7} lb$_f$sec/ft^2, the density to be 5×10^{-4} g/cm^3, and assume that the flow is laminar.

10-15. (10.7) A vertical plate 2 ft high is maintained at 180°F and is in contact with steam at 30 psia. Estimate the average heat transfer coefficient. Is the flow laminar or turbulent? What is the film thickness at the bottom of the plate?

10-16. (10.7) Derive Eq. 10.7-30.

10-17. (10.7) Derive an expression for the Reynolds number, N_{Re}, for laminar condensation on a horizontal cylinder.

REFERENCES

1. Slattery, J. C., "General Balance Equation for a Phase Interface," *I&EC Fund. Quart.* **6**, 108 (1967).
2. Whitaker, S., *Introduction to Fluid Mechanics*, Prentice-Hall, Inc., Englewood Cliffs, N.J., 1968.
3. Rohsenow, W. M., "Heat Transfer with Boiling," in *Developments in Heat Transfer*, edited by W. M. Rohsenow, The M.I.T. Press, Cambridge, Mass., 1964.
4. Rohsenow, W. M., "A Method of Correlating Heat Transfer Data for Surface Boiling Liquids," *Trans. ASME* **48**, 969 (1952).
5. Leppert, G., and Pitts, C. C., "Boiling," in *Advances in Heat Transfer*, Vol. 1, edited by T. F. Irvine and J. P. Hartnett, Academic Press, New York, 1964.
6. Siegel, R., "Effects of Reduced Gravity on Heat Transfer," in *Advances in Heat Transfer*, Vol. 4, edited by J. P. Hartnett and T. F. Irvine, Academic Press, New York, 1967.
7. Mikic, B. B., and Rohsenow, W. M., "A New Correlation of Pool-Boiling Data Including the Effect of Heating Surface Characteristics," *J. Heat Transfer* **91**, 245 (1969).
8. Westwater, J. W., "Nucleate Pool Boiling," in *Advanced Heat Transfer*, edited by B. T. Chao, University of Illinois Press, Urbana, Illinois, 1969.
9. Noyes, R. C., "An Experimental Study of Sodium Pool Boiling Heat Transfer," *Trans. ASME* **85C**, 125 (1963).
10. Bromley, L. A., "Heat Transfer in Stable Film Boiling," *Chem. Engr. Prog.* **46**, 221 (1950).
11. Jordan, D. P., "Film and Transition Boiling," in *Advances in Heat Transfer*, edited by T. F. Irvine and J. P. Hartnett, Academic Press, New York, 1968.
12. Breen, B. P., and Westwater, J. W., "Effect of Diameter of Horizontal Tubes on Film Boiling Heat Transfer," *Chem. Engr. Prog.* **58**, 67 (1962).
13. Bromley, L. A., "Heat Transfer in Stable Film Boiling," PhD Thesis, Dept. of Chem., University of California, Berkeley, California, 1948.
14. Westwater, J. W., "Dropwise Condensation," in *Advanced Heat Transfer*, edited by B. T. Chao, University of Illinois Press, Urbana, Illinois, 1969.
15. Khan, R. A., "Effect of Noncondensables in Sea Water Evaporators," *Chem. Engr. Prog.* **68**, No. 7, 79 (1972).
16. Tanner, D. W., Pope, D., Potter, C. J., and West, D., "Heat Transfer in Dropwise Condensation, Part II," *Int. J. Heat Mass Transfer* **8**, 427 (1965).
17. McCormick, J. L., and Westwater, J. W., "Nucleation Sites for Dropwise Condensation," *Chem. Engr. Sci.* **20**, 1021 (1965).

11

Design of Heat Exchangers

In the previous ten chapters we encountered various aspects of heat transfer design. In Design Problem I we considered the use of insulation to reduce heat losses, and in Probs. II and IV we explored the problem of insulating a heated vessel so that the outer surface would be safe to touch. Problem III dealt with the use of hot water to heat apartments, while in Prob. V we were again concerned with reducing heat losses from homes and office buildings. Problem VI dealt with the design of a thermal mixing system which was used to dispose of excess heat, and Prob. VII was our first introduction to the design of a heat exchanger. Clearly there is a wide range of heat transfer design problems that an engineer might encounter, but one of the most important processes to be considered is simply the exchange of heat between two process streams. A great deal of research, some of which we encountered in Secs. 7.6–7.9, has been devoted to this subject, and books [1, 2] are available which treat only the subject of heat exchanger design. In our treatment we will cover the main points concerning the thermal design of heat exchangers while leaving the equally important mechanical design for further study by the interested student. Although the double-pipe heat exchanger has been discussed in Prob. VII, we will begin our analysis of heat exchangers with a thorough treatment of the double-pipe heat exchanger.

11.1 The Double-Pipe Heat Exchanger

One of the simplest means of transferring heat between two process streams is the double-pipe heat exchanger shown in Fig. 11.1.1. The configuration shown is for *co-current flow*; however, *counter-current* flows are usually used since they require less heat transfer surface to accomplish the same total heat transfer rate. Throughout this chapter we will use the subscripts i and o to designate the *inlet* and *outlet* temperature respectively. In addition we will designate one end of the exchanger by "1" and the other end by "2". This allows us to express the inlet temperatures as T_1^{I} and T_1^{II} rather than T_i^{I} and T_i^{II}, and the outlet temperatures as T_2^{I} and T_2^{II} instead of T_o^{I} and T_o^{II}. In subsequent sections we will see that this dual nomenclature is a help rather than a hindrance.

For a steady process and a fixed control volume the macroscopic thermal energy balance can be written as†

$$\int_{A_e} \rho c_p (\bar{T} - T_0)\bar{\mathbf{v}} \cdot \mathbf{n}\, dA = -\int_{\mathscr{A}} \bar{\mathbf{q}}^{(T)} \cdot \mathbf{n}\, dA \tag{11.1-1}$$

†Viscous dissipation and reversible work have been neglected and T_0 is a reference temperature not an outlet temperature.

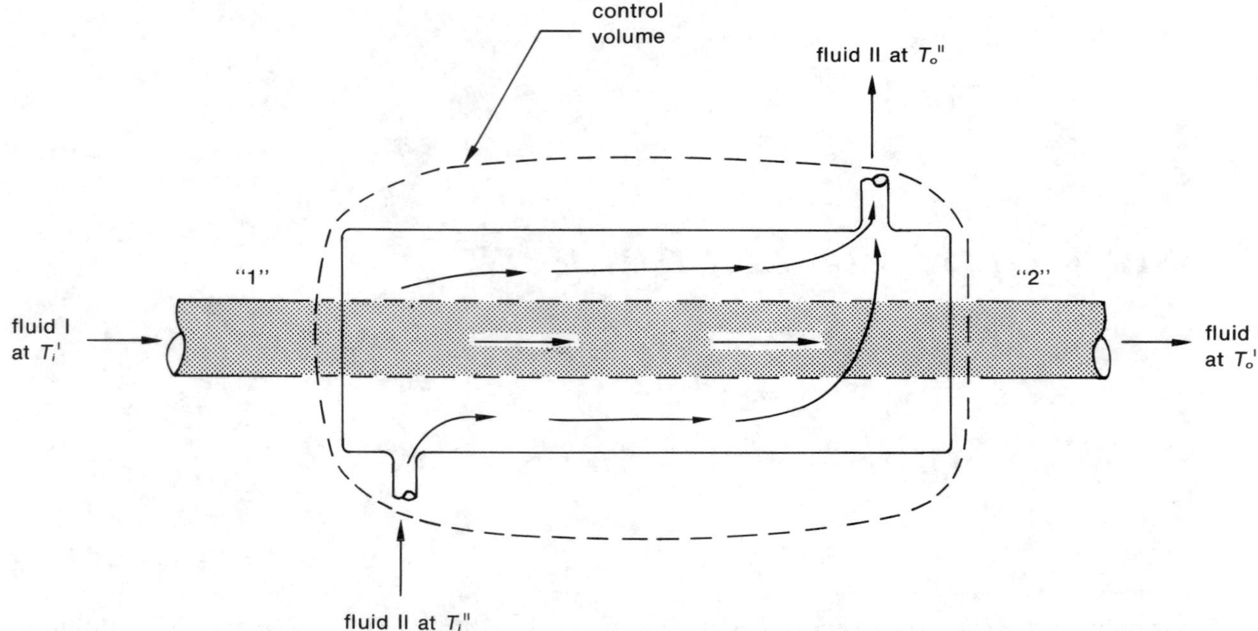

Fig. 11.1.1 Double-pipe heat exchanger.

If we take the heat capacity for both fluids to be constant, and neglect axial conduction or turbulent transport relative to convective transport, Eq. 11.1-1 can be applied to the control volume shown in Fig. 11.1.1 to yield

$$\dot{m}_I c_p^I(T_2^I - T_1^I) = -\dot{m}_{II} c_p^{II}(T_2^{II} - T_1^{II}), \quad \text{for co-current flow} \tag{11.1-2a}$$

$$\dot{m}_I c_p^I(T_2^I - T_1^I) = +\dot{m}_{II} c_p^{II}(T_2^{II} - T_1^{II}), \quad \text{for counter-current flow} \tag{11.1-2b}$$

If we had used the i and o subscripts for the temperatures, Eqs. 11.1-2 could be replaced by the single expression,

$$\dot{m}_I c_p^I(T_o^I - T_i^I) = \dot{m}_{II} c_p^{II}(T_i^{II} - T_o^{II}), \quad \text{for co-current and counter-current flows}$$

however, we will continue to work with the nomenclature used in Eqs. 11.1-2 and remember that the $(+)$ refers to counter-current flow while the $(-)$ indicates co-current flow. In Eqs. 11.1-2 all temperatures are *bulk* or *cup-mixing* temperatures defined by

$$T_b \equiv \frac{\int_{A_e} T\mathbf{v}\cdot\mathbf{n}\,dA}{\int_{A_e} \mathbf{v}\cdot\mathbf{n}\,dA} \tag{11.1-3}$$

and $\dot{m}$ represents the mass flow rate given by

$$\dot{m} = \int_{A_e} \rho\mathbf{v}\cdot\mathbf{n}\,dA \tag{11.1-4}$$

Strictly speaking, we require that the density be constant across the entrances and exits and the heat capacity be a constant in order to use Eq. 11.1-3 along with Eq. 11.1-1 to obtain Eqs. 11.1-2.

The actual temperature variations within the exchanger depends on whether the flow is co-current or counter-current, and on the ratio $\dot{m}_I c_p^I/\dot{m}_2 c_p^{II}$. In Fig. 11.1.2 we have sketched T^I and T^{II}, assuming that I is the "cold" fluid and II is the "hot" fluid, for $\dot{m}_I c_p^I > \dot{m}_{II} c_p^{II}$ and for $\dot{m}_I c_p^I < \dot{m}_{II} c_p^{II}$. For co-current flow the driving force for heat transfer $(T^{II} - T^I)$ is a maximum at the entrance of the exchanger and steadily

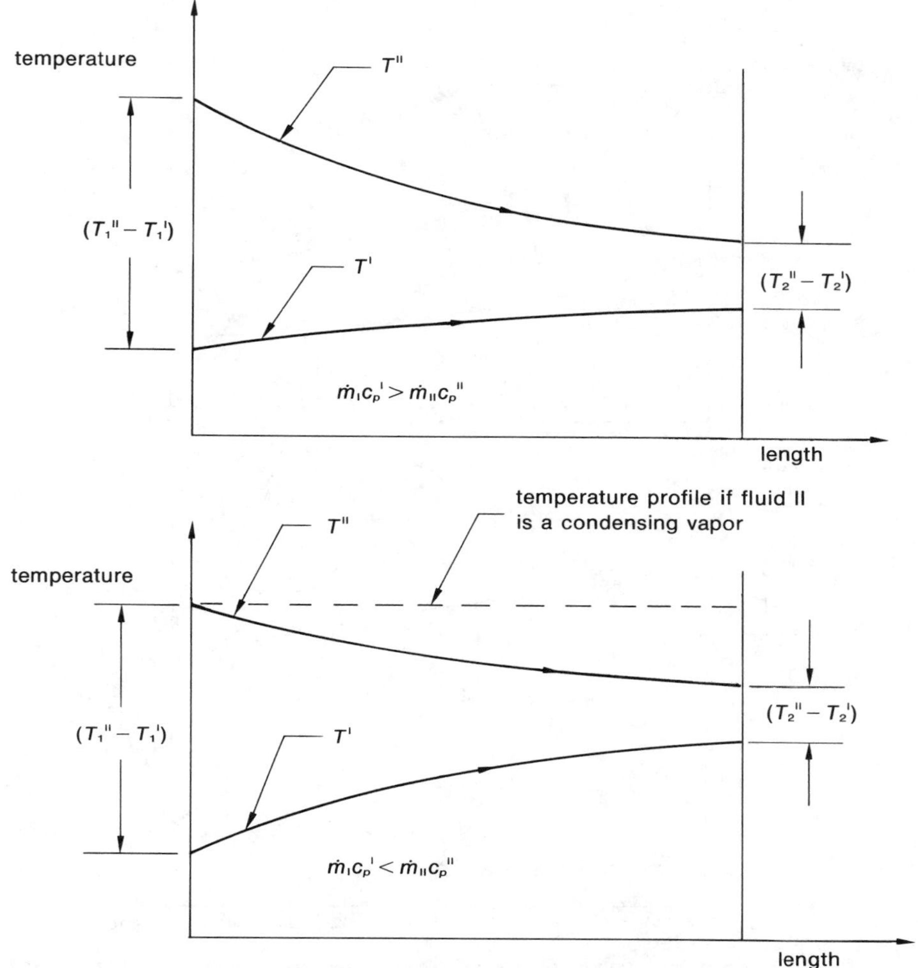

Fig. 11.1.2 Temperature variations for co-current flow in a double-pipe heat exchanger.

decreases as the fluid approaches the exit of the exchanger. Since T_2^{II} is always greater than or equal to T_2^{I} there is a minimum value for T_2^{II} and a maximum value for T_2^{I}. These are given by

$$T_2^{\text{II}} \geqslant \frac{\left(\dfrac{\dot{m}_{\text{I}} c_p^{\text{I}}}{\dot{m}_{\text{II}} c_p^{\text{II}}}\right) T_1^{\text{I}} + T_1^{\text{II}}}{\left(\dfrac{\dot{m}_{\text{I}} c_p^{\text{I}}}{\dot{m}_{\text{II}} c_p^{\text{II}}}\right) + 1}, \quad \text{for co-current flow} \tag{11.1-5a}$$

$$T_2^{\text{I}} \leqslant \frac{\left(\dfrac{\dot{m}_{\text{I}} c_p^{\text{I}}}{\dot{m}_{\text{II}} c_p^{\text{II}}}\right) T_1^{\text{I}} + T_1^{\text{II}}}{\left(\dfrac{\dot{m}_{\text{I}} c_p^{\text{I}}}{\dot{m}_{\text{II}} c_p^{\text{II}}}\right) + 1}, \quad \text{for co-current flow} \tag{11.1-5b}$$

The temperature profiles for counter-current flow in a double-pipe heat exchanger are shown in Fig. 11.1.3. This type of flow has the advantage of providing a greater overall driving force for heat transfer, and the restrictions on the amount of cooling or heating that can be accomplished are less severe than those given

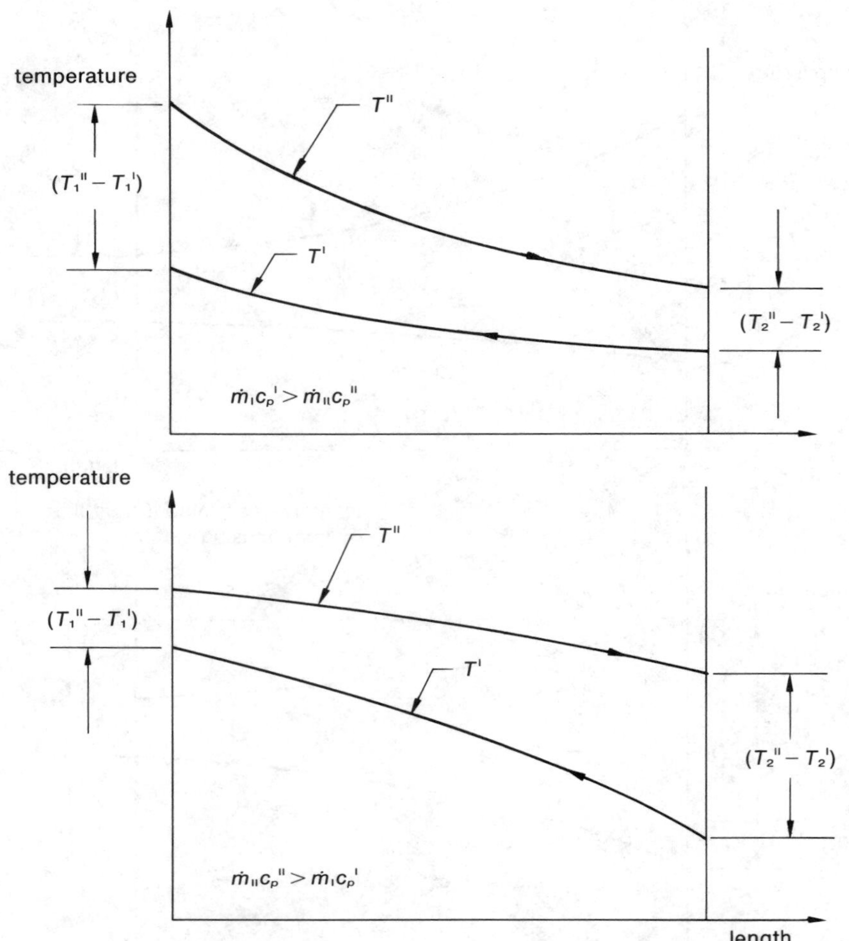

Fig. 11.1.3 Temperature variations for a counter-current flow in a double-pipe heat exchanger.

by Eqs. 11.1-5. For counter-current flow the temperatures are limited by

$$T_2^{\mathrm{II}} \geqslant T_2^{\mathrm{I}}, \quad \text{for counter-current flow} \tag{11.1-6a}$$

$$T_1^{\mathrm{I}} \leqslant T_1^{\mathrm{II}}, \quad \text{for counter-current flow} \tag{11.1-6b}$$

Since the driving force for heat transfer, $(T^{\mathrm{II}} - T^{\mathrm{I}})$, varies with position in the exchanger we must determine $T^{\mathrm{II}} - T^{\mathrm{I}}$ as a function of position if we are to calculate the total rate of heat transfer, $\dot{Q}$. We will follow the approach presented in Sec. 7.4 and apply Eq. 11.1-1 to the two control volumes illustrated in Fig. 11.1.4. Applying Eq. 11.1-1 to the control volume for fluid I we obtain

$$-\int_{A_e} \rho c_p(\bar{T} - T_0)\bar{v}_z\, dA\big|_z + \int_{A_e} \rho c_p(\bar{T} - T_0)\bar{v}_z\, dA\big|_{z+\Delta z}$$

$$= -\Delta z \int_0^{2\pi} \bar{q}_r r\, d\theta\big|_{r=D_i/2} + \int_{A_e} \bar{q}_z^{(T)}\, dA\big|_z - \int_{A_e} \bar{q}_z^{(T)}\, dA\big|_{z+\Delta z} \tag{11.1-7}$$

Note that the turbulent heat flux is zero at the pipe wall so that $\bar{\mathbf{q}}^{(T)}$ is replaced by $\bar{\mathbf{q}}$ in the integral over that solid surface. Dividing by Δz and taking the limit $\Delta z \to 0$ yields

$$\frac{d}{dz}\int_{A_e} \rho c_p(\bar{T} - T_0)\bar{v}_z\, dA = -\langle \bar{q}_r \rangle\big|_{r=D_i/2}\pi D_i - \frac{d}{dz}\int_{A_e} \bar{q}_z^{(T)}\, dA \tag{11.1-8}$$

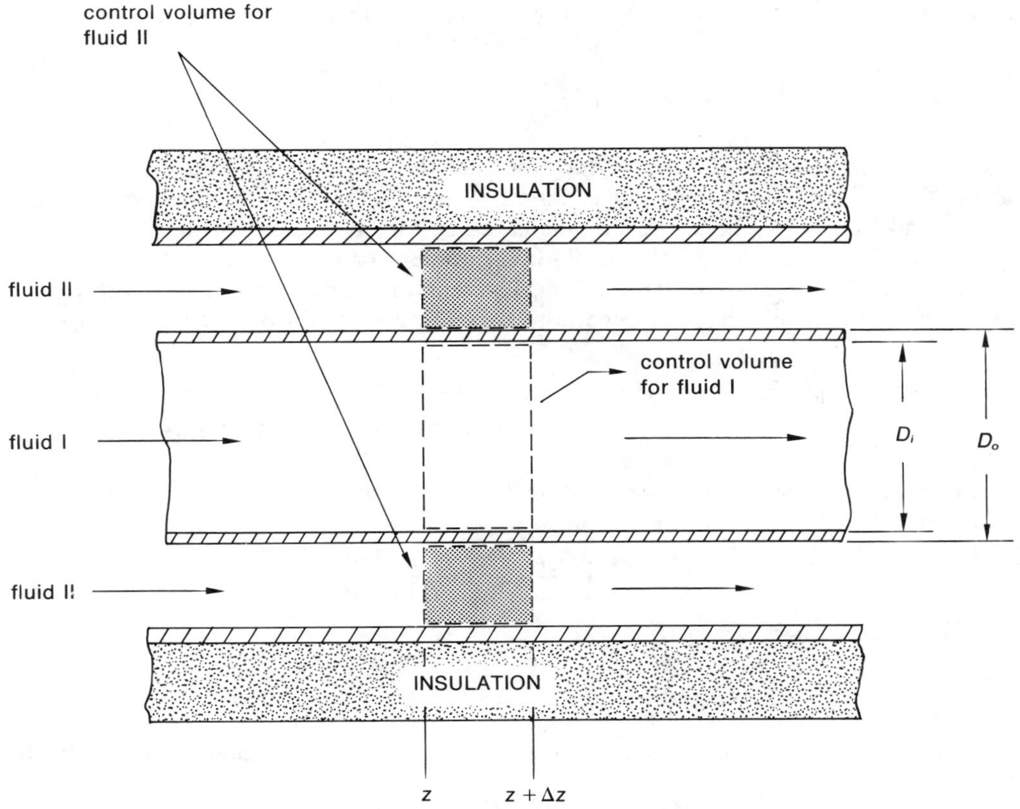

Fig. 11.1.4 Control volumes for double-pipe heat exchanger.

If the density and heat capacity are constant we can express the left-hand-side of Eq. 11.1-8 as

$$\frac{d}{dz}\int_{A_e} \rho c_p(\bar{T} - T_0)\bar{v}_z\, dA = \rho c_p \frac{d}{dz}\int_{A_e} (\bar{T} - T_0)\bar{v}_z\, dA = \rho c_p \frac{d}{dz}\Big[(T^{\mathrm{I}} - T_0)\langle v_z\rangle\Big]\left(\frac{\pi D_i^2}{4}\right) \tag{11.1-9}$$

where T^{I} represents the cup-mixing temperature as defined by Eq. 11.1-3. We can now use the mass balance

$$\frac{d}{dz}\langle \bar{v}_z\rangle = 0 \tag{11.1-10}$$

to simplify Eq. 11.1-9 to the form

$$\frac{d}{dz}\int_{A_e} \rho c_p(\bar{T} - T_0)\bar{v}_z\, dA = \rho^{\mathrm{I}} c_p^{\mathrm{I}}\langle \bar{v}_z\rangle^{\mathrm{I}}\left(\frac{dT^{\mathrm{I}}}{dz}\right)\left(\frac{\pi D_i^2}{4}\right) \tag{11.1-11}$$

If we neglect the axial molecular and turbulent transport relative to the convective transport, i.e.,

$$\frac{d}{dz}\int_{A_e} \bar{q}_z^{(T)}\, dA \ll \frac{d}{dz}\int_{A_e} \rho c_p(\bar{T} - T_0)\bar{v}_z\, dA \tag{11.1-12}$$

and express the mass flow rate as

$$\dot{m}_{\mathrm{I}} = \rho^{\mathrm{I}}\langle v_z\rangle^{\mathrm{I}}\left(\frac{\pi D_i^2}{4}\right) \tag{11.1-13}$$

we can write Eq. 11.1-8 as

$$\dot{m}_{\mathrm{I}} c_p^{\mathrm{I}}\left(\frac{dT^{\mathrm{I}}}{dz}\right) = -\langle \bar{q}_r\rangle|_{r=D_i/2}\,\pi D_i \tag{11.1-14}$$

A similar analysis for fluid II can be developed using the other control volume illustrated in Fig. 11.1.4. The result is

$$\pm \dot{m}_{II} c_p{}^{II} \left(\frac{dT^{II}}{dz}\right) = -\langle \bar{q}_r \rangle|_{r=D_o/2} \pi D_o \tag{11.1-15}$$

The ($\pm$) sign on the left-hand-side results from the fact that we wish to consider both co-current and counter-current flow of the fluid in the annular region. When the flow is in the positive z-direction the sign is negative ($-$) and the flow is co-current as indicated in Fig. 11.1.4. When the flow is in the negative z-direction the sign is positive ($+$) and the flow is counter-current. Note that the sign convection is consistent with Eqs. 11.1-2; positive ($+$) for counter-current flow and negative ($-$) for co-current flow.

Drawing upon our work in Chapter 2, we note that Eq. 2.4-13 can be used to show that

$$\langle \bar{q}_r \rangle|_{r=D_i/2} \pi D_i = \langle \bar{q}_r \rangle|_{r=D_o/2} \pi D_o = \frac{\pi D_o (T^I - T^{II})}{\frac{1}{h^I}\left(\frac{D_o}{D_i}\right) + \frac{D_o}{2k} \ln\left(\frac{D_o}{D_i}\right) + \frac{1}{h^{II}}} \tag{11.1-16}$$

provided that $q_z \ll q_r$ in the pipe wall. The local *overall* heat transfer coefficient *based on the outer area*, U_o, is defined as

$$\frac{1}{U_o} = \frac{1}{h^I}\left(\frac{D_o}{D_i}\right) + \frac{D_o}{2k} \ln\left(\frac{D_o}{D_i}\right) + \frac{1}{h^{II}} \tag{11.1-17}$$

so that Eq. 11.1-16 can be expressed as

$$\langle \bar{q}_r \rangle|_{r=D_i/2} \pi D_i = \langle \bar{q}_r \rangle|_{r=D_o/2} \pi D_o = U_o \pi D_o (T^I - T^{II}) \tag{11.1-18}$$

Substitution of this expression into Eqs. 11.1-14 and 11.1-15 and rearranging the result leads to

$$\left(\frac{dT^I}{dz}\right) = -\left(\frac{U_o \pi D_o}{\dot{m}_I c_p{}^I}\right)(T^I - T^{II}) \tag{11.1-19}$$

$$\left(\frac{dT^{II}}{dz}\right) = -\left(\frac{U_o \pi D_o}{\pm \dot{m}_{II} c_p{}^{II}}\right)(T^I - T^{II}) \tag{11.1-20}$$

Subtracting Eq. 11.1-20 from Eq. 11.1-19 leads to a differential equation for the local driving force for heat transfer, $(T^I - T^{II})$.

$$\frac{d}{dz}(T^I - T^{II}) = -U_o \pi D_o \left(\frac{1}{\dot{m}_I c_p{}^I} - \frac{1}{\pm \dot{m}_{II} c_p{}^{II}}\right)(T^I - T^{II}) \tag{11.1-21}$$

Remember once again that in the term $\pm \dot{m}_{II} c_p{}^{II}$ the plus sign ($+$) is for counter-current flow and the minus sign ($-$) is for co-current flow. If we now *define* $\dot{Q}$ as the *total* rate of heat transfer to fluid I, we can write Eqs. 11.1-2 as

$$\dot{Q} = \dot{m}_I c_p{}^I (T_2{}^I - T_1{}^I) = (\pm \dot{m}_{II} c_p{}^{II})(T_2{}^{II} - T_1{}^{II}) \tag{11.1-22}$$

We can rearrange Eq. 11.1-21 and substitute Eq. 11.1-22 to obtain

$$\frac{1}{(T^I - T^{II})} \frac{d}{dz}(T^I - T^{II}) = -\frac{U_o \pi D_o}{\dot{Q}}\left[(T_2{}^I - T_1{}^I) - (T_2{}^{II} - T_1{}^{II})\right] \tag{11.1-23}$$

Note that here we have finally rid ourselves of the troublesome plus–minus ($\pm$) sign, but we do need to remember that $\dot{Q}$ is positive when heat is transferred from fluid II to fluid I, and negative when the opposite occurs. Separating variables and integrating from $z = 0$ where $(T^I - T^{II}) = (T_1{}^I - T_1{}^{II})$ to $z = L$ where $(T^I - T^{II}) = (T_2{}^I - T_2{}^{II})$ yields

$$\ln\left(\frac{T_2{}^I - T_2{}^{II}}{T_1{}^I - T_1{}^{II}}\right) = \frac{U_o \pi D_o L}{\dot{Q}}\left[(T_1{}^I - T_1{}^{II}) - (T_2{}^I - T_2{}^{II})\right] \tag{11.1-24}$$

Further rearrangement leads to the traditional form for the total rate of heat transfer to fluid I

$$\dot{Q} = U_o A_o \left[\frac{(T_2^{\mathrm{II}} - T_2^{\mathrm{I}}) - (T_1^{\mathrm{II}} - T_1^{\mathrm{I}})}{\ln \left(\dfrac{T_2^{\mathrm{II}} - T_2^{\mathrm{I}}}{T_1^{\mathrm{II}} - T_1^{\mathrm{I}}} \right)} \right] \tag{11.1-25}$$

Here we have replaced $\pi D_o L$ with A_o, the *outer* area. Most often this result is expressed in terms of the log-mean temperature difference as

$$\dot{Q} = U_o A_o \, \Delta T_{\ln} \tag{11.1-26}$$

In Eq. 11.1-25 we can see the advantage of designating the temperatures in terms of the conditions at the two ends of the heat exchanger, for that allows us to write a single expression for the log-mean temperature regardless of whether the flow is co-current or counter-current. This would not be the case if we used i and o to indicate *inlet* and *outlet* conditions. Often the expression for the log-mean temperature difference is simplified to

$$\Delta T_{\ln} = \frac{\Delta T_2 - \Delta T_1}{\ln \left(\dfrac{\Delta T_2}{\Delta T_1} \right)} = \frac{\Delta T_1 - \Delta T_2}{\ln \left(\dfrac{\Delta T_1}{\Delta T_2} \right)} \tag{11.1-27}$$

where ΔT_1 refers to the absolute value of the temperature difference between the two streams at the "1" end of the exchanger and ΔT_2 is the absolute value of the temperature difference between the two streams at the "2" end of the exchanger.

At this point we are in a position to explore the advantage of counter-current flow over co-current flow. Imagine that we have a fluid stream at 200°F and wish to raise the temperature to 400°F. There is a second process stream which can be used to accomplish this heating. The temperature of this stream is 800°F and the heat capacity and flow rate are such that the final temperature of this stream will be 700°F. For co-current and counter-current flow this gives

co-current

$$T_1^{\mathrm{I}} = 200°\mathrm{F}, \qquad T_2^{\mathrm{I}} = 400°\mathrm{F}$$
$$T_1^{\mathrm{II}} = 800°\mathrm{F}, \qquad T_2^{\mathrm{II}} = 700°\mathrm{F}$$
$$\Delta T_{\ln} = 433°\mathrm{F}$$

counter-current

$$T_1^{\mathrm{I}} = 200°\mathrm{F}, \qquad T_2^{\mathrm{I}} = 400°\mathrm{F}$$
$$T_1^{\mathrm{II}} = 700°\mathrm{F}, \qquad T_2^{\mathrm{II}} = 800°\mathrm{F}$$
$$\Delta T_{\ln} = 448°\mathrm{F}$$

In this case the area required for a co-current heat exchanger would be $3\frac{1}{2}$ per cent larger than the area required for a counter-current exchanger. There is essentially no difference between the two types of exchanger for this case because the temperature difference is large throughout the entire exchanger. If the heating fluid is available at 600°F, a different situation results

co-current

$$T_1^{\mathrm{I}} = 200°\mathrm{F}, \qquad T_2^{\mathrm{II}} = 400°\mathrm{F}$$
$$T_1^{\mathrm{II}} = 600°\mathrm{F}, \qquad T_2^{\mathrm{II}} = 500°\mathrm{F}$$
$$\Delta T_{\ln} = 217°\mathrm{F}$$

counter-current

$$T_1^{\mathrm{I}} = 200°\mathrm{F}, \qquad T_2^{\mathrm{I}} = 400°\mathrm{F}$$
$$T_1^{\mathrm{II}} = 500°\mathrm{F}, \qquad T_2^{\mathrm{II}} = 600°\mathrm{F}$$
$$\Delta T_{\ln} = 247°\mathrm{F}$$

In this case the area of the co-current heat exchanger is 14 per cent larger than the area of the counter-current exchanger. This difference is still not especially significant, but what if the heating fluid is available at 500°F? We would then require an *infinite* area for the co-current heat exchanger, i.e., $\Delta T_{\ln} = 0$, whereas the counter-current heat exchanger would have a log-mean temperature difference of 144°F and therefore a finite area. For this reason the counter-current flow configuration is always preferred.

Non-constant overall coefficient

We know from our studies in Chapter 7 that film heat transfer coefficients depend on the Reynolds number, Prandtl number, and the viscosity ratio, (μ_b/μ_0). Since these dimensionless groups depend on temperature we can expect the film heat transfer coefficients and thus U_o to depend on temperature in a complex manner. The temperature dependence of the viscosity is of major importance for liquids since ρ, c_p, and k vary only slowly with temperature. For gases the Prandtl number is essentially constant, while the viscosity is proportional to $\sqrt{T}$ and the kinematic viscosity varies roughly as $T^{3/2}$.

Allowing U_o to be variable, we return to Eq. 11.1-23, separate variables, and integrate between $z = 0$ and $z = L$

$$\ln\left(\frac{T_2^{\mathrm{I}} - T_2^{\mathrm{II}}}{T_1^{\mathrm{I}} - T_1^{\mathrm{II}}}\right) = -\frac{\pi D_o}{\dot{Q}}\left[(T_2^{\mathrm{I}} - T_1^{\mathrm{I}}) - (T_2^{\mathrm{II}} - T_1^{\mathrm{II}})\right] \int_0^L U_o\, dz \tag{11.1-28}$$

Solving for $\dot{Q}$ and rearranging the temperature term on the right-hand-side allows us to write

$$\dot{Q} = U_{o,\mathrm{av}} A_o \left[\frac{(T_2^{\mathrm{II}} - T_2^{\mathrm{I}}) - (T_1^{\mathrm{II}} - T_1^{\mathrm{I}})}{\ln\left(\dfrac{T_2^{\mathrm{II}} - T_2^{\mathrm{I}}}{T_1^{\mathrm{II}} - T_1^{\mathrm{I}}}\right)}\right] \tag{11.1-29}$$

where the average value of U_o is defined by

$$U_{o,\mathrm{av}} = \frac{1}{L} \int_0^L U_o\, dz \tag{11.1-30}$$

If values of U_o can be determined at the entrance and exit we could partially account for variation in U_o by assuming a linear dependence on z so that the average value is given by

$$U_{o,\mathrm{av}}\ \tfrac{1}{2}(U_{o,1} + U_{o,2}) \tag{11.1-31}$$

and Eq. 11.1-29 could be expressed as

$$\dot{Q} = \tfrac{1}{2}(U_{o,1} + U_{o,2}) A_o\, \Delta T_{\ln} \tag{11.1-32}$$

11.2 Shell and Tube Heat Exchangers

For most process streams we require a more efficient heat exchanger than the double-pipe heat exchanger discussed in the previous section. From the point of cost, space, and pressure drop requirements the shell and tube heat exchanger shown in Fig. 11.2.1 is preferred for a great many heat transfer processes, especially those encountered in the petroleum industry. These exchangers consist of a bundle of tubes through which one fluid passes, while the other fluid flows past the tubes and is contained by the shell. The configuration shown in Fig. 11.2.1 would be referred to as a one shell-pass, one tube-pass, co-current exchanger. Baffles are used to direct the flow of the shell fluid across the tube bundle in order to obtain the high heat transfer rates associated with flow past tube banks. Sufficiently large headers are required at the entrance and exit for the tube fluid in order that the flow be uniformly distributed throughout all the tubes. The mechanical design of a shell and tube heat exchanger is not a trivial matter for the tube sheets, baffles, and headers must be constructed in a way which will withstand the thermal strains which are set up when the exchanger is in operation [3]. There are a number of general rules regarding the use of shell and tube exchangers. These are given by McAdams [4] as:

1. If one of the fluids fouls the surface more rapidly than the other it should be routed through the

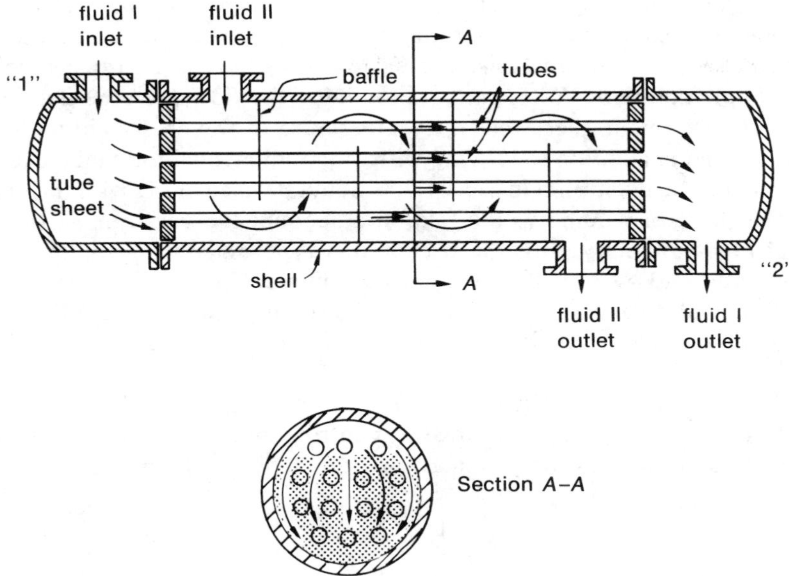

Fig. 11.2.1 Shell and tube heat exchanger (a one tube-pass, one shell-pass, baffled, shell and tube heat exchanger).

tubes, since the inside of the tubes can be cleaned by simply removing the headers and scouring the tubes with an appropriate tool.

2. If one stream is at a high pressure it is advantageous to have it flow through the tubes, since this eliminates the cost of a high-pressure shell.
3. Corrosive fluids should flow in the tubes in order to avoid the expense of a corrosion resistant metal for both the shell and tubes.
4. In general the more viscous fluid should be routed through the shell where the pressure drop is relatively low, and the heat transfer coefficient is higher than that for flow in a tube (compare Figs. 7.6.2 and 7.8.5 at the same Reynolds number).
5. If the major resistance to heat transfer is in the tube fluid, a two tube-pass, one shell-pass exchanger may be desirable. This arrangement is illustrated in Fig. 11.2.2. The overall temperature driving force will be reduced somewhat over that obtained with a one tube-pass exchanger; on the other hand, the Reynolds number for the tube flow will be doubled and the heat transfer coefficient increased by approximately a factor of 1.8 (see Fig. 7.6.2).

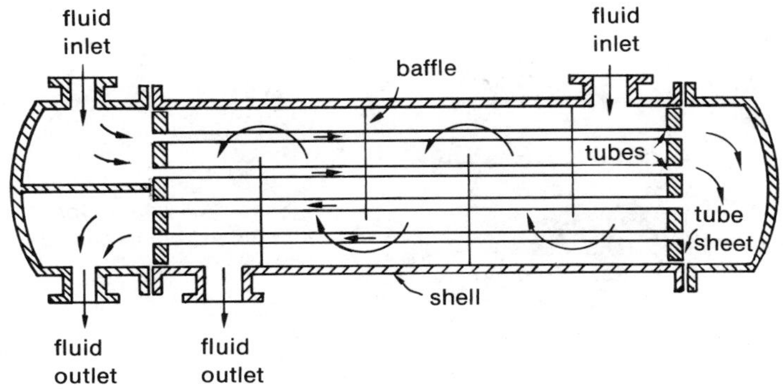

Fig. 11.2.2 Two tube-pass, one shell-pass, baffled, shell and tube heat exchanger.

Our analysis of the one shell-pass, one tube-pass exchanger shown in Fig. 11.2.1 will follow precisely that for the double-pipe heat exchanger, and our final result will be the same as that given by Eq. 11.1-25. However, it is necessary to repeat the analysis in order to clarify the assumptions which must be imposed in order to obtain a simple solution. We begin by examining the flow patterns illustrated in Fig. 11.2.1. From these flow patterns we might guess that the temperature of the shell fluid varies significantly as it flows across the tube bundle, in addition to varying with longitudinal position in the exchanger. This would suggest that the control volume illustrated in Fig. 11.2.3 should be used along with the macroscopic thermal energy balance, for that control volume would take into account the variation of the fluid temperatures with y and z. The primary difficulty with the use of this type of control volume is that it requires a knowledge of the velocity field averaged over the x-coordinate. This average velocity field would be a complex function of y and z, thus the resulting differential equation for $(T^{\mathrm{I}} - T^{\mathrm{II}})$ would contain coefficients which would be functions of y and z and the solution of the equation would present a tedious problem.

In order to simplify the analysis of a shell and tube heat exchanger we will choose as a control volume the "slice" illustrated in Fig. 11.2.4. In considering this control volume we must remember that the *bulk* or *cup-mixing* temperature that appears in the macroscopic balance is defined by

$$T_b = \frac{\int_{A_e} T\mathbf{v}\cdot\mathbf{n}\,dA}{\int_{A_e} \mathbf{v}\cdot\mathbf{n}\,dA} \tag{11.2-1}$$

and is therefore dependent on the velocity profile. If the velocity profile is flat, as it nearly is for turbulent flow in a pipe, the bulk temperature is equal to the area average temperature:

$$T_b = \langle T\rangle, \quad \text{for a flat velocity profile} \tag{11.2-2}$$

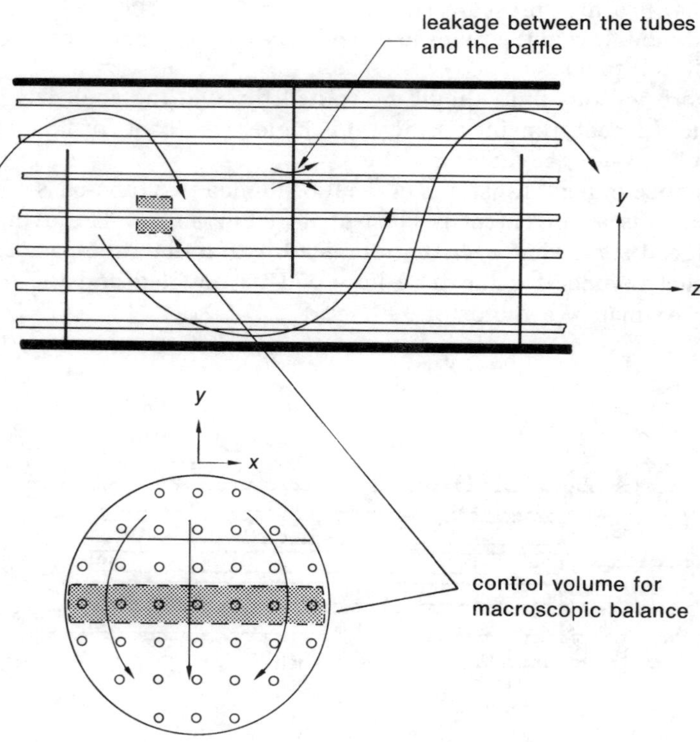

Fig. 11.2.3 Control volume for a two-dimensional analysis of the shell fluid.

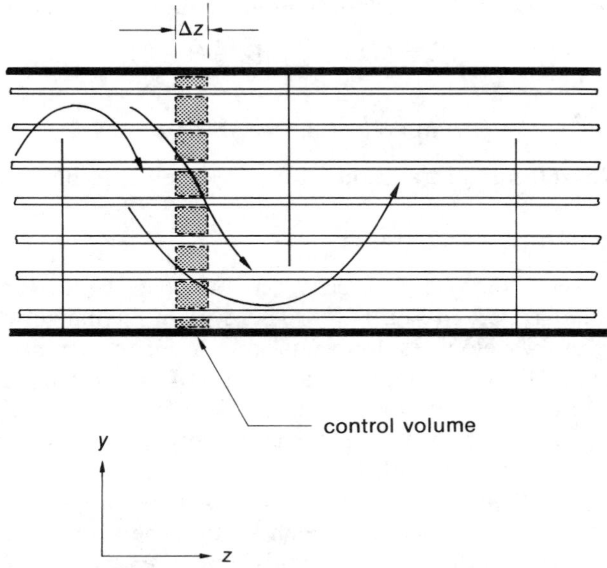

Fig. 11.2.4 Control volume for a one-dimensional analysis of the shell fluid.

however, the z-component of the velocity vector for the flow shown in Fig. 11.2.4 is anything but flat. There are certainly drawbacks to analyzing shell and tube heat exchangers in terms of a one-dimensional model, and we must always keep in mind the possibility of large deviations between this type of theory and experimental results.

Once we have committed ourselves to the one-dimensional model the analysis follows Eqs. 11.1-7 through 11.1-25 to yield

$$\dot{Q} = U_o A_o \left[\frac{(T_2^{\text{II}} - T_2^{\text{I}}) - (T_1^{\text{II}} - T_1^{\text{I}})}{\ln\left(\dfrac{T_2^{\text{II}} - T_2^{\text{I}}}{T_1^{\text{II}} - T_1^{\text{I}}}\right)} \right] \tag{11.2-3}$$

Here A_o is the total outside area of all the tubes and U_o is the overall heat transfer coefficient defined by Eq. 11.1-17. Before passing on to other aspects of shell and tube heat exchangers we must consider how to evaluate the film heat transfer coefficients in Eq. 11.1-17. The coefficient for the tube fluid, h^{I}, presents no problem for we can draw directly upon the correlations presented in Sec. 7.6 for laminar and turbulent flow in tubes. In Sec. 7.8 a satisfactory correlation for staggered tube bundles was presented (see Eq. 7.8-27 and Fig. 7.8.5); however, the flow in that case was directly across the tube bundle and is therefore somewhat different than the kind of flow illustrated in Fig. 11.2.3. In order to estimate h^{II} it would seem reasonable to use the average mass average velocity in the cross flow section in conjunction with Eq. 7.8-27. If the diameter of the shell is D_s and the distance between baffles is L_b, then an average mass velocity could be expressed as

$$G_{\text{av}}^{\text{II}} = \frac{4\dot{m}_{\text{II}}}{\pi D_s L_b} \tag{11.2-4}$$

The appropriate Reynolds number is given by

$$N_{\text{Re}}^{\text{II}} = \frac{D_p G_{\text{av}}^{\text{II}}}{\mu_{\text{II}}(1-\epsilon)} = \frac{4 D_p \dot{m}_{\text{II}}}{\pi \mu_{\text{II}} D_s L_b (1-\epsilon)} \tag{11.2-5}$$

where ϵ is the void fraction. The definition of D_p is given by Eq. 7.9-3 and for tube bundles it indicates that

$$D_p = \tfrac{3}{2} D, \quad \text{for tube bundles} \tag{11.2-6}$$

where D is the outer tube diameter. The Reynolds number now takes the form

$$N_{\mathrm{Re}}^{\mathrm{II}} = 6D\dot{m}_{\mathrm{II}}/\pi\mu_{\mathrm{II}}D_s L_b(1-\epsilon) \tag{11.2-7}$$

which is to be used in Eq. 7.8-27

$$N_{\mathrm{Nu}} = (0.4N_{\mathrm{Re}}^{1/2} + 0.2N_{\mathrm{Re}}^{2/3})N_{\mathrm{Pr}}^{0.4}(\mu_b/\mu_0)^{0.14} \tag{7.8-27}$$

in order to calculate the Nusselt number and therefore the shell side film heat transfer coefficient.

Two tube-pass, one shell-pass exchangers

The most obvious extension of the one shell-pass, one tube-pass heat exchanger is the one shell-pass, two tube-pass configuration illustrated in Fig. 11.2.5. This type of exchanger might be used instead of the one tube-pass version if high tube velocities are required in order to increase the tube side heat transfer coefficient. This could be accomplished by doubling the length of the exchanger, and using half the number of tubes in a one tube-pass exchanger. As we shall see, this would provide a better overall temperature driving force and thus require a smaller heat transfer area; however, the length of an exchanger is often dictated by the necessity for removing the tube bundle for cleaning or repair, and its placement relative to other process equipment such as distillation columns or chemical reactors. Because of this multi tube-pass exchangers are often used for their compactness even though they require a larger heat transfer area.

The control volumes to be used in the analysis of this type of exchanger are shown in Fig. 11.2.6. The shell fluid will be treated with a single control volume which will yield a differential equation for the bulk temperature T^{II}. We will determine the tube fluid temperature in both the first and second passes by using the two control volumes shown in Fig. 11.2.6. In addition to using the *differential* control volume we will also make use of the macroscopic thermal energy balance for the entire exchanger. Defining $\dot{Q}$ as the total rate of heat transfer from fluid II to fluid I we find

$$\dot{Q} = \dot{m}_{\mathrm{I}}c_p{}^{\mathrm{I}}(T_o^{\mathrm{I}} - T_i^{\mathrm{I}}) = \dot{m}_{\mathrm{II}}c_p{}^{\mathrm{II}}(T_i^{\mathrm{II}} - T_o^{\mathrm{II}}) \tag{11.2-8}$$

Application of Eq. 11.1-1 to the shell fluid control volume, and following the same type of development given in Eqs. 11.7-7 through 11.1-14, yields

$$-\dot{m}_{\mathrm{II}}c_p{}^{\mathrm{II}}\left(\frac{dT^{\mathrm{II}}}{dz}\right) = \left\{\langle\bar{q}_r\rangle_o\left(\frac{n}{2}\right)\pi D_o\right\}_{\substack{\text{over the tubes in}\\\text{the first pass}}} + \left\{\langle\bar{q}_r\rangle_o\left(\frac{n}{2}\right)\pi D_o\right\}_{\substack{\text{over the tubes in}\\\text{the second pass}}} \tag{11.2-9}$$

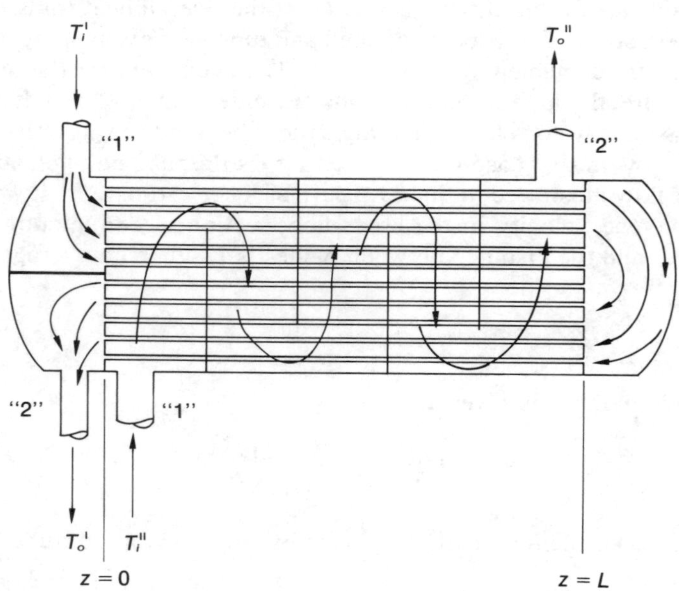

Fig. 11.2.5 Two tube-pass, one shell-pass shell and tube heat exchanger.

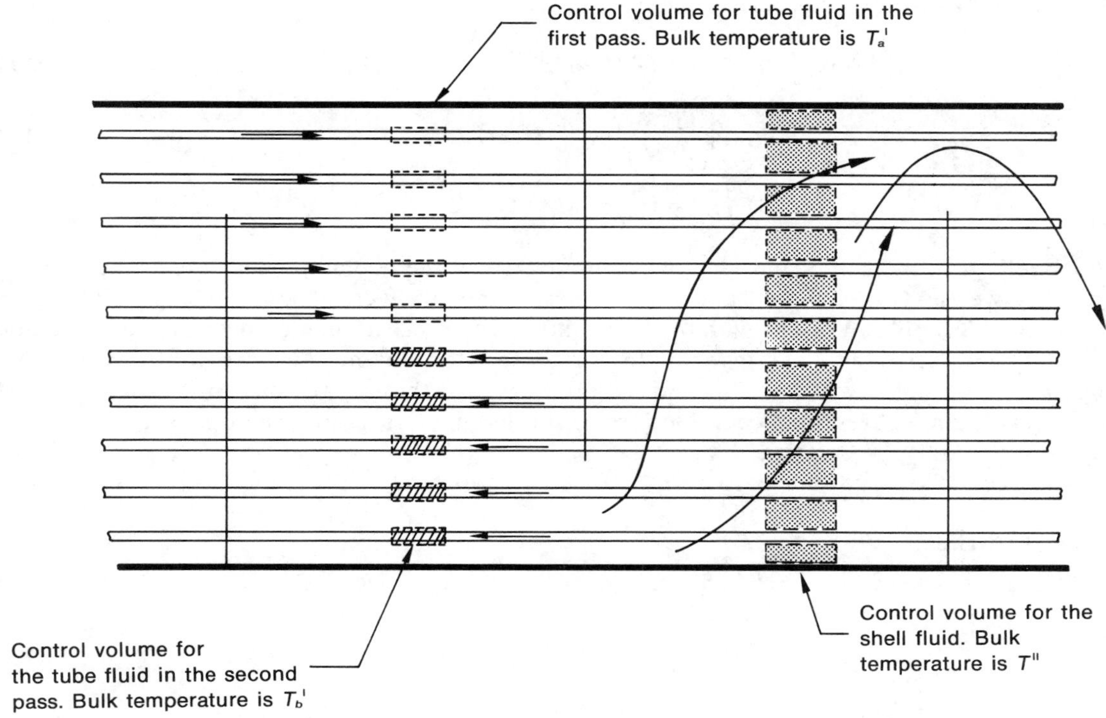

Fig. 11.2.6 Control volumes for the analysis of a one shell-pass, two tube-pass heat exchanger.

where n is the total number of tubes. For the control volume consisting of a "slice" of the *first pass* tubes, this type of analysis gives

$$\dot{m}_1 c_p{}^{\mathrm{I}}\left(\frac{dT_a^{\mathrm{I}}}{dz}\right) = -\left\{\langle\bar{q}_r\rangle_i\left(\frac{n}{2}\right)\pi D_i\right\}_{\substack{\text{over the tubes in}\\\text{the first pass}}} \tag{11.2-10}$$

and for the *second pass* tubes we find

$$-\dot{m}_1 c_p{}^{\mathrm{I}}\left(\frac{dT_b^{\mathrm{I}}}{dz}\right) = -\left\{\langle\bar{q}_r\rangle_i\left(\frac{n}{2}\right)\pi D_i\right\}_{\substack{\text{over the tubes in}\\\text{the second pass}}} \tag{11.2-11}$$

Following Eq. 11.1-18 we express the heat flux through the tube wall as

$$\left\{\langle\bar{q}_r\rangle_i\left(\frac{n}{2}\right)\pi D_i\right\}_{\substack{\text{over the tubes}\\\text{in the first pass}}} = \left\{\langle\bar{q}_r\rangle_o\left(\frac{n}{2}\right)\pi D_o\right\}_{\substack{\text{over the tubes in}\\\text{the first pass}}} = \left(\frac{n}{2}\right)U_o\pi D_o(T_a^{\mathrm{I}} - T^{\mathrm{II}}) \tag{11.2-12a}$$

$$\left\{\langle\bar{q}_r\rangle_i\left(\frac{n}{2}\right)\pi D_i\right\}_{\substack{\text{over the tubes}\\\text{in the second pass}}} = \left\{\langle\bar{q}_r\rangle_o\left(\frac{n}{2}\right)\pi D_o\right\}_{\substack{\text{over the tubes in}\\\text{the second pass}}} = \left(\frac{n}{2}\right)U_o\pi D_o(T_b^{\mathrm{I}} - T^{\mathrm{II}}) \tag{11.2-12b}$$

where U_o is assumed constant over the entire exchanger, and the total number of tubes is designated by n. We should remember that the best representation of the heat flux across the wall of a single tube would be given in terms of the local temperature difference

$$\{\text{heat flux across a single tube wall}\} = U_o\pi D_o(T_{\mathrm{loc}}^{\mathrm{I}} - T_{\mathrm{loc}}^{\mathrm{II}}) \tag{11.2-13}$$

and the use of $(T_a^{\mathrm{I}} - T^{\mathrm{II}})$ and $(T_b^{\mathrm{I}} - T^{\mathrm{II}})$ as the temperature difference in Eqs. 11.2-12 undoubtedly causes some error.

We can now substitute Eqs. 11.2-12 into Eqs. 11.2-9 through 11.2-11 to obtain

$$-\dot{m}_{\mathrm{II}} c_p{}^{\mathrm{II}}\left(\frac{dT^{\mathrm{II}}}{dz}\right)=\left(\frac{n}{2}\right) U_o \pi D_o\left[(T_b{}^{\mathrm{I}}-T^{\mathrm{II}})+(T_a{}^{\mathrm{I}}-T^{\mathrm{II}})\right] \tag{11.2-14}$$

$$\dot{m}_{\mathrm{I}} c_p{}^{\mathrm{I}}\left(\frac{dT_a{}^{\mathrm{I}}}{dz}\right)=-\left(\frac{n}{2}\right) U_o \pi D_o (T_a{}^{\mathrm{I}}-T^{\mathrm{II}}) \tag{11.2-15}$$

$$\dot{m}_{\mathrm{I}} c_p{}^{\mathrm{I}}\left(\frac{dT_b{}^{\mathrm{I}}}{dz}\right)=\left(\frac{n}{2}\right) U_o \pi D_o (T_b{}^{\mathrm{I}}-T^{\mathrm{II}}) \tag{11.2-16}$$

Returning briefly to Eqs. 11.1-19 and 11.1-20 in our analysis of the double-pipe heat exchanger we should note that there we had two equations and two unknowns, thus we were able to develop a single equation for the unknown $(T^{\mathrm{I}}-T^{\mathrm{II}})$. Working with the temperature difference as an unknown allowed us to obtain a solution for $\dot{Q}$ in a relatively easy manner. In our present development we are confronted with three equations and three unknowns $T_a{}^{\mathrm{I}}$, $T_b{}^{\mathrm{I}}$, and T^{II}. We can use these equations to eliminate two of the unknowns and obtain a differential equation for the third temperature. Before doing so, we will simplify these equations slightly by defining

$$\beta_1=\frac{nU_o\pi D_o}{\dot{m}_{\mathrm{I}} c_p{}^{\mathrm{I}}}, \qquad \beta_2=\frac{nU_o\pi D_o}{\dot{m}_{\mathrm{II}} c_p{}^{\mathrm{II}}} \tag{11.2-17}$$

so that we can write

$$\left(\frac{dT^{\mathrm{II}}}{dz}\right)=-\beta_2\left[(T_b{}^{\mathrm{I}}-T^{\mathrm{II}})+(T_a{}^{\mathrm{I}}-T^{\mathrm{II}})\right] \tag{11.2-18}$$

$$\left(\frac{dT_a{}^{\mathrm{I}}}{dz}\right)=-\beta_1(T_a{}^{\mathrm{I}}-T^{\mathrm{II}}) \tag{11.2-19}$$

$$\left(\frac{dT_b{}^{\mathrm{I}}}{dz}\right)=\beta_1(T_b{}^{\mathrm{I}}-T^{\mathrm{II}}) \tag{11.2-20}$$

Differentiation of Eq. 11.2-18 with respect to z and substitution of Eqs. 11.2-19 and 11.2-20 yields

$$\left(\frac{d^2T^{\mathrm{II}}}{dz^2}\right)=2\beta_2\left(\frac{dT^{\mathrm{II}}}{dz}\right)-\beta_2\beta_1(T_b{}^{\mathrm{I}}-T_a{}^{\mathrm{I}}) \tag{11.2-21}$$

Here we need to express $(T_b{}^{\mathrm{I}}-T_a{}^{\mathrm{I}})$ in terms of T^{II} if we are to obtain an equation containing only one temperature. We can accomplish this by substituting Eqs. 11.2-19 and 11.2-20 into Eq. 11.2-18 to obtain

$$\left(\frac{\beta_1}{\beta_2}\right)\left(\frac{dT^{\mathrm{II}}}{dz}\right)=\left(\frac{dT_a{}^{\mathrm{I}}}{dz}\right)-\left(\frac{dT_b{}^{\mathrm{I}}}{dz}\right) \tag{11.2-22}$$

Integration from any arbitrary value of z to $z=L$ gives

$$\left(\frac{\beta_1}{\beta_2}\right)\int_z^L\left(\frac{dT^{\mathrm{II}}}{dz}\right)dz=\int_z^L\left(\frac{dT_a{}^{\mathrm{I}}}{dz}\right)dz-\int_z^L\left(\frac{dT_b{}^{\mathrm{I}}}{dz}\right)dz \tag{11.2-23}$$

which may be expressed as

$$\left(\frac{\beta_1}{\beta_2}\right)(T_L{}^{\mathrm{II}}-T^{\mathrm{II}})=(T^{\mathrm{I}}_{a,L}-T_a{}^{\mathrm{I}})-(T^{\mathrm{I}}_{b,L}-T_b{}^{\mathrm{I}}) \tag{11.2-24}$$

Noting that

$$T_L{}^{\mathrm{II}}=T_i^{\mathrm{II}}, \qquad T^{\mathrm{I}}_{a,L}=T^{\mathrm{I}}_{b,L}$$

allows us to obtain the desired expression

$$(T_b{}^{\mathrm{I}}-T_a{}^{\mathrm{I}})=\left(\frac{\beta_1}{\beta_2}\right)(T_i^{\mathrm{II}}-T^{\mathrm{II}}) \tag{11.2-25}$$

Substitution of Eq. 11.2-25 into Eq. 11.2-21 gives us our differential equation for the shell fluid

$$\left(\frac{d^2T^{\mathrm{II}}}{dz^2}\right)-2\beta_2\left(\frac{dT^{\mathrm{II}}}{dz}\right)+\beta_1^2(T_i^{\mathrm{II}}-T^{\mathrm{II}})=0 \tag{11.2-26}$$

which is to be solved subject to the boundary conditions

B.C.1 $$T^{\text{II}} = T_o^{\text{II}}, \qquad z = 0 \tag{11.2-27}$$

B.C.2 $$T^{\text{II}} = T_i^{\text{II}}, \qquad z = L \tag{11.2-28}$$

Defining the dimensionless variables

$$\Theta^{\text{II}} = \frac{T_i^{\text{II}} - T^{\text{II}}}{T_i^{\text{II}} - T_o^{\text{II}}}, \qquad Z = z/L, \qquad \mathscr{B}_1 = \beta_1 L, \qquad \mathscr{B}_2 = \beta_2 L$$

allows us to write Eqs. 11.2-26 through 11.2-28 as

$$\left(\frac{d^2\Theta^{\text{II}}}{dZ^2}\right) - 2\mathscr{B}_2\left(\frac{d\Theta^{\text{II}}}{dZ}\right) - \mathscr{B}_1^2\Theta^{\text{II}} = 0 \tag{11.2-29}$$

B.C.1′ $$\Theta^{\text{II}} = 1, \qquad Z = 0 \tag{11.2-30}$$

B.C.2′ $$\Theta^{\text{II}} = 0, \qquad Z = 1 \tag{11.2-31}$$

It will be left as an exercise for the student to show that

$$\Theta^{\text{II}} = C_1\, e^{m_1 Z} + C_2\, e^{m_2 Z} \tag{11.2-32}$$

where

$$m_1, \quad m_2 = \mathscr{B}_2[1 \pm \sqrt{1 + (\mathscr{B}_1/\mathscr{B}_2)^2}] \tag{11.2-33}$$

$$C_1 = e^{m_2}/(e^{m_2} - e^{m_1}) \tag{11.2-34}$$

$$C_2 = -e^{m_1}/(e^{m_2} - e^{m_1}) \tag{11.2-35}$$

From Eq. 11.2-32 we can express T^{II} as

$$T^{\text{II}} = T_i^{\text{II}} - (T_i^{\text{II}} - T_o^{\text{II}})(C_1\, e^{m_1 Z} + C_2\, e^{m_2 Z}) \tag{11.2-36}$$

and the gradient of T^{II} as†

$$\left(\frac{dT^{\text{II}}}{dz}\right) = -(T_i^{\text{II}} - T_o^{\text{II}})\left(\frac{C_1 m_1}{L}\, e^{m_1 Z} + \frac{C_2 m_2}{L}\, e^{m_2 Z}\right) \tag{11.2-37}$$

Substitution of this latter equation into Eq. 11.2-18 and rearranging yields

$$T_b^{\text{I}} + T_a^{\text{I}} - 2T^{\text{II}} = \frac{1}{\beta_2 L}(T_i^{\text{II}} - T_o^{\text{II}})(C_1 m_1\, e^{m_1 Z} + C_2 m_2\, e^{m_2 Z}) \tag{11.2-38}$$

Setting $Z = 0$ gives

$$T_o^{\text{I}} + T_i^{\text{I}} - 2T_o^{\text{II}} = \frac{1}{\beta_2 L}(T_i^{\text{II}} - T_o^{\text{II}})(C_1 m_1 + C_2 m_2) \tag{11.2-39}$$

Substituting for C_1, C_2, m_1, and m_2 gives

$$T_o^{\text{I}} + T_i^{\text{I}} - 2T_o^{\text{II}} = (T_i^{\text{II}} - T_o^{\text{II}})\left\{\frac{(1+\mu)\, e^{\beta_2 L(1+\mu)} - (1-\mu)\, e^{\beta_2 L(1+\mu)}}{e^{\beta_2 L(1-\mu)} - e^{\beta_2 L(1+\mu)}}\right\} \tag{11.2-40}$$

Here we have substituted $\mathscr{B}_2 = \beta_2 L$ and μ is given by

$$\mu = \sqrt{1 + (\mathscr{B}_1/\mathscr{B}_2)^2} = \sqrt{1 + (\beta_1/\beta_2)^2} \tag{11.2-41}$$

Carrying out the multiplication in the numerator on the right-hand-side of Eq. 11.2-40 allows some simplification

$$(T_o^{\text{I}} - T_o^{\text{II}}) + (T_i^{\text{I}} - T_i^{\text{II}}) = \mu(T_i^{\text{II}} - T_o^{\text{II}})\left[\frac{e^{-\mu\beta_2 L} + e^{\mu\beta_2 L}}{e^{-\mu\beta_2 L} - e^{\mu\beta_2 L}}\right] \tag{11.2-42}$$

†Remember that $Z = z/L$.

We can multiply the numerator and denominator on the right-hand-side by $\exp(\mu\beta_2 L)$ and solve for $\exp(2\mu\beta_2 L)$

$$e^{2\mu\beta_2 L} = \frac{(T_o^{\mathrm{I}} - T_o^{\mathrm{II}}) + (T_i^{\mathrm{I}} - T_i^{\mathrm{II}}) - \mu(T_i^{\mathrm{II}} - T_o^{\mathrm{II}})}{(T_o^{\mathrm{I}} - T_o^{\mathrm{II}}) + (T_i^{\mathrm{I}} - T_i^{\mathrm{II}}) + \mu(T_i^{\mathrm{II}} - T_o^{\mathrm{II}})} \tag{11.2-43}$$

Taking the logarithm of both sides and substituting for β_2 from Eq. 11.2-17 gives

$$\frac{\mu\eta U_o\pi D_o L}{\dot{m}_{\mathrm{II}} c_p^{\mathrm{II}}} = \ln\frac{(T_o^{\mathrm{I}} - T_o^{\mathrm{II}}) + (T_i^{\mathrm{I}} - T_i^{\mathrm{II}}) - \mu(T_i^{\mathrm{II}} - T_o^{\mathrm{II}})}{(T_o^{\mathrm{I}} - T_o^{\mathrm{II}}) + (T_i^{\mathrm{I}} - T_i^{\mathrm{II}}) + \mu(T_i^{\mathrm{II}} - T_o^{\mathrm{II}})} \tag{11.2-44}$$

From Eq. 11.2-8 we can write

$$\dot{m}_{\mathrm{II}} c_p^{\mathrm{II}} = \dot{Q}/(T_i^{\mathrm{II}} - T_o^{\mathrm{II}})$$

and $\eta U_o\pi D_o L$ can be replaced by $U_o A_o$ so Eq. 11.2-44 can be put in the form

$$\dot{Q} = \frac{\mu U_o A_o (T_i^{\mathrm{II}} - T_o^{\mathrm{II}})}{\ln\left\{\dfrac{(T_o^{\mathrm{I}} - T_o^{\mathrm{II}}) + (T_i^{\mathrm{I}} - T_i^{\mathrm{II}}) - \mu(T_i^{\mathrm{II}} - T_o^{\mathrm{II}})}{(T_o^{\mathrm{I}} - T_o^{\mathrm{II}}) + (T_i^{\mathrm{I}} - T_i^{\mathrm{II}}) + \mu(T_i^{\mathrm{II}} - T_o^{\mathrm{II}})}\right\}} \tag{11.2-45}$$

We can now express μ as

$$\mu = \sqrt{1 + (\beta_1/\beta_2)^2} = \sqrt{1 + (\dot{m}_{\mathrm{II}} c_p^{\mathrm{II}}/\dot{m}_{\mathrm{I}} c_p^{\mathrm{I}})^2} \tag{11.2-46}$$

Making use of Eq. 11.2-8 leads to

$$\mu = \sqrt{(T_o^{\mathrm{II}} - T_i^{\mathrm{II}})^2 + (T_o^{\mathrm{I}} - T_i^{\mathrm{I}})^2}/(T_i^{\mathrm{II}} - T_o^{\mathrm{II}}) \tag{11.2-47}$$

which can be substituted into Eq. 11.2-45 to give us our final form of the equation for $\dot{Q}$.

$$\dot{Q} = \frac{U_o A_o \sqrt{(T_i^{\mathrm{I}} - T_o^{\mathrm{I}})^2 + (T_i^{\mathrm{II}} - T_o^{\mathrm{II}})^2}}{\ln\left\{\dfrac{(T_i^{\mathrm{II}} + T_o^{\mathrm{II}}) - (T_i^{\mathrm{I}} + T_o^{\mathrm{I}}) + \sqrt{(T_i^{\mathrm{I}} - T_o^{\mathrm{I}})^2 + (T_i^{\mathrm{II}} - T_o^{\mathrm{II}})^2}}{(T_i^{\mathrm{II}} + T_o^{\mathrm{II}}) - (T_i^{\mathrm{I}} + T_o^{\mathrm{I}}) - \sqrt{(T_i^{\mathrm{I}} - T_o^{\mathrm{I}})^2 + (T_i^{\mathrm{II}} - T_o^{\mathrm{II}})^2}}\right\}} \tag{11.2-48}$$

This result was apparently first presented by Underwood [5]. We should note that the only sign convention associated with this result is that $\dot{Q}$ is *positive* when energy is transferred *from* fluid II *to* fluid I. This is the same convention that applies to Eq. 11.2-3 for the one tube-pass, one shell-pass heat exchanger.

The expression for $\dot{Q}$ for a two tube-pass exchanger is certainly more complex than the result for a one tube-pass exchanger given by Eq. 11.2-3 and for easy use we need a graphical representation of the characteristic temperature difference in Eq. 11.2-48. Because of the prevalence of the log-mean temperature difference in heat transfer processes, it is traditional to represent the temperature difference for the two tube-pass exchanger in terms of the log-mean temperature difference and a correction factor. Remember from Sec. 11.1 that we found it convenient to represent the log-mean temperature difference in terms of the temperature differences at the ends of the exchanger rather than in terms of inlet and outlet temperatures. This allowed us to write a single expression for $\Delta T_{\ln}$ for both co-current and counter-current flow, as illustrated by Eqs. 11.1-25 and 11.1-27. We would also like to retain this convenience in our discussion of multi-pass heat exchangers; however, designation of the "ends" of the exchanger, as we did in Fig. 11.1.1, is not suitable and we must go on to a somewhat more complicated designation of the "1" and "2" ends as illustrated in Fig. 11.2.5. Using this nomenclature the log-mean temperature difference for the two tube-pass, one shell-pass heat exchanger takes the simple form

$$\Delta T_{\ln} = \frac{\Delta T_2 - \Delta T_1}{\ln\left(\dfrac{\Delta T_2}{\Delta T_1}\right)}, \quad \text{for a two tube-pass, one shell-pass heat exchanger} \tag{11.2-49}$$

which is identical to that given in Eqs. 11.1-25 and 11.1-27. The rational behind the designation of the ends of the exchanger shown in Fig. 11.2.5 is illustrated in Fig. 11.2.7. There we see that the double tube-pass is

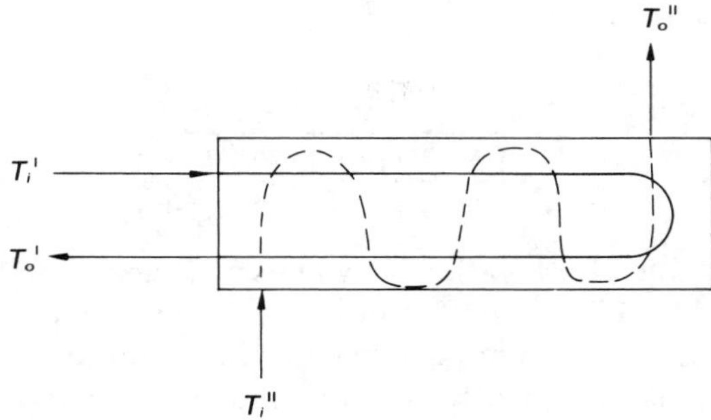

(a) Real configuration

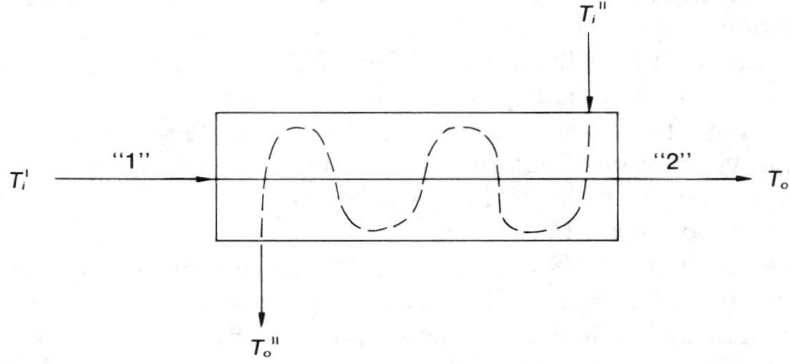

(b) Hypothetical configuration

Fig. 11.2.7 Designation of the ends of a two tube-pass heat exchanger.

simply "straightened out" to give an uni-directional flow for both streams, and the inlet and outlet temperatures are then designated by

tube fluid	*shell fluid*
$T_i^{\mathrm{I}} = T_1^{\mathrm{I}}$	$T_i^{\mathrm{II}} = T_2^{\mathrm{II}}$
$T_o^{\mathrm{I}} = T_2^{\mathrm{I}}$	$T_o^{\mathrm{II}} = T_1^{\mathrm{II}}$

We can now define a correction factor F by the expression

$$\Delta T^* = F\,\Delta T_{\ln} \qquad (11.2\text{-}50)$$

where ΔT^* is the temperature function in Eq. 11.2-48 and $\Delta T_{\ln}$ is given by Eq. 11.2-49. If we define two dimensionless quantities characterizing heat exchanger as

$$\text{Capacity ratio:}\quad R = \frac{\dot{m}_{\mathrm{I}} c_p^{\mathrm{I}}}{\dot{m}_{\mathrm{II}} c_p^{\mathrm{II}}} = \frac{T_i^{\mathrm{II}} - T_o^{\mathrm{II}}}{T_o^{\mathrm{I}} - T_i^{\mathrm{I}}} \qquad (11.2\text{-}51)$$

$$\text{Effectiveness:}\quad P = \frac{T_o^{\mathrm{I}} - T_i^{\mathrm{I}}}{T_i^{\mathrm{II}} - T_i^{\mathrm{I}}} \qquad (11.2\text{-}52)$$

we can rewrite Eq. 11.2-48 as

$$\dot{Q} = U_o A_o \left\{ F \left[\frac{(T_2^{\mathrm{II}} - T_2^{\mathrm{I}}) - (T_1^{\mathrm{II}} - T_1^{\mathrm{I}})}{\ln\left(\dfrac{T_2^{\mathrm{II}} - T_2^{\mathrm{I}}}{T_1^{\mathrm{II}} - T_1^{\mathrm{I}}}\right)} \right] \right\} \qquad (11.2\text{-}53)$$

where the correction factor F is given by

$$F = \left(\frac{\sqrt{R^2+1}}{R-1}\right) \frac{\ln\left(\frac{1-P}{1-PR}\right)}{\ln\left[\frac{2-P(R+1-\sqrt{R^2+1})}{2-P(R+1+\sqrt{R^2+1})}\right]} \tag{11.2-54}$$

This correction factor has been determined for a variety of values of P and R and the results are plotted in Fig. 11.2.8. As we might have guessed the correction factor is always less than one, i.e., the one shell-pass, one tube-pass arrangement provides the maximum heat transfer rate, and under certain circumstances F can become quite small. In general it is considered economically unsatisfactory to operate a heat exchanger under conditions such that $F < 0.75$. We can also see from Fig. 11.2.8 that there are certain conditions for which no positive solution for F exists (for example, large values of R and P) and under those conditions some other shell and tube arrangement must be used.

A variety of other shell and tube configurations has been studied[6] and the correction factor for the two shell-pass configuration is given in Fig. 11.2.9. The designation of the "1" and "2" ends of the exchanger for the calculation of ΔT_{ln} is illustrated in Fig. 11.2.10. Once again we see that the hypothetical configuration is obtained by "straightening out" the two streams so that the flow is uni-directional. It should be clear from both Figs. 11.2.7 and 11.2.9 that under circumstances where R is large and the value of P is small it may be very difficult to determine the correction factor with satisfactory accuracy and under these conditions one may wish to use Eq. 11.2-48 directly. A comparable expression for the two shell-pass exchanger is given by Jakob[6].

While the results given in Figs. 11.2.8 and 11.2.9 illustrate very clearly how the overall temperature difference is reduced for multi-pass heat exchangers, they are somewhat difficult to use since all four terminal temperatures must be known in order to determine F. If these temperatures are specified then Eq. 11.2-53 can be used to determine the area required in a given heat exchanger. Often this is not the case and an alternate analysis, described in the next section, is preferable to the trial-and-error calculations required by the use of the correction factor charts.

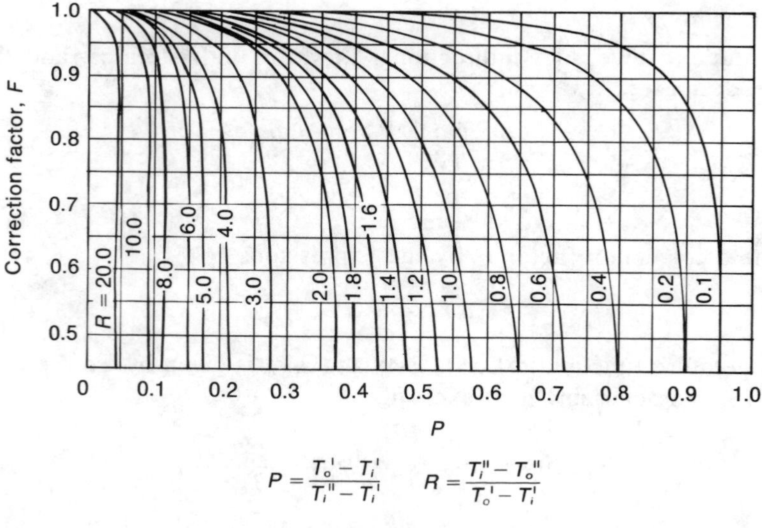

$$P = \frac{T_o' - T_i'}{T_i'' - T_i'} \qquad R = \frac{T_i'' - T_o''}{T_o' - T_i'}$$

T_i'' = inlet temperature, shell side
T_o'' = outlet temperature, shell side
T_i' = inlet temperature, tube side
T_o' = outlet temperature, tube side

Fig. 11.2.8 Correction factors for shell and tube heat exchangers having one shell-pass and two or a multiple of two tube-passes. (Adapted from M. Jakob and G. A. Hawkins, *Elements of Heat Transfer and Insulation*, Second Edition, John Wiley & Sons, Inc., New York, 1950.)

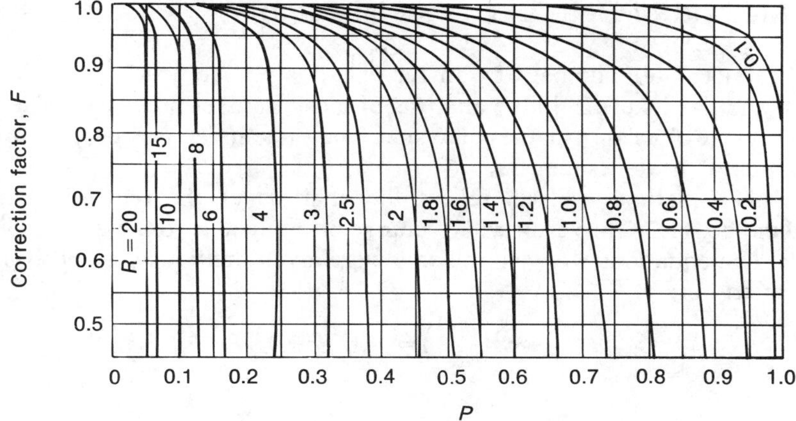

Fig. 11.2.9 Correction factors for shell and tube heat exchangers having two shell-passes and four or a multiple of four tube-passes. (Adapted from M. Jakob and G. A. Hawkins, *Elements of Heat Transfer and Insulation*, Second Edition, John Wiley & Sons, Inc., New York, 1950.)

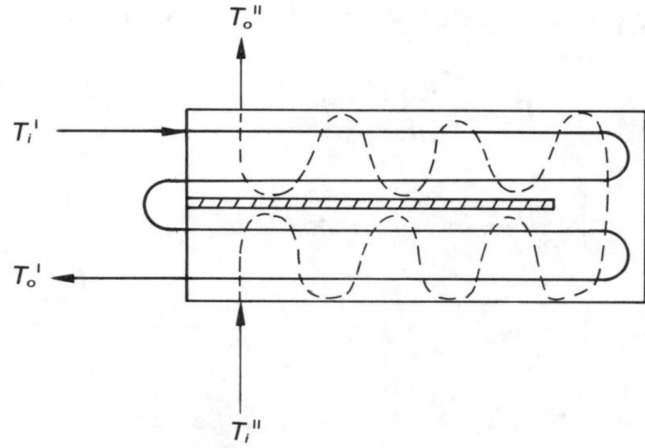

(a) Real configuration

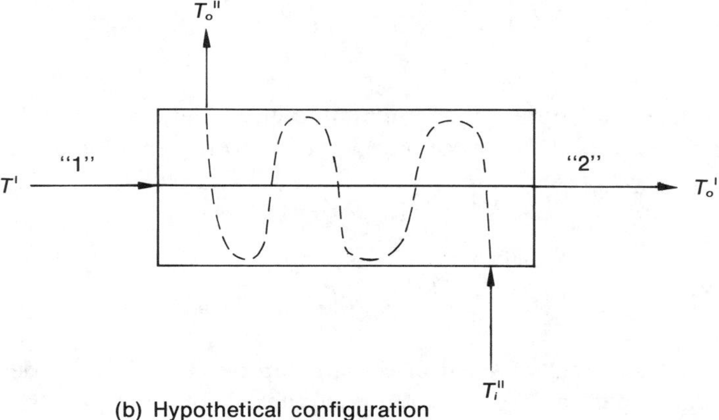

(b) Hypothetical configuration

Fig. 11.2.10 Designation of the ends of multi-pass heat exchangers.

11.3 The NTU-Method of Heat Exchanger Design

The letters NTU refer to the "number of transfer units," a phrase which is common in the chemical engineering literature and has its origin in the analysis of mass transfer processes. The NTU-method was first used by Chilton and Colburn[7] in the analysis of mass transfer processes, later by London and Kays[8] for the analysis of heat exchangers.

To illustrate the NTU-method we will repeat the analysis of the one tube-pass, one shell-pass exchanger discussed in Sec. 11.2. The result will of course be applicable to the double-pipe heat exchanger analyzed in Sec. 11.1. The equations we wish to solve were given previously as Eqs. 11.1-14, 11.1-15, and 11.1-18 and are rewritten here as

$$\dot{m}_{\mathrm{I}} c_p{}^{\mathrm{I}} \left(\frac{dT^{\mathrm{I}}}{dz} \right) = -\langle q_r \rangle_i n\pi D_i \tag{11.3-1}$$

$$\pm \dot{m}_{\mathrm{II}} c_p{}^{\mathrm{II}} \left(\frac{dT^{\mathrm{II}}}{dz} \right) = -\langle q_r \rangle_o n\pi D_o \tag{11.3-2}$$

$$\langle q_r \rangle_i n\pi D_i = \langle q_r \rangle_o n\pi D_o = U_o n\pi D_o (T^{\mathrm{I}} - T^{\mathrm{II}}) \tag{11.3-3}$$

In the equations in Sec. 11.1 we had $n = 1$ since there was only a single tube, and Eqs. 11.3-1 through 11.3-3 represent the general case for a shell and tube heat exchanger having n tubes with an inner diameter D_i and an outer diameter D_o. The tube fluid, designated as fluid I, is assumed to be flowing in the positive z-direction, while the shell fluid may be flowing in either the positive (co-current flow) or negative (counter-current flow) z-direction. In Eq. 11.3-2 the positive (+) sign represents counter-current flow while the negative (−) sign is for co-current flow.

In order to use the NTU-method we define a new *capacity ratio* which is a *minimum capacity* ratio given by

$$R_{\min} = \frac{(\dot{m}c_p)_{\min}}{(\dot{m}c_p)_{\max}} \tag{11.3-4}$$

or

$$R_{\min} = \begin{cases} \dfrac{\dot{m}_{\mathrm{I}} c_p{}^{\mathrm{I}}}{\dot{m}_{\mathrm{II}} c_p{}^{\mathrm{II}}}, & \text{when } \dot{m}_{\mathrm{I}} c_p{}^{\mathrm{I}} < \dot{m}_{\mathrm{II}} c_p{}^{\mathrm{II}} \\[2ex] \dfrac{\dot{m}_{\mathrm{II}} c_p{}^{\mathrm{II}}}{\dot{m}_{\mathrm{I}} c_p{}^{\mathrm{I}}}, & \text{when } \dot{m}_{\mathrm{II}} c_p{}^{\mathrm{II}} < \dot{m}_{\mathrm{I}} c_p{}^{\mathrm{I}} \end{cases} \tag{11.3-5}$$

so that $R_{\min}$ is bounded by zero and one. Similarly a *minimum effectiveness* is defined by

$$\epsilon = \begin{cases} \dfrac{T_o^{\mathrm{I}} - T_i^{\mathrm{I}}}{T_i^{\mathrm{II}} - T_i^{\mathrm{I}}}, & \text{when } \dot{m}_{\mathrm{I}} c_p{}^{\mathrm{I}} < \dot{m}_{\mathrm{II}} c_p{}^{\mathrm{II}} \\[2ex] \dfrac{T_i^{\mathrm{II}} - T_o^{\mathrm{II}}}{T_i^{\mathrm{II}} - T_i^{\mathrm{I}}}, & \text{when } \dot{m}_{\mathrm{II}} c_p{}^{\mathrm{II}} < \dot{m}_{\mathrm{I}} c_p{}^{\mathrm{I}} \end{cases} \tag{11.3-6}$$

where it is traditional to use ϵ to represent the minimum effectiveness where $0 \leqslant \epsilon \leqslant 1$. The number of transfer units, NTU, is defined as the ratio of $U_oA_o = U_iA_i$ to the smaller of $\dot{m}_{\mathrm{I}} c_p{}^{\mathrm{I}}$ and $\dot{m}_{\mathrm{II}} c_p{}^{\mathrm{II}}$, thus

$$\mathrm{NTU} = \begin{cases} \dfrac{U_oA_o}{\dot{m}_{\mathrm{I}} c_p{}^{\mathrm{I}}}, & \text{when } \dot{m}_{\mathrm{I}} c_p{}^{\mathrm{I}} < \dot{m}_{\mathrm{II}} c_p{}^{\mathrm{II}} \\[2ex] \dfrac{U_oA_o}{\dot{m}_{\mathrm{II}} c_p{}^{\mathrm{II}}}, & \text{when } \dot{m}_{\mathrm{II}} c_p{}^{\mathrm{II}} < \dot{m}_{\mathrm{I}} c_p{}^{\mathrm{I}} \end{cases} \tag{11.3-7}$$

In our analysis in Secs. 11.1 and 11.2 we used three parameters (P, R, $\Delta T_{\ln}$) to describe heat exchangers. Here we will exchange those parameters for three new ones (NTU, $R_{\min}$, ϵ); the advantage being that ϵ may be determined as an *explicit* function of $R_{\min}$ and NTU. Under these circumstances we can solve for the outlet temperatures directly when the inlet temperatures, the flow rates and heat capacities, and the exchanger geometry and overall coefficient are specified. This is always the case when existing equipment is to be used in a new process, and is generally the case when new equipment is "designed." In the development of a new process one might think that the geometry of an exchanger might be specified in terms of the required inlet and outlet temperatures for the two process streams; however, heat exchangers are expensive items and it is not economically practical to construct a new heat exchanger for each new process. Because of this we must consider the large shell and tube heat exchangers to be "shelf items" and the designer must choose that model which best suits his purposes.

Returning to Eqs. 11.3-1 and 11.3-2 we use Eq. 11.3-3 to equate the right-hand-sides giving

$$\dot{m}_{\mathrm{I}} c_p{}^{\mathrm{I}} \left(\frac{dT^{\mathrm{I}}}{dz}\right) = \pm \dot{m}_{\mathrm{II}} c_p{}^{\mathrm{II}} \left(\frac{dT^{\mathrm{II}}}{dz}\right) \tag{11.3-8}$$

Our objective here is to derive the governing differential equation for $(T^{\mathrm{I}} - T^{\mathrm{II}})$ in terms of flow rates, heat capacities, exchanger area, and the overall coefficient. In order to do this we first subtract the quantity $\dot{m}_{\mathrm{I}} c_p{}^{\mathrm{I}}(dT^{\mathrm{II}}/dz)$ from both sides to obtain

$$\dot{m}_{\mathrm{I}} c_p{}^{\mathrm{I}} \frac{d}{dz}(T^{\mathrm{I}} - T^{\mathrm{II}}) = \left[-\dot{m}_{\mathrm{I}} c_p{}^{\mathrm{I}} \pm \dot{m}_{\mathrm{II}} c_p{}^{\mathrm{II}}\right] \frac{dT^{\mathrm{II}}}{\mathrm{dz}} \tag{11.3-9}$$

From Eq. 11.3-2 we obtain

$$\left(\frac{dT^{\mathrm{II}}}{dz}\right) = \frac{-\langle q_r \rangle_o n\pi D_o}{\pm \dot{m}_{\mathrm{II}} c_p{}^{\mathrm{II}}} \tag{11.3-10}$$

which may be substituted into Eq. 11.3-9 to yield

$$\dot{m}_{\mathrm{I}} c_p{}^{\mathrm{I}} \frac{d}{dz}(T^{\mathrm{I}} - T^{\mathrm{II}}) = \frac{-\langle q_r \rangle_o n\pi D_o}{\pm \dot{m}_{\mathrm{II}} c_p{}^{\mathrm{II}}} \left[-\dot{m}_{\mathrm{I}} c_p{}^{\mathrm{I}} \pm \dot{m}_{\mathrm{II}} c_p{}^{\mathrm{II}}\right] \tag{11.3-11}$$

Dividing Eq. 11.3-11 by $\dot{m}_{\mathrm{I}} c_p{}^{\mathrm{I}}$ leads to

$$\frac{d}{dz}(T^{\mathrm{I}} - T^{\mathrm{II}}) = \frac{-\langle q_r \rangle_o n\pi D_o}{\dot{m}_{\mathrm{I}} c_p{}^{\mathrm{I}}} \left[\frac{-\dot{m}_{\mathrm{I}} c_p{}^{\mathrm{I}}}{\pm \dot{m}_{\mathrm{II}} c_p{}^{\mathrm{II}}} + 1\right] \tag{11.3-12}$$

Substitution of Eq. 11.3-3 allows us to eliminate $\langle q_r \rangle_o$ and write

$$\frac{d}{dz}(T^{\mathrm{I}} - T^{\mathrm{II}}) = -\frac{U_o n\pi D_o T^{\mathrm{I}} - T^{\mathrm{II}}}{\dot{m}_{\mathrm{I}} c_p{}^{\mathrm{I}}} \left[\frac{-\dot{m}_{\mathrm{I}} c_p{}^{\mathrm{I}}}{\pm \dot{m}_{\mathrm{II}} c_p{}^{\mathrm{II}}} + 1\right] \tag{11.3-13}$$

We can now separate variables and integrate from $z = 0$ to $z = L$ to obtain

$$\ln\left(\frac{T^{\mathrm{I}}_{z=L} - T^{\mathrm{II}}_{z=L}}{T^{\mathrm{I}}_{z=0} - T^{\mathrm{II}}_{z=L}}\right) = -\frac{U_o A_o}{\dot{m}_{\mathrm{I}} c_p{}^{\mathrm{I}}} \left[\frac{-\dot{m}_{\mathrm{I}} c_p{}^{\mathrm{I}}}{\pm \dot{m}_{\mathrm{II}} c_p{}^{\mathrm{II}}} + 1\right] \tag{11.3-14a}$$

or

$$\left(\frac{T^{\mathrm{I}}_{z=L} - T^{\mathrm{II}}_{z=L}}{T^{\mathrm{I}}_{z=0} - T^{\mathrm{II}}_{z=0}}\right) = \exp\left\{-\frac{U_o A_o}{\dot{m}_{\mathrm{I}} c_p{}^{\mathrm{I}}} \left[\frac{-\dot{m}_{\mathrm{I}} c_p{}^{\mathrm{I}}}{\pm \dot{m}_{\mathrm{II}} c_p{}^{\mathrm{II}}} + 1\right]\right\} \tag{11.3-14b}$$

Here we have replaced $n\pi D_o$ with A_o, and we have refrained from specifying the temperatures at $z = 0$ and $z = L$ in terms of inlet or outlet temperatures. Eqs. 11.3-14 are completely general and can be used to calculate outlet temperatures if the inlet temperatures are given along with $U_o A_o$ and the mass flow rates and heat capacities; however, we would like to express this result in terms of ϵ, $R_{\min}$, and NTU, and in order to do so we must consider the different cases that can occur with a one shell-pass, one tube-pass heat exchanger.

In Fig. 11.3.1a we have shown a co-current exchanger for which we can express the temperatures at $z = 0$ and $z = L$ as

$$\left.\begin{aligned} T^{\mathrm{I}}_{z=L} &= T_o{}^{\mathrm{I}}, \qquad T^{\mathrm{I}}_{z=0} = T_i^{\mathrm{I}} \\ T^{\mathrm{II}}_{z=L} &= T_o{}^{\mathrm{II}}, \qquad T^{\mathrm{II}}_{z=o} = T_i^{\mathrm{I}} \end{aligned}\right\} \quad \text{co-current flow}$$

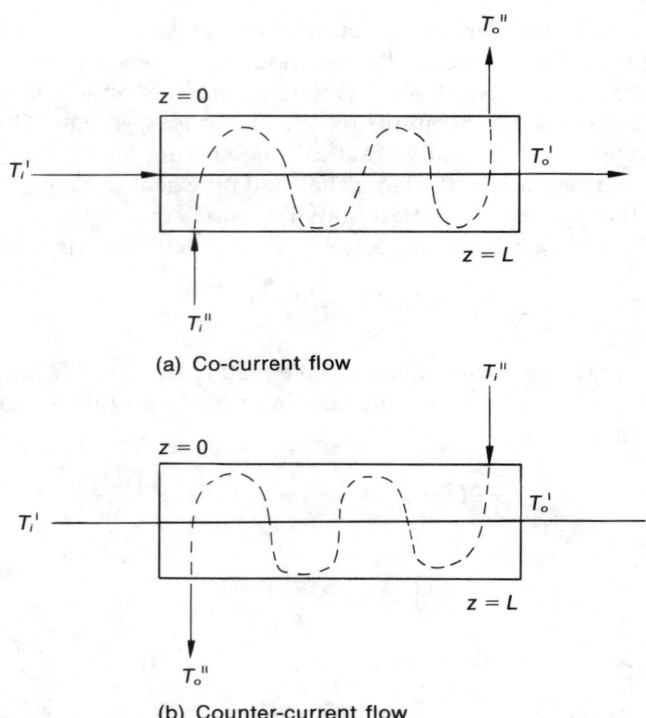

Fig. 11.3.1 One-pass heat exchangers.

and Eq. 11.3-14b takes the form

$$\left(\frac{T_o^{\mathrm{I}} - T_o^{\mathrm{II}}}{T_i^{\mathrm{I}} - T_i^{\mathrm{II}}}\right) = \exp\left\{-\frac{U_o A_o}{\dot{m}_{\mathrm{I}} c_p^{\mathrm{I}}}\left[\frac{\dot{m}_{\mathrm{I}} c_p^{\mathrm{I}}}{\dot{m}_{\mathrm{II}} c_p^{\mathrm{II}}} + 1\right]\right\}, \quad \text{co-current flow} \tag{11.3-15}$$

We now consider the special case, $\dot{m}_{\mathrm{I}} c_p^{\mathrm{I}} < \dot{m}_{\mathrm{II}} c_p^{\mathrm{II}}$ and make use of Eqs. 11.3-5 and 11.3-6 to express ϵ as

$$\epsilon = \frac{T_o^{\mathrm{I}} - T_i^{\mathrm{I}}}{T_i^{\mathrm{II}} - T_i^{\mathrm{I}}} = \frac{1 - (T_o^{\mathrm{I}} - T_o^{\mathrm{II}})/(T_i^{\mathrm{I}} - T_i^{\mathrm{II}})}{1 + R_{\min}}, \quad \dot{m}_{\mathrm{I}} c_p^{\mathrm{I}} < \dot{m}_{\mathrm{II}} c_p^{\mathrm{II}} \tag{11.3-16}$$

Substitution of Eq. 11.3-15 into Eq. 11.3-16, and noting that for this case

$$R_{\min} = \dot{m}_{\mathrm{I}} c_p^{\mathrm{I}} / \dot{m}_{\mathrm{II}} c_p^{\mathrm{II}}$$
$$\mathrm{NTU} = U_o A_o / \dot{m}_{\mathrm{I}} c_p^{\mathrm{I}}$$

we obtain

$$\epsilon = \frac{1 - e^{-\mathrm{NTU}(1+R_{\min})}}{(1 + R_{\min})}, \quad \text{co-current flow, } \dot{m}_{\mathrm{I}} c_p^{\mathrm{I}} < \dot{m}_{\mathrm{II}} c_p^{\mathrm{II}} \tag{11.3-17}$$

One can also show that Eq. 11.3-17 is valid for the case where $\dot{m}_{\mathrm{II}} c_p^{\mathrm{II}} < \dot{m}_{\mathrm{I}} c_p^{\mathrm{I}}$; however, the proof will be left as an exercise for the student. In using Eq. 11.3-17 we note that once $R_{\min}$ and NTU are specified we can compute ϵ which does not contain the outlet temperature of fluid II. An energy balance around the entire exchanger yields

$$\frac{\dot{m}_{\mathrm{I}} c_p^{\mathrm{I}}}{\dot{m}_{\mathrm{II}} c_p^{\mathrm{II}}} = \frac{T_i^{\mathrm{II}} - T_o^{\mathrm{II}}}{T_o^{\mathrm{I}} - T_i^{\mathrm{I}}}, \quad \text{for co-current and counter-current flow, and arbitrary values of } \dot{m}_{\mathrm{I}} c_p^{\mathrm{I}} \text{ and } \dot{m}_{\mathrm{II}} c_p^{\mathrm{II}} \tag{11.3-18}$$

thus knowledge of $R_{\min}$ provides a second equation relating the terminal temperatures. If any two terminal temperatures are specified we can use Eqs. 11.3-17 and 11.3-18 to compute the other two terminal temperatures and thus the total heat $\dot{Q}$ transferred from fluid II to fluid I by

$$\dot{Q} = \dot{m}_{\text{I}} c_p^{\text{I}} (T_o^{\text{I}} - T_i^{\text{I}}) \tag{11.3-19}$$

A graphical representation of Eq. 11.3-17 is given in Fig. 11.3.2, and there we see that the effectiveness, ϵ, is essentially independent of the number of transfer units for NTU > 5.

Continuing with our exploration of the special forms of Eqs. 11.3-4, we now consider the case of counter-current flow illustrated in Fig. 11.3.1b. The temperatures at $z = 0$ and $z = L$ are now expressed as

$$\left.\begin{array}{ll} T^{\text{I}}_{z=L} = T_o^{\text{I}}, & T^{\text{I}}_{z=0} = T_i^{\text{I}} \\ T^{\text{II}}_{z=L} = T_i^{\text{II}}, & T^{\text{II}}_{z=0} = T_o^{\text{II}} \end{array}\right\}, \quad \text{counter-current flow}$$

and Eq. 11.3-14b takes the form

$$\left(\frac{T_o^{\text{I}} - T_i^{\text{II}}}{T_i^{\text{I}} - T_o^{\text{II}}}\right) = \exp\left\{-\frac{U_o A_o}{\dot{m}_{\text{I}} c_p^{\text{I}}}\left[1 - \frac{\dot{m}_{\text{I}} c_p^{\text{I}}}{\dot{m}_{\text{II}} c_p^{\text{II}}}\right]\right\}, \quad \text{counter-current flow} \tag{11.3-20}$$

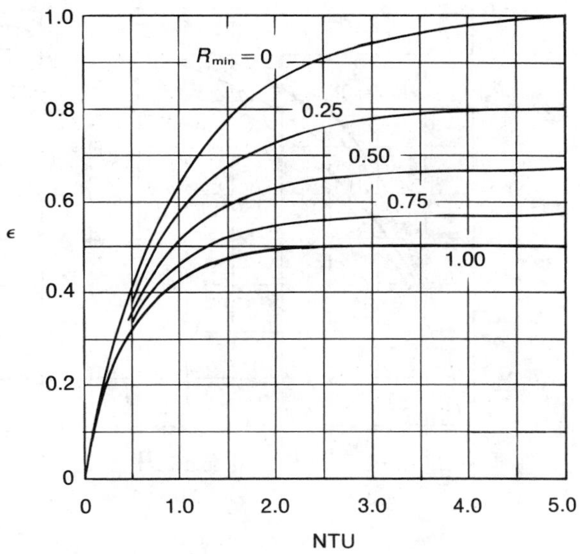

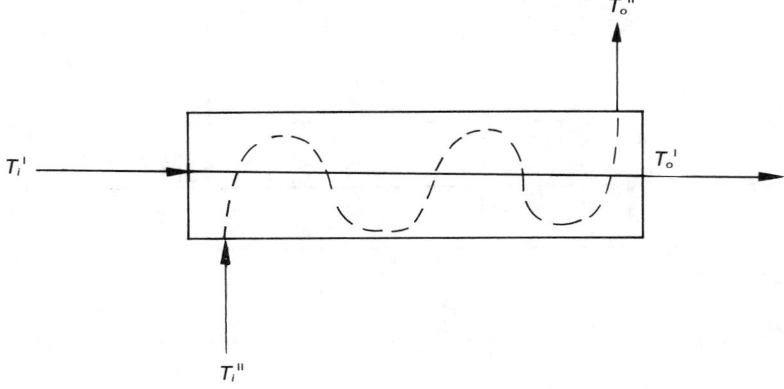

Fig. 11.3.2 Effectiveness as a function of NTU and $R_{\min}$ for a single pass co-current heat exchanger. (Adapted from W. M. Kays and A. L. London, *Compact Heat Exchangers*, McGraw-Hill Book Co., Inc., New York, 1964.)

For the case where $\dot{m}_{\rm I} c_p^{\rm I} < \dot{m}_{\rm II} c_p^{\rm II}$ we can write Eq. 11.3-20 as

$$\left(\frac{T_o^{\rm I} - T_i^{\rm II}}{T_i^{\rm I} - T_o^{\rm II}}\right) = e^{-{\rm NTU}(1 - R_{\rm min})}, \quad \text{counter-current flow, } \dot{m}_{\rm I} c_p^{\rm I} < \dot{m}_{\rm II} c_p^{\rm II} \tag{11.3-21}$$

and from Eq. 11.3-6 we find ϵ to be

$$\epsilon = \frac{T_o^{\rm I} - T_i^{\rm I}}{T_i^{\rm II} - T_i^{\rm I}}, \quad \dot{m}_{\rm I} c_p^{\rm I} < \dot{m}_{\rm II} c_p^{\rm II} \tag{11.3-22}$$

Making use of

$$R_{\rm min} = \frac{T_i^{\rm II} - T_o^{\rm II}}{T_o^{\rm I} - T_i^{\rm I}}, \quad \dot{m}_{\rm I} c_p^{\rm I} < \dot{m}_{\rm II} c_p^{\rm II} \tag{11.3-23}$$

we can express ϵ as

$$\epsilon = \frac{1 - e^{-{\rm NTU}(1-R_{\rm min})}}{1 - R_{\rm min}\, e^{-{\rm NTU}(1-R_{\rm min})}}, \quad \text{counter-current flow, } \dot{m}_{\rm I} c_p^{\rm I} < \dot{m}_{\rm II} c_p^{\rm II} \tag{11.3-24}$$

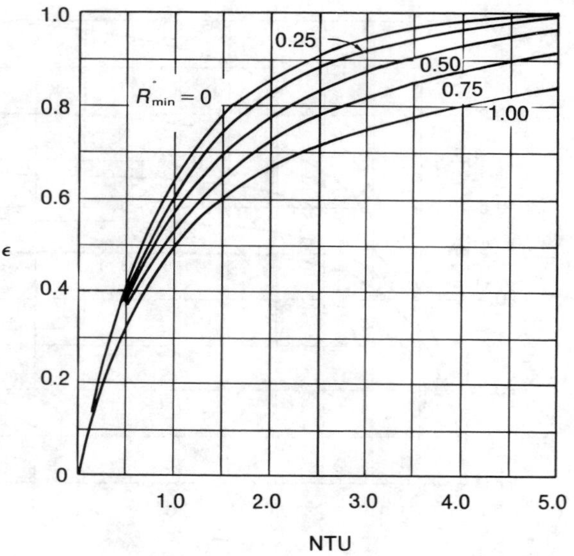

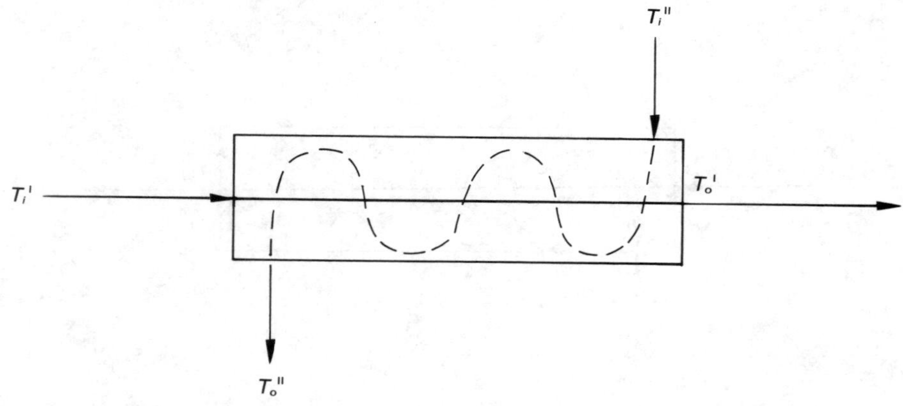

Fig. 11.3.3 Effectiveness as a function of NTU and $R_{\rm min}$ for a single pass counter-current heat exchanger. (Adapted from W. M. Kays and A. L. London, *Compact Heat Exchangers*, McGraw-Hill Book Co., Inc., New York, 1964.)

Eq. 11.3-24 is represented in graphical form in Fig. 11.3.3, and comparing these results with those in Fig. 11.3.2 we see that the effectiveness of the counter-current exchanger is always greater than the co-current exchanger except for the condition $R_{min} = 0$ where there is no difference. In examining Eqs. 11.3-17 and 11.3-24 and Figs. 11.3.2 and 11.3.3 we should note that two equations are required to describe the single-pass heat exchanger when the NTU-method is used, while only one equation (Eq. 11.1-26) is required for both co- and counter-current flows when the method outlined in Sec. 11.1 is used. However, we must remember that the NTU-method allows us to calculate directly the exit temperatures of the two streams when flow rates, heat capacities, exchanger area and overall heat transfer coefficient are given.

The NTU-method can of course be applied to multi-pass heat exchangers and the results for the multi-pass exchangers discussed in Sec. 11.2 are presented in Figs. 11.3.4 and 11.3.5. Other shell and tube configurations are discussed by Kays and London along with a thorough treatment of finned tubed heat exchangers and other types of compact cross-flow exchangers.

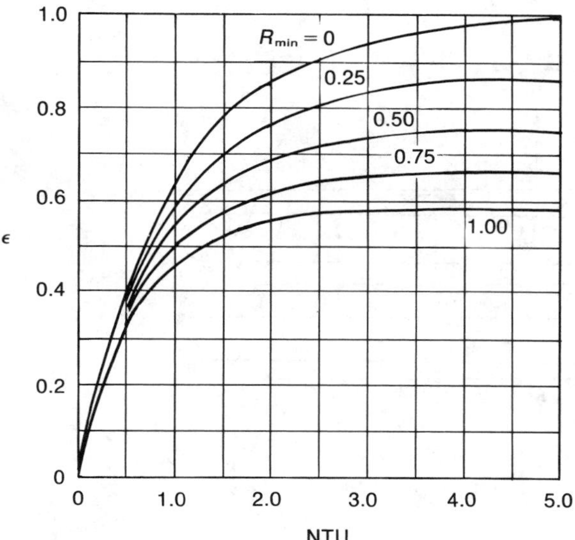

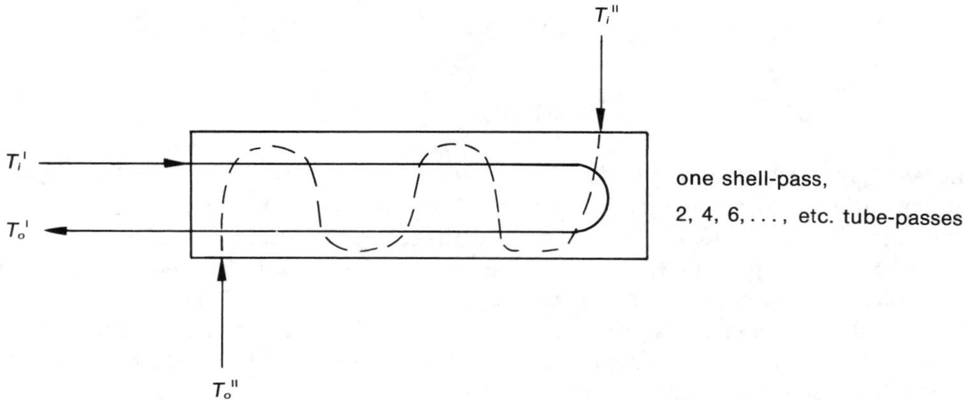

Fig. 11.3.4 Effectiveness as a function of NTU and R_{min} for one shell-pass and an even number of tube-passes. (Adapted from W. M. Kays and A. L. London, *Compact Heat Exchangers*, McGraw-Hill Book Co., Inc., New York, 1964.)

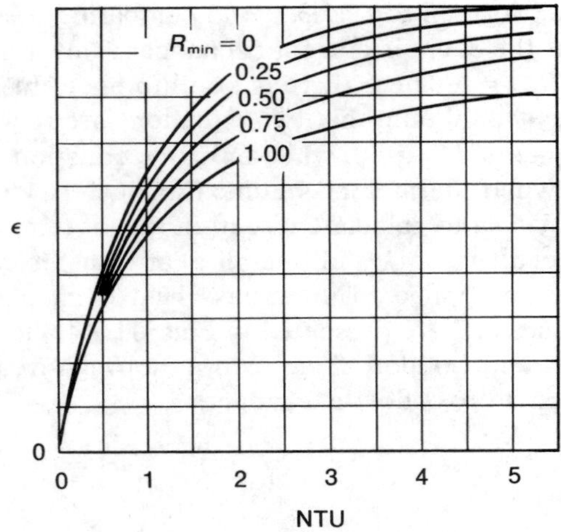

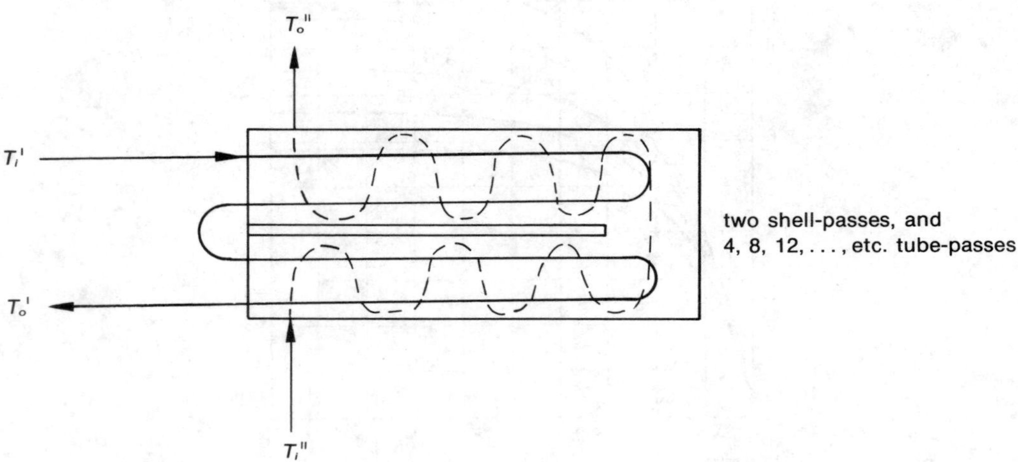

Fig. 11.3.5 Effectiveness as a function of NTU and R_{min} for two shell-passes and a multiple of four tube-passes. (Adapted from W. M. Kays and A. L. London, *Compact Heat Exchangers*, McGraw-Hill Book Co., Inc., New York, 1964.)

11.4 Fouling of Heat Exchange Surfaces

At this point we have developed methods of analyzing shell and tube heat exchangers in terms of flow rates and heat capacities, heat exchanger geometry and the overall heat transfer coefficient U_o or U_i. In order to determine the overall coefficient we must know the tube dimensions and thermal conductivity, and we must be able to specify the shell-side and tube-side film heat transfer coefficients. The tube-side coefficients can usually be estimated with reasonable accuracy by means of the correlations presented in Sec. 7.6, and the shell-side coefficients are related to the film heat transfer coefficients for tube bundles discussed in Sec. 7.8. The difficulties associated with estimating shell-side coefficients from tube bundle correlations were discussed briefly in Sec. 11.2.

One of the most difficult aspects of heat exchanger design is the reduction of the heat transfer rate across the tube walls owing to the deposition of "scale" or insoluble inorganic compounds on the tube wall. The magnitude of this effect depends on the thickness of the deposit and the effect is usually reported in terms of a film heat transfer coefficient for the scale or its inverse which is often referred to as the "fouling factor."

$$h_s = \{\text{film heat transfer coefficient for the scale}\} \tag{11.4-1}$$

$$h_s^{-1} = \{\text{fouling factor}\} \tag{11.4-2}$$

If there is appreciable scale deposited on both the inside and outside of a tube we must have two fouling factors $h_{s,i}^{-1}$ and $h_{s,o}^{-1}$ in order to determine U_o by the expression

$$\frac{1}{U_o} = \frac{1}{h^{\text{I}}}\left(\frac{D_o}{D_i}\right) + (h_{s,i}^{-1})\left(\frac{D_o}{D_i}\right) + \frac{D_o}{2k}\ln\left(\frac{D_o}{D_i}\right) + (h_{s,o}^{-1}) + \frac{1}{h^{\text{II}}}$$

which is simply Eq. 11.1-17 modified to include the effect of the scale.

Scale deposits are built up continuously during the operation of the exchanger, thus if fouling is a serious problem one must be prepared for a steadily decreasing exchanger efficiency. In order to minimize the cost of removing scale the fluid stream having the largest fouling factor should always be contained in the tubes for the inside of the tubes in the tube bundle are easily cleaned by mechanical means. If the shell side of the tubes requires cleaning in order to maintain heat exchanger performance, one must resort to chemical treatments for there is no practical method of cleaning the exterior surface of a tube bundle.

Fouling factor data are extremely difficult to obtain since experiments must be performed on process streams and in general with process equipment. It is much more difficult to perform experiments under these conditions than it is under the usual laboratory conditions, and for this reason one must use fouling factors with caution. In Table 11.4-1 we have listed some fouling factors for various water supplies. These factors must be used cautiously for they simply indicate the proper magnitude of the fouling factor while

Table 11.4-1 Fouling Factors for Water, hr ft^2 °F/Btu†

Temperature of heating medium	Up to 240°F		240–400°F	
Temperature of water	125°F or less		Over 125°F	
	Water velocity, fps		*Water velocity, fps*	
Types of water	(1) *3 ft and less*	(2) *Over 3 ft*	(3) *3 ft and less*	(4) *Over 3 ft*
Seawater	0.0005	0.0005	0.001	0.001
Brackish water	0.002	0.001	0.003	0.002
Cooling tower and artificial spray pond:				
Treated makeup	0.001	0.001	0.002	0.002
Untreated	0.003	0.003	0.005	0.004
City or well water (such as Great Lakes)	0.001	0.001	0.002	0.002
Great Lakes	0.001	0.001	0.002	0.002
River water:				
Minimum	0.002	0.001	0.003	0.002
Mississippi	0.003	0.002	0.004	0.003
Delaware, Schuylkill	0.003	0.002	0.004	0.003
East River and New York Bay	0.003	0.002	0.004	0.003
Chicago Sanitary Canal	0.008	0.006	0.010	0.008
Muddy or silty	0.003	0.002	0.004	0.003
Hard (over 15 grains/gal)	0.003	0.003	0.005	0.005
Engine jacket	0.001	0.001	0.001	0.001
Distilled	0.0005	0.0005	0.0005	0.0005
Treated boiler feedwater	0.001	0.0005	0.001	0.001
Boiler blowdown	0.002	0.002	0.002	0.002

†From *Standards of Tubular Exchanger Manufacturers Association*, 1959.

giving no information regarding the transient nature of the process. This is also true of the fouling factors listed in Table 11.4-2 for a variety of liquids and gases. At best these tabulated data should alert the engineer to the problem of fouling, and provide some estimate of the magnitude of the effect. For a semi-analytical analysis of fouling the interested student is referred to the work of Taborek *et al.*[9].

Table 11.4-2 Fouling Factors for Miscellaneous Fluids, hr ft²/Btu†

Industrial gases and vapors	
Manufactured gas	0.01
Engine exhaust gas	0.01
Steam (non-oil-bearing)	0.0005
Exhaust steam (oil-bearing)	0.001
Refrigerating vapors (oil-bearing)	0.002
Natural gas	0.001
Compressed air	0.002
Industrial liquids	
Industrial organic heat transfer media	0.001
Refrigerating liquids	0.001
Molten heat transfer salts	0.0005
Hydraulic fluid	0.001
Industrial oils	
Fuel oil	0.005
Engine lube oil	0.001
Transformer oil	0.001
Quench oil	0.004
Vegetable oils	0.003

†From *Standards of Tubular Exchanger Manufacturers Association,* 1959.

PROBLEMS

11-1. (11.1) Derive Eqs. 11.1-2 from Eq. 11.1-1 being careful to express the assumptions in an analytic manner.

11-2. (11.1) If the flow is compressible one can express the density as $\rho = \bar{\rho} + \rho'$ where $\bar{\rho}$ is the time-averaged value and ρ' is the fluctuating component of the density. Using this expression for the density and expressing the velocity as $\mathbf{v} = \bar{\mathbf{v}} + \mathbf{v}'$ derive an expression for the time-averaged mass flow rate, $\dot{m}$, which is different from that given by Eq. 11.1-4.

11-3. (11.1) Derive Eqs. 11.1-5.

11-4. (11.1) Derive Eq. 11.1-15 from Eq. 11.1-1 indicating how the sign changes are related to the direction of flow.

11-5. (11.1) List the assumptions that we used in the derivation of Eq. 11.1-26.

11-6. (11.1) Indicate what form Eq. 11.1-27 takes when $\Delta T_1 = \Delta T_2$.

11-7. (11.1) If the inlet and outlet temperatures T_i^{I}, T_o^{I}, T_i^{II}, T_o^{II} for a double-pipe heat exchanger are specified and U_o is fixed derive an expression relating the area required for counter-current flow to the area required for current flow.

11-8. (11.1) Lubricating oil at 150°F is to be cooled to 105°F by water available at 70°F in a double-pipe, counter-current flow, heat exchanger. The oil and water flow rates are 225 and 195 lb_m/hr respectively, and the specific heat of the oil is 0.46 Btu/lb_m°F. The overall heat transfer coefficient is 58 Btu/hr ft²°F based on the outside area: (a) Determine the required heat transfer area. (b) If this exchanger is used to cool this same oil entering the exchanger at 210°F at a rate of 225 lb_m/hr, what is the exit temperature of the oil if the water inlet temperature and flow rate are kept constant?

11-9. (11.2) A shell and tube heat exchanger is used to heat 85 000 lb_m/hr of water from 187°F to 255°F with 40 psia steam condensing on the tube side. The exchanger has one shell-side pass and two tube-side passes, and there are 120 tubes with an inside diameter of 1 in. and an outside diameter of $1\frac{1}{8}$ in. If the overall coefficient based on the inside area is 572 Btu/hr ft^2°F, how long must the tubes be?

11-10. (11.2) Water at a flow rate of 5 gal/min is to be cooled from 57°F to 44°F by brine ($c_p = 0.68$ Btu/lb_m °F) at 32°F and a flow rate of 3400 lb_m/hr. For an overall heat transfer coefficient of 200 Btu/hr ft^2°F, compare the required exchanger area for one and two shell-pass exchangers when the brine flows through the tubes. There are four tube passes.

11-11. (11.2) Derive Eqs. 11.2-32 through 11.2-35.

11-12. (11.2) Show what form Eq. 11.2-54 takes when $R = 1$.

11-13. (11.3) Prove that Eq. 11.3-17 is valid for $\dot{m}_{I} c_p{}^{I} > \dot{m}_{II} c_p{}^{II}$.

11-14. (11.3) Explain why $R = R_{min} = 0$ represents the case of a condensing fluid.

11-15. (11.3) If the water flow rate in Prob. 11-9 is increased from 85 000 lb_m/hr to 200 000 lb_m/hr what is the outlet water temperature for the exchanger designed in Prob. 11-9? Note: Prob. 11-9 must be solved before this temperature can be computed.

11-16. (11.4) If a fouling factor of 0.003 hr ft^2°F/Btu is included for the inside of the tubes in Prob. 11-9, how long must the tubes be?

REFERENCES

1. Kays, W. M., and London, A. L., *Compact Heat Exchangers*, McGraw-Hill Book Co., Inc., New York, 1964.
2. Kern, D. Q., *Process Heat Transfer*, McGraw-Hill Book Co., Inc., New York, 1950.
3. *Standards of Tubular Exchangers Manufacturers Association*, Fourth Edition, Tubular Exchanger Manufacturers Association, Inc., New York, 1959.
4. McAdams, W. H., *Heat Transmission*, McGraw-Hill Book Co., Inc., New York, 1954.
5. Underwood, A. J. V., "The Calculation of the Mean Temperature Difference in Multi-Pass Heat Exchangers," *J. Inst. Petroleum Tech. (London)* **20**, 145 (1934).
6. Jakob, M., *Heat Transfer*, Vol. II, John Wiley & Sons, Inc., New York, 1957.
7. Chilton, T. H., and Colburn, A. P., "Distillation and Absorption in Packed Columns. A Convenient Design and Correlation Method," *Ind. Engr. Chem.* **27**, 255 (1935).
8. London, A. L., and Kays, W. M., "The Liquid Coupled Indirect Transfer Regenerator for Gas Turbine Plants," *Trans. ASME* **73**, 529 (1951).
9. Taborek, J., Aoki, T., Ritter, R. B., Palen, J. W., and Knudsen, J. G., "Predictive Methods for Fouling Behavior," *Chem. Engr. Prog.* **68**, No. 7, 69 (1972).

Appendix A

Properties of Materials

Table A-1 Properties of Saturated Water

T °F	k Btu/hr ft °F	c_p Btu/lb$_m$ °F	μ lb$_m$/ft hr	ρ lb$_m$/ft^3	ν ft^2/hr	α ft^2/hr	N_{Pr}	β °R^{-1}
32	0.327	1.009	4.33	62.42	0.0694	0.0052	13.37	0.03×10^{-3}
40	0.332	1.005	3.75	62.42	0.0601	0.0053	11.36	0.045
50	0.338	1.002	3.17	62.38	0.0508	0.0054	9.41	0.070
60	0.344	1.000	2.71	62.34	0.0435	0.0055	7.88	0.10
70	0.349	0.998	2.37	62.27	0.0381	0.0056	6.78	0.13
80	0.355	0.998	2.08	62.17	0.0334	0.0057	5.85	0.15
90	0.360	0.997	1.85	62.11	0.0298	0.0058	5.13	0.18
100	0.364	0.997	1.65	61.99	0.0266	0.0059	4.52	0.20
110	0.368	0.997	1.49	61.84	0.0241	0.0060	4.04	0.22×10^{-3}
120	0.372	0.997	1.36	61.73	0.0220	0.0060	3.65	0.24
130	0.375	0.998	1.24	61.54	0.0202	0.0061	3.30	0.27
140	0.378	0.998	1.14	61.39	0.0186	0.0062	3.01	0.29
150	0.381	0.999	1.04	61.20	0.0170	0.0063	2.72	0.31
160	0.384	1.000	0.97	61.01	0.0159	0.0063	2.53	0.33
170	0.386	1.001	0.90	60.79	0.0148	0.0064	2.33	0.35
180	0.389	1.002	0.84	60.57	0.0139	0.0064	2.16	0.37
190	0.390	1.003	0.79	60.35	0.0131	0.0065	2.03	0.39
200	0.392	1.004	0.74	60.13	0.0123	0.0065	1.90	0.41
210	0.393	1.005	0.69	59.88	0.0115	0.0065	1.76	0.43×10^{-3}
220	0.395	1.007	0.65	59.63	0.0109	0.0066	1.66	0.45
230	0.395	1.009	0.62	59.38	0.0104	0.0066	1.58	0.47
240	0.396	1.011	0.59	59.10	0.0100	0.0066	1.51	0.48
250	0.396	1.013	0.56	58.82	0.0095	0.0066	1.43	0.50
260	0.396	1.015	0.53	58.51	0.0091	0.0067	1.36	0.51
270	0.396	1.017	0.50	58.24	0.0086	0.0067	1.28	0.53
280	0.396	1.020	0.48	57.94	0.0083	0.0067	1.24	0.55
290	0.396	1.023	0.46	57.64	0.0080	0.0067	1.19	0.56
300	0.395	1.026	0.45	57.31	0.0079	0.0067	1.17	0.58
350	0.391	1.044	0.38	55.59	0.0068	0.0067	1.01	0.62×10^{-3}
400	0.384	1.067	0.33	53.65	0.0062	0.0068	0.91	0.72
450	0.373	1.095	0.29	51.55	0.0056	0.0066	0.85	0.93
500	0.356	1.130	0.26	49.02	0.0053	0.0064	0.83	1.18
550	0.330	1.200	0.23	45.92	0.0050	0.0060	0.84	1.63
600	0.298	1.362	0.21	42.37	0.0050	0.0052	0.96	—

Table A-2 Properties of Some Saturated Liquids

T °F	k Btu/hr ft °F	c_p Btu/lb$_m$ °F	μ lb$_m$/ft hr	ρ lb$_m$/ft^3	ν ft^2/hr	α ft^2/hr	N_{Pr}	β °R^{-1}
				Carbon Dioxide				
−58	0.0494	0.44	0.333	72.19	4.61×10^{-3}	1.558×10^{-3}	2.96	3.67×10^{-3}
−40	0.0584	0.45	0.319	69.78	4.57	1.864	2.46	
−22	0.0645	0.47	0.305	67.22	4.54	2.043	2.22	
−4	0.0665	0.49	0.287	64.45	4.46	2.110	2.12	
14	0.0635	0.52	0.270	61.39	4.39	1.989	2.20	
32	0.0604	0.59	0.244	57.87	4.21	1.774	2.38	
50	0.0561	0.75	0.210	53.69	3.92	1.398	2.80	
68	0.0504	1.2	0.170	48.23	3.53	0.860	4.10	
86	0.0406	8.7	0.116	37.32	3.10	0.108	28.7	
				Sulfur Dioxide				
−58	0.140	0.3247	1.831	97.44	1.88×10^{-2}	4.42×10^{-3}	4.24	1.08×10^{-3}
−40	0.136	0.3250	1.573	95.94	1.64	4.38	3.74	
−22	0.133	0.3252	1.360	94.43	1.44	4.33	3.31	
−4	0.130	0.3254	1.171	92.93	1.26	4.29	2.93	
14	0.126	0.3255	1.023	91.37	1.12	4.25	2.62	
32	0.122	0.3257	0.895	89.80	0.997	4.19	2.38	
50	0.118	0.3259	0.794	88.18	0.900	4.13	2.18	
68	0.115	0.3261	0.705	86.55	0.814	4.07	2.00	
86	0.111	0.3263	0.623	84.86	0.734	4.01	1.83	
104	0.107	0.3266	0.556	82.98	0.670	3.95	1.70	
122	0.102	0.3268	0.508	81.10	0.626	3.87	1.61	
				Ammonia				
−58	0.316	1.066	0.742	43.93	1.69×10^{-2}	6.75×10^{-3}	2.60	1.36×10^{-3}
−40	0.316	1.067	0.678	43.18	1.57	6.88	2.28	
−22	0.317	1.069	0.636	42.41	1.50	6.98	2.15	
−4	0.316	1.077	0.616	41.62	1.48	7.05	2.09	
14	0.314	1.090	0.600	40.80	1.47	7.07	2.07	
32	0.312	1.107	0.579	39.96	1.45	7.05	2.05	
50	0.307	1.126	0.559	39.09	1.43	6.98	2.04	
68	0.301	1.146	0.531	38.19	1.39	6.88	2.02	
86	0.293	1.168	0.503	37.23	1.35	6.75	2.01	
104	0.285	1.194	0.479	36.27	1.32	6.59	2.00	
122	0.275	1.222	0.451	35.23	1.28	6.41	1.99	
				Dichlorodifluoromethane				
−58	0.039	0.2090	1.159	96.56	1.20×10^{-2}	1.94×10^{-3}	6.2	
−40	0.040	0.2113	1.024	94.81	1.08	1.99	5.4	
−22	0.040	0.2139	0.910	92.99	0.079	2.04	4.8	
−4	0.041	0.2167	0.831	91.18	0.911	2.09	4.4	
14	0.042	0.2198	0.765	89.24	0.857	2.13	4.0	
32	0.042	0.2232	0.722	87.24	0.828	2.16	3.8	
50	0.042	0.2268	0.671	85.17	0.788	2.17	3.6	
68	0.042	0.2307	0.637	83.04	0.767	2.17	3.5	
86	0.041	0.2349	0.608	80.85	0.752	2.17	3.5	
104	0.040	0.2393	0.582	78.48	0.742	2.15	3.5	
122	0.039	0.2440	0.557	75.91	0.734	2.11	3.5	

Table A-2 (*Contd.*)

T °F	k Btu/hr ft °F	c_p Btu/lb$_m$ °F	μ lb$_m$/ft hr	ρ lb$_m$/ft^3	ν ft^2/hr	α ft^2/hr	N_{Pr}	β °R^{-1}
				Glycerine				
32	0.163	0.540	25650	79.66	0.322×10^3	3.81×10^{-3}	84700	0.28×10^{-3}
50	0.164	0.554	9200	79.29	0.116	3.74	31000	
68	0.165	0.570	3610	78.91	0.0457	3.67	12500	
86	0.165	0.584	1520	78.54	0.0194	3.60	5380	
104	0.165	0.600	672	78.16	0.0086	3.54	2450	
122	0.166	0.617	451	77.72	0.0058	3.46	1630	
				Lubricating Oil				
32	0.085	0.429	9318	56.13	166	3.53×10^{-3}	47100	0.39×10^{-3}
68	0.084	0.449	1935	55.45	34.9	3.38	10400	
104	0.083	0.469	512	54.69	9.36	3.23	2870	
140	0.081	0.489	175	53.94	3.25	3.10	1050	
176	0.080	0.509	77.1	53.19	1.45	2.98	490	
212	0.079	0.530	41.3	52.44	0.788	2.86	276	
248	0.078	0.551	24.8	51.75	0.479	2.75	175	
284	0.077	0.572	15.8	51.00	0.310	2.66	116	
320	0.076	0.593	10.9	50.31	0.216	2.57	84	
				Mercury				
32	4.74	0.0335	4.08	850.78	4.79×10^{-3}	166.6×10^{-3}	0.0288	1.01×10^{-3}
68	5.02	0.0333	3.75	847.71	4.42	178.5	0.0249	
122	5.43	0.0331	3.40	843.14	4.03	194.6	0.0207	
212	6.07	0.0328	3.01	835.57	3.60	221.5	0.0162	
302	6.64	0.0326	2.73	828.06	3.30	246.2	0.0134	
392	7.13	0.0325	2.55	820.61	3.11	267.7	0.0116	
482	7.55	0.0324	2.41	813.16	2.96	287.0	0.0103	

Table A-3 Properties of Liquid Metals

T °F	k Btu/hr ft °F	c_p Btu/lb$_m$ °F	μ lb$_m$/ft hr	ρ lb$_m$/ft^3	ν ft^2/hr	α ft^2/hr	N_{Pr}
				Bismuth			
600	9.5	0.0345	3.88	625	0.0062	0.44	0.014
800	9.0	0.0357	3.26	616	0.0053	0.41	0.013
1000	9.0	0.0369	2.68	608	0.0044	0.40	0.011
1200	9.0	0.0381	2.22	600	0.0037	0.39	0.0094
1400	9.0	0.0393	1.95	591	0.0033	0.39	0.0084
				Lead			
700	9.3	0.038	5.86	658	0.0089	0.37	0.024
850	9.0	0.037	4.82	652	0.0074	0.37	0.020
1000	8.9	0.037	4.07	646	0.0063	0.37	0.017
1150	8.7	0.037	3.77	639	0.0059	0.37	0.016
1300	8.6			633			

Table A-3 (*Contd.*)

T °F	k Btu/hr ft °F	c_p Btu/lb$_m$ °F	μ lb$_m$/ft hr	ρ lb$_m$/ft^3	ν ft^2/hr	α ft^2/hr	N_{Pr}
				Mercury			
50	4.7	0.033	3.90	847	0.0046	0.17	0.027
200	6.0	0.033	2.92	834	0.0035	0.22	0.016
300	6.7	0.033	2.48	826	0.0030	0.25	0.012
400	7.2	0.032	2.45	817	0.0030	0.27	0.011
600	8.1	0.032	2.08	802	0.0026	0.31	0.0084
				Sodium			
200	49.8	0.33	1.68	58.0	0.029	2.6	0.011
400	46.4	0.32	1.07	56.3	0.019	2.6	0.0072
700	41.8	0.31	0.70	53.7	0.013	2.5	0.0050
1000	37.8	0.30	0.49	51.2	0.0096	2.4	0.0040
1300	34.5	0.30	0.44	48.6	0.0091	2.4	0.0038
				Zinc			
850	33.7	0.119	7.76	431	0.018	0.66	0.027
1000	33.2	0.116	6.42	428	0.015	0.67	0.022
1200	32.8	0.113	5.06	422	0.012	0.69	0.017
1500	32.6	0.107	4.08	408	0.010	0.74	0.014

Table A-4 Properties of Gases at Atmospheric Pressure

T °F	k Btu/hr ft °F	c_p Btu/lb$_m$ °F	μ lb$_m$/ft hr	ρ lb$_m$/ft^3	ν ft^2/hr	α ft^2/hr	N_{Pr}
				Air			
−100	0.01045	0.2405	0.03214	0.11028	0.2914	0.3940	0.739
−80	0.01099	0.2404	0.03365	0.10447	0.3221	0.4377	0.736
−60	0.01153	0.2404	0.03513	0.09924	0.3540	0.4832	0.733
−40	0.01207	0.2403	0.03658	0.09451	0.3870	0.5315	0.728
−20	0.01260	0.2403	0.03800	0.09021	0.4212	0.5812	0.725
0	0.01312	0.2403	0.03939	0.08629	0.4565	0.6326	0.722
20	0.01364	0.2403	0.04075	0.08269	0.4928	0.6865	0.718
40	0.01416	0.2404	0.04208	0.07938	0.5301	0.7421	0.714
60	0.01466	0.2404	0.04339	0.07633	0.5685	0.7989	0.712
80	0.01516	0.2405	0.04467	0.07350	0.6078	0.8575	0.709
100	0.01566	0.2406	0.04594	0.07087	0.6482	0.9185	0.706
120	0.01615	0.2407	0.04718	0.06843	0.6895	0.9806	0.703
140	0.01664	0.2409	0.04839	0.06614	0.7316	1.0446	0.700
160	0.01712	0.2411	0.04959	0.06401	0.7747	1.1095	0.698
180	0.01759	0.2413	0.05077	0.06201	0.8187	1.1758	0.696
200	0.01806	0.2415	0.05193	0.06013	0.8636	1.2438	0.694
220	0.01853	0.2418	0.05308	0.05836	0.9095	1.3133	0.693
240	0.01899	0.2421	0.05420	0.05669	0.9561	1.3841	0.691
260	0.01945	0.2424	0.05531	0.05512	1.0034	1.4558	0.689
280	0.01990	0.2427	0.05640	0.05363	1.0517	1.5284	0.688

Table A-4 (*Contd.*)

T °F	k Btu/hr ft °F	c_p Btu/lb$_m$°F	μ lb$_m$/ft hr	ρ lb$_m$/ft^3	ν ft^2/hr	α ft^2/hr	N_{Pr}
Air							
300	0.02034	0.2431	0.05748	0.05221	1.1009	1.6028	0.687
320	0.02079	0.2435	0.05854	0.05087	1.1508	1.6780	0.686
340	0.02122	0.2439	0.05959	0.04960	1.2014	1.7537	0.685
360	0.02166	0.2443	0.06063	0.04839	1.2529	1.8325	0.684
380	0.02208	0.2447	0.06165	0.04724	1.3050	1.9100	0.683
400	0.02251	0.2452	0.06266	0.04614	1.3580	1.9902	0.682
420	0.02293	0.2457	0.06366	0.04509	1.4118	2.0695	0.682
440	0.02335	0.2462	0.06464	0.04409	1.4660	2.2331	0.681
460	0.02376	0.2467	0.06561	0.04313	1.5212	2.3310	0.681
480	0.02417	0.2472	0.06657	0.04211	1.5771	2.3174	0.680
500	0.02458	0.2478	0.06752	0.04133	1.6337	2.4004	0.680
520	0.02498	0.2483	0.06846	0.04049	1.6908	2.4856	0.680
540	0.02538	0.2489	0.06939	0.03968	1.7487	2.5688	0.680
560	0.02577	0.2495	0.07031	0.03890	1.8075	2.6540	0.681
580	0.02616	0.2501	0.07122	0.03815	1.8668	2.7421	0.681
Nitrogen							
−100	0.01054	0.2491	0.03132	0.1068	0.2932	0.3962	0.747
80	0.01514	0.2486	0.04316	0.0713	0.6055	0.8542	0.713
260	0.01927	0.2498	0.05317	0.0533	0.9976	1.447	0.691
440	0.02302	0.2521	0.06217	0.0426	1.4593	2.143	0.684
620	0.02646	0.2569	0.07416	0.0355	1.9847	2.901	0.686
800	0.02960	0.2620	0.07772	0.0308	2.5244	3.668	0.691
980	0.03241	0.2681	0.08476	0.0267	3.1562	4.528	0.700
1160	0.03507	0.2738	0.09068	0.0237	3.5296	5.404	0.711
1340	0.03741	0.2789	0.09677	0.0213	4.5433	6.297	0.724
1520	0.03958	0.2832	0.10228	0.0194	5.2701	7.204	0.736
1700	0.04151	0.2875	0.10764	0.0178	6.0485	8.111	0.748
Oxygen							
−190	0.00790	0.2192	0.02779	0.1635	0.1700	0.2204	0.773
−100	0.01054	0.2181	0.03592	0.1221	0.3302	0.3958	0.745
−10	0.01305	0.2187	0.04324	0.0975	0.4435	0.6120	0.725
80	0.01546	0.2198	0.04896	0.0812	0.6145	0.8662	0.709
170	0.01774	0.2219	0.05602	0.0695	0.8060	1.150	0.702
260	0.02000	0.2250	0.06177	0.0609	1.0145	1.460	0.695
350	0.02212	0.2285	0.06718	0.0542	1.2395	1.786	0.694
440	0.02411	0.2322	0.07236	0.0487	1.4857	2.132	0.697
530	0.02610	0.2360	0.07733	0.0443	1.7456	2.496	0.700
620	0.02792	0.2399	0.08204	0.0406	2.0207	2.867	0.704
Hydrogen							
−190	0.0567	3.010	0.01354	0.01022	1.3244	1.84	0.718
−100	0.741	3.234	0.01648	0.00766	2.1517	2.99	0.719
−10	0.0902	3.358	0.01916	0.00613	3.1248	4.38	0.713
80	0.105	3.419	0.02168	0.00511	4.2444	6.02	0.706
170	0.119	3.448	0.02408	0.00438	5.4972	7.87	0.697
260	0.132	3.461	0.02628	0.00383	6.8616	9.95	0.690
350	0.145	3.463	0.02849	0.00341	8.3556	12.26	0.682
440	0.157	3.465	0.03057	0.00307	10.066	14.79	0.675

Table A-4 (*Contd.*)

T °F	k Btu/hr ft °F	c_p Btu/lb$_m$ °F	μ lb$_m$/ft hr	ρ lb$_m$/ft^3	ν ft^2/hr	α ft^2/hr	N_{Pr}
			Hydrogen (*Contd.*)				
530	0.169	3.471	0.03260	0.00279	11.686	17.50	0.668
620	0.182	3.472	0.03456	0.00255	13.550	20.56	0.664
800	0.203	3.481	0.03845	0.00218	17.636	26.75	0.659
980	0.222	3.505	0.04208	0.00191	22.03	33.18	0.664
1160	0.238	3.540	0.04543	0.00170	26.75	39.59	0.676
			Helium				
−200	0.0536	1.242	0.03035	0.211	1.4382	2.044	0.70
−100	0.0680	1.242	0.03787	0.0152	2.4948	3.599	0.694
0	0.0784	1.242	0.04396	0.0119	3.7008	5.299	0.70
200	0.0977	1.242	0.05576	0.00829	6.7284	9.490	0.71
400	0.114	1.242	0.06653	0.00637	10.436	14.40	0.72
600	0.130	1.242	0.07531	0.00517	14.562	20.21	0.72
800	0.145	1.242	0.08406	0.00439	19.148	25.81	0.72
1000	0.159	1.242	0.09234	0.00376	24.57	34.00	0.72
			Carbon dioxide				
−64	0.006243	0.187	0.02686	0.1544	0.1740	0.2294	0.818
−10	0.007444	0.192	0.03046	0.1352	0.2252	0.2868	0.793
80	0.009575	0.208	0.03618	0.1122	0.3224	0.4103	0.770
170	0.01183	0.215	0.04162	0.0959	0.4338	0.5738	0.755
260	0.01422	0.225	0.04673	0.0838	0.5576	0.7542	0.738
350	0.01674	0.234	0.05162	0.0744	0.6937	0.9615	0.721
440	0.01937	0.242	0.05627	0.0670	0.8399	1.195	0.702
530	0.02208	0.250	0.06066	0.0608	0.9976	1.453	0.685
620	0.02491	0.257	0.06491	0.0558	1.1632	1.737	0.608

Table A-5 Properties of Some Metals at 68 °F

Metal	k Btu/hr ft °F	c_p Btu/lb$_m$ °F	ρ lb$_m$/ft^3	α ft^2/hr
Aluminum	132	0.214	169	3.66
Lead	20	0.031	710	0.92
Iron	42	0.108	493	0.78
Steel (1% carbon)	25	0.113	487	0.45
Copper	223	0.092	559	4.35
Brass (70% copper, 30% zinc)	64	0.092	532	1.32
Magnesium	99	0.242	109	3.76
Molybdenum	79	0.060	638	2.07
Nickel	52	0.106	556	0.88
Silver	242	0.056	657	6.60
Tungsten	94	0.032	1208	2.43
Tin	37	0.054	456	1.50
Zinc	65	0.092	446	1.59

Table A-6 Properties of Some Nonmetals† at 68°F

Material	k Btu/hr ft °F	c_p Btu/lb$_m$ °F	ρ lb$_m$/ft^3	α ft^2/hr
Common red brick	0.40	0.20	100	0.02
Asphalt	0.4			
Concrete	0.6	0.2	130	0.023
Glass	0.44	0.2	168	0.013
Plaster	0.28	0.2	90	0.016
Limestone	0.73	0.2	155	0.023
Marble	1.6	0.2	160	0.05
Wood				
pine	0.07	0.6	40	0.0029
oak	0.10	0.6	38	0.0044
Asbestos	0.09		36	
Diatomaceous earth	0.02		10	
Glass wool	0.022		1.5	
Rock wool	0.023		10	
Fiber board	0.028			
Sawdust	0.03			
Corkboard	0.025		10	

†The physical properties of these structural materials can vary considerably and the values listed in this table should be considered as reasonable estimates.

Appendix B

Tables of Mathematical Functions

Bessel Functions of the First Kind

Bessel's equation of the form

$$x^2\left(\frac{d^2y}{dx^2}\right)+x\left(\frac{dy}{dx}\right)+(x^2-n^2)y=0$$

has the independent solutions $J_n(x)$ and $J_{-n}(x)$ where

$$J_n(x)=\sum_{m=0}^{\infty}\frac{(-1)^m}{m!\Gamma(m+n+1)}\left(\frac{x}{2}\right)^{n+2m}$$

except when n is an integer. Under those conditions $J_n(x)=(-1)^nJ_{-n}(x)$. Recurrence formulas can be obtained relating the functions and their derivatives

$$J_{n-1}(x)+J_{n+1}(x)=\left(\frac{2n}{x}\right)J_n(x)$$

$$J_{n-1}(x)-J_{n+1}(x)=2J'_n(x)$$

$$nJ_n(x)+xJ'_n(x)=xJ_{n-1}(x)$$

$$nJ_n(x)-xJ'_n(x)=xJ_{n+1}(x)$$

For small values of the argument $J_n(x)$ can be approximated by

$$J_n(x)\sim\left(\frac{x}{2}\right)^n\frac{1}{\Gamma(n+1)},\qquad x\to 0$$

provided $n\neq -1, -2, -3, \ldots$.

The Gamma function $\Gamma(x)$ has the property that

$$\Gamma(x+1)=x!$$

when x is an integer, and is given in general by

$$\Gamma(x)=\int_0^{\infty}\eta^{x-1}e^{-\eta}\,d\eta$$

Tabulated values are available in the *Handbook of Mathematical Functions*, U.S. Department of Commerce, Applied Mathematics Series No. 55.

Table B-1

x	$J_0(x)$	$J_1(x)$	x	$J_0(x)$	$J_1(x)$
0	1.000	0.000	2.50	−0.048	0.497
0.10	0.998	0.050	2.60	−0.097	0.471
0.20	0.990	0.100	2.70	−0.142	0.442
0.30	0.978	0.148	2.80	−0.185	0.410
0.40	0.960	0.196	2.90	−0.224	0.375
0.50	0.938	0.242	3.00	−0.260	0.339
0.60	0.912	0.287	3.10	−0.292	0.301
0.70	0.881	0.329	3.20	−0.320	0.261
0.80	0.846	0.369	3.30	−0.344	0.221
0.90	0.808	0.406	3.40	−0.364	0.179
1.00	0.765	0.440	3.50	−0.380	0.137
1.10	0.720	0.471	3.60	−0.392	0.095
1.20	0.671	0.498	3.70	−0.399	0.054
1.30	0.646	0.511	3.80	−0.402	0.013
1.40	0.567	0.542	3.90	−0.402	−0.027
1.50	0.512	0.558	4.00	−0.397	−0.066
1.60	0.455	0.570	4.10	−0.389	−0.103
1.70	0.398	0.578	4.20	−0.376	−0.139
1.80	0.340	0.582	4.30	−0.361	−0.172
1.90	0.282	0.581	4.40	−0.342	−0.203
2.00	0.224	0.577	4.50	−0.320	−0.231
2.10	0.167	0.568	4.60	−0.296	−0.256
2.20	0.110	0.556	4.70	−0.269	−0.279
2.30	0.055	0.540	4.80	−0.240	−0.298
2.40	0.002	0.520	4.90	−0.210	−0.315
			5.00	−0.178	−0.328

Bessel Functions of the Second Kind

When n is an integer $J_n(x)$ and $J_{-n}(x)$ are not independent solutions of Bessel's equation of the form

$$x^2\left(\frac{d^2y}{dx^2}\right)+x\left(\frac{dy}{dx}\right)+(x^2-n^2)y=0$$

however, $Y_n(x)$ is an independent solution.

Recurrence formulas can be obtained relating the various functions and their derivatives.

$$Y_{n-1}(x)+Y_{n+1}(x)=\frac{2n}{x}Y_n(x)$$

$$Y_{n-1}(x)-Y_{n+1}(x)=2Y_n'(x)$$

$$nY_n(x)+xY_n'(x)=xY_{n-1}(x)$$

$$nY_n(x)-xY_n'(x)=xY_{n+1}(x)$$

For small values of the argument the limiting forms are

$$Y_0(x)\sim\left(\frac{2}{\pi}\right)\ln x,\quad Y_n(x)\sim-\left(\frac{1}{\pi}\right)\Gamma(n)\left(\frac{x}{2}\right)^{-n},\qquad \text{for } n>0$$

Table B-2

x	$Y_0(x)$	$Y_1(x)$	x	$Y_0(x)$	$Y_1(x)$
0	$-\infty$	$-\infty$	2.30	+0.518	+0.052
0.05	−1.979	−12.790	2.40	+0.510	+0.100
0.10	−1.534	−6.459	2.50	+0.498	+0.146
0.15	−1.271	−4.364	2.60	+0.481	+0.188
0.20	−1.081	−3.324	2.70	+0.460	+0.228
0.25	−0.932	−2.704	2.80	+0.436	+0.263
0.30	−0.807	−2.293	2.90	+0.408	+0.296
0.35	−0.700	−2.000	3.00	+0.377	+0.325
0.40	−0.606	−1.781	3.10	+0.343	+0.350
0.45	−0.521	−1.610	3.20	+0.307	+0.371
0.50	−0.444	−1.471	3.30	+0.269	+0.388
0.60	−0.308	−1.260	3.40	+0.230	+0.401
0.70	−0.191	−1.103	3.50	+0.189	+0.410
0.80	−0.087	−0.978	3.60	+0.148	+0.415
0.90	+0.0056	−0.873	3.70	+0.106	+0.417
1.00	+0.088	−0.781	3.80	+0.064	+0.414
1.10	+0.162	−0.698	3.90	+0.023	+0.408
1.20	+0.228	−0.621	4.00	−0.017	+0.398
1.30	+0.286	−0.548	4.10	−0.056	+0.384
1.40	+0.338	−0.479	4.20	−0.094	+0.368
1.50	+0.382	−0.412	4.30	−0.130	+0.348
1.60	+0.420	−0.347	4.40	−0.163	+0.326
1.70	+0.452	−0.285	4.50	−0.195	+0.301
1.80	+0.477	−0.224	4.60	−0.223	+0.274
1.90	+0.497	−0.164	4.70	−0.249	+0.244
2.00	+0.510	−0.107	4.80	−0.272	+0.213
2.10	+0.518	−0.052	4.90	−0.292	+0.181
2.20	+0.521	+0.0015	5.00	−0.308	+0.148

Modified Bessel Functions of the First Kind

Bessel's equation of the form

$$x^2\left(\frac{d^2y}{dx^2}\right)+x\left(\frac{dy}{dx}\right)-(x^2+n^2)y=0$$

has the independent solutions $I_n(x)$ and $I_{-n}(x)$ where

$$I_n(x)=\sum_{m=0}^{\infty}\frac{1}{m!\Gamma(m+n+1)}\left(\frac{x}{2}\right)^{n+2m}$$

except when n is an integer. Under those conditions $I_n(x)=I_{-n}(x)$. Recurrence formulas can be obtained relating the functions and their derivatives.

$$I_{n-1}(x)-I_{n+1}(x)=\frac{2n}{x}I_n(x)$$

$$I_{n-1}(x)+I_{n+1}(x)=2I_n'(x)$$

$$nI_n(x)+xI_n'(x)=xI_{n-1}(x)$$

$$nI_n(x)-xI_n'(x)=-xI_{n+1}(x)$$

For small values of the argument the limiting form of $I_n(x)$ is

$$I_n(x)\sim\left(\frac{x}{2}\right)^n\Big/\Gamma(n+1),\qquad x\to 0$$

provided $n\neq -1, -2, -3, \ldots$.

Table B-3

x	$I_0(x)$	$I_1(x)$	x	$I_0(x)$	$I_1(x)$
0	1.000	0.000	2.50	3.290	2.517
0.10	1.002	0.050	2.60	3.553	2.755
0.20	1.010	0.100	2.70	3.842	3.016
0.30	1.023	0.152	2.80	4.157	3.301
0.40	1.040	0.204	2.90	4.503	3.613
0.50	1.063	0.258	3.00	4.881	3.953
0.60	1.092	0.314	3.10	5.294	4.326
0.70	1.126	0.372	3.20	5.747	4.734
0.80	1.166	0.433	3.30	6.243	5.181
0.90	1.213	0.497	3.40	6.785	5.670
1.00	1.266	0.565	3.50	7.378	6.206
1.10	1.326	0.637	3.60	8.028	6.793
1.20	1.394	0.715	3.70	8.739	7.436
1.30	1.469	0.797	3.80	9.517	8.140
1.40	1.553	0.886	3.90	10.369	8.913
1.50	1.647	0.982	4.00	11.30	9.759
1.60	1.750	1.085	4.10	12.32	10.69
1.70	1.864	1.196	4.20	13.44	11.70
1.80	1.990	1.317	4.30	14.67	12.82
1.90	2.128	1.448	4.40	16.01	14.04
2.00	2.280	1.591	4.50	17.48	15.39
2.10	2.446	1.745	4.60	19.09	16.86
2.20	2.629	1.914	4.70	20.86	18.48
2.30	2.830	2.098	4.80	22.79	20.25
2.40	3.049	2.298	4.90	24.91	22.20
			5.00	27.24	24.34

Modified Bessel Functions of the Second Kind

When n is an integer $I_n(x)$ and $I_{-n}(x)$ are not independent solutions of Bessel's equation of the form

$$x^2\left(\frac{d^2y}{dx^2}\right)+x\left(\frac{dy}{dx}\right)-(x^2+n^2)y=0$$

however, $K_n(x)$ is an independent solution. Recurrence formulas can be obtained relating the various functions and their derivatives.

$$K_{n-1}(x)-K_{n+1}(x)=-\frac{2n}{x}K_n(x)$$

$$K_{n-1}(x)+K_{n+1}(x)=-2K_n'(x)$$

$$nK_n(x)+xK_n'(x)=-xK_{n-1}(x)$$

$$nK_n(x)-xK_n'(x)=xK_{n+1}(x)$$

The limiting forms for small values of x are

$$K_0(x)\sim-\ln(x),\quad K_n(x)\sim\frac{1}{2}\Gamma(n)\left(\frac{x}{2}\right)^{-n},\qquad \text{for } n>0$$

Table B-4

x	$K_0(x)$	$K_1(x)$	x	$K_0(x)$	$K_1(x)$
0.0	∞	∞	2.30	0.0791	0.0950
0.05	3.114	19.910	2.40	0.0702	0.0837
0.10	2.427	9.854	2.50	0.0623	0.0739
0.15	2.030	6.477	2.60	0.0554	0.0653
0.20	1.753	4.776	2.70	0.0492	0.0577
0.25	1.541	3.747	2.80	0.0438	0.0511
0.30	1.372	3.056	2.90	0.0390	0.0453
0.35	1.233	2.559	3.00	0.0347	0.0402
0.40	1.114	2.184	3.10	0.0310	0.0356
0.45	1.013	1.892	3.20	0.0276	0.0316
0.50	0.924	1.656	3.30	0.0246	0.0281
0.60	0.778	1.303	3.40	0.0220	0.0250
0.70	0.660	1.050	3.50	0.0196	0.0222
0.80	0.565	0.862	3.60	0.0175	0.0198
0.90	0.487	0.716	3.70	0.0156	0.0176
1.00	0.421	0.602	3.80	0.0140	0.0157
1.10	0.366	0.510	3.90	0.0125	0.0140
1.20	0.318	0.434	4.00	0.0112	0.0125
1.30	0.278	0.372	4.10	0.0100	0.0111
1.40	0.244	0.321	4.20	0.0089	0.0099
1.50	0.214	0.277	4.30	0.0080	0.0089
1.60	0.188	0.241	4.40	0.0071	0.0079
1.70	0.165	0.209	4.50	0.0064	0.0071
1.80	0.146	0.183	4.60	0.0057	0.0063
1.90	0.129	0.160	4.70	0.0051	0.0056
2.00	0.114	0.140	4.80	0.0046	0.0050
2.10	0.101	0.123	4.90	0.0041	0.0045
2.20	0.0893	0.108	5.00	0.0037	0.0040

The Error Function

The *error function* of the argument η is denoted as $\operatorname{erf}(\eta)$ and defined by

$$\operatorname{erf}(\eta)=\frac{2}{\sqrt{\pi}}\int_{\xi=0}^{\xi=\eta} e^{-\xi^2}\,d\xi$$

The *complimentary error function* of the argument η is denoted as $\operatorname{erfc}(\eta)$ and is defined by

$$\operatorname{erfc}(\eta)=1-\operatorname{erf}(\eta)=\frac{2}{\sqrt{\pi}}\int_{\xi=\eta}^{\xi=\infty} e^{-\xi^2}\,d\xi$$

Some important properties of the error function are

$$\operatorname{erf}(\infty)=1,\quad \operatorname{erf}(-\eta)=-\operatorname{erf}(\eta)$$

$$\frac{d}{d\eta}[\operatorname{erf}(\eta)]=\frac{2}{\sqrt{\pi}}e^{-\eta^2}$$

Table B-5

η	$\text{erf}(\eta)$	$\text{erfc}(\eta)$	$\frac{2}{\sqrt{\pi}} e^{-\eta^2}$
0	0	1.00	1.128
0.05	0.0564	0.944	1.126
0.10	0.112	0.888	1.117
0.15	0.168	0.832	1.103
0.20	0.223	0.777	1.084
0.25	0.276	0.724	1.060
0.30	0.329	0.671	1.031
0.35	0.379	0.621	0.998
0.40	0.428	0.572	0.962
0.45	0.475	0.525	0.922
0.50	0.520	0.480	0.879
0.55	0.563	0.437	0.834
0.60	0.604	0.396	0.787
0.65	0.642	0.378	0.740
0.70	0.678	0.322	0.691
0.75	0.711	0.289	0.643
0.80	0.742	0.258	0.595
0.85	0.771	0.229	0.548
0.90	0.797	0.203	0.502
0.95	0.821	0.179	0.458
1.00	0.843	0.157	0.415
1.1	0.880	0.120	0.337
1.2	0.910	0.090	0.267
1.3	0.934	0.066	0.208
1.4	0.952	0.048	0.159
1.5	0.966	0.034	0.119
1.6	0.976	0.024	0.087
1.7	0.984	0.016	0.063
1.8	0.989	0.011	0.044
1.9	0.993	0.007	0.030
2.0	0.995	0.005	0.021

Author Index

Subject Index